# The Elements

| Element | Symbol | Atomic Number | Relative Atomic Mass* | Element | Symbol | Atomic Number | Relative Atomic Mass* |
|---|---|---|---|---|---|---|---|
| Actinium | Ac | 89 | (227) | Molybdenum | Mo | 42 | 95.94 |
| Aluminum | Al | 13 | 26.98 | Neodymium | Nd | 60 | 144.2 |
| Americium | Am | 95 | (243) | Neon | Ne | 10 | 20.18 |
| Antimony | Sb | 51 | 121.8 | Neptunium | Np | 93 | (237) |
| Argon | Ar | 18 | 39.95 | Nickel | Ni | 28 | 58.69 |
| Arsenic | As | 33 | 74.92 | Niobium | Nb | 41 | 92.91 |
| Astatine | At | 85 | (210) | Nitrogen | N | 7 | 14.01 |
| Barium | Ba | 56 | 137.3 | Nobelium | No | 102 | (259) |
| Berkelium | Bk | 97 | (247) | Osmium | Os | 76 | 190.2 |
| Beryllium | Be | 4 | 9.012 | Oxygen | O | 8 | 16.00 |
| Bismuth | Bi | 83 | 209.0 | Palladium | Pd | 46 | 106.4 |
| Bohrium | Bh | 107 | (272) | Phosphorus | P | 15 | 30.97 |
| Boron | B | 5 | 10.81 | Platinum | Pt | 78 | 195.1 |
| Bromine | Br | 35 | 79.90 | Plutonium | Pu | 94 | (244) |
| Cadmium | Cd | 48 | 112.4 | Polonium | Po | 84 | (209) |
| Calcium | Ca | 20 | 40.08 | Potassium | K | 19 | 39.10 |
| Californium | Cf | 98 | (251) | Praseodymium | Pr | 59 | 140.9 |
| Carbon | C | 6 | 12.01 | Promethium | Pm | 61 | (145) |
| Cerium | Ce | 58 | 140.1 | Protactinium | Pa | 91 | 231.0 |
| Cesium | Cs | 55 | 132.9 | Radium | Ra | 88 | (226) |
| Chlorine | Cl | 17 | 35.45 | Radon | Rn | 86 | (222) |
| Chromium | Cr | 24 | 52.00 | Rhenium | Re | 75 | 186.2 |
| Cobalt | Co | 27 | 58.93 | Rhodium | Rh | 45 | 102.9 |
| Copernicium | Cn | 112 | (285) | Roentgenium | Rg | 111 | (280) |
| Copper | Cu | 29 | 63.55 | Rubidium | Rb | 37 | 85.47 |
| Curium | Cm | 96 | (247) | Ruthenium | Ru | 44 | 101.1 |
| Darmstadtium | Ds | 110 | (281) | Rutherfordium | Rf | 104 | (267) |
| Dubnium | Db | 105 | (268) | Samarium | Sm | 62 | 150.4 |
| Dysprosium | Dy | 66 | 162.5 | Scandium | Sc | 21 | 44.96 |
| Einsteinium | Es | 99 | (252) | Seaborgium | Sg | 106 | (271) |
| Erbium | Er | 68 | 167.3 | Selenium | Se | 34 | 78.96 |
| Europium | Eu | 63 | 152.0 | Silicon | Si | 14 | 28.09 |
| Fermium | Fm | 100 | (257) | Silver | Ag | 47 | 107.9 |
| Fluorine | F | 9 | 19.00 | Sodium | Na | 11 | 22.99 |
| Francium | Fr | 87 | (223) | Strontium | Sr | 38 | 87.62 |
| Gadolinium | Gd | 64 | 157.3 | Sulfur | S | 16 | 32.07 |
| Gallium | Ga | 31 | 69.72 | Tantalum | Ta | 73 | 180.9 |
| Germanium | Ge | 32 | 72.64 | Technetium | Tc | 43 | (98) |
| Gold | Au | 79 | 197.0 | Tellurium | Te | 52 | 127.6 |
| Hafnium | Hf | 72 | 178.5 | Terbium | Tb | 65 | 158.9 |
| Hassium | Hs | 108 | (270) | Thallium | Tl | 81 | 204.4 |
| Helium | He | 2 | 4.003 | Thorium | Th | 90 | 232.0 |
| Holmium | Ho | 67 | 164.9 | Thulium | Tm | 69 | 168.9 |
| Hydrogen | H | 1 | 1.008 | Tin | Sn | 50 | 118.7 |
| Indium | In | 49 | 114.8 | Titanium | Ti | 22 | 47.88 |
| Iodine | I | 53 | 126.9 | Tungsten | W | 74 | 183.8 |
| Iridium | Ir | 77 | 192.2 | Uranium | U | 92 | 238.0 |
| Iron | Fe | 26 | 55.85 | Vanadium | V | 23 | 50.94 |
| Krypton | Kr | 36 | 83.80 | Xenon | Xe | 54 | 131.3 |
| Lanthanum | La | 57 | 138.9 | Ytterbium | Yb | 70 | 173.0 |
| Lawrencium | Lr | 103 | (262) | Yttrium | Y | 39 | 88.91 |
| Lead | Pb | 82 | 207.2 | Zinc | Zn | 30 | 65.41 |
| Lithium | Li | 3 | 6.941 | Zirconium | Zr | 40 | 91.22 |
| Lutetium | Lu | 71 | 175.0 | | | 113** | |
| Magnesium | Mg | 12 | 24.31 | | | | |
| Manganese | Mn | 25 | 54.94 | | | | |
| Meitnerium | Mt | 109 | (276) | | | | |
| Mendelevium | Md | 101 | (258) | | | | |
| Mercury | Hg | 80 | 200.6 | | | | |

*Values in parentheses represent the mass number of the most stable isotope.

**The names and symbols for elements 113 through 118 have not been chosen.

# Student Quick Tips

Use this Student Quick Tips guide for a quick and easy start with McGraw-Hill Connect. You'll get valuable tips on registering, doing assignments, and accessing resources, as well as information about the support center hours.

## Getting Started

**TIP:** To get started in Connect, you will need the following:

- Your instructor's Connect Web Address

> Sample of Connect Web Address:
>
> http://www.mcgrawhillconnect.com/class/instructorname_section_name

- Connect Access Code

**TIP:** If you do not have an access code or have not yet secured your tuition funds, you can click "Free Trial" during registration. This trial will provide temporary Connect access (typically three weeks) and will remind you to purchase online access before the end of your trial.

## Registration and Sign In

1. Go to the Connect Web Address provided by your instructor
2. Click on **Register Now**
3. Enter your email address

**TIP:** If you already have a McGraw-Hill account, you will be asked for your password and will not be required to create a new account.

4. Enter a registration code or choose **Buy Online** to purchase access online

5. Follow the on-screen directions

**TIP:** Please choose your Security Question and Answer carefully. We will ask you for this information if you forget your password.

6. When registration is complete, click on **Go to Connect Now**

7. You are now ready to use **Connect**

## Trouble Logging In?

- Ensure you are using the same email address you used during registration

- If you have forgotten your password, click on the "Forgot Password?" link at your Instructor's Connect Course Web Address

- When logged into Connect, you can update your account information (e.g. email address, password, and security question/answer) by clicking on the *"My Account"* link located at the top-right corner

## Home (Assignments)

**TIP:** If you are unable to begin an assignment, verify the following:

- The assignment is available (start and due dates)

- That you have not exceeded the maximum number of attempts

- That you have not achieved a score of 100%

- If your assignment contains questions that require manual grading, you will not be able to begin your next attempt until your instructor has graded those questions

(Continued: **Home Assignments**)

> **TIP:** Based on the assignment policy settings established by your Instructor, you may encounter the following limitations when working on your assignment(s):
>
> - Ability to Print Assignment
>
> - Timed assignments – once you begin a "*timed assignment*," the timer will not stop by design
>
> **TIP:** "*Save & Exit*" vs. "*Submit*" button
>
> - If you are unable to complete your assignment in one sitting, utilize the "*Save & Exit*" button to save your work and complete it at a later time
>
> - Once you have completed your assignment, utilize the "*Submit*" button in order for your assignment to be graded

## Library

> **TIP:** The *Library* section of your Connect account provides shortcuts to various resources.
>
> - If you purchased ConnectPlus, you will see an *eBook* link, which can also be accessed from the section information widget of the *Home* tab
>
> - *Recorded Lectures* can be accessed if your instructor is using *Tegrity Campus* to capture lectures. You may also access recorded lectures when taking an assignment by clicking on the projector icon in the navigation bar
>
> - Many McGraw-Hill textbooks offer additional resources such as narrated slides and additional problems, which are accessible through the *Student Resources* link

## Reports

**TIP:** Once you submit your assignment, you can view your available results in the *Reports* tab.

- If you see a dash (-) as your score, your instructor has either delayed or restricted your ability to see the assignment feedback

- Your instructor has the ability to limit the amount of information (e.g. questions, answers, scores) you can view for each submitted assignment

## Need More Help?

### CONTACT US ONLINE

Visit us at:

www.mcgrawhillconnect.com/support

Browse our support materials including tutorial videos and our searchable Connect knowledge base. If you cannot find an answer to your question, click on "Contact Us" button to send us an email.

### GIVE US A CALL

Call us at:

1-800-331-5094

Our live support is available:

Mon-Thurs:   8 am – 11 pm CT
Friday:         8 am –  6  pm CT
Sunday:        6 pm – 11 pm CT

# Chemistry 2AB

## Riverside Community College

Contains Material From

## General, Organic & Biological Chemistry

Second Edition

### Janice Gorzynski Smith
University of Hawai'i at Mānoa

**Learning Solutions**

Boston  Burr Ridge, IL  Dubuque, IA  New York  San Francisco  St. Louis
Bangkok  Bogotá  Caracas  Lisbon  London  Madrid
Mexico City  Milan  New Delhi  Seoul  Singapore  Sydney  Taipei  Toronto

Chemistry 2AB
Riverside Community College

This book is a McGraw-Hill Learning Solutions textbook and contains select material from *General, Organic, & Biological Chemistry*, Second Edition by Janice Gorzynski Smith. Copyright © 2013, 2010 by The McGraw-Hill Companies, Inc. Reprinted with permission of the publisher. Many custom published texts are modified versions or adaptations of our best-selling textbooks. Some adaptations are printed in black and white to keep prices at a minimum, while others are in color.

8 9 0  CCC CCC  14

ISBN-13: 978-0-07-769937-6
ISBN-10: 0-07-769937-8
Part of
ISBN-13: 978-0-07-769938-3
ISBN-10: 0-07-769938-6

*Learning Solutions Consultant: Kimberly Scheyving*
*Production Editor: Kelsey Streif*
*Printer/Binder: Commercial Communications, Inc.*
*Cover Images © 2012 JupiterImages Corporation*

# About the Author

**Janice Gorzynski Smith** was born in Schenectady, New York, and grew up following the Yankees, listening to the Beatles, and water skiing on Sacandaga Reservoir. She became interested in chemistry in high school, and went on to major in chemistry at Cornell University where she received an A.B. degree *summa cum laude*. Jan earned a Ph.D. in Organic Chemistry from Harvard University under the direction of Nobel Laureate E. J. Corey, and she also spent a year as a National Science Foundation National Needs Postdoctoral Fellow at Harvard. During her tenure with the Corey group, she completed the total synthesis of the plant growth hormone gibberellic acid.

Following her postdoctoral work, Jan joined the faculty of Mount Holyoke College where she was employed for 21 years. During this time she was active in teaching chemistry lecture and lab courses, conducting a research program in organic synthesis, and serving as department chair. Her organic chemistry class was named one of Mount Holyoke's "Don't-miss courses" in a survey by *Boston* magazine. After spending two sabbaticals amidst the natural beauty and diversity in Hawai'i in the 1990s, Jan and her family moved there permanently in 2000. Most recently, she has served as a faculty member at the University of Hawai'i at Mānoa, where she has taught a one-semester organic and biological chemistry course for nursing students, as well as the two-semester organic chemistry lecture and lab courses. She has also served as the faculty advisor to the student affiliate chapter of the American Chemical Society. In 2003, she received the Chancellor's Citation for Meritorious Teaching.

Jan resides in Hawai'i with her husband Dan, an emergency medicine physician. She has four children: Matthew and Zachary (margin photo on page 477); Jenna, a 2011 graduate of Temple University School of Law; and Erin (married with one son, Max), a 2006 graduate of Brown University School of Medicine and co-author of the Student Study Guide/Solutions Manual for this text. When not teaching, writing, or enjoying her family, Jan bikes, hikes, snorkels, and scuba dives in sunny Hawai'i, and time permitting, enjoys travel and Hawaiian quilting.

*Dedicated to my family*

# Brief Contents

# Contents

**5  Chemical Reactions   123**

**6  Energy Changes, Reaction Rates, and Equilibrium   167**

## 9   Acids and Bases   273

## 10   Nuclear Chemistry   315

## 11    Introduction to Organic Molecules and Functional Groups   341

## 12    Alkanes   376

13   Unsaturated Hydrocarbons   402

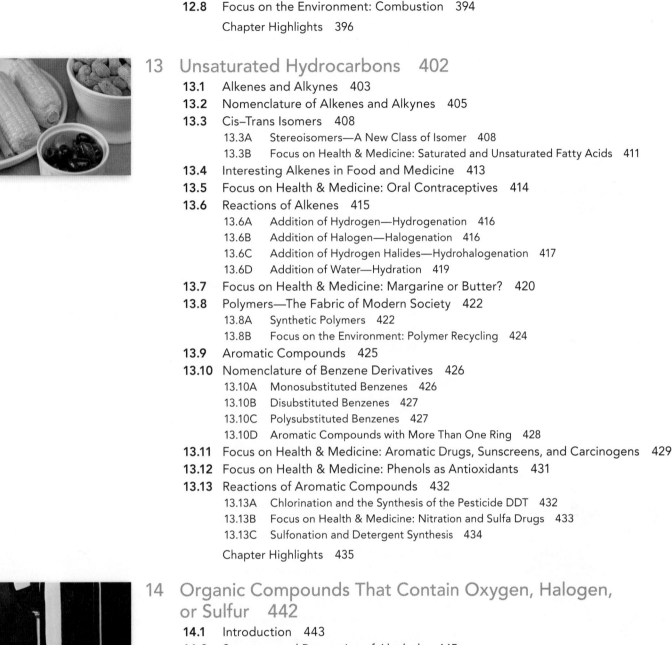

14   Organic Compounds That Contain Oxygen, Halogen, or Sulfur   442

# Preface

My goal in writing this text was to relate the fundamental concepts of general, organic, and biological chemistry to the world around us, and in this way illustrate how chemistry explains many aspects of everyday life. I have followed two guiding principles:

- use relevant and interesting applications for all basic chemical concepts
- present the material in a student-friendly fashion using bulleted lists, extensive illustrations, and step-by-step problem solving.

This text is different—by design. Since today's students rely more heavily on visual imagery to learn than ever before, this text uses less prose and more diagrams and figures to reinforce the major themes of chemistry. A key feature is the use of molecular art to illustrate and explain common phenomena we encounter every day. Each topic is broken down into small chunks of information that are more manageable and easily learned. Students are given enough detail to understand basic concepts, such as how soap cleans away dirt and why trans fats are undesirable in the diet, without being overwhelmed.

This textbook is written for students who have an interest in nursing, nutrition, environmental science, food science, and a wide variety of other health-related professions. The content of this book is designed for an introductory chemistry course with no chemistry prerequisite, and is suitable for either a two-semester sequence or a one-semester course. I have found that by introducing one new concept at a time, keeping the basic themes in focus, and breaking down complex problems into small pieces, many students in these chemistry courses acquire a new appreciation of both the human body and the larger world around them.

## Building the Text

Writing a textbook is a multifaceted process. McGraw-Hill's 360° Development Process is an ongoing, never ending market-oriented approach to building accurate and innovative print and digital products. It is dedicated to continual large scale and incremental improvement, driven by multiple customer feedback loops and checkpoints. This is initiated during the early planning stages of new products, intensifies during the development and production stages, and then begins again upon publication, in anticipation of the next edition. This process is designed to provide a broad, comprehensive spectrum of feedback for refinement and innovation of learning tools, for both student and instructor. The 360° Development Process includes market research, content reviews, faculty and student focus groups, course- and product-specific symposia, accuracy checks, and art reviews.

## The Learning System Used in *General, Organic, & Biological Chemistry*

▶ **Writing Style**  A concise writing style allows students to focus on learning major concepts and themes of general, organic, and biological chemistry. Relevant materials from everyday life are used to illustrate concepts, and topics are broken into small chunks of information that are more easily learned.

▶ **Chapter Outline**  The chapter outline lists the main headings of the chapter, to help students map out the organization of each chapter's content.

**Chapter Goals, tied to end-of-chapter Key Concepts** The Chapter Goals at the beginning of each chapter identify what students will learn, and are tied numerically to the end-of-chapter Key Concepts, which serve as bulleted summaries of the most important concepts for study.

**Macro-to-Micro Illustrations** Because today's students are visual learners, and because visualizing molecular-level representations of macroscopic phenomena is critical to the understanding of any chemistry course, many illustrations in this text include photos or drawings of everyday objects, paired with their molecular representation, to help students understand the chemistry behind ordinary occurrences.

Figure 3.1
Sodium Chloride, an Ionic Compound

Sodium metal | Chlorine gas | Sodium chloride crystals

Na

$Cl_2$

$Na^+$ (sodium ion)

$Cl^-$ (chloride ion)

Sodium metal and chlorine gas are both elements. Sodium chloride is an ionic compound composed of sodium ions and chloride ions.

**Problem Solving** Sample Problems lead students through the thought process tied to successful problem solving by employing Analysis and Solution parts. Sample Problems are categorized sequentially by topic to match chapter organization, and are often paired with practice problems to allow students to apply what they have just learned. Students can immediately verify their answers to the follow-up problems in the appendix at the end of the book.

*How To* Name an Ionic Compound That Contains a Metal with Variable Charge

Example: Give the name for $CuCl_2$.

Step [1] Determine the charge on the cation.
- Since there are two $Cl^-$ anions, each of which has a –1 charge, the copper cation must have a +2 charge to make the overall charge zero.

$CuCl_2$ 2 $Cl^-$ anions ---→ The total negative charge is –2.

Cu must have a +2 charge to balance the –2 charge of the anions.

→ $Cu^{2+}$

Step [2] Name the cation and anion.
- Name the cation using its element name followed by a Roman numeral to indicate its charge. In the common system, use the suffix *-ous* or *-ic* to indicate charge.
- Name the anion by changing the ending of the element name to the suffix *-ide*.

$Cu^{2+}$ ---→ copper(II) or cupric
$Cl^-$ ---→ chloride

Step [3] Write the name of the cation first, then the anion.
- **Answer:** Copper(II) chloride or cupric chloride.

**How To's** Key processes are taught to students in a straightforward and easy-to-understand manner by using examples and multiple, detailed steps to solving problems.

**Applications** Common applications of chemistry to everyday life are found in margin-placed Health Notes, Consumer Notes, and Environmental Notes, as well as sections entitled "Focus on Health & Medicine," "Focus on the Environment," and "Focus on the Human Body."

# New to This Edition

## Chapter Specific

- Atomic weights are now reported more systematically, using four significant digits for all weights. The periodic table of elements has also been revised accordingly in Chapter 2 and on the inside cover.
- Examples of ions with variable charge have been added to Chapter 3 to present a clearer discussion of the fact that some of the transition metals have a fixed charge while others are variable.
- A section on limiting reactants has been added to Chapter 5. This additional coverage instructs students on how to determine which reactant is limiting and how much product is formed using the mole ratios in a balanced equation.
- A more detailed discussion of the transition state in energy diagrams was added to Chapter 6.
- A discussion of heating and cooling curves was added to Chapter 7 in order to provide a more complete illustration of energy and phase changes.
- Material on optical activity and polarimetry has been added to Chapter 15.
- More photos have been added to Chapters 22 through 24 to aid students in visualizing and better relating to the concepts in the text.

## General

- **Problem sets.** More problems with molecular art and 3-D models have been added to the text and end-of-chapter. A set of Challenge Problems has also been added at the end of each chapter.
- **Design.** The problem and sample problem headings have been moved out of the margin to leave more room for marginal photos and tables, allowing for photos and tables to be placed closer to relevant material in the text.
- **Photos.** About one-third to one-half of the chapter opening photos have been replaced with photos emphasizing relevance and student interest. More marginal photos of relevant applications have been added.
- **Art.** The representations of the human body have been given a much cleaner and androgynous appearance.

# Our Commitment to Serving Teachers and Learners

**TO THE INSTRUCTOR**  Writing a chemistry textbook is a colossal task. Teaching chemistry for over 20 years at both a private, liberal arts college and a large state university has given me a unique perspective with which to write this text. I have found that students arrive with vastly different levels of preparation and widely different expectations for their college experience. As an instructor and now an author I have tried to channel my love and knowledge of chemistry into a form that allows this spectrum of students to understand chemical science more clearly, and then see everyday phenomena in a new light.

**TO THE STUDENT**  I hope that this text and its ancillary program will help you to better understand and appreciate the world of chemistry. My interactions with thousands of students in my long teaching career have profoundly affected the way I teach and write about chemistry, so please feel free to email me with any comments or questions at **jgsmith@hawaii.edu.**

# P.A.V.E. the Way to Student Learning

Ginkgo extracts from the tree *Ginkgo biloba* contain ginkgolide B (Problem 5.17), a complex compound that was synthesized by a series of chemical reactions in the laboratory of Nobel Laureate E. J. Corey at Harvard University in 1988.

**P**ractice chemistry through stepped-out practice problems and end-of-chapter problems categorized sequentially by topic to match chapter organization. *How-To* **boxes** offer step-by-step strategies for difficult concepts.

**A**pply chemistry through **"Focus on Health & Medicine," "Focus on the Human Body,"** and **"Focus on the Environment"** sections woven throughout the text. Chemistry applications are also woven into marginal notes that cover topics on consumer, health, and environmental issues.

CONSUMER NOTE

Some anti-aging creams contain vitamin A.

Figure 5.2    Chemistry of an Automobile Airbag

a. The chemical reaction that inflates an airbag

inflated airbag

inflator

crash sensor

Na

N₂

NaN₃
sodium azide

b. An airbag deployed in a head-on collision

A severe car crash triggers an airbag to deploy when an electric sensor causes sodium azide (NaN₃) to ignite, converting it to sod[ium] and nitrogen gas (N₂). The nitrogen gas causes the bag to inflate fully in 40 milliseconds, helping to protect passengers from seri[ous]. The sodium atoms formed in this first reaction are hazardous and subsequently converted to a safe sodium salt. It took 30 years [to develop a] reliable airbag system for automobiles.

**V**isualize chemistry through a dynamic art program that brings together macroscopic and microscopic representations of images to help students comprehend on a molecular level. Many illustrations include photos or drawings of everyday objects, paired with their molecular representation, to help students understand the chemistry behind ordinary occurrences. Many illustrations of the human body include magnifications for specific anatomic regions, as well as representations at the microscopic level, for today's visual learners.

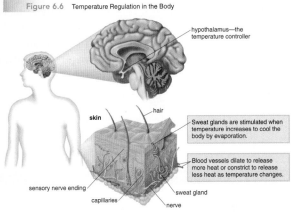

Figure 6.6    Temperature Regulation in the Body

hypothalamus—the
temperature controller

skin

hair

Sweat glands are stimulated when temperature increases to cool the body by evaporation.

Blood vessels dilate to release more heat or constrict to release less heat as temperature changes.

sensory nerve ending

capillaries

sweat gland

nerve

When the temperature in the environment around the body changes, the body works to counteract the change, in a method similar to Le Châtelier's principle. The hypothalamus acts as a thermostat, which signals the body to respond to temperature changes. When the temperature increases, the body must dissipate excess heat by dilating blood vessels and sweating. When the temperature decreases, blood vessels constrict and the body shivers.

### 7.8A    Vapor Pressure

When a liquid is placed in an open container, liquid molecules near the surface that have enough kinetic energy to overcome the intermolecular forces, escape to the gas phase. This process, **evaporation,** will continue until all of the liquid has become gas. A puddle of water formed after a rainstorm evaporates as all of the liquid water is converted to gas molecules called water **vapor.** **Evaporation is an *endothermic* process**—it absorbs heat from the surroundings. This explains why the skin is cooled as sweat evaporates.

Chloroethane (CH₃CH₂Cl), commonly called ethyl chloride, is a local anesthetic. When chloroethane is sprayed on a wound it quickly evaporates, causing a cooling sensation that numbs the site of an injury.

HEALTH NOTE

H₂O

evaporation

In a closed container, some liquid molecules evaporate from the surface and enter the gas phase. As more molecules accumulate in the gas phase, some molecules re-enter the liquid phase in the process of **condensation. Condensation is an *exothermic* process**—it gives off heat to the surroundings. At equilibrium, the rate of evaporation and the rate of condensation are equal.

In **evaporation,** molecules go from liquid to gas.

In **condensation,** molecules go from gas to liquid.

H₂O

liquid in a closed container

The gas laws we have already learned can describe the behavior of the gas molecules above a liquid. In particular, these gas molecules exert pressure, called **vapor pressure.**

• Vapor pressure is the pressure exerted by gas molecules in equilibrium with the liquid phase.

The vapor pressure exerted by a particular liquid depends on the identity of the liquid and the temperature. As the temperature is increased, the kinetic energy of the molecules increases and more molecules escape into the gas phase.

• Vapor pressure increases with increasing temperature.

When the temperature is high enough that the vapor pressure above the liquid equals the atmospheric pressure, even molecules below the surface of the liquid have enough kinetic energy to enter the gas phase and the liquid boils. The *normal boiling point* of a liquid is the temperature at which its vapor pressure equals 760 mm Hg.

**E**ngage students with a unique writing style that matches the method in which students learn. Key points of general, organic, and biological chemistry, along with attention-grabbing applications to consumer, environmental, and health-related fields, are woven together in a succinct style for today's to-the-point readers.

# Learning Resources for Instructors and Students

## McGraw-Hill Connect® Chemistry

Featuring *CambridgeSoft* *ChemDraw*

**www.mcgrawhillconnect.com/chemistry**

McGraw-Hill Connect® Chemistry is a web-based assignment and assessment platform that gives students the means to better connect with their coursework, with their instructors, and with the important concepts that they will need to know for success now and in the future. The chemical drawing tool found within Connect Chemistry is CambridgeSoft's ChemDraw, which is widely considered the "gold standard" of scientific drawing programs and the cornerstone application for scientists who draw and annotate molecules, reactions, and pathways. This collaboration of Connect and ChemDraw features an easy-to-use, intuitive, and comprehensive course management and homework system with professional-grade drawing capabilities.

With Connect Chemistry, instructors can deliver assignments, quizzes, and tests online. Questions from the text are presented in an auto-gradable format and tied to the text's learning objectives. Instructors can edit existing questions and author entirely new problems. They also can track individual student performance—by question, assignment, or in relation to the class overall—with detailed grade reports; integrate grade reports easily with Learning Management Systems (LMS) such as WebCT and Blackboard; and much more.

By choosing Connect Chemistry, instructors are providing their students with a powerful tool for improving academic performance and truly mastering course material. Connect Chemistry allows students to practice important skills at their own pace and on their own schedule. Importantly, students' assessment results and instructors' feedback are all saved online—so students can continually review their progress and plot their course to success.

## McGraw-Hill ConnectPlus® Chemistry

Like Connect Chemistry, **McGraw-Hill ConnectPlus® Chemistry** provides students with online assignments and assessments, plus 24/7 online access to an eBook—an online edition of the text—to aid them in successfully completing their work, wherever and whenever they choose.

The **Best** of
**Both Worlds**

## McGraw-Hill Higher Education and Blackboard®

McGraw-Hill Higher Education and Blackboard® have teamed up! What does this mean for you?

1. **Your life, simplified.** Now you and your students can access McGraw-Hill's Connect® and Create™ right from within your Blackboard course—all with one single sign-on. Say good-bye to the days of logging in to multiple applications.

2. **Deep integration of content and tools.** Not only do you get single sign-on with Connect and Create, you also get deep integration of McGraw-Hill content and content engines right in Blackboard. Whether you're choosing a book for your course or building Connect assignments, all the tools you need are right where you want them—inside of Blackboard.

3. **Seamless Gradebooks.** Are you tired of keeping multiple gradebooks and manually synchronizing grades into Blackboard? We thought so. When a student completes an integrated Connect assignment, the grade for that assignment automatically (and instantly) feeds your Blackboard grade center.

4. **A solution for everyone.** Whether your institution is already using Blackboard or you just want to try Blackboard on your own, we have a solution for you. McGraw-Hill and Blackboard can now offer you easy access to industry-leading technology and content, whether your campus hosts it, or we do. Be sure to ask your local McGraw-Hill representative for details.

## McGraw-Hill LearnSmart™

This adaptive diagnostic learning system, powered by Connect Chemistry and based on artificial intelligence, constantly assesses a student's knowledge of the course material. As students work within the system, LearnSmart develops a personal learning path adapted to what each student has actively learned and retained. This innovative study tool

also has features to allow the instructor to see exactly what students have accomplished, with a built-in assessment tool for graded assignments. You can access LearnSmart for *General, Organic, & Biological Chemistry* at **www.mcgrawhillconnect.com/chemistry.**

## Customizable Textbooks: McGraw-Hill Create™

Create what you've only imagined. Introducing McGraw-Hill Create™—a new, self-service website that allows you to create custom course materials (print and eBooks) by drawing upon McGraw-Hill's comprehensive, cross-disciplinary content. Add your own content quickly and easily. Tap into other rights-secured third party sources as well. Then, arrange the content in a way that makes the most sense for your course, and if you wish, personalize your book with your course name and information. Choose the best delivery format for your course: color print, black-and-white print, or eBook. The eBook is now viewable for the iPad! And when you are finished customizing, you will receive a free PDF review copy in just minutes! Visit McGraw-Hill Create (**www.mcgrawhillcreate.com**) today and begin building your perfect book.

## Presentation Center

Within the Instructor's Presentation Center, instructors have access to editable PowerPoint lecture outlines, which appear as ready-made presentations that combine art and lecture notes for each chapter of the text. For instructors who prefer to create their lecture notes from scratch, all illustrations, photos, and tables are pre-inserted by chapter into a separate set of PowerPoint slides.

An online digital library contains photos, artwork, animations, and other media types that can be used to create customized lectures, visually enhanced tests and quizzes, compelling course websites, or attractive printed support materials. All assets are copyrighted by McGraw-Hill Higher Education, but can be used by instructors for classroom purposes. The visual resources in this collection include:

- **Art** Full-color digital files of all illustrations in the book can be readily incorporated into lecture presentations, exams, or custom-made classroom materials.
- **Photos** The photo collection contains digital files of photographs from the text, which can be reproduced for multiple classroom uses.
- **Tables** Every table that appears in the text has been saved in electronic form for use in classroom presentations and/or quizzes.
- **Animations** Numerous full-color animations illustrating important processes are also provided. Harness the visual impact of concepts in motion by importing these files into classroom presentations or online course materials.

## Digital Lecture Capture: Tegrity®

McGraw-Hill Tegrity® records and distributes your lecture with just a click of a button. Students can view anytime/anywhere via computer, iPod, or mobile device. Tegrity indexes as it records your slideshow presentations and anything shown on your computer, so students can use keywords to find exactly what they want to study.

## Instructor's Solutions Manual

This supplement contains complete, worked out solutions for all the end-of-chapter problems in the text. It can be found within the Instructor's Resources for this text at **www.mcgrawhillconnect.com/chemistry.**

## Computerized Test Bank Online

A comprehensive bank of test questions prepared by Jennifer Adamski is provided within a computerized test bank enabling you to create paper and online tests or quizzes in an easy-to-use program that allows you to prepare and access your test or quiz anywhere, at anytime. Instructors can create or edit questions, or drag-and-drop questions, to prepare tests quickly and easily. Tests may be published to an online course, or printed for paper-based assignments.

## Student Study Guide/Solutions Manual

The Student Solutions Manual, prepared by Erin Smith Berk and Janice Gorzynski Smith, begins each chapter with a detailed chapter review that is organized around the chapter goals and key concepts. The Problem Solving section provides a number of examples for solving each type of problem essential to that chapter. The Self-Test section of each chapter quizzes chapter highlights, with answers provided. Finally, each chapter ends with the solutions to all in-chapter problems, as well as the solutions to all odd-numbered end-of-chapter problems.

# Acknowledgments

Publishing a modern chemistry textbook requires a team of knowledgeable and hard-working individuals who are able to translate an author's vision into a reality. I am thankful to work with such a group of dedicated publishing professionals at McGraw-Hill. Much thanks goes to Sponsoring Editor Todd Turner and Senior Developmental Editor Mary Hurley, both of whom managed the day-to-day details of the project with timeliness and professionalism. Jayne Klein, Senior Project Manager, skillfully directed the production process, and Publisher Ryan Blankenship guided the project to assure that all the needed resources were available to see it to completion.

I am especially grateful to freelance Developmental Editor John Murdzek, whose unique blend of humor, chemical knowledge, and attention to detail were key ingredients at numerous stages in the creation of both the text and the student solutions manual. I have also greatly benefited from a team of advisors who helped guide me through the preparation of the first edition, as well as a panel of art reviewers who oversaw the creation of the beautiful figures present in the finished text.

Finally, I thank my family for their support and patience during the long process of publishing a textbook. My husband Dan, an emergency medicine physician, read the entire manuscript, took several photos that appear in the text, and served as a consultant for many medical applications. My daughter Erin co-authored the *Student Study Guide/Solutions Manual* with me, which was written while she was working as a full-time physician in emergency medicine.

## Reviewers

The following people were instrumental in reading and providing feedback on the text and illustrations, which helped to shape my ideas into cohesive pages:

Madeline Adamczeski, *San Jose City College*
Karen Atkinson, *Bunker Hill Community College*
Dan Black, *Snow College*
Albert Bobst, *University of Cincinnati*
David Butcher, *Western Carolina University*
Ling Chen, *Borough of Manhattan Community College/CUNY*
Pam Clevenger, *Hinds Community College*
Rajeev Dabke, *Columbus State University*
William Daniel, *Bakersfield College*
Brahmadeo Dewprashad, *Borough of Manhattan Community College*
Pam Doyle, *Essex County College*
Coretta Fernandes, *Lansing Community College*
Zewdu Gebeyehu, *Columbus State University*
Arlene Haffa, *University of Wisconsin, Oshkosh*
Amy Hanks, *Brigham Young University, Idaho*
Blaine Harrison, *West Valley College*
John Haseltine, *Kennesaw State University*
Shirley Hino, *Santa Rosa Junior College*
Michael Hurst, *Georgia Southern University*
Tom Huxford, *San Diego State University*
Martina Kaledin, *Kennesaw State University*

Margaret Leslie, *Kent State University*
Julie Lowe, *Bakersfield College*
Ying Mao, *Camden Community College*
Craig McClure, *University of Alabama at Birmingham*
Mary Bethe Neely, *University of Colorado at Colorado Springs*
Felix Ngassa, *Grand Valley State University*
Amanda Norick, *Foothill College*
Kenneth O'Connor, *Marshall University*
Katherine Olsen, *Pierce College*
Johanna Petridou–Fisher, *Spokane Falls Community College*
Allan Pinhas, *University of Cincinnati*
Tomislav Pintauer, *Duquesne University*
Mike Ray, *California State University Fresno*
Jonathan Rhoad, *Missouri Western State University*
Jennifer Robertson–Honecker, *West Virginia University*
Paul Root, *Henry Ford Community College*
Raymond Sadeghi, *University of Texas at San Antonio*
Susan Marie Sawyer, *Kellogg Community College*
Colleen Scott, *Southern Illinois University Carbondale*
Nicholas Servis, *Vincennes University–Jasper Campus*
Heather Sklenicka, *Rochester Community and Technical College*
David Stanislawski, *Chattanooga State Technical Community College*
Denise Stiglich, *Antelope Valley College*
Susan Thomas, *University of Texas at San Antonio*
Lois Gilbert Waters, *Baltimore City Community College*
Lawrence Williams, *Wake Tech Community College*
Lawrence Yee, *Hartnell College*

McGraw-Hill Connect® Chemistry has been greatly enhanced by the efforts of Danae Quirk Dorr of Minnesota State University–Mankato, who worked to improve the content, author feedback and hints, and select problems for the second edition site; and Shirley Hino of Santa Rosa Junior College, who authored the interactive problem content, also authored feedback and hints, and performed accuracy checking of all Connect: Chemistry content. In addition, the following instructors also did a masterful job of authoring hints and feedback to augment all of the Connect: Chemistry homework problems: Eric Elisabeth of Johnson County Community College; Patrick Greco of Sinclair Community College; Paul Root of Henry Ford Community College; Emily Tansey of Otterbein College; John Tansey of Otterbein College; and Dave Tramontozzi of Macomb Community College. The following instructors performed accuracy checks of the Connect: Chemistry content to ensure the reliability and correctness:  Jennifer Adamski (formally of Old Dominion University); Eric Elisabeth of Johnson County Community College; and Annise Goodman of Eastern Michigan University.

The following individuals helped write and review learning goal-oriented content for McGraw-Hill LearnSmart™ for *General, Organic, & Biological Chemistry:* Susan Bane, Binghamton University; Anne M. Distler, Cuyahoga Community College; Patrick Greco, Sinclair Community College; Lenore K. Hoyt, University of Louisville; David G. Jones, North Carolina Central University; Adam I. Keller, Columbus State Community College; Michael Koerner, University of Arizona; Jerry Mundell, Cleveland State University; Anne O'Connor, Cleveland State University; Shadrick I. Paris, Ohio University; Paul D. Root, Henry Ford Community College; Kathleen Thrush Shaginaw, Particular Solutions, Inc.; and David Tramontozzi, Macomb Community College.

We are also extremely grateful to the authors of the other ancillaries to accompany *General, Organic, & Biological Chemistry,* Second Edition: Lauren McMills of Ohio University–Athens for her authoring of the Instructor Solutions Manual; Andrea Leonard of the University of Louisiana at Lafayette for her authoring of the PowerPoint Lecture Outlines; and Jennifer Adamski for her authoring of the Test Bank.

# List of *How To's*

# List of Applications

Determining the weight and length of a newborn are common measurements performed by healthcare professionals.

# Matter and Measurement

## CHAPTER GOALS

*In this chapter you will learn how to:*

1. Describe the three states of matter

2. Classify matter as a pure substance, mixture, element, or compound

3. Report measurements using the metric units of length, mass, and volume

4. Use significant figures

5. Use scientific notation for very large and very small numbers

6. Use conversion factors to convert one unit to another

7. Convert temperature from one scale to another

8. Define density and specific gravity and use density to calculate the mass or volume of a substance

Everything you touch, feel, or taste is composed of chemicals—that is, **matter**—so an understanding of its composition and properties is crucial to our appreciation of the world around us. Some matter—lakes, trees, sand, and soil—is naturally occurring, while other examples of matter—aspirin, CDs, nylon fabric, plastic syringes, and vaccines—are made by humans. To understand the properties of matter, as well as how one form of matter is converted to another, we must also learn about measurements. Following a recipe, pumping gasoline, and figuring out drug dosages involve manipulating numbers. Thus, Chapter 1 begins our study of chemistry by examining the key concepts of matter and measurement.

## 1.1   Chemistry—The Science of Everyday Experience

What activities might occupy the day of a typical student? You may have done some or all of the following tasks: eaten some meals, drunk coffee or cola, taken a shower with soap, taken notes in a class, checked email on a computer, watched some television, ridden a bike or car to a part-time job, taken an aspirin to relieve a headache, and spent some of the evening having snacks and refreshments with friends. Perhaps, without your awareness, your life was touched by chemistry in each of these activities. What, then, is this discipline we call **chemistry?**

- *Chemistry* is the study of matter—its composition, properties, and transformations.

What is **matter?**

- *Matter* is anything that has mass and takes up volume.

In other words, **chemistry studies anything that we touch, feel, see, smell, or taste,** from simple substances like water or salt, to complex substances like proteins and carbohydrates that combine to form the human body. Some matter—cotton, sand, an apple, and the cardiac drug digoxin—is **naturally occurring,** meaning it is isolated from natural sources. Other substances—nylon, Styrofoam, the plastic used in soft drink bottles, and the pain reliever ibuprofen—are **synthetic,** meaning they are produced by chemists in the laboratory (Figure 1.1).

**Figure 1.1**   Naturally Occurring and Synthetic Materials

a. Naturally occurring materials

b. Synthetic materials

Matter occurs in nature or is synthesized in the lab. (a) Sand and apples are two examples of natural materials. Cotton fabric is woven from cotton fiber, obtained from the cotton plant. The drug digoxin (Trade name: Lanoxin), widely prescribed for decades for patients with congestive heart failure, is extracted from the leaves of the woolly foxglove plant. (b) Nylon was the first synthetic fiber made in the laboratory. It quickly replaced the natural fiber silk in parachutes and ladies' stockings. Styrofoam and PET (polyethylene terephthalate), the plastic used for soft drink bottles, are strong yet lightweight synthetic materials used for food storage. Over-the-counter pain relievers like ibuprofen are synthetic. The starting materials for all of these useful products are obtained from petroleum.

MATTER

**Figure 1.2**

Transforming Natural Materials into Useful Synthetic Products

a.

b.
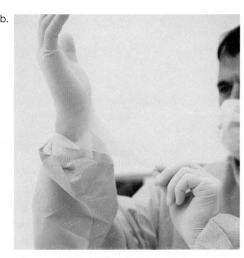

(a) Latex, the sticky liquid that oozes from a rubber tree when it is cut, is too soft for most applications.
(b) Vulcanization converts latex to the stronger, elastic rubber used in tires and other products.

Sometimes a chemist studies what a substance is made of, while at other times he or she might be interested in its properties. Alternatively, the focus may be how to convert one material into a new material with unique and useful properties. As an example, naturally occurring rubber exists as the sticky liquid latex, which is too soft for most applications. The laboratory process of vulcanization converts it to the stronger, more elastic material used in tires and other products (Figure 1.2).

Chemistry is truly the science of everyday experience. Soaps and detergents, newspapers and CDs, condoms and oral contraceptives, Tylenol and penicillin—all of these items are products of chemistry. Without a doubt, advances in chemistry have transformed life in modern times.

**PROBLEM 1.1**

Look around you and identify five objects. Decide if they are composed of natural or synthetic materials.

**PROBLEM 1.2**

Imagine that your job as a healthcare professional is to take a blood sample from a patient and store it in a small container in a refrigerator until it is picked up for analysis in the hospital lab. You might have to put on gloves and a mask, use a plastic syringe with a metal needle, store the sample in a test tube or vial, and place it in a cold refrigerator. Pick five objects you might encounter during the process and decide if they are made of naturally occurring or synthetic materials.

## 1.2 States of Matter

**Matter exists in three common states—solid, liquid, and gas.**

- A *solid* has a definite volume, and maintains its shape regardless of the container in which it is placed. The particles of a solid lie close together, and are arranged in a regular three-dimensional array.
- A *liquid* has a definite volume, but takes on the shape of the container it occupies. The particles of a liquid are close together, but they can randomly move around, sliding past one another.
- A *gas* has no definite shape or volume. The particles of a gas move randomly and are separated by a distance much larger than their size. The particles of a gas expand to fill the volume and assume the shape of whatever container they are put in.

For example, water exists in its solid state as ice or snow, liquid state as liquid water, and gaseous state as steam or water vapor. Blow-up circles like those in Figure 1.3 will be used commonly in this text to indicate the composition and state of the particles that compose a substance. In this molecular art, different types of particles are shown in color-coded spheres, and the distance between the spheres signals its state—solid, liquid, or gas.

Matter is characterized by its **physical properties** and **chemical properties.**

• *Physical properties* are those that can be observed or measured without changing the composition of the material.

Common physical properties include melting point (mp), boiling point (bp), solubility, color, and odor. **A *physical change* alters a substance without changing its composition.** The most common physical changes are **changes in state.** Melting an ice cube to form liquid water, and boiling liquid water to form steam are two examples of physical changes. Water is the substance at the beginning and end of both physical changes. More details about physical changes are discussed in Chapter 7.

**Figure 1.3**    The Three States of Water—Solid, Liquid, and Gas

a. Solid water        b. Liquid water        c. Gaseous water

• The particles of a solid are close together and highly organized. (Photo: snow-capped Mauna Kea on the Big Island of Hawaii)

• The particles of a liquid are close together but more disorganized than the solid. (Photo: Akaka Falls on the Big Island of Hawaii)

• The particles of a gas are far apart and disorganized. (Photo: steam formed by a lava flow on the Big Island of Hawaii)

Each red sphere joined to two gray spheres represents a single water particle. In proceeding from left to right, from solid to liquid to gas, the molecular art shows that the level of organization of the water particles decreases. Color-coding and the identity of the spheres within the particles will be addressed in Chapter 2.

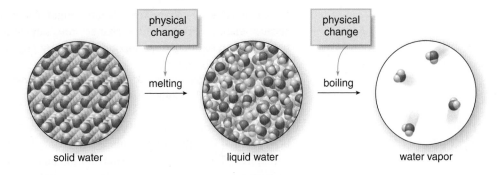

solid water      liquid water      water vapor

> • *Chemical properties* are those that determine how a substance can be converted to another substance.

A *chemical change,* or a *chemical reaction,* **converts one material to another.** The conversion of hydrogen and oxygen to water is a chemical reaction because the composition of the material is different at the beginning and end of the process. Chemical reactions are discussed in Chapters 5 and 6.

### PROBLEM 1.3

Characterize each process as a physical change or a chemical change: (a) making ice cubes; (b) burning natural gas; (c) silver jewelry tarnishing; (d) a pile of snow melting; (e) baking bread.

### PROBLEM 1.4

Does the molecular art represent a chemical change or a physical change? Explain your choice.

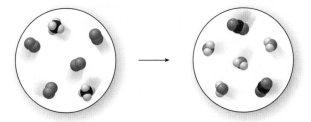

## 1.3    Classification of Matter

All matter can be classified as either a **pure substance** or a **mixture.**

> • A *pure substance* is composed of a single component and has a constant composition, regardless of the sample size and the origin of the sample.

A pure substance, such as water or table sugar, can be characterized by its physical properties, because these properties do not change from sample to sample. **A pure substance cannot be broken down to other pure substances by any physical change.**

- A *mixture* is composed of more than one component. The composition of a mixture can vary depending on the sample.

The physical properties of a mixture may also vary from one sample to another. **A mixture can be separated into its components by physical changes.** Dissolving table sugar in water forms a mixture, whose sweetness depends on the amount of sugar added. If the water is allowed to evaporate from the mixture, pure table sugar and pure water are obtained.

| sugar | water | sugar dissolved in water |
|:-----:|:-----:|:------------------------:|
| pure substances | | mixture |

Mixtures can be formed from solids, liquids, and gases, as shown in Figure 1.4. The compressed air breathed by a scuba diver consists mainly of the gases oxygen and nitrogen. A saline solution used in an IV bag contains solid sodium chloride (table salt) dissolved in liquid water.

**Figure 1.4**    Two Examples of Mixtures

a. Two gases

oxygen        nitrogen

b. A solid and a liquid

water        sodium

chloride (from chlorine)

## Figure 1.5    Elements and Compounds

a. Aluminum foil

aluminum

b. Nitrogen gas

nitrogen

c. Water

hydrogen                    oxygen

d. Table salt

chloride                    sodium
(from chlorine)

- Aluminum foil and nitrogen gas are elements. The molecular art for an element shows spheres of one color only. Thus, aluminum is a solid shown with gray spheres, while nitrogen is a gas shown with blue spheres. Water and table salt are compounds. Color-coding of the spheres used in the molecular art indicates that water is composed of two elements—hydrogen shown as gray spheres, and oxygen shown in red. Likewise, the gray (sodium) and green (chlorine) spheres illustrate that sodium chloride is formed from two elements as well.

A pure substance is classified as either an **element** or a **compound.**

- An *element* is a pure substance that cannot be broken down into simpler substances by a chemical reaction.
- A *compound* is a pure substance formed by chemically combining (joining together) two or more elements.

An alphabetical list of elements is located on the inside front cover of this text. The elements are commonly organized into a periodic table, also shown on the inside front cover, and discussed in much greater detail in Section 2.4.

Nitrogen gas, aluminum foil, and copper wire are all elements. Water is a compound because it is composed of the elements hydrogen and oxygen. Table salt, sodium chloride, is also a compound since it is formed from the elements sodium and chlorine (Figure 1.5). Although only 118 elements are currently known, over 20 million compounds occur naturally or have been synthesized in the laboratory. We will learn much more about elements and compounds in Chapter 2. Figure 1.6 summarizes the categories into which matter is classified.

### SAMPLE PROBLEM 1.1

Classify each example of molecular art as an element or a compound:

a.

b.

### Analysis

In molecular art, an element is composed of spheres of the same color, while a compound is composed of spheres of different colors.

### Solution

Representation (a) is an element since each particle contains only gray spheres. Representation (b) is a compound since each particle contains both red and black spheres.

### PROBLEM 1.5

Classify each example of molecular art as a pure substance or a mixture:

a.    b.

### PROBLEM 1.6

Classify each item as a pure substance or a mixture: (a) blood; (b) ocean water; (c) a piece of wood; (d) a chunk of ice.

### PROBLEM 1.7

Classify each item as an element or a compound: (a) the gas inside a helium balloon; (b) table sugar; (c) the rust on an iron nail; (d) aspirin. All elements are listed alphabetically on the inside front cover.

**Figure 1.6**   Classification of Matter

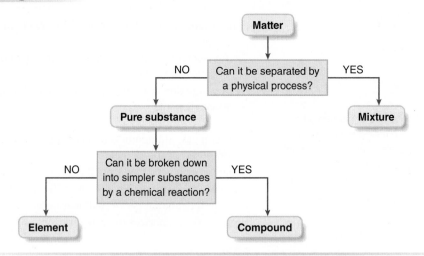

## 1.4   Measurement

Any time you check your weight on a scale, measure the ingredients of a recipe, or figure out how far it is from one location to another, you are measuring a quantity. Measurements are routine for healthcare professionals who use weight, blood pressure, pulse, and temperature to chart a patient's progress.

Length:
21.0 in.
or
53.3 cm

number    unit

Mass
(Weight):
8 lb 8 oz
or
3.9 kg

number    unit

**CONSUMER NOTE**

The metric system is slowly gaining acceptance in the United States, as seen in the gallon jug of milk and the two-liter bottle of soda.

### Table 1.1 The Basic Metric Units

| Quantity | Metric Base Unit | Symbol |
|---|---|---|
| Length | Meter | m |
| Mass | Gram | g |
| Volume | Liter | L |
| Time | Second | s |

- Every measurement is composed of a *number* and a *unit*.

Reporting the value of a measurement is meaningless without its unit. For example, if you were told to give a patient an aspirin dosage of 325, does this mean 325 ounces, pounds, grams, milligrams, or tablets? Clearly there is a huge difference among these quantities.

## 1.4A The Metric System

In the United States, most measurements are made with the **English system,** using units like miles (mi), gallons (gal), pounds (lb), and so forth. A disadvantage of this system is that the units are not systematically related to each other and require memorization. For example, 1 lb = 16 oz, 1 gal = 4 qt, and 1 mi = 5,280 ft.

Scientists, health professionals, and people in most other countries use the **metric system,** with units like meter (m) for length, gram (g) for mass, and liter (L) for volume. The metric system is slowly gaining popularity in the United States. The weight of packaged foods is often given in both ounces and grams. Distances on many road signs are shown in miles and kilometers. Most measurements in this text will be reported using the metric system, but learning to convert English units to metric units is also a necessary skill that will be illustrated in Section 1.7.

The important features of the metric system are the following:

- Each type of measurement has a base unit—the meter (m) for length; the gram (g) for mass; the liter (L) for volume; the second (s) for time.
- All other units are related to the base unit by powers of 10.
- The prefix of the unit name indicates if the unit is larger or smaller than the base unit.

The base units of the metric system are summarized in Table 1.1, and the most common prefixes used to convert the base units to smaller or larger units are summarized in Table 1.2. **The same prefixes are used for all types of measurement.** For example, the prefix *kilo-* means 1,000 times as large. Thus,

| 1 **kilo**meter = **1,000** meters | or | 1 km = 1,000 m |
|---|---|---|
| 1 **kilo**gram = **1,000** grams | or | 1 kg = 1,000 g |
| 1 **kilo**liter = **1,000** liters | or | 1 kL = 1,000 L |

The prefix *milli-* means one thousandth as large (1/1,000 or 0.001). Thus,

| 1 **milli**meter = **0.001** meters | or | 1 mm = 0.001 m |
|---|---|---|
| 1 **milli**gram = **0.001** grams | or | 1 mg = 0.001 g |
| 1 **milli**liter = **0.001** liters | or | 1 mL = 0.001 L |

### Table 1.2  Common Prefixes Used for Metric Units

| Prefix | Symbol | Meaning | Numerical Value[a] | Scientific Notation[b] |
|--------|--------|---------|-------------------|----------------------|
| Mega- | M | Million | 1,000,000. | $10^6$ |
| Kilo- | k | Thousand | 1,000. | $10^3$ |
| Deci- | d | Tenth | 0.1 | $10^{-1}$ |
| Centi- | c | Hundredth | 0.01 | $10^{-2}$ |
| Milli- | m | Thousandth | 0.001 | $10^{-3}$ |
| Micro- | μ[c] | Millionth | 0.000 001 | $10^{-6}$ |
| Nano- | n | Billionth | 0.000 000 001 | $10^{-9}$ |

[a]Numbers that contain five or more digits to the right of the decimal point are written with a small space separating each group of three digits.
[b]How to express numbers in scientific notation is explained in Section 1.6.
[c]The symbol μ is the lower case Greek letter mu. The prefix *micro-* is sometimes abbreviated as **mc.**

The metric symbols are all lower case except for the unit **liter** (L) and the prefix **mega-** (M). Liter is capitalized to distinguish it from the number *one.* Mega is capitalized to distinguish it from the symbol for the prefix *milli-*.

### PROBLEM 1.8

What term is used for each of the following units: (a) a million liters; (b) a thousandth of a second; (c) a hundredth of a gram; (d) a tenth of a liter?

## 1.4B  Measuring Length

**The base unit of length in the metric system is the *meter* (m).** A meter, 39.4 inches in the English system, is slightly longer than a yard (36 inches). The three most common units derived from a meter are the kilometer (km), centimeter (cm), and millimeter (mm).

$$1,000 \text{ m} = 1 \text{ km}$$
$$1 \text{ m} = 100 \text{ cm}$$
$$1 \text{ m} = 1,000 \text{ mm}$$

Note how these values are related to those in Table 1.2. Since a centimeter is one *hundredth* of a meter (0.01 m), there are *100* centimeters in a meter.

### PROBLEM 1.9

If a nanometer is one billionth of a meter (0.000 000 001 m), how many nanometers are there in one meter?

## 1.4C  Measuring Mass

Although the terms mass and weight are often used interchangeably, they really have different meanings.

- *Mass* is a measure of the amount of matter in an object.
- *Weight* is the force that matter feels due to gravity.

The mass of an object is independent of its location. The weight of an object changes slightly with its location on the earth, and drastically when the object is moved from the earth to the moon, where the gravitational pull is only one-sixth that of the earth. Although we often speak of *weighing* an object, we are really *measuring its mass.*

**The base unit of mass in the metric system is the *gram* (g),** a small quantity compared to the English pound (1 lb = 454 g). The two most common units derived from a gram are the kilogram (kg) and milligram (mg).

$$1,000 \text{ g} = 1 \text{ kg}$$
$$1 \text{ g} = 1,000 \text{ mg}$$

## PROBLEM 1.10

If a microgram is one millionth of a gram (0.000 001 g), how many micrograms are there in one gram?

## 1.4D Measuring Volume

**The base unit of volume in the metric system is the *liter* (L),** which is slightly larger than the English quart (1 L = 1.06 qt). One liter is defined as the volume of a cube 10 cm on an edge.

Note the difference between the units **cm** and **cm³**. The centimeter (cm) is a unit of length. A cubic centimeter (cm³ or cc) is a unit of volume.

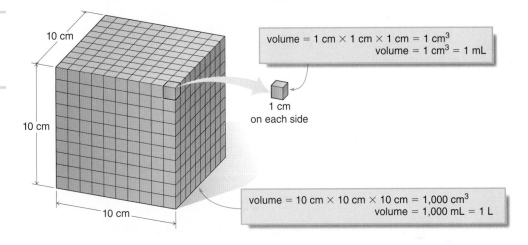

volume = 1 cm × 1 cm × 1 cm = 1 cm³
volume = 1 cm³ = 1 mL

1 cm on each side

volume = 10 cm × 10 cm × 10 cm = 1,000 cm³
volume = 1,000 mL = 1 L

Three common units derived from a liter used in medicine and laboratory research are the deci-liter (dL), milliliter (mL), and microliter (μL). **One milliliter is the same as one cubic centimeter (cm³), which is abbreviated as cc.**

$$1 \text{ L} = 10 \text{ dL}$$
$$1 \text{ L} = 1,000 \text{ mL}$$
$$1 \text{ L} = 1,000,000 \text{ μL}$$
$$1 \text{ mL} = 1 \text{ cm}^3 = 1 \text{ cc}$$

Table 1.3 summarizes common metric units of length, mass, and volume. Table 1.4 lists English units of measurement, as well as their metric equivalents.

## PROBLEM 1.11

Using the prefixes in Table 1.2, determine which quantity in each pair is larger.

a. 3 mL or 3 cL

b. 1 ng or 1 μg

c. 5 km or 5 cm

d. 2 mL or 2 μL

### Table 1.3 Summary of the Common Metric Units of Length, Mass, and Volume

| Length | Mass | Volume |
|---|---|---|
| 1 km = 1,000 m | 1 kg = 1,000 g | 1 L = 10 dL |
| 1 m = 100 cm | 1 g = 1,000 mg | 1 L = 1,000 mL |
| 1 m = 1,000 mm | 1 mg = 1,000 μg | 1 L = 1,000,000 μL |
| 1 cm = 10 mm | | 1 dL = 100 mL |
| | | 1 mL = 1 cm³ = 1 cc |

### Table 1.4 English Units and Their Metric Equivalents

| Quantity | English Unit | Metric–English Relationship |
|---|---|---|
| Length | 1 ft = 12 in. | 2.54 cm = 1 in. |
| | 1 yd = 3 ft | 1 m = 39.4 in. |
| | 1 mi = 5,280 ft | 1 km = 0.621 mi |
| Mass | 1 lb = 16 oz | 1 kg = 2.20 lb |
| | 1 ton = 2,000 lb | 454 g = 1 lb |
| | | 28.3 g = 1 oz |
| Volume | 1 qt = 4 cups | 946 mL = 1 qt |
| | 1 qt = 2 pints | 1 L = 1.06 qt |
| | 1 qt = 32 fl oz | 29.6 mL = 1 fl oz |
| | 1 gal = 4 qt | |

Common abbreviations for English units: inch (in.), foot (ft), yard (yd), mile (mi), pound (lb), ounce (oz), gallon (gal), quart (qt), and fluid ounce (fl oz).

## 1.5   Significant Figures

Numbers used in chemistry are either **exact** or **inexact.**

- An *exact* number results from counting objects or is part of a definition.

Our bodies have 10 fingers, 10 toes, and two kidneys. A meter is composed of 100 centimeters. These numbers are exact because there is no uncertainty associated with them.

- An *inexact* number results from a measurement or observation and contains some uncertainty.

Whenever we measure a quantity there is a degree of uncertainty associated with the result. The last number (farthest to the right) is an estimate, and it depends on the type of measuring device we use to obtain it. For example, the length of a fish caught on a recent outing could be reported as 53 cm or 53.5 cm depending on the tape measure used.

A container of 71 macadamia nuts weighs 125 g. The number of nuts (71) is exact, while the mass of the nuts (125 g) is inexact.

- *Significant figures* are all the digits in a measured number including *one* estimated digit.

Thus, the length 53 cm has two significant figures, and the length 53.5 cm has three significant figures.

## 1.5A  Determining the Number of Significant Figures

How many significant figures are contained in a number?

> • **All nonzero digits are always significant.**

| | |
|---|---|
| 65.2 g | three significant figures |
| 1,265 m | four significant figures |
| 25 µL | two significant figures |
| 255.345 g | six significant figures |

Whether a zero counts as a significant figure depends on its location in the number.

> **Rules to Determine When a Zero is a Significant Figure**
>
> **Rule [1]**  A zero *counts* as a significant figure when it occurs:
>
> - Between two nonzero digits
>   - 29.05 g—four significant figures
>   - 1.0087 mL—five significant figures
> - At the end of a number with a decimal point
>   - 25.70 cm—four significant figures
>   - 3.7500 g—five significant figures
>   - 620. lb—three significant figures
>
> **Rule [2]**  A zero does *not* count as a significant figure when it occurs:
>
> - At the beginning of a number
>   - 0.0245 mg—three significant figures
>   - 0.008 mL—one significant figure
> - At the end of a number that does not have a decimal point
>   - 2,570 m—three significant figures
>   - 1,245,500 m—five significant figures

In reading a number with a decimal point from left to right, all digits starting with the first nonzero number are significant figures. The number 0.003 450 120 has seven significant figures, shown in red.

### SAMPLE PROBLEM 1.2

How many significant figures does each number contain?

   a. 34.08      b. 0.0054      c. 260.00      d. 260

### Analysis

All nonzero digits are significant. A zero is significant only if it occurs between two nonzero digits, or at the end of a number with a decimal point.

### Solution

Significant figures are shown in red.

   a. 34.08 (four)      b. 0.0054 (two)      c. 260.00 (five)      d. 260 (two)

### PROBLEM 1.12

How many significant figures does each number contain?

| | | | |
|---|---|---|---|
| a. 23.45 | c. 230 | e. 0.202 | g. 1,245,006 |
| b. 23.057 | d. 231.0 | f. 0.003 60 | h. 1,200,000 |

### PROBLEM 1.13

How many significant figures does each number contain?

| | | | |
|---|---|---|---|
| a. 10,040 | c. 1,004.00 | e. 1.0040 | g. 0.001 004 |
| b. 10,040. | d. 1.004 | f. 0.1004 | h. 0.010 040 0 |

### PROBLEM 1.14

Indicate whether each zero in the following numbers is significant.

| | | | |
|---|---|---|---|
| a. 0.003 04 | b. 26,045 | c. 1,000,034 | d. 0.304 00 |

## 1.5B   Using Significant Figures in Multiplication and Division

We often must perform calculations with numbers that contain a different number of significant figures. The number of significant figures in the answer of a problem depends on the type of mathematical calculation—multiplication (and division) or addition (and subtraction).

> • In multiplication and division, the answer has the same number of significant figures as the original number with the *fewest* significant figures.

Let's say you drove a car 351.2 miles in 5.5 hours, and you wanted to calculate how many miles per hour you traveled. Entering these numbers on a calculator would give the following result:

The answer to this problem can have only *two* significant figures, since one of the original numbers (5.5 hours) has only *two* significant figures. To write the answer in proper form, we must **round off the number** to give an answer with only two significant figures. Two rules are used in rounding off numbers.

> • If the first number that must be dropped is 4 or less, drop it and all remaining numbers.
> • If the first number that must be dropped is 5 or greater, *round the number up* by adding one to the last digit that will be retained.

In this problem:

Table 1.5 gives other examples of rounding off numbers.

### Table 1.5  Rounding Off Numbers

| Original Number | Rounded To | Rounded Number |
| --- | --- | --- |
| 61.2537 | Two places | 61 |
| 61.2537 | Three places | 61.3 |
| 61.2537 | Four places | 61.25 |
| 61.2537 | Five places | 61.254 |

The first number to be dropped is indicated in red in each original number. When this number is 4 or fewer, it and all other digits to its right are dropped. When this number is 5 or greater, 1 is added to the digit to its left.

### SAMPLE PROBLEM 1.3

Round off each number to three significant figures.

  a.  1.2735      b.  0.002 536 22      c.  3,836.9

### Analysis

If the answer is to have *three* significant figures, look at the *fourth* number from the left. If this number is 4 or less, drop it and all remaining numbers to the right. If the fourth number from the left is 5 or greater, round the number up by adding one to the third digit.

Solution

a. 1.27          b. 0.002 54          c. 3,840 (Omit the decimal point after the 0. The number
                                          3,840. has four significant figures.)

## PROBLEM 1.15

Round off each number in Sample Problem 1.3 to two significant figures.

## SAMPLE PROBLEM 1.4

Carry out each calculation and give the answer using the proper number of significant figures.

a. $3.81 \times 0.046$          b. $120.085 \div 106$

### Analysis

Since these calculations involve multiplication and division, the answer must have the same number of significant figures as the original number with the fewest number of significant figures.

### Solution

a. $3.81 \times 0.046 = 0.1753$

- Since 0.046 has only two significant figures, round the answer to give it two significant figures.

  0.1753     Since this number is 5 (5 or greater),
             round the 7 to its left up by one.

  **Answer: 0.18**

b. $120.085 \div 106 = 1.132\ 877\ 36$

- Since 106 has three significant figures, round the answer to give it three significant figures.

  1.132 877 36     Since this number is 2 (4 or less),
                   drop it and all numbers to its right.

  **Answer: 1.13**

## PROBLEM 1.16

Carry out each calculation and give the answer using the proper number of significant figures.

a. $10.70 \times 3.5$          b. $0.206 \div 25,993$          c. $1,300 \div 41.2$          d. $120.5 \times 26$

## 1.5C   Using Significant Figures in Addition and Subtraction

In determining significant figures in addition and subtraction, the decimal place of the last significant digit determines the number of significant figures in the answer.

- In addition and subtraction, the answer has the same number of decimal places as the original number with the *fewest* decimal places.

Suppose a baby weighed 3.6 kg at birth and 10.11 kg on his first birthday. To figure out how much weight the baby gained in his first year of life, we subtract these two numbers and report the answer using the proper number of significant figures.

weight at one year = 10.11 kg

weight at birth =     3.6 kg

                                    two digits after the decimal point
                          10.11 kg
                                    one digit after the decimal point
                        − 3.6  kg
weight gain = 6.51 kg

last significant digit

- The answer can have only **one** digit after the decimal point.
- Round 6.51 to 6.5.
- The baby gained 6.5 kg during his first year of life.

Since 3.6 kg has only one significant figure after the decimal point, the answer can have only one significant figure after the decimal point as well.

## SAMPLE PROBLEM 1.5

While on a diet, a woman lost 3.52 lb the first week, 2.2 lb the second week, and 0.59 lb the third week. How much weight did she lose in all?

### Analysis

Add up the amount of weight loss each week to get the total weight loss. When adding, the answer has the same number of decimal places as the original number with the fewest decimal places.

### Solution

$$
\begin{array}{l}
3.52 \text{ lb} \\
2.2 \text{ lb} \quad \text{one digit after the decimal point} \\
0.59 \text{ lb} \\
\hline
6.31 \text{ lb} \quad \text{-----}\rightarrow \quad 6.3 \text{ lb} \\
\qquad\qquad\quad \text{round off}
\end{array}
$$

last significant digit

- Since 2.2 lb has only one digit after the decimal point, the answer can have only one digit after the decimal point.
- Round 6.31 to 6.3.
- Total weight loss: 6.3 lb.

## PROBLEM 1.17

Carry out each calculation and give the answer using the proper number of significant figures.

a. 27.8 cm + 0.246 cm

b. 102.66 mL + 0.857 mL + 24.0 mL

c. 54.6 mg – 25 mg

d. 2.35 s – 0.266 s

# 1.6   Scientific Notation

Hospital laboratory technicians determine thousands of laboratory results each day.

Healthcare professionals and scientists must often deal with very large and very small numbers. For example, the blood platelet count of a healthy adult might be 250,000 platelets per mL. At the other extreme, the level of the female sex hormone estriol during pregnancy might be 0.000 000 250 g per mL of blood plasma. Estriol is secreted by the placenta and its concentration is used as a measure of the health of the fetus.

To write numbers that contain many leading zeros (at the beginning) or trailing zeros (at the end), scientists use **scientific notation.**

- In scientific notation, a number is written as $y \times 10^x$.
- The term $y$, called the coefficient, is a number between 1 and 10.
- The value $x$ is an exponent, which can be any positive or negative whole number.

First, let's recall what powers of 10 with *positive* exponents, such as $10^2$ or $10^5$, mean. These correspond to numbers greater than one, and the positive exponent tells how many zeros are to be written after the number one. Thus, $10^2 = 100$, a number with two zeros after the number one.

The product has two zeros.

$$10^2 = 10 \times 10 = 100$$

The exponent 2 means "multiply two 10s."

The product has five zeros.

$$10^5 = 10 \times 10 \times 10 \times 10 \times 10 = 100,000$$

The exponent 5 means "multiply five 10s."

Powers of 10 that contain *negative* exponents, such as $10^{-3}$, correspond to numbers less than one. In this case the exponent tells how many places (*not* zeros) are located to the right of the decimal point.

The answer has three places to the right of the decimal point, including the number one.

$$10^{-3} = \frac{1}{10 \times 10 \times 10} = 0.001$$

The exponent −3 means "divide by three 10s."

To write a number in scientific notation, we follow a stepwise procedure.

## How To Convert a Standard Number to Scientific Notation

**Example:** Write each number in scientific notation: (a) 2,500; (b) 0.036.

**Step [1]** **Move the decimal point to give a number between 1 and 10.**

a. 2500.

Move the decimal point three places to the left to give the number 2.5.

b. 0.036

Move the decimal point two places to the right to give the number 3.6.

**Step [2]** **Multiply the result by $10^x$, where $x$ is the number of places the decimal point was moved.**

- If the decimal point is moved to the **left,** $x$ is **positive.**
- If the decimal point is moved to the **right,** $x$ is **negative.**

a. Since the decimal point was moved three places to the **left,** the exponent is +3, and the coefficient is multiplied by $10^3$.

**Answer: $2,500 = 2.5 \times 10^3$**

b. Since the decimal point was moved two places to the **right,** the exponent is –2, and the coefficient is multiplied by $10^{-2}$.

**Answer: $0.036 = 3.6 \times 10^{-2}$**

Notice that the number of significant figures in the coefficient in scientific notation must equal the number of significant figures in the original number. Thus, the coefficients for both 2,500 and 0.036 need two significant figures and no more. Figure 1.7 shows two more examples of numbers written in standard form and scientific notation.

$$2,500 = 2.5 \times 10^3 \quad \textbf{\textit{not}} \quad 2.50 \times 10^3 \text{ (three significant figures)}$$

two significant figures

$$\textbf{\textit{not}} \quad 2.500 \times 10^3 \text{ (four significant figures)}$$

**Figure 1.7** Numbers in Standard Form and Scientific Notation

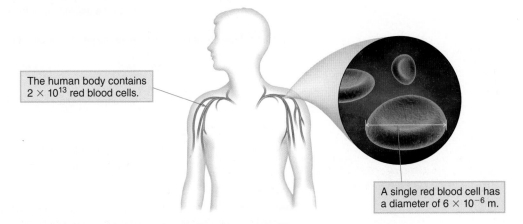

The human body contains $2 \times 10^{13}$ red blood cells.

A single red blood cell has a diameter of $6 \times 10^{-6}$ m.

Very large and very small numbers are more conveniently written in scientific notation.

| Quantity | Number | Scientific Notation |
|---|---|---|
| Number of red blood cells | 20,000,000,000,000 | $2 \times 10^{13}$ |
| Diameter of a red blood cell | 0.000 006 m | $6 \times 10^{-6}$ m |

### SAMPLE PROBLEM 1.6

Write the recommended daily dietary intake of each nutrient in scientific notation: (a) sodium, 2,400 mg; (b) vitamin $B_{12}$, 0.000 006 g.

### Analysis

Move the decimal point to give a number between 1 and 10. Multiply the number by $10^x$, where $x$ is the number of places the decimal point was moved. The exponent $x$ is (+) when the decimal point moves to the left and (–) when it moves to the right.

## Solution

a.

$$2400. = 2.4 \times 10^3 \qquad \text{the number of places the decimal point was moved to the left}$$

Move the decimal point three places to the left.

- Write the coefficient as 2.4 (two significant figures), since 2,400 contains two significant figures.

b.

$$0.000\,006 = 6 \times 10^{-6} \qquad \text{the number of places the decimal point was moved to the right}$$

Move the decimal point six places to the right.

- Write the coefficient as 6 (one significant figure), since 0.000 006 contains one significant figure.

## PROBLEM 1.18

Lab results for a routine check-up showed an individual's iron level in the blood to be 0.000 098 g per deciliter, placing it in the normal range. Convert this number to scientific notation.

## PROBLEM 1.19

Write each number in scientific notation.

a. 93,200
b. 0.000 725

c. 6,780,000
d. 0.000 030

e. 4,520,000,000,000
f. 0.000 000 000 028

To convert a number in scientific notation to a standard number, reverse the procedure, as shown in Sample Problem 1.7. It is often necessary to add leading or trailing zeros to write the number.

- **When the exponent $x$ is positive, move the decimal point $x$ places to the *right*.**

$$2.800 \times 10^2 \qquad\qquad 2.800 \quad \dashrightarrow \quad 280.0$$

Move the decimal point to the right two places.

- **When the exponent $x$ is negative, move the decimal point $x$ places to the *left*.**

$$2.80 \times 10^{-2} \qquad\qquad 002.80 \quad \dashrightarrow \quad 0.0280$$

Move the decimal point to the left two places.

## SAMPLE PROBLEM 1.7

As we will learn in Chapter 4, the element hydrogen is composed of two hydrogen atoms, separated by a distance of $7.4 \times 10^{-11}$ m. Convert this value to a standard number.

### Analysis

The exponent in $10^x$ tells how many places to move the decimal point in the coefficient to generate a standard number. The decimal point goes to the right when $x$ is positive and to the left when $x$ is negative.

Solution      $7.4 \times 10^{-11}$            $000\,000\,000\,07.4 \quad \dashrightarrow \quad 0.000\,000\,000\,074$ m

Move the decimal point to the left 11 places.                                                          **Answer**

The answer, 0.000 000 000 074, has two significant figures, just like $7.4 \times 10^{-11}$.

## PROBLEM 1.20

There are $6.02 \times 10^{21}$ "particles" called molecules (Chapter 4) of aspirin in 1.8 g. Write this number in standard form.

## PROBLEM 1.21

Convert each number to its standard form.

a. $6.5 \times 10^3$
b. $3.26 \times 10^{-5}$

c. $3.780 \times 10^{-2}$
d. $1.04 \times 10^8$

e. $2.221 \times 10^6$
f. $4.5 \times 10^{-10}$

## 1.7  Problem Solving Using the Factor–Label Method

Often a measurement is recorded in one unit, and then it must be converted to another unit. For example, a patient may weigh 130 lb, but we may need to know her weight in kilograms to calculate a drug dosage. The recommended daily dietary intake of potassium is 3,500 mg, but we may need to know how many grams this corresponds to.

### 1.7A  Conversion Factors

To convert one unit to another we use one or more **conversion factors.**

- A *conversion factor* is a term that converts a quantity in one unit to a quantity in another unit.

A conversion factor is formed by taking an equality, such as 2.20 lb = 1 kg, and writing it as a ratio. We can always write a conversion factor in two different ways.

$$\frac{2.20 \text{ lb}}{1 \text{ kg}} \quad \text{or} \quad \frac{1 \text{ kg}}{2.20 \text{ lb}}$$

numerator
denominator

conversion factors for pounds and kilograms

With pounds and kilograms, either of these values can be written above the division line of the fraction (the numerator) or below the division line (the denominator). The way the conversion factor is written will depend on the problem.

Refer to Tables 1.3 and 1.4 for metric and English units needed in problem solving. Common metric and English units are also listed on the inside back cover.

### SAMPLE PROBLEM 1.8

Write two conversion factors for each pair of units: (a) kilograms and grams; (b) quarts and liters.

#### Analysis

Use the equalities in Tables 1.3 and 1.4 to write a ratio that shows the relationship between the two units.

#### Solution

a. Conversion factors for kilograms and grams:

$$\frac{1000 \text{ g}}{1 \text{ kg}} \quad \text{or} \quad \frac{1 \text{ kg}}{1000 \text{ g}}$$

b. Conversion factors for quarts and liters:

$$\frac{1.06 \text{ qt}}{1 \text{ L}} \quad \text{or} \quad \frac{1 \text{ L}}{1.06 \text{ qt}}$$

### PROBLEM 1.22

Write two conversion factors for each pair of units.

a. miles and kilometers
b. meters and millimeters
c. grams and pounds
d. milligrams and micrograms

### 1.7B  Solving a Problem Using One Conversion Factor

Using conversion factors to convert a quantity in one unit to a quantity in another unit is called the **factor–label method.** In this method, if a unit appears in the numerator in one term and the denominator in another term, the units *cancel.* **The goal in setting up a problem is to make sure all unwanted units cancel.**

How many grams of aspirin are contained in a 325-mg tablet?

Let's say we want to convert 130 lb to kilograms.

$$\underset{\text{original quantity}}{130 \text{ lb}} \quad \times \quad \boxed{\textbf{conversion factor}} \quad = \quad \underset{\text{desired quantity}}{? \quad \text{kg}}$$

Two possible conversion factors: $\dfrac{2.20 \text{ lb}}{1 \text{ kg}}$ or $\dfrac{1 \text{ kg}}{2.20 \text{ lb}}$

To solve this problem we must use a conversion factor that satisfies two criteria.

- **The conversion factor must relate the two quantities in question—pounds and kilograms.**
- **The conversion factor must cancel out the unwanted unit—pounds.**

This means choosing the conversion factor with the unwanted unit—pounds—*in the denominator* to cancel out pounds in the original quantity. This leaves kilograms as the only remaining unit, and the problem is solved.

$$\boxed{\textbf{conversion factor}}$$

$$130 \text{ l\!b} \quad \times \quad \frac{1 \text{ kg}}{2.20 \text{ l\!b}} \quad = \quad \boxed{59 \text{ kg}} \quad \textbf{answer in kilograms}$$

Pounds (lb) must be the denominator to cancel
the unwanted unit (lb) in the original quantity.

We must use the correct number of significant figures in reporting an answer to each problem. In this case, the value 1 kg is *defined* as 2.20 lb; in other words, 1 kg contains the exact number "1" with *no* uncertainty, so it does not limit the number of digits in the answer. Since 130 lb has two significant figures, the answer is rounded to two significant figures (59 kg).

As problems with units get more complicated, keep in mind the following general steps that are useful for solving any problem using conversion factors.

## *How To* Solve a Problem Using Conversion Factors

**Example:** How many grams of aspirin are contained in a 325-mg tablet?

**Step [1]** Identify the original quantity and the desired quantity, including units.

- In this problem the original quantity is reported in milligrams and the desired quantity is in grams.

$$\underset{\text{original quantity}}{325 \text{ mg}} \qquad \underset{\text{desired quantity}}{? \text{ g}}$$

**Step [2]** Write out the conversion factor(s) needed to solve the problem.

- We need a conversion factor that relates milligrams and grams (Table 1.3). Since the unwanted unit is in milligrams, **choose the conversion factor that contains milligrams in the denominator so that the *units cancel.***

$$\text{Two possible conversion factors:} \quad \frac{1000 \text{ mg}}{1 \text{ g}} \quad \text{or} \quad \boxed{\frac{1 \text{ g}}{1000 \text{ mg}}} \quad \underset{\text{Choose this factor to cancel the unwanted unit, mg.}}{\Longleftarrow}$$

- Sometimes one conversion factor is all that is needed in a problem. At other times (Section 1.7C) more than one conversion factor is needed.
- If the desired answer has a single unit (grams in this case), **the conversion factor must contain the desired unit in the numerator and the unwanted unit in the denominator.**

**Step [3]** Set up and solve the problem.

- Multiply the original quantity by the conversion factor to obtain the desired quantity.

$$\boxed{\textbf{conversion factor}}$$

$$\underset{\text{original quantity}}{325 \text{ m\!g}} \quad \times \quad \frac{1 \text{ g}}{1000 \text{ m\!g}} \quad = \quad \underset{\text{desired quantity}}{0.325 \text{ g of aspirin}}$$

The number of mg (unwanted unit) cancels.

**How To, continued . . .**

**Step [4]** **Write the answer using the correct number of significant figures and check it by estimation.**

- Use the number of significant figures in each inexact (measured) number to determine the number of significant figures in the answer. In this case the answer is limited to three significant figures by the original quantity (325 mg).
- Estimate the answer using a variety of methods. In this case we knew our answer had to be less than one, since it is obtained by dividing 325 by a number larger than itself.

**PROBLEM 1.23**

The distance between Honolulu, HI, and Los Angeles, CA, is 4,120 km. How many frequent flyer miles will you earn by traveling between the two cities?

**PROBLEM 1.24**

Carry out each of the following conversions.

a. 25 L to dL          b. 40.0 oz to g          c. 32 in. to cm          d. 10 cm to mm

## 1.7C   Solving a Problem Using Two or More Conversion Factors

Some problems require the use of more than one conversion factor to obtain the desired units in the answer. The same stepwise procedure is followed no matter how many conversion factors are needed. Keep in mind:

- **Always arrange the factors so that the denominator in one term cancels the numerator in the preceding term.**

Sample Problem 1.9 illustrates how to solve a problem with two conversion factors.

**SAMPLE PROBLEM 1.9**

An individual donated 1.0 pint of blood at the local blood bank. How many liters of blood does this correspond to?

**Analysis and Solution**

**[1] Identify the original quantity and the desired quantity.**

1.0 pt                              ? L

original quantity          desired quantity

**[2] Write out the conversion factors.**

- We have no conversion factor that relates pints to liters directly. We do, however, know conversions for pints to quarts, and quarts to liters.

pint–quart conversion                                    quart–liter conversion

$\dfrac{2\ pt}{1\ qt}$  or  $\boxed{\dfrac{1\ qt}{2\ pt}}$                 $\dfrac{1.06\ qt}{1\ L}$  or  $\boxed{\dfrac{1\ L}{1.06\ qt}}$

Choose the conversion factors with the unwanted units—pt and qt—in the denominator.

**[3] Solve the problem.**

- To set up the problem so that unwanted units cancel, arrange each term so that the units in the numerator of one term cancel the units of the denominator of the adjacent term. In this problem we need to cancel both pints and quarts to get liters.
- The single desired unit, liters, must be in the **numerator** of one term.

Liters do not cancel.

$$1.0\ \cancel{pt}\ \times\ \frac{1\ \cancel{qt}}{2\ \cancel{pt}}\ \times\ \frac{1\ L}{1.06\ \cancel{qt}}\ =\ 0.47\ L$$

Pints cancel.          Quarts cancel.

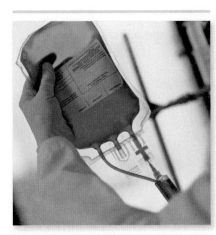

How many liters of blood does this pint of blood contain?

**[4] Check.**

- Since there are two pints in a quart and a quart is about the same size as a liter, one pint should be about half a liter. The answer, 0.47, is just about 0.5.
- Write the answer with two significant figures since one term, 1.0 pt, has two significant figures.

### PROBLEM 1.25

Carry out each of the following conversions.

   a.  6,250 ft to km         b.  3 cups to L         c.  4.5 ft to cm

## 1.8 FOCUS ON HEALTH & MEDICINE
### Problem Solving Using Clinical Conversion Factors

Sometimes conversion factors don't have to be looked up in a table; they are stated in the problem. If a drug is sold as a 250-mg tablet, this fact becomes a conversion factor relating milligrams to tablets.

$$\frac{250 \text{ mg}}{1 \text{ tablet}} \quad \text{or} \quad \frac{1 \text{ tablet}}{250 \text{ mg}}$$

mg–tablet conversion factors

Alternatively, a drug could be sold as a liquid solution with a specific concentration. For example, Children's Tylenol contains 80 mg of the active ingredient acetaminophen in 2.5 mL. This fact becomes a conversion factor relating milligrams to milliliters.

$$\frac{80 \text{ mg}}{2.5 \text{ mL}} \quad \text{or} \quad \frac{2.5 \text{ mL}}{80 \text{ mg}}$$

mg of acetaminophen–mL conversion factors

Sample Problems 1.10 and 1.11 illustrate how these conversion factors are used in determining drug dosages.

### SAMPLE PROBLEM 1.10

A patient is prescribed 1.25 g of amoxicillin, which is available in 250-mg tablets. How many tablets are needed?

#### Analysis and Solution

**[1] Identify the original quantity and the desired quantity.**

- We must convert the number of grams of amoxicillin needed to the number of tablets that must be administered.

                   1.25 g                      ? tablets

             original quantity         desired quantity

**[2] Write out the conversion factors.**

- We have no conversion factor that relates grams to tablets directly. We do know, however, how to relate grams to milligrams, and milligrams to tablets.

    g–mg conversion factors                  mg–tablet conversion factors

$$\frac{1 \text{ g}}{1000 \text{ mg}} \quad \text{or} \quad \boxed{\frac{1000 \text{ mg}}{1 \text{ g}}} \qquad\qquad \frac{250 \text{ mg}}{1 \text{ tablet}} \quad \text{or} \quad \boxed{\frac{1 \text{ tablet}}{250 \text{ mg}}}$$

Choose the conversion factors with the unwanted units—g and mg—in the denominator.

**[3] Solve the problem.**

- Arrange each term so that the units in the numerator of one term cancel the units in the denominator of the adjacent term. In this problem we need to cancel both grams and milligrams to get tablets.

The active ingredient in Children's Tylenol is acetaminophen.

- The single desired unit, tablets, must be located in the **numerator** of one term.

$$1.25 \text{ g} \times \frac{1000 \text{ mg}}{1 \text{ g}} \times \frac{1 \text{ tablet}}{250 \text{ mg}} = 5 \text{ tablets}$$

Grams cancel. Milligrams cancel.

**[4] Check.**

- The answer of 5 tablets of amoxicillin (not 0.5 or 50) is reasonable. Since the dose in a single tablet (250 mg) is a fraction of a gram, and the required dose is more than a gram, the answer must be greater than one.

### SAMPLE PROBLEM 1.11

A dose of 240 mg of acetaminophen is prescribed for a 20-kg child. How many mL of Children's Tylenol (80. mg of acetaminophen per 2.5 mL) are needed?

### Analysis and Solution

**[1] Identify the original quantity and the desired quantity.**

- We must convert the number of milligrams of acetaminophen needed to the number of mL that must be administered.

$$\underset{\text{original quantity}}{240 \text{ mg}} \qquad \underset{\text{desired quantity}}{? \text{ mL}}$$

**[2] Write out the conversion factors.**

mg of acetaminophen–mL conversion factors

$$\frac{80. \text{ mg}}{2.5 \text{ mL}} \quad \text{or} \quad \boxed{\frac{2.5 \text{ mL}}{80. \text{ mg}}}$$

Choose the conversion factor to cancel mg.

**[3] Solve the problem.**

- Arrange the terms so that the units in the numerator of one term cancel the units of the denominator of the adjacent term. In this problem we need to cancel milligrams to obtain milliliters.
- In this problem we are given a fact we don't need to use—the child weighs 20 kg. We can ignore this quantity in carrying out the calculation.

$$240 \text{ mg} \times \frac{2.5 \text{ mL}}{80. \text{ mg}} = 7.5 \text{ mL of Children's Tylenol}$$

Milligrams cancel.

**[4] Check.**

- The answer of 7.5 mL (not 0.75 or 75) is reasonable. Since the required dose is larger than the dose in 2.5 mL, the answer must be larger than 2.5 mL.

### PROBLEM 1.26

If one teaspoon contains 5.0 mL, how many teaspoons of Children's Tylenol must be administered in Sample Problem 1.11?

### PROBLEM 1.27

A patient is prescribed 0.100 mg of a drug that is available in 25-µg tablets. How many tablets are needed?

### PROBLEM 1.28

How many milliliters of Children's Motrin (100 mg of ibuprofen per 5 mL) are needed to give a child a dose of 160 mg?

## 1.9 Temperature

**Temperature is a measure of how hot or cold an object is.** Three temperature scales are used: **Fahrenheit** (most common in the United States), **Celsius** (most commonly used by scientists and countries other than the United States), and **Kelvin** (Figure 1.8).

The Fahrenheit and Celsius scales are both divided into **degrees.** On the Fahrenheit scale, water freezes at 32 °F and boils at 212 °F. On the Celsius scale, water freezes at 0 °C and boils at 100 °C. To convert temperature values from one scale to another, we use two equations, where °C is the Celsius temperature and °F is the Fahrenheit temperature.

To convert from Celsius to Fahrenheit:

$$°F = 1.8(°C) + 32$$

To convert from Fahrenheit to Celsius:

$$°C = \frac{°F - 32}{1.8}$$

The Kelvin scale is divided into **kelvins (K),** not degrees. **The only difference between the Kelvin scale and the Celsius scale is the zero point.** A temperature of –273 °C corresponds to 0 K. The zero point on the Kelvin scale is called **absolute zero,** the lowest temperature possible. To convert temperature values from Celsius to Kelvin, or vice versa, use two equations.

To convert from Celsius to Kelvin:

$$K = °C + 273$$

To convert from Kelvin to Celsius:

$$°C = K - 273$$

### SAMPLE PROBLEM 1.12

An infant had a temperature of 104 °F. Convert this temperature to both °C and K.

### Analysis

First convert the Fahrenheit temperature to degrees Celsius using the equation °C = (°F – 32)/1.8. Then convert the Celsius temperature to kelvins by adding 273.

Although mercury thermometers were used in hospitals to measure temperature for many years, temperature is now more commonly recorded with a digital thermometer. Tympanic thermometers, which use an infrared sensing device placed in the ear, are also routinely used.

**Figure 1.8** Fahrenheit, Celsius, and Kelvin Temperature Scales Compared

Since the freezing point and boiling point of water span 180° on the Fahrenheit scale, but only 100° on the Celsius scale, a Fahrenheit degree and a Celsius degree differ in size. The Kelvin scale is divided into kelvins (K), not degrees. Since the freezing point and boiling point of water span 100 kelvins, one kelvin is the same size as one Celsius degree.

Solution

**[1] Convert °F to °C:**

$$°C = \frac{°F - 32}{1.8}$$

$$= \frac{104 - 32}{1.8} = 40. \ °C$$

**[2] Convert °C to K:**

$$K = °C + 273$$

$$= 40. + 273 = 313 \ K$$

### PROBLEM 1.29

When the human body is exposed to extreme cold, hypothermia can result and the body's temperature can drop to 28.5 °C. Convert this temperature to °F and K.

### PROBLEM 1.30

Convert each temperature to the requested temperature scale.

a.  20. °C to °F          c.  298 K to °F

b.  150. °F to °C         d.  75 °C to K

## 1.10    Density and Specific Gravity

Two additional quantities used to characterize substances are **density** and **specific gravity.**

### 1.10A    Density

*Density* **is a physical property that relates the mass of a substance to its volume.** Density is reported in grams per milliliter (g/mL) or grams per cubic centimeter (g/cc).

$$\text{density} = \frac{\text{mass (g)}}{\text{volume (mL or cc)}}$$

The density of a substance depends on temperature. For most substances, the solid state is more dense than the liquid state, and as the temperature increases, the density decreases. This phenomenon occurs because the volume of a sample of a substance generally increases with temperature but the mass is always constant.

Water is an exception to this generalization. Solid water, ice, is *less* dense than liquid water, and from 0 °C to 4 °C, the density of water *increases*. Above 4 °C, water behaves like other liquids and its density decreases. Thus, water's maximum density of 1.00 g/mL occurs at 4 °C. Some representative densities are reported in Table 1.6.

The density (not the mass) of a substance determines whether it floats or sinks in a liquid.

- **A less dense substance floats on a more dense liquid.**

### Table 1.6  Representative Densities at 25 °C

| Substance | Density [g/(mL or cc)] | Substance | Density [g/(mL or cc)] |
|---|---|---|---|
| Oxygen (0 °C) | 0.001 43 | Urine | 1.003–1.030 |
| Gasoline | 0.66 | Blood plasma | 1.03 |
| Ice (0 °C) | 0.92 | Table sugar | 1.59 |
| Water (4 °C) | 1.00 | Bone | 1.80 |

Although a can of a diet soft drink floats in water because it is less dense, a can of a regular soft drink that contains sugar is more dense than water so it sinks.

Ice floats on water because it is less dense. When petroleum leaks from an oil tanker or gasoline is spilled when fueling a boat, it floats on water because it is less dense. In contrast, a cannonball or torpedo sinks because it is more dense than water.

Knowing the density of a liquid allows us to convert the volume of a substance to its mass, or the mass of a substance to its volume.

To convert volume (mL) to mass (g):

$$\text{mL} \quad \times \quad \boxed{\frac{\text{g}}{\text{mL}}} \quad = \quad \text{g}$$

density

Milliliters cancel.

To convert mass (g) to volume (mL):

$$\text{g} \quad \times \quad \boxed{\frac{\text{mL}}{\text{g}}} \quad = \quad \text{mL}$$

inverse of the density

Grams cancel.

For example, one laboratory synthesis of aspirin uses the liquid acetic acid, which has a density of 1.05 g/mL. If we need 5.0 g for a synthesis, we could use density to convert this mass to a volume that could then be easily measured out using a syringe or pipette.

$$5.0 \text{ g acetic acid} \quad \times \quad \frac{1 \text{ mL}}{1.05 \text{ g}} \quad = \quad 4.8 \text{ mL of acetic acid}$$

Grams cancel.

### SAMPLE PROBLEM 1.13

Calculate the mass in grams of 15.0 mL of a saline solution that has a density 1.05 g/mL.

### Analysis

Use density (g/mL) to interconvert the mass and volume of a liquid.

### Solution

$$15.0 \text{ mL} \quad \times \quad \boxed{\frac{1.05 \text{ g}}{1 \text{ mL}}} \quad = \quad 15.8 \text{ g of saline solution}$$

density

Milliliters cancel.

The answer, 15.8 g, is rounded to three significant figures to match the number of significant figures in both factors in the problem.

### PROBLEM 1.31

Calculate the mass in grams of 10.0 mL of diethyl ether, an anesthetic that has a density of 0.713 g/mL.

### PROBLEM 1.32

(a) Calculate the volume in milliliters of 100. g of coconut oil, which has a density of 0.92 g/mL.
(b) How many liters does this correspond to?

### PROBLEM 1.33

Suppose we have two substances, **A** and **B,** and the density of **A** is greater than the density of **B.**
(a) If we have equal volumes of **A** and **B,** which one has the larger mass? (b) If we have equal masses of **A** and **B,** which one has the larger volume?

The specific gravity of a urine sample is measured to check if a patient has an imbalance in metabolism.

## 1.10B Specific Gravity

*Specific gravity* **is a quantity that compares the density of a substance with the density of water at 4 °C.**

$$\text{specific gravity} \quad = \quad \frac{\text{density of a substance (g/mL)}}{\text{density of water (g/mL)}}$$

Unlike most other quantities, specific gravity is a quantity without units, since the units in the numerator (g/mL) cancel the units in the denominator (g/mL). Since the density of water is 1.00 g/mL at 4 °C, **the specific gravity of a substance equals its density, but it contains no units.** For example, if the density of a liquid is 1.5 g/mL, its specific gravity is 1.5.

The specific gravity of urine samples is often measured in a hospital lab. Normal urine has a density in the range of 1.003–1.030 g/mL (Table 1.6), so it has a specific gravity in the range of 1.003–1.030. Consistently high or low values can indicate an imbalance in metabolism. For example, the specific gravity of urine samples from patients with poorly controlled diabetes is abnormally high, because a large amount of glucose is excreted in the urine.

### PROBLEM 1.34

(a) If the density of a liquid is 0.80 g/mL, what is its specific gravity? (b) If the specific gravity of a substance is 2.3, what is its density?

# CHAPTER HIGHLIGHTS

## KEY TERMS

| | | |
|---|---|---|
| Celsius scale (1.9) | Fahrenheit scale (1.9) | Mixture (1.3) |
| Chemical properties (1.2) | Gas (1.2) | Physical properties (1.2) |
| Chemistry (1.1) | Gram (1.4) | Pure substance (1.3) |
| Compound (1.3) | Inexact number (1.5) | Scientific notation (1.6) |
| Conversion factor (1.7) | Kelvin scale (1.9) | SI units (1.4) |
| Cubic centimeter (1.4) | Liquid (1.2) | Significant figures (1.5) |
| Density (1.10) | Liter (1.4) | Solid (1.2) |
| Element (1.3) | Mass (1.4) | Specific gravity (1.10) |
| English system of measurement (1.4) | Matter (1.1) | States of matter (1.2) |
| Exact number (1.5) | Meter (1.4) | Temperature (1.9) |
| Factor–label method (1.7) | Metric system (1.4) | Weight (1.4) |

## KEY CONCEPTS

**❶ Describe the three states of matter. (1.1, 1.2)**

- Matter is anything that has mass and takes up volume. Matter has three common states:
  - The solid state is composed of highly organized particles that lie close together. A solid has a definite shape and volume.
  - The liquid state is composed of particles that lie close together but are less organized than the solid state. A liquid has a definite volume but not a definite shape.
  - The gas state is composed of highly disorganized particles that lie far apart. A gas has no definite shape or volume.

**❷ How is matter classified? (1.3)**

- Matter is classified in one of two categories:
  - A pure substance is composed of a single component with a constant composition. A pure substance is either an element, which cannot be broken down into simpler substances by a chemical reaction, or a compound, which is formed by combining two or more elements.
  - A mixture is composed of more than one component and its composition can vary depending on the sample.

**❸ What are the key features of the metric system of measurement? (1.4)**

- The metric system is a system of measurement in which each type of measurement has a base unit and all other units are related to the base unit by a prefix that indicates if the unit is larger or smaller than the base unit.
- The base units are meter (m) for length, gram (g) for mass, liter (L) for volume, and second (s) for time.

**❹ What are significant figures and how are they used in calculations? (1.5)**

- Significant figures are all digits in a measured number, including one estimated digit. All nonzero digits are significant. A zero is significant only if it occurs between two nonzero digits, or at the end of a number with a decimal point. A trailing zero in a number without a decimal point is not considered significant.
- In multiplying and dividing with significant figures, the answer has the same number of significant figures as the original number with the fewest significant figures.
- In adding or subtracting with significant figures, the answer has the same number of decimal places as the original number with the fewest decimal places.

**❺ What is scientific notation? (1.6)**

- Scientific notation is a method of writing a number as $y \times 10^x$, where $y$ is a number between 1 and 10, and $x$ is a positive or negative exponent.

- To convert a standard number to a number in scientific notation, move the decimal point to give a number between 1 and 10. Multiply the result by $10^x$, where $x$ is the number of places the decimal point was moved. When the decimal point is moved to the left, $x$ is positive. When the decimal point is moved to the right, $x$ is negative.

**❻ How are conversion factors used to convert one unit to another? (1.7, 1.8)**

- A conversion factor is a term that converts a quantity in one unit to a quantity in another unit. To use conversion factors to solve a problem, set up the problem with any unwanted unit in the numerator of one term and the denominator of another term, so that unwanted units cancel.

**❼ What is temperature and how are the three temperature scales related? (1.9)**

- Temperature is a measure of how hot or cold an object is. The Fahrenheit and Celsius temperature scales are divided into degrees. Both the size of the degree and the zero point of these scales differ. The Kelvin scale is divided into kelvins, and one kelvin is the same size as one degree Celsius.

**❽ What are density and specific gravity? (1.10)**

- Density is a physical property reported in g/mL or g/cc that relates the mass of an object to its volume. A less dense substance floats on top of a more dense liquid.
- Specific gravity is a unitless quantity that relates the density of a substance to the density of water at 4 °C. Since the density of water is 1.00 g/mL at this temperature, the specific gravity of a substance equals its density, but it contains no units.

## PROBLEMS

Selected in-chapter and odd-numbered end-of-chapter problems have brief answers in Appendix B. The *Student Study Guide and Solutions Manual* contains detailed solutions to all in-chapter and odd-numbered end-of-chapter problems, as well as additional worked examples and a chapter self-test.

### Matter

**1.35** Classify each example of molecular art as a pure element, a pure compound, or a mixture.

a.

c.

b.

d.

**1.36** (a) Which representation(s) in Problem 1.35 illustrate a mixture of two elements? (b) Which representation(s) in Problem 1.35 illustrate a mixture of a compound and an element?

**1.37** What is the difference between an element and a compound?

**1.38** What is the difference between a compound and a mixture?

**1.39** Describe solids, liquids, and gases in terms of (a) volume (how they fill a container); (b) shape; (c) level of organization of the particles that comprise them; (d) how close the particles that comprise them lie.

**1.40** How do physical properties and chemical properties differ?

**1.41** Classify each process as a chemical or physical change.
  a. dissolving calcium chloride in water
  b. burning gasoline to power a car
  c. heating wax so that it melts

**1.42** Classify each process as a chemical or physical change.
  a. the condensation of water on the outside of a cold glass
  b. mixing a teaspoon of instant coffee with hot water
  c. baking a cake

**1.43** When a chunk of dry ice (solid carbon dioxide) is placed out in the air, the solid gradually disappears and a gas is formed above the solid. Does the molecular art drawn below indicate that a chemical or physical change has occurred? Explain your choice.

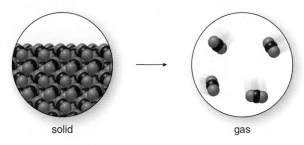

solid                          gas

**1.44** The inexpensive preparation of nitrogen-containing fertilizers begins with mixing together two elements, hydrogen and nitrogen, at high temperature and pressure in the presence of a metal. Does the molecular art depicted below indicate that a chemical or physical change occurs under these conditions? Explain your choice.

metal
heat

## Measurement

**1.45**

a. What is the temperature on the given Fahrenheit thermometer?
b. How many significant figures does your answer contain?
c. Convert this temperature into °C.

**1.46** (a) What is the length of the given crayon in centimeters? (b) How many significant figures does this value contain? (c) Convert this value to meters, and write the answer in scientific notation.

**1.47** What is the difference between an exact number and an inexact number? Give an example of each type of number.

**1.48** Label each quantity as an exact or inexact number.
a. A recipe requires 10 cloves of garlic and two tablespoons of oil.
b. A dog had five puppies whose combined weight was 10 lb.
c. The four bicycles in the family have been ridden for a total of 250 mi.
d. A child fell and had a 4-cm laceration that required 12 stitches.

**1.49** Which quantity in each pair is larger?
a. 5 mL or 5 dL          c. 5 cm or 5 mm
b. 10 mg or 10 µg        d. 10 Ms or 10 ms

**1.50** Which quantity in each pair is larger?
a. 10 km or 10 m         c. 10 g or 10 µg
b. 10 L or 10 mL         d. 10 cm or 10 mm

## Significant Figures

**1.51** How many significant figures does each number contain?
a. 16.00      c. 0.001 60     e. 1.06       g. $1.060 \times 10^{10}$
b. 160        d. 1,600,000    f. 0.1600     h. $1.6 \times 10^{-6}$

**1.52** How many significant figures does each number contain?
a. 160.       c. 0.000 16     e. 1,600.     g. $1.600 \times 10^{-10}$
b. 160.0      d. 1.60         f. 1.060      h. $1.6 \times 10^{6}$

**1.53** Round each number to three significant figures.
a. 25,401         c. 0.001 265 982     e. 195.371
b. 1,248,486      d. 0.123 456         f. 196.814

**1.54** Round each number in Problem 1.53 to four significant figures.

**1.55** Carry out each calculation and report the answer using the proper number of significant figures.
a. $53.6 \times 0.41$      c. $65.2 \div 12$      e. $694.2 \times 0.2$
b. $25.825 - 3.86$         d. $41.0 + 9.135$      f. $1,045 - 1.26$

**1.56** Carry out each calculation and report the answer using the proper number of significant figures.
a. $49,682 \times 0.80$    c. $1,000 \div 2.34$   e. $25,000 \div 0.4356$
b. $66.815 + 2.82$         d. $21 - 0.88$         f. $21.5381 + 26.55$

## Scientific Notation

**1.57** Write each quantity in scientific notation.
a. 1,234 g          c. 5,244,000 L       e. 44,000 km
b. 0.000 016 2 m    d. 0.005 62 g

**1.58** Write each quantity in scientific notation.
a. 0.001 25 m       c. 54,235.6 m        e. 4,440 s
b. 8,100,000,000 lb d. 0.000 001 899 L

**1.59** Convert each number to its standard form.
a. $3.4 \times 10^{8}$       c. $3 \times 10^{2}$
b. $5.822 \times 10^{-5}$    d. $6.86 \times 10^{-8}$

**1.60** Convert each number to its standard form.
a. $4.02 \times 10^{10}$     c. $6.86 \times 10^{9}$
b. $2.46 \times 10^{-3}$     d. $1.00 \times 10^{-7}$

**1.61** Which number in each pair is larger?
a. $4.44 \times 10^3$ or $4.8 \times 10^2$    c. $1.3 \times 10^8$ or 52,300,000
b. $5.6 \times 10^{-6}$ or $5.6 \times 10^{-5}$    d. $9.8 \times 10^{-4}$ or 0.000 089

**1.62** Rank the numbers in each group from smallest to largest.
a. $5.06 \times 10^6$, $7 \times 10^4$, and $2.5 \times 10^8$
b. $6.3 \times 10^{-2}$, $2.5 \times 10^{-4}$, and $8.6 \times 10^{-6}$

**1.63** Write the recommended daily intake of each nutrient in scientific notation.
a. 0.000 400 g of folate    c. 0.000 080 g of vitamin K
b. 0.002 g of copper    d. 3,400 mg of chloride

**1.64** A blood vessel is 0.40 μm in diameter. (a) Convert this quantity to meters and write the answer in scientific notation. (b) Convert this quantity to inches and write the answer in scientific notation.

## Problem Solving and Unit Conversions

**1.65** The average mass of a human liver is 1.5 kg. Convert this quantity to (a) grams; (b) pounds; (c) ounces.

**1.66** A *grain* is a unit of measurement sometimes used in medicine to indicate the dose of a medication, where 1 grain = 65 mg. How many grains are contained in a typical 325-mg aspirin tablet?

**1.67** Carry out each of the following conversions.
a. 300 g to mg    d. 300 g to oz
b. 2 L to μL    e. 2 ft to m
c. 5.0 cm to m    f. 3.5 yd to m

**1.68** Carry out each of the following conversions.
a. 25 μL to mL    d. 300 mL to qt
b. 35 kg to g    e. 3 cups to L
c. 2.36 mL to L    f. 2.5 tons to kg

**1.69** Carry out each of the following conversions.
a. What is the mass in kilograms of an individual who weighs 234 lb?
b. What is the height in centimeters of a child who is 50. in. tall?
c. A patient required 3.0 pt of blood during surgery. How many liters does this correspond to?
d. A patient had a body temperature of 37.7 °C. What is his body temperature in °F?

**1.70** Carry out each of the following conversions.
a. What is the mass in pounds of an individual who weighs 53.2 kg?
b. What is the height in inches of a child who is 90. cm tall?
c. How many mL are contained in the 5.0 qt of blood in the human body?
d. A patient had a body temperature of 103.5 °F. What is his body temperature in °C?

**1.71** (a) How many milliliters are contained in 1 qt of milk? (b) How many fluid ounces are contained in 1 L of soda?

**1.72** The official distance of a marathon is 26 miles and 385 yards. Convert this value to kilometers.

## Temperature

**1.73** Carry out each of the following temperature conversions.
a. An over-the-counter pain reliever melts at 53 °C. Convert this temperature to °F and K.
b. A cake is baked at 350. °F. Convert this temperature to °C and K.

**1.74** Methane, the main component of the natural gas used for cooking and heating homes, melts at −183 °C and boils at −162 °C. Convert each temperature to °F and K.

**1.75** Which temperature in each pair is higher?
a. −10 °C or 10 °F    b. −50 °C or −50 °F

**1.76** Rank the temperatures in each group from lowest to highest.
a. 0 °F, 0 °C, 0 K    b. 100 K, 100 °C, 100 °F

## Density and Specific Gravity

**1.77** What is the difference between density and specific gravity?

**1.78** The density of sucrose, table sugar, is 1.56 g/cc. What volume (in cubic centimeters) does 20.0 g of sucrose occupy?

**1.79** If a urine sample has a mass of 122 g and a volume of 121 mL, what is its density in g/mL?

**1.80** A volume of saline solution had a mass of 25.6 g at 4 °C. An equal volume of water at the same temperature had a mass of 24.5 g. What is the density of the saline solution?

**1.81** If milk has a density of 1.03 g/mL, what is the mass of one quart, reported in kilograms?

**1.82** If gasoline has a density of 0.66 g/mL, what is the mass of one gallon, reported in kilograms?

**1.83** Which is the upper layer when each of the following liquids is added to water?
a. heptane (density = 0.684 g/mL)
b. olive oil (density = 0.92 g/mL)
c. chloroform (density = 1.49 g/mL)
d. carbon tetrachloride (density = 1.59 g/mL)

**1.84** Which of the following solids float on top of water and which sink?
a. aluminum (density = 1.70 g/cc)
b. lead (density = 11.34 g/cc)
c. Styrofoam (density = 0.100 g/cc)
d. maple wood (density = 0.74 g/cc)

**1.85** (a) What is the specific gravity of mercury, the liquid used in thermometers, if it has a density of 13.6 g/mL? (b) What is the density of ethanol if it has a specific gravity of 0.789?

**1.86** Why is specific gravity a unitless quantity?

## Applications

**1.87** A lab test showed an individual's cholesterol level to be 186 mg/dL. (a) Convert this quantity to g/dL. (b) Convert this quantity to mg/L.

**1.88** Hemoglobin is a protein that transports oxygen from the lungs to the rest of the body. Lab results indicated a patient had a hemoglobin concentration in the blood of 15.5 g/dL, which is in the normal range. (a) Convert the number of grams to milligrams and write the answer in scientific notation. (b) Convert the number of grams to micrograms and write the answer in scientific notation.

**1.89** A woman was told to take a dose of 1.5 g of calcium daily. How many 500-mg tablets should she take?

**1.90** A soccer player weighed 70.7 kg before a match, drank 1.8 L of liquid (density 1.05 g/mL) during the match, and weighed 69.3 kg after the match. How many pounds of sweat did the soccer player lose?

**1.91** A medium banana contains 451 mg of the nutrient potassium. How many bananas would you have to eat in one day to obtain the recommended daily intake of 3.5 g of potassium?

**1.92** A single 1-oz serving of tortilla chips contains 250 mg of sodium. If an individual ate the entire 13-oz bag, how many grams of sodium would he ingest? If the recommended daily intake of sodium is 2.4 g, does this provide more or less than the recommended daily value, and by how much?

**1.93** A bottle of liquid medication contains 300. mL and costs $10.00. (a) If the usual dose is 20. mL, how much does each dose cost? (b) If the usual dose is two tablespoons (1 tablespoon = 15 mL), how much does each dose cost?

**1.94** The average nicotine content of a Camel cigarette is 1.93 mg. (a) Convert this quantity to both grams and micrograms. (b) Nicotine patches, which are used to help quit smoking, release nicotine into the body by absorption through the skin. The patches come with different amounts of nicotine. A smoker begins with the amount of nicotine that matches his typical daily intake. The maximum amount of nicotine in one brand of patch supplies a smoker with 21 mg of nicotine per day. If an individual smoked one pack of 20 Camel cigarettes each day, would a smoker get more or less nicotine per day using this patch?

**1.95** A chemist synthesized 0.510 kg of aspirin in the lab. If the normal dose of aspirin is two 325-mg tablets, how many doses did she prepare?

**1.96** Maalox is the trade name for an antacid and antigas medication used for relief of heartburn, bloating, and acid indigestion. Each 5.0-mL portion of Maalox contains 400. mg of aluminum hydroxide, 400. mg of magnesium hydroxide, and 40. mg of simethicone. If the recommended dose is two teaspoons four times a day, how many grams of each substance would an individual take in a 24-hour period? (1 teaspoon = 5.0 mL.)

**1.97** A patient is prescribed 2.0 g of a medication to be taken four times a day. If the medicine is available in 500.-mg tablets, how many tablets are needed in a 24-hour period?

**1.98** A patient receives an intravenous (IV) solution that flows at the rate of 150 mL per hour. (a) How much fluid does the patient receive in 20. min? (b) How long does it take for the patient to receive 90. mL of fluid? (c) If the IV bag holds 600. mL of fluid, how many minutes does it take to empty the bag? (d) If the solution contains 90. mg of glucose per mL, how long will it take to give the patient 2.0 g of glucose?

## CHALLENGE PROBLEMS

**1.99** Often the specific amount of a drug to be administered must be calculated from a given dose in mg per kilogram of body weight. This assures that individuals who have very different body mass get the proper dose. If the proper dosage of a drug is 2.0 mg/kg of body weight, how many milligrams would a 110-lb individual need?

**1.100** Quinine, a drug isolated from the bark of the cinchona tree native to the Andes Mountains, is an effective treatment for malaria. Children typically receive a dose of 10. mg/kg three times a day for seven days. How many grams would a 28-kg child receive during the course of a treatment?

**1.101** Children's Chewable Tylenol contains 80 mg of acetaminophen per tablet. If the recommended dosage is 10 mg/kg, how many tablets are needed for a 42-lb child?

**1.102** Artemether, an antimalarial drug prepared from the Chinese antimalarial plant *Artemisia annua,* can be given either orally or by injection. When the drug is given in pill form, the patient receives 160 mg on the first day, and then 80. mg daily for the next four days. When the drug is given by injection, the patient receives 3.2 mg/kg of body weight on the first day, and then 1.6 mg/kg daily for the next four days. (a) Which method gives a 40.-kg individual the larger dose? (b) Which method gives a 100.-kg individual the larger dose?

**1.103** Children's Liquid Motrin contains 100. mg of the pain reliever ibuprofen per 5 mL. If the dose for a 45-lb child is 1.5 teaspoons, how many grams of ibuprofen would the child receive? (1 teaspoon = 5.0 mL.)

**1.104** If the proper dose of a medication is 10 μg/kg of body weight, how many milligrams would a 200-lb individual need?

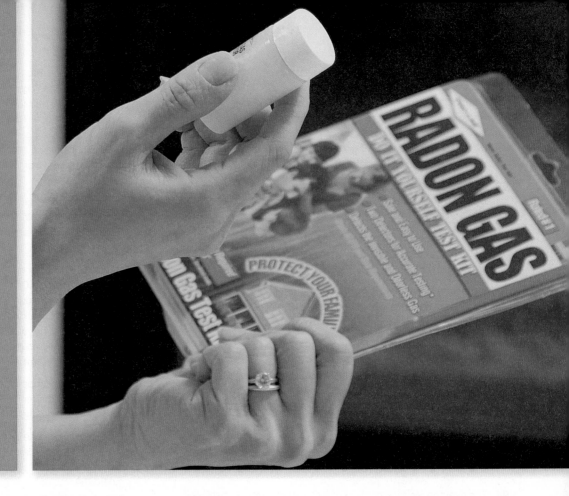

Radon detectors are used to measure high levels of radon, a radioactive noble gas linked to an increased incidence of lung cancer.

# Atoms and the Periodic Table

## CHAPTER GOALS

*In this chapter you will learn how to:*

1 Identify an element by its symbol and classify it as a metal, nonmetal, or metalloid

2 Describe the basic parts of an atom

3 Distinguish isotopes and calculate atomic weight

4 Describe the basic features of the periodic table

5 Understand the electronic structure of an atom

6 Write an electronic configuration for an element

7 Relate the location of an element in the periodic table to its electronic configuration

8 Draw an electron-dot symbol for an atom

9 Use the periodic table to predict the relative size and ionization energy of atoms

E xamine the ingredients listed on a box of crackers. They may include flour, added vitamins, sugar for sweetness, a natural or synthetic coloring agent, baking soda, salt for flavor, and BHT as a preservative. No matter how simple or complex each of these substances is, it is composed of the basic building block, the **atom.** The word *atom* comes from the Greek word *atomos* meaning *unable to cut.* In Chapter 2, we examine the structure and properties of atoms, the building blocks that comprise all forms of matter.

## 2.1  Elements

You were first introduced to elements in Section 1.3.

> • An *element* is a pure substance that cannot be broken down into simpler substances by a chemical reaction.

Of the 118 elements currently known, 90 are naturally occurring and the remaining 28 have been prepared by scientists in the laboratory. Some elements, like oxygen in the air we breathe and aluminum in a soft drink can, are familiar to you, while others, like samarium and seaborgium, are probably not. An alphabetical list of all elements appears on the inside front cover.

**Each element is identified by a one- or two-letter symbol.** The element carbon is symbolized by the single letter **C,** while the element chlorine is symbolized by **Cl.** When two letters are used in the element symbol, the first is upper case while the second is lower case. Thus, **Co** refers to the element cobalt, but CO is carbon monoxide, which is composed of the elements carbon (C) and oxygen (O). Table 2.1 lists common elements and their symbols.

While most element symbols are derived from the first one or two letters of the element name, 11 elements have symbols derived from Latin or German origins. Table 2.2 lists these elements and their symbols.

### PROBLEM 2.1

Give the symbol for each element.

a. calcium, a nutrient needed for strong teeth and bones
b. radon, a radioactive gas produced in the soil
c. nitrogen, the main component of the earth's atmosphere
d. gold, a precious metal used in coins and jewelry

Elements are named for people, places, and things. For example, *carbon* (C) comes from the Latin word *carbo,* meaning *coal* or *charcoal; neptunium* (Np) was named for the planet Neptune; *einsteinium* (Es) was named for scientist Albert Einstein; and *californium* (Cf) was named for the state of California.

## ENVIRONMENTAL NOTE

Carbon monoxide (CO), formed in small amounts during the combustion of fossil fuels like gasoline, is a toxic component of the smoggy air in many large cities. Carbon monoxide contains the elements carbon (C) and oxygen (O). We will learn about carbon monoxide in Section 12.8.

### Table 2.1  Common Elements and Their Symbols

| Element | Symbol | Element | Symbol |
|---------|--------|---------|--------|
| Bromine | Br | Magnesium | Mg |
| Calcium | Ca | Manganese | Mn |
| Carbon | C | Molybdenum | Mo |
| Chlorine | Cl | Nitrogen | N |
| Chromium | Cr | Oxygen | O |
| Cobalt | Co | Phosphorus | P |
| Copper | Cu | Potassium | K |
| Fluorine | F | Sodium | Na |
| Hydrogen | H | Sulfur | S |
| Iodine | I | Zinc | Zn |
| Lead | Pb | | |

### Table 2.2  Unusual Element Symbols

| Element | Symbol |
|---------|--------|
| Antimony | Sb (stibium) |
| Copper | Cu (cuprum) |
| Gold | Au (aurum) |
| Iron | Fe (ferrum) |
| Lead | Pb (plumbum) |
| Mercury | Hg (hydrargyrum) |
| Potassium | K (kalium) |
| Silver | Ag (argentum) |
| Sodium | Na (natrium) |
| Tin | Sn (stannum) |
| Tungsten | W (wolfram) |

**PROBLEM 2.2**

An alloy is a mixture of two or more elements that has metallic properties. Give the element symbol for the components of each alloy: (a) brass (copper and zinc); (b) bronze (copper and tin); (c) pewter (tin, antimony, and lead).

**PROBLEM 2.3**

Give the name corresponding to each element symbol: (a) Ne; (b) S; (c) I; (d) Si; (e) B; (f) Hg.

## 2.1A    Elements and the Periodic Table

A periodic table appears on the inside front cover for easy reference.

Long ago it was realized that groups of elements have similar properties, and that these elements could be arranged in a schematic way called the **periodic table** (Figure 2.1). The position of an element in the periodic table tells us much about its chemical properties.

**Figure 2.1**    The Periodic Table of the Elements

- **Metals** are shiny substances that conduct heat and electricity. Metals are ductile, meaning they can be drawn into wires, and malleable, meaning they can be hammered into shapes.

- **Metalloids** have properties intermediate between metals and nonmetals.

- **Nonmetals** are poor conductors of heat and electricity.

The elements in the periodic table are divided into three categories—**metals, nonmetals,** and **metalloids.** The solid line that begins with boron (B) and angles in steps down to astatine (At) marks the three regions corresponding to these groups. All metals are located to the *left* of the line. All nonmetals except hydrogen are located to the *right.* Metalloids are located along the steps.

- *Metals* are shiny materials that are good conductors of heat and electricity. All metals are solids at room temperature except for mercury, which is a liquid.
- *Nonmetals* do not have a shiny appearance, and they are generally poor conductors of heat and electricity. Nonmetals like sulfur and carbon are solids at room temperature; bromine is a liquid; and nitrogen, oxygen, and nine other elements are gases.
- *Metalloids* have properties intermediate between metals and nonmetals. Only seven elements are categorized as metalloids: boron (B), silicon (Si), germanium (Ge), arsenic (As), antimony (Sb), tellurium (Te), and astatine (At).

## PROBLEM 2.4

Locate each element in the periodic table and classify it as a metal, nonmetal, or metalloid.

| a. titanium | c. krypton | e. arsenic | g. selenium |
|---|---|---|---|
| b. chlorine | d. palladium | f. cesium | h. osmium |

## 2.1B  FOCUS ON THE HUMAN BODY
### The Elements of Life

Because living organisms selectively take up elements from their surroundings, the abundance of elements in the human body is very different from the distribution of elements in the earth's crust. **Four nonmetals—oxygen, carbon, hydrogen, and nitrogen—comprise 96% of the mass of the human body, and are called the** *building-block elements* (Figure 2.2). Hydrogen and oxygen are the elements that form water, the most prevalent substance in the body. Carbon, hydrogen, and oxygen are found in the four main types of biological molecules—proteins, carbohydrates, lipids, and nucleic acids. Proteins and nucleic acids contain the element nitrogen as well. These biological molecules are discussed in Chapters 19–22.

**Figure 2.2**   The Elements of Life

**Building-Block Elements**

Oxygen (O)
Carbon (C)
Hydrogen (H)
Nitrogen (N)

These four elements compose almost 96% of the mass of the human body. Muscle tissue contains all four building-block elements.

**Trace Elements**

| Arsenic (As) | Fluorine (F) | Nickel (Ni) |
|---|---|---|
| Boron (B) | Iodine (I) | Selenium (Se) |
| Chromium (Cr) | Iron (Fe) | Silicon (Si) |
| Cobalt (Co) | Manganese (Mn) | Zinc (Zn) |
| Copper (Cu) | Molybdenum (Mo) | |

Each trace element is present in less than 0.1% by mass. A small quantity (15 mg or less) of each element is needed in the daily diet.

**Major Minerals**

Potassium (K), sodium (Na), and chlorine (Cl) are present in body fluids.

Magnesium (Mg) and sulfur (S) are present in the proteins found in muscle.

Calcium (Ca) and phosphorus (P) are present in teeth and bones.

Each major mineral is present in 0.1–2% by mass. At least 100 mg of each mineral is needed in the daily diet.

**Nutrition Facts**
Serving Size 3/4 cup (30g)
Servings Per Container about 17

| Amount Per Serving | Cereal | Cereal with 1/2 cup Fat Free Milk |
|---|---|---|
| **Calories** | 120 | 160 |
| Calories from Fat | 15 | 15 |
| | **% Daily Value**** | |
| Vitamin A | 15% | 20% |
| Vitamin C | 0% | 0% |
| Calcium | 0% | 15% |
| Iron | 60% | 60% |
| Vitamin D | 10% | 25% |
| Thiamin | 25% | 30% |
| Riboflavin | 25% | 35% |
| Niacin | 25% | 25% |
| Vitamin B6 | 25% | 25% |
| Folic Acid | 50% | 50% |
| Vitamin B12 | 25% | 35% |
| Phosphorus | 4% | 15% |
| Magnesium | 4% | 8% |
| Zinc | 2% | 6% |
| Copper | 2% | 2% |

**INGREDIENTS:** CORN, WHOLE GRAIN WHEAT, SUGAR, WHOLE GRAIN ROLLED OATS, BROWN SUGAR, HIGH OLEIC VEGETABLE OIL† (CANOLA OR SUNFLOWER OIL), RICE FLOUR, WHEAT FLOUR, MALTED BARLEY FLOUR, SALT, RICE, CORN SYRUP, WHEY (FROM MILK†), HONEY, MALTED CORN AND BARLEY SYRUP, CARAMEL COLOR, ARTIFICIAL FLAVOR, ANNATTO EXTRACT (COLOR). BHT ADDED TO PACKAGING MATERIAL TO PRESERVE PRODUCT FRESHNESS.
**VITAMINS AND MINERALS:** REDUCED IRON, NIACINAMIDE, VITAMIN B6, VITAMIN A PALMITATE, RIBOFLAVIN (VITAMIN B2), THIAMIN MONONITRATE (VITAMIN B1), ZINC OXIDE (SOURCE OF ZINC), FOLIC ACID, VITAMIN B12, VITAMIN D

Many breakfast cereals are fortified with iron to provide the consumer with this essential micronutrient.

Seven other elements, called the **major minerals** or **macronutrients,** are also present in the body in much smaller amounts (0.1–2% by mass). Sodium, potassium, and chlorine are present in body fluids. Magnesium and sulfur occur in proteins, and calcium and phosphorus are present in teeth and bones. Phosphorus is also contained in all nucleic acids, such as the DNA that transfers genetic information from one generation to another. At least 100 mg of each macronutrient is needed in the daily diet.

Many other elements occur in very small amounts in the body, but are essential to good health. These **trace elements** or **micronutrients** are required in the daily diet in small quantities, usually less than 15 mg. Each trace element has a specialized function that is important for proper cellular function. For example, iron is needed for hemoglobin, the protein that carries oxygen in red blood cells, and myoglobin, the protein that stores oxygen in muscle. Zinc is needed for the proper functioning of many enzymes in the liver and kidneys, and iodine is needed for proper thyroid function. Although most of the trace elements are metals, nonmetals like fluorine and selenium are micronutrients as well.

### PROBLEM 2.5

Classify each micronutrient in Figure 2.2 as a metal, nonmetal, or metalloid.

## 2.1C  Compounds

In Section 1.3 we learned that a *compound* **is a pure substance formed by chemically combining two or more elements together.** Element symbols are used to write chemical formulas for compounds.

- A *chemical formula* uses element symbols to show the identity of the elements forming a compound and subscripts to show the ratio of atoms (the building blocks of matter) contained in the compound.

For example, table salt is formed from sodium (Na) and chlorine (Cl) in a ratio of 1:1, so its formula is NaCl. Water, on the other hand, is formed from two hydrogens for each oxygen, so its formula is $H_2O$. The subscript "1" is understood when no subscript is written. Other examples of chemical formulas are shown below.

$$H_2O \quad\quad 2\ H\text{'s for each O}$$

$$CO_2 \quad\quad 2\ O\text{'s for each C}$$

$$C_3H_8 \quad\quad 3\ C\text{'s} \quad\quad 8\ H\text{'s}$$

water                carbon dioxide (dry ice)                propane

As we learned in Section 1.2, molecular art will often be used to illustrate the composition and state of elements and compounds. Color-coded spheres, shown in Figure 2.3, are used to identify the common elements that form compounds.

For example, a red sphere is used for the element oxygen and gray is used for the element hydrogen, so $H_2O$ is represented as a red sphere joined to two gray spheres. Sometimes the spheres will be connected by "sticks" to generate a **ball-and-stick** representation for a compound. At other times, the spheres will be drawn close together to form a **space-filling** representation. No matter

**Figure 2.3**   Common Element Colors Used in Molecular Art

C   H   O   N   F   Cl   Br   I   S   P

how the spheres are depicted, $H_2O$ always consists of one red sphere for the oxygen and two gray spheres for the two hydrogens.

$H_2O$ = ball-and-stick representation

water

oxygen

hydrogen

$H_2O$ drawn in a space-filling representation

water in the gas phase

## SAMPLE PROBLEM 2.1

Identify the elements used in each example of molecular art.

a.

b.

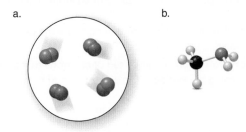

### Analysis

Use Figure 2.3 to determine the identity of the color-coded spheres.

### Solution

a. The blue spheres in this space-filling representation correspond to the element nitrogen and the red spheres correspond to the element oxygen. Thus, one "particle" contains two nitrogens, one contains two oxygens, and two contain one oxygen and one nitrogen.

b. This ball-and-stick representation contains the elements carbon (black), nitrogen (blue), and hydrogen (gray).

## PROBLEM 2.6

Identify the elements used in each example of molecular art.

a.

b.

c.

## PROBLEM 2.7

Identify the elements in each chemical formula, and give the number of atoms of each element.

a. NaCN (sodium cyanide)
b. $H_2S$ (hydrogen sulfide)

c. $C_2H_6$ (ethane)
d. $SnF_2$ (stannous fluoride)

e. CO (carbon monoxide)
f. $C_3H_8O_3$ (glycerol)

## PROBLEM 2.8

Halothane is an inhaled general anesthetic, commonly used since the 1950s. Identify the elements in the ball-and-stick representation of halothane.

halothane

## 2.2   Structure of the Atom

**All matter is composed of the same basic building blocks called** *atoms.* An atom is much too small to be seen even by the most powerful light microscopes. The period at the end of this sentence holds about $1 \times 10^8$ atoms, and a human cheek cell contains about $1 \times 10^{16}$ atoms. An atom is composed of three subatomic particles.

- A proton, symbolized by p, has a positive (+) charge.
- An electron, symbolized by e⁻, has a negative (–) charge.
- A neutron, symbolized by n, has no charge.

Protons and neutrons have approximately the same, exceedingly small mass, as shown in Table 2.3. The mass of an electron is much less, 1/1,836 the mass of a proton. These subatomic particles are not evenly distributed in the volume of an atom. There are two main components of an atom.

- The *nucleus* is a dense core that contains the protons and neutrons. Most of the mass of an atom resides in the nucleus.
- The *electron cloud* is composed of electrons that move rapidly in the almost empty space surrounding the nucleus. The electron cloud comprises most of the volume of an atom.

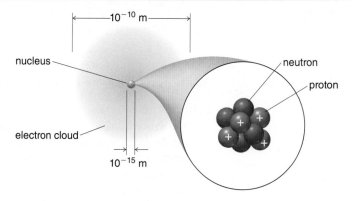

main components of an atom

While the diameter of an atom is about $10^{-10}$ m, the diameter of a nucleus is only about $10^{-15}$ m. For a macroscopic analogy, if the nucleus were the size of a baseball, an atom would be the size of Yankee Stadium!

The charged particles of an atom can either attract or repel each other.

- Opposite charges attract while like charges repel each other.

Thus, two electrons or two protons repel each other, while a proton and an electron attract each other.

Positive charges repel.          Negative charges repel.          Opposite charges attract.

### Table 2.3  Summary: The Properties of the Three Subatomic Particles

| Subatomic Particle | Charge | Mass (g) | Mass (amu) |
|---|---|---|---|
| Proton | +1 | $1.6726 \times 10^{-24}$ | 1 |
| Neutron | 0 | $1.6749 \times 10^{-24}$ | 1 |
| Electron | −1 | $9.1093 \times 10^{-28}$ | Negligible |

The element lithium is found in many consumer products, from long-lasting lithium batteries to the prescription medication lithium carbonate, used to treat individuals with bipolar disorder.

Since the mass of an individual atom is so small (on the order of $10^{-24}$ g), chemists use a standard mass unit, the **atomic mass unit,** which defines the mass of individual atoms relative to a standard mass.

- One atomic mass unit (amu) equals one-twelfth the mass of a carbon atom that has six protons and six neutrons; 1 amu = $1.661 \times 10^{-24}$ g.

Using this scale, one proton has a mass of 1.0073 amu, a value typically rounded to 1 amu. One neutron has a mass of 1.0087 amu, a value also typically rounded to 1 amu. The mass of an electron is so small that it is ignored.

**Every atom of a given type of element always has the *same* number of protons in the nucleus, a value called the *atomic number,* symbolized by Z.** Conversely, two *different* elements have *different* atomic numbers.

- The *atomic number* (Z) = the number of protons in the nucleus of an atom.

Thus, the element hydrogen has one proton in its nucleus, so its atomic number is one. Lithium has three protons in its nucleus, so its atomic number is three. The periodic table is arranged in order of increasing atomic number beginning at the upper left-hand corner. The atomic number appears just above the element symbol for each entry in the table.

Since a neutral atom has no overall charge:

- Z = the number of protons in the nucleus = the number of electrons.

Thus, the atomic number tells us *both* the number of protons in the nucleus and the number of electrons in the electron cloud of a neutral atom.

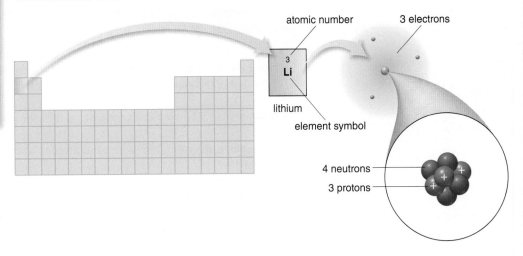

### SAMPLE PROBLEM 2.2

For the given atom: (a) determine the number of protons, neutrons, and electrons in the neutral atom; (b) give the atomic number; (c) identify the element.

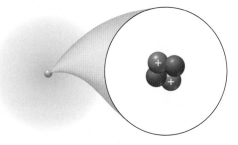

### Analysis

- The number of protons = the number of positively charged particles = the atomic number.
- The number of neutrons = the number of uncharged particles.
- The number of protons = the number of electrons in a neutral atom.
- The atomic number determines the identity of an element.

### Solution

a. The element contains two protons and two neutrons. Since a neutral atom has the same number of protons and electrons, the element has two electrons.

b. The two protons give the element an atomic number of two.

c. The element with two protons in the nucleus is **helium.**

### PROBLEM 2.9

An element has nine protons and 10 neutrons in the neutral atom. (a) How many electrons are present in the neutral atom? (b) What is the atomic number of this element? (c) Identify the element.

### SAMPLE PROBLEM 2.3

Identify the element that has an atomic number of 19, and give the number of protons and electrons in the neutral atom.

### Analysis

The atomic number is unique to an element and tells the number of protons in the nucleus and the number of electrons in the electron cloud of a neutral atom.

### Solution

According to the periodic table, the element potassium has atomic number 19. A neutral potassium atom has 19 protons and 19 electrons.

### PROBLEM 2.10

Identify the element with each atomic number, and give the number of protons and electrons in the neutral atom: (a) 2; (b) 11; (c) 20; (d) 47; (e) 78.

Both protons and neutrons contribute to the mass of an atom. The **mass number,** symbolized by *A,* is the sum of the number of protons and neutrons.

- **Mass number (*A*) = the number of protons (*Z*) + the number of neutrons.**

For example, a fluorine atom with nine protons and 10 neutrons in the nucleus has a mass number of 19.

### SAMPLE PROBLEM 2.4

For the given atom: (a) determine the number of protons and neutrons; (b) give the atomic number and the mass number; (c) identify the element.

### Analysis

- The number of protons = the number of positively charged particles = the atomic number. The atomic number determines the identity of an element.
- The number of neutrons = the number of uncharged particles.
- The mass number = the number of protons + the number of neutrons.

**Solution**

a. The element contains six protons and seven neutrons.

b. The six protons give the element an atomic number of six. The mass number = the number of protons + the number of neutrons = 6 + 7 = 13.

c. The element with six protons in the nucleus is **carbon.**

## PROBLEM 2.11

For the given atom: (a) determine the number of protons and neutrons; (b) give the atomic number and the mass number; (c) identify the element.

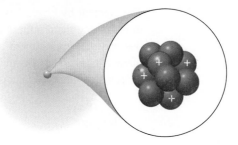

## SAMPLE PROBLEM 2.5

How many protons, neutrons, and electrons are contained in an atom of argon, which has an atomic number of 18 and a mass number of 40?

**Analysis**

- In a neutral atom, the atomic number ($Z$) = the number of protons = the number of electrons.
- The mass number ($A$) = the number of protons + the number of neutrons.

**Solution**

The atomic number of 18 means that argon has 18 protons and 18 electrons. To find the number of neutrons, subtract the atomic number ($Z$) from the mass number ($A$).

$$
\begin{aligned}
\text{number of neutrons} &= \text{mass number} - \text{atomic number} \\
&= \quad\quad 40 \quad\quad\quad - \quad\quad 18 \\
&= \quad\quad 22 \text{ neutrons}
\end{aligned}
$$

## PROBLEM 2.12

How many protons, neutrons, and electrons are contained in each atom with the given atomic number and mass number?

a. $Z = 17$, $A = 35$       b. $Z = 14$, $A = 28$       c. $Z = 92$, $A = 238$

## PROBLEM 2.13

What is the mass number of an atom that contains

a. 42 protons, 42 electrons, and 53 neutrons?       b. 24 protons, 24 electrons, and 28 neutrons?

# 2.3 Isotopes

Two atoms of the same element always have the same number of protons, but the number of neutrons can vary.

- *Isotopes* are atoms of the same element having a different number of neutrons.

## 2.3A Isotopes, Atomic Number, and Mass Number

Most elements in nature exist as a mixture of isotopes. For example, all atoms of the element chlorine contain 17 protons in the nucleus, but some of these atoms have 18 neutrons in the nucleus and some have 20 neutrons. Thus, chlorine has two isotopes with different mass numbers, 35 and 37. These isotopes are often referred to as chlorine-35 (or Cl-35) and chlorine-37 (or Cl-37).

An isotope symbol is also written using the element symbol with the atomic number as a subscript and the mass number as a superscript, both to the left.

Two isotopes of the element chlorine

mass number $\qquad$ $^{35}_{17}Cl$ $\qquad$ $^{37}_{17}Cl$
atomic number

chlorine-35    chlorine-37

The element hydrogen has three isotopes. Most hydrogen atoms have one proton and no neutrons, giving them a mass number of one. About 1% of hydrogen atoms have one proton and one neutron, giving them a mass number of two. This isotope is called **deuterium,** and it is often symbolized as **D.** An even smaller number of hydrogen atoms contain one proton and two neutrons, giving them a mass number of three. This isotope is called **tritium,** symbolized as **T.**

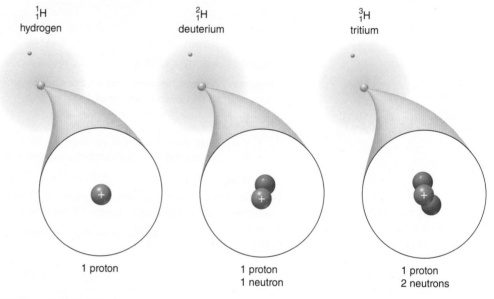

| $^1_1H$ | $^2_1H$ | $^3_1H$ |
| hydrogen | deuterium | tritium |

1 proton          1 proton          1 proton
                  1 neutron         2 neutrons

### SAMPLE PROBLEM 2.6

For each atom give the following information: [1] the atomic number; [2] the mass number; [3] the number of protons; [4] the number of neutrons; [5] the number of electrons.

a. $^{118}_{50}Sn$      b. $^{195}_{78}Pt$

#### Analysis

- The superscript gives the mass number and the subscript gives the atomic number for each element.
- The atomic number = the number of protons = the number of electrons.
- The mass number = the number of protons + the number of neutrons.

#### Solution

|  | Atomic Number | Mass Number | Number of Protons | Number of Neutrons | Number of Electrons |
|---|---|---|---|---|---|
| a. $^{118}_{50}Sn$ | 50 | 118 | 50 | 118 − 50 = 68 | 50 |
| b. $^{195}_{78}Pt$ | 78 | 195 | 78 | 195 − 78 = 117 | 78 |

### PROBLEM 2.14

For each atom give the following information: [1] the atomic number; [2] the mass number; [3] the number of protons; [4] the number of neutrons; [5] the number of electrons.

a. $^{13}_6C$      b. $^{121}_{51}Sb$

### SAMPLE PROBLEM 2.7

Determine the number of neutrons in each isotope: (a) carbon-14; (b) $^{81}Br$.

#### Analysis

- The identity of the element tells us the atomic number.
- The number of neutrons = mass number ($A$) – atomic number ($Z$).

#### Solution

a. Carbon's atomic number ($Z$) is 6. Carbon-14 has a mass number ($A$) of 14.

$$\text{number of neutrons} = A - Z$$
$$= 14 - 6 = 8 \text{ neutrons}$$

b. Bromine's atomic number is 35 and the mass number of the given isotope is 81.

$$\text{number of neutrons} = A - Z$$
$$= 81 - 35 = 46 \text{ neutrons}$$

### PROBLEM 2.15

Magnesium has three isotopes that contain 12, 13, and 14 neutrons. For each isotope give the following information: (a) the number of protons; (b) the number of electrons; (c) the atomic number; (d) the mass number. Write the isotope symbol of each isotope.

**ENVIRONMENTAL NOTE**

Although gasoline sold in the United States no longer contains lead, leaded gasoline is still used extensively in Asia, Africa, and Latin America. Gasoline exhaust containing lead pollutes the air and soil, and individuals exposed to high lead levels can suffer from circulatory, digestive, and nervous disorders. Lead (Pb) is a metal with atomic number 82 and atomic weight 207.2, as shown in the periodic table.

## 2.3B    Atomic Weight

Some elements like fluorine occur naturally as a single isotope. More commonly, an element is a mixture of isotopes, and it is useful to know the average mass, called the **atomic weight** (or **atomic mass**), of the atoms in a sample.

- The *atomic weight* is the weighted average of the mass of the naturally occurring isotopes of a particular element reported in atomic mass units.

The atomic weights of the elements appear in the alphabetical list of elements on the inside front cover. The atomic weight is also given under the element symbol in the periodic table on the inside front cover.

lead

To determine the atomic weight of an element, two quantities must be known: the mass of each isotope in atomic mass units, and the abundance with which each isotope occurs.

---

### *How To*  Determine the Atomic Weight of an Element

**Example:**  What is the atomic weight of the element chlorine?

**Step [1]**  List each isotope, along with its mass in atomic mass units (amu) and the percentage that each isotope occurs in nature.

- Chlorine has two isotopes—Cl-35 and Cl-37.
- To solve the problem, the masses and abundances of the isotopes must be known.

|        | Mass (amu) | Isotopic Abundance |
|--------|-----------|--------------------|
| Cl-35  | 34.97     | 75.78% = 0.7578    |
| Cl-37  | 36.97     | 24.22% = 0.2422    |

- The mass of any isotope is very close to the mass number of the isotope.
- To convert a percent to a decimal, divide by 100%, which is the same as moving the decimal point two places to the left; thus,

$$75.78\% = 0.7578$$

—Continued

Step [2] Multiply the isotopic abundance by the mass of each isotope, and add up the products. The sum is the atomic weight for the element.

Mass due to Cl-35:   0.7578 × 34.97 amu  = 26.5003 amu

Mass due to Cl-37:   0.2422 × 36.97 amu  =  8.9541 amu

Atomic weight  = 35.4544 amu rounded to 35.45 amu

**Answer**

### SAMPLE PROBLEM 2.8

Calculate the atomic weight of copper, which has two isotopes with the following properties: Cu-63 (62.93 amu, 69.17% natural occurrence) and Cu-65 (64.93 amu, 30.83% natural occurrence).

### Analysis

Multiply the isotopic abundance by the mass of each isotope, and add up the products to give the atomic weight for the element.

### Solution

Mass due to Cu-63:   0.6917 × 62.93 amu  = 43.5287 amu

Mass due to Cu-65:   0.3083 × 64.93 amu  = 20.0179 amu

Atomic weight  = 63.5466 amu rounded to 63.55 amu

**Answer**

### PROBLEM 2.16

Calculate the atomic weight of each element given the mass and natural occurrence of each isotope.

| a. Magnesium | Mass (amu) | Isotopic Abundance | b. Vanadium | Mass (amu) | Isotopic Abundance |
|---|---|---|---|---|---|
| Mg-24 | 23.99 | 78.99% | V-50 | 49.95 | 0.250% |
| Mg-25 | 24.99 | 10.00% | V-51 | 50.94 | 99.750% |
| Mg-26 | 25.98 | 11.01% | | | |

## 2.3C  FOCUS ON HEALTH & MEDICINE
### Isotopes in Medicine

Generally the chemical properties of isotopes are identical. Sometimes, however, one isotope of an element is radioactive—that is, it emits particles or energy as some form of radiation. Radioactive isotopes have both diagnostic and therapeutic uses in medicine.

As an example, iodine-131 is used in at least two different ways for thyroid disease. Iodine is a micronutrient needed by the body to synthesize the thyroid hormone thyroxine, which contains four iodine atoms. To evaluate the thyroid gland, a patient can be given sodium iodide (NaI) that contains radioactive iodine-131. Iodine-131 is taken up in the thyroid gland and as it emits radiation, it produces an image in a thyroid scan, which is then used to determine the condition of the thyroid gland, as shown in Figure 2.4.

Other applications of radioactive isotopes in medicine are discussed in Chapter 10.

Higher doses of iodine-131 can also be used to treat thyroid disease. Since the radioactive isotope is taken up by the thyroid gland, the radiation it emits can kill overactive or cancerous cells in the thyroid.

Figure 2.4    Iodine-131 in Medicine

a.

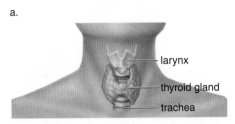

- larynx
- thyroid gland
- trachea

b.

c.

The thyroid gland is a butterfly-shaped gland in the neck, shown in (a). Uptake of radioactive iodine-131 can reveal the presence of a healthy thyroid as in (b), or an unsymmetrical thyroid gland with dense areas of iodine uptake as in (c), which may be indicative of cancer or other thyroid disease.

## 2.4   The Periodic Table

Every beginning chemistry text has a periodic table in a prominent location—often the inside front cover—because it is a valuable list of all known elements organized so that groups of elements with similar characteristics are arranged together. The periodic table evolved over many years, and it resulted from the careful observations and experiments of many brilliant scientists in the nineteenth century. Most prominent was Russian chemist Dmitri Mendeleev, whose arrangement in 1869 of the 60 known elements into groups having similar properties in order of increasing atomic number became the precursor of the modern periodic table (inside front cover and Figure 2.5).

### 2.4A   Basic Features of the Periodic Table

The periodic table is arranged into seven horizontal rows and 18 vertical columns. The particular row and column tell us much about the properties of an element.

- A row in the periodic table is called a *period.* Elements in the same row are similar in size.
- A column in the periodic table is called a *group.* Elements in the same group have similar electronic and chemical properties.

The rows in the periodic table are numbered 1–7. The number of elements in each row varies. The first period has just two elements, hydrogen and helium. The second and third rows have eight elements each, and the fourth and fifth rows have 18 elements. Also note that two rows of 14 elements appear at the bottom of the periodic table. The **lanthanides,** beginning with the element cerium ($Z = 58$), immediately follow the element lanthanum (La). The **actinides,** beginning with thorium ($Z = 90$), immediately follow the element actinium (Ac).

Each column in the periodic table is assigned a **group number.** Groups are numbered in two ways. In one system, the 18 columns of the periodic table are assigned the numbers 1–18, beginning with the column farthest to the left. An older but still widely used system numbers the groups 1–8, followed by the letter A or B.

- The *main group elements* consist of the two columns on the far left and the six columns on the far right of the table. These groups are numbered 1A–8A.
- The *transition metal elements* are contained in the 10 short columns in the middle of the table, numbered 1B–8B.
- The *inner transition metal elements* consist of the lanthanides and actinides, and they are not assigned group numbers.

The periodic table in Figure 2.5 has both systems of numbering groups. For example, the element carbon (C) is located in the second row (period 2) of the periodic table. Its group number is 4A (or 14).

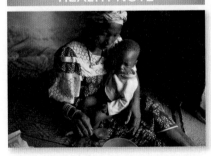

**Figure 2.5**    Basic Features of the Periodic Table

Period

| | 1A 1 | 2A 2 | | | | | | | | | | | 3A 13 | 4A 14 | 5A 15 | 6A 16 | 7A 17 | 8A 18 | |
|---|---|---|---|---|---|---|---|---|---|---|---|---|---|---|---|---|---|---|---|
| 1 | 1 **H** 1.008 | | | | | | | | | | | | | | | | | | 2 **He** 4.003 | 1 |
| 2 | 3 **Li** 6.941 | 4 **Be** 9.012 | | | | | | | | | | | 5 **B** 10.81 | 6 **C** 12.01 | 7 **N** 14.01 | 8 **O** 16.00 | 9 **F** 19.00 | 10 **Ne** 20.18 | 2 |
| 3 | 11 **Na** 22.99 | 12 **Mg** 24.31 | 3B 3 | 4B 4 | 5B 5 | 6B 6 | 7B 7 | 8 | 8B 9 | 10 | 1B 11 | 2B 12 | 13 **Al** 26.98 | 14 **Si** 28.09 | 15 **P** 30.97 | 16 **S** 32.07 | 17 **Cl** 35.45 | 18 **Ar** 39.95 | 3 |
| 4 | 19 **K** 39.10 | 20 **Ca** 40.08 | 21 **Sc** 44.96 | 22 **Ti** 47.88 | 23 **V** 50.94 | 24 **Cr** 52.00 | 25 **Mn** 54.94 | 26 **Fe** 55.85 | 27 **Co** 58.93 | 28 **Ni** 58.69 | 29 **Cu** 63.55 | 30 **Zn** 65.41 | 31 **Ga** 69.72 | 32 **Ge** 72.64 | 33 **As** 74.92 | 34 **Se** 78.96 | 35 **Br** 79.90 | 36 **Kr** 83.80 | 4 |
| 5 | 37 **Rb** 85.47 | 38 **Sr** 87.62 | 39 **Y** 88.91 | 40 **Zr** 91.22 | 41 **Nb** 92.91 | 42 **Mo** 95.94 | 43 **Tc** (98) | 44 **Ru** 101.1 | 45 **Rh** 102.9 | 46 **Pd** 106.4 | 47 **Ag** 107.9 | 48 **Cd** 112.4 | 49 **In** 114.8 | 50 **Sn** 118.7 | 51 **Sb** 121.8 | 52 **Te** 127.6 | 53 **I** 126.9 | 54 **Xe** 131.3 | 5 |
| 6 | 55 **Cs** 132.9 | 56 **Ba** 137.3 | 57 **La** 138.9 | 72 **Hf** 178.5 | 73 **Ta** 180.9 | 74 **W** 183.8 | 75 **Re** 186.2 | 76 **Os** 190.2 | 77 **Ir** 192.2 | 78 **Pt** 195.1 | 79 **Au** 197.0 | 80 **Hg** 200.6 | 81 **Tl** 204.4 | 82 **Pb** 207.2 | 83 **Bi** 209.0 | 84 **Po** (209) | 85 **At** (210) | 86 **Rn** (222) | 6 |
| 7 | 87 **Fr** (223) | 88 **Ra** (226) | 89 **Ac** (227) | 104 **Rf** (267) | 105 **Db** (268) | 106 **Sg** (271) | 107 **Bh** (272) | 108 **Hs** (270) | 109 **Mt** (276) | 110 **Ds** (281) | 111 **Rg** (280) | 112 **Cn** (285) | 113 – (284) | 114 – (289) | 115 – (289) | 116 – (293) | 117 – (294) | 118 – (294) | 7 |

Group number

| Lanthanides | 6 | 58 **Ce** 140.1 | 59 **Pr** 140.9 | 60 **Nd** 144.2 | 61 **Pm** (145) | 62 **Sm** 150.4 | 63 **Eu** 152.0 | 64 **Gd** 157.3 | 65 **Tb** 158.9 | 66 **Dy** 162.5 | 67 **Ho** 164.9 | 68 **Er** 167.3 | 69 **Tm** 168.9 | 70 **Yb** 173.0 | 71 **Lu** 175.0 | 6 |
|---|---|---|---|---|---|---|---|---|---|---|---|---|---|---|---|---|
| Actinides | 7 | 90 **Th** 232.0 | 91 **Pa** 231.0 | 92 **U** 238.0 | 93 **Np** (237) | 94 **Pu** (244) | 95 **Am** (243) | 96 **Cm** (247) | 97 **Bk** (247) | 98 **Cf** (251) | 99 **Es** (252) | 100 **Fm** (257) | 101 **Md** (258) | 102 **No** (259) | 103 **Lr** (262) | 7 |

▢ Main group elements     ▢ Transition metal elements     ▢ Inner transition metal elements

- Each element of the periodic table is part of a horizontal row and a vertical column.
- The periodic table consists of seven rows, labeled periods 1–7, and 18 columns that are assigned a group number. Two different numbering systems are indicated.
- Elements are divided into three categories: main group elements (groups 1A–8A, shown in light blue), transition metals (groups 1B–8B, shown in tan), and inner transition metals (shown in light green).

## SAMPLE PROBLEM 2.9

Give the period and group number for each element: (a) magnesium; (b) manganese.

### Analysis

Use the element symbol to locate an element in the periodic table. Count down the rows of elements to determine the period. The group number is located at the top of each column.

### Solution

a. Magnesium (Mg) is located in the third row (period 3), and has group number 2A (or 2).

b. Manganese (Mn) is located in the fourth row (period 4), and has group number 7B (or 7).

PROBLEM 2.17

Give the period and group number for each element: (a) oxygen; (b) calcium; (c) phosphorus; (d) platinum; (e) iodine.

## 2.4B   Characteristics of Groups 1A, 2A, 7A, and 8A

Four columns of main group elements illustrate an important fact about the periodic table.

- • Elements that comprise a particular group have similar chemical properties.

### Alkali Metals (Group 1A) and Alkaline Earth Elements (Group 2A)

The alkali metals and the alkaline earth elements are located on the far left side of the periodic table.

Although hydrogen is also located in group 1A, it is *not* an alkali metal.

The **alkali metals,** located in group 1A (group 1), include lithium (Li), sodium (Na), potassium (K), rubidium (Rb), cesium (Cs), and francium (Fr). Alkali metals share the following characteristics:

- • They are soft and shiny and have low melting points.
- • They are good conductors of heat and electricity.
- • They react readily with water to form basic solutions.

The **alkaline earth elements,** located in group 2A (group 2), include beryllium (Be), magnesium (Mg), calcium (Ca), strontium (Sr), barium (Ba), and radium (Ra). Alkaline earth metals are also shiny solids but less reactive than the alkali metals.

None of the metals in groups 1A or 2A exist in nature as pure elements; rather, they are always combined with other elements to form compounds. Examples of compounds from group 1A elements include sodium chloride (NaCl), table salt, and potassium iodide (KI), an essential nutrient added to make iodized salt. Examples of compounds from group 2A elements include magnesium sulfate ($MgSO_4$), an anticonvulsant used to prevent seizures in pregnant women, and barium sulfate ($BaSO_4$), which is used to improve the quality of X-ray images of the gastrointestinal tract.

Chlorpheniramine is an antihistamine that contains the halogen chlorine. Antihistamines are drugs used to treat the symptoms of the common cold and allergies. We will learn more about antihistamines in Chapter 18.

## Halogens (Group 7A) and Noble Gases (Group 8A)

The halogens and noble gases are located on the far right side of the periodic table.

The **halogens,** located in group 7A (group 17), include fluorine (F), chlorine (Cl), bromine (Br), iodine (I), and the rare radioactive element astatine (At). In their elemental form, halogens contain two atoms joined together—$F_2$, $Cl_2$, $Br_2$, and $I_2$. Fluorine and chlorine are gases at room temperature, bromine is a liquid, and iodine is a solid. Halogens are very reactive and combine with many other elements to form compounds. In Chapter 14, we will learn about carbon compounds that contain halogen atoms.

The **noble gases,** located in group 8A (group 18), include helium (He), neon (Ne), argon (Ar), krypton (Kr), xenon (Xe), and radon (Rn). Unlike other elements, the noble gases are especially stable as atoms, and so they rarely combine with other elements to form compounds.

The noble gas **radon** has received attention in recent years. Radon is a radioactive gas, and generally its concentration in the air is low and therefore its presence harmless. In some types of soil, however, radon levels can be high and radon detectors are recommended for the basement of homes to monitor radon levels. High radon levels are linked to an increased risk of lung cancer.

### PROBLEM 2.18

Identify the element fitting each description.

  a. an alkali metal in period 4
  b. a second-row element in group 7A
  c. a noble gas in the third period

  d. a main group element in period 5 and group 2A
  e. a transition metal in group 12, period 4
  f. a transition metal in group 5, period 5

### PROBLEM 2.19

Identify each highlighted element in the periodic table and give its [1] element name and symbol; [2] group number; [3] period; [4] classification (main group element, transition metal, or inner transition metal).

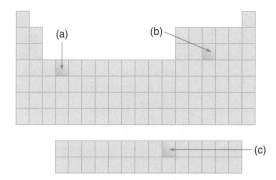

## 2.4C  The Unusual Nature of Carbon

Carbon, a second-row element in group 4A of the periodic table, is different from most other elements in that it has three elemental forms (Figure 2.6). The two most common forms of carbon are diamond and graphite. **Diamond** is hard because it contains a dense three-dimensional network of carbon atoms in six-membered rings. **Graphite,** on the other hand, is a slippery black substance used as a lubricant. It contains parallel sheets of carbon atoms in flat six-membered rings.

**Buckminsterfullerene,** also referred to as a bucky ball, is a third form that contains 60 carbon atoms joined together in a sphere of 20 hexagons and 12 pentagons in a pattern that resembles a soccer ball. A component of soot, this form of carbon was not discovered until 1985. Its unusual name stems from its shape, which resembles the geodesic dome invented by R. Buckminster Fuller.

**Carbon's ability to join with itself and other elements gives it versatility not seen with any other element in the periodic table.** In the unscientific but eloquent description by writer Bill Bryson in *A Short History of Nearly Everything,* carbon is described as "the party animal of the atomic world, latching on to many other atoms (including itself) and holding tight, forming molecular conga lines of hearty robustness—the very trick of nature necessary to build proteins and DNA." As a result, millions of compounds that contain the element carbon are known. The chemistry of these compounds is discussed at length in Chapters 11–24.

**Figure 2.6**   Three Elemental Forms of Carbon

a. Diamond

b. Graphite

c. Buckminsterfullerene

• Diamond consists of an intricate three-dimensional network of carbon atoms.

• Graphite contains parallel sheets of carbon atoms.

• Buckminsterfullerene contains a sphere with 60 carbon atoms.

## 2.5  Electronic Structure

Why do elements in a group of the periodic table have similar chemical properties? **The chemical properties of an element are determined by the number of *electrons* in an atom.** To understand the properties of an element, therefore, we must learn more about the electrons that surround the nucleus.

The modern description of the electronic structure of an atom is based on the following principles.

- Electrons do not move freely in space; rather, an electron is confined to a specific region, giving it a particular energy.
- Electrons occupy discrete energy levels. The energy of electrons is *quantized;* that is, the energy is restricted to specific values.

The electrons that surround a nucleus are confined to regions called the **principal energy levels** or **shells.**

- The shells are numbered, $n = 1, 2, 3, 4$, and so forth, beginning closest to the nucleus.
- Electrons closer to the nucleus are held more tightly and are lower in energy.
- Electrons farther from the nucleus are held less tightly and are higher in energy.

The number of electrons that can occupy a given shell is determined by the value of $n$. **The farther a shell is from the nucleus, the larger its volume becomes, and the more electrons it can hold.** Thus, the first shell can hold only two electrons, the second holds eight, the third 18, and so forth. The maximum number of electrons is given by the formula $2n^2$, where $n$ = the shell number.

**Distribution of electrons in the first four shells**

| Shell | Number of electrons in a shell |
|---|---|
| 4 | 32 |
| 3 | 18 |
| 2 | 8 |
| lowest energy → 1 | 2 |

*Increasing energy* →    *Increasing number of electrons* →

Shells are divided into **subshells,** identified by the letters *s, p, d,* and *f.* The subshells consist of **orbitals.**

- An *orbital* is a region of space where the probability of finding an electron is high. Each orbital can hold *two* electrons.

The two electrons in an orbital must have opposite spins. If one electron has a clockwise spin, the second electron in the orbital must have a counterclockwise spin.

**A particular type of subshell contains a specific number of orbitals.** An *s* subshell contains only **one** *s* orbital. A *p* subshell has **three** *p* orbitals. A *d* subshell has **five** *d* orbitals. An *f* subshell has **seven** *f* orbitals. The number of subshells in a given shell equals the value of *n*. The energy of orbitals shows the following trend:

| *s* orbital | *p* orbital | *d* orbital | *f* orbital |
|---|---|---|---|
| lowest energy | | | highest energy |

Increasing energy

The first shell of electrons around a nucleus ($n = 1$) has only one *s* orbital. This orbital is called the 1*s* orbital since it is the *s* orbital in the first shell. Since each orbital can hold two electrons and the first shell has only one orbital, the **first shell can hold two electrons.**

shell number (principal energy level)    1*s* = the *s* orbital in the first shell

The second shell of electrons ($n = 2$) has two types of orbitals—one $s$ and three $p$ orbitals. These orbitals are called the $2s$ and $2p$ orbitals since they are located in the second shell. Since each orbital can hold two electrons and there are four orbitals, the **second shell can hold eight electrons.**

The third shell of electrons ($n = 3$) has three types of orbitals—one $s$, three $p$, and five $d$ orbitals. These orbitals are called the $3s$, $3p$, and $3d$ orbitals since they are located in the third shell. Since each orbital can hold two electrons and the third shell has a total of nine orbitals, the **third shell can hold 18 electrons.**

| one 3s orbital | three 3p orbitals | five 3d orbitals | | |
|---|---|---|---|---|
| 3s | 3p 3p 3p | 3d 3d 3d 3d 3d | = | **9 orbitals** in the third shell |

Each orbital holds **two** electrons.

$$9 \text{ orbitals} \times \frac{2 \text{ electrons}}{1 \text{ orbital}} =$$

**18 electrons** in the third shell

The fourth shell of electrons ($n = 4$) has four types of orbitals—one $s$, three $p$, five $d$, and seven $f$ orbitals. These orbitals are called the $4s$, $4p$, $4d$, and $4f$ orbitals since they are located in the fourth shell. Since each orbital can hold two electrons and the fourth shell has a total of sixteen orbitals, the **fourth shell can hold 32 electrons.**

| one 4s orbital | three 4p orbitals | five 4d orbitals | seven 4f orbitals | |
|---|---|---|---|---|
| 4s | 4p 4p 4p | 4d 4d 4d 4d 4d | 4f 4f 4f 4f 4f 4f 4f | = **16 orbitals** in the fourth shell |

$$16 \text{ orbitals} \times \frac{2 \text{ electrons}}{1 \text{ orbital}} = \boxed{\textbf{32 electrons} \text{ in the fourth shell}}$$

**Thus, the maximum number of electrons that can occupy a shell is determined by the number of orbitals in the shell.** Table 2.4 summarizes the orbitals and electrons in the first four shells.

Table 2.4  Orbitals and Electrons Contained in the Principal Energy Levels ($n = 1–4$)

| Shell | Orbitals | Electrons in Each Subshell | Maximum Number of Electrons |
|---|---|---|---|
| 1 | 1s | 2 | 2 |
| 2 | 2s | 2 | 8 |
|   | 2p 2p 2p | $3 \times 2 = 6$ | |
| 3 | 3s | 2 | 18 |
|   | 3p 3p 3p | $3 \times 2 = 6$ | |
|   | 3d 3d 3d 3d 3d | $5 \times 2 = 10$ | |
| 4 | 4s | 2 | 32 |
|   | 4p 4p 4p | $3 \times 2 = 6$ | |
|   | 4d 4d 4d 4d 4d | $5 \times 2 = 10$ | |
|   | 4f 4f 4f 4f 4f 4f 4f | $7 \times 2 = 14$ | |

Each type of orbital has a particular shape.

- An *s* orbital has a sphere of electron density. It is lower in energy than other orbitals in the same shell because electrons are kept closer to the positively charged nucleus.
- A *p* orbital has a dumbbell shape. A *p* orbital is higher in energy than an *s* orbital in the same shell because its electron density is farther from the nucleus.

All *s* orbitals are spherical, but the orbital gets larger in size as the shell number increases. Thus, both a 1*s* orbital and a 2*s* orbital are spherical, but the 2*s* orbital is larger. The three *p* orbitals in a shell are perpendicular to each other along the *x, y,* and *z* axes.

### PROBLEM 2.20

How many electrons are present in each shell, subshell, or orbital?

  a. a 2*p* orbital       b. the 3*d* subshell       c. a 3*d* orbital       d. the third shell

## 2.6   Electronic Configurations

We can now examine the **electronic configuration** of an individual atom—that is, how the electrons are arranged in an atom's orbitals. **The lowest energy arrangement of electrons is called the** *ground state*. Three rules are followed.

### Rules to Determine the Ground State Electronic Configuration of an Atom

**Rule [1]**   Electrons are placed in the lowest energy orbitals beginning with the 1*s* orbital.

- In comparing similar types of orbitals from one shell to another (e.g., 2*s* and 3*s*), an orbital closer to the nucleus is lower in energy. Thus, the energy of a 2*s* orbital is lower than a 3*s* orbital.
- Within a shell, orbital energies increase in the following order: *s, p, d, f.*

These guidelines result in the following order of energies in the first three periods: 1*s,* 2*s,* 2*p,* 3*s,* 3*p.* Above the 3*p* level, however, all orbitals of one shell do *not* have to be filled before any orbital in the next higher shell gets electrons. For example, a 4*s* orbital is lower in energy than a 3*d* orbital, so it is filled first. Figure 2.7 lists the relative energy of the orbitals used by atoms in the periodic table.

**Rule [2]**   Each orbital holds a maximum of two electrons.

**Rule [3]**   When orbitals are equal in energy, one electron is added to each orbital until the orbitals are half-filled, before any orbital is completely filled.

- For example, one electron is added to each of the three *p* orbitals before filling any *p* orbital with two electrons.
- Because like charges repel each other (Section 2.2), adding electrons to *different p* orbitals keeps them farther away from each other, which is energetically favorable.

**Figure 2.7** Relative Energies of Orbitals

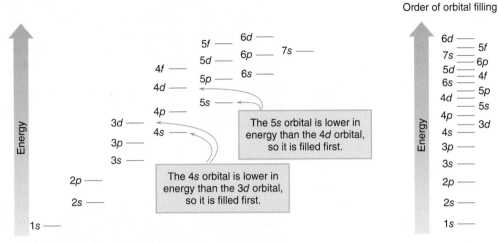

Order of orbital filling

Electrons are added to orbitals in order of increasing energy. The 4s orbital is filled with electrons before the 3d orbital since it is lower in energy. The same is true for filling the 5s orbital with electrons before the 4d orbital. Likewise, the 6s orbital is filled before both the 4f and 5d orbitals, and the 7s orbital is filled before both the 5f and 6d orbitals.

To illustrate how these rules are used, we can write the electronic configuration for several elements using **orbital diagrams.** An orbital diagram uses a box to represent each orbital and arrows to represent electrons. A single electron, called an **unpaired electron,** is shown with a single arrow pointing up ($\uparrow$). Two electrons in an orbital have **paired spins**—that is, the spins are opposite in direction—so up and down arrows ($\uparrow\downarrow$) are used.

Finally, it is not necessary to memorize the order of orbital filling that appears in Figure 2.7. Rather, the periodic table can be used to determine the electronic configuration of an element, as shown in Section 2.6C. This method is especially useful for elements in the fourth row and later, in which an orbital of a higher shell gets electrons before filling a lower shell completely.

## 2.6A First-Row Elements (Period 1)

The first row of the periodic table contains only two elements—hydrogen and helium. Since the number of protons in the nucleus equals the number of electrons in a neutral atom, the **atomic number tells us how many electrons must be placed in orbitals.**

**Hydrogen** (H, $Z = 1$) has one electron. In the ground state, this electron is added to the lowest energy orbital, the 1s orbital. To draw an orbital diagram we use one box to represent the 1s orbital, and one up arrow to represent the electron. We can also write out the electron configuration without boxes and arrows, using a superscript with each orbital to show how many electrons it contains.

H $\qquad$ $\uparrow$ $\quad$ or $\quad$ $1s^1$ $\quad$ one electron in the 1s orbital

1 electron $\quad$ 1s

**Helium** (He, $Z = 2$) has two electrons. In the ground state, both electrons are added to the 1s orbital. To draw an orbital diagram we use one box to represent the 1s orbital, and a set of up and down arrows to represent the two electrons with paired spins. The electron configuration can also be written as $1s^2$, meaning the 1s orbital has two electrons. Helium has a filled first shell of electrons.

He $\qquad$ $\uparrow\downarrow$ $\quad$ or $\quad$ $1s^2$ $\quad$ two electrons in the 1s orbital

2 electrons $\quad$ 1s

Because the element helium is lighter than air, balloons filled with helium must be secured with ropes or strings so they don't float away.

## 2.6B  Second-Row Elements (Period 2)

To write orbital diagrams for the second-row elements, we must now use the four orbitals in the second shell—the $2s$ orbital and the three $2p$ orbitals. Since electrons are always added to the lowest energy orbitals first, all second-row elements have the $1s$ orbital filled with electrons, and then the remaining electrons are added to the orbitals in the second shell. Since the $2s$ orbital is lower in energy than the $2p$ orbitals, it is completely filled before adding electrons to the $2p$ orbitals.

**Lithium** (Li, $Z = 3$) has three electrons. In the ground state, two electrons are added to the $1s$ orbital and the remaining electron is an unpaired electron in the $2s$ orbital. Lithium's electronic configuration can also be written as $1s^2 2s^1$ to show the placement of its three electrons.

**Carbon** (C, $Z = 6$) has six electrons. In the ground state, two electrons are added to both the $1s$ and $2s$ orbitals. The two remaining electrons are added to two different $2p$ orbitals, giving carbon **two unpaired electrons.** These electrons spin in the same direction, so the arrows used to represent them are drawn in the same direction as well (both ↑ in this case). Carbon's electronic configuration is also written as $1s^2 2s^2 2p^2$. This method of writing an electronic configuration indicates that carbon has two electrons in its $2p$ orbitals, but it does not explicitly show that the two $2p$ electrons occupy *different* $2p$ orbitals.

**Oxygen** (O, $Z = 8$) has eight electrons. In the ground state, two electrons are added to both the $1s$ and $2s$ orbitals. The remaining four electrons must be distributed among the three $2p$ orbitals to give the lowest energy arrangement. This is done by pairing two electrons in one $2p$ orbital, and giving the remaining $2p$ orbitals one electron each. Oxygen has two unpaired electrons.

**Neon** (Ne, $Z = 10$) has 10 electrons. In the ground state, two electrons are added to the $1s$, $2s$, and each of the three $2p$ orbitals, so that the second shell of orbitals is now completely filled with electrons.

Sometimes the electronic configuration of an element is shortened by using the name of the noble gas that has a filled shell of electrons from the preceding row, and then adding the electronic configuration of all remaining electrons using orbitals and superscripts. For example, each second-row element has a $1s^2$ configuration like the noble gas helium in the preceding row, so the electronic configuration for carbon can be shortened to $[He]2s^2 2p^2$.

Electronic configuration for helium:    $[He]$    $=$    $1s^2$

For carbon:   $1s^2 2s^2 2p^2$          $[He]2s^2 2p^2$

replace

carbon's electronic configuration using noble gas notation

The electronic configurations of all the first- and second-row elements are listed in Table 2.5.

## Table 2.5 Electronic Configurations of the First- and Second-Row Elements

| Atomic Number | Element | Orbital Diagram 1s | 2s | 2p | | | Electronic Configuration | Noble Gas Notation |
|---|---|---|---|---|---|---|---|---|
| 1 | H | ↑ | | | | | $1s^1$ | |
| 2 | He | ↑↓ | | | | | $1s^2$ | |
| 3 | Li | ↑↓ | ↑ | | | | $1s^2 2s^1$ | [He] $2s^1$ |
| 4 | Be | ↑↓ | ↑↓ | | | | $1s^2 2s^2$ | [He] $2s^2$ |
| 5 | B | ↑↓ | ↑↓ | ↑ | | | $1s^2 2s^2 2p^1$ | [He] $2s^2 2p^1$ |
| 6 | C | ↑↓ | ↑↓ | ↑ | ↑ | | $1s^2 2s^2 2p^2$ | [He] $2s^2 2p^2$ |
| 7 | N | ↑↓ | ↑↓ | ↑ | ↑ | ↑ | $1s^2 2s^2 2p^3$ | [He] $2s^2 2p^3$ |
| 8 | O | ↑↓ | ↑↓ | ↑↓ | ↑ | ↑ | $1s^2 2s^2 2p^4$ | [He] $2s^2 2p^4$ |
| 9 | F | ↑↓ | ↑↓ | ↑↓ | ↑↓ | ↑ | $1s^2 2s^2 2p^5$ | [He] $2s^2 2p^5$ |
| 10 | Ne | ↑↓ | ↑↓ | ↑↓ | ↑↓ | ↑↓ | $1s^2 2s^2 2p^6$ | [He] $2s^2 2p^6$ |

### PROBLEM 2.21

What element has each electronic configuration?

a. $1s^2 2s^2 2p^6 3s^2 3p^2$

b. [Ne]$3s^2 3p^4$

c. $1s^2 2s^2 2p^6 3s^2 3p^6 4s^2 3d^1$

d. [Ar]$4s^2 3d^{10}$

### PROBLEM 2.22

What element(s) in the first and second period fit each description?

a. The element has one electron in the second energy level.

b. There are two electrons in the 2s orbital.

c. The electronic configuration is $1s^2 2s^2 2p^5$.

d. The element contains six electrons in the second energy level.

## 2.6C   Electronic Configurations of Other Elements Using the Periodic Table

Orbital diagrams can be written for every element in the periodic table. We can use the location of an element in the periodic table to determine what orbitals are filled with electrons.

Considering electronic configuration, the periodic table can be divided into four regions called **blocks**, labeled *s*, *p*, *d*, and *f*, and illustrated in Figure 2.8. **The blocks are labeled according to the subshells that are filled with electrons *last*.**

- The *s block* consists of groups 1A and 2A and the element helium. The *s* subshell is filled last in these elements.
- The *p block* consists of groups 3A–8A (except helium). The *p* subshell is filled last in these elements.
- The *d block* consists of the 10 columns of transition metals. The *d* subshell is filled last in these elements.
- The *f block* consists of the two groups of 14 inner transition metals. The *f* subshell is filled last in these elements.

Sample Problems 2.10 and 2.11 illustrate how to use the blocks in Figure 2.8 to write the electronic configuration for two different elements.

Figure 2.8 The Blocks of Elements in the Periodic Table

Coal that is high in **sulfur** content burns to form sulfur oxides, which in turn react with water to form sulfurous and sulfuric acids. Rain that contains these acids has destroyed acres of forests worldwide.

## SAMPLE PROBLEM 2.10

Give the orbital diagram for the ground state electronic configuration of the element sulfur.

### Analysis

- Use the atomic number to determine the number of electrons.
- Locate the element in the periodic table, and use Figure 2.8 to determine the order of orbitals filled with electrons. Read the table from left-to-right, row-by-row, beginning at the upper left corner and ending at the element in question.
- To fill orbitals of the same energy, place electrons one at a time in the orbitals until they are half-filled.

### Solution

Sulfur is located in the $p$ block with an atomic number of 16, so 16 electrons must be placed in orbitals. Reading the periodic table in blocks row-by-row from left-to-right ending at sulfur gives the following order of orbitals to be filled with electrons: $1s$, $2s$, $2p$ (three orbitals), $3s$, and $3p$ (three orbitals).

Give each orbital two electrons. In adding the last four electrons to the three 3p orbitals, give one orbital two electrons and place one unpaired electron in the remaining two orbitals.

**Answer:**

two unpaired electrons

S

sulfur
16 electrons

1s  2s      2p          3s      3p

### SAMPLE PROBLEM 2.11

Give the ground state electronic configuration of the element calcium. Convert the electronic configuration to noble gas notation.

#### Analysis

- Use the atomic number to determine the number of electrons.
- Locate the element in the periodic table and use Figure 2.8 to determine the order of orbitals filled with electrons.
- To convert the electronic configuration to noble gas notation, replace the electronic configuration corresponding to the noble gas in the preceding row by the symbol for the noble gas in brackets.

#### Solution

The atomic number of calcium is 20, so 20 electrons must be placed in orbitals. Figure 2.8 shows the following order of orbitals to be filled: 1s, 2s, 2p (three orbitals), 3s, 3p (three orbitals), and 4s. Give each orbital two electrons. Since calcium is an element in period 4, use the noble gas argon in period 3 to write the noble gas configuration. **Substitute [Ar] for all of the electrons in the first three shells.**

$$\text{Electronic configuration for Ca} \quad = \quad 1s^2 2s^2 2p^6 3s^2 3p^6 4s^2 \quad = \quad [\text{Ar}]4s^2$$

(20 electrons)

The noble gas argon contains
these 18 electrons.

noble gas notation

Replace with [Ar].

### PROBLEM 2.23

Draw an orbital diagram for each element: (a) magnesium; (b) aluminum; (c) bromine.

### PROBLEM 2.24

Give the electronic configuration for each element and then convert it to noble gas notation: (a) sodium; (b) silicon; (c) iodine.

## 2.7  Valence Electrons

The chemical properties of an element depend on the most loosely held electrons—that is, those electrons in the outermost shell, called the **valence shell.** The period number tells the number of the valence shell.

- **The electrons in the outermost shell are called the *valence electrons.***

### 2.7A  Relating Valence Electrons to Group Number

To identify the electrons in the valence shell, always look for the shell with the *highest* number. Thus, beryllium has two valence electrons that occupy the 2s orbital. Chlorine has seven valence electrons since it has a total of seven electrons in the third shell, two in the 3s orbital and five in the 3p orbitals.

Be (beryllium):

Cl (chlorine):

$1s^2 2s^2$    2 valence electrons

valence shell

$1s^2 2s^2 2p^6 3s^2 3p^5$    7 valence electrons

valence shell

If we examine the electronic configuration of a group in the periodic table, two facts become apparent.

- Elements in the same group have the same number of valence electrons and similar electronic configurations.
- The group number (using the 1A–8A system) equals the number of valence electrons for main group elements (except helium).

As an example, the alkali metals in group 1A all have one valence electron that occupies an $s$ orbital. Thus, a general electronic configuration for the valence electrons of an alkali metal is $ns^1$, where $n$ = the period in which the element is located.

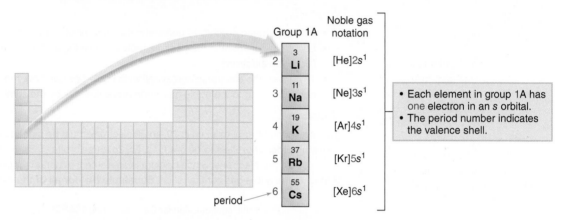

- Each element in group 1A has one electron in an $s$ orbital.
- The period number indicates the valence shell.

**Thus, the periodic table is organized into groups of elements with similar valence electronic configurations in the same column.** The valence electronic configurations of the main group elements in the first three rows of the periodic table are given in Table 2.6.

- The chemical properties of a group are similar because these elements contain the same electronic configuration of valence electrons.

Take particular note of the electronic configuration of the noble gases in group 8A. **All of these elements have a completely filled outer shell of valence electrons.** Helium has a filled first shell ($1s^2$ configuration). The remaining elements have a completely filled valence shell of $s$ and $p$ orbitals ($s^2p^6$). This electronic arrangement is especially stable, and as a result, these elements exist in nature as single atoms. We will learn about the consequences of having a completely filled valence shell in Chapter 3.

**Table 2.6** Valence Electronic Configurations for the Main Group Elements in Periods 1–3

| Group Number | 1A | 2A | 3A | 4A | 5A | 6A | 7A | 8A[a] |
|---|---|---|---|---|---|---|---|---|
| Period 1 | H $1s^1$ | | | | | | | He $1s^2$ |
| Period 2 | Li $2s^1$ | Be $2s^2$ | B $2s^22p^1$ | C $2s^22p^2$ | N $2s^22p^3$ | O $2s^22p^4$ | F $2s^22p^5$ | Ne $2s^22p^6$ |
| Period 3 | Na $3s^1$ | Mg $3s^2$ | Al $3s^23p^1$ | Si $3s^23p^2$ | P $3s^23p^3$ | S $3s^23p^4$ | Cl $3s^23p^5$ | Ar $3s^23p^6$ |
| General configuration | $ns^1$ | $ns^2$ | $ns^2np^1$ | $ns^2np^2$ | $ns^2np^3$ | $ns^2np^4$ | $ns^2np^5$ | $ns^2np^6$ |

[a]The general electronic configuration in group 8A applies to all of the noble gases except helium. Since helium is a first-row element, it has only two electrons, and these occupy the only available orbital in the first shell, the $1s$ orbital.

Mercury (Sample Problem 2.12) is safely used in dental amalgam to fill cavities in teeth. Mercury released into the environment, however, is converted to toxic methylmercury by microorganisms in water, so hazardous levels of this soluble mercury compound can accumulate in fish at the top of the food chain, such as sharks and swordfish.

## SAMPLE PROBLEM 2.12

Identify the total number of electrons, the number of valence electrons, and the name of the element with each electronic configuration.

a. $1s^2 2s^2 2p^6 3s^2 3p^2$  b. $1s^2 2s^2 2p^6 3s^2 3p^6 4s^2 3d^{10} 4p^6 5s^2 4d^{10} 5p^6 6s^2 4f^{14} 5d^{10}$

### Analysis

To obtain the total number of electrons, add up the superscripts. This gives the atomic number and identifies the element. To determine the number of valence electrons, add up the number of electrons in the shell with the highest number.

### Solution

a.  valence shell

$1s^2 2s^2 2p^6 3s^2 3p^2$

**4** valence electrons

Total number of electrons =
$2 + 2 + 6 + 2 + 2 = \mathbf{14}$

**Answer:** Silicon (Si), 14 total electrons and 4 valence electrons

b.  valence shell

$1s^2 2s^2 2p^6 3s^2 3p^6 4s^2 3d^{10} 4p^6 5s^2 4d^{10} 5p^6 6s^2 4f^{14} 5d^{10}$

**2** valence electrons

Total number of electrons = **80**

**Answer:** Mercury (Hg), 80 total electrons and 2 valence electrons

### PROBLEM 2.25

Identify the total number of electrons, the number of valence electrons, and the name of the element with each electronic configuration.

a. $1s^2 2s^2 2p^6 3s^2$

b. $1s^2 2s^2 2p^6 3s^2 3p^3$

c. $1s^2 2s^2 2p^6 3s^2 3p^6 4s^2 3d^{10} 4p^6 5s^2 4d^2$

d. $[Ar]4s^2 3d^6$

## SAMPLE PROBLEM 2.13

Determine the number of valence electrons and give the electronic configuration of the valence electrons of each element: (a) nitrogen; (b) potassium.

### Analysis

The group number of a main group element = the number of valence electrons. Use the general electronic configurations in Table 2.6 to write the configuration of the valence electrons.

### Solution

a.  Nitrogen is located in group 5A so it has five valence electrons. Since nitrogen is a second-period element, its valence electronic configuration is $2s^2 2p^3$.

b.  Potassium is located in group 1A so it has one valence electron. Since potassium is a fourth-period element, its valence electronic configuration is $4s^1$.

### PROBLEM 2.26

Determine the number of valence electrons and give the electronic configuration of the valence electrons of each element: (a) fluorine; (b) krypton; (c) magnesium; (d) germanium.

### PROBLEM 2.27

Write the valence shell electronic configuration for the elements in periods 4, 5, and 6 of group 6A.

## 2.7B  Electron-Dot Symbols

The number of valence electrons around an atom is often represented by an **electron-dot symbol.** Representative examples are shown.

|  | H | C | O | Cl |
|---|---|---|---|---|
| Number of valence electrons: | 1 | 4 | 6 | 7 |
| Electron-dot symbol: | H· | ·Ċ· | ·Ö· | ·Ċl: |

- Each dot represents one electron.
- The dots are placed on the four sides of an element symbol.
- For one to four valence electrons, single dots are used. With more than four electrons, the dots are paired.

The location of the dots around the symbol—side, top, or bottom—does not matter. Each of the following representations for the five valence electrons of nitrogen is equivalent.

### SAMPLE PROBLEM 2.14

Write an electron-dot symbol for each element: (a) sodium; (b) phosphorus.

#### Analysis

Write the symbol for each element and use the group number to determine the number of valence electrons for a main group element. Represent each valence electron with a dot.

#### Solution

a. The symbol for sodium is Na. Na is in group 1A and has one valence electron. Electron-dot symbol:

$$Na\cdot$$

b. The symbol for phosphorus is P. P is in group 5A and has five valence electrons. Electron-dot symbol:

### PROBLEM 2.28

Give the electron-dot symbol for each element: (a) bromine; (b) lithium; (c) aluminum; (d) sulfur; (e) neon.

## 2.8  Periodic Trends

Many properties of atoms exhibit **periodic trends;** that is, they change in a regular way across a row or down a column of the periodic table. Two properties that illustrate this phenomenon are **atomic size** and **ionization energy.**

### 2.8A  Atomic Size

The size of an atom is measured by its atomic radius—that is, the distance from the nucleus to the outer edge of the valence shell. Two periodic trends characterize the size of atoms.

- The size of atoms increases down a column of the periodic table, as the valence electrons are farther from the nucleus.

• The size of atoms decreases across a row of the periodic table as the number of protons in the nucleus increases. An increasing number of protons pulls the electrons closer to the nucleus, so the atom gets smaller.

For period 2:

## PROBLEM 2.29

Rank the atoms in each group in order of increasing size.

a. boron, carbon, neon
b. calcium, magnesium, beryllium
c. silicon, sulfur, magnesium

d. krypton, neon, xenon
e. sulfur, oxygen, silicon
f. fluorine, sulfur, aluminum

## 2.8B  Ionization Energy

Since a negatively charged electron is attracted to a positively charged nucleus, energy is required to remove an electron from a neutral atom. The more tightly the electron is held, the greater the energy required to remove it. Removing an electron from a neutral atom forms a **cation.**

• The *ionization energy* is the energy needed to remove an electron from a neutral atom.
• A *cation* is positively charged, and has fewer electrons than the neutral atom.

Two periodic trends characterize ionization energy.

• Ionization energies decrease down a column of the periodic table as the valence electrons get farther from the positively charged nucleus.

For group 1A:

- Ionization energies generally increase across a row of the periodic table as the number of protons in the nucleus increases.

For period 2:

Increasing ionization energy

## PROBLEM 2.30

Arrange the elements in each group in order of increasing ionization energy.

a. phosphorus, silicon, sulfur
b. magnesium, calcium, beryllium
c. carbon, fluorine, beryllium
d. neon, krypton, argon
e. tin, silicon, sulfur
f. calcium, aluminum, nitrogen

# CHAPTER HIGHLIGHTS

## KEY TERMS

Actinide (2.4)

Alkali metal (2.4)

Alkaline earth element (2.4)

Atom (2.2)

Atomic mass unit (2.2)

Atomic number (2.2)

Atomic weight (2.3)

Building-block element (2.1)

Cation (2.8)

Chemical formula (2.1)

Compound (2.1)

d Block (2.6)

Deuterium (2.3)

Electron (2.2)

Electron cloud (2.2)

Electron-dot symbol (2.7)

Electronic configuration (2.6)

Element (2.1)

f Block (2.6)

Ground state (2.6)

Group (2.4)

Group number (2.4)

Halogen (2.4)

Inner transition metal element (2.4)

Ionization energy (2.8)

Isotope (2.3)

Lanthanide (2.4)

Main group element (2.4)

Major mineral (Macronutrient, 2.1)

Mass number (2.2)

Metal (2.1)

Metalloid (2.1)

Neutron (2.2)

Noble gas (2.4)

Nonmetal (2.1)

Nucleus (2.2)

Orbital (2.5)

p Block (2.6)

Period (2.4)

Periodic table (2.1)

p Orbital (2.5)

Proton (2.2)

s Block (2.6)

Shell (2.5)

s Orbital (2.5)

Subshell (2.5)

Trace element (Micronutrient, 2.1)

Transition metal element (2.4)

Tritium (2.3)

Unpaired electron (2.6)

Valence electron (2.7)

## KEY CONCEPTS

❶ **How is the name of an element abbreviated and how does the periodic table help to classify it as a metal, nonmetal, or metalloid? (2.1)**

- An element is abbreviated by a one- or two-letter symbol. The periodic table contains a stepped line from boron to astatine. All metals are located to the left of the line. All nonmetals except hydrogen are located to the right of the line. The seven elements located along the line are metalloids.

❷ **What are the basic components of an atom? (2.2)**

- An atom is composed of two parts: a dense nucleus containing positively charged protons and neutral neutrons, and an electron cloud containing negatively charged electrons. Most of the mass of an atom resides in the nucleus, while the electron cloud contains most of its volume.

- The atomic number ($Z$) of a neutral atom tells the number of protons and the number of electrons. The mass number ($A$) is the sum of the number of protons ($Z$) and the number of neutrons.

**③ What are isotopes and how are they related to the atomic weight? (2.3)**

- Isotopes are atoms that have the same number of protons but a different number of neutrons. The atomic weight is the weighted average of the mass of the naturally occurring isotopes of a particular element.

**④ What are the basic features of the periodic table? (2.4)**

- The periodic table is a schematic of all known elements, arranged in rows (periods) and columns (groups), organized so that elements with similar properties are grouped together.
- The vertical columns are assigned group numbers using two different numbering schemes—1–8 plus the letters A or B; or 1–18.
- The periodic table is divided into the main group elements (groups 1A–8A), the transition metals (groups 1B–8B), and the inner transition metals located at the bottom.

**⑤ How are electrons arranged around an atom? (2.5)**

- Electrons occupy discrete energy levels, organized into shells (numbered 1, 2, 3, and so on), subshells (*s, p, d,* and *f*), and orbitals.
- Each orbital can hold two electrons.

**⑥ What rules determine the electronic configuration of an atom? (2.6)**

- To write the ground state electronic configuration of an atom, electrons are added to the lowest energy orbitals, giving each

orbital two electrons. When two orbitals are equal in energy, one electron is added to each orbital until the orbitals are half-filled.

- Orbital diagrams that use boxes for orbitals and arrows for electrons indicate electronic configuration. Electron configuration can also be shown using superscripts to show how many electrons an orbital contains. For example, the electron configuration of the six electrons in a carbon atom is $1s^2 2s^2 2p^2$.

**⑦ How is the location of an element in the periodic table related to its electronic configuration? (2.6, 2.7)**

- The periodic table is divided into four regions—the *s* block, *p* block, *d* block, and *f* block—based on the subshells that are filled with electrons last.
- Elements in the same group have the same number of valence electrons and similar electronic configurations.

**⑧ What is an electron-dot symbol? (2.7)**

- An electron-dot symbol uses a dot to represent each valence electron around the symbol for an element.

**⑨ How are atomic size and ionization energy related to location in the periodic table? (2.8)**

- The size of an atom decreases across a row and increases down a column.
- Ionization energy—the energy needed to remove an electron from an atom—increases across a row and decreases down a column.

# PROBLEMS

Selected in-chapter and odd-numbered end-of-chapter problems have brief answers in Appendix B. The *Student Study Guide and Solutions Manual* contains detailed solutions to all in-chapter and odd-numbered end-of-chapter problems, as well as additional worked examples and a chapter self-test.

## Elements

**2.31** Identify the elements used in each example of molecular art.

a.                                              b.

**2.32** Write a chemical formula for each example of molecular art.

a.            b.            c.

**2.33** Give the name of the elements in each group of three element symbols.
- a. Au, At, Ag       d. Ca, Cr, Cl
- b. N, Na, Ni        e. P, Pb, Pt
- c. S, Si, Sn        f. Ti, Ta, Tl

**2.34** What element(s) are designated by each symbol or group of symbols?
- a. CU and Cu        c. Ni and NI
- b. Os and OS        d. BIN, BiN, and BIn

**2.35** Does each chemical formula represent an element or a compound?
- a. $H_2$    b. $H_2O_2$    c. $S_8$    d. $Na_2CO_3$    e. $C_{60}$

**2.36** Identify the elements in each chemical formula and tell how many atoms of each are present.
- a. $K_2Cr_2O_7$
- b. $C_5H_8NNaO_4$ (MSG, flavor enhancer)
- c. $C_{10}H_{16}N_2O_3S$ (vitamin $B_7$)

**2.37** Identify the element that fits each description.
- a. an alkali metal in period 6
- b. a transition metal in period 5, group 8
- c. a main group element in period 3, group 7A
- d. a main group element in period 2, group 2A
- e. a halogen in period 2
- f. an inner transition metal with one 4*f* electron

**2.38** Identify the element that fits each description.
  a. an alkaline earth element in period 3
  b. a noble gas in period 6
  c. a main group element in period 3 that has *p* orbitals half-filled with electrons
  d. a transition metal in period 4, group 11
  e. an inner transition metal with its 5*f* orbitals completely filled with electrons
  f. a transition metal in period 6, group 10

**2.39** Give all of the terms that apply to each element: [1] metal; [2] nonmetal; [3] metalloid; [4] alkali metal; [5] alkaline earth element; [6] halogen; [7] noble gas; [8] main group element; [9] transition metal; [10] inner transition metal.
  a. sodium       c. xenon        e. uranium
  b. silver       d. platinum     f. tellurium

**2.40** Give all of the terms that apply to each element: [1] metal; [2] nonmetal; [3] metalloid; [4] alkali metal; [5] alkaline earth element; [6] halogen; [7] noble gas; [8] main group element; [9] transition metal; [10] inner transition metal.
  a. bromine      c. cesium       e. calcium
  b. silicon      d. gold         f. chromium

## Atomic Structure

**2.41** Give the following information about the atom shown: (a) the number of protons and neutrons in the nucleus; (b) the atomic number; (c) the mass number; (d) the number of electrons in the neutral atom; and (e) the element symbol.

**2.42** Give the following information about the atom shown: (a) the number of protons and neutrons in the nucleus; (b) the atomic number; (c) the mass number; (d) the number of electrons in the neutral atom; and (e) the element symbol.

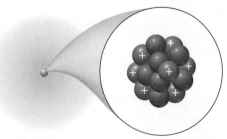

**2.43** Complete the following table for neutral elements.

| Element Symbol | Atomic Number | Mass Number | Number of Protons | Number of Neutrons | Number of Electrons |
|---|---|---|---|---|---|
| a. C |  | 12 |  |  |  |
| b. |  | 31 |  |  | 15 |
| c. |  |  |  | 35 | 30 |
| d. Mg |  | 24 |  |  |  |
| e. |  |  | 53 | 74 |  |
| f. | 4 |  |  | 5 |  |
| g. | 40 | 91 |  |  |  |
| h. |  |  |  | 16 | 16 |

**2.44** For the given atomic number (*Z*) and mass number (*A*): [1] identify the element; [2] give the element symbol; [3] give the number of protons, neutrons, and electrons.
  a. $Z = 10, A = 20$      d. $Z = 55, A = 133$
  b. $Z = 13, A = 27$      e. $Z = 28, A = 59$
  c. $Z = 38, A = 88$      f. $Z = 79, A = 197$

## Periodic Table

**2.45** Label each region on the periodic table.
  a. noble gases          e. alkaline earth elements
  b. period 3             f. *f* block elements
  c. group 4A             g. transition metals
  d. *s* block elements   h. group 10

**2.46** Identify each highlighted element in the periodic table and give its [1] element name and symbol; [2] group number; [3] period; [4] classification (i.e., main group element, transition metal, or inner transition metal).

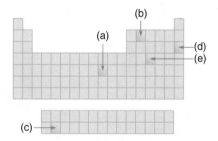

**2.47** What element is located in group 1A but is not an alkali metal?

**2.48** What *s* block element is not located in either group 1A or group 2A in the periodic table?

**2.49** Classify each element in the fourth row of the periodic table as a metal, nonmetal, or metalloid.

**2.50** To which blocks do the elements in the fifth period belong?

**2.51** Which group(s) in the periodic table contain only nonmetals?

**2.52** Which groups in the periodic table contain metals, nonmetals, and metalloids?

## Isotopes and Atomic Weight

**2.53** The most common isotope of oxygen has a mass number of 16, but two other isotopes having mass numbers of 17 and 18 are also known. For each isotope, give the following information: (a) the number of protons; (b) the number of neutrons; (c) the number of electrons in the neutral atom; (d) the group number; (e) the element symbols using superscripts and subscripts.

**2.54** The three most common isotopes of tin have mass numbers 116, 118, and 120. For each isotope, give the following information: (a) the number of protons; (b) the number of neutrons; (c) the number of electrons in the neutral atom; (d) the group number; (e) the element symbols using superscripts and subscripts.

**2.55** How many protons, neutrons, and electrons are contained in each element?
a. $^{27}_{13}Al$      b. $^{35}_{17}Cl$      c. $^{34}_{16}S$

**2.56** Give the number of protons, neutrons, and electrons in each element: (a) silver-115; (b) Au-197; (c) Rn-222; (d) osmium-192.

**2.57** Write the element symbol that fits each description, using a superscript for the mass number and a subscript for the atomic number.
a. an element that contains 53 protons and 74 neutrons
b. an element with 35 electrons and a mass number of 79
c. an element with 47 protons and 60 neutrons

**2.58** Write the element symbol that fits each description. Use a superscript for the mass number and a subscript for the atomic number.
a. an element that contains 10 protons and 12 neutrons
b. an element with atomic number 24 and mass number 52
c. an element with 10 electrons and 10 neutrons

**2.59** Calculate the atomic weight of silver, which has two isotopes with the following properties: Ag-107 (106.91 amu, 51.84% natural occurrence) and Ag-109 (108.90 amu, 48.16% natural occurrence).

**2.60** Calculate the atomic weight of antimony, which has two isotopes with the following properties: Sb-121 (120.90 amu, 57.21% natural occurrence) and Sb-123 (122.90 amu, 42.79% natural occurrence).

**2.61** Can the neutral atoms of two different elements have the same number of electrons? Explain.

**2.62** Can the neutral atoms of two different elements have the same number of neutrons? Explain.

## Electronic Configuration

**2.63** How many orbitals are contained in each of the following shells of electrons: (a) first shell ($n = 1$); (b) second shell ($n = 2$); (c) third shell ($n = 3$); (d) fourth shell ($n = 4$)?

**2.64** What is the maximum number of electrons that can be contained in each shell, subshell, or orbital?
a. second shell      c. 3p subshell      e. fourth shell
b. 3s orbital         d. 4f orbital        f. 5p orbital

**2.65** Write the electronic configuration of each element using an orbital diagram: (a) B; (b) K; (c) Se; (d) Ar; (e) Zn.

**2.66** Write the electronic configuration of each element using an orbital diagram: (a) N; (b) I; (c) Ga; (d) Ti; (e) Mn.

**2.67** For each element in Problem 2.65: (a) Write out the electronic configuration using a superscript with each orbital; (b) write out the electronic configuration using noble gas notation.

**2.68** For each element in Problem 2.66: (a) Write out the electronic configuration using a superscript with each orbital; (b) write out the electronic configuration using noble gas notation.

**2.69** How many unpaired electrons are contained in each element: (a) Al; (b) P; (c) Na?

**2.70** How many unpaired electrons are contained in each element: (a) Cl; (b) Se; (c) Cs?

**2.71** Give the total number of electrons, the number of valence electrons, and the identity of the element with each electronic configuration.
a. $1s^22s^22p^63s^23p^64s^23d^{10}4p^65s^2$      c. $1s^22s^22p^63s^1$
b. $1s^22s^22p^63s^23p^4$      d. $[Ne]3s^23p^5$

**2.72** Give the total number of electrons, the number of valence electrons, and the identity of the element with each electronic configuration.
a. $1s^22s^22p^63s^23p^6$      c. $1s^22s^22p^3$
b. $1s^22s^22p^63s^23p^64s^23d^7$      d. $[Kr]5s^24d^{10}5p^2$

**2.73** How do an alkali metal and an alkaline earth element in the same row differ in the electronic configuration of the valence shell electrons?

**2.74** How do a halogen and a noble gas in the same row differ in the electronic configuration of the valence shell electrons?

**2.75** For each element, give the following information: [1] total number of electrons; [2] group number; [3] number of valence electrons; [4] period; [5] number of the valence shell.
a. carbon      b. calcium      c. krypton

**2.76** For each element, give the following information: [1] total number of electrons; [2] group number; [3] number of valence electrons; [4] period; [5] number of the valence shell.
a. oxygen      b. sodium      c. phosphorus

**2.77** For each element in Problem 2.75, first write the electronic configuration of all the electrons. Then give the electronic configuration of the valence electrons only.

**2.78** For each element in Problem 2.76, first write the electronic configuration of all the electrons. Then give the electronic configuration of the valence electrons only.

**2.79** How many valence electrons does an element in each group contain: (a) 2A; (b) 4A; (c) 7A?

**2.80** In what shell do the valence electrons reside for an element in period: (a) 2; (b) 3; (c) 4; (d) 5?

**2.81** Give the number of valence electrons in each element. Write out the electronic configuration for the valence electrons.
a. sulfur     b. chlorine     c. barium     d. titanium     e. tin

**2.82** Give the number of valence electrons in each element. Write out the electronic configuration for the valence electrons.
a. neon              c. aluminum              e. zirconium
b. rubidium          d. manganese

**2.83** Write an electron-dot symbol for each element: (a) beryllium; (b) silicon; (c) iodine; (d) magnesium; (e) argon.

**2.84** Write an electron-dot symbol for each element: (a) K; (b) B; (c) F; (d) Ca; (e) Se.

## Periodic Trends

**2.85** Which element in each pair is larger?
a. bromine and iodine              c. silicon and potassium
b. carbon and nitrogen             d. chlorine and selenium

**2.86** Which element in each pair has its valence electrons farther from the nucleus?
a. sodium and magnesium            c. neon and krypton
b. carbon and fluorine             d. argon and bromine

**2.87** For each pair of elements in Problem 2.85, label the element with the higher ionization energy.

**2.88** For each pair of elements in Problem 2.86, label the element from which it is easier to remove an electron.

**2.89** Rank the following elements in order of increasing size: sulfur, silicon, oxygen, magnesium, and fluorine.

**2.90** Rank the following elements in order of increasing size: aluminum, nitrogen, potassium, oxygen, and phosphorus.

**2.91** Rank the following elements in order of increasing ionization energy: nitrogen, fluorine, magnesium, sodium, and phosphorus.

**2.92** Rank the following elements in order of decreasing ionization energy: calcium, silicon, oxygen, magnesium, and carbon.

## Applications

**2.93** Answer the following questions about the macronutrients sodium, potassium, and chlorine.
a. Is each element classified as a metal, nonmetal, or metalloid?
b. In which block does each element reside?
c. Which element has the smallest atomic radius?
d. Which element has the largest atomic radius?
e. Which element has the largest ionization energy?
f. Which element has the smallest ionization energy?
g. How many valence electrons does each element possess?

**2.94** Platinum is a precious metal used in a wide variety of products. Besides fine jewelry, platinum is also the catalyst found in the catalytic converters of automobile exhaust systems, and platinum-containing drugs like cisplatin are used to treat some lung and ovarian cancers. Answer the following questions about the element platinum.
a. What is its element symbol?
b. What group number and period are assigned to platinum?
c. What is its atomic number?
d. Is platinum classified as a main group element, transition metal, or inner transition metal?
e. In what block does platinum reside?
f. What is unusual about the electronic configuration for platinum: $[Xe]6s^14f^{14}5d^9$?

**2.95** Carbon-11 is an unnatural isotope used in positron emission tomography (PET) scans. PET scans are used to monitor brain activity and diagnose dementia. How does carbon-11 compare to carbon-12 in terms of the number of protons, neutrons, and electrons? Write the element symbol of carbon-11 using superscripts and subscripts.

**2.96** Answer the following questions about the macronutrients calcium, magnesium, and sulfur.
a. Is each element classified as a metal, nonmetal, or metalloid?
b. In which block does each element reside?
c. Which element has the smallest atomic radius?
d. Which element has the largest atomic radius?
e. Which element has the largest ionization energy?
f. Which element has the smallest ionization energy?
g. How many valence electrons does each element possess?

## CHALLENGE PROBLEMS

**2.97** Sesame seeds, sunflower seeds, and peanuts are good dietary sources of the trace element copper. Copper is needed for the synthesis of neurotransmitters, compounds that transmit nerve signals from one nerve cell to another. Copper is also needed for the synthesis of collagen, a protein found in bone, tendons, teeth, and blood vessels. What is unusual about the electronic configuration of the trace element copper: $1s^22s^22p^63s^23p^64s^13d^{10}$?

**2.98** Strontium-90 is a radioactive element formed in nuclear reactors. When an unusually high level of strontium is released into the air, such as occurred during the Chernobyl nuclear disaster in 1986, the strontium can be incorporated into the bones of exposed individuals. High levels of strontium can cause bone cancer and leukemia. Why does Sr-90 cause this particular health problem?

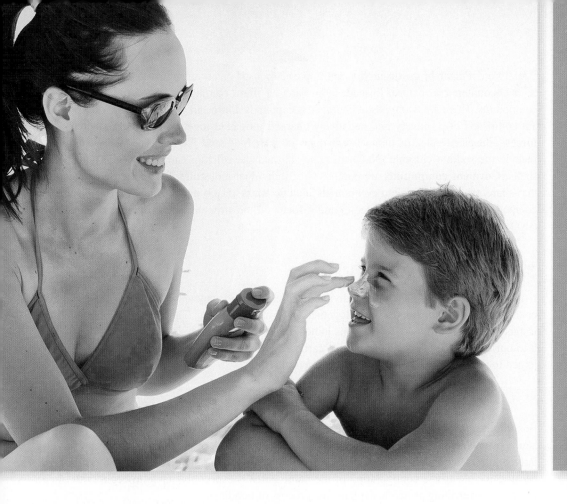

**Zinc oxide** is an ionic compound widely used in sunblocks to protect the skin from harmful ultraviolet radiation.

# 3

# Ionic Compounds

## CHAPTER GOALS

*In this chapter you will learn how to:*

1. Describe the basic features of ionic and covalent bonds
2. Use the periodic table to determine whether an atom forms a cation or an anion, and determine its charge using the group number
3. Describe the octet rule
4. Write the formula for an ionic compound
5. Name ionic compounds
6. Describe the properties of ionic compounds
7. Recognize the structures of common polyatomic ions and name compounds that contain them
8. List useful consumer products and drugs that are composed of ionic compounds

Although much of the discussion in Chapter 2 focused on atoms, individual atoms are rarely encountered in nature. Instead, atoms are far more commonly joined together to form compounds. There are two types of chemical compounds, **ionic** and **covalent. Ionic compounds** are composed of positively and negatively charged ions held together by strong **electrostatic forces**—the electrical attraction between oppositely charged ions. Examples of ionic compounds include the sodium chloride ($NaCl$) in table salt and the calcium carbonate ($CaCO_3$) in snail shells. **Covalent compounds** are composed of individual molecules, discrete groups of atoms that share electrons. Covalent compounds include water ($H_2O$) and methane ($CH_4$), the main component of natural gas. Chapters 3 and 4 focus on the structure and properties of ionic and covalent compounds, respectively.

## 3.1   Introduction to Bonding

It is rare in nature to encounter individual atoms. Instead, anywhere from two to hundreds or thousands of atoms tend to join together to form compounds. The oxygen we breathe, for instance, consists of two oxygen atoms joined together, whereas the hemoglobin that transports it to our tissues consists of thousands of carbon, hydrogen, oxygen, nitrogen, and sulfur atoms joined together. We say **two atoms are *bonded* together.**

- *Bonding* is the joining of two atoms in a stable arrangement.

Bonding is a favorable process because it always forms a compound that is more stable than the atoms from which it is made. Only the noble gases in group 8A of the periodic table are particularly stable as individual atoms; that is, the **noble gases do *not* readily react to form bonds,** because the electronic configuration of the noble gases is especially stable to begin with. As a result, one overriding principle explains the process of bonding.

- In bonding, elements gain, lose, or share electrons to attain the electronic configuration of the noble gas closest to them in the periodic table.

Bonding involves only the valence electrons of an atom. There are two different kinds of bonding: **ionic** and **covalent.**

- *Ionic bonds* result from the transfer of electrons from one element to another.
- *Covalent bonds* result from the sharing of electrons between two atoms.

The position of an element in the periodic table determines the type of bonds it makes. **Ionic bonds form between a metal on the left side of the periodic table and a nonmetal on the right side.** As shown in Figure 3.1, when the metal sodium (Na) bonds to the nonmetal chlorine ($Cl_2$), the ionic compound sodium chloride (NaCl) forms. Since ionic compounds are composed of *ions*—**charged species in which the number of protons and electrons in an atom is *not* equal**—we begin our discussion of ionic compounds with how ions are formed in Section 3.2.

Covalent bonds are formed when two nonmetals combine, or when a metalloid bonds to a nonmetal. **A *molecule* is a compound containing two or more atoms joined together with covalent bonds.** For example, when two hydrogen atoms bond they form the molecule $H_2$, and two electrons are shared. Covalent bonds and molecules are discussed in Chapter 4.

hydrogen molecule

Figure 3.1

Sodium Chloride, an Ionic Compound

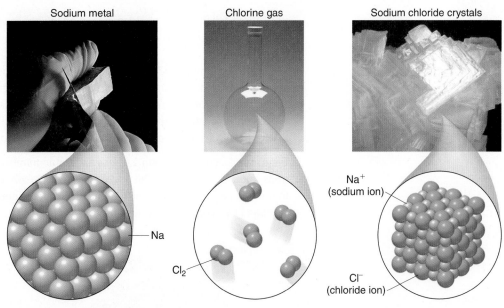

Sodium metal          Chlorine gas          Sodium chloride crystals

Na

$Cl_2$

$Na^+$
(sodium ion)

$Cl^-$
(chloride ion)

Sodium metal and chlorine gas are both elements. Sodium chloride is an ionic compound composed of sodium ions and chloride ions.

## SAMPLE PROBLEM 3.1

Predict whether the bonds in the following compounds are ionic or covalent: (a) NaI (sodium iodide); (b) $H_2O_2$ (hydrogen peroxide).

### Analysis

The position of the elements in the periodic table determines the type of bonds they form. When a metal and nonmetal combine, the bond is ionic. When two nonmetals combine, or a metalloid bonds to a nonmetal, the bond is covalent.

### Solution

a. Since Na is a metal on the left side and I is a nonmetal on the right side of the periodic table, the bonds in NaI are ionic.

b. Since $H_2O_2$ contains only the nonmetals hydrogen and oxygen, the bonds must be covalent.

## PROBLEM 3.1

Predict whether the bonds in the following species are ionic or covalent.

a. CO          b. $CaF_2$          c. MgO          d. $Cl_2$          e. HF          f. $C_2H_6$

## PROBLEM 3.2

Label each of the following as a compound, element, or molecule. In some cases, more than one term applies.

a. $CO_2$          b. $H_2O$          c. NaF          d. $MgBr_2$          e. $F_2$          f. CaO

## PROBLEM 3.3

Vitamin C has the chemical formula $C_6H_8O_6$. Even if you know nothing about how the atoms in vitamin C are arranged, what type of bonds are likely to be present in vitamin C?

HEALTH NOTE

Vitamin C is important in the formation of collagen, a protein that holds together the connective tissue of skin, muscle, and blood vessels. Oranges and other citrus fruits are an excellent source of vitamin C.

# 3.2   Ions

Ionic compounds consist of oppositely charged **ions** that have a strong **electrostatic attraction**—electrical attraction between oppositely charged ions—for each other.

## 3.2A   Cations and Anions

There are two types of ions called **cations** and **anions**.

- *Cations* are positively charged ions. A cation has fewer electrons than protons.
- *Anions* are negatively charged ions. An anion has more electrons than protons.

The nature and magnitude of the charge on an ion depend on the position of an element in the periodic table. In forming an ion, an atom of a main group element loses or gains electrons to obtain the electronic configuration of the noble gas closest to it in the periodic table. This gives the ion an especially stable electronic arrangement with a **completely filled shell of electrons;** that is, the electrons completely fill the shell farthest from the nucleus.

For example, sodium (group 1A) has an atomic number of 11, giving it 11 protons and 11 electrons in the neutral atom. This gives sodium one *more* electron than neon, the noble gas closest to it in the periodic table. In losing one electron, sodium forms a cation with a +1 charge, which still has 11 protons, but now has only 10 electrons in its electron cloud.

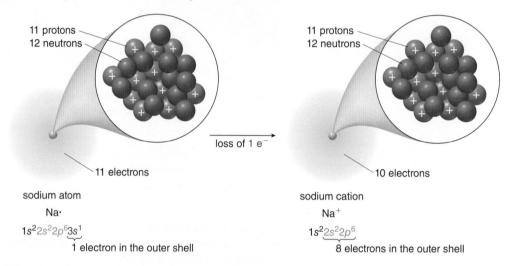

What does this mean in terms of valence electrons? A neutral sodium atom, with an electronic configuration of $1s^2 2s^2 2p^6 3s^1$, has a single valence electron. Loss of this valence electron forms a **sodium cation,** symbolized as **Na$^+$,** which has the especially stable electronic configuration of the noble gas neon, $1s^2 2s^2 2p^6$. The sodium cation now has **eight electrons** that fill the $2s$ and three $2p$ orbitals.

Magnesium (group 2A) has 12 protons and 12 electrons in the neutral atom. This gives magnesium two *more* electrons than neon, the noble gas closest to it in the periodic table. In losing two electrons, magnesium forms a cation with a +2 charge, which still has 12 protons, but now has only 10 electrons in its electron cloud.

In terms of valence electrons, a neutral magnesium atom, with an electronic configuration of $1s^2 2s^2 2p^6 3s^2$, has two valence electrons. Loss of these valence electrons forms a **magnesium cation,** symbolized as $Mg^{2+}$, which has the especially stable electronic configuration of the noble gas neon, $1s^2 2s^2 2p^6$. The magnesium cation now has **eight electrons** that fill the $2s$ and three $2p$ orbitals.

Sodium and magnesium are examples of metals.

Some metals—notably tin and lead—can lose *four* electrons to form cations.

- Metals form *cations.*
- By losing one, two, or three electrons, an atom forms a cation with a completely filled outer shell of electrons.

A neutral chlorine atom (group 7A), on the other hand, has 17 protons and 17 electrons. This gives it one *fewer* electron than argon, the noble gas closest to it in the periodic table. By gaining one electron, chlorine forms an anion with a –1 charge because it still has 17 protons, but now has 18 electrons in its electron cloud.

17 protons
18 neutrons

17 protons
18 neutrons

gain of 1 e⁻

17 electrons

18 electrons

chlorine atom
:Cl·
$1s^2 2s^2 2p^6 \underbrace{3s^2 3p^5}$
7 electrons in the outer shell

chloride anion
:Cl:⁻
$1s^2 2s^2 2p^6 \underbrace{3s^2 3p^6}$
8 electrons in the outer shell

In terms of valence electrons, a neutral chlorine atom, with an electronic configuration of $1s^2 2s^2 2p^6 3s^2 3p^5$, has seven valence electrons. Gain of one electron forms a **chloride anion,** symbolized as $Cl^-$, which has the especially stable electronic configuration of the noble gas argon, $1s^2 2s^2 2p^6 3s^2 3p^6$. The chloride anion now has **eight valence electrons** that fill the $3s$ and three $3p$ orbitals.

Chlorine is an example of a nonmetal.

- Nonmetals form *anions.*
- By gaining one, two, or sometimes three electrons, an atom forms an anion with a completely filled outer shell of electrons.

Ions are written with the element symbol followed by a superscript to indicate the charge. The number "1" is omitted in ions that have a +1 or –1 charge, as in $Na^+$ or $Cl^-$. When the charge is "2" or greater, it is written as 2+ or 2–, as in $Mg^{2+}$ or $O^{2-}$.

Each of these ions formed from a main group element has the $s$ and three $p$ orbitals filled with **eight electrons.** This illustrates the **octet rule.**

- A main group element is especially stable when it possesses an *octet* of electrons in its outer shell.

## SAMPLE PROBLEM 3.2

Write the ion symbol for an atom with: (a) nine protons and 10 electrons; (b) three protons and two electrons.

### Analysis

Since the number of protons equals the atomic number (Section 2.2), this quantity identifies the element. The charge is determined by comparing the number of protons and electrons. If the number of electrons is greater than the number of protons, the charge is negative (an anion). If the number of protons is greater than the number of electrons, the charge is positive (a cation).

### Solution

a.  An element with nine protons has an atomic number of nine, identifying it as fluorine (F). Since there is one more electron than proton (10 vs. 9), the charge is –1.

**Answer:**
$F^-$

b.  An element with three protons has an atomic number of three, identifying it as lithium (Li). Since there is one more proton than electron (3 vs. 2), the charge is +1.

**Answer:**
$Li^+$

## PROBLEM 3.4

Write the ion symbol for an atom with the given number of protons and electrons.

a.  19 protons and 18 electrons
b.  seven protons and 10 electrons

c.  35 protons and 36 electrons
d.  23 protons and 21 electrons

## SAMPLE PROBLEM 3.3

How many protons and electrons are present in each ion: (a) $Ca^{2+}$; (b) $O^{2-}$?

### Analysis

Use the identity of the element to determine the number of protons. The charge tells how many more or fewer electrons there are compared to the number of protons. A positive charge means more protons than electrons, while a negative charge means more electrons than protons.

### Solution

a.  $Ca^{2+}$: The element calcium (Ca) has an atomic number of 20, so it has 20 protons. Since the charge is +2, there are two more protons than electrons, giving the ion 18 electrons.

b.  $O^{2-}$: The element oxygen (O) has an atomic number of eight, so it has eight protons. Since the charge is –2, there are two more electrons than protons, giving the ion 10 electrons.

## PROBLEM 3.5

How many protons and electrons are present in each ion?

a.  $Ni^{2+}$      b.  $Se^{2-}$      c.  $Zn^{2+}$      d.  $Fe^{3+}$

## 3.2B    Relating Group Number to Ionic Charge for Main Group Elements

Since elements with similar electronic configurations are grouped together in the periodic table, **elements in the same group form ions of similar charge.** The group number of a main group element can be used to determine the charge on an ion derived from that element.

- Metals form cations. For metals in groups 1A, 2A, and 3A, the group number = the charge on the cation.

Group **1A** elements (Li, Na, K, Rb, and Cs) have **one** valence electron. Loss of this electron forms a cation with a **+1** charge. Group **2A** elements (Be, Mg, Ca, Sr, and Ba) have **two** valence electrons. Loss of both electrons forms a cation with a **+2** charge. Group **3A** elements (Al, Ga, In, and Tl) form cations, too, but only aluminum is commonly found in ionic compounds. It has **three** valence electrons, so loss of three electrons from aluminum forms a cation with a **+3** charge.

All of the cations derived from group 1A–3A elements have an octet of outer shell electrons except for $Li^+$ and $Be^{2+}$. $Li^+$ and $Be^{2+}$ have a $1s^2$ electronic configuration like helium, the noble gas to which they are closest in the periodic table. Thus, these cations are especially stable because they have a filled outer shell of electrons, although they do *not* have an octet of electrons.

- Nonmetals form anions. For nonmetals in groups 5A, 6A, and 7A, the anion charge = 8 – (the group number).

Group **5A** elements have **five** valence electrons. A gain of **three** electrons forms an anion with a –3 charge (anion charge = 8 – 5). Group **6A** elements have **six** valence electrons. A gain of **two** electrons forms an anion with a –2 charge (anion charge = 8 – 6). Group **7A** elements have **seven** valence electrons. A gain of one electron forms an anion with a –1 charge (anion charge = 8 – 7).

Table 3.1 summarizes the ionic charges of the main group elements. The periodic table in Figure 3.2 gives the common ions formed by the main group elements.

**Table 3.1  Ionic Charges of the Main Group Elements**

| Group Number | Number of Valence Electrons | Number of Electrons Gained or Lost | General Structure of the Ion |
|---|---|---|---|
| 1A (1) | 1 | 1 $e^-$ lost | $M^+$ |
| 2A (2) | 2 | 2 $e^-$ lost | $M^{2+}$ |
| 3A (3) | 3 | 3 $e^-$ lost | $M^{3+}$ |
| 5A (15) | 5 | 3 $e^-$ gained | $X^{3-}$ |
| 6A (16) | 6 | 2 $e^-$ gained | $X^{2-}$ |
| 7A (17) | 7 | 1 $e^-$ gained | $X^-$ |

Figure 3.2    Common Ions Formed by Main Group Elements

Group 2A metals form cations with a +2 charge.

Group 6A nonmetals form anions with a −2 charge.

Group 5A nonmetals form anions with a −3 charge.

Transition metals

Group 1A metals form cations with a +1 charge.

Halogens form anions with a −1 charge.

## SAMPLE PROBLEM 3.4

Use the group number to determine the charge on an ion derived from each element: (a) barium; (b) sulfur.

### Analysis

Locate the element in the periodic table. A metal in groups 1A, 2A, or 3A forms a cation equal in charge to the group number. A nonmetal in groups 5A, 6A, and 7A forms an anion whose charge equals 8 − (the group number).

### Solution

a.  Barium (Ba) is located in group 2A, so it forms a cation with a +2 charge; $Ba^{2+}$.

b.  Sulfur (S) is located in group 6A, so it forms an anion with a negative charge of 8 − 6 = 2; $S^{2-}$.

## PROBLEM 3.6

Use the group number to determine the charge on an ion derived from each element.

a. magnesium        b. iodine         c. selenium          d. rubidium

## PROBLEM 3.7

What noble gas has the same electronic configuration as each ion derived from the elements in Problem 3.6?

## 3.2C    Metals with Variable Charge

The transition metals form cations like other metals, but the magnitude of the charge on the cation is harder to predict. Some transition metals, and a few main group metals as well, form more than one type of cation. For example, iron forms two different cations, $Fe^{2+}$ and $Fe^{3+}$. $Fe^{2+}$ is formed by losing two valence electrons from the $4s$ orbital. $Fe^{3+}$ is formed by loss of three electrons, two from a $4s$ orbital and one from a $3d$ orbital.

**Figure 3.3** Common Cations Derived from Transition Metals and Group 4A Metals

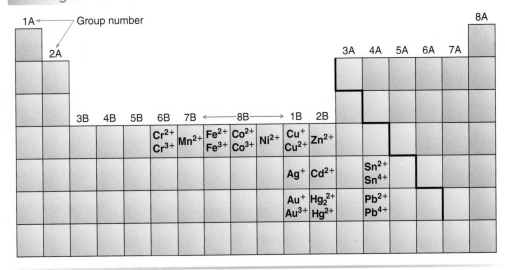

Because transition metal cations generally have additional *d* electrons that the nearest noble gas does not, the octet rule is not usually followed. Figure 3.3 illustrates the common cations formed from transition metals, as well as some main group elements that form more than one cation.

### PROBLEM 3.8

How many electrons and protons are contained in each cation?

a. $Au^+$  b. $Au^{3+}$  c. $Sn^{2+}$  d. $Sn^{4+}$

### 3.2D  FOCUS ON THE HUMAN BODY
Important Ions in the Body

Many different ions are required for proper cellular and organ function (Figure 3.4). The major cations in the body are $Na^+$, $K^+$, $Ca^{2+}$, and $Mg^{2+}$. $K^+$ and $Mg^{2+}$ are present in high concentrations inside cells, while $Na^+$ and $Ca^{2+}$ are present in a higher concentration outside cells, in the extracellular fluids. $Na^+$ is the major cation present in blood and extracellular bodily fluids and its concentration is carefully regulated through a number of mechanisms to maintain blood volume and blood pressure within acceptable ranges that permit organ function. $Ca^{2+}$ is found mainly in solid body parts such as teeth and bones, but it is also needed for proper nerve conduction and muscle contraction, as is $Mg^{2+}$.

In addition to these four cations, $Fe^{2+}$ and $Cl^-$ are also important ions. $Fe^{2+}$ is essential for oxygen transport by red blood cells. $Cl^-$ is present in red blood cells, gastric juices, and other body fluids. Along with $Na^+$, it plays a major role in regulating the fluid balance in the body.

Although $Na^+$ is an essential mineral needed in the daily diet, the average American consumes three to five times the recommended daily allowance (RDA) of 2,400 mg. Excess sodium intake is linked to high blood pressure and heart disease. Dietary $Na^+$ comes from salt, NaCl, added during cooking or at the table. $Na^+$ is also added during the preparation of processed foods and canned products. For example, one 3.5-oz serving of fresh asparagus has only 1 mg of $Na^+$, but the same serving size of canned asparagus contains 236 mg of $Na^+$. Potato chips, snack foods, ketchup, processed meats, and many cheeses are particularly high in $Na^+$. Table 3.2 lists the $Na^+$ content of some common foods.

All of these foods are high in sodium.

Figure 3.4    Common Ions in the Human Body

Ca$^{2+}$ is found in teeth and bones.

Fe$^{2+}$ is present in the hemoglobin of the blood.

Na$^+$ and K$^+$ are found in all body fluids.

Cl$^-$ is present in the gastric juices of the stomach and other fluids.

Mg$^{2+}$ is needed for nerve transmission and muscle control.

Na$^+$, K$^+$, Ca$^{2+}$, Mg$^{2+}$, Fe$^{2+}$, and Cl$^-$ are all common ions present throughout the organs of the human body.

Table 3.2  Na$^+$ Content in Common Foods

| Foods High in Na$^+$ | | Foods Low in Na$^+$ | |
|---|---|---|---|
| Food | Na$^+$ (mg) | Food | Na$^+$ (mg) |
| Potato chips (30) | 276 | Banana (1) | 1 |
| Hot dog (1) | 504 | Orange juice (1 cup) | 2 |
| Ham, smoked (3 oz) | 908 | Oatmeal, cooked (1 cup) | 2 |
| Chicken soup, canned (1 cup) | 1,106 | Cereal, shredded wheat (3.5 oz) | 3 |
| Tomato sauce, canned (1 cup) | 1,402 | Raisins, dried (3.5 oz) | 27 |
| Parmesan cheese (1 cup) | 1,861 | Salmon (3 oz) | 55 |

PROBLEM 3.9

Mn$^{2+}$ is an essential nutrient needed for blood clotting and the formation of the protein collagen. (a) How many protons and electrons are found in a neutral manganese atom? (b) How many electrons and protons are found in the cation Mn$^{2+}$? (c) Write the electronic configuration of the element manganese and suggest which electrons are lost to form the Mn$^{2+}$ cation.

## 3.3  Ionic Compounds

When a metal (on the left side of the periodic table) transfers one or more electrons to a nonmetal (on the right side), **ionic bonds** are formed.

> • **Ionic compounds are composed of cations and anions.**

The ions in an ionic compound are arranged to maximize the attractive force between the oppositely charged species. For example, sodium chloride, NaCl, is composed of sodium cations ($Na^+$) and chloride anions ($Cl^-$), packed together in a regular arrangement in a crystal lattice. Each $Na^+$ cation is surrounded by six $Cl^-$ anions, and each $Cl^-$ anion is surrounded by six $Na^+$ cations. In this way, the positively charged cations are located closer to the charged particles to which they are attracted—anions—and farther from the particles from which they are repelled—cations.

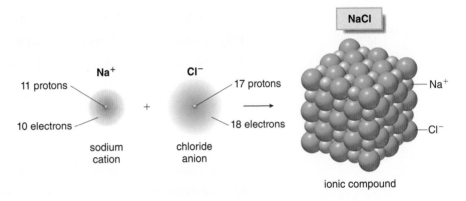

> • **The sum of the charges in an ionic compound must always be zero overall.**

The formula for an ionic compound shows the ratio of ions that combine to give zero charge. Since the sodium cation has a +1 charge and the chloride anion has a –1 charge, there must be one $Na^+$ cation for each $Cl^-$ anion; thus, the formula is **NaCl.**

When cations and anions having charges of different magnitude combine, the number of cations per anion is not equal. Consider an ionic compound formed from calcium (Ca) and fluorine (F). Since calcium is located in group 2A, it loses two valence electrons to form $Ca^{2+}$. Since fluorine is located in group 7A, it gains one electron to form $F^-$ like other halogens. When $Ca^{2+}$ combines with the fluorine anion $F^-$, **there must be two $F^-$ anions for each $Ca^{2+}$ cation to have an overall charge of zero.**

In writing a formula for an ionic compound, we use subscripts when the number of ions needed to achieve zero charge is greater than one. Since two $F^-$ anions are needed for each calcium cation, the formula is **$CaF_2$.** Figure 3.5 illustrates additional examples of how cations and anions combine to give zero overall charge.

**Figure 3.5**

Examples of Ionic Compounds with Zero Overall Charge

| NaCl | Li$_2$O | BaI$_2$ | Al$_2$O$_3$ |
|---|---|---|---|
| Na$^+$ Cl$^-$ | Li$^+$ O$^{2-}$ | Ba$^{2+}$ I$^-$ | Al$^{3+}$ O$^{2-}$ |
| +1 −1 | +2 −2 | +2 −2 | +6 −6 |

The ratio of oppositely charged ions that combine to form an ionic compound depends on the charge of the ions.

- NaCl: One Na$^+$ cation (+1 charge) combines with one Cl$^-$ anion (−1 charge).

- Li$_2$O: Two Li$^+$ cations (+2 charge total) combine with one O$^{2-}$ anion (−2 charge).

- BaI$_2$: One Ba$^{2+}$ cation (+2 charge) combines with two I$^-$ anions (−2 charge total).

- Al$_2$O$_3$: Two Al$^{3+}$ cations (+6 charge total) combine with three O$^{2-}$ anions (−6 charge total).

**PROBLEM 3.10**

Which pairs of elements will form ionic compounds?

a. lithium and bromine      c. calcium and magnesium

b. chlorine and oxygen      d. barium and chlorine

## 3.3A   Formulas for Ionic Compounds

Writing a formula for an ionic compound from two elements is a useful skill that can be practiced by following a series of steps.

**How To** Write a Formula for an Ionic Compound

**Step [1]** Identify which element is the cation and which is the anion.
- **Metals form *cations* and nonmetals form *anions*.**
- Use the group number of a main group element to determine the charge.

An ionic compound derived from calcium and oxygen has the metal calcium as the cation and the nonmetal oxygen as the anion. Calcium (group 2A) loses two electrons to form Ca$^{2+}$. Oxygen (group 6A) gains two electrons to form O$^{2-}$.

**Step [2]** Determine how many of each ion type are needed for an overall charge of zero.
- When the cation and anion have the *same* charge only *one* of each is needed.

The charges are equal in magnitude,
+2 and −2.

$$Ca^{2+} \ + \ O^{2-} \longrightarrow \boxed{\textbf{CaO}}$$

One of each ion is needed
to balance charge.

—Continued

**How To, continued . . .**

- When the cation and anion have different charges, as is the case with the $Ca^{2+}$ cation and $Cl^-$ anion, use the ion charges to determine the number of ions of each needed. **The charges on the ions tell us how many of the *oppositely* charged ions are needed to balance charge.**
- Write a subscript for the cation that is equal in magnitude to the charge on the anion. Write a subscript for the anion that is equal in magnitude to the charge on the cation.

The charges are not equal in magnitude, +2 and –1.

$Ca^{2+}$    $Cl^{1-}$    The "1" is written for emphasis.

$Ca_1Cl_2$  =  $\boxed{CaCl_2}$   2 $Cl^-$ anions for each $Ca^{2+}$

**Step [3]** **To write the formula, place the cation first and then the anion, and omit charges.**

- Use subscripts to show the number of each ion needed to have zero overall charge. When no subscript is written it is assumed to be "1."

As shown in step [2], the formula for the ionic compound formed from one calcium cation ($Ca^{2+}$) and one oxygen anion ($O^{2-}$) is CaO. The formula for the ionic compound formed from one calcium cation ($Ca^{2+}$) and two chlorine anions ($Cl^-$) is $CaCl_2$.

The tarnish on sterling silver is composed of an ionic compound formed from silver and sulfur (Sample Problem 3.5).

### SAMPLE PROBLEM 3.5

When sterling silver tarnishes it forms an ionic compound derived from silver and sulfur. Write the formula for this ionic compound.

#### Analysis

- Identify the cation and the anion, and use the periodic table to determine the charges.
- When ions of equal charge combine, one of each ion is needed. When ions of unequal charge combine, use the ionic charges to determine the relative number of each ion.
- Write the formula with the cation first and then the anion, omitting charges, and using subscripts to indicate the number of each ion.

#### Solution

Silver is a metal, so it forms the cation. Sulfur is a nonmetal, so it forms the anion. The charge on silver is +1 ($Ag^+$), as shown in Figure 3.3. Sulfur (group 6A) is a main group element with a –2 charge ($S^{2-}$). Since the charges are unequal, use their magnitudes to determine the relative number of each ion to give an overall charge of zero.

The "1" is written for emphasis.    $Ag^{1+}$    $S^{2-}$

$Ag_2S_1$  =  $\boxed{Ag_2S}$   2 $Ag^+$ cations for each $S^{2-}$

**Answer:** Since two $Ag^+$ cations are needed for each $S^{2-}$ anion, the formula is **$Ag_2S$.**

### PROBLEM 3.11

Write the formula for the ionic compound formed from each pair of elements.

a. sodium and bromine

b. barium and oxygen

c. magnesium and iodine

d. lithium and oxygen

## SAMPLE PROBLEM 3.6

Match the given representations of two ionic compounds dissolved in water with the following formulas: (a) KCl; (b) $CaCl_2$.

[1]   [2]

### Analysis

Determine the charges on the cation and anion. When the cation and anion have the same charge, an equal number of cations and anions must be present for an overall charge of zero. When the cation and anion have different charges, use the charges on the ions to tell how many of the oppositely charged ions are needed so that the solution has an overall charge of zero.

### Solution

a. Since KCl contains a cation ($K^+$) and anion ($Cl^-$) with charges of the same magnitude (+1 and −1), an equal number of cations and anions must be present in solution. Representation [1] contains an equal number of yellow and green spheres.

b. Since $CaCl_2$ contains a cation ($Ca^{2+}$) and anion ($Cl^-$) with charges of different magnitude (+2 and −1), the solution must contain twice as many anions as cations to have an overall charge of zero. Representation [2] contains twice as many green spheres ($Cl^-$) as purple spheres ($Ca^{2+}$).

### PROBLEM 3.12

Draw a representation using molecular art for a solution of each of the following ionic compounds dissolved in water: (a) $Na_2S$; (b) $MgCl_2$.

## 3.3B FOCUS ON HEALTH & MEDICINE
### Ionic Compounds in Consumer Products

Simple ionic compounds are added to food or consumer products to prevent disease or maintain good health. For example, **potassium iodide** (KI) is an essential nutrient added to table salt. Iodine is needed to synthesize thyroid hormones. A deficiency of iodine in the diet can lead to insufficient thyroid hormone production. In an attempt to compensate, the thyroid gland may become enlarged, producing a swollen thyroid referred to as a goiter. **Sodium fluoride** (NaF) is added to toothpaste to strengthen tooth enamel and help prevent tooth decay.

potassium iodide in table salt            sodium fluoride in toothpaste

Potassium is a critical cation for normal heart and skeletal muscle function and nerve impulse conduction. Drinking electrolyte replacement beverages like Gatorade or Powerade can replenish K⁺ lost in sweat.

**Potassium chloride** (KCl), sold under trade names such as K–Dur, Klor–Con, and Micro–K, is an ionic compound used for patients whose potassium levels are low. Potassium chloride can be given as tablets, an oral suspension, or intravenously. Adequate potassium levels are needed for proper fluid balance and organ function. Although potassium is readily obtained from many different food sources (e.g., potatoes, beans, melon, bananas, and spinach), levels can become low when too much potassium is lost in sweat and urine or through the use of certain medications.

### PROBLEM 3.13

Zinc oxide, an ionic compound formed from zinc and oxygen, is a common component of sunblocks, as mentioned in the chapter opener. The zinc oxide crystals reflect sunlight away from the skin, and in this way, protect it from sun exposure. What is the ionic formula for zinc oxide?

## 3.4 Naming Ionic Compounds

Now that we have learned how to write the formulas of some simple ionic compounds, we must learn how to name them. Assigning an unambiguous name to each compound is called chemical **nomenclature.**

### 3.4A Naming Cations

Cations of main group metals are given the name of the element from which they are formed.

| $Na^+$ | $K^+$ | $Ca^{2+}$ | $Mg^{2+}$ |
|---|---|---|---|
| sodium | potassium | calcium | magnesium |

It is common to add the word "ion" after the name of the metal cation to distinguish it from the neutral metal itself. For example, when the concentration of sodium in a blood sample is determined, what is really measured is the concentration of sodium *ions* ($Na^+$).

When a metal is able to form two different cations, a method is needed to distinguish these cations. Two systems are used, the systematic method and the common method. The systematic method (Method [1]) will largely be followed in this text. Since many ions are still identified by older names, however, the common method (Method [2]) is also given.

- **Method [1]: Follow the name of the cation by a Roman numeral in parentheses to indicate its charge.**
- **Method [2]: Use the suffix *-ous* for the cation with the lower charge, and the suffix *-ic* for the cation with the higher charge. These suffixes are often added to the Latin names of the elements.**

For example, the element iron (Fe) forms two cations, $Fe^{2+}$ and $Fe^{3+}$, which are named in the following way:

| | **Systematic Name** | **Common Name** |
|---|---|---|
| $Fe^{2+}$ | iron(II) | ferr**ous** |
| $Fe^{3+}$ | iron(III) | ferr**ic** |

Table 3.3 lists the systematic and common names for several cations.

### 3.4B Naming Anions

Anions are named by replacing the ending of the element name by the suffix *-ide*. For example:

| Cl | ---→ | Cl⁻ | [Change *-ine* to *-ide.*] |
|---|---|---|---|
| chlor*ine* | | chlor**ide** | |
| O | ---→ | $O^{2-}$ | [Change *-ygen* to *-ide.*] |
| oxy*gen* | | ox**ide** | |

Table 3.4 lists the names of common anions derived from nonmetal elements.

## Table 3.3 Systematic and Common Names for Some Metal Ions

| Element | Ion Symbol | Systematic Name | Common Name |
|---|---|---|---|
| Chromium | $Cr^{2+}$ | Chromium(II) | Chromous |
|  | $Cr^{3+}$ | Chromium(III) | Chromic |
| Copper | $Cu^+$ | Copper(I) | Cuprous |
|  | $Cu^{2+}$ | Copper(II) | Cupric |
| Iron | $Fe^{2+}$ | Iron(II) | Ferrous |
|  | $Fe^{3+}$ | Iron(III) | Ferric |
| Mercury | $Hg_2^{2+}$ | Mercury(I)[a] | Mercurous |
|  | $Hg^{2+}$ | Mercury(II) | Mercuric |
| Tin | $Sn^{2+}$ | Tin(II) | Stannous |
|  | $Sn^{4+}$ | Tin(IV) | Stannic |

[a]Mercury(I) exists as $Hg_2^{2+}$, containing two atoms of mercury, each with a +1 charge.

## Table 3.4 Names of Common Anions

| Element | Ion Symbol | Name |
|---|---|---|
| Bromine | $Br^-$ | Bromide |
| Chlorine | $Cl^-$ | Chloride |
| Fluorine | $F^-$ | Fluoride |
| Iodine | $I^-$ | Iodide |
| Nitrogen | $N^{3-}$ | Nitride |
| Oxygen | $O^{2-}$ | Oxide |
| Phosphorus | $P^{3-}$ | Phosphide |
| Sulfur | $S^{2-}$ | Sulfide |

### PROBLEM 3.14

Give the name of each ion.

   a. $S^{2-}$      b. $Cu^+$      c. $Cs^+$      d. $Al^{3+}$      e. $Sn^{4+}$

### PROBLEM 3.15

Give the symbol for each ion.

   a. stannic      b. iodide      c. manganese ion      d. lead(II)      e. selenide

## 3.4C Naming Ionic Compounds with Cations from Main Group Metals

To name an ionic compound with a main group metal cation whose charge never varies, **name the cation and then the anion.** Do *not* specify the charge on the cation. Do *not* specify how many ions of each type are needed to balance charge.

$$Na^+ \quad\quad F^- \quad\quad \text{- - -} \rightarrow \quad\quad NaF$$
sodium     fluoride            sodium fluoride

$$Mg^{2+} \quad\quad Cl^- \quad\quad \text{- - -} \rightarrow \quad\quad MgCl_2$$
magnesium   chloride         magnesium chloride

Thus, $BaCl_2$ is named barium chloride (*not* barium *di*chloride). The number of ions of each type is inferred in the name because the net charge must be zero.

### SAMPLE PROBLEM 3.7

Name each ionic compound: (a) $Na_2S$; (b) $AlBr_3$.

#### Analysis

Name the cation and then the anion.

#### Solution

   a. $Na_2S$: The cation is sodium and the anion is sulfide (derived from sulfur); thus, the name is sodium sulfide.

   b. $AlBr_3$: The cation is aluminum and the anion is bromide (derived from bromine); thus, the name is aluminum bromide.

## PROBLEM 3.16

Name each ionic compound.

a. NaF      b. MgO      c. $SrBr_2$      d. $Li_2O$      e. $TiO_2$      f. $AlCl_3$

## 3.4D    Naming Ionic Compounds Containing Metals with Variable Charge

To name an ionic compound that contains a metal with variable charge, we must specify the charge on the cation. The formula of the ionic compound—that is, how many cations there are per anion—allows us to determine the charge on the cation.

### How To   Name an Ionic Compound That Contains a Metal with Variable Charge

**Example:** Give the name for $CuCl_2$.

**Step [1] Determine the charge on the cation.**

- Since there are two $Cl^-$ anions, each of which has a –1 charge, the copper cation must have a +2 charge to make the overall charge zero.

$CuCl_2$   2 $Cl^-$ anions   - - - →   The total negative charge is –2.

Cu must have a +2 charge to balance the –2 charge of the anions.

$Cu^{2+}$

**Step [2] Name the cation and anion.**

- Name the cation using its element name followed by a Roman numeral to indicate its charge. In the common system, use the suffix *-ous* or *-ic* to indicate charge.
- Name the anion by changing the ending of the element name to the suffix *-ide.*

$Cu^{2+}$   - - - →   copper(II)   or   cupric

$Cl^-$   - - - →   chloride

**Step [3] Write the name of the cation first, then the anion.**

- **Answer:** Copper(II) chloride or cupric chloride.

Sample Problem 3.8 illustrates the difference in naming ionic compounds derived from metals that have fixed or variable charge.

### SAMPLE PROBLEM 3.8

$SnF_2$ and $Al_2O_3$ are both ingredients in commercial toothpastes. $SnF_2$ contains fluoride, which strengthens tooth enamel. $Al_2O_3$ is an abrasive that helps to scrub the teeth clean when they are brushed. Give names for (a) $SnF_2$; (b) $Al_2O_3$.

#### Analysis

First determine if the cation has a fixed or variable charge. To name an ionic compound that contains a cation that always has the same charge, name the cation and then the anion (using the suffix *-ide*). When the metal has a variable charge, use the overall anion charge to determine the charge on the cation. Then name the cation (using a Roman numeral or the suffix *-ous* or *-ic*), followed by the anion.

#### Solution

a. $SnF_2$: Sn cations have variable charge so the overall anion charge determines the cation charge.

$SnF_2$   2 $F^-$ anions   - - - →   The total negative charge is –2.

Sn must have a +2 charge to balance the –2 charge of the anions.

tin(II) or stannous        fluoride

**Answer:** tin(II) fluoride or stannous fluoride

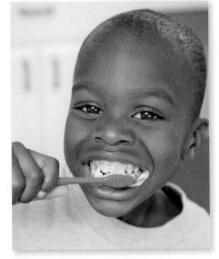

Some toothpastes contain the ionic compounds $SnF_2$ as a source of fluoride and $Al_2O_3$ as an abrasive.

b. $Al_2O_3$: Al has a fixed charge of +3. To name the compound, name the cation as the element (aluminum), and the anion by changing the ending of the element name to the suffix -ide (oxygen → oxide).

$Al_2O_3$  aluminum oxide     **Answer:** aluminum oxide

### PROBLEM 3.17

Name each ionic compound.

  a. $CrCl_3$      b. $PbS$      c. $SnF_4$      d. $PbO_2$      e. $FeBr_2$      f. $AuCl_3$

### PROBLEM 3.18

Several copper salts are brightly colored. Give the name for each of the following ionic copper compounds.

  a. $Cu_2O$ (brown)      b. $CuO$ (black)      c. $CuCl$ (green)      d. $CuCl_2$ (blue)

### PROBLEM 3.19

When iron rusts it forms $Fe_2O_3$. Name this product of air oxidation.

## 3.4E   Writing a Formula from the Name of an Ionic Compound

Thus far, we have focused on assigning a name to a formula for an ionic compound. Writing a formula from a name is also a useful skill.

### How To   Derive a Formula from the Name of an Ionic Compound

**Example:** Write the formula for tin(IV) oxide.

**Step [1]**   **Identify the cation and the anion and determine their charges.**
- The name of the cation appears first, followed by the anion.
- For metals with variable charge, the Roman numeral gives the charge on the cation.

In this example, tin is the cation. The Roman numeral tells us that its charge is +4, making the cation $Sn^{4+}$. Oxide is the name of the oxygen anion, $O^{2-}$ (Table 3.4).

**Step [2]**   **Balance charges.**
- Use the charge on the cation to determine the number of ions of the anion needed to balance charge.

    $Sn^{4+}$    $O^{2-}$    Two –2 anions are needed
                   for each +4 cation.
    cation    anion

**Step [3]**   **Write the formula with the cation first, and use subscripts to show the number of each ion needed to have zero overall charge.**
    **Answer:** $SnO_2$

### PROBLEM 3.20

Write the formula for each ionic compound.

  a. calcium bromide          c. ferric bromide          e. chromium(II) chloride
  b. copper(I) iodide          d. magnesium sulfide        f. sodium oxide

## 3.5   Physical Properties of Ionic Compounds

Ionic compounds are crystalline solids composed of ions packed to maximize the interaction of the positive charge of the cations and negative charge of the anions. The relative size and charge of the ions determine the way they are packed in the crystal lattice. Ionic solids are held together by extremely strong interactions of the oppositely charged ions. How is this reflected in the melting point and boiling point of an ionic compound?

When a compound melts to form a liquid, energy is needed to overcome some of the attractive forces of the ordered solid to form the less ordered liquid phase. Since an ionic compound is held together by very strong electrostatic interactions, it takes a great deal of energy to separate the ions from each other. As a result, **ionic compounds have very high melting points.** For example, the melting point of NaCl is 801 °C.

A great deal of energy is needed to overcome the attractive forces present in the liquid phase, too, to form ions that are far apart and very disorganized in the gas phase, so **ionic compounds have extremely high boiling points.** The boiling point of liquid NaCl is 1413 °C.

A great many ionic compounds are soluble in water. When an ionic compound dissolves in water, the ions are separated, and each anion and cation is surrounded by water molecules, as shown in Figure 3.6. The interaction of the water solvent with the ions provides the energy needed to overcome the strong ion–ion attractions of the crystalline lattice. We will learn much more about solubility in Chapter 8.

An **aqueous solution** contains a substance dissolved in liquid water.

When an ionic compound dissolves in water, the resulting aqueous solution conducts an electric current. This distinguishes ionic compounds from other compounds discussed in Chapter 4, some of which dissolve in water but do not form ions and therefore do not conduct electricity.

PROBLEM 3.21

List five physical properties of ionic compounds.

Figure 3.6    Dissolving NaCl in Water

When NaCl dissolves in water, each Na$^+$ ion and each Cl$^-$ ion are surrounded by water molecules. The interactions of these ions with water molecules provide the energy needed to break apart the ions of the crystal lattice.

## 3.6   Polyatomic Ions

Sometimes ions are composed of more than one element. The ion bears a charge because the total number of electrons it contains is different from the total number of protons in the nuclei of all of the atoms.

> • A *polyatomic ion* is a cation or anion that contains more than one atom.

The atoms in the polyatomic ion are held together by covalent bonds, but since the ion bears a charge, it bonds to other ions by ionic bonding. For example, calcium sulfate, $CaSO_4$, is composed of a calcium cation, $Ca^{2+}$, and the polyatomic anion sulfate, $SO_4^{2-}$. $CaSO_4$ is used to make plaster casts for broken bones.

We will encounter only two polyatomic cations: **$H_3O^+$, the hydronium ion,** which will play a key role in the acid–base chemistry discussed in Chapter 9, and **$NH_4^+$, the ammonium ion.**

In contrast, there are several common polyatomic anions, most of which contain a nonmetal like carbon, sulfur, or phosphorus, usually bonded to one or more oxygen atoms. Common examples include **carbonate ($CO_3^{2-}$), sulfate ($SO_4^{2-}$), and phosphate ($PO_4^{3-}$).** Table 3.5 lists the most common polyatomic anions.

The names of most polyatomic anions end in the suffix *-ate.* Exceptions to this generalization include hydroxide ($OH^-$) and cyanide ($CN^-$). Two other aspects of nomenclature are worthy of note.

> • The suffix *-ite* is used for an anion that has one fewer oxygen atom than a similar anion named with the *-ate* ending. Thus, $SO_4^{2-}$ is sul*fate*, but $SO_3^{2-}$ is sul*fite.*
> • When two anions differ in the presence of a hydrogen, the word *hydrogen* or the prefix *bi-* is added to the name of the anion. Thus, $SO_4^{2-}$ is sulfate, but $HSO_4^-$ is *hydrogen* sulfate or *bi*sulfate.

### Table 3.5  Names of Common Polyatomic Anions

| Nonmetal | Formula | Name |
|---|---|---|
| Carbon | $CO_3^{2-}$ | **Carbonate** |
| | $HCO_3^-$ | Hydrogen carbonate or bicarbonate |
| | $CH_3CO_2^-$ | Acetate |
| | $CN^-$ | Cyanide |
| Nitrogen | $NO_3^-$ | **Nitrate** |
| | $NO_2^-$ | Nitrite |
| Oxygen | $OH^-$ | **Hydroxide** |
| Phosphorus | $PO_4^{3-}$ | **Phosphate** |
| | $HPO_4^{2-}$ | Hydrogen phosphate |
| | $H_2PO_4^-$ | Dihydrogen phosphate |
| Sulfur | $SO_4^{2-}$ | **Sulfate** |
| | $HSO_4^-$ | Hydrogen sulfate or bisulfate |
| | $SO_3^{2-}$ | Sulfite |
| | $HSO_3^-$ | Hydrogen sulfite or bisulfite |

### 3.6A   Writing Formulas for Ionic Compounds with Polyatomic Ions

Writing the formula for an ionic compound with a polyatomic ion is no different than writing a formula for an ion with a single charged atom, so we follow the procedure outlined in Section 3.3A.

Spam, a canned meat widely consumed in Alaska, Hawaii, and other parts of the United States, contains the preservative sodium nitrite, $NaNO_2$. Sodium nitrite inhibits the growth of *Clostridium botulinum,* a bacterium responsible for a lethal form of food poisoning.

When the cation and anion have the *same* charge, only *one* of each ion is needed for an overall charge of zero.

The charges are equal in magnitude, +1 and −1.

$$Na^+ + NO_2^- \longrightarrow NaNO_2$$
sodium    nitrite        sodium nitrite

One of each ion is needed to balance charge.

The charges are equal in magnitude, +2 and −2.

$$Ba^{2+} + SO_4^{2-} \longrightarrow BaSO_4$$
barium    sulfate        barium sulfate

One of each ion is needed to balance charge.

In a compound formed from ions of unequal charge, such as magnesium ($Mg^{2+}$) and hydroxide ($OH^-$), **the charges on the ions tell us how many of the *oppositely* charged ions are needed to balance the charge.**

The charges are not equal in magnitude, +2 and −1.

$$Mg^{2+} + OH^- \longrightarrow Mg(OH)_2$$

Use a subscript outside the parentheses.

Two $OH^-$ anions are needed to balance charge.    Use parentheses around all atoms of the ion.

Parentheses are used around the polyatomic ion, and a subscript indicates how many of each are needed to balance charge. The formula is written as $Mg(OH)_2$ (*not* $MgO_2H_2$ or $MgOH_2$).

### SAMPLE PROBLEM 3.9

A dietary supplement used to prevent and treat calcium deficiencies consists of an ionic compound formed from calcium and phosphate. What is its formula?

### Analysis

- Identify the cation and anion and determine the charges.
- When ions of equal charge combine, one of each is needed. When ions of unequal charge combine, use the ionic charges to determine the relative number of each ion.
- Write the formula with the cation first and then the anion, omitting charges. Use parentheses around polyatomic ions when more than one appears in the formula, and use subscripts to indicate the number of each ion.

### Solution

The cation ($Ca^{2+}$) and anion ($PO_4^{3-}$) have different charges so the magnitude of the ionic charges determines the number of each ion giving an overall charge of zero.

$$Ca^{2+} \qquad PO_4^{3-}$$

$$Ca_3(PO_4)_2 \qquad \text{parentheses around the anion}$$

**Answer:** Since three $Ca^{2+}$ cations are needed for two $PO_4^{3-}$ anions, the formula is $Ca_3(PO_4)_2$.

### PROBLEM 3.22

Write the formula for the compound formed when the sulfate anion ($SO_4^{2-}$) combines with a cation from each of the following elements: (a) magnesium; (b) sodium; (c) nickel; (d) aluminum; (e) lithium.

### PROBLEM 3.23

Write the formula of the ionic compound formed from each pair of cations and anions.

a. sodium and bicarbonate
b. potassium and nitrate
c. ammonium and sulfate
d. magnesium and phosphate
e. calcium and bisulfate
f. barium and hydroxide

### PROBLEM 3.24

Write the formula for the compound formed when $K^+$ combines with each anion.

a. $OH^-$    b. $NO_2^-$    c. $SO_4^{2-}$    d. $HSO_3^-$    e. $PO_4^{3-}$    f. $CN^-$

Barium sulfate is used to visualize the digestive system during an X-ray procedure.

### 3.6B  Naming Ionic Compounds with Polyatomic Ions

Naming ionic compounds derived from polyatomic anions follows the same procedures outlined in Sections 3.4C and 3.4D. There is no easy trick for remembering the names and structures of the anions listed in Table 3.5. The names of the anions in boldface type are especially common and should be committed to memory.

#### SAMPLE PROBLEM 3.10

Name each ionic compound: (a) $NaHCO_3$, the active ingredient in baking soda; (b) $Al_2(SO_4)_3$, an ingredient once used in antiperspirants, but no longer considered effective.

#### Analysis

First determine if the cation has a fixed or variable charge. To name an ionic compound that contains a cation that always has the same charge, name the cation and then the anion. When the metal has a variable charge, use the overall anion charge to determine the charge on the cation. Then name the cation (using a Roman numeral or the suffix -ous or -ic), followed by the anion.

#### Solution

a. $NaHCO_3$: Sodium cations have a fixed charge of +1. The anion $HCO_3^-$ is called bicarbonate or hydrogen carbonate.

   **Answer:** sodium bicarbonate or sodium hydrogen carbonate

b. $Al_2(SO_4)_3$: Aluminum cations have a fixed charge of +3. The anion $SO_4^{2-}$ is called sulfate.

   **Answer:** aluminum sulfate

#### PROBLEM 3.25

Name each compound.

a. $Na_2CO_3$     b. $Ca(OH)_2$     c. $Mg(NO_3)_2$     d. $Mn(CH_3CO_2)_2$     e. $Fe(HSO_3)_3$     f. $Mg_3(PO_4)_2$

### 3.6C  FOCUS ON HEALTH & MEDICINE
#### Useful Ionic Compounds

Ionic compounds are the active ingredients in several over-the-counter drugs. Examples include **calcium carbonate ($CaCO_3$),** the antacid in Tums; **magnesium hydroxide [$Mg(OH)_2$],** one of the active components in the antacids Maalox and milk of magnesia; and **iron(II) sulfate ($FeSO_4$),** an iron supplement used to treat anemia.

The shells of oysters and other mollusks are composed largely of calcium carbonate, $CaCO_3$.

$Ca^{2+}$

$CO_3^{2-}$

$CaCO_3$

$OH^-$

$Mg^{2+}$

$Mg(OH)_2$

$SO_4^{2-}$

$Fe^{2+}$

$FeSO_4$

(top) Normal bone; (bottom) brittle bone due to osteoporosis. Osteoporosis results in a decrease in bone density, making bones brittle and easily fractured.

Some ionic compounds are given as intravenous drugs. Bicarbonate ($HCO_3^-$) is an important polyatomic anion that controls the acid–base balance in the blood. When the blood becomes too acidic, sodium bicarbonate ($NaHCO_3$) is administered intravenously to decrease the acidity. Magnesium sulfate ($MgSO_4$), an over-the-counter laxative, is also given intravenously to prevent seizures caused by extremely high blood pressure associated with some pregnancies.

### 3.6D FOCUS ON HEALTH & MEDICINE
Treating Osteoporosis

Although much of the body is composed of compounds held together by covalent bonds, about 70% of bone is composed largely of a complex ionic solid with the formula $Ca_{10}(PO_4)_6(OH)_2$ called **hydroxyapatite.** Throughout an individual's life, hydroxyapatite is constantly broken down and rebuilt. In postmenopausal women, however, the rate of bone loss often becomes greater than bone synthesis, and bones get brittle and easily broken. This condition is called **osteoporosis.**

In recent years, some prescription drugs have proven effective in combating osteoporosis. Sodium alendronate, trade name Fosamax, increases bone density by decreasing the rate of bone loss. Fosamax is an ionic compound with the formula $Na(C_4H_{12}NO_7P_2)$. This compound contains a sodium cation, $Na^+$, and a polyatomic anion, $(C_4H_{12}NO_7P_2)^-$.

#### PROBLEM 3.26
Using the charges on the ions that compose hydroxyapatite, show that it has zero overall charge.

## CHAPTER HIGHLIGHTS

### KEY TERMS

Ammonium ion (3.6)
Anion (3.2)
Bonding (3.1)
Carbonate (3.6)
Cation (3.2)
Covalent bond (3.1)

Hydronium ion (3.6)
Hydroxide (3.6)
Ion (3.1)
Ionic bond (3.1)
Molecule (3.1)

Nomenclature (3.4)
Octet rule (3.2)
Phosphate (3.6)
Polyatomic ion (3.6)
Sulfate (3.6)

### KEY CONCEPTS

**❶ What are the basic features of ionic and covalent bonds? (3.1)**

- Both ionic bonding and covalent bonding follow one general rule: Elements gain, lose, or share electrons to attain the electronic configuration of the noble gas closest to them in the periodic table.
- Ionic bonds result from the transfer of electrons from one element to another. Ionic bonds form between a metal and a nonmetal. Ionic compounds consist of oppositely charged ions that feel a strong electrostatic attraction for each other.
- Covalent bonds result from the sharing of electrons between two atoms. Covalent bonds occur between two nonmetals, or when a metalloid combines with a nonmetal. Covalent bonding forms discrete molecules.

**❷ How can the periodic table be used to determine whether an atom forms a cation or an anion, and its resulting ionic charge? (3.2)**

- Metals form cations and nonmetals form anions.
- By gaining or losing one, two, or three electrons, an atom forms an ion with a completely filled outer shell of electrons.
- The charge on main group ions can be predicted from the position in the periodic table. For metals in groups 1A, 2A, and 3A, the group number = the charge on the cation. For nonmetals in groups 5A, 6A, and 7A, the anion charge = 8 – (the group number).

**3** **What is the octet rule? (3.2)**
- Main group elements are especially stable when they possess an octet of electrons. Main group elements gain or lose one, two, or three electrons to form ions with eight outer shell electrons.

**4** **What determines the formula of an ionic compound? (3.3)**
- Cations and anions always form ionic compounds that have zero overall charge.
- Ionic compounds are written with the cation first, and then the anion, with subscripts to show how many of each are needed to have zero net charge.

**5** **How are ionic compounds named? (3.4)**
- Ionic compounds are always named with the name of the cation first.
- With cations having a fixed charge, the cation has the same name as its neutral element. The name of the anion usually ends in the suffix -ide if it is derived from a single atom or -ate (or -ite) if it is polyatomic.
- When the metal has a variable charge, use the overall anion charge to determine the charge on the cation. Then name the cation using a Roman numeral or the suffix -ous (for the ion with the smaller charge) or -ic (for the ion with the larger charge).

**6** **Describe the properties of ionic compounds. (3.5)**
- Ionic compounds are crystalline solids with the ions arranged to maximize the interactions of the oppositely charged ions.
- Ionic compounds have high melting points and boiling points.
- Most ionic compounds are soluble in water and their aqueous solutions conduct an electric current.

**7** **What are polyatomic ions and how are they named? (3.6)**
- Polyatomic ions are charged species that are composed of more than one element.
- The names for polyatomic cations end in the suffix -onium.
- Many polyatomic anions have names that end in the suffix -ate. The suffix -ite is used for an anion that has one fewer oxygen atom than a similar anion named with the -ate ending. When two anions differ in the presence of a hydrogen, the word hydrogen or the prefix bi- is added to the name of the anion.

**8** **List useful consumer products and drugs that are composed of ionic compounds.**
- Useful ionic compounds that contain alkali metal cations and halogen anions include KI (iodine supplement), NaF (source of fluoride in toothpaste), and KCl (potassium supplement). (3.3)
- Other products contain $SnF_2$ (fluoride source in toothpaste), $Al_2O_3$ (abrasive in toothpaste), and ZnO (sunblock agent). (3.4)
- Useful ionic compounds with polyatomic anions include $CaCO_3$ (antacid and calcium supplement), magnesium hydroxide (antacid), and $FeSO_4$ (iron supplement). (3.6)

## PROBLEMS

Selected in-chapter and odd-numbered end-of-chapter problems have brief answers in Appendix B. The *Student Study Guide and Solutions Manual* contains detailed solutions to all in-chapter and odd-numbered end-of-chapter problems, as well as additional worked examples and a chapter self-test.

### Ionic and Covalent Bonding

**3.27** Which formulas represent ionic compounds and which represent covalent compounds?
   a. $CO_2$      b. $H_2SO_4$      c. KF      d. $CH_5N$

**3.28** Which formulas represent ionic compounds and which represent covalent compounds?
   a. $C_3H_8$      b. ClBr      c. CuO      d. $CH_4O$

**3.29** Which pairs of elements are likely to form ionic bonds and which pairs are likely to form covalent bonds?
   a. potassium and oxygen      c. two bromine atoms
   b. sulfur and carbon          d. carbon and oxygen

**3.30** Which pairs of elements are likely to form ionic bonds and which pairs are likely to form covalent bonds?
   a. carbon and hydrogen        c. hydrogen and oxygen
   b. sodium and sulfur          d. magnesium and bromine

**3.31** Why do ionic bonds form between a metal and a nonmetal?

**3.32** Is it proper to speak of sodium chloride molecules? Explain.

### Ions

**3.33** Write the ion symbol for an atom with the given number of protons and electrons.
   a. four protons and two electrons
   b. 22 protons and 20 electrons
   c. 16 protons and 18 electrons
   d. 13 protons and 10 electrons
   e. 17 protons and 18 electrons
   f. 20 protons and 18 electrons

**3.34** How many protons and electrons are present in each ion?
   a. $K^+$   b. $S^{2-}$   c. $Mn^{2+}$   d. $Fe^{2+}$   e. $Cs^+$   f. $I^-$

**3.35** What element fits each description?
   a. a period 2 element that forms a +2 cation
   b. an ion from group 7A with 18 electrons
   c. a cation from group 1A with 36 electrons

**3.36** What element fits each description?
   a. a period 3 element that forms an ion with a –1 charge
   b. an ion from group 2A with 36 electrons
   c. an ion from group 6A with 18 electrons

**3.37** Why do elements in group 6A gain electrons to form anions?

**3.38** Why do elements in group 2A lose electrons to form cations?

**3.39** Give the ion symbol for each ion.
   a. sodium ion        c. manganese ion      e. stannic
   b. selenide          d. gold(III)          f. mercurous

**3.40** Give the ion symbol for each ion.
  a. barium ion      c. oxide      e. lead(IV)
  b. iron(II)      d. ferrous      f. cobalt(III)

**3.41** What noble gas has the same electronic configuration as each ion?
  a. $O^{2-}$   b. $Mg^{2+}$   c. $Al^{3+}$   d. $S^{2-}$   e. $F^-$   f. $Be^{2+}$

**3.42** Give two cations and two anions that have the same electronic configuration as each noble gas: (a) neon; (b) argon.

**3.43** How many electrons must be gained or lost by each element to achieve a noble gas configuration of electrons?
  a. lithium      b. iodine      c. sulfur      d. strontium

**3.44** How many electrons must be gained or lost by each element to achieve a noble gas configuration of electrons?
  a. cesium      b. barium      c. selenium      d. aluminum

**3.45** Which ions are likely to form? For those ions that are not likely to form, explain why this is so.
  a. $S^-$   b. $S^{2-}$   c. $S^{3-}$   d. $Na^+$   e. $Na^{2+}$   f. $Na^-$

**3.46** Which ions are likely to form? For those ions that are not likely to form, explain why this is so.
  a. $Mg^+$   b. $Mg^{2+}$   c. $Mg^{3+}$   d. $Cl^+$   e. $Cl^-$   f. $Cl^{2-}$

**3.47** For each of the general electron-dot formulas for elements, give the following information: [1] the number of valence electrons; [2] the group number of the element; [3] how many electrons would be gained or lost to achieve a noble gas configuration; [4] the charge on the resulting ion; [5] an example of the element.
  a. X·      b. ·Q·      c. ·Z̈·      d. :Ä·

**3.48** Label each of the following elements or regions in the periodic table.

  a. a group that forms cations with a +2 charge
  b. a group that forms anions with a –2 charge
  c. a group that forms cations with a +1 charge
  d. a group that forms anions with a –1 charge
  e. elements that form ions with the same electronic configuration as Ne
  f. elements that form ions with the same electronic configuration as He

**3.49** Use the element colors in Figure 2.3 (also shown on the inside back cover) and the information in Table 3.5 to identify each of the following anions. Give the name and proper formula, including the charge.

  a.    b.    c.

**3.50** Use the element colors in Figure 2.3 (also shown on the inside back cover) and the information in Table 3.5 to identify each of the following anions. Give the name and proper formula, including the charge.

  a.    b.    c.

**3.51** Give the formula for each polyatomic ion.
  a. sulfate      c. hydrogen carbonate
  b. ammonium      d. cyanide

**3.52** Give the formula for each polyatomic ion.
  a. acetate      c. dihydrogen phosphate
  b. bisulfite      d. hydronium

**3.53** How many protons and electrons are contained in each polyatomic ion?
  a. $OH^-$      b. $H_3O^+$      c. $PO_4^{3-}$

**3.54** How many protons and electrons are contained in each polyatomic ion?
  a. $NH_4^+$      b. $CN^-$      c. $CO_3^{2-}$

**3.55** Why isn't the octet rule followed by transition metals when they form cations?

**3.56** Do all isotopes of an element form the same type of ions? Explain.

## Ionic Compounds

**3.57** How does the compound NaF illustrate the octet rule?

**3.58** How does the compound LiF "violate" the octet rule?

**3.59** Write the formula for the ionic compound formed from each pair of elements.
  a. calcium and sulfur      d. nickel and chlorine
  b. aluminum and bromine      e. sodium and selenium
  c. lithium and iodine

**3.60** Write the formula for the ionic compound formed from each pair of elements.
  a. barium and bromine
  b. aluminum and sulfur
  c. manganese and chlorine
  d. zinc and sulfur
  e. magnesium and fluorine

**3.61** Write the formula for the ionic compound formed from each cation and anion.
  a. lithium and nitrite
  b. calcium and acetate
  c. sodium and bisulfite
  d. manganese and phosphate
  e. magnesium and hydrogen sulfite

**3.62** Write the formula for the ionic compound formed from each cation and anion.

    a. potassium and bicarbonate

    b. magnesium and nitrate

    c. lithium and carbonate

    d. potassium and cyanide

    e. ammonium and phosphate

**3.63** Considering the indicated charges on the cation **X** and the anion **Y,** fill in the table with the formula of the ionic compound that results in zero overall charge. One entry is filled in.

|           | $Y^-$   | $Y^{2-}$ | $Y^{3-}$ |
| --------- | ------- | -------- | -------- |
| $X^+$     |         |          |          |
| $X^{2+}$  | $XY_2$  |          |          |
| $X^{3+}$  |         |          |          |

**3.64** What is the charge on the cation **M** in each of the following ionic compounds?

    a. $MCl_2$      b. $MO$      c. $M_3O_2$      d. $M_3N$

**3.65** Complete the following table by filling in the formula of the ionic compound derived from the cations on the left and each of the anions across the top.

|           | $Br^-$ | $OH^-$ | $HCO_3^-$ | $SO_3^{2-}$ | $PO_4^{3-}$ |
| --------- | ------ | ------ | --------- | ----------- | ----------- |
| $Na^+$    |        |        |           |             |             |
| $Co^{2+}$ |        |        |           |             |             |
| $Al^{3+}$ |        |        |           |             |             |

**3.66** Complete the following table by filling in the formula of the ionic compound derived from the cations on the left and each of the anions across the top.

|           | $I^-$ | $CN^-$ | $NO_3^-$ | $SO_4^{2-}$ | $HPO_4^{2-}$ |
| --------- | ----- | ------ | -------- | ----------- | ------------ |
| $K^+$     |       |        |          |             |              |
| $Mg^{2+}$ |       |        |          |             |              |
| $Cr^{3+}$ |       |        |          |             |              |

**3.67** Write the formula for the ionic compound formed from the bisulfate anion ($HSO_4^-$) and each cation: (a) $K^+$; (b) $Ba^{2+}$; (c) $Al^{3+}$; (d) $Zn^{2+}$.

**3.68** Write the formula for the ionic compound formed from the sulfite anion ($SO_3^{2-}$) and each cation: (a) $K^+$; (b) $Ba^{2+}$; (c) $Al^{3+}$; (d) $Zn^{2+}$.

**3.69** Write the formula for the ionic compound formed from the barium cation ($Ba^{2+}$) and each anion: (a) $CN^-$; (b) $PO_4^{3-}$; (c) $HPO_4^{2-}$; (d) $H_2PO_4^-$.

**3.70** Write the formula for the ionic compound formed from the iron(III) cation ($Fe^{3+}$) and each anion: (a) $CN^-$; (b) $PO_4^{3-}$; (c) $HPO_4^{2-}$; (d) $H_2PO_4^-$.

## Naming Ionic Compounds

**3.71** Name each ionic compound.

    a. $Na_2O$      d. $AgCl$      f. $RbBr$

    b. $BaS$      e. $CoBr_2$      g. $PbBr_2$

    c. $PbS_2$

**3.72** Name each ionic compound.

    a. $KF$      d. $SnO$      f. $Li_2S$

    b. $ZnCl_2$      e. $AuBr_3$      g. $SnBr_4$

    c. $Cu_2S$

**3.73** Name each ionic compound.

    a. $FeCl_2$    b. $FeBr_3$    c. $FeS$    d. $Fe_2S_3$

**3.74** Name each ionic compound.

    a. $CrCl_2$    b. $CrBr_3$    c. $CrO$    d. $Cr_2O_3$

**3.75** Why is a Roman numeral needed in the name for $CuBr_2$ but not $CaBr_2$? Name both compounds.

**3.76** Why is a Roman numeral needed in the name for $PbO$ but not $ZnO$? Name both compounds.

**3.77** Write formulas to illustrate the difference between each pair of compounds.

    a. sodium sulfide and sodium sulfate

    b. magnesium oxide and magnesium hydroxide

    c. magnesium sulfate and magnesium bisulfate

**3.78** Write formulas to illustrate the difference between each pair of compounds.

    a. lithium sulfite and lithium sulfide

    b. sodium carbonate and sodium hydrogen carbonate

    c. calcium phosphate and calcium dihydrogen phosphate

**3.79** Name each ionic compound.

    a. $NH_4Cl$      c. $Cu(NO_3)_2$      e. $Fe(NO_3)_2$

    b. $PbSO_4$      d. $Ca(HCO_3)_2$

**3.80** Name each ionic compound.

    a. $(NH_4)_2SO_4$      c. $Cr(CH_3CO_2)_3$      e. $Ni_3(PO_4)_2$

    b. $NaH_2PO_4$      d. $Sn(HPO_4)_2$

**3.81** Write a formula from each name.

    a. magnesium carbonate

    b. nickel sulfate

    c. copper(II) hydroxide

    d. potassium hydrogen phosphate

    e. gold(III) nitrate

    f. lithium phosphate

    g. aluminum bicarbonate

    h. chromous cyanide

**3.82** Write a formula from each name.

    a. copper(I) sulfite

    b. aluminum nitrate

    c. tin(II) acetate

    d. lead(IV) carbonate

    e. zinc hydrogen phosphate

    f. manganese dihydrogen phosphate

    g. ammonium cyanide

    h. iron(II) nitrate

**3.83** Write the formula for the ionic compound formed from $Pb^{4+}$ and each anion. Then name each compound.

   a. $OH^-$       c. $HCO_3^-$       e. $PO_4^{3-}$

   b. $SO_4^{2-}$      d. $NO_3^-$       f. $CH_3CO_2^-$

**3.84** Write the formula for the ionic compound formed from $Fe^{3+}$ and each anion. Then name each compound.

   a. $OH^-$       c. $HPO_4^{2-}$      e. $PO_4^{3-}$

   b. $CO_3^{2-}$     d. $NO_2^-$       f. $CH_3CO_2^-$

## Properties of Ionic Compounds

**3.85** Label each statement as "true" or "false." Correct any false statement to make it true.

   a. Ionic compounds have high melting points.

   b. Ionic compounds can be solid, liquid, or gas at room temperature.

   c. Most ionic compounds are insoluble in water.

   d. An ionic solid like sodium chloride consists of discrete pairs of sodium cations and chloride anions.

**3.86** Label each statement as "true" or "false." Correct any false statement to make it true.

   a. Ionic compounds have high boiling points.

   b. The ions in a crystal lattice are arranged randomly and the overall charge is zero.

   c. When an ionic compound dissolves in water, the solution conducts electricity.

   d. In an ionic crystal, ions having like charges are arranged close to each other.

**3.87** Which compound has the highest melting point: $NaCl$, $CH_4$, or $H_2SO_4$?

**3.88** Which compound or element has the lowest boiling point: $Cl_2$, $KI$, or $LiF$?

## Applications

**3.89** Zinc is an essential nutrient needed by many enzymes to maintain proper cellular function. Zinc is obtained in many dietary sources, including oysters, beans, nuts, whole grains, and sunflower seeds. (a) How many protons and electrons are found in a neutral zinc atom? (b) How many electrons and

protons are found in the $Zn^{2+}$ cation? (c) Write the electronic configuration of the element zinc, and suggest which electrons are lost to form the $Zn^{2+}$ cation.

**3.90** Wilson's disease is an inherited defect in copper metabolism in which copper accumulates in tissues, causing neurological problems and liver disease. The disease can be treated with compounds that bind to copper and thus remove it from the tissues. (a) How many protons and electrons are found in a neutral copper atom? (b) How many electrons and protons are found in the $Cu^+$ cation? (c) How many electrons and protons are found in the $Cu^{2+}$ cation? (d) Zinc acetate inhibits copper absorption and so it is used to treat Wilson's disease. What is the structure of zinc acetate?

**3.91** $Na^+$, $K^+$, $Ca^{2+}$, and $Mg^{2+}$ are the four major cations in the body. For each cation, give the following information: (a) the number of protons; (b) the number of electrons; (c) the noble gas that has the same electronic configuration; (d) its role in the body.

**3.92** Unlike many ionic compounds, calcium carbonate is insoluble in water. What information contained in this chapter suggested that calcium carbonate is water insoluble?

**3.93** Write the formula for silver nitrate, an antiseptic and germ killing agent.

**3.94** Ammonium carbonate is the active ingredient in smelling salts. Write its formula.

**3.95** $CaSO_3$ is used to preserve cider and fruit juices. Name this ionic compound.

**3.96** Many ionic compounds are used as paint pigments. Name each of the following pigments.

   a. $CdS$ (yellow)      c. $Cr_2O_3$ (white)

   b. $TiO_2$ (white)      d. $Mn_3(PO_4)_2$ (purple)

**3.97** Ammonium nitrate is the most common source of the element nitrogen in fertilizers. When it is mixed with water, the solution gets cold, so it is used in instant cold packs. When mixed with diesel fuel it forms an explosive mixture that can be used as a bomb. Write the formula of ammonium nitrate.

**3.98** Write the formula for sodium phosphate, a key ingredient in many commercial detergents.

## CHALLENGE PROBLEMS

**3.99** Energy bars contain ionic compounds that serve as a source of the trace elements that the body needs each day for proper cellular function. Answer the following questions about some of the ingredients in one commercial product.

   a. Write the formulas for magnesium oxide and potassium iodide.

   b. The ingredient $CaHPO_4$ is called dicalcium phosphate on the label. What name would you give to this ionic compound?

   c. Give two different names for the ingredient $FePO_4$.

   d. Sodium selenite is one ingredient. Selenite is a polyatomic anion that contains a selenium atom in place of the sulfur atom in sulfite. With this in mind, suggest a formula for sodium selenite.

   e. Another ingredient is listed as chromium chloride. What is wrong with this name?

**3.100** Some polyatomic anions contain a metal as part of the anion. For example, the anion dichromate has the formula $Cr_2O_7^{2-}$ and the anion permanganate has the formula $MnO_4^-$. Write the formula of the ionic compound formed from each of these anions and a potassium cation. Name each compound.

Like many drugs, **acetaminophen,** the active ingredient in the pain reliever Tylenol, is composed of covalent bonds.

# Covalent Compounds

## CHAPTER GOALS

*In this chapter you will learn how to:*

① Recognize the bonding characteristics of covalent compounds

② Draw Lewis structures for covalent compounds

③ Draw resonance structures for some ions and molecules

④ Name covalent compounds that contain two types of elements

⑤ Predict the shape around an atom in a molecule

⑥ Use electronegativity to determine whether a bond is polar or nonpolar

⑦ Determine whether a molecule is polar or nonpolar

Although all of Chapter 3 was devoted to ionic compounds, in truth, most compounds that we come in contact with in our daily lives are **covalent compounds,** formed by sharing electrons between atoms. The air we breathe is composed largely of the gases nitrogen and oxygen, two covalent molecules. The body is mostly water, which contains two covalent hydrogen–oxygen bonds. Most of the drugs routinely used—aspirin, acetaminophen, ibuprofen, and all antibiotics—are covalent compounds. Virtually all products of the chemical industry—polyethylene, nylon, synthetic dyes, gasoline, and pesticides, to name a few—are covalent compounds. In Chapter 4, we learn about the important features of covalent compounds.

## 4.1  Introduction to Covalent Bonding

In Section 3.1 we learned that **covalent bonds result from the *sharing* of electrons between two atoms.** For example, when two hydrogen atoms with one electron each (H·) combine, they form a covalent bond that contains two electrons. The two negatively charged electrons are now attracted to both positively charged hydrogen nuclei, forming the hydrogen **molecule,** $H_2$. This is an especially stable arrangement, since the shared electrons give each hydrogen atom the noble gas configuration of helium.

- A covalent bond is a two-electron bond in which the bonding atoms share valence electrons.
- A *molecule* is a discrete group of atoms held together by covalent bonds.

We use a **solid line between two element symbols to represent a two-electron bond.** Thus, the $H_2$ molecule can be drawn as:

$$H_2 \quad = \quad H\!:\!H \quad = \quad H\!-\!H \quad \text{two-electron bond}$$

Hydrogen is called a **diatomic molecule** because it contains just two atoms. In addition to hydrogen, six other elements exist as diatomic molecules: nitrogen ($N_2$), oxygen ($O_2$), fluorine ($F_2$), chlorine ($Cl_2$), bromine ($Br_2$), and iodine ($I_2$).

Hydrogen fluoride, HF, is an example of a diatomic molecule formed between two different atoms, hydrogen and fluorine. Hydrogen has one valence electron and fluorine has seven. H and F each donate one electron to form a single two-electron bond.

$$H\cdot \quad + \quad \cdot\ddot{F}\!: \quad \longrightarrow \quad H\!:\!\ddot{F}\!: \quad \text{or} \quad H\!-\!\ddot{F}\!: \leftarrow \textbf{three lone pairs}$$

two electrons around H        eight electrons around F

The resulting molecule gives both H and F a filled valence shell: H is surrounded by two electrons, giving it the noble gas configuration of helium, and F is surrounded by eight electrons, giving it the noble gas configuration of neon. The F atom shares two electrons in one covalent bond, and it also contains three pairs of electrons that it does not share with hydrogen. These unshared electron pairs are called **nonbonded electron pairs** or **lone pairs.**

Nonbonded electron pair = lone pair.

• In covalent bonding, atoms share electrons to attain the electronic configuration of the noble gas closest to them in the periodic table.

As a result, hydrogen shares two electrons. Other main group elements are especially stable when they possess an *octet* **of electrons in their outer shell.**

### PROBLEM 4.1
Use electron-dot symbols to show how a hydrogen atom and a chlorine atom form the diatomic molecule HCl. Explain how each atom has the electronic configuration of the noble gas closest to it in the periodic table.

### PROBLEM 4.2
Use electron-dot symbols to show how two chlorine atoms form the diatomic molecule $Cl_2$. Explain how each atom has the electronic configuration of the noble gas closest to it in the periodic table.

## 4.1A   Covalent Bonding and the Periodic Table

When do two atoms form covalent bonds rather than ionic bonds? **Covalent bonds are formed when two nonmetals combine.** Nonmetals do not easily lose electrons, and as a result, one nonmetal does not readily transfer an electron to another nonmetal. **Covalent bonds are also formed when a metalloid bonds to a nonmetal.** Covalent bonding is preferred with elements that would otherwise have to gain or lose several electrons to form an ion with a complete outer shell of electrons.

Methane ($CH_4$), ammonia ($NH_3$), and water ($H_2O$) are three examples of covalent molecules in which each main group element is surrounded by eight electrons. Methane, the main component of natural gas, contains four covalent carbon–hydrogen bonds, each having two electrons. The nitrogen atom in $NH_3$, an agricultural fertilizer, is surrounded by an octet since it has three bonds and one lone pair. The oxygen atom in $H_2O$ is also surrounded by an octet since it has two bonds and two lone pairs.

**These electron-dot structures for molecules are called Lewis structures.** Lewis structures show the location of all valence electrons in a molecule, both the shared electrons in bonds, and the non-bonded electron pairs. In Section 4.2, we will learn a general procedure for drawing Lewis structures.

How many covalent bonds will a particular atom typically form? As you might expect, it depends on the location of the atom in the periodic table. In the first row, hydrogen forms one covalent bond with its one valence electron. Other main group elements generally have no more than eight electrons around them. For neutral molecules, two consequences result.

- Atoms with one, two, or three valence electrons generally form one, two, or three bonds, respectively.
- Atoms with four or more valence electrons form enough bonds to give an octet. Thus, for atoms with four or more valence electrons:

$$\boxed{\text{Predicted number of bonds}} \quad = \quad 8 \quad - \quad \text{number of valence electrons}$$

These guidelines are used in Figure 4.1 to summarize the usual number of covalent bonds formed by some common atoms. Except for hydrogen, these common elements generally follow one rule in bonding:

$$\boxed{\text{Number of bonds}} \quad + \quad \boxed{\text{Number of lone pairs}} \quad = \quad \boxed{4}$$

### SAMPLE PROBLEM 4.1

Without referring to Figure 4.1, how many covalent bonds are predicted for each atom: (a) B; (b) N?

### Analysis

Atoms with one, two, or three valence electrons form one, two, or three bonds, respectively. Atoms with four or more valence electrons form enough bonds to give an octet.

### Solution

a. B has three valence electrons. Thus, it is expected to form three bonds.

b. N has five valence electrons. Since it contains more than four valence electrons, it is expected to form 8 – 5 = 3 bonds.

### PROBLEM 4.3

How many covalent bonds are predicted for each atom: (a) F; (b) Si; (c) Br; (d) O; (e) P; (f) S?

### PROBLEM 4.4

Fill in the lone pairs on each atom to give every main group element except hydrogen an octet.

a. H—C—Cl (with H above and below C)  b. H—N—O—H (with H below N)  c. H—C—O—H (with H above and below C)  d. Br—C—Br (with H above and below C)

---

**Figure 4.1**

Bonding Patterns for Common Main Group Elements

| | Lone pairs of electrons | | |
|---|---|---|---|
| —H | —C— | —N— | —Ö— | —Ẍ: | X = F, Cl, Br, I |
| hydrogen | carbon | nitrogen | oxygen | halogen | |

| | | | | | |
|---|---|---|---|---|---|
| Number of bonds | 1 | 4 | 3 | 2 | 1 |
| Number of nonbonded electron pairs | 0 | 0 | 1 | 2 | 3 |

### PROBLEM 4.5

A nonmetal like oxygen forms both ionic and covalent bonds, depending on the identity of the element to which it bonds. What type of bonding is observed in CaO and $CO_2$? Explain why two different types of bonding are observed.

## 4.1B FOCUS ON THE HUMAN BODY
### Covalent Molecules and the Cardiovascular System

Living organisms are a sea of covalent molecules. The major component in the body, water, is a covalent molecule. In addition, the proteins that compose muscle, the carbohydrates that are metabolized for energy, stored fat, and DNA, the carrier of genetic information, are all covalent molecules. Some of these molecules are very large, and are composed of hundreds or thousands of covalent bonds.

Figure 4.2 contains a schematic of a blood vessel inside the heart, and it illustrates a few covalent molecules—water, hemoglobin, oxygen, glycine, and nitroglycerin—that play a role in the cardiovascular system. Blood is composed of water and red blood cells that contain the protein hemoglobin. Hemoglobin is a large covalent compound that complexes oxygen molecules, and carries oxygen to tissues throughout the body. Heart muscle is composed of complex covalent

**Figure 4.2**

Covalent Molecules and the Human Heart

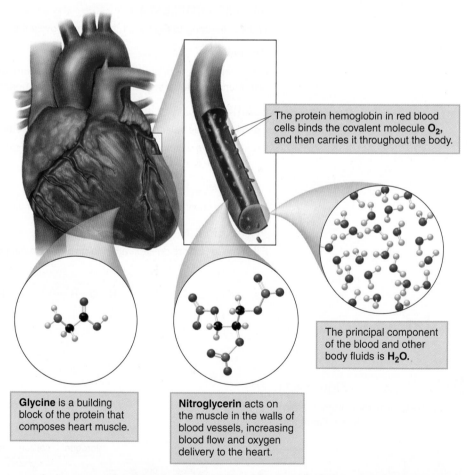

The protein hemoglobin in red blood cells binds the covalent molecule $O_2$, and then carries it throughout the body.

The principal component of the blood and other body fluids is $H_2O$.

**Glycine** is a building block of the protein that composes heart muscle.

**Nitroglycerin** acts on the muscle in the walls of blood vessels, increasing blood flow and oxygen delivery to the heart.

Some covalent compounds related to the chemistry of the heart include **water,** the most prevalent covalent compound in the body; **oxygen,** which is carried by the protein **hemoglobin** to the tissues; **glycine,** a building block of the proteins that compose heart muscle; and **nitroglycerin,** a drug used to treat some forms of heart disease.

protein molecules, which are synthesized from smaller molecules. The three-dimensional structure of one of those molecules, glycine, is pictured. Finally, covalent compounds are used to treat heart disease. For example, nitroglycerin, a drug used when blood vessels have become narrow, increases blood flow and thereby oxygen delivery to the heart.

## 4.2  Lewis Structures

**A molecular formula shows the number and identity of all of the atoms in a covalent compound,** but it does not tell us what atoms are bonded to each other. Thus, the molecular formula $NH_3$ for ammonia shows that ammonia contains one nitrogen atom and three hydrogen atoms, but it does not tell us that ammonia has three covalent nitrogen–hydrogen bonds and that the N atom has a lone pair. **A Lewis structure, in contrast, shows the connectivity between the atoms, as well as where all the bonding and nonbonding valence electrons reside.**

### 4.2A  Drawing Lewis Structures

There are three general rules for drawing Lewis structures.

1. Draw only the *valence electrons*.
2. Give every main group element (except hydrogen) an *octet* of electrons.
3. Give each hydrogen two electrons.

In Section 4.1, Lewis structures were drawn for several covalent molecules. While drawing a Lewis structure for a diatomic molecule with one bond is straightforward, drawing Lewis structures for compounds with three or more atoms is easier if you follow a general procedure.

---

*How To*  Draw a Lewis Structure

Step [1]  **Arrange the atoms next to each other that you think are bonded together.**
- **Always place hydrogens and halogens on the periphery** since these atoms form only one bond.

- As a first approximation, **use the common bonding patterns** in Figure 4.1 to arrange the atoms.

In truth, sometimes atom arrangement is not obvious. For this reason, atom arrangement will be specified for you in some problems.

Step [2]  **Count the valence electrons.**
- Use the group number of a main group element to give the number of valence electrons.
- This sum gives the total number of electrons that must be used in drawing the Lewis structure.

—Continued

## How To, continued . . .

Step [3] **Arrange the electrons around the atoms.**
- **Place one bond between every two atoms,** giving two electrons to each H and no more than eight to all other main group atoms.
- Use all remaining electrons to **fill octets with lone pairs,** beginning with atoms on the periphery.
- If all valence electrons are used and an atom does not have an octet, proceed to Step [4].

Step [4] **Use multiple bonds to fill octets when needed.**
- **Convert one lone pair to one bonding pair of electrons for each two electrons needed to complete an octet.**
  This forms double or triple bonds in some molecules, as shown in Section 4.2B. While a single covalent bond contains two electrons, a double bond consists of four electrons and a triple bond consists of six electrons.

Sample Problems 4.2 and 4.3 illustrate how to draw Lewis structures in two molecules that contain only single bonds.

### SAMPLE PROBLEM 4.2

Draw a Lewis structure for chloromethane, $CH_3Cl$, a compound produced by giant kelp and a component of volcanic emissions.

### Analysis and Solution

**[1] Arrange the atoms.**

$$
\begin{array}{c}
H \\
H \quad C \quad Cl \\
H
\end{array}
$$

- Place C in the center and 3 H's and 1 Cl on the periphery.
- In this arrangement, C is surrounded by four atoms, its usual number.

**[2] Count the electrons.**

$$
\begin{aligned}
1\,C &\times 4\,e^- = 4\,e^- \\
3\,H &\times 1\,e^- = 3\,e^- \\
1\,Cl &\times 7\,e^- = 7\,e^- \\
\hline
&\quad\quad\;\; \textbf{14 e}^- \textbf{ total}
\end{aligned}
$$

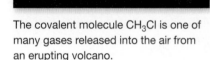

The covalent molecule $CH_3Cl$ is one of many gases released into the air from an erupting volcano.

**[3] Add the bonds and lone pairs.**

$$
\begin{array}{ccc}
H & & H \;\text{— eight electrons around C} \\
H \quad C \quad Cl & \xrightarrow{\text{Add a bond between the C and each atom.}} & H\text{—}\overset{|}{\underset{|}{C}}\text{—}Cl \\
H & & H
\end{array}
\xrightarrow{\text{Add three lone pairs to Cl to form an octet.}}
\begin{array}{c}
H \;\text{— eight electrons around Cl} \\
H\text{—}\overset{|}{\underset{|}{C}}\text{—}\ddot{\underset{\cdot\cdot}{Cl}}{:} \\
H
\end{array}
$$

two electrons around H

14 e⁻ used altogether

First add four single bonds, three C—H bonds and one C—Cl bond. This uses eight valence electrons, and gives carbon an octet (four two-electron bonds) and each hydrogen two electrons. Next, give Cl an octet by adding three lone pairs. This uses all 14 valence electrons. To check if a Lewis structure is valid, we must answer YES to three questions.

- Have all the electrons been used?
- Is each H surrounded by two electrons?
- Is every other main group element surrounded by eight electrons?

Since the answer to all three questions is YES, we have drawn a valid Lewis structure for $CH_3Cl$.

## SAMPLE PROBLEM 4.3

Draw a Lewis structure for methanol, a compound with molecular formula $CH_4O$. Methanol is a toxic compound that can cause blindness and even death when ingested in small quantities (Section 14.4).

### Analysis and Solution

**[1] Arrange the atoms.**

$$\begin{array}{ccc} & H & \\ H & C & O & H \\ & H & \end{array}$$

- four atoms around C
- two atoms around O

**[2] Count the electrons.**

$$1\,C \times 4\,e^- = 4\,e^-$$
$$1\,O \times 6\,e^- = 6\,e^-$$
$$4\,H \times 1\,e^- = 4\,e^-$$
$$\overline{\phantom{xxxxxxxxx}}$$
**14 $e^-$ total**

**[3] Add the bonds and lone pairs.**

Add bonds first...                    ...then lone pairs.

$$\begin{array}{c} H \\ | \\ H-C-O-H \\ | \\ H \end{array} \quad ---\rightarrow \quad \begin{array}{c} H \\ | \\ H-C-\overset{..}{\underset{..}{O}}-H \\ | \\ H \end{array}$$

no octet

only 10 $e^-$ used                    14 $e^-$ used

In step [3], placing bonds between all atoms uses only 10 electrons, and the O atom, with only four electrons, does not yet have a complete octet. To complete the structure, give the O atom two lone pairs. This uses all 14 electrons, giving every H two electrons and every main group element eight. We have now drawn a valid Lewis structure.

## PROBLEM 4.6

Draw a Lewis structure for each covalent molecule.

a. HBr     b. $CH_3F$     c. $H_2O_2$     d. $N_2H_4$     e. $C_2H_6$     f. $CH_2Cl_2$

## PROBLEM 4.7

Draw a Lewis structure for dimethyl ether ($C_2H_6O$) with the given arrangement of atoms.

$$\begin{array}{ccccc} & H & & H & \\ H & C & O & C & H \\ & H & & H & \end{array}$$

## 4.2B  Multiple Bonds

Sometimes it is not possible to give every main group element (except hydrogen) an octet of electrons by placing only single bonds in a molecule. For example, in drawing a Lewis structure for $N_2$, each N has five valence electrons, so there are 10 electrons to place. If there is only one N—N bond, adding lone pairs gives one or both N's fewer than eight electrons.

Add one bond.

For $N_2$:
Each N has five
valence electrons.
total 10 $e^-$

$$N-N \quad ----\rightarrow \quad \overset{..}{N}-\overset{..}{N} \quad or \quad \overset{..}{N}-\overset{..}{\underset{..}{N}}:$$

Add lone pairs.

N has only 4 $e^-$.

N has 8 $e^-$.

Each N has only 6 $e^-$.

In this case, we must convert a lone pair to a bonding pair of electrons to form a multiple bond. Since we have four fewer electrons than needed, **we must convert** *two* **lone pairs to** *two* **bonding pairs of electrons and form a** *triple* **bond.**

For example:

- **A triple bond contains six electrons in three two-electron bonds.**

Sample Problem 4.4 illustrates another example of a Lewis structure that contains a double bond.

- **A double bond contains four electrons in two two-electron bonds.**

### SAMPLE PROBLEM 4.4

Draw a Lewis structure for ethylene, a compound of molecular formula $C_2H_4$ in which each carbon is bonded to two hydrogens.

#### Analysis and Solution

Follow steps [1]–[3] to draw a Lewis structure.

[1] **Arrange the atoms.**

$$H \quad C \quad C \quad H$$
$$H \quad H$$

- Each C gets 2 H's.

[2] **Count the electrons.**

$$2\,C \times 4\,e^- = 8\,e^-$$
$$4\,H \times 1\,e^- = 4\,e^-$$
$$\overline{\phantom{4\,H \times 1\,e^- =\ } 12\,e^-\ \text{total}}$$

[3] **Add the bonds and lone pairs.**

Add bonds first...        ...then lone pairs.

After placing five bonds between the atoms and adding the two remaining electrons as a lone pair, one C still has no octet.

[4] **To give both C's an octet, change** *one* **lone pair into** *one* **bonding pair of electrons between the two C atoms, forming a** *double* **bond.**

- Each C now has four bonds.
- Each C is now surrounded by eight electrons.

This uses all 12 electrons, each C has an octet, and each H has two electrons. The Lewis structure is valid. **Ethylene contains a carbon–carbon double bond.**

- **After placing all electrons in bonds and lone pairs, use a lone pair to form a multiple bond if an atom does not have an octet.**

Formic acid ($CH_2O_2$, Problem 4.9) is responsible for the sting of some types of ants.

### PROBLEM 4.8

Draw a valid Lewis structure for each compound, using the given arrangement of atoms.

a.　HCN　　H　C　N　　b.　$CH_2O$　　H　C　O　　c.　$C_2H_3Cl$　　H　C　C　Cl
　　hydrogen cyanide　　　　　formaldehyde　　H　　　　vinyl chloride　　H　H

### PROBLEM 4.9

Draw a Lewis structure for formic acid with the given arrangement of atoms.

O

H　C　O　H

### PROBLEM 4.10

(a) Use the element colors in Figure 2.3 (and shown on the inside back cover) to determine the molecular formula of glycine, depicted as a ball-and-stick model in Figure 4.2. (b) Draw a Lewis structure for glycine and include all nonbonded electron pairs on atoms that contain them.

## 4.3　Exceptions to the Octet Rule

Most of the common elements in covalent compounds—carbon, nitrogen, oxygen, and the halogens—generally follow the octet rule. **Hydrogen is a notable exception, because it accommodates only two electrons in bonding.** Additional exceptions include elements such as **boron** in group 3A, and elements in the third row and later in the periodic table, particularly **phosphorus** and **sulfur.**

### 4.3A　Elements in Group 3A

Elements in group 3A of the periodic table, such as boron, do not have enough valence electrons to form an octet in a neutral molecule. A Lewis structure for $BF_3$ illustrates that the boron atom has only six electrons around it. There is nothing we can do about this! There simply aren't enough electrons to form an octet.

:F:
|
:F—B—F:　only six electrons around B

### 4.3B　Elements in the Third Row

Another exception to the octet rule occurs with some elements located in the third row and later in the periodic table. These elements have empty *d* orbitals available to accept electrons, and thus they may have *more than eight* electrons around them. The two most common elements in this category are phosphorus and sulfur, which can have 10 or even 12 electrons around them.

While $PCl_3$ and $H_2S$ contain phosphorus and sulfur atoms that follow the octet rule, $H_3PO_4$ (phosphoric acid) and $H_2SO_4$ (sulfuric acid) do not. The phosphorus atom in $H_3PO_4$ is surrounded by 10 electrons, and the sulfur atom in $H_2SO_4$ is surrounded by 12 electrons.

Glyphosate (Problem 4.12) is an effective herbicide because it interferes with the synthesis of key compounds needed for weed growth.

## PROBLEM 4.11

Draw a Lewis structure for $BBr_3$, and explain why it does not follow the octet rule.

## PROBLEM 4.12

Glyphosate is the most widely used weed killer and the active ingredient in Roundup and other lawn products. (a) Add lone pairs around all N and O atoms to complete octets. (b) How many electrons surround phosphorus in the given structure? (c) Which atoms in glyphosate do not follow the octet rule?

$$
\begin{array}{c}
\quad\;\; O \quad\; H \qquad\;\; H \;\; O \\
\quad\;\; \| \qquad | \qquad\quad | \;\; \| \\
H-O-P-C-N-C-C-O-H \\
\quad\;\; | \qquad | \qquad | \;\; | \\
\quad H-O \;\; H \quad\; H \;\; H
\end{array}
$$

glyphosate

# 4.4  Resonance

We sometimes must draw Lewis structures for ions that contain covalent bonds—that is, polyatomic ions. In this case, the charge on the ion must be taken into account when counting the number of valence electrons that must be placed around the atoms. In counting valence electrons:

- Add one electron for each negative charge.
- Subtract one electron for each positive charge.

For example, in drawing a Lewis structure for the cyanide anion, $CN^-$, there are 10 valence electrons—four from carbon, five from nitrogen, and one additional electron from the negative charge. In order to give each atom an octet, the two atoms must be joined by a triple bond, and both carbon and nitrogen have a lone pair.

Number of valence electrons          Lewis structure

$$1\,e^- \quad CN \quad\quad\quad \left[:C\equiv N:\right]^-$$

$$4\,e^- \quad 5\,e^-$$

10 valence electrons                    Each atom has an octet.

## 4.4A  Drawing Resonance Structures

Sometimes two or more valid Lewis structures are possible for a given arrangement of atoms. Sample Problem 4.5 illustrates that two Lewis structures are possible for the bicarbonate anion ($HCO_3^-$).

## SAMPLE PROBLEM 4.5

Draw a Lewis structure for $HCO_3^-$ with the following arrangement of atoms:

$$
\begin{array}{c}
O \\
H \quad O \quad C \quad O
\end{array}
$$

### Analysis and Solution

Follow steps [1]–[3] to draw a Lewis structure.

**[1] Arrange the atoms.**

$$
\begin{array}{c}
O \\
H \quad O \quad C \quad O
\end{array}
$$

**[2] Count the electrons.**

$$
\begin{array}{rcll}
1\,C & \times & 4\,e^- & = \quad 4\,e^- \\
3\,O & \times & 6\,e^- & = \quad 18\,e^- \\
1\,H & \times & 1\,e^- & = \quad 1\,e^- \\
1\,(-) & \times & 1\,e^- & = \quad 1\,e^- \\
\hline
& & & \mathbf{24\,e^-\ total}
\end{array}
$$

**[3] Add the bonds and lone pairs.**

Add bonds first...          ...then lone pairs.

After placing four bonds and adding the remaining 16 electrons as lone pairs, the carbon atom does not have an octet.

**[4] Convert one lone pair on O into one bonding pair to form a double bond. There are two ways to do this.**

Thus, there are two different Lewis structures, **A** and **B,** for the bicarbonate anion.

The two different Lewis structures (**A** and **B**) for $HCO_3^-$ are called **resonance structures.**

- Resonance structures are two Lewis structures having the same arrangement of atoms but a different arrangement of electrons.

**Two resonance structures differ in the location of multiple bonds and the position of lone pairs.** In Lewis structures **A** and **B,** the location of one C=O and one lone pair is different. We often use a **double-headed arrow** ($\longleftrightarrow$) to show that two Lewis structures are resonance structures.

The position of the double bond is different.

The position of a lone pair is different.

Which structure, **A** or **B,** is an accurate representation for $HCO_3^-$? The answer is **neither of them.** The true structure is a composite of both resonance forms and is called a **hybrid.** Experimentally it is shown that the carbon–oxygen bonds that appear as a double bond in one resonance structure and a single bond in the other, are really somewhere in between a C=O and a C—O. **Resonance stabilizes a molecule** by spreading out lone pairs and electron pairs in multiple bonds over a larger region of space. We say a molecule or ion that has two or more resonance structures is **resonance-stabilized.**

**PROBLEM 4.13**

Draw a second resonance structure for each ion.

a. ![structure a]   b. ![structure b]

**PROBLEM 4.14**

Draw resonance structures for each polyatomic anion.

a. $NO_2^-$ (two resonance structures, central N atom)

b. $HCO_2^-$ (two resonance structures, central C atom)

## 4.4B  FOCUS ON THE ENVIRONMENT
### Ozone

In addition to polyatomic ions, resonance structures can be drawn for neutral molecules as well. For example, the molecule **ozone, $O_3$,** can be drawn as two resonance structures that differ in the placement of a double bond and a lone pair.

$$O_3: \quad \ddot{O}=\ddot{O}-\ddot{O}: \quad \longleftrightarrow \quad \ddot{O}-\ddot{O}=\ddot{O}:$$

Bonds and lone pairs that differ in the two resonance structures are drawn in red.

**Ozone** is formed in the upper atmosphere (the stratosphere) by the reaction of oxygen molecules ($O_2$) with oxygen atoms (O). Stratospheric ozone is vital to life: it acts as a shield, protecting the earth's surface from destructive ultraviolet radiation (Figure 4.3). A decrease in ozone concentration in this protective layer would have some immediate consequences, including an increase in the incidence of skin cancer and eye cataracts. We will learn about the interaction of ozone with covalent molecules that contain carbon–chlorine bonds in Chapter 14.

### PROBLEM 4.15

When fossil fuels containing sulfur are burned in power plants to generate electricity, large amounts of sulfur dioxide ($SO_2$) are formed and released into the atmosphere, where some of it eventually forms the acid in acid rain. If the structure of $SO_2$ consists of a central sulfur atom surrounded by an octet of electrons and bonded to both oxygen atoms, draw two resonance structures for sulfur dioxide.

### PROBLEM 4.16

Nitrous oxide, $N_2O$, is a sweet-smelling gas sometimes used as an anesthetic in dentistry. Draw two resonance structures for $N_2O$ that contain a central nitrogen atom.

Nitrous oxide ($N_2O$, Problem 4.16) is a weak general anesthetic used for some dental procedures. Nitrous oxide is sometimes called laughing gas because it induces euphoria and mild hallucinations.

**Figure 4.3**    Ozone in the Upper Atmosphere

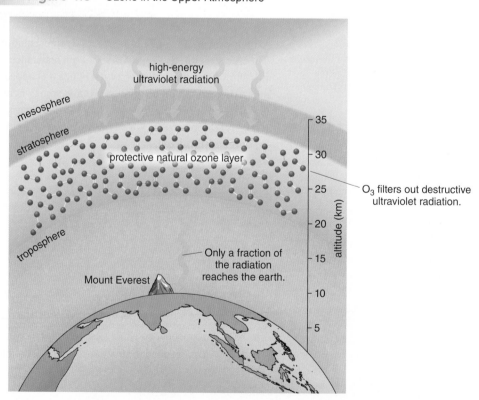

## 4.5 Naming Covalent Compounds

Although some covalent compounds are always referred to by their common names—$H_2O$ (water) and $NH_3$ (ammonia)—these names tell us nothing about the atoms that the molecule contains. Other covalent compounds with two elements are named to indicate the identity and number of elements they contain.

---

### *How To* Name a Covalent Molecule with Two Elements

**Example:** Name each covalent molecule: (a) $NO_2$; (b) $N_2O_4$.

**Step [1] Name the first nonmetal by its element name and the second using the suffix *-ide*.**
- In both compounds the first nonmetal is nitrogen.
- To name the second element, change the name oxygen to **oxide.**

**Step [2] Add prefixes to show the number of atoms of each element.**
- Use a prefix from Table 4.1 for each element.
- Usually, the prefix *mono-* is omitted when only one atom of an element is present. An exception to this rule is the molecule CO, named as carbon monoxide, to distinguish it from $CO_2$, carbon dioxide.
- When the prefix and element name would place two vowels next to each other, omit the first vowel. For example, mono- + oxide = monoxide (*not* monooxide).
  a. $NO_2$ contains one N atom, so the prefix *mono-* is understood. Since $NO_2$ contains two O atoms, use the prefix *di- → di*oxide. Thus, $NO_2$ is **nitrogen dioxide.**
  b. $N_2O_4$ contains two N atoms, so use the prefix *di- → di*nitrogen. Since $N_2O_4$ contains four O atoms, use the prefix *tetra-* and omit the *a → tetr*oxide (*not* tetraoxide). Thus, $N_2O_4$ is **dinitrogen tetroxide.**

---

### Table 4.1 Common Prefixes in Nomenclature

| Number of Atoms | Prefix |
|---|---|
| 1 | Mono |
| 2 | Di |
| 3 | Tri |
| 4 | Tetra |
| 5 | Penta |
| 6 | Hexa |
| 7 | Hepta |
| 8 | Octa |
| 9 | Nona |
| 10 | Deca |

### PROBLEM 4.17

Name each compound: (a) $CS_2$; (b) $SO_2$; (c) $PCl_5$; (d) $BF_3$.

To write a formula from a name, write the element symbols in the order of the elements in the name. Then use the prefixes to determine the subscripts of the formula, as shown in Sample Problem 4.6.

### SAMPLE PROBLEM 4.6

Give the formula for each compound: (a) silicon tetrafluoride; (b) diphosphorus pentoxide.

#### Analysis
- Determine the symbols for the elements in the order given in the name.
- Use the prefixes to write the subscripts.

#### Solution

a. silicon   tetrafluoride

      Si     4 F atoms

      **Answer: $SiF_4$**

b. diphosphorus pentoxide

      2 P atoms     5 O atoms

      **Answer: $P_2O_5$**

### PROBLEM 4.18

Give the formula for each compound: (a) silicon dioxide; (b) phosphorus trichloride; (c) sulfur trioxide; (d) dinitrogen trioxide.

## 4.6  Molecular Shape

We can now use Lewis structures to determine the shape around a particular atom in a molecule. Consider the $H_2O$ molecule. The Lewis structure tells us only which atoms are connected to each other, but it implies nothing about the geometry. Is $H_2O$ a bent or linear molecule?

What is the bond angle?

H—Ö—H

To determine the shape around a given atom, we must first determine how many groups surround the atom. **A group is either an atom or a lone pair of electrons.** Then we use the **valence shell electron pair repulsion (VSEPR) theory** to determine the shape. VSEPR is based on the fact that electron pairs repel each other; thus:

- **The most stable arrangement keeps these groups as far away from each other as possible.**

In general, an atom has three possible arrangements of the groups that surround it.

| linear | trigonal planar | tetrahedral |

- **An atom surrounded by two groups is linear and has a bond angle of 180°.**
- **An atom surrounded by three groups is trigonal planar and has bond angles of 120°.**
- **An atom surrounded by four groups is tetrahedral and has bond angles of 109.5°.**

Let's examine several molecules. In each case we use the number of groups around a given atom in a Lewis structure to predict its geometry.

### 4.6A  Two Groups Around an Atom

**To determine geometry: [1] Draw a valid Lewis structure. [2] Count groups around a given atom.**

**Any atom surrounded by only two groups is linear and has a bond angle of 180°.** Two examples illustrating this geometry are **$CO_2$** (carbon dioxide) and **HCN** (hydrogen cyanide). To determine the shape around the central atom in both molecules, we draw the Lewis structure and count the number of groups—atoms and lone pairs—that surround the central atom.

The Lewis structure for $CO_2$ contains a central carbon atom surrounded by two oxygen atoms. To give every atom an octet and the usual number of bonds requires two carbon–oxygen double bonds. The carbon atom is surrounded by two oxygen atoms and no lone pairs; that is, it is surrounded by two groups, making the molecule linear and the O—C—O bond angle 180°.

four bonds

:Ö=C=Ö:

two bonds          two bonds

180°

:Ö=C=Ö:   =   ●—●—●

two atoms around C          linear molecule
**two groups**

Carbon dioxide illustrates another important feature of VSEPR theory: *ignore multiple bonds in predicting geometry.* **Count only atoms and lone pairs.**

Similarly, the Lewis structure for HCN contains a central carbon atom surrounded by one hydrogen and one nitrogen. To give carbon and nitrogen an octet and the usual number of bonds requires a carbon–nitrogen triple bond. The carbon atom is surrounded by two atoms and no lone pairs; that is, it is surrounded by two groups, making the molecule linear and the H—C—N bond angle 180°.

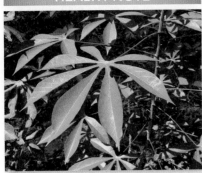

Cassava is a widely grown root crop, first introduced to Africa by Portuguese traders from Brazil in the sixteenth century. The root must be boiled or roasted to remove linamarin before ingestion. Eating the root without processing affords high levels of HCN, a cellular poison with a characteristic almond odor.

Trigonal = three-sided.

Over time, some adhesives and insulation made from formaldehyde can decompose back to formaldehyde, a reactive and potentially hazardous substance. Spider plants act as natural air purifiers by removing formaldehyde ($H_2CO$) from the air.

four bonds

three bonds

180°

two atoms around C
**two groups**

linear molecule

HCN, an extremely toxic gas, is produced by some naturally occurring molecules. For example, cassava, a woody shrub grown as a root crop in South America and Africa, contains the compound linamarin. Linamarin is not toxic itself, but it forms HCN in the presence of water and some enzymes. Cassava is safe to eat when the root has been peeled and boiled, so that the linamarin is removed during processing. If the root is eaten without processing, illness and even death can result from high levels of HCN formed from linamarin.

## 4.6B   Three Groups Around an Atom

**Any atom surrounded by three groups is trigonal planar and has bond angles of 120°.** Two examples illustrating this geometry are **BF₃** (boron trifluoride) and **H₂C=O** (formaldehyde).

120°

three atoms around B
**three groups**

trigonal planar
molecule

120°

three atoms around C
**three groups**

trigonal planar
molecule

In $BF_3$, the boron atom is surrounded by three fluorines and no lone pairs; that is, the boron is surrounded by three groups. A similar situation occurs with the carbon atom in $H_2C=O$. The carbon atom is surrounded by three atoms (two H's and one O) and no lone pairs—that is, three groups. To keep the three groups as far from each other as possible, they are arranged in a trigonal planar fashion, with bond angles of 120°.

## 4.6C   Four Groups Around an Atom

**Any atom surrounded by four groups is tetrahedral and has bond angles of (approximately) 109.5°.** For example, the simple organic compound methane, **CH₄**, has a central carbon atom with four bonds to hydrogen, each pointing to the corners of a tetrahedron.

109.5°

tetrahedral carbon

How can we represent the three-dimensional geometry of a tetrahedron on a two-dimensional piece of paper? **Place two of the bonds in the plane of the paper, one bond in front, and one bond behind,** using the following conventions:

- A solid line is used for bonds in the plane.
- A wedge is used for a bond in front of the plane.
- A dashed line is used for a bond behind the plane.

bonds **in the plane**

bond **behind**

bond **in front**

tetrahedral molecule

Up to now, each of the groups around the central atom has been another atom. **A group can also be a lone pair of electrons.** $NH_3$ and $H_2O$ represent two examples of molecules with atoms surrounded by four groups, some of which are lone pairs.

The Lewis structure for ammonia, **$NH_3$,** has an N atom surrounded by three hydrogen atoms and one lone pair of electrons—four groups. To keep four groups as far apart as possible, the three H atoms and the one lone pair around N point to the corners of a tetrahedron. The H—N—H bond angle of 107° is close to the tetrahedral bond angle of 109.5°. This shape is referred to as a **trigonal pyramid,** since one of the groups around the N is a nonbonded electron pair, not another atom.

One corner of the tetrahedron has an **electron pair,** not a bond.

H—N̈—H
   |
   H

**four** groups around N
• three atoms
• one lone pair

=

107°

trigonal pyramidal molecule

The Lewis structure for water, **$H_2O$,** has an O atom surrounded by two hydrogen atoms and two lone pairs of electrons—four groups. In **$H_2O$,** the two H atoms and the two lone pairs around O point to the corners of a tetrahedron. The H—O—H bond angle of 105° is close to the tetrahedral bond angle of 109.5°. Water has a *bent* shape, because two of the groups around oxygen are lone pairs of electrons.

Two corners of the tetrahedron have **electron pairs,** not bonds.

H—Ö—H

**four** groups around O
• two atoms
• two lone pairs

=

105°

bent molecule

Common molecular shapes are summarized in Table 4.2. The three-dimensional shape determines the polarity of a molecule, which is discussed in Section 4.8. All of Chapter 15 is devoted to the importance of the three-dimensional shapes of molecules.

### SAMPLE PROBLEM 4.7

Using the given Lewis structure, determine the shape around the second-row elements in each compound.

a. H—C≡C—H

acetylene

b. $\left[ \begin{array}{c} H \\ | \\ H-N-H \\ | \\ H \end{array} \right]^+$

ammonium ion

### Analysis

To predict the shape around an atom, we need a valid Lewis structure, which is given in this problem. Then count groups around the atom to determine molecular shape using the information in Table 4.2.

### Solution

a. Each C in H—C≡C—H is surrounded by two atoms (one C and one H) and no lone pairs—that is, two groups. An atom surrounded by two groups is linear with a 180° bond angle.

180°
H—C≡C—H
            180°

b. The N atom in $NH_4^+$ is surrounded by four H atoms—that is, four groups. An atom surrounded by four groups is tetrahedral, with 109.5° bond angles.

H
109.5° N⁺
H     H
   H
tetrahedral

## Table 4.2 Common Molecular Shapes Around Atoms

| Total Number of Groups | Number of Atoms | Number of Lone Pairs | Shape Around an Atom (A) | Approximate Bond Angle (°) | Example |
|:---:|:---:|:---:|:---:|:---:|:---:|
| 2 | 2 | 0 | A—A linear | 180 | $CO_2$, HCN |
| 3 | 3 | 0 | A trigonal planar | 120 | $BF_3$, $H_2C{=}O$ |
| 4 | 4 | 0 | A tetrahedral | 109.5 | $CH_4$ |
| 4 | 3 | 1 | A trigonal pyramidal | ~109.5[a] | $NH_3$ |
| 4 | 2 | 2 | A bent | ~109.5[a] | $H_2O$ |

[a]The symbol "~" means approximately.

### PROBLEM 4.19

What is the shape around each carbon atom in ethylene, $H_2C{=}CH_2$?

### PROBLEM 4.20

What is the shape around the indicated atom in each molecule? Don't forget to draw in all needed lone pairs before determining molecular shape.

a. $H_2S$          b. $CH_2Cl_2$          c. $NCl_3$          d. $BBr_3$

### PROBLEM 4.21

$NaNH_2$, sodium amide, is a salt that contains a sodium cation, $Na^+$, and the polyatomic anion $NH_2^-$. Draw a Lewis structure for $NH_2^-$. Use the Lewis structure to determine which of the following ball-and-stick models represents the geometry of $NH_2^-$.

a.           b.

## 4.7 Electronegativity and Bond Polarity

When two atoms share electrons in a covalent bond, are the electrons in the bond attracted to both nuclei to the same extent? That depends on the **electronegativity** of the atoms in the bond.

- *Electronegativity* is a measure of an atom's attraction for electrons in a bond. Electronegativity tells us how much a particular atom "*wants*" electrons.

Figure 4.4    Electronegativity Values for Main Group Elements

The electronegativity of an atom is assigned a value from 0 to 4; **the *higher* the value, the *more electronegative* an atom is, and the *more it is attracted* to the electrons in a bond.** The electronegativity values for main group elements are shown in Figure 4.4. The noble gases are not assigned values, since they do not typically form bonds.

Electronegativity values exhibit periodic trends.

- Electronegativity *increases* across a row of the periodic table as the nuclear charge increases (excluding the noble gases).
- Electronegativity *decreases* down a column of the periodic table as the atomic radius increases, pushing the valence electrons farther from the nucleus.

Thus, nonmetals have high electronegativity values compared to metals, because nonmetals have a strong tendency to hold on to and attract electrons. As a result, the most electronegative elements—fluorine and oxygen—are located at the **upper right-hand corner** of the periodic table, and the least electronegative elements are located in the lower left-hand corner.

PROBLEM 4.22

Using the trends in the periodic table, rank the following atoms in order of increasing electronegativity.

a. Li, Na, H          b. O, C, Be          c. Cl, I, F          d. B, O, N

Electronegativity values are used as a guideline to indicate whether the electrons in a bond are *equally* shared or *unequally* shared between two atoms. For example, whenever two *identical* atoms are bonded together, each atom attracts the electrons in the bond to the same extent. The electrons are equally shared, and the bond is said to be **nonpolar.** Thus, a **carbon–carbon bond is nonpolar,** as is the fluorine–fluorine bond in $F_2$. The same is true whenever two different atoms having *similar* electronegativities are bonded together. **C—H bonds are considered to be nonpolar,** because the electronegativity difference between C (2.5) and H (2.1) is small.

The small electronegativity difference
between C and H is ignored.

In contrast, bonding between atoms of *different* electronegativity results in the *unequal* sharing of electrons. For example, in a C—O bond, the electrons are pulled away from C (2.5) towards the element of higher electronegativity, O (3.5). **The bond is *polar,* or *polar covalent.*** The bond is said to have a **dipole**—that is, **a separation of charge.**

**A C–O bond is a *polar* bond.**

The direction of polarity in a bond is often indicated by an arrow, with the head of the arrow pointing towards the more electronegative element. The tail of the arrow, with a perpendicular line drawn through it, is drawn at the less electronegative element. Alternatively, the lower case Greek letter delta ($\delta$) with a positive or negative charge is used, resulting in the symbols $\delta^+$ and $\delta^-$ to indicate this unequal sharing of electron density.

- The symbol $\delta^+$ is given to the less electronegative atom.
- The symbol $\delta^-$ is given to the more electronegative atom.

Students often wonder how large an electronegativity difference must be to consider a bond polar. That's hard to say. We will set an arbitrary value for this difference and use it as an approximation. **Usually, a polar bond will be one in which the electronegativity difference between two atoms is 0.5 units or greater.**

As the electronegativity difference between the two atoms in a bond increases, the shared electrons are pulled more and more towards the more electronegative element. When the electronegativity difference is larger than 1.9 units, the electrons are essentially transferred from the less electronegative element to the more electronegative element and the bond is considered ionic. Table 4.3 summarizes the relationship between the electronegativity difference of the atoms in a bond and the type of bond formed.

### Table 4.3 Electronegativity Difference and Bond Type

| Electronegativity Difference | Bond Type | Electron Sharing |
|---|---|---|
| Less than 0.5 units | Nonpolar | Electrons are equally shared. |
| 0.5–1.9 units | Polar covalent | Electrons are unequally shared; they are pulled towards the more electronegative element. |
| Greater than 1.9 units | Ionic | Electrons are transferred from the less electronegative element to the more electronegative element. |

### SAMPLE PROBLEM 4.8

Use electronegativity values to classify each bond as nonpolar, polar covalent, or ionic: (a) $Cl_2$; (b) HCl; (c) NaCl.

#### Analysis

Calculate the electronegativity difference between the two atoms and use the following rules: less than 0.5 (nonpolar); 0.5–1.9 (polar covalent); and greater than 1.9 (ionic).

#### Solution

| | Electronegativity Difference | Bond Type |
|---|---|---|
| a. $Cl_2$ | 3.0 (Cl) – 3.0 (Cl) = 0 | Nonpolar |
| b. HCl | 3.0 (Cl) – 2.1 (H) = 0.9 | Polar covalent |
| c. NaCl | 3.0 (Cl) – 0.9 (Na) = 2.1 | Ionic |

Use electronegativity values to classify the bond(s) in each compound as nonpolar, polar covalent, or ionic.

  a. HF        b. MgO        c. $F_2$        d. ClF        e. $H_2O$        f. $NH_3$

Show the direction of the dipole in each bond. Label the atoms with $\delta^+$ and $\delta^-$.

  a. H—F        b. —B—C—        c. —C—Li        d. —C—Cl

# 4.8 Polarity of Molecules

Thus far, we have been concerned with the polarity of a single bond. Is an entire covalent molecule polar or nonpolar? That depends on two factors: the polarity of the individual bonds and the overall shape. When a molecule contains zero or one polar bond, the following can be said:

- A molecule with no polar bonds is a nonpolar molecule.
- A molecule with one polar bond is a polar molecule.

Thus, $CH_4$ is a nonpolar molecule because all of the C—H bonds are nonpolar. In contrast, $CH_3Cl$ contains only one polar bond, so it is a polar molecule. The dipole is in the same direction as the dipole of the only polar bond.

CH₄
no polar bonds
nonpolar molecule

CH₃Cl
one polar bond
polar molecule

With covalent compounds that have more than one polar bond, the shape of the molecule determines the overall polarity.

- If the individual bond dipoles do not cancel, the molecule is polar.
- If the individual bond dipoles cancel, the molecule is nonpolar.

To determine the polarity of a molecule that has two or more polar bonds:

1. Identify all polar bonds based on electronegativity differences.
2. Determine the shape around individual atoms by counting groups.
3. Decide if individual dipoles cancel or reinforce.

Figure 4.5 illustrates several examples of polar and nonpolar molecules that contain polar bonds. The net dipole is the sum of all the bond dipoles in a molecule.

### Figure 4.5    Examples of Polar and Nonpolar Molecules

| one polar bond | three polar bonds<br>All dipoles cancel.<br>NO net dipole | three polar bonds<br>All dipoles reinforce. | two polar bonds<br>Two dipoles reinforce. |
|---|---|---|---|
| **polar** molecule | **nonpolar** molecule | **polar** molecule | **polar** molecule |

### SAMPLE PROBLEM 4.9

Determine whether each molecule is polar or nonpolar: (a) $H_2O$; (b) $CO_2$.

### Analysis

To determine the overall polarity of a molecule: identify the polar bonds; determine the shape around individual atoms; decide if the individual bond dipoles cancel or reinforce.

### Solution

a. **$H_2O$:** Each O—H bond is polar because the electronegativity difference between O (3.5) and H (2.1) is 1.4. Since the O atom of $H_2O$ has two atoms and two lone pairs around it, $H_2O$ is a bent molecule around the O atom. The two dipoles reinforce (both point *up*), so **$H_2O$ has a net dipole;** that is, **$H_2O$ is a polar molecule.**

> The two individual dipoles reinforce.

The net dipole bisects the H—O—H bond angle.
The bent representation shows that the dipoles reinforce.

Do NOT draw $H_2O$ as:

**Note: We must know the geometry to determine if two dipoles cancel or reinforce.** For example, do **not** draw $H_2O$ as a linear molecule, because you might think that the two dipoles cancel, when in reality, they reinforce.

b. **$CO_2$:** Each C—O bond is polar because the electronegativity difference between O (3.5) and C (2.5) is 1.0. The Lewis structure of $CO_2$ (Section 4.6A) shows that the C atom is surrounded by two groups (two O atoms), making it linear. In this case, the two dipoles are equal and opposite in direction so they cancel. Thus, $CO_2$ is a **nonpolar molecule** with **no net dipole.**

> The two dipoles cancel.

NO net dipole

### PROBLEM 4.25

Label the polar bonds in each molecule, and then decide if the molecule is polar or nonpolar.

a. HCl      b. $C_2H_6$      c. $CH_2F_2$      d. HCN      e. $CCl_4$

## 4.9 FOCUS ON HEALTH & MEDICINE
### Covalent Drugs and Medical Products

Most drugs and products used in medicine are made up of covalent molecules. Some are simple molecules containing only a few atoms, while others are very complex. The principles learned in this chapter apply to all molecules regardless of size. Two examples are shown.

**Hydrogen peroxide, $H_2O_2$,** is a simple covalent molecule used to disinfect wounds. We now know a great deal about the structure of $H_2O_2$. The Lewis structure for $H_2O_2$ contains an O—O bond and each O atom has two lone pairs to give it an octet of electrons. Since each O atom is surrounded by two atoms and two lone pairs, it has a bent structure. While the O—O bond is nonpolar, both O—H bonds are polar, since the electronegativity difference between oxygen (3.5) and hydrogen (2.1) is large (1.4).

**Acetaminophen,** a pain-reliever and antipyretic (an agent that reduces fever), is more complex, but we still know much about its structure. Each O atom has two lone pairs and the N atom has one lone pair. Acetaminophen has six polar bonds, labeled in red. The number of groups around each atom determines its shape. One tetrahedral C surrounded by four groups and two trigonal planar C's are labeled.

### SAMPLE PROBLEM 4.10

Glycolic acid is a starting material used to manufacture dissolving sutures. (a) Place lone pairs where needed in the Lewis structure. (b) Give the shape around each atom in red. (c) Label all polar bonds.

glycolic acid

Analysis and Solution

a. Each O atom needs two lone pairs to make an octet.

b. Count groups to determine shape.

c. Since O is much more electronegative (3.5) than hydrogen (2.1) and carbon (2.5), all C—O and O—H bonds are polar and are labeled in red.

### PROBLEM 4.26

In each compound: [1] determine the geometry around each carbon; [2] label each bond as polar or nonpolar.

a. ethanol      b. acetaldehyde

Ethanol, the "alcohol" in alcoholic beverages, is the world's most widely abused drug. It is metabolized to acetaldehyde, a toxic compound that produces some of the ill effects of ingesting too much ethanol. Ethanol is discussed in greater detail in Chapter 14.

# CHAPTER HIGHLIGHTS

## KEY TERMS

Covalent bond (4.1)

Diatomic molecule (4.1)

Dipole (4.7)

Double bond (4.2)

Double-headed arrow (4.4)

Electronegativity (4.7)

Hybrid (4.4)

Lewis structure (4.1)

Lone pair (4.1)

Molecular formula (4.2)

Molecule (4.1)

Multiple bond (4.2)

Nonbonded electron pair (4.1)

Nonpolar bond (4.7)

Polar bond (4.7)

Resonance structure (4.4)

Triple bond (4.2)

Valence shell electron pair repulsion (VSEPR) theory (4.6)

## KEY CONCEPTS

**❶ What are the characteristic bonding features of covalent compounds? (4.1)**

- Covalent bonds result from the sharing of electrons between two atoms, forming molecules. Atoms share electrons to attain the electronic configuration of the noble gas nearest them in the periodic table. For many main group elements, this results in an octet of electrons.

- Covalent bonds are formed when two nonmetals combine or when a metalloid bonds to a nonmetal. Covalent bonds are preferred with elements that would have to gain or lose too many electrons to form an ion.

- Except for hydrogen, the common elements—C, N, O, and the halogens—follow one rule: the number of bonds + the number of lone pairs = four.

**❷ What are Lewis structures and how are they drawn? (4.2)**

- Lewis structures are electron-dot representations of molecules. Two-electron bonds are drawn with a solid line and nonbonded electrons are drawn with dots (:).

- Lewis structures contain only valence electrons. Each H gets two electrons and main group elements generally get eight.

- After placing all electrons in bonds and lone pairs in a Lewis structure, it may be necessary to use lone pairs to form double or triple bonds if an atom does not have an octet.

**❸ What are resonance structures? (4.4)**

- Resonance structures are two Lewis structures having the same arrangement of atoms but a different arrangement of electrons.

- The hybrid is a composite of all resonance structures that spreads out electron pairs in multiple bonds and lone pairs.

**4** **How are covalent compounds with two elements named? (4.5)**
- Name the first nonmetal by its element name and the second using the suffix *-ide*. Add prefixes to indicate the number of atoms of each element.

**5** **How is the molecular shape around an atom determined? (4.6)**
- To determine the shape around an atom, count groups—atoms and lone pairs—and keep the groups as far away from each other as possible.
- Two groups = linear, 180° bond angle; three groups = trigonal planar, 120° bond angle; four groups = tetrahedral, 109.5° bond angle.

**6** **How does electronegativity determine bond polarity? (4.7)**
- Electronegativity is a measure of an atom's attraction for electrons in a bond.
- When two atoms have the same electronegativity value, or the difference is less than 0.5 units, the electrons are equally shared and the bond is nonpolar.
- When two atoms have very different electronegativity values—a difference of 0.5–1.9 units—the electrons are unequally shared and the bond is polar.

**7** **When is a molecule polar or nonpolar? (4.8)**
- A polar molecule has either one polar bond, or two or more bond dipoles that do not cancel.
- A nonpolar molecule has either all nonpolar bonds, or two or more bond dipoles that cancel.

## PROBLEMS

Selected in-chapter and odd-numbered end-of-chapter problems have brief answers in Appendix B. The *Student Study Guide and Solutions Manual* contains detailed solutions to all in-chapter and odd-numbered end-of-chapter problems, as well as additional worked examples and a chapter self-test.

### Covalent Bonding

**4.27** For each pair of compounds, classify the bonding as ionic or covalent and explain your choice.
   a. LiCl and HCl          b. KBr and HBr

**4.28** For each pair of compounds, classify the bonding as ionic or covalent and explain your choice.
   a. $BeH_2$ and $BeCl_2$          b. $Na_3N$ and $NH_3$

**4.29** How many bonds and lone pairs are typically observed with each element: (a) C; (b) Se; (c) I; (d) P?

**4.30** How many bonds and lone pairs are typically observed with each element: (a) O; (b) Si; (c) Ge; (d) B?

**4.31** Fill in the lone pairs needed to give the main group elements (except hydrogen) an octet. Acrylonitrile is a starting material used to manufacture synthetic Orlon and Acrilan fibers. Cysteine is an amino acid used to synthesize proteins.

a.
```
       H   H
       |   |
   H—C=C—C≡N
```
   acrylonitrile

b.
```
       H   H   O
       |   |   ‖
   H—S—C—C—C—O—H
       |   |
       H   N—H
           |
           H
```
   cysteine

**4.32** Fill in the lone pairs needed to give the main group elements (except hydrogen) an octet. Glycerol is a product of the metabolism of fats. Acrylamide is used to make polyacrylamide, which is used in some cosmetics and food packaging.

a.
```
       H  H  H
       |  |  |
   H—O—C—C—C—O—H
       |  |  |
       H  O  H
          |
          H
```
   glycerol

b.
```
           O
           ‖
   H—C=C—C—N—H
     |  |     |
     H  H     H
```
   acrylamide

**4.33** Convert the 3-D model of oxalic acid into a Lewis structure and include all nonbonded electron pairs on atoms that contain them. Oxalic acid occurs naturally in spinach and rhubarb. Although oxalic acid is toxic, you would have to eat about nine pounds of spinach at one time to ingest a fatal dose.

oxalic acid

**4.34** Convert the 3-D model of the general anesthetic methoxyflurane into a Lewis structure and include all nonbonded electron pairs on atoms that contain them.

methoxyflurane

## Lewis Structures

**4.35** Draw a valid Lewis structure for each molecule.
   a. HI     b. $CH_2F_2$     c. $H_2Se$     d. CO     e. $C_2Cl_6$

**4.36** Draw a valid Lewis structure for each molecule.
   a. $CH_3Br$     b. $PH_3$     c. HBr     d. $SiF_4$     e. $C_2HCl$

**4.37** Draw a valid Lewis structure for each compound using the given arrangement of atoms.

a. $CH_5N$
```
        H
  H  C  N  H
     H  H
```

b. $HNO_2$
```
  H  O  N  O
```

c. $C_3H_4$
```
  H  C  C  C  H
        H
```

**4.38** Draw a valid Lewis structure for each compound using the given arrangement of atoms.

a. $C_2H_3N$
```
        H
  H  C  C  N
     H
```

b. $HNO_3$
```
  H  O  N  O
           O
```

c. $C_3H_6$
```
        H
  H  C  C  C  H
     H  H  H
```

**4.39** Draw a valid Lewis structure for tetrafluoroethylene, $C_2F_4$, the industrial starting material used to prepare Teflon. Teflon is most widely used as a nonstick surface on pots and pans, but it has also found application in tape used by plumbers to seal joints, nail polish, and coatings on eye glasses. Assume that each carbon is bonded to two fluorine atoms.

**4.40** Draw a valid Lewis structure for phosgene, $CCl_2O$, which contains a central carbon atom. Phosgene is an extremely toxic gas used as a chemical weapon during World War I. It is now an important industrial starting material for the synthesis of Lexan, a lightweight transparent material used in bike helmets, goggles, and catcher's masks.

**4.41** Draw a valid Lewis structure for each ion: (a) $OH^-$; (b) $H_3O^+$.

**4.42** Draw a valid Lewis structure for each ion: (a) $OCl^-$; (b) $CH_3O^-$.

**4.43** Keeping in mind that some elements violate the octet rule, draw a Lewis structure for each compound: (a) $BCl_3$; (b) $SO_3$.

**4.44** Keeping in mind that some elements violate the octet rule, draw a Lewis structure for each compound: (a) $BeH_2$; (b) $PCl_5$.

## Resonance Structures

**4.45** What is the difference between a resonance structure and a resonance hybrid?

**4.46** Briefly explain why having two resonance structures for a molecule stabilizes it.

**4.47** Draw a second resonance structure for the following anion:

**4.48** Draw a second resonance structure for nitromethane, a compound used in drag racing fuels and in the manufacture of pharmaceuticals, pesticides, and fibers.

nitromethane

**4.49** Label each pair of compounds as resonance structures or not resonance structures.

a.

b.

**4.50** Label each pair of compounds as resonance structures or not resonance structures.

a.

b.

**4.51** Draw three resonance structures for the carbonate anion $(CO_3^{2-})$ that contain a central carbon atom.

**4.52** Draw three resonance structures for the nitrate anion $(NO_3^-)$ that contain a central N atom.

## Naming Covalent Compounds

**4.53** Name each covalent compound.
   a. $PBr_3$     b. $SO_3$     c. $NCl_3$     d. $P_2S_5$

**4.54** Name each covalent compound.
   a. $SF_6$     b. $CBr_4$     c. $N_2O$     d. $P_4O_{10}$

**4.55** Write a formula that corresponds to each name.
   a. selenium dioxide
   b. carbon tetrachloride
   c. dinitrogen pentoxide

**4.56** Write a formula that corresponds to each name.

    a. silicon tetrafluoride

    b. nitrogen oxide

    c. phosphorus triiodide

**4.57** What is the common name for dihydrogen oxide?

**4.58** What is the systematic name for $H_2S$, the compound we commonly call hydrogen sulfide?

## Molecular Shape

**4.59** Add lone pairs where needed to give octets and then determine the shape around each indicated atom.

a. H—C—O—H

b. $NF_3$

c. H—C—C=C—C—H

**4.60** Add lone pairs where needed to give octets and then determine the shape around each indicated atom.

a. H—C—S—H

b. $PCl_3$

c. H—C≡C—C—Cl

**4.61** Add lone pairs where needed to give octets and then determine the shape around each indicated atom.

a. H—N—O—H

b. H—C—C—H

c. [H—C—N—H]⁺

**4.62** Add lone pairs where needed to give octets and then determine the shape around each indicated atom.

a. H—N—N—H

b. H—C—O—O—H

c. H—C—C—O—H

**4.63** Considering each of the given ball-and-stick models: [1] Does the dark red atom have one or more lone pairs of electrons on it? Explain your choice. [2] Give an example of a molecule that has the indicated geometry.

a.     b.

**4.64** Considering each of the given ball-and-stick models: [1] Does the dark red atom have one or more lone pairs of electrons on it? Explain your choice. [2] Give an example of a molecule that has the indicated geometry.

a.     b.

**4.65** Give the molecular shape around the boron atom in $BCl_3$ and the nitrogen atom in $NCl_3$ and explain why they are different.

**4.66** Give the molecular shape for the oxygen atom in $H_2O$ and $H_3O^+$ and explain why they are different.

**4.67** Predict the bond angles around the indicated atoms in each compound. Don't forget to draw in lone pairs where needed to give octets.

a. H—C—F

b. H—C≡C—C—O—H

c. H—C=C=O

**4.68** Predict the bond angles around the indicated atoms in each compound. Don't forget to draw in lone pairs where needed to give octets.

a. H—C—C—Cl

b. H—C≡C—C—N—H

c. H—C=C—H

**4.69** Draw Lewis structures for $CCl_4$ and $C_2Cl_4$. Give the molecular shape around each carbon atom. Explain why the carbon atoms in the two molecules have different shapes.

**4.70** Draw a Lewis structure for $N_2H_4$ and explain why the shape around each N atom should be described as trigonal pyramidal.

## Electronegativity and Polarity

**4.71** Rank the atoms in each group in order of increasing electronegativity.
    a. Se, O, S         c. Cl, S, F
    b. P, Na, Cl      d. O, P, N

**4.72** Rank the atoms in each group in order of increasing electronegativity.
    a. Si, P, S         c. Se, Cl, Br
    b. Be, Mg, Ca     d. Li, Be, Na

**4.73** Using electronegativity values, classify the bond formed between each pair of elements as polar covalent or ionic.
    a. hydrogen and bromine     c. sodium and sulfur
    b. nitrogen and carbon      d. lithium and oxygen

**4.74** Using electronegativity values, classify the bond formed between each pair of elements as polar covalent or ionic.
    a. nitrogen and oxygen     c. sulfur and chlorine
    b. oxygen and hydrogen    d. sodium and chlorine

**4.75** Label the bond formed between carbon and each of the following elements as nonpolar, polar, or ionic.
    a. carbon       c. lithium       e. hydrogen
    b. oxygen      d. chlorine

**4.76** Label the bond formed between fluorine and each of the following elements as nonpolar, polar, or ionic.
    a. hydrogen      c. carbon       e. sulfur
    b. fluorine       d. lithium

**4.77** Which bond in each pair is more polar—that is, has the larger electronegativity difference between atoms?
    a. C—O or C—N
    b. C—F or C—Cl
    c. Si—C or P—H

**4.78** Which bond in each pair is more polar—that is, has the larger electronegativity difference between atoms?
    a. Si—O or Si—S
    b. H—F or H—Br
    c. C—B or C—Li

**4.79** Label each bond in Problem 4.77 with $\delta^+$ and $\delta^-$ to show the direction of polarity.

**4.80** Label each bond in Problem 4.78 with $\delta^+$ and $\delta^-$ to show the direction of polarity.

**4.81** Explain why the carbon atom in $CH_3NH_2$ bears a partial positive charge ($\delta^+$), but the carbon atom in $CH_3MgBr$ bears a partial negative charge ($\delta^-$).

**4.82** Explain why the carbon atom in $CH_3Cl$ bears a partial positive charge ($\delta^+$), but the carbon atom in $CH_3Li$ bears a partial negative charge ($\delta^-$).

**4.83** Can a compound be nonpolar if it contains one polar bond? Explain.

**4.84** Is a compound that contains polar bonds always polar? Explain.

**4.85** Label the polar bonds and then decide if each molecule is polar or nonpolar.

**4.86** Label the polar bonds and then decide if each molecule is polar or nonpolar.

**4.87** Explain why $CHCl_3$ is a polar molecule but $CCl_4$ is not.

**4.88** Explain why $H_2O$ is a polar molecule but $H_2S$ is not.

## General Questions

**4.89** Answer the following questions about the molecule $Cl_2O$.
    a. How many valence electrons does $Cl_2O$ contain?
    b. Draw a valid Lewis structure.
    c. Label all polar bonds.
    d. What is the shape around the O atom?
    e. Is $Cl_2O$ a polar molecule? Explain.

**4.90** Answer the following questions about the molecule OCS.
    a. How many valence electrons does OCS contain?
    b. Draw a valid Lewis structure.
    c. Label all polar bonds.
    d. What is the shape around the C atom?
    e. Is OCS a polar molecule? Explain.

## Applications

**4.91** Glycine is a building block used to make proteins, such as those in heart muscle (Figure 4.2).

glycine

    a. Add lone pairs where needed, and then count the total number of valence electrons in glycine.
    b. Determine the shape around the four indicated atoms.
    c. Label all of the polar bonds.
    d. Is glycine a polar or nonpolar molecule? Explain.

**4.92** Lactic acid gives sour milk its distinctive taste. Lactic acid is also an ingredient in several skin care products that purportedly smooth fine lines and improve skin texture.

lactic acid

a. Add lone pairs where needed, and then count the total number of valence electrons in lactic acid.

b. Determine the shape around the four indicated atoms.

c. Label all of the polar bonds.

d. Is lactic acid a polar or nonpolar molecule? Explain.

**4.93** Serotonin ($C_{10}H_{12}N_2O$) is a neurotransmitter that is important in mood, sleep, perception, and temperature regulation. Fill in all lone pairs and double bonds to give every atom its usual bonding pattern.

serotonin

**4.94** Phenylephrine ($C_9H_{13}NO_2$) is the decongestant in Sudafed PE. Phenylephrine replaced the decongestant pseudoephedrine, which was readily converted to the illegal stimulant methamphetamine. Fill in all lone pairs and double bonds to give every atom its usual bonding pattern.

phenylephrine

# CHALLENGE PROBLEMS

**4.95** Cyclopropane is a stable compound that contains three carbon atoms in a three-membered ring.

cyclopropane

a. What is the predicted shape around each carbon atom in the ring, given the number of groups around carbon?

b. What is the predicted $C-C-C$ bond angle, given the shape and size of the ring?

c. Explain why cyclopropane is less stable than similar three-carbon compounds that do not contain a ring.

**4.96** Although carbon has four bonds in stable molecules, sometimes reactive carbon intermediates that contain carbon atoms without four bonds are formed for very short time periods. Examples of these unstable intermediates include the methyl carbocation $(CH_3)^+$ and the methyl carbanion $(CH_3)^-$. Draw Lewis structures for both unstable ions and predict the shape around carbon.

Aspirin, a widely used over-the-counter pain reliever, is one of the countless products synthesized by the chemical industry using chemical reactions.

# Chemical Reactions

## CHAPTER GOALS

*In this chapter you will learn how to:*

1. Write and balance chemical equations
2. Define a mole and use Avogadro's number in calculations
3. Calculate formula weight and molar mass
4. Relate the mass of a substance to its number of moles
5. Carry out mole and mass calculations in chemical equations
6. Calculate percent yield
7. Determine the limiting reactant in a reaction
8. Define oxidation and reduction and recognize the components of a redox reaction
9. Give examples of common or useful redox reactions

Having learned about atoms, ionic compounds, and covalent molecules in Chapters 2–4, we now turn our attention to chemical reactions. Reactions are at the heart of chemistry. An understanding of chemical processes has made possible the conversion of natural substances into new compounds with different and sometimes superior properties. Aspirin, ibuprofen, and nylon are all products of chemical reactions utilizing substances derived from petroleum. Chemical reactions are not limited to industrial processes. The metabolism of food involves a series of reactions that both forms new compounds and also provides energy for the body's maintenance and growth. Burning gasoline, baking a cake, and photosynthesis involve chemical reactions. In Chapter 5 we learn the basic principles about chemical reactions.

## 5.1   Introduction to Chemical Reactions

Now that we have learned about compounds and the atoms that compose them, we can better understand the difference between the physical and chemical changes that were first discussed in Section 1.2.

### 5.1A   General Features of Physical and Chemical Changes

- **A physical change alters the physical state of a substance without changing its composition.**

Changes in state—such as melting and boiling—are familiar examples of physical changes. When ice (solid water) melts to form liquid water, the highly organized water molecules in the solid phase become more disorganized in the liquid phase, but no bonds are broken or formed. Each water molecule ($H_2O$) is composed of two O—H bonds in both the solid and liquid phases.

2 O—H bonds

solid $H_2O$

physical change | melting

$H_2O$ molecules are unchanged before and after melting.

2 O—H bonds

liquid $H_2O$

- **A chemical change—chemical reaction—converts one substance into another.**

**Chemical reactions involve breaking bonds in the starting materials, called *reactants*, and forming new bonds in the *products*.** The combustion of methane ($CH_4$), the main constituent of natural gas, in the presence of oxygen ($O_2$) to form carbon dioxide ($CO_2$) and water ($H_2O$) is an example of a chemical reaction. The carbon–hydrogen bonds in methane and the oxygen–oxygen bond in elemental oxygen are broken, and new carbon–oxygen and hydrogen–oxygen bonds are formed in the products.

$CH_4$

$O_2$

chemical reaction

$CO_2$

new bonds formed

$H_2O$

new bonds formed

reactants

products

## SAMPLE PROBLEM 5.1

Identify each process as a chemical reaction or a physical change.

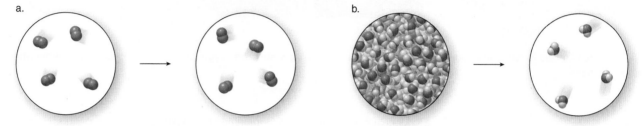

a.

b.

### Analysis

A chemical reaction occurs when the bonds in the reactants are broken and new bonds are formed in the products. A physical change occurs when the bonds in the reactants are the same as the bonds in the products.

### Solution

Part (a) represents a chemical reaction—the reactants contain two $N_2$ molecules (with blue spheres joined) and two $O_2$ molecules (two red spheres joined), while the product contains four NO molecules (a red sphere joined to a blue sphere). Part (b) represents a physical change—boiling—since liquid $H_2O$ molecules are converted to gaseous $H_2O$ molecules and the bonds do not change.

## PROBLEM 5.1

Use the molecular art to identify the process as a chemical reaction or a physical change, and explain your choice.

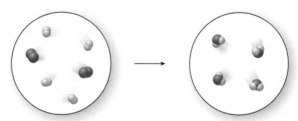

## PROBLEM 5.2

Use the molecular art to identify the process as a chemical reaction or a physical change, and explain your choice.

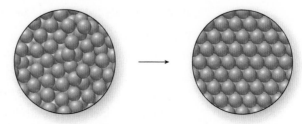

**Figure 5.1**    Treating Wounds with Hydrogen Peroxide—A Visible Chemical Reaction

The enzyme catalase in red blood converts hydrogen peroxide ($H_2O_2$) to water and oxygen gas, which appears as a visible white foam on the bloody surface.

A chemical reaction may be accompanied by a visible change: two colorless reactants can form a colored product; a gas may be given off; two liquid reactants may yield a solid product. Sometimes heat is produced so that a reaction flask feels hot. A reaction having a characteristic visible change occurs when hydrogen peroxide ($H_2O_2$) is used to clean a bloody wound. An enzyme in the blood called catalase converts the $H_2O_2$ to water ($H_2O$) and oxygen ($O_2$), and bubbles of oxygen appear as a foam, as shown in Figure 5.1.

## 5.1B   Writing Chemical Equations

- A *chemical equation* is an expression that uses chemical formulas and other symbols to illustrate what reactants constitute the starting materials in a reaction and what products are formed.

Chemical equations are written with the **reactants on the left** and the **products on the right,** separated by a horizontal arrow—a **reaction arrow**—that points from the reactants to the products. In the combustion of methane, methane ($CH_4$) and oxygen ($O_2$) are the reactants on the left side of the arrow, and carbon dioxide ($CO_2$) and water ($H_2O$) are the products on the right side.

The numbers written in front of any formula are called **coefficients. Coefficients show the number of molecules of a given element or compound that react or are formed.** When no number precedes a formula, the coefficient is assumed to be "1." In the combustion of methane, the coefficients tell us that one molecule of $CH_4$ reacts with two molecules of $O_2$ to form one molecule of $CO_2$ and two molecules of $H_2O$.

When a formula contains a subscript, **multiply its coefficient by the subscript** to give the total number of atoms of a given type in that formula.

$$2\ O_2 = 4\ O\ \text{atoms}$$
$$2\ H_2O = 4\ H\ \text{atoms} + 2\ O\ \text{atoms}$$

Coefficients are used because all chemical reactions follow a fundamental principle of nature, the **law of conservation of mass,** which states:

- Atoms cannot be created or destroyed in a chemical reaction.

Although bonds are broken and formed in reactions, the number of atoms of each element in the reactants must be the same as the number of atoms of each type in the products. **Coefficients are used to *balance* an equation,** making the number of atoms of each element the same on both sides of the equation.

$$CH_4 \ + \ 2\,O_2 \ \longrightarrow \ CO_2 \ + \ 2\,H_2O$$

**Atoms in the reactants:**
- 1 C atom
- 4 H atoms
- 4 O atoms

**Atoms in the products:**
- 1 C atom
- 4 H atoms
- 4 O atoms

Two other important features are worthy of note. If heat is needed for a reaction to occur, the Greek letter delta ($\Delta$) may be written over the arrow. The physical states of the reactants and products are sometimes indicated next to each formula—solid ($s$), liquid ($l$), or gas ($g$). If an aqueous solution is used—that is, if a reactant is dissolved in water—the symbol ($aq$) is used next to the reactant. When these features are added, the equation for the combustion of methane becomes:

| Combustion of methane | $CH_4(g) \ + \ 2\,O_2(g) \ \xrightarrow{\ \Delta\ } \ CO_2(g) \ + \ 2\,H_2O(g)$ |
|---|---|

The symbols used for chemical equations are summarized in Table 5.1.

**Table 5.1 Symbols Used in Chemical Equations**

| Symbol | Meaning |
|---|---|
| $\longrightarrow$ | Reaction arrow |
| $\Delta$ | Heat |
| ($s$) | Solid |
| ($l$) | Liquid |
| ($g$) | Gas |
| ($aq$) | Aqueous solution |

### SAMPLE PROBLEM 5.2

Label the reactants and products, and indicate how many atoms of each type of element are present on each side of the equation.

$$C_2H_6O(l) \ + \ 3\,O_2(g) \ \longrightarrow \ 2\,CO_2(g) + 3\,H_2O(g)$$

### Analysis

Reactants are on the left side of the arrow and products are on the right side in a chemical equation. When a formula contains a subscript, multiply its coefficient by the subscript to give the total number of atoms of a given type in the formula.

### Solution

In this equation, the reactants are $C_2H_6O$ and $O_2$, while the products are $CO_2$ and $H_2O$. If no coefficient is written, it is assumed to be "1." To determine the number of each type of atom when a formula has both a coefficient and a subscript, multiply the coefficient by the subscript.

| | |
|---|---|
| $1\,C_2H_6O = 2$ C's $+$ 6 H's $+$ 1 O | |
| $3\,O_2 \quad = 6$ O's | Multiply the coefficient 3 by the subscript 2. |
| $2\,CO_2 \quad = 2$ C's $+$ 4 O's | Multiply the coefficient 2 by each subscript; $2 \times 1$ C $= 2$ C's; $2 \times 2$ O's $= 4$ O's. |
| $3\,H_2O \quad = 6$ H's $+$ 3 O's | Multiply the coefficient 3 by each subscript; $3 \times 2$ H's $= 6$ H's; $3 \times 1$ O $= 3$ O's. |

Add up the atoms on each side to determine the total number for each type of element.

$$C_2H_6O(l) \ + \ 3\,O_2(g) \ \longrightarrow \ 2\,CO_2(g) \ + \ 3\,H_2O(g)$$

**Atoms in the reactants:**
- 2 C's  6 H's  7 O's

**Atoms in the products:**
- 2 C's  6 H's  7 O's

**PROBLEM 5.3**

Label the reactants and products, and indicate how many atoms of each type of element are present on each side of the following equations.

a. $2\ H_2O_2(aq) \longrightarrow 2\ H_2O(l) + O_2(g)$
b. $2\ C_8H_{18} + 25\ O_2 \longrightarrow 16\ CO_2 + 18\ H_2O$
c. $2\ Na_3PO_4(aq) + 3\ MgCl_2(aq) \longrightarrow Mg_3(PO_4)_2(s) + 6\ NaCl(aq)$

**PROBLEM 5.4**

One term in a balanced chemical equation contained the coefficient 3 in front of the formula $Al_2(SO_4)_3$. How many atoms of each type of element does this represent?

**PROBLEM 5.5**

Write a chemical equation from the following description of a reaction: One molecule of gaseous methane ($CH_4$) is heated with four molecules of gaseous chlorine ($Cl_2$), forming one molecule of liquid carbon tetrachloride ($CCl_4$) and four molecules of gaseous hydrogen chloride ($HCl$).

## 5.2 Balancing Chemical Equations

In order to carry out a reaction in the laboratory, we must know how much of each reactant we must combine to give the desired product. For example, if we wanted to synthesize aspirin ($C_9H_8O_4$) from a given amount of salicylic acid ($C_7H_6O_3$), say 100 g, we would have to determine how much acetic acid would be needed to carry out the reaction. A calculation of this sort begins with a **balanced chemical equation.**

salicylic acid $\quad$ acetic acid $\quad$ aspirin
$C_7H_6O_3 \qquad\qquad C_2H_4O_2 \qquad\qquad C_9H_8O_4$

In this example, the equation is balanced as written and the coefficient in front of each formula is "1." Thus, one molecule of salicylic acid reacts with one molecule of acetic acid to form one molecule of aspirin and one molecule of water. More often, however, an equation must be balanced by adding coefficients in front of some formulas so that the **number of atoms of each element is equal on both sides of the equation.**

**ENVIRONMENTAL NOTE**

The reaction of propane with oxygen forms carbon dioxide, water, and a great deal of energy that can be used for cooking, heating homes and water, drying clothes, and powering generators and vehicles. The combustion of propane and other fossil fuels adds a tremendous amount of $CO_2$ to the atmosphere each year, with clear environmental consequences (Section 12.8).

---

## How To Balance a Chemical Equation

**Example:** Write a balanced chemical equation for the reaction of propane ($C_3H_8$) with oxygen ($O_2$) to form carbon dioxide ($CO_2$) and water ($H_2O$).

**Step [1] Write the equation with the correct formulas.**

• Write the reactants on the left side and the products on the right side of the reaction arrow, and check if the equation is balanced without adding any coefficients.

$$C_3H_8 + O_2 \longrightarrow CO_2 + H_2O$$

• This equation is not balanced as written since none of the elements—carbon, hydrogen, and oxygen—has the same number of atoms on both sides of the equation. For example, there are 3 C's on the left and only 1 C on the right.

• **The subscripts in a formula can *never* be changed to balance an equation.** Changing a subscript changes the identity of the compound. For example, changing $CO_2$ to $CO$ would balance oxygen (there would be 2 O's on both sides of the equation), but that would change $CO_2$ (carbon dioxide) into $CO$ (carbon monoxide).

—Continued

Step [2]   **Balance the equation with coefficients one element at a time.**

- Begin with the most complex formula, and start with an element that appears in only one formula on both sides of the equation. In this example, begin with either the C's or H's in $C_3H_8$. Since there are 3 C's on the left, place the coefficient 3 before $CO_2$ on the right.

$$C_3H_8 \;+\; O_2 \;\longrightarrow\; 3\,CO_2 \;+\; H_2O$$

  3 C's on the left          Place a 3 to balance C's.

- To balance the 8 H's in $C_3H_8$, place the coefficient 4 before $H_2O$ on the right.

$$C_3H_8 \;+\; O_2 \;\longrightarrow\; 3\,CO_2 \;+\; 4\,H_2O$$

  8 H's on the left          Place a 4 to balance H's.
                             ($4 \times 2$ H's in $H_2O$ = 8 H's)

- The only element not balanced is oxygen, and at this point there are a total of 10 O's on the right—six from three $CO_2$ molecules and four from four $H_2O$ molecules. To balance the 10 O's on the right, place the coefficient 5 before $O_2$ on the left.

$$C_3H_8 \;+\; 5\,O_2 \;\longrightarrow\; 3\,CO_2 \;+\; 4\,H_2O$$

  Place a 5 to balance O's.        10 O's on the right

Step [3]   **Check to make sure that the smallest set of whole numbers is used.**

$$C_3H_8 \;+\; 5\,O_2 \;\longrightarrow\; 3\,CO_2 \;+\; 4\,H_2O$$

O
H
C

Atoms in the reactants:                    Atoms in the products:
- 3 C's   8 H's   10 O's ($5 \times 2$ O's)     - 3 C's   8 H's   10 O's [($3 \times 2$ O's) + ($4 \times 1$ O)]

- This equation is balanced because the same number of C's, O's, and H's is present on both sides of the equation.
- Sometimes an equation is balanced but the lowest set of whole numbers is not used as coefficients. Say, for example, that balancing yielded the following equation:

$$2\,C_3H_8 \;+\; 10\,O_2 \;\longrightarrow\; 6\,CO_2 \;+\; 8\,H_2O$$

- This equation has the same number of C's, O's, and H's on both sides, but *each coefficient must be divided by two* to give the lowest set of whole numbers for the balanced equation, as drawn in the first equation in step [3].

Sample Problems 5.3–5.5 illustrate additional examples of balancing chemical equations. Sample Problem 5.4 shows how to balance an equation when there is an odd–even relationship of atoms in the reactants and products. Sample Problem 5.5 illustrates how to balance an equation that contains several polyatomic anions.

### SAMPLE PROBLEM 5.3

Write a balanced equation for the reaction of glucose ($C_6H_{12}O_6$) with oxygen ($O_2$) to form carbon dioxide ($CO_2$) and water ($H_2O$).

### Analysis

Balance an equation with coefficients, one element at a time, beginning with the most complex formula and starting with an element that appears in only one formula on both sides of the equation. Continue placing coefficients until the **number of atoms of each element is equal on both sides of the equation.**

Bagels, pasta, bread, and rice are high in starch, which is hydrolyzed to the simple carbohydrate glucose after ingestion. The metabolism of glucose forms $CO_2$ and $H_2O$ and provides energy for bodily functions.

## Solution

**[1] Write the equation with correct formulas.**

$$C_6H_{12}O_6 + O_2 \longrightarrow CO_2 + H_2O$$
glucose

- None of the elements is balanced in this equation. As an example, there are 6 C's on the left side, but only 1 C on the right side.

**[2] Balance the equation with coefficients one element at a time.**

- Begin with glucose, since its formula is most complex. Balance the 6 C's of glucose by placing the coefficient 6 before $CO_2$. Balance the 12 H's of glucose by placing the coefficient 6 before $H_2O$.

Place a 6 to balance C's.

$$C_6H_{12}O_6 \quad + \quad O_2 \longrightarrow 6\ CO_2 \quad + \quad 6\ H_2O$$

Place a 6 to balance H's.

- The right side of the equation now has 18 O's. Since glucose already has 6 O's on the left side, 12 additional O's are needed on the left side. The equation will be balanced if the coefficient 6 is placed before $O_2$.

$$C_6H_{12}O_6 \quad + \quad 6\ O_2 \longrightarrow 6\ CO_2 \quad + \quad 6\ H_2O$$

Place a 6 to balance O's.

**[3] Check.**

- The equation is balanced since the number of atoms of each element is the same on both sides.

**Answer:**  $C_6H_{12}O_6 \quad + \quad 6\ O_2 \longrightarrow 6\ CO_2 \quad + \quad 6\ H_2O$

| Atoms in the reactants: | Atoms in the products: |
|---|---|
| • 6 C's | • 6 C's ($6 \times 1$ C) |
| • 12 H's | • 12 H's ($6 \times 2$ H's) |
| • 18 O's ($1 \times 6$ O's) + ($6 \times 2$ O's) | • 18 O's ($6 \times 2$ O's) + ($6 \times 1$ O) |

## PROBLEM 5.6

Write a balanced equation for each reaction.

a. $H_2 + O_2 \longrightarrow H_2O$      b. $NO + O_2 \longrightarrow NO_2$      c. $CH_4 + Cl_2 \longrightarrow CH_2Cl_2 + HCl$

## PROBLEM 5.7

Write a balanced equation for the following reaction, shown with molecular art.

## SAMPLE PROBLEM 5.4

The airbag in an automobile inflates when ionic sodium azide ($NaN_3$), which is composed of $Na^+$ cations and the polyatomic anion, $N_3^-$ (azide), rapidly decomposes to sodium (Na) and gaseous $N_2$ (Figure 5.2). Write a balanced equation for this reaction.

## Analysis

Balance an equation with coefficients, one element at a time, beginning with the most complex formula and starting with an element that appears in only one formula on both sides of the equation. Continue placing coefficients until the **number of atoms of each element is equal on both sides of the equation.**

### Solution

**[1] Write the equation with correct formulas.**

$$NaN_3 \longrightarrow Na + N_2$$

sodium azide

- The N atoms are not balanced since there are 3 N's on the left side and only 2 N's on the right.

**[2] Balance the equation with coefficients.**

- To balance the odd number of N atoms (3 N's) on the reactant side with the even number of N atoms on the product side (2 N's) requires the placement of two coefficients. Place the coefficient 2 on the left side (for a total of 6 N's in the reactants). Then place the coefficient 3 before $N_2$ (for a total of 6 N's in the product). Placing two coefficients is necessary whenever there is an odd–even relationship of atoms in the reactants and products (for any odd number other than one).

Place a 2 to give 6 N's on the left.

$$2\,NaN_3 \longrightarrow Na + 3\,N_2$$

Place a 3 to give 6 N's on the right.

- Note the relationship between the nitrogen-containing species. The subscript of $N_2$ on the right side is numerically equal to the coefficient (2) before $NaN_3$ on the left side; similarly, the subscript of $NaN_3$ on the left side is numerically equal to the coefficient (3) before $N_2$ on the right side.
- Balance the 2 Na atoms on the left side by placing a 2 before the Na atoms on the right.

$$2\,NaN_3 \longrightarrow 2\,Na + 3\,N_2$$

Place a 2 to balance Na's.

**[3] Check and simplify.**

- The equation is balanced since the number of atoms of each element is the same on both sides.

$$2\,NaN_3 \longrightarrow 2\,Na + 3\,N_2$$

| Atoms in the reactants: | Atoms in the products: |
|---|---|
| • 2 Na's | • 2 Na's |
| • 6 N's ($2 \times 3$ N's) | • 6 N's ($3 \times 2$ N's) |

---

**Figure 5.2**    Chemistry of an Automobile Airbag

a. The chemical reaction that inflates an airbag

inflated airbag

inflator

crash sensor

$NaN_3$
sodium azide

Na

$N_2$

b. An airbag deployed in a head-on collision

A severe car crash triggers an airbag to deploy when an electric sensor causes sodium azide ($NaN_3$) to ignite, converting it to sodium (Na) and nitrogen gas ($N_2$). The nitrogen gas causes the bag to inflate fully in 40 milliseconds, helping to protect passengers from serious injury. The sodium atoms formed in this first reaction are hazardous and subsequently converted to a safe sodium salt. It took 30 years to develop a reliable airbag system for automobiles.

### PROBLEM 5.8

Write a balanced equation for the reaction of ethane ($C_2H_6$) with $O_2$ to form $CO_2$ and $H_2O$.

### PROBLEM 5.9

The Haber process is an important industrial reaction that converts $N_2$ and $H_2$ to ammonia ($NH_3$), an agricultural fertilizer and starting material for the synthesis of nitrate fertilizers. Write a balanced equation for the Haber process.

### SAMPLE PROBLEM 5.5

Balance the following equation.

$$Ca_3(PO_4)_2 \quad + \quad H_2SO_4 \quad \longrightarrow \quad CaSO_4 \quad + \quad H_3PO_4$$
calcium phosphate    sulfuric acid        calcium sulfate   phosphoric acid

### Analysis

Balance an equation with coefficients, one element at a time, beginning with the most complex formula and starting with an element that appears in only one formula on both sides of the equation. Continue placing coefficients until the **number of atoms of each element is equal on both sides of the equation.**

### Solution

**[1] Write the equation with correct formulas.**

- The correct formula for each compound is given in the problem statement. When the reactants and products contain polyatomic ions, $PO_4^{3-}$ and $SO_4^{2-}$ in this case, **balance each ion as a _unit_,** rather than balancing the individual atoms. Thus, phosphate is not balanced in the equation as written, because the left side has two $PO_4^{3-}$ anions while the right side has only one.

**[2] Balance the equation with coefficients.**

- Begin with $Ca_3(PO_4)_2$. Balance the 3 Ca's by placing the coefficient 3 before $CaSO_4$. Balance the 2 $PO_4^{3-}$ anions by placing the coefficient 2 before $H_3PO_4$.

Place a 3 to balance Ca's.
$$Ca_3(PO_4)_2 \quad + \quad H_2SO_4 \quad \longrightarrow \quad 3\, CaSO_4 \quad + \quad 2\, H_3PO_4$$
Place a 2 to balance $PO_4^{3-}$.

- Two components are still not balanced—H atoms and sulfate anions ($SO_4^{2-}$). Both can be balanced by placing the coefficient 3 before $H_2SO_4$ on the left.

6 H's                                              6 H's
$$Ca_3(PO_4)_2 \quad + \quad 3\, H_2SO_4 \quad \longrightarrow \quad 3\, CaSO_4 \quad + \quad 2\, H_3PO_4$$
3 $SO_4^{2-}$ in both

Place a 3 to balance H and $SO_4^{2-}$.

**[3] Check.**

- The equation is balanced since the number of atoms and polyatomic anions is the same on both sides.

Ammonium hydrogen phosphate [$(NH_4)_2HPO_4$], the major phosphorus fertilizer, is formed from phosphoric acid, $H_3PO_4$, which is synthesized industrially by the chemical reaction in Sample Problem 5.5.

**Answer:**   $Ca_3(PO_4)_2 \quad + \quad 3\, H_2SO_4 \quad \longrightarrow \quad 3\, CaSO_4 \quad + \quad 2\, H_3PO_4$

| **Atoms or ions in the reactants:** | | **Atoms or ions in the products:** | |
|---|---|---|---|
| • 3 Ca's | • 6 H's | • 3 Ca's | • 6 H's |
| • 2 $PO_4^{3-}$ | • 3 $SO_4^{2-}$ | • 2 $PO_4^{3-}$ | • 3 $SO_4^{2-}$ |

### PROBLEM 5.10

Balance each chemical equation.

a.  $Al + H_2SO_4 \longrightarrow Al_2(SO_4)_3 + H_2$

b.  $Na_2SO_3 + H_3PO_4 \longrightarrow H_2SO_3 + Na_3PO_4$

## 5.3 The Mole and Avogadro's Number

Although the chemical equations in Section 5.2 were discussed in terms of individual atoms and molecules, atoms are exceedingly small. It is more convenient to talk about larger quantities of atoms, and for this reason, scientists use the **mole.** A mole defines a quantity, much like a dozen items means 12, and a case of soda means 24 cans. The only difference is that a mole is much larger.

- A *mole* is a quantity that contains $6.02 \times 10^{23}$ items—usually atoms, molecules, or ions.

The definition of a mole is based on the number of atoms contained in exactly 12 g of the carbon-12 isotope. This number is called **Avogadro's number,** after the Italian scientist Amadeo Avogadro, who first proposed the concept of a mole in the nineteenth century. One mole, abbreviated as **mol,** always contains an Avogadro's number of particles.

| | |
|---|---|
| 1 mole of C atoms = | $6.02 \times 10^{23}$ C atoms |
| 1 mole of $H_2O$ molecules = | $6.02 \times 10^{23}$ $H_2O$ molecules |
| 1 mole of vitamin C molecules = | $6.02 \times 10^{23}$ vitamin C molecules |

### PROBLEM 5.11

How many items are contained in one mole of (a) baseballs; (b) bicycles; (c) Cheerios; (d) $CH_4$ molecules?

We can use Avogadro's number as a conversion factor to relate the number of moles of a substance to the number of atoms or molecules it contains.

Two possible conversion factors: $\dfrac{1 \text{ mol}}{6.02 \times 10^{23} \text{ atoms}}$ or $\dfrac{6.02 \times 10^{23} \text{ atoms}}{1 \text{ mol}}$

These conversion factors allow us to determine how many atoms or molecules are contained in a given number of moles. To carry out calculations that contain numbers written in scientific notation, we must first learn how to multiply and divide numbers written in this form.

- To multiply two numbers in scientific notation, multiply the coefficients together and add the exponents in the powers of 10.

Add exponents.
(5 + 2)

$(3.0 \times 10^5)$ × $(2.0 \times 10^2)$ = $6.0 \times 10^7$

Multiply coefficients.
(3.0 × 2.0)

- To divide two numbers in scientific notation, divide the coefficients and subtract the exponents in the powers of 10.

Divide coefficients.
(6.0/2.0)

$\dfrac{6.0 \times 10^2}{2.0 \times 10^{20}}$ Subtract exponents. = $3.0 \times 10^{-18}$
(2 − 20)

Sample Problems 5.6 and 5.7 illustrate how to interconvert moles and molecules. In both problems we follow the stepwise procedure for problem solving using conversion factors outlined in Section 1.7B.

Each sample contains one mole of the substance—water ($H_2O$ molecules), salt (NaCl, one mole of $Na^+$ and one mole of $Cl^-$), and aspirin ($C_9H_8O_4$ molecules). Pictured is a mole of aspirin *molecules,* not a mole of aspirin *tablets,* which is a quantity too large to easily represent. If a mole of aspirin tablets were arranged next to one another to cover a football field and then stacked on top of each other, they would occupy a volume 100 yards long, 53.3 yards wide, and over 20,000,000,000 miles high!

For a number written in scientific notation as $y \times 10^x$, $y$ is the coefficient and $x$ is the exponent in the power of 10 (Section 1.6).

## SAMPLE PROBLEM 5.6

How many molecules are contained in 5.0 moles of carbon dioxide ($CO_2$)?

### Analysis and Solution

**[1] Identify the original quantity and the desired quantity.**

$$5.0 \text{ mol of } CO_2 \qquad \text{? number of molecules of } CO_2$$
original quantity                     desired quantity

**[2] Write out the conversion factors.**

- Choose the conversion factor that places the unwanted unit, mol, in the denominator so that the units cancel.

$$\frac{1 \text{ mol}}{6.02 \times 10^{23} \text{ molecules}} \quad \text{or} \quad \boxed{\frac{6.02 \times 10^{23} \text{ molecules}}{1 \text{ mol}}}$$

Choose this conversion factor to cancel mol.

**[3] Set up and solve the problem.**

- Multiply the original quantity by the conversion factor to obtain the desired quantity.

Convert to a number between 1 and 10.

$$5.0 \text{ mol} \quad \times \quad \frac{6.02 \times 10^{23} \text{ molecules}}{1 \text{ mol}} \quad = \quad 30. \times 10^{23} \text{ molecules}$$

Moles cancel.

$$= \quad 3.0 \times 10^{24} \text{ molecules of } CO_2$$

**Answer**

- Multiplication first gives an answer that is not written in scientific notation since the coefficient (30.) is greater than 10. Moving the decimal point one place to the *left* and *increasing* the exponent by one gives the answer written in the proper form.

## PROBLEM 5.12

How many carbon atoms are contained in each of the following number of moles: (a) 2.00 mol; (b) 6.00 mol; (c) 0.500 mol; (d) 25.0 mol?

## PROBLEM 5.13

How many molecules are contained in each of the following number of moles?

a. 2.5 mol of penicillin molecules

b. 0.25 mol of $NH_3$ molecules

c. 0.40 mol of sugar molecules

d. 55.3 mol of acetaminophen molecules

## SAMPLE PROBLEM 5.7

How many moles of aspirin contain $8.62 \times 10^{25}$ molecules?

### Analysis and Solution

**[1] Identify the original quantity and the desired quantity.**

$$8.62 \times 10^{25} \text{ molecules of aspirin} \qquad \text{? mole of aspirin}$$
original quantity                          desired quantity

**[2] Write out the conversion factors.**

- Choose the conversion factor that places the unwanted unit, number of molecules, in the denominator so that the units cancel.

$$\frac{6.02 \times 10^{23} \text{ molecules}}{1 \text{ mol}} \quad \text{or} \quad \boxed{\frac{1 \text{ mol}}{6.02 \times 10^{23} \text{ molecules}}}$$

Choose this conversion factor to cancel molecules.

**[3] Set up and solve the problem.**

- Multiply the original quantity by the conversion factor to obtain the desired quantity.
- To divide numbers using scientific notation, divide the coefficients (8.62/6.02) and subtract the exponents (25 – 23).

$$8.62 \times 10^{25} \text{ molecules} \quad \times \quad \frac{1 \text{ mol}}{6.02 \times 10^{23} \text{ molecules}} \quad = \quad 1.43 \times 10^2 \text{ mol}$$

Molecules cancel.

$$= \quad 143 \text{ mol of aspirin}$$

**Answer**

### PROBLEM 5.14

How many moles of water contain each of the following number of molecules?

a. $6.02 \times 10^{25}$ molecules    b. $3.01 \times 10^{22}$ molecules    c. $9.0 \times 10^{24}$ molecules

## 5.4 Mass to Mole Conversions

In Section 2.3, we learned that the *atomic weight* **is the average mass of an element,** reported in atomic mass units (amu), and that the atomic weight of each element appears just below its chemical symbol in the periodic table. Thus, carbon has an atomic weight of 12.01 amu. We use atomic weights to calculate the mass of a compound.

- The *formula weight* is the sum of the atomic weights of all the atoms in a compound, reported in atomic mass units (amu).

The term "formula weight" is used for both ionic and covalent compounds. Often the term **"molecular weight"** is used in place of formula weight for covalent compounds, since they are composed of molecules, not ions. The formula weight of ionic sodium chloride (NaCl) is 58.44 amu, which is determined by adding up the atomic weights of Na (22.99 amu) and Cl (35.45 amu). The stepwise procedure for calculating the formula weight of compounds whose chemical formulas contain subscripts is shown in the accompanying *How To*.

**Formula weight of NaCl:**

| | | |
|---|---|---|
| Atomic weight of 1 Na | = | 22.99 amu |
| Atomic weight of 1 Cl | = | 35.45 amu |
| Formula weight of NaCl | = | 58.44 amu |

### How To Calculate the Formula Weight of a Compound

**Example:** Calculate the formula weight for iron(II) sulfate, $FeSO_4$, an iron supplement used to treat anemia.

**Step [1]** Write the correct formula and determine the number of atoms of each element from the subscripts.

- $FeSO_4$ contains 1 Fe atom, 1 S atom, and 4 O atoms.

**Step [2]** Multiply the number of atoms of each element by the atomic weight and add the results.

| | | |
|---|---|---|
| 1 Fe atom $\times$ 55.85 amu | = | 55.85 amu |
| 1 S atom $\times$ 32.07 amu | = | 32.07 amu |
| 4 O atoms $\times$ 16.00 amu | = | 64.00 amu |
| Formula weight of $FeSO_4$ | = | 151.92 amu |

### PROBLEM 5.15

Calculate the formula weight of each ionic compound.

a. $CaCO_3$, a common calcium supplement
b. KI, the essential nutrient added to NaCl to make iodized salt

## PROBLEM 5.16

Calculate the molecular weight of each covalent compound.

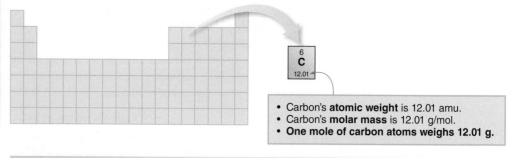

a. ethanol
(alcohol in alcoholic beverages)

b. phenol
(antiseptic)

c. halothane
(general anesthetic)

## 5.4A    Molar Mass

When reactions are carried out in the laboratory, single atoms and molecules are much too small to measure out. Instead, substances are weighed on a balance and amounts are typically reported in grams, not atomic mass units. To determine how many atoms or molecules are contained in a given mass, we use its **molar mass.**

- The *molar mass* is the mass of one mole of any substance, reported in grams per mole.

**The value of the molar mass of an element in the periodic table (in grams per mole) is the same as the value of its atomic weight (in amu).** Thus, the molar mass of carbon is 12.01 g/mol, since its atomic weight is 12.01 amu; that is, one mole of carbon atoms weighs 12.01 g.

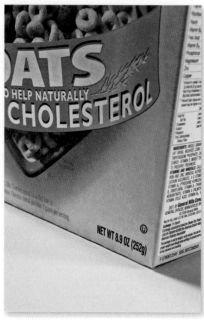

When a consumer product contains a great many lightweight small objects—for example, Cheerios—it is typically sold by weight, not by the number of objects. We buy Cheerios in an 8.9-oz box, not a box that contains 2,554 Cheerios.

| 6 |
| C |
| 12.01 |

- Carbon's **atomic weight** is 12.01 amu.
- Carbon's **molar mass** is 12.01 g/mol.
- **One mole of carbon atoms weighs 12.01 g.**

- The value of the molar mass of a compound in grams equals the value of its formula weight in amu.

Since the formula weight of NaCl is 58.44 amu, its molar mass is 58.44 g/mol. One mole of NaCl weighs 58.44 g. We use a compound's formula weight to calculate its molar mass, as shown in Sample Problem 5.8.

## SAMPLE PROBLEM 5.8

What is the molar mass of nicotine ($C_{10}H_{14}N_2$), the toxic and addictive stimulant in tobacco?

### Analysis

Determine the number of atoms of each element from the subscripts in the chemical formula, multiply the number of atoms of each element by the atomic weight, and add up the results.

### Solution

$$10 \text{ C atoms} \times 12.01 \text{ amu} = 120.1 \text{ amu}$$
$$14 \text{ H atoms} \times 1.008 \text{ amu} = 14.11 \text{ amu}$$
$$2 \text{ N atoms} \times 14.01 \text{ amu} = 28.02 \text{ amu}$$

Formula weight of nicotine = 162.23 amu rounded to 162.2 amu

**Answer:** Since the formula weight of nicotine is 162.2 amu, the molar mass of nicotine is 162.2 g/mol.

Ginkgo extracts from the tree *Ginkgo biloba* contain ginkgolide B (Problem 5.17), a complex compound that was synthesized by a series of chemical reactions in the laboratory of Nobel Laureate E. J. Corey at Harvard University in 1988.

### PROBLEM 5.17

What is the molar mass of ginkgolide B ($C_{20}H_{24}O_{10}$), a complex compound isolated from the ginkgo tree? Extracts of the roots, bark, and seeds of the ginkgo tree comprise the most widely taken herbal supplements used today.

## 5.4B  Relating Grams to Moles

**The molar mass is a very useful quantity because it relates the number of *moles* to the number of *grams* of a substance.** In this way, the molar mass can be used as a conversion factor. For example, since the molar mass of $H_2O$ is 18.02 g/mol, two conversion factors can be written.

$$\frac{18.02 \text{ g } H_2O}{1 \text{ mol}} \quad \text{or} \quad \frac{1 \text{ mol}}{18.02 \text{ g } H_2O}$$

Using these conversion factors, we can convert a given number of moles of water to grams, or a specific number of grams of water to moles.

### SAMPLE PROBLEM 5.9

**Converting moles to mass:** What is the mass of 0.25 moles of water?

### Analysis and Solution

**[1] Identify the original quantity and the desired quantity.**

$$\begin{array}{cc} 0.25 \text{ mol of } H_2O & \text{? g of } H_2O \\ \text{original quantity} & \text{desired quantity} \end{array}$$

**[2] Write out the conversion factors.**

- Choose the conversion factor that places the unwanted unit, moles, in the denominator so that the units cancel.

$$\frac{1 \text{ mol}}{18.02 \text{ g } H_2O} \quad \text{or} \quad \boxed{\frac{18.02 \text{ g } H_2O}{1 \text{ mol}}}$$ 

Choose this conversion factor to cancel mol.

**[3] Set up and solve the problem.**

- Multiply the original quantity by the conversion factor to obtain the desired quantity.

$$0.25 \text{ mol} \quad \times \quad \frac{18.02 \text{ g } H_2O}{1 \text{ mol}} \quad = \quad 4.5 \text{ g of } H_2O$$

Moles cancel.  **Answer**

### PROBLEM 5.18

Calculate the number of grams contained in each of the following number of moles.

a. 0.500 mol of NaCl          c. 3.60 mol of $C_2H_4$ (ethylene)
b. 2.00 mol of KI             d. 0.820 mol of $CH_4O$ (methanol)

### SAMPLE PROBLEM 5.10

**Converting mass to moles:** How many moles are present in 100. g of aspirin ($C_9H_8O_4$, molar mass 180.2 g/mol)?

### Analysis and Solution

**[1] Identify the original quantity and the desired quantity.**

$$\begin{array}{cc} 100. \text{ g of aspirin} & \text{? mol of aspirin} \\ \text{original quantity} & \text{desired quantity} \end{array}$$

**[2] Write out the conversion factors.**

- Choose the conversion factor that places the unwanted unit, grams, in the denominator so that the units cancel.

$$\frac{180.2 \text{ g aspirin}}{1 \text{ mol}} \quad \text{or} \quad \boxed{\frac{1 \text{ mol}}{180.2 \text{ g aspirin}}} \quad \text{Choose this conversion factor to cancel g.}$$

**[3] Set up and solve the problem.**

- Multiply the original quantity by the conversion factor to obtain the desired quantity.

$$100. \cancel{g} \quad \times \quad \frac{1 \text{ mol}}{180.2 \cancel{g} \text{ aspirin}} \quad = \quad 0.555 \text{ mol of aspirin}$$

Grams cancel. **Answer**

## PROBLEM 5.19

How many moles are contained in each of the following?

a. 100. g of NaCl

b. 25.5 g of $CH_4$

c. 0.250 g of aspirin ($C_9H_8O_4$)

d. 25.0 g of $H_2O$

## 5.4C  Relating Grams to Number of Atoms or Molecules

Since the molar mass of a substance gives the number of grams in a mole and a mole contains $6.02 \times 10^{23}$ molecules (or atoms), **we can use molar mass to show the relationship between** *grams* **and** *number of molecules* **(or atoms).** For example, since the molar mass of aspirin is 180.2 g/mol, the following relationships exist:

$$\frac{180.2 \text{ g aspirin}}{1 \text{ mol}} \quad = \quad \frac{180.2 \text{ g aspirin}}{6.02 \times 10^{23} \text{ molecules}}$$

1 mol = $6.02 \times 10^{23}$ molecules

## SAMPLE PROBLEM 5.11

**Converting mass to number of molecules:** How many molecules are contained in a 325-mg tablet of aspirin ($C_9H_8O_4$, molar mass 180.2 g/mol)?

### Analysis and Solution

**[1] Identify the original quantity and the desired quantity.**

325 mg of aspirin
original quantity

? molecules of aspirin
desired quantity

**[2] Write out the conversion factors.**

- We have no conversion factor that directly relates milligrams to number of molecules. We do know, however, how to relate milligrams to grams, and grams to number of molecules. In other words, we need two conversion factors to solve this problem.
- Choose the conversion factors that place the unwanted units, grams and milligrams, in the denominator so that the units cancel.

g–mg conversion factors

gram–number of molecules conversion factors

$$\frac{1000 \text{ mg}}{1 \text{ g}} \quad \text{or} \quad \boxed{\frac{1 \text{ g}}{1000 \text{ mg}}} \qquad \frac{180.2 \text{ g aspirin}}{6.02 \times 10^{23} \text{ molecules}} \quad \text{or} \quad \boxed{\frac{6.02 \times 10^{23} \text{ molecules}}{180.2 \text{ g aspirin}}}$$

Choose the conversion factors with the unwanted units—mg and g—in the denominator.

**[3] Set up and solve the problem.**

- Arrange each term so that the units in the numerator of one term cancel the units in the denominator of the adjacent term. The single desired unit, number of molecules, must be located in the numerator of one term.

$$325 \text{ mg aspirin} \quad \times \quad \frac{1 \text{ g}}{1000 \text{ mg}} \quad \times \quad \frac{6.02 \times 10^{23} \text{ molecules}}{180.2 \text{ g aspirin}} \quad = \quad 1.09 \times 10^{21} \text{ molecules of aspirin}$$

**Answer**

Milligrams cancel.    Grams cancel.

### PROBLEM 5.20

How many molecules are contained in two 500.-mg tablets of penicillin ($C_{16}H_{18}N_2O_4S$, molar mass 334.4 g/mol)?

## 5.5 Mole Calculations in Chemical Equations

NO, nitrogen monoxide, is formed from $N_2$ and $O_2$ at very high temperature in automobile engines and coal-burning furnaces. NO is a reactive air pollutant that goes on to form other air pollutants, such as ozone ($O_3$) and nitric acid ($HNO_3$). $HNO_3$ is one component of acid rain that can devastate forests and acidify streams, making them unfit for fish and other wildlife.

Having learned about moles and molar mass, we can now return to balanced chemical equations. As we learned in Section 5.2, the coefficients in a balanced chemical equation tell us the number of *molecules* of each compound that react or are formed in a given reaction.

- A balanced chemical equation also tells us the number of *moles* of each reactant that combine and the number of *moles* of each product formed.

$$1 \text{ N}_2(g) \quad + \quad 1 \text{ O}_2(g) \quad \xrightarrow{\Delta} \quad 2 \text{ NO}(g)$$

one molecule of $N_2$      one molecule of $O_2$      two molecules of NO
one mole of $N_2$          one mole of $O_2$          two moles of NO

[The coefficient "1" has been written for emphasis.]

For example, the balanced chemical equation for the high temperature reaction of $N_2$ and $O_2$ to form nitrogen monoxide, NO, shows that one *molecule* of $N_2$ combines with one *molecule* of $O_2$ to form two *molecules* of NO. It also shows that one *mole* of $N_2$ combines with one *mole* of $O_2$ to form two *moles* of NO.

**Coefficients are used to form mole ratios, which can serve as conversion factors.** These ratios tell us the relative number of moles of reactants that combine in a reaction, as well as the relative number of moles of product formed from a given reactant, as shown in Sample Problem 5.12.

Mole ratios:
$$\frac{1 \text{ mol N}_2}{1 \text{ mol O}_2} \qquad \frac{1 \text{ mol N}_2}{2 \text{ mol NO}} \qquad \frac{1 \text{ mol O}_2}{2 \text{ mol NO}}$$

two reactants          reactant–product          reactant–product
$N_2$ and $O_2$        $N_2$ and NO              $O_2$ and NO

- Use the mole ratio from the coefficients in the balanced equation to convert the number of moles of one compound (A) into the number of moles of another compound (B).

Moles of **A** ⟶ Moles of **B**

mole–mole
conversion factor

Meters that measure CO levels in homes are sold commercially. CO, a colorless, odorless gas, is a minor product formed whenever fossil fuels and wood are burned. In poorly ventilated rooms, such as those found in modern, well-insulated homes, CO levels can reach unhealthy levels.

### SAMPLE PROBLEM 5.12

Carbon monoxide (CO) is a poisonous gas that combines with hemoglobin in the blood, thus reducing the amount of oxygen that can be delivered to tissues. Under certain conditions, CO is formed when ethane ($C_2H_6$) in natural gas is burned in the presence of oxygen. Using the balanced equation, how many moles of CO are produced from 3.5 mol of $C_2H_6$?

$$2\ C_2H_6(g)\ +\ 5\ O_2(g)\ \xrightarrow{\Delta}\ 4\ CO(g)\ +\ 6\ H_2O(g)$$

### Analysis and Solution

**[1] Identify the original quantity and the desired quantity.**

| 3.5 mol of $C_2H_6$ | ? mol of CO |
|---|---|
| original quantity | desired quantity |

**[2] Write out the conversion factors.**

- Use the coefficients in the balanced equation to write mole–mole conversion factors for the two compounds, $C_2H_6$ and CO. Choose the conversion factor that places the unwanted unit, moles of $C_2H_6$, in the denominator so that the units cancel.

$$\frac{2\ \text{mol}\ C_2H_6}{4\ \text{mol}\ CO}\quad \text{or}\quad \boxed{\frac{4\ \text{mol}\ CO}{2\ \text{mol}\ C_2H_6}}\quad \text{Choose this conversion factor to cancel mol } C_2H_6.$$

**[3] Set up and solve the problem.**

- Multiply the original quantity by the conversion factor to obtain the desired quantity.

$$3.5\ \cancel{\text{mol}\ C_2H_6}\ \times\ \frac{4\ \text{mol}\ CO}{2\ \cancel{\text{mol}\ C_2H_6}}\ =\ 7.0\ \text{mol}\ CO$$

Moles $C_2H_6$ cancel.　　**Answer**

### PROBLEM 5.21

Use the balanced equation for the reaction of $N_2$ and $O_2$ to form NO at the beginning of Section 5.5 to answer each question.

a. How many moles of NO are formed from 3.3 moles of $N_2$?
b. How many moles of NO are formed from 0.50 moles of $O_2$?
c. How many moles of $O_2$ are needed to completely react with 1.2 moles of $N_2$?

### PROBLEM 5.22

Use the balanced equation in Sample Problem 5.12 to answer each question.

a. How many moles of $O_2$ are needed to react completely with 3.0 moles of $C_2H_6$?
b. How many moles of $H_2O$ are formed from 0.50 moles of $C_2H_6$?
c. How many moles of $C_2H_6$ are needed to form 3.0 moles of CO?

Lightning produces $O_3$ from $O_2$ during an electrical storm. $O_3$ at the ground level is an unwanted pollutant. In the stratosphere, however, it protects us from harmful radiation from the sun (Section 4.4B).

## 5.6　Mass Calculations in Chemical Equations

Since a mole represents an enormously large number of very small molecules, there is no way to directly count the number of moles or molecules used in a chemical reaction. Instead, we utilize a balance to measure the number of grams of a compound used and the number of grams of product formed. The number of grams of a substance and the number of moles it contains are related by the molar mass (Section 5.4).

## 5.6A　Converting Moles of Reactant to Grams of Product

To determine how many grams of product are expected from a given number of moles of reactant, two operations are necessary. First, we must determine how many moles of product to expect using the coefficients of the balanced chemical equation (Section 5.5). Then, we convert the number of moles of product to the number of grams using the molar mass (Section 5.4). Each step needs a conversion factor. The stepwise procedure is outlined in the accompanying *How To,* and then illustrated with an example in Sample Problem 5.13.

## How To Convert Moles of Reactant to Grams of Product

**Example:** In the upper atmosphere, high-energy radiation from the sun converts oxygen ($O_2$) to ozone ($O_3$). Using the balanced equation, how many grams of $O_3$ are formed from 9.0 mol of $O_2$?

$$3\ O_2(g) \xrightarrow{\text{sunlight}} 2\ O_3(g)$$

**Step [1]** **Convert the number of moles of reactant to the number of moles of product using a mole–mole conversion factor.**

- Use the coefficients in the balanced chemical equation to write mole–mole conversion factors.

- Multiply the number of moles of starting material (9.0 mol) by the conversion factor to give the number of moles of product. In this example, 6.0 mol of $O_3$ are formed.

| **Moles of reactant** | | | | **Moles of product** |
|---|---|---|---|---|

$$9.0\ \text{mol}\ O_2 \quad \times \quad \frac{2\ \text{mol}\ O_3}{3\ \text{mol}\ O_2} \quad = \quad 6.0\ \text{mol}\ O_3$$

Moles $O_2$ cancel.

**Step [2]** **Convert the number of moles of product to the number of grams of product using the product's molar mass.**

- Use the molar mass of the product ($O_3$) to write a conversion factor. The molar mass of $O_3$ is 48.00 g/mol (3 O atoms × 16.00 g/mol for each O atom = 48.00 g/mol).

$$\frac{1\ \text{mol}\ O_3}{48.00\ \text{g}\ O_3} \quad \text{or} \quad \frac{48.00\ \text{g}\ O_3}{1\ \text{mol}\ O_3} \quad \overset{\curvearrowright}{\text{Choose this conversion factor to cancel mol.}}$$

- Multiply the number of moles of product (from step [1]) by the conversion factor to give the number of grams of product.

| **Moles of product** | | | | **Grams of product** |
|---|---|---|---|---|

$$6.0\ \text{mol}\ O_3 \quad \times \quad \frac{48.00\ \text{g}\ O_3}{1\ \text{mol}\ O_3} \quad = \quad 288\ \text{g, rounded to 290 g of}\ O_3$$

Moles cancel.

**Answer**

It is also possible to combine the multiplication operations from steps [1] and [2] into a single operation using both conversion factors. This converts the moles of starting material to grams of product all at once. Both the one-step and stepwise approaches give the same overall result.

Ethanol ($C_2H_6O$) is the alcohol in red wine, formed by the fermentation of grapes. Ethanol depresses the central nervous system, increases the production of stomach acid, and dilates blood vessels. Excessive alcohol consumption is a major health problem in the United States.

## SAMPLE PROBLEM 5.13

Wine is produced by the fermentation of grapes. In fermentation, the carbohydrate glucose ($C_6H_{12}O_6$) is converted to ethanol and carbon dioxide according to the given balanced equation. How many grams of ethanol ($C_2H_6O$, molar mass 46.07 g/mol) are produced from 5.00 mol of glucose?

$$C_6H_{12}O_6(aq) \longrightarrow 2\ C_2H_6O(aq)\ +\ 2\ CO_2(g)$$
$$\text{glucose} \qquad\qquad \text{ethanol}$$

### Analysis and Solution

**[1] Convert the number of moles of reactant to the number of moles of product using a mole–mole conversion factor.**

- Use the coefficients in the balanced chemical equation to write mole–mole conversion factors for the two compounds—one mole of glucose ($C_6H_{12}O_6$) forms two moles of ethanol ($C_2H_6O$).
- Multiply the number of moles of reactant (glucose) by the conversion factor to give the number of moles of product (ethanol).

| Moles of reactant | | mole–mole conversion factor | | Moles of product |

$$5.00\ \text{mol}\ C_6H_{12}O_6 \quad \times \quad \frac{2\ \text{mol}\ C_2H_6O}{1\ \text{mol}\ C_6H_{12}O_6} \quad = \quad 10.0\ \text{mol}\ C_2H_6O$$

Moles $C_6H_{12}O_6$ cancel.

**[2] Convert the number of moles of product to the number of grams of product using the product's molar mass.**

- Use the molar mass of the product ($C_2H_6O$, molar mass 46.07 g/mol) to write a conversion factor.
- Multiply the number of moles of product (from step [1]) by the conversion factor to give the number of grams of product.

| Moles of product | | molar mass conversion factor | | Grams of product |

$$10.0\ \text{mol}\ C_2H_6O \quad \times \quad \frac{46.07\ \text{g}\ C_2H_6O}{1\ \text{mol}\ C_2H_6O} \quad = \quad 461\ \text{g}\ C_2H_6O$$

Moles cancel.                                                                        **Answer**

## PROBLEM 5.23

Using the balanced equation for fermentation written in Sample Problem 5.13, answer the following questions.

a. How many grams of ethanol are formed from 0.55 mol of glucose?
b. How many grams of $CO_2$ are formed from 0.25 mol of glucose?
c. How many grams of glucose are needed to form 1.0 mol of ethanol?

## PROBLEM 5.24

Using the balanced equation for the combustion of ethanol, answer the following questions.

$$C_2H_6O(l) + 3\ O_2(g) \longrightarrow 2\ CO_2(g) + 3\ H_2O(g)$$
$$\text{ethanol}$$

a. How many grams of $CO_2$ are formed from 0.50 mol of ethanol?
b. How many grams of $H_2O$ are formed from 2.4 mol of ethanol?
c. How many grams of $O_2$ are needed to react with 0.25 mol of ethanol?

## 5.6B   Converting Grams of Reactant to Grams of Product

**The coefficients in chemical equations tell us the ratio of the number of *molecules* or *moles* that are involved in a chemical reaction.** The coefficients do *not*, however, tell us directly about the number of grams. That's because the molar mass—the number of grams in one mole—of a substance depends on the identity of the elements that compose it. One mole of $H_2O$ molecules weighs 18.02 g, one mole of NaCl weighs 58.44 g, and one mole of sugar molecules weighs 342.3 g (Figure 5.3).

In the laboratory, we measure out the number of grams of a reactant on a balance. This does not tell us directly the number of grams of a particular product that will form, because in all likelihood, the molar masses of the reactant and product are different. To carry out this type of calculation—grams of one compound (reactant) to grams of another compound (product)—three operations are necessary.

First, we must determine how many moles of reactant are contained in the given number of grams using the molar mass. Then, we can determine the number of moles of product expected using the coefficients of the balanced chemical equation. Finally, we convert the number of moles of product to the number of grams of product using its molar mass. Now there are three steps and three conversion factors. The stepwise procedure is outlined in the accompanying *How To,* and then illustrated with an example in Sample Problem 5.14.

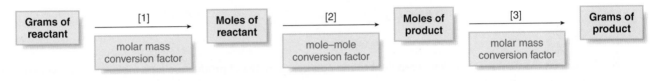

**Figure 5.3**   One Mole of Water, Table Salt, and Table Sugar

one mole of table sugar
**$C_{12}H_{22}O_{11}$**
342.3 g/mol

one mole of table salt
**NaCl**
58.44 g/mol

one mole of water molecules
**$H_2O$**
18.02 g/mol

One mole of each substance has the same number of units—$6.02 \times 10^{23}$ $H_2O$ molecules, $6.02 \times 10^{23}$ $Na^+$ and $Cl^-$ ions, and $6.02 \times 10^{23}$ sugar molecules. The molar mass of each substance is *different,* however, because they are each composed of *different* elements.

## How To Convert Grams of Reactant to Grams of Product

**Example:** Ethanol ($C_2H_6O$, molar mass 46.07 g/mol) is synthesized by reacting ethylene ($C_2H_4$, molar mass 28.05 g/mol) with water. How many grams of ethanol are formed from 14 g of ethylene?

ethylene                                          ethanol

**Step [1]** Convert the number of grams of reactant to the number of moles of reactant using the reactant's molar mass.

- Use the molar mass of the reactant ($C_2H_4$) to write a conversion factor.

$$\frac{28.05 \text{ g } C_2H_4}{1 \text{ mol } C_2H_4} \quad \text{or} \quad \boxed{\frac{1 \text{ mol } C_2H_4}{28.05 \text{ g } C_2H_4}} \quad \text{Choose this conversion factor to cancel g.}$$

- Multiply the number of grams of reactant by the conversion factor to give the number of moles of reactant.

| Grams of reactant | | Moles of reactant |
|---|---|---|

$$14 \text{ g } C_2H_4 \quad \times \quad \frac{1 \text{ mol } C_2H_4}{28.05 \text{ g } C_2H_4} \quad = \quad 0.50 \text{ mol } C_2H_4$$

Grams cancel.

**Step [2]** Convert the number of moles of reactant to the number of moles of product using a mole–mole conversion factor.

- Use the coefficients in the balanced chemical equation to write mole–mole conversion factors.

$$\frac{1 \text{ mol } C_2H_4}{1 \text{ mol } C_2H_6O} \quad \text{or} \quad \boxed{\frac{1 \text{ mol } C_2H_6O}{1 \text{ mol } C_2H_4}} \quad \text{Choose this conversion factor to cancel mol } C_2H_4.$$

- Multiply the number of moles of reactant by the conversion factor to give the number of moles of product. In this example, 0.50 mol of $C_2H_6O$ is formed.

| Moles of reactant | | Moles of product |
|---|---|---|

$$0.50 \text{ mol } C_2H_4 \quad \times \quad \frac{1 \text{ mol } C_2H_6O}{1 \text{ mol } C_2H_4} \quad = \quad 0.50 \text{ mol } C_2H_6O$$

Moles $C_2H_4$ cancel.

**Step [3]** Convert the number of moles of product to the number of grams of product using the product's molar mass.

- Use the molar mass of the product ($C_2H_6O$) to write a conversion factor.

$$\frac{1 \text{ mol } C_2H_6O}{46.07 \text{ g } C_2H_6O} \quad \text{or} \quad \boxed{\frac{46.07 \text{ g } C_2H_6O}{1 \text{ mol } C_2H_6O}} \quad \text{Choose this conversion factor to cancel mol } C_2H_6O.$$

- Multiply the number of moles of product (from step [2]) by the conversion factor to give the number of grams of product.

| Moles of product | | Grams of product |
|---|---|---|

$$0.50 \text{ mol } C_2H_6O \quad \times \quad \frac{46.07 \text{ g } C_2H_6O}{1 \text{ mol } C_2H_6O} \quad = \quad 23 \text{ g } C_2H_6O$$

Moles $C_2H_6O$ cancel.

**Answer**

It is also possible to combine the multiplication operations from steps [1], [2], and [3] into a single operation using all three conversion factors. This converts grams of starting material to grams of product all at once. Both the one-step and stepwise approaches give the same overall result.

| Grams of reactant | | molar mass conversion factor | | mole–mole conversion factor | | molar mass conversion factor | | Grams of product |
|---|---|---|---|---|---|---|---|---|
| $14 \text{ g } C_2H_4$ | $\times$ | $\dfrac{1 \text{ mol } C_2H_4}{28.05 \text{ g } C_2H_4}$ | $\times$ | $\dfrac{1 \text{ mol } C_2H_6O}{1 \text{ mol } C_2H_4}$ | $\times$ | $\dfrac{46.07 \text{ g } C_2H_6O}{1 \text{ mol } C_2H_6O}$ | $=$ | $23 \text{ g } C_2H_6O$ |

Grams cancel.   Moles $C_2H_4$ cancel.   Moles $C_2H_6O$ cancel.

**Answer**

### SAMPLE PROBLEM 5.14

How many grams of aspirin are formed from 10.0 g of salicylic acid using the given balanced equation?

$$C_7H_6O_3(s) \;+\; C_2H_4O_2(l) \longrightarrow C_9H_8O_4(s) \;+\; H_2O(l)$$

salicylic acid      acetic acid            aspirin

### Analysis and Solution

**[1] Convert the number of grams of reactant to the number of moles of reactant using the reactant's molar mass.**

- Use the molar mass of the reactant ($C_7H_6O_3$, molar mass 138.1 g/mol) to write a conversion factor. Multiply the number of grams of reactant by the conversion factor to give the number of moles of reactant.

| Grams of reactant | | molar mass conversion factor | | Moles of reactant |
|---|---|---|---|---|
| $10.0 \text{ g } C_7H_6O_3$ | $\times$ | $\dfrac{1 \text{ mol } C_7H_6O_3}{138.1 \text{ g } C_7H_6O_3}$ | $=$ | $0.0724 \text{ mol } C_7H_6O_3$ |

Grams cancel.

**[2] Convert the number of moles of reactant to the number of moles of product using a mole–mole conversion factor.**

- Use the coefficients in the balanced chemical equation to write mole–mole conversion factors for the two compounds—one mole of salicylic acid ($C_7H_6O_3$) forms one mole of aspirin ($C_9H_8O_4$).
- Multiply the number of moles of reactant (salicylic acid) by the conversion factor to give the number of moles of product (aspirin).

| Moles of reactant | | mole–mole conversion factor | | Moles of product |
|---|---|---|---|---|
| $0.0724 \text{ mol } C_7H_6O_3$ | $\times$ | $\dfrac{1 \text{ mol } C_9H_8O_4}{1 \text{ mol } C_7H_6O_3}$ | $=$ | $0.0724 \text{ mol } C_9H_8O_4$ |

Moles $C_7H_6O_3$ cancel.

**[3] Convert the number of moles of product to the number of grams of product using the product's molar mass.**

- Use the molar mass of the product ($C_9H_8O_4$, molar mass 180.2 g/mol) to write a conversion factor. Multiply the number of moles of product (from step [2]) by the conversion factor to give the number of grams of product.

| Moles of product | | molar mass conversion factor | | Grams of product |
|---|---|---|---|---|
| $0.0724 \text{ mol } C_9H_8O_4$ | $\times$ | $\dfrac{180.2 \text{ g } C_9H_8O_4}{1 \text{ mol } C_9H_8O_4}$ | $=$ | $13.0 \text{ g } C_9H_8O_4$ |

Moles cancel.

**Answer**

### PROBLEM 5.25

Use the balanced equation in Sample Problem 5.14 for the conversion of salicylic acid and acetic acid to aspirin to answer the following questions.

    a. How many grams of aspirin are formed from 55.5 g of salicylic acid?
    b. How many grams of acetic acid are needed to react with 55.5 g of salicylic acid?
    c. How many grams of water are formed from 55.5 g of salicylic acid?

### PROBLEM 5.26

Use the balanced equation, $N_2 + O_2 \longrightarrow 2\ NO$, to answer the following questions.

    a. How many grams of NO are formed from 10.0 g of $N_2$?
    b. How many grams of NO are formed from 10.0 g of $O_2$?
    c. How many grams of $O_2$ are needed to react completely with 10.0 g of $N_2$?

## 5.7  Percent Yield

In determining the number of moles or grams of product in Sections 5.5 and 5.6, we assumed that each reaction gives the maximum amount of product from a given amount of reactant. This value is called the **theoretical yield** of a reaction.

The actual yield is an experimental value determined by weighing the product obtained on a balance. The theoretical yield, on the other hand, is calculated from the coefficients of the balanced equation.

- The *theoretical yield* is the amount of product expected from a given amount of reactant based on the coefficients in the balanced chemical equation.

Usually, however, the amount of product formed is *less* than the maximum amount predicted. Sometimes other undesired reactions, called **side reactions,** occur between the reactants. At other times the desired product is formed, but it goes on to react further to form another product. Moreover, each time material is weighed and transferred to a reaction vessel, or anytime a separation or purification step is carried out, material is inadvertently lost.

- The *actual yield* is the amount of product isolated from a reaction.

### 5.7A  Calculating Percent Yield

The theoretical and actual yields are typically reported in grams. The amount of product actually formed in a particular reaction is reported as a **percent yield.**

$$\text{Percent yield} = \frac{\text{actual yield (g)}}{\text{theoretical yield (g)}} \times 100\%$$

For example, if a reaction forms 25.0 g of product and the theoretical yield is 40.0 g, the percent yield is calculated as follows.

$$\text{Percent yield} = \frac{25.0\ \text{g}}{40.0\ \text{g}} \times 100\% = 62.5\%$$

### SAMPLE PROBLEM 5.15

Consider the reaction of ethylene ($C_2H_4$) and water to form ethanol ($C_2H_6O$), which was mentioned in Section 5.6B. If the theoretical yield of ethanol is 23 g in a reaction, what is the percent yield of ethanol if only 15 g of ethanol are actually formed?

#### Analysis

Use the formula, percent yield = (actual yield/theoretical yield) × 100% to calculate the percent yield.

#### Solution

$$\text{Percent yield} = \frac{\text{actual yield (g)}}{\text{theoretical yield (g)}} \times 100\%$$

$$= \frac{15\ \text{g}}{23\ \text{g}} \times 100\% = 65\%$$

**Answer**

## SAMPLE PROBLEM 5.16

When charcoal is burned, the carbon (C) it contains reacts with oxygen ($O_2$) to form carbon dioxide ($CO_2$). (a) What is the theoretical yield of $CO_2$ in grams from 0.50 mol of C? (b) What is the percent yield if 10.0 g of $CO_2$ are formed?

$$C(s) + O_2(g) \longrightarrow CO_2(g)$$

### Analysis

To answer part (a), convert the number of moles of reactant to the number of moles of product, as in Section 5.6A. Then, convert the number of moles of product to the number of grams of product using the product's molar mass. This is the theoretical yield. To answer part (b), use the formula, percent yield = (actual yield/theoretical yield) × 100%.

### Solution

a. Calculate the theoretical yield using the procedure outlined in Sample Problem 5.13.

[1] **Convert the number of moles of reactant to the number of moles of product using a mole–mole conversion factor.**

- Use the coefficients in the balanced equation to write a mole–mole conversion factor for the two compounds—one mole of carbon forms one mole of $CO_2$. Multiply the number of moles of reactant (carbon) by the conversion factor to give the number of moles of product ($CO_2$).

| Moles of reactant | | mole–mole conversion factor | | Moles of product |
|---|---|---|---|---|
| 0.50 mol C | × | $\dfrac{1 \text{ mol } CO_2}{1 \text{ mol C}}$ | = | 0.50 mol $CO_2$ |

[2] **Convert the number of moles of product to the number of grams of product—the theoretical yield—using the product's molar mass.**

- Use the molar mass of the product ($CO_2$, molar mass 44.01 g/mol) to write a conversion factor. Multiply the number of moles of product (from step [1]) by the conversion factor to give the number of grams of product.

| Moles of product | | molar mass conversion factor | | Grams of product |
|---|---|---|---|---|
| 0.50 mol $CO_2$ | × | $\dfrac{44.01 \text{ g } CO_2}{1 \text{ mol } CO_2}$ | = | 22 g $CO_2$ |

Theoretical yield
**Answer: part (a)**

b. Use the theoretical yield from part (a) and the given actual yield to calculate the percent yield.

$$\text{Percent yield} = \frac{\text{actual yield (g)}}{\text{theoretical yield (g)}} \times 100\%$$

$$= \frac{10.0 \text{ g}}{22 \text{ g}} \times 100\% = 45\%$$

**Answer: part (b)**

## PROBLEM 5.27

Using the chemical equation in Sample Problem 5.16, answer each question. (a) What is the theoretical yield of $CO_2$ from 3.50 mol of charcoal? (b) What is the percent yield if the reaction gives 53.5 g of $CO_2$?

## PROBLEM 5.28

Consider the conversion of oxygen ($O_2$) to ozone ($O_3$) described in Section 5.6A; that is, $3 O_2 \longrightarrow 2 O_3$. (a) What is the theoretical yield of $O_3$ in grams from 8.0 mol of $O_2$? (b) What is the percent yield if the reaction actually gives 155 g of $O_3$?

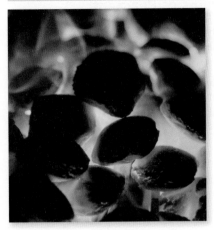

Charcoal is composed of a network of covalently bonded carbon atoms. When charcoal is burned in a grill or coal is burned in a furnace, carbon atoms combine with $O_2$ from the air to form carbon dioxide ($CO_2$).

## 5.7B   Calculating Percent Yield from Grams of Reactant

Since we weigh the amount of reactants and products on a balance, we must be able to calculate a percent yield from the number of grams of reactant used and the number of grams of product formed. This latter quantity is the **actual yield,** and it is always experimentally determined; that is, it is *not* a calculated value. We can carry out this lengthy calculation by putting together the steps in Sample Problems 5.14 and 5.15. Sample Problem 5.17 illustrates the steps used to calculate a percent yield when the number of grams of reactant used and the actual yield of product formed are both known.

### SAMPLE PROBLEM 5.17

Acetaminophen, the active ingredient in Tylenol, can be prepared by the chemical reaction given below. What is the percent yield when 60.0 g of 4-aminophenol reacts with acetyl chloride to form 70.0 g of acetaminophen?

4-aminophenol   acetyl    acetaminophen
molar mass 109.1 g/mol chloride   molar mass 151.2 g/mol

### Analysis

To find the theoretical yield, convert grams of reactant to grams of product, following the three steps in Sample Problem 5.14. Then, use the formula, percent yield = (actual yield/theoretical yield) × 100%.

### Solution

**[1] Convert the number of grams of reactant to the number of moles of reactant using the reactant's molar mass.**

- Use the molar mass of the reactant, 4-aminophenol, to write a conversion factor. Multiply the number of grams of reactant by the conversion factor to give the number of moles of reactant.

| Grams of reactant | | molar mass conversion factor | | Moles of reactant |
|---|---|---|---|---|

$$60.0 \text{ g 4-aminophenol} \quad \times \quad \frac{1 \text{ mol 4-aminophenol}}{109.1 \text{ g 4-aminophenol}} \quad = \quad 0.550 \text{ mol 4-aminophenol}$$

**[2] Convert the number of moles of reactant to the number of moles of product using a mole–mole conversion factor.**

- Use the coefficients in the balanced chemical equation to write a mole–mole conversion factor—one mole of 4-aminophenol forms one mole of acetaminophen. Multiply the number of moles of reactant by the conversion factor to give the number of moles of product.

| Moles of reactant | | mole–mole conversion factor | | Moles of product |
|---|---|---|---|---|

$$0.550 \text{ mol 4-aminophenol} \quad \times \quad \frac{1 \text{ mol acetaminophen}}{1 \text{ mol 4-aminophenol}} \quad = \quad 0.550 \text{ mol acetaminophen}$$

**[3] Convert the number of moles of product to the number of grams of product using the product's molar mass.**

- Use the molar mass of the product to write a conversion factor. Multiply the number of moles of product (from step [2]) by the conversion factor to give the number of grams of product.

| Moles of product | | molar mass conversion factor | | Grams of product |
|---|---|---|---|---|

$$0.550 \text{ mol acetaminophen} \quad \times \quad \frac{151.2 \text{ g acetaminophen}}{1 \text{ mol acetaminophen}} \quad = \quad 83.2 \text{ g acetaminophen}$$

**Theoretical yield**

**[4] Use the theoretical yield and the given actual yield to calculate the percent yield.**

$$\text{Percent yield} = \frac{\text{actual yield (g)}}{\text{theoretical yield (g)}} \times 100\%$$

$$= \frac{70.0 \text{ g}}{83.2 \text{ g}} \times 100\% = 84.1\%$$

**Answer**

### PROBLEM 5.29

Using the equation in Sample Problem 5.17, answer each question. (a) What is the theoretical yield of acetaminophen from 80.0 g of 4-aminophenol? (b) What is the percent yield if the reaction gives 65.5 g of acetaminophen?

### PROBLEM 5.30

Consider the conversion of oxygen ($O_2$) to ozone ($O_3$) described in Section 5.6A; that is, $3 O_2 \longrightarrow 2 O_3$. (a) What is the theoretical yield of $O_3$ in grams from 324 g of $O_2$? (b) What is the percent yield if the reaction actually gives 122 g of $O_3$?

## 5.7C FOCUS ON HEALTH & MEDICINE
### The Importance of Percent Yield in the Pharmaceutical Industry

Although some drugs, like the cardiac drug digoxin (used to treat congestive heart failure, Section 1.1), are isolated directly from a natural source, most widely used drugs are synthesized in the laboratory. All common pain relievers—aspirin, acetaminophen, and ibuprofen—are synthetic. The same is true for the bronchodilator albuterol (trade name Proventil or Ventolin), the antidepressant fluoxetine (trade name Prozac), and the cholesterol-lowering medication atorvastatin (trade name Lipitor), whose three-dimensional structures are shown in Figure 5.4.

Once it has been determined that a drug is safe and effective, a pharmaceutical company must be able to prepare large quantities of the material cost-efficiently. This means that cheap and readily available starting materials must be used. It also means that the reactions used to synthesize a drug must proceed in high yield. Rarely is a drug prepared in a single step, and typically, five or more steps may be required in a synthesis.

- To determine the overall percent yield in a synthesis that has more than one step, multiply the percent yield for each step.

For example, if a synthesis has five steps and each step has a 90.% yield (0.90 written as a decimal), the overall yield is

$$0.90 \times 0.90 \times 0.90 \times 0.90 \times 0.90 = 0.59 = 59\%$$

yield for each step, written as a decimal

**overall yield for five steps**

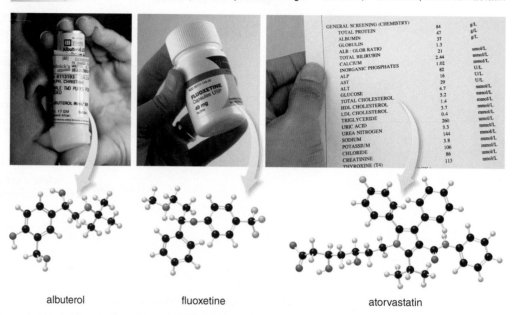

**Figure 5.4**    Three Widely Used Synthetic Drugs—Albuterol, Fluoxetine, and Atorvastatin

albuterol                         fluoxetine                              atorvastatin

Most commonly prescribed drugs are synthesized in the laboratory. Albuterol (Proventil, Ventolin) is a bronchodilator—that is, it widens airways—and so it is used to treat asthma. Fluoxetine (Prozac) is one of the most common antidepressants currently on the market, used by over 40 million individuals since 1986. Atorvastatin (Lipitor) lowers cholesterol levels, and in this way decreases the risk of heart attack and stroke.

Thus, even if all steps proceed in high yield, the overall yield is considerably lower—59% in this example. If only one step has a lower yield, say 50.%, the overall yield drops even more, from 59% to 33%.

$$0.50 \times 0.90 \times 0.90 \times 0.90 \times 0.90 = 0.33 = 33\%$$

one low-yield reaction                                    **overall yield
                                                          for five steps**

Moreover, many drugs are synthesized by routes that require 10 or more steps, resulting in a low overall yield. Thus, pharmaceutical companies are faced with the task of developing drugs that have the desired physiological effects, which are prepared by reactions that give high yields of the desired compounds.

## PROBLEM 5.31

The synthetic antiviral drug Tamiflu, currently the most effective agent against avian influenza, is prepared by a 10-step synthesis. What is the overall yield of Tamiflu in each of the following 10-step syntheses?

a. Each step proceeds in 90.% yield.
b. Each step proceeds in 80.% yield.
c. One step proceeds in 50.% yield, while the rest occur in 90.% yield.
d. The following yields are recorded: 20.% (one reaction), 50.% (two reactions), 80.% (all remaining reactions).

## 5.8   Limiting Reactants

Up to now we have assumed that we have the exact ratio of the reactants needed to carry out a reaction. In the following reaction, the mole ratio of **A** to **B** is 1:1, so one molecule of **A** is needed to react with one molecule of **B** to form one molecule of the product, **AB.**

Suppose, instead, that the reaction contains an *excess* of **B,** as shown in the molecular art, where the reaction mixture contains six molecules of **A** and eight molecules of **B.** In this case, all six **A** molecules react with six **B** molecules, and two **B** molecules are left over. Reactant **A** is all used up, so the amount of **A** *limits* how much product **AB** can be formed.

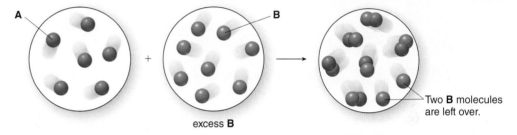

- The *limiting reactant* is the reactant that is completely used up in a reaction.

In this example, **A** is the limiting reactant since **B** is present in excess.

### 5.8A   Determining the Limiting Reactant

We deal with the concept of limiting reactants often in everyday life. To make turkey sandwiches, we may use two pieces of bread for each slice of turkey. If we had eight slices of bread and three slices of turkey, we could make three sandwiches using six slices of bread and three pieces of turkey, leaving two pieces of bread left over. In this case, the turkey is the limiting reactant and the bread is present in excess.

excess reactant          limiting reactant                    product                    leftovers

Sample Problem 5.18 illustrates how to determine which reactant is limiting using the mole ratios in a balanced equation.

### SAMPLE PROBLEM 5.18

Consider the reaction of hydrogen and oxygen to form water, according to the balanced equation: $2 H_2(g) + O_2(g) \longrightarrow 2 H_2O(l)$. Identify the limiting reactant in the molecular art, and draw a representation showing how much product is formed and what reactant molecules are left over.

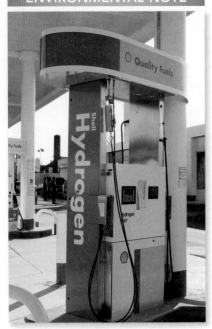

The reaction of hydrogen with oxygen (Sample Problem 5.18) releases a great deal of energy and offers an alternative to burning fossil fuels for powering vehicles. Current research efforts are underway to make this process economical and feasible for widespread use.

## Analysis

Use the amount of each reactant and the mole ratio from the balanced equation to determine the limiting reactant. Use the amount of limiting reactant to determine the amount of product formed.

## Solution

**[1]** **To determine how much of one reactant is needed to react with a second reactant, label one reactant as the original quantity and the second reactant as the unknown quantity.**

- These labels are completely arbitrary. In this example we identify the number of molecules of $H_2$ as the original quantity.

$$\begin{array}{cc} 4 \text{ molecules of } H_2 & ? \text{ molecules of } O_2 \\ \text{original quantity} & \text{unknown quantity} \end{array}$$

**[2]** **Write out the conversion factors that relate the number of moles (or molecules) of reactants.**

- Use the coefficients in the balanced equation to write a mole–mole (or molecule–molecule) conversion factor for $H_2$ and $O_2$.

$$\frac{2 \text{ molecules } H_2}{1 \text{ molecule } O_2} \quad \text{or} \quad \boxed{\frac{1 \text{ molecule } O_2}{2 \text{ molecules } H_2}}$$

Choose this conversion factor to cancel molecules of $H_2$.

**[3]** **Calculate the number of moles (or molecules) of the second reactant needed for complete reaction.**

$$4 \text{ molecules } H_2 \times \frac{1 \text{ molecule } O_2}{2 \text{ molecules } H_2} = 2 \text{ molecules of } O_2 \text{ needed}$$

**[4]** **Analyze the two possible outcomes.**

- If the amount present of the second reactant is *less than* what is needed, the *second reactant is the limiting reactant.*
- If the amount present of the second reactant is *greater than* what is needed, the *second reactant is in excess.*

In this reaction only two molecules of $O_2$ are needed but three molecules of $O_2$ are present, so $O_2$ is present in excess and **$H_2$ is the limiting reactant.** To draw the molecular art representing the product, we must know what happens to each reactant and how much product is formed.

4 molecules of $H_2O$

1 $O_2$ left over

- Since $H_2$ is the limiting reactant, all of the $H_2$ is consumed and none is left.
- Since two molecules of $O_2$ react and three were present at the outset, one molecule of $O_2$ is left over.
- Using the balanced equation, the number of molecules of product formed equals the number of molecules of the limiting reactant consumed. Thus, four molecules of $H_2$ yield four molecules of $H_2O$.

| Summary | Reactants | | Product |
|---|---|---|---|
| Equation | $2 H_2$          +          $O_2$ | $\longrightarrow$ | $2 H_2O$ |
| Initial quantities | 4 molecules | 3 molecules | 0 molecules |
| Used or formed | −4 molecules | −2 molecules | +4 molecules |
| Molecules remaining | 0 molecules | 1 molecule | 4 molecules |
| | Limiting reactant | Excess reactant | |

### PROBLEM 5.32

Consider the reaction of hydrogen and nitrogen to form ammonia, according to the balanced equation: $3 H_2(g) + N_2(g) \longrightarrow 2 NH_3(g)$. Identify the limiting reactant in the molecular art, and draw a representation showing how much product is formed and what reactant molecules are left over.

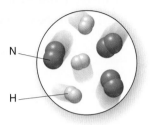

### PROBLEM 5.33

Using the balanced equation for the reaction of $H_2$ with $O_2$ to form $H_2O$ in Sample Problem 5.18, determine the limiting reactant under each of the following conditions.

a. 5.0 mol $H_2$ and 5.0 mol $O_2$        c. 8.0 mol $H_2$ and 2.0 mol $O_2$

b. 5.0 mol $H_2$ and 8.0 mol $O_2$        d. 2.0 mol $H_2$ and 5.0 mol $O_2$

## 5.8B Using the Limiting Reactant to Determine How Much Product Is Formed

When a reaction has a limiting reactant,

- **The number of moles of limiting reactant determines the number of moles of product that can form.**

For example, the molecular art shows the reaction of $A_2$ with $B_2$ to form $AB$, with $B_2$ present in excess. The amount of $A_2$, the limiting reactant, determines how much $AB$ can form. Since the balanced equation shows that each $A_2$ molecule forms two $AB$ molecules, three $A_2$ molecules form six $AB$ molecules.

Sample Problem 5.19 illustrates how to determine the amount of product formed from a limiting reactant using mole ratios in a balanced equation. **Keep in mind that the number of moles (*not* grams) of the limiting reactant determines the number of moles (*not* grams) of product.**

## SAMPLE PROBLEM 5.19

Using the balanced equation, $3 H_2(g) + N_2(g) \longrightarrow 2 NH_3(g)$, calculate the number of moles of product formed from 5.0 moles of $H_2$ and 3.0 moles of $N_2$.

### Analysis and Solution

**[1] Determine the limiting reactant as in Sample Problem 5.18.**

- Identify $H_2$ as the original quantity and use the mole ratio from the balanced equation as a conversion factor to calculate how much $N_2$ is needed for complete reaction.

$$\underset{\text{conversion factor}}{\boxed{\text{mole–mole}}}$$

$$5.0 \text{ mol } H_2 \qquad \times \qquad \frac{1 \text{ mol } N_2}{3 \text{ mol } H_2} \qquad = \qquad 1.7 \text{ mol } N_2 \text{ needed}$$

- Since the amount of $N_2$ present is greater than what is needed, $N_2$ is present in excess and **$H_2$ is the limiting reactant.**

**[2] Convert the number of moles of limiting reactant to the number of moles of product using a mole–mole conversion factor.**

$$\underset{\text{conversion factor}}{\boxed{\text{mole–mole}}}$$

$$5.0 \text{ mol } H_2 \qquad \times \qquad \frac{2 \text{ mol } NH_3}{3 \text{ mol } H_2} \qquad = \qquad 3.3 \text{ mol } NH_3 \text{ formed}$$

**Answer**

## PROBLEM 5.34

Using the balanced equation, $3 H_2(g) + N_2(g) \longrightarrow 2 NH_3(g)$, calculate the number of moles of product formed under each of the following reaction conditions.

a. 1.5 mol $H_2$ and 1.0 mol $N_2$            c. 2.0 mol $H_2$ and 3.0 mol $N_2$

b. 1.0 mol $H_2$ and 2.0 mol $N_2$            d. 7.5 mol $H_2$ and 2.0 mol $N_2$

## 5.8C    Determining the Limiting Reactant Using the Number of Grams

In the laboratory, we measure out the number of grams (not the number of moles) of each reactant on a balance. To determine the limiting reactant from the number of grams, we must first determine the number of moles of each reactant using the molar mass, as shown in Sample Problem 5.20.

## SAMPLE PROBLEM 5.20

Using the balanced equation, $N_2(g) + O_2(g) \longrightarrow 2 NO(g)$, determine the limiting reactant when 10.0 g of $N_2$ (molar mass 28.02 g/mol) react with 10.0 g of $O_2$ (molar mass 32.00 g/mol).

### Analysis

Convert the number of grams to the number of moles for each reactant, and then use the steps in Sample Problem 5.18 to determine the limiting reactant.

### Solution

**[1] Convert the number of grams of each reactant to the number of moles using the molar masses.**

$$\boxed{\text{Moles of } N_2\text{:}} \qquad 10.0 \text{ g } N_2 \quad \times \quad \frac{1 \text{ mol } N_2}{28.02 \text{ g } N_2} \quad = \quad 0.357 \text{ mol } N_2$$

$$\boxed{\text{Moles of } O_2\text{:}} \qquad 10.0 \text{ g } O_2 \quad \times \quad \frac{1 \text{ mol } O_2}{32.00 \text{ g } O_2} \quad = \quad 0.313 \text{ mol } O_2$$

**[2] Determine the limiting reactant as in Sample Problem 5.18.**

- Identify $N_2$ as the original quantity and use the mole ratio from the balanced equation as a conversion factor to calculate how much $O_2$ is needed for complete reaction.

$$\boxed{\begin{array}{c}\text{mole–mole}\\\text{conversion factor}\end{array}}$$

$$0.357 \text{ mol } N_2 \quad \times \quad \frac{1 \text{ mol } O_2}{1 \text{ mol } N_2} \quad = \quad 0.357 \text{ mol } O_2 \text{ needed}$$

- Since the amount of $O_2$ present is less than what is needed, **$O_2$ is the limiting reactant.**

## PROBLEM 5.35

Using the balanced equation, $N_2(g) + O_2(g) \longrightarrow 2\ NO(g)$, determine the limiting reactant under the following conditions ($N_2$, molar mass 28.02 g/mol; $O_2$, molar mass 32.00 g/mol).

   a. 12.5 g $N_2$ and 15.0 g $O_2$          b. 14.0 g $N_2$ and 13.0 g $O_2$

## SAMPLE PROBLEM 5.21

Using the balanced equation, $N_2(g) + O_2(g) \longrightarrow 2\ NO(g)$, calculate the number of grams of NO (molar mass 30.01 g/mol) formed when 10.0 g of $N_2$ (molar mass 28.02 g/mol) react with 10.0 g of $O_2$ (molar mass 32.00 g/mol).

### Analysis

Three steps are required:

- Determine the limiting reactant.
- Use the mole ratio from the balanced equation to calculate the number of moles of product formed.
- Convert the moles of product to grams using the molar mass.

### Solution

**[1] Determine the limiting reactant.**

- Convert the number of grams of each reactant to the number of moles using the molar masses.
- Use a mole–mole conversion factor to determine which reactant is present in excess.
- As shown in Sample Problem 5.20, when 10.0 g of $N_2$ (0.357 mol) react with 10.0 g (0.313 mol) of $O_2$, $O_2$ is the limiting reactant.

**[2] Convert the number of moles of limiting reactant to the number of moles of product using a mole–mole conversion factor.**

$$\boxed{\begin{array}{c}\text{mole–mole}\\\text{conversion factor}\end{array}}$$

$$0.313 \text{ mol } O_2 \quad \times \quad \frac{2 \text{ mol NO}}{1 \text{ mol } O_2} \quad = \quad 0.626 \text{ mol NO formed}$$

**[3] Convert the number of moles of product to the number of grams using the molar mass.**

$$0.626 \text{ mol NO} \times \frac{30.01 \text{ g NO}}{1 \text{ mol NO}} = 18.8 \text{ g NO formed}$$

$$\textbf{Answer}$$

## PROBLEM 5.36

For each set of reaction conditions in Problem 5.35, calculate the number of grams of product formed.

## PROBLEM 5.37

Using the balanced equation, $2\ H_2(g) + O_2(g) \longrightarrow 2\ H_2O(l)$, calculate the number of grams of $H_2O$ (molar mass 18.02 g/mol) formed when 5.00 g of $H_2$ (molar mass 2.016 g/mol) react with 10.0 g of $O_2$ (molar mass 32.00 g/mol).

## 5.9   Oxidation and Reduction

Another group of reactions—acid–base reactions—is discussed in Chapter 9.

Thus far we have examined features that are common to all types of chemical reactions. We conclude with an examination of one class of reactions that involves electron transfer—oxidation–reduction reactions.

### 5.9A   General Features of Oxidation–Reduction Reactions

A common type of chemical reaction involves the transfer of electrons from one element to another. When iron rusts, methane and wood burn, and a battery generates electricity, one element gains electrons and another loses them. These reactions involve **oxidation** and **reduction.**

- Oxidation is the loss of electrons from an atom.
- Reduction is the gain of electrons by an atom.

Oxidation and reduction are opposite processes, and both occur together in a single reaction called an **oxidation–reduction** or **redox reaction.** A redox reaction always has two components—one that is oxidized and one that is reduced.

- A redox reaction involves the transfer of electrons from one element to another.

An example of an oxidation–reduction reaction occurs when Zn metal reacts with $Cu^{2+}$ cations, as shown in Figure 5.5.

- Zn loses two electrons to form $Zn^{2+}$, so Zn is oxidized.
- $Cu^{2+}$ gains two electrons to form Cu metal, so $Cu^{2+}$ is reduced.

Benzoyl peroxide ($C_{14}H_{10}O_4$) is the active ingredient in several acne medications. Benzoyl peroxide kills bacteria by oxidation reactions.

**Figure 5.5**   A Redox Reaction—The Transfer of Electrons from Zn to $Cu^{2+}$

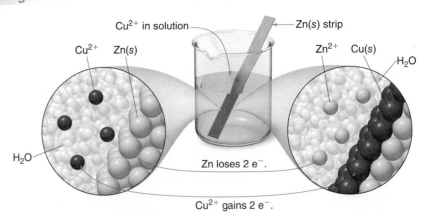

A redox reaction occurs when a strip of Zn metal is placed in a solution of $Cu^{2+}$ ions. In this reaction, Zn loses two electrons to form $Zn^{2+}$, which goes into solution. $Cu^{2+}$ gains two electrons to form Cu metal, which precipitates out of solution, forming a coating on the zinc strip.

Figure 5.6   Examples of Oxidation and Reduction Reactions

Each of these processes can be written as individual reactions, called **half reactions,** to emphasize which electrons are gained and lost.

- A compound that gains electrons (is reduced) while causing another compound to be oxidized is called an *oxidizing agent.*
- A compound that loses electrons (is oxidized) while causing another compound to be reduced is called a *reducing agent.*

In this example, Zn loses electrons to $Cu^{2+}$. We can think of Zn as a **reducing agent** since it causes $Cu^{2+}$ to gain electrons and become reduced. We can think of $Cu^{2+}$ as an **oxidizing agent** since it causes Zn to lose electrons and become oxidized.

To draw the products of an oxidation–reduction reaction, we must decide which element or ion gains electrons and which element or ion loses electrons. Use the following guidelines.

- When considering neutral atoms, metals lose electrons and nonmetals gain electrons.
- When considering ions, cations tend to gain electrons and anions tend to lose electrons.

Thus, the metals sodium (Na) and magnesium (Mg) readily lose electrons to form the cations $Na^+$ and $Mg^{2+}$, respectively; that is, they are oxidized. The nonmetals $O_2$ and $Cl_2$ readily gain electrons to form $2\ O^{2-}$ and $2\ Cl^-$, respectively; that is, they are reduced. A positively charged ion like $Cu^{2+}$ is reduced to Cu by gaining two electrons, while two negatively charged $Cl^-$ anions are oxidized to $Cl_2$ by losing two electrons. These reactions and additional examples are shown in Figure 5.6.

## SAMPLE PROBLEM 5.22

Identify the species that is oxidized and the species that is reduced in the following reaction. Write out half reactions to show how many electrons are gained or lost by each species.

$$Mg(s) + 2\ H^+(aq) \longrightarrow Mg^{2+}(aq) + H_2(g)$$

### Analysis

Metals and anions tend to lose electrons and thus undergo oxidation. Nonmetals and cations tend to gain electrons and thus undergo reduction.

### Solution

The metal Mg is oxidized to $Mg^{2+}$, thus losing two electrons. Two $H^+$ cations gain a total of two electrons, and so are reduced to the nonmetal $H_2$.

$$Mg(s) \longrightarrow Mg^{2+}(aq) + 2\,e^- \qquad\qquad 2\,H^+(aq) + 2\,e^- \longrightarrow H_2(g)$$

Mg is oxidized.                                  $H^+$ is reduced.    Two electrons are needed
                                                                     to balance charge.

We need enough electrons so that **the total charge is the same on both sides of the equation.** Since 2 $H^+$ cations have a +2 overall charge, this means that 2 $e^-$ must be gained so that the total charge on both sides of the equation is zero.

### PROBLEM 5.38

Identify the species that is oxidized and the species that is reduced in each reaction. Write out half reactions to show how many electrons are gained or lost by each species.

a. $Zn(s) + 2\,H^+(aq) \longrightarrow Zn^{2+}(aq) + H_2(g)$
b. $Fe^{3+}(aq) + Al(s) \longrightarrow Al^{3+}(aq) + Fe(s)$

c. $2\,I^- + Br_2 \longrightarrow I_2 + 2\,Br^-$
d. $2\,AgBr \longrightarrow 2\,Ag + Br_2$

### PROBLEM 5.39

Classify each reactant in Problem 5.38 as an oxidizing agent or a reducing agent.

## 5.9B   Examples of Oxidation–Reduction Reactions

Many common processes involve oxidation and reduction. For example, common antiseptics like iodine ($I_2$) and hydrogen peroxide ($H_2O_2$) are oxidizing agents that clean wounds by oxidizing, thereby killing bacteria that might cause infection.

When iron (Fe) rusts, it is oxidized by the oxygen in air to form iron(III) oxide, $Fe_2O_3$. In this redox reaction, neutral iron atoms are oxidized to $Fe^{3+}$ cations, and elemental $O_2$ is reduced to $O^{2-}$ anions.

Fe atom

$Fe^{3+}$

$O^{2-}$

$$4\,Fe(s) + 3\,O_2(g) \longrightarrow 2\,Fe_2O_3(s)$$

neutral elements

Each Fe ion has a
+3 charge.

Each O ion has a
−2 charge.

Batteries consist of a metal and a cation that undergo a redox reaction. When the electrons are transferred from the metal to the cation, an electric current results, which can supply power for a lightbulb, radio, computer, or watch. For example, an alkaline battery usually contains zinc powder and $Mn^{4+}$ cations, together with sodium or potassium hydroxide (NaOH or KOH), as shown in Figure 5.7.

$$Zn + 2\,MnO_2 \longrightarrow ZnO + Mn_2O_3$$

$Mn^{4+}$              $Zn^{2+}$    $Mn^{3+}$

### Figure 5.7 A Flashlight Battery—An Example of a Redox Reaction

Zn is oxidized. ⌐ ⌐ $MnO_2$ is reduced.

brass pin   Zn   $MnO_2$

**Redox Reaction**

Oxidation: $Zn \longrightarrow Zn^{2+} + 2\,e^-$

Reduction: $2\,Mn^{4+} + 2\,e^- \longrightarrow 2\,Mn^{3+}$

Alkaline batteries consist of zinc powder (Zn) and manganese dioxide ($MnO_2$), along with a paste of sodium hydroxide (NaOH) or potassium hydroxide (KOH). When electrical contact is made, Zn atoms lose electrons, which flow towards the $Mn^{4+}$ cations in $MnO_2$. The resulting electric current can be used to power a lightbulb, radio, or other electrical device.

In this redox reaction, neutral Zn atoms are oxidized to $Zn^{2+}$ cations. $Mn^{4+}$ cations are reduced to $Mn^{3+}$ cations. The oxygen anions ($O^{2-}$) just balance the charge of the metal cations and are neither oxidized nor reduced.

In some reactions it is much less apparent which reactant is oxidized and which is reduced. For example, in the combustion of methane ($CH_4$) with oxygen to form $CO_2$ and $H_2O$, there are no metals or cations that obviously lose or gain electrons, yet this is a redox reaction. In these instances, it is often best to count oxygen and hydrogen atoms.

- Oxidation results in the gain of oxygen atoms or the loss of hydrogen atoms.
- Reduction results in the loss of oxygen atoms or the gain of hydrogen atoms.

$O_2$ is reduced.

$$CH_4 + 2\,O_2 \longrightarrow CO_2 + 2\,H_2O$$

4 H atoms   0 H atoms   2 O atoms   2 H atoms for each $H_2O$

$CH_4$ is oxidized.

$CH_4$ is oxidized since it gains two oxygen atoms to form $CO_2$. $O_2$ is reduced since it gains two hydrogen atoms to form $H_2O$.

### PROBLEM 5.40

The following redox reaction occurs in mercury batteries for watches. Identify the species that is oxidized and the species that is reduced, and write out two half reactions to show how many electrons are gained or lost.

$$Zn + HgO \longrightarrow ZnO + Hg$$

### PROBLEM 5.41

Identify the species that is oxidized and the species that is reduced in the following redox reaction. Explain your choices.

$$C_2H_4O_2 + 2\,H_2 \longrightarrow C_2H_6O + H_2O$$

## 5.10 FOCUS ON HEALTH & MEDICINE
### Pacemakers

A pacemaker is a small electrical device implanted in an individual's chest and used to maintain an adequate heart rate (Figure 5.8). When a pacemaker detects that the heart is beating too slowly, it sends an electrical signal to the heart so that the heart muscle beats faster. A pacemaker contains a small, long-lasting battery that generates an electrical impulse by a redox reaction.

Most pacemakers used today contain a lithium–iodine battery. Each neutral lithium atom is oxidized to $Li^+$ by losing one electron. Each $I_2$ molecule is reduced by gaining two electrons and forming $2\ I^-$. Since the balanced equation contains two Li atoms for each $I_2$ molecule, the number of electrons lost by Li atoms equals the number of electrons gained by $I_2$.

- $I_2$ gains $2\ e^-$, forming $2\ I^-$.
- $I_2$ is **reduced.**

$$2\ Li \quad + \quad I_2 \quad \longrightarrow \quad 2\ LiI$$

- Each Li atom loses $1\ e^-$, forming $Li^+$.
- Li metal is **oxidized.**

The lithium–iodine battery has a much longer battery life (over 10 years) than earlier batteries, greatly improving the quality of life for the many individuals with pacemakers.

### PROBLEM 5.42

Early pacemakers generated an electrical impulse by the following reaction. What species is the oxidizing agent and what species is the reducing agent in this reaction?

$$Zn + Hg^{2+} \longrightarrow Zn^{2+} + Hg$$

**Figure 5.8**   The Lithium–Iodine Battery in a Pacemaker

A pacemaker generates a small electrical impulse that triggers the heart to beat. Today's pacemakers sense when the heart beats normally and provide an electrical signal only when the heart rate slows. Such devices are called "demand" pacemakers, and they quickly replaced earlier "fixed" rate models that continuously produced impulses to set the heart rate at a fixed value.

# CHAPTER HIGHLIGHTS

## KEY TERMS

Actual yield (5.7)

Avogadro's number (5.3)

Balanced chemical equation (5.2)

Chemical equation (5.1)

Formula weight (5.4)

Half reaction (5.9)

Law of conservation of mass (5.1)

Limiting reactant (5.8)

Molar mass (5.4)

Mole (5.3)

Molecular weight (5.4)

Oxidation (5.9)

Oxidizing agent (5.9)

Percent yield (5.7)

Product (5.1)

Reactant (5.1)

Redox reaction (5.9)

Reducing agent (5.9)

Reduction (5.9)

Theoretical yield (5.7)

## KEY CONCEPTS

**❶ What do the terms in a chemical equation mean and how is an equation balanced? (5.1, 5.2)**

- A chemical equation contains the reactants on the left side of an arrow and the products on the right. The coefficients tell how many molecules or moles of a substance react or are formed.

- A chemical equation is balanced by placing coefficients in front of chemical formulas one at a time, beginning with the most complex formula, so that the number of atoms of each element is the same on both sides. You must *not* balance the chemical equation by changing the subscripts in the chemical formulas of the reactants or products.

**❷ Define the terms mole and Avogadro's number. (5.3)**

- A mole is a quantity that contains $6.02 \times 10^{23}$ atoms, molecules, or ions.

- Avogadro's number is the number of particles in a mole—$6.02 \times 10^{23}$.

- The number of molecules in a given number of moles is calculated using Avogadro's number.

**❸ How are formula weight and molar mass calculated? (5.4)**

- The formula weight is the sum of the atomic weights of all the atoms in a compound, reported in atomic mass units.

- The molar mass is the mass of one mole of a substance, reported in grams. The molar mass is numerically equal to the formula weight but the units are different (g/mol not amu).

**❹ How are the mass of a substance and its number of moles related? (5.4)**

- The molar mass is used as a conversion factor to determine how many grams are contained in a given number of moles of a substance. Similarly, the molar mass is used to determine how many moles of a substance are contained in a given number of grams.

**❺ How can a balanced equation and molar mass be used to calculate the number of moles and mass of a reaction product? (5.5, 5.6)**

- The coefficients in a balanced chemical equation tell us the number of moles of each reactant that combine and the number of moles of each product formed. Coefficients are used to form mole ratios that serve as conversion factors relating the number of moles of reactants and products.

- When the mass of a substance in a reaction must be calculated, first its number of moles is determined using mole ratios, and then the molar mass is used to convert moles to grams.

**❻ What is percent yield? (5.7)**

- Percent yield = (actual yield/theoretical yield) $\times$ 100%.

- The actual yield is the amount of product formed in a reaction, determined by weighing a product on a balance. The theoretical yield is a quantity calculated from a balanced chemical equation, using mole ratios and molar masses. The theoretical yield is the maximum amount of product that can form in a chemical reaction from the amount of reactants used.

**❼ What is the limiting reactant in a reaction? (5.8)**

- The limiting reactant is the reactant that is completely used up in a reaction. The number of moles of limiting reactant determines the number of moles of product formed using mole ratios in the balanced equation.

**❽ What are oxidation and reduction reactions? (5.9)**

- Oxidation–reduction or redox reactions are electron transfer reactions.

- Oxidation results in the loss of electrons. Metals and anions tend to undergo oxidation. In some reactions, oxidation results in the gain of O atoms or the loss of H atoms.

- Reduction results in the gain of electrons. Nonmetals and cations tend to undergo reduction. In some reactions, reduction results in the loss of O atoms or the gain of H atoms.

**❾ Give some examples of common or useful redox reactions. (5.9, 5.10)**

- Common examples of redox reactions include the rusting of iron and the combustion of methane. The electric current generated in batteries used for flashlights and pacemakers results from redox reactions.

# PROBLEMS

Selected in-chapter and odd-numbered end-of-chapter problems have brief answers in Appendix B. The *Student Study Guide and Solutions Manual* contains detailed solutions to all in-chapter and odd-numbered end-of-chapter problems, as well as additional worked examples and a chapter self-test.

## Chemical Reactions and Chemical Equations

**5.43** Use the molecular art to identify the process as a chemical reaction or a physical change. If a chemical reaction occurs, write the equation from the molecular art. If a physical change occurs, identify the phase change.

**5.44** Diagram [1] represents the compound **AB,** which contains two elements, **A** shown with red spheres, and **B** shown with blue spheres. Label each transformation as a physical change or a chemical reaction: (a) [1] ⟶ [2]; (b) [1] ⟶ [3].

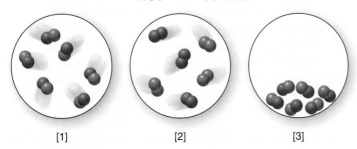

| [1] | [2] | [3] |

**5.45** What is the difference between a coefficient in a chemical equation and a subscript in a chemical formula?

**5.46** Why is it not possible to change the subscripts of a chemical formula to balance an equation?

**5.47** How many atoms of each element are drawn on each side of the following equations? Label the equations as balanced or not balanced.
   a. $2 HCl(aq) + Ca(s) \longrightarrow CaCl_2(aq) + H_2(g)$
   b. $TiCl_4 + 2 H_2O \longrightarrow TiO_2 + HCl$
   c. $Al(OH)_3 + H_3PO_4 \longrightarrow AlPO_4 + 3 H_2O$

**5.48** How many atoms of each element are drawn on each side of the following equations? Label the equations as balanced or not balanced.
   a. $3 NO_2 + H_2O \longrightarrow HNO_3 + 2 NO$
   b. $2 H_2S + 3 O_2 \longrightarrow H_2O + 2 SO_2$
   c. $Ca(OH)_2 + 2 HNO_3 \longrightarrow 2 H_2O + Ca(NO_3)_2$

**5.49** Use the molecular art to write a balanced equation for the given reaction.

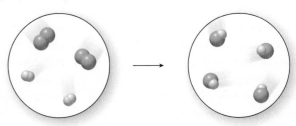

**5.50** Use the molecular art to write a balanced equation for the given reaction.

**5.51** Balance each equation.
   a. $Ni(s) + HCl(aq) \longrightarrow NiCl_2(aq) + H_2(g)$
   b. $CH_4(g) + Cl_2(g) \longrightarrow CCl_4(g) + HCl(g)$
   c. $KClO_3 \longrightarrow KCl + O_2$
   d. $Al_2O_3 + HCl \longrightarrow AlCl_3 + H_2O$
   e. $Al(OH)_3 + H_2SO_4 \longrightarrow Al_2(SO_4)_3 + H_2O$

**5.52** Balance each equation.
   a. $Mg(s) + HBr(aq) \longrightarrow MgBr_2(s) + H_2(g)$
   b. $CO(g) + O_2(g) \longrightarrow CO_2(g)$
   c. $PbS(s) + O_2(g) \longrightarrow PbO(s) + SO_2(g)$
   d. $H_2SO_4 + NaOH \longrightarrow Na_2SO_4 + H_2O$
   e. $H_3PO_4 + Ca(OH)_2 \longrightarrow Ca_3(PO_4)_2 + H_2O$

**5.53** Hydrocarbons are compounds that contain only C and H atoms. When a hydrocarbon reacts with $O_2$, $CO_2$ and $H_2O$ are formed. Write a balanced equation for the combustion of each of the following hydrocarbons, all of which are high-octane components of gasoline.
   a. $C_6H_6$ (benzene)
   b. $C_7H_8$ (toluene)
   c. $C_8H_{18}$ (isooctane)

**5.54** MTBE ($C_5H_{12}O$) is a high-octane gasoline additive with a sweet, nauseating odor. Because small amounts of MTBE have contaminated the drinking water in some towns, it is now banned as a fuel additive in many areas. MTBE reacts with $O_2$ to form $CO_2$ and $H_2O$. Write a balanced equation for the combustion of MTBE.

**5.55** Some coal is high in sulfur (S) content, and when it burns, it forms sulfuric acid ($H_2SO_4$), a major component of acid rain, by a series of reactions. Balance the equation for the overall conversion drawn below.

$$S(s) + O_2(g) + H_2O(l) \longrightarrow H_2SO_4(l)$$

**5.56** Balance the equation for the formation of magnesium hydroxide [Mg(OH)₂], one of the active ingredients in milk of magnesia.

$$MgCl_2 + NaOH \longrightarrow Mg(OH)_2 + NaCl$$

**5.57** Consider the reaction, $O_3 + CO \longrightarrow O_2 + CO_2$. Molecular art is used to show the starting materials for this reaction. Fill in the molecules of the products using the balanced equation and following the law of conservation of mass.

**5.58** Consider the reaction, $2\ NO + 2\ CO \longrightarrow N_2 + 2\ CO_2$. Molecular art is used to show the starting materials for this reaction. Fill in the molecules of the products using the balanced equation and following the law of conservation of mass.

## Formula Weight and Molar Mass

**5.59** Calculate the formula weight and molar mass of each compound.
   a. NaNO₂ (sodium nitrite), a preservative in hot dogs, ham, and other cured meats
   b. Al₂(SO₄)₃ (aluminum sulfate), once used as a common antiperspirant
   c. C₆H₈O₆ (vitamin C)

**5.60** Calculate the formula weight and molar mass of each compound.
   a. MgSO₄ (magnesium sulfate), a laxative
   b. Ca₃(PO₄)₂ (calcium phosphate), a calcium supplement
   c. C₁₆H₁₆ClNO₂S (Plavix), a drug used to treat coronary artery disease

**5.61** L-Dopa is a drug used to treat Parkinson's disease.

L-dopa

   a. What is the molecular formula of L-dopa?
   b. What is the formula weight of L-dopa?
   c. What is the molar mass of L-dopa?

**5.62** Niacin, vitamin B₃, is found in soybeans, which contain it naturally, and cereals, which are fortified with it.

niacin

   a. What is the molecular formula of niacin?
   b. What is the formula weight of niacin?
   c. What is the molar mass of niacin?

## Moles, Mass, and Avogadro's Number

**5.63** Which quantity has the greater mass?
   a. 1 mol of Fe atoms or 1 mol of Sn atoms
   b. 1 mol of C atoms or $6.02 \times 10^{23}$ N atoms
   c. 1 mol of N atoms or 1 mol of N₂ molecules
   d. 1 mol of CO₂ molecules or $3.01 \times 10^{23}$ N₂O molecules

**5.64** Which quantity has the greater mass?
   a. 1 mol of Si atoms or 1 mol of Ar atoms
   b. 1 mol of He atoms or $6.02 \times 10^{23}$ H atoms
   c. 1 mol of Cl atoms or 1 mol of Cl₂ molecules
   d. 1 mol of C₂H₄ molecules or $3.01 \times 10^{23}$ C₂H₄ molecules

**5.65** How many grams are contained in 5.00 mol of each compound?
   a. HCl      b. Na₂SO₄      c. C₂H₂      d. Al(OH)₃

**5.66** How many grams are contained in 0.50 mol of each compound?
   a. NaOH      b. CaSO₄      c. C₃H₆      d. Mg(OH)₂

**5.67** How many moles are contained in each number of grams of table sugar (C₁₂H₂₂O₁₁, molar mass 342.3 g/mol)?
   a. 0.500 g      b. 5.00 g      c. 25.0 g      d. 0.0250 g

**5.68** How many moles are contained in each number of grams of fructose (C₆H₁₂O₆, molar mass 180.2 g/mol), a carbohydrate that is about twice as sweet as table sugar? "Lite" food products use half as much fructose as table sugar to achieve the same sweet taste, but with fewer calories.
   a. 0.500 g      b. 5.00 g      c. 25.0 g      d. 0.0250 g

**5.69** How many molecules of butane (C₄H₁₀) are contained in the following number of moles: (a) 2.00 mol; (b) 0.250 mol; (c) 26.5 mol; (d) 222 mol; (e) $5.00 \times 10^5$ mol?

**5.70** How many moles of pentane (C₅H₁₂) are contained in the following number of molecules?
   a. $5.00 \times 10^{19}$ molecules      c. $8.32 \times 10^{21}$ molecules
   b. $6.51 \times 10^{28}$ molecules      d. $3.10 \times 10^{20}$ molecules

**5.71** What is the mass in grams of each quantity of lactic acid (C₃H₆O₃, molar mass 90.08 g/mol), the compound responsible for the aching feeling of tired muscles during vigorous exercise?
   a. 3.60 mol                          c. $7.3 \times 10^{24}$ molecules
   b. 0.580 mol                         d. $6.56 \times 10^{22}$ molecules

**5.72** What is the mass in grams of each quantity of vitamin D (molar mass 384.7 g/mol), which is needed for forming and maintaining healthy bones?

    a. 3.6 mol                c. $7.3 \times 10^{24}$ molecules

    b. 0.58 mol              d. $6.56 \times 10^{22}$ molecules

## Mass and Mole Calculations in Chemical Equations

**5.73** Using the balanced equation for the combustion of acetylene, answer the following questions.

$$2\ H\!-\!C\!\equiv\!C\!-\!H\ +\ 5\ O_2\ \longrightarrow\ 4\ CO_2\ +\ 2\ H_2O$$
$$\text{acetylene}$$

    a. How many moles of $O_2$ are needed to react completely with 5.00 mol of $C_2H_2$?

    b. How many moles of $CO_2$ are formed from 6.0 mol of $C_2H_2$?

    c. How many moles of $H_2O$ are formed from 0.50 mol of $C_2H_2$?

    d. How many moles of $C_2H_2$ are needed to form 0.80 mol of $CO_2$?

**5.74** Sodium metal (Na) reacts violently when added to water according to the following balanced equation.

$$2\ Na(s)\ +\ 2\ H_2O(l)\ \longrightarrow\ 2\ NaOH(aq)\ +\ H_2(g)$$

    a. How many moles of $H_2O$ are needed to react completely with 3.0 mol of Na?

    b. How many moles of $H_2$ are formed from 0.38 mol of Na?

    c. How many moles of $H_2$ are formed from 3.64 mol of $H_2O$?

**5.75** Using the balanced equation for the combustion of acetylene in Problem 5.73, answer the following questions.

    a. How many grams of $CO_2$ are formed from 2.5 mol of $C_2H_2$?

    b. How many grams of $CO_2$ are formed from 0.50 mol of $C_2H_2$?

    c. How many grams of $H_2O$ are formed from 0.25 mol of $C_2H_2$?

    d. How many grams of $O_2$ are needed to react with 3.0 mol of $C_2H_2$?

**5.76** Using the balanced equation for the reaction of Na with $H_2O$ in Problem 5.74, answer the following questions.

    a. How many grams of NaOH are formed from 3.0 mol of Na?

    b. How many grams of $H_2$ are formed from 0.30 mol of Na?

    c. How many grams of $H_2O$ are needed to react completely with 0.20 mol of Na?

## Theoretical Yield and Percent Yield

**5.77** What is the percent yield of **B** in a reaction that uses 10.0 g of starting material **A,** has a theoretical yield of 12.0 g of **B,** and an actual yield of 9.0 g of **B?**

**5.78** What is the percent yield of **B** in a reaction that uses 25.0 g of starting material **A,** has a theoretical yield of 20.0 g of **B,** and an actual yield of 17.0 g of **B?**

**5.79** The reaction of methane ($CH_4$) with $Cl_2$ forms chloroform ($CHCl_3$) and HCl. Although $CHCl_3$ is a general anesthetic, it is no longer used for this purpose since it is also carcinogenic. The molar masses for all substances are given under the balanced equation.

$$CH_4(g)\ +\ 3\ Cl_2(g)\ \longrightarrow\ CHCl_3(l)\ +\ 3\ HCl(g)$$
$$\text{16.04 g/mol}\quad\text{70.90 g/mol}\qquad\text{119.4 g/mol}\quad\text{36.46 g/mol}$$

    a. What is the theoretical yield of $CHCl_3$ in grams from 3.20 g of $CH_4$?

    b. What is the percent yield if 15.0 g of $CHCl_3$ are actually formed in this reaction?

**5.80** Methanol ($CH_4O$), which is used as a fuel in high-performance racing cars, burns in the presence of $O_2$ to form $CO_2$ and $H_2O$. The molar masses for all substances are given under the balanced equation.

$$2\ CH_4O(l)\ +\ 3\ O_2(g)\ \longrightarrow\ 2\ CO_2(g)\ +\ 4\ H_2O(g)$$
$$\text{32.04 g/mol}\quad\text{32.00 g/mol}\qquad\text{44.01 g/mol}\quad\text{18.02 g/mol}$$

    a. What is the theoretical yield of $CO_2$ from 48.0 g of methanol?

    b. What is the percent yield of $CO_2$ if 48.0 g of $CO_2$ are formed?

## Limiting Reactants

**5.81** Consider the given reaction mixture that contains **A** and **B** molecules, represented by red and blue spheres, respectively. Given each of the following chemical equations, which reactant, **A** or **B**, is present in excess? Which reactant is the limiting reactant?

    a. $\mathbf{A} + \mathbf{B} \longrightarrow \mathbf{C}$

    b. $2\ \mathbf{A} + \mathbf{B} \longrightarrow \mathbf{C}$

    c. $\mathbf{A} + 2\ \mathbf{B} \longrightarrow \mathbf{C}$

**5.82** Consider the reaction of $\mathbf{A_2}$ and $\mathbf{B_2}$ to form $\mathbf{A_2B}$, according to the balanced equation: $2\ \mathbf{A_2} + \mathbf{B_2} \longrightarrow 2\ \mathbf{A_2B}$. Identify the limiting reactant in the molecular art, and draw a representation showing how much product is formed and what reactant molecules are left over.

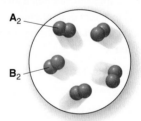

**5.83** Using the balanced equation, $2 NO + O_2 \longrightarrow 2 NO_2$, determine the limiting reactant under each of the following conditions.

    a. 1.0 mol NO and 1.0 mol $O_2$    c. 10.0 g NO and 10.0 g $O_2$

    b. 2.0 mol NO and 0.50 mol $O_2$   d. 28.0 g NO and 16.0 g $O_2$

**5.84** Use the balanced equation in Problem 5.83 to determine the limiting reactant under each of the following conditions.

    a. 2.0 mol NO and 1.1 mol $O_2$    c. 15.0 g NO and 10.0 g $O_2$

    b. 4.2 mol NO and 2.0 mol $O_2$   d. 10.0 g NO and 4.00 g $O_2$

**5.85** For each set of reaction conditions in Problem 5.83, calculate how many moles of the product $NO_2$ forms. Then, calculate the number of grams of product that forms.

**5.86** For each set of reaction conditions in Problem 5.84, calculate how many moles of the product $NO_2$ forms. Then, calculate the number of grams of product that forms.

**5.87** The local anesthetic ethyl chloride ($C_2H_5Cl$, molar mass 64.51 g/mol) can be prepared by reaction of ethylene ($C_2H_4$, molar mass 28.05 g/mol) with HCl (molar mass 36.46 g/mol), according to the balanced equation, $C_2H_4 + HCl \longrightarrow C_2H_5Cl$.

    a. If 8.00 g of ethylene and 12.0 g of HCl are used, how many moles of each reactant are used?

    b. What is the limiting reactant?

    c. How many moles of product are formed?

    d. How many grams of product are formed?

    e. If 10.6 g of product are formed, what is the percent yield of the reaction?

**5.88** The solvent dichloromethane ($CH_2Cl_2$, molar mass 84.93 g/mol) can be prepared by reaction of methane ($CH_4$, molar mass 16.04 g/mol) with $Cl_2$ (molar mass 70.90 g/mol), according to the balanced equation, $CH_4 + 2 Cl_2 \longrightarrow CH_2Cl_2 + 2 HCl$.

    a. If 5.00 g of methane and 15.0 g of $Cl_2$ are used, how many moles of each reactant are used?

    b. What is the limiting reactant?

    c. How many moles of product are formed?

    d. How many grams of product are formed?

    e. If 15.6 g of product are formed, what is the percent yield of the reaction?

## Oxidation–Reduction Reactions

**5.89** What is the difference between a substance that is oxidized and an oxidizing agent?

**5.90** What is the difference between a substance that is reduced and a reducing agent?

**5.91** Identify the species that is oxidized and the species that is reduced in each reaction. Write out two half reactions to show how many electrons are gained or lost by each species.

    a. $Fe + Cu^{2+} \longrightarrow Fe^{2+} + Cu$

    b. $Cl_2 + 2 I^- \longrightarrow I_2 + 2 Cl^-$

    c. $2 Na + Cl_2 \longrightarrow 2 NaCl$

**5.92** Identify the species that is oxidized and the species that is reduced in each reaction. Write out two half reactions to show how many electrons are gained or lost by each species.

    a. $Mg + Fe^{2+} \longrightarrow Mg^{2+} + Fe$

    b. $Cu^{2+} + Sn \longrightarrow Sn^{2+} + Cu$

    c. $4 Na + O_2 \longrightarrow 2 Na_2O$

**5.93** Zinc–silver oxide batteries are used in cameras and hearing aids. Identify the species that is oxidized and the species that is reduced in the following redox reaction. Identify the oxidizing agent and the reducing agent.

$$Zn + Ag_2O \longrightarrow ZnO + 2 Ag$$

**5.94** Rechargeable nickel–cadmium batteries are used in appliances and power tools. Identify the species that is oxidized and the species that is reduced in the following redox reaction. Identify the oxidizing agent and the reducing agent.

$$Cd + Ni^{4+} \longrightarrow Cd^{2+} + Ni^{2+}$$

**5.95** The reaction of hydrogen ($H_2$) with acetylene ($C_2H_2$) forms ethane ($C_2H_6$). Is acetylene oxidized or reduced in this reaction? Explain your choice.

**5.96** When $Cl_2$ is used to disinfect drinking water, $Cl^-$ is formed. Is $Cl_2$ oxidized or reduced in this process?

**5.97** The reaction of magnesium metal (Mg) with oxygen ($O_2$) forms MgO. Write a balanced equation for this redox reaction. Write two half reactions to show how many electrons are gained or lost by each species.

**5.98** The reaction of aluminum metal (Al) with oxygen ($O_2$) forms $Al_2O_3$. Write a balanced equation for this redox reaction. Write two half reactions to show how many electrons are gained or lost by each species.

## General Questions

**5.99** Answer the following questions about the conversion of the sucrose ($C_{12}H_{22}O_{11}$) in sugarcane to ethanol ($C_2H_6O$) and $CO_2$ according to the following unbalanced equation. In this way sugarcane is used as a renewable source of ethanol, which is used as a fuel additive in gasoline.

$$C_{12}H_{22}O_{11}(s) + H_2O(l) \longrightarrow C_2H_6O(l) + CO_2(g)$$
$$\text{sucrose} \qquad\qquad\qquad\qquad \text{ethanol}$$

    a. What is the molar mass of sucrose?

    b. Balance the given equation.

    c. How many moles of ethanol are formed from 2 mol of sucrose?

    d. How many moles of water are needed to react with 10 mol of sucrose?

    e. How many grams of ethanol are formed from 0.550 mol of sucrose?

    f. How many grams of ethanol are formed from 34.2 g of sucrose?

    g. What is the theoretical yield of ethanol in grams from 17.1 g of sucrose?

    h. If 1.25 g of ethanol are formed in the reaction in part (g), what is the percent yield of ethanol?

**5.100** Answer the following questions about diethyl ether ($C_4H_{10}O$), the first widely used general anesthetic. Diethyl ether can be prepared from ethanol according to the following unbalanced equation.

$$C_2H_6O(l) \longrightarrow C_4H_{10}O(l) + H_2O(l)$$
ethanol             diethyl ether

a. What is the molar mass of diethyl ether?

b. Balance the given equation.

c. How many moles of diethyl ether are formed from 2 mol of ethanol?

d. How many moles of water are formed from 10 mol of ethanol?

e. How many grams of diethyl ether are formed from 0.55 mol of ethanol?

f. How many grams of diethyl ether are formed from 4.60 g of ethanol?

g. What is the theoretical yield of diethyl ether in grams from 2.30 g of ethanol?

h. If 1.80 g of diethyl ether are formed in the reaction in part (g), what is the percent yield of diethyl ether?

## Applications

**5.101** A bottle of the pain reliever ibuprofen ($C_{13}H_{18}O_2$, molar mass 206.3 g/mol) contains 500 200.-mg tablets. (a) How many moles of ibuprofen does the bottle contain? (b) How many molecules of ibuprofen does the bottle contain?

**5.102** One dose of Maalox contains 500. mg each of $Mg(OH)_2$ and $Al(OH)_3$. How many moles of each compound are contained in a single dose?

**5.103** The average nicotine ($C_{10}H_{14}N_2$, molar mass 162.3 g/mol) content of a Camel cigarette is 1.93 mg. Suppose an individual smokes one pack of 20 cigarettes a day.

a. How many moles of nicotine are smoked in a day?

b. How many molecules of nicotine are smoked in a day?

**5.104** How many moles of sucrose (table sugar, $C_{12}H_{22}O_{11}$, molar mass 342.3 g/mol) are contained in a 5-lb bag of sugar?

**5.105** If the daily recommended intake of sodium ions is 2,400 mg, how many $Na^+$ ions does this correspond to?

**5.106** How many molecules are contained in a glass that holds 250 g of water? How many moles does that correspond to?

**5.107** DDT, a pesticide that kills disease-carrying mosquitoes, is synthesized by the given equation. DDT is now banned in the United States because it is a persistent environmental pollutant that only slowly degrades.

chlorobenzene
112.6 g/mol

DDT
$C_{14}H_9Cl_5$

a. What is the molar mass of DDT?

b. How many grams of DDT would be formed from 0.10 mol of chlorobenzene?

c. What is the theoretical yield of DDT in grams from 11.3 g of chlorobenzene?

d. If 15.0 g of DDT are formed in the reaction in part (c), what is the percent yield of DDT?

**5.108** Fats, such as butter, and oils, such as corn oil, are formed from compounds called fatty acids, one of which is linolenic acid ($C_{18}H_{30}O_2$). Linolenic acid undergoes reactions with hydrogen and oxygen to form the products shown in each equation.

[1]   $C_{18}H_{30}O_2 + H_2 \longrightarrow C_{18}H_{36}O_2$
linolenic acid

[2]   $C_{18}H_{30}O_2 + O_2 \longrightarrow CO_2 + H_2O$
linolenic acid

a. Calculate the molar mass of linolenic acid.

b. Balance Equation [1], which shows the reaction with hydrogen.

c. Balance Equation [2], which shows the reaction with oxygen.

d. How many grams of product are formed from 10.0 g of linolenic acid in Equation [1]?

## CHALLENGE PROBLEMS

**5.109** TCDD, also called dioxin ($C_{12}H_4Cl_4O_2$, molar mass 322.0 g/mol), is a potent poison. The average lethal dose in humans is estimated to be $3.0 \times 10^{-2}$ mg per kg of body weight. (a) How many grams constitute a lethal dose for a 70.-kg individual? (b) How many molecules of TCDD does this correspond to?

**5.110** The lead–acid battery in a car consists of lead (Pb), lead(IV) oxide ($PbO_2$), and sulfuric acid ($H_2SO_4$), which undergo a redox reaction according to the given equation. Explain the oxidation and reduction reactions that occur with the lead atoms and ions in this battery.

$$Pb + PbO_2 + 2\,H_2SO_4 \longrightarrow 2\,PbSO_4 + 2\,H_2O$$

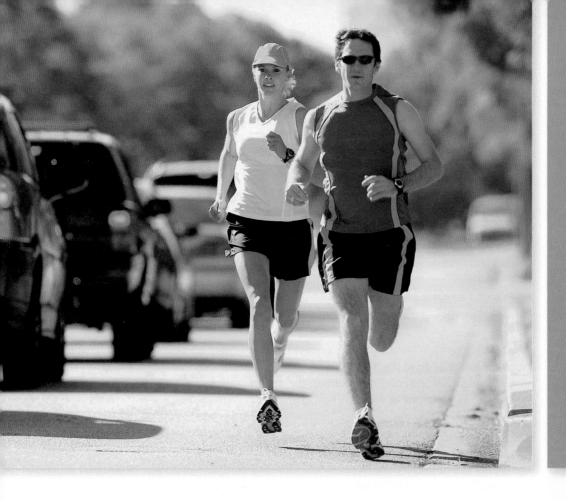

**6**

The combustion of gasoline and the metabolism of carbohydrates during exercise are examples of oxidation reactions that release a great deal of useful energy.

# Energy Changes, Reaction Rates, and Equilibrium

## CHAPTER OUTLINE

## CHAPTER GOALS

*In this chapter you will learn how to:*

1. Define energy and become familiar with the units of energy

2. Use bond dissociation energies to predict bond strength

3. Describe energy changes in a reaction, and classify reactions as endothermic or exothermic

4. Draw energy diagrams

5. Predict the effect of concentration, temperature, and the presence of a catalyst on the rate of a reaction

6. Describe the basic features of chemical equilibrium and write an expression for an equilibrium constant

7. Use Le Châtelier's principle to predict what happens when equilibrium is disturbed

8. Use Le Châtelier's principle and reaction rates to explain the regulation of body temperature

In Chapter 6 we turn our attention to two facets of chemical reactions: energy changes and reaction rates. Why do some reactions—like the combustion of fossil fuels or the metabolism of carbohydrates—release a great deal of energy that can be used for powering a car or running a marathon, while other reactions absorb energy from the environment? What factors affect how fast a reaction proceeds? To answer these and related questions, we must learn about what happens when molecules come together in a reaction, as well as what energy changes are observed when bonds are broken and formed.

## 6.1 Energy

***Energy* is the capacity to do work.** Whenever you throw a ball, ride a bike, or read a newspaper, you use energy to do work. There are two types of energy.

- Potential energy is stored energy.
- Kinetic energy is the energy of motion.

A ball at the top of a hill or the water in a reservoir behind a dam are examples of potential energy. When the ball rolls down the hill or the water flows over the dam, the stored potential energy is converted to the kinetic energy of motion. Although energy can be converted from one form to another, one rule, the **law of conservation of energy,** governs the process.

- The total energy in the universe does not change. Energy cannot be created or destroyed.

The energy stored in chemical bonds—both ionic and covalent—is a form of potential energy. In chemical reactions, potential energy may be released and converted to heat, the kinetic energy of the moving particles of the product. **Reactions that form products having *lower* potential energy than the reactants are favored.**

- A compound with lower potential energy is more stable than a compound with higher potential energy.

The water at the top of a waterfall has potential energy because of its position. This potential energy becomes kinetic energy as the water falls.

The joule, named after the nineteenth-century English physicist James Prescott Joule, is pronounced *jewel*.

### 6.1A The Units of Energy

Energy can be measured using two different units, **calories (cal)** and **joules (J)**. A **calorie** is the amount of energy needed to raise the temperature of 1 g of water 1 °C. Joules and calories are related in the following way.

$$1 \text{ cal} = 4.184 \text{ J}$$

Since both the calorie and the joule are small units of measurement, more often energies in reactions are reported with kilocalories (kcal) and kilojoules (kJ). Recall from Table 1.2 that the prefix *kilo* means 1,000.

$$1 \text{ kcal} = 1,000 \text{ cal}$$
$$1 \text{ kJ} = 1,000 \text{ J}$$
$$1 \text{ kcal} = 4.184 \text{ kJ}$$

To convert a quantity from one unit of measurement to another, set up conversion factors and use the method first shown in Section 1.7B and illustrated in Sample Problem 6.1.

## SAMPLE PROBLEM 6.1

A reaction releases 421 kJ of energy. How many kilocalories does this correspond to?

### Analysis and Solution

**[1] Identify the original quantity and the desired quantity.**

421 kJ         ? kcal
original quantity    desired quantity

**[2] Write out the conversion factors.**

- Choose the conversion factor that places the unwanted unit, kilojoules, in the denominator so that the units cancel.

kJ–kcal conversion factors

$$\frac{4.184 \text{ kJ}}{1 \text{ kcal}} \quad or \quad \boxed{\frac{1 \text{ kcal}}{4.184 \text{ kJ}}}$$

Choose this conversion factor to cancel kJ.

**[3] Set up and solve the problem.**

- Multiply the original quantity by the conversion factor to obtain the desired quantity.

$$421 \text{ k\!\!\!/J} \quad \times \quad \frac{1 \text{ kcal}}{4.184 \text{ k\!\!\!/J}} \quad = \quad 100.6 \text{ kcal, rounded to 101 kcal}$$

Kilojoules cancel.              **Answer**

## PROBLEM 6.1

Carry out each of the following conversions.

a. 42 J to cal      b. 55.6 kcal to cal      c. 326 kcal to kJ      d. 25.6 kcal to J

## PROBLEM 6.2

Combustion of 1 g of gasoline releases 11.5 kcal of energy. How many kilojoules of energy is released? How many joules does this correspond to?

## 6.1B   FOCUS ON THE HUMAN BODY
### Energy and Nutrition

When we eat food, the protein, carbohydrates, and fat (lipid) in the food are metabolized to form simpler molecules that in turn are used to prepare new molecules that cells need for maintenance and growth. This process also generates the energy needed for the organs to function, allowing the heart to beat, the lungs to breathe, and the brain to think.

The amount of stored energy in food is measured using nutritional Calories (upper case C), where 1 Cal = 1,000 cal. Since 1,000 cal = 1 kcal, the following relationships exist.

Nutritional Calorie

1 Cal = 1 kcal
1 Cal = 1,000 cal

Upon metabolism, proteins, carbohydrates, and fat each release a predictable amount of energy, the **caloric value** of the substance. For example, one gram of protein or one gram of carbohydrate typically releases about 4 Cal/g, while fat releases 9 Cal/g (Table 6.1). If we know the amount of each of these substances contained in a food product, we can make a first approximation of the number of Calories it contains by using caloric values as conversion factors, as illustrated in Sample Problem 6.2.

**WHEATS**

**Nutrition Facts**
Serving Size 1 cup (55 g)
Servings Per Container about 13

**Amount Per Serving**
**Calories** 200   Calories from Fat 10

| | % Daily Value* |
|---|---|
| **Total Fat** 1g | **2%** |
| Saturated Fat 0g | **0%** |
| Trans Fat 0g | |
| **Cholesterol** 0mg | **0%** |
| **Sodium** 0mg | **0%** |
| **Potassium** 180mg | **5%** |
| **Total Carbohydrate** 42g | **14%** |
| Dietary Fiber 5g | **20%** |
| Sugars 12g | |
| **Protein** 5g | |

Vitamin A 0%   • Vitamin C 0%
Calcium 0%   • Iron 90%
Thiamine 25%   • Riboflavin 25%
Niacin 25%   • Vitamin B6 25%

**Table 6.1** Caloric Value for Three Classes of Compounds

| | Cal/g | cal/g |
|---|---|---|
| Protein | 4 | 4,000 |
| Carbohydrate | 4 | 4,000 |
| Fat | 9 | 9,000 |

One nutritional Calorie (1 Cal) = 1,000 cal = 1 kcal.

When an individual eats more Calories than are needed for normal bodily maintenance, the body stores the excess as fat. The average body fat content for men and women is about 20% and 25%, respectively. This stored fat can fill the body's energy needs for two or three months. Frequent ingestion of a large excess of Calories results in a great deal of stored fat, causing an individual to be overweight.

### SAMPLE PROBLEM 6.2

If a baked potato contains 3 g of protein, a trace of fat, and 23 g of carbohydrates, estimate its number of Calories.

### Analysis

Use the caloric value (Cal/g) of each class of molecule to form a conversion factor to convert the number of grams to Calories and add up the results.

### Solution

**[1] Identify the original quantity and the desired quantity.**

3 g protein
23 g carbohydrates                           ? Cal
original quantities                          desired quantity

**[2] Write out the conversion factors.**

- Write out conversion factors that relate the number of grams to the number of Calories for each substance. Each conversion factor must place the unwanted unit, grams, in the denominator so that the units cancel.

Cal–g conversion factor for protein　　　　　Cal–g conversion factor for carbohydrates

$\dfrac{4\ \text{Cal}}{1\ \text{g protein}}$　　　　　　　　$\dfrac{4\ \text{Cal}}{1\ \text{g carbohydrate}}$

**[3] Set up and solve the problem.**

- Multiply the original quantity by the conversion factor for both protein and carbohydrates and add up the results to obtain the desired quantity.

Total Calories = 12 Cal + 92 Cal

Total Calories = 104 Cal, rounded to 100 Cal

**Answer**

### PROBLEM 6.3

How many Calories are contained in one tablespoon of olive oil, which has 14 g of fat?

### PROBLEM 6.4

One serving (36 crackers) of wheat crackers contains 6 g of fat, 20 g of carbohydrates, and 2 g of protein. Estimate the number of Calories.

## 6.2 Energy Changes in Reactions

When molecules come together and react, bonds are broken in the reactants and new bonds are formed in the products. **Breaking a bond requires energy.** For example, 58 kcal of energy is needed to break the chlorine–chlorine bond in a mole of chlorine molecules ($Cl_2$).

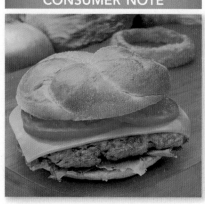

**CONSUMER NOTE**

Knowing the number of grams of protein, carbohydrates, and fat allows you to estimate how many Calories a food product contains. A quarter-pound burger with cheese with 29 g of protein, 40 g of carbohydrates, and 26 g of fat contains 510 Calories.

To cleave this bond...

$$:\ddot{C}l—\ddot{C}l: \longrightarrow :\ddot{C}l\cdot + \cdot\ddot{C}l:$$

...58 kcal/mol of energy must be added.

In contrast, when the chlorine–chlorine bond is formed, 58 kcal of energy is *released*. The amount of energy needed to break a bond is the same amount that is released when that bond is formed.

When this bond is formed...

$$:\ddot{C}l\cdot + \cdot\ddot{C}l: \longrightarrow :\ddot{C}l—\ddot{C}l:$$

...58 kcal/mol of energy is released.

- Bond breaking always requires an input of energy and bond formation always releases energy.

The energy absorbed or released in any reaction is called the **heat of reaction** or the **enthalpy change,** symbolized by $\Delta H$. The heat of reaction is given a positive (+) or negative (–) sign depending on whether energy is absorbed or released.

- When energy is absorbed, the reaction is said to be *endothermic* and $\Delta H$ is positive (+).
- When energy is released, the reaction is said to be *exothermic* and $\Delta H$ is negative (–).

Thus, $\Delta H = +58$ kcal/mol for cleaving the Cl—Cl bond and the reaction is endothermic; on the other hand, $\Delta H = -58$ kcal/mol for forming the Cl—Cl bond and that reaction is exothermic. The heat of reaction is reported as the number of kilocalories *per mole*. The cleavage of two moles of chlorine–chlorine bonds requires twice as much energy; that is, (2 mol)(+58 kcal/mol) = +116 kcal.

## 6.2A Bond Dissociation Energy

The heat of reaction ($\Delta H$) for breaking a covalent bond by equally dividing the electrons between the two atoms in the bond is called the **bond dissociation energy.** Because bond breaking requires energy, **bond dissociation energies are always *positive* numbers,** and breaking a covalent bond into the atoms that compose it is always **endothermic.** Since **bond formation always *releases* energy,** forming a bond is **exothermic and $\Delta H$ is a *negative* number.** The H—H bond requires +104 kcal/mol to cleave and releases –104 kcal/mol when formed. Table 6.2 lists bond dissociation energies for some simple molecules.

Bond breaking is **endothermic.**
Energy must be added.

$$H—H \longrightarrow H\cdot + \cdot H \quad \Delta H = +104 \text{ kcal/mol}$$

$$H\cdot + \cdot H \longrightarrow H—H \quad \Delta H = -104 \text{ kcal/mol}$$

Bond making is **exothermic.**
Energy is released.

### Table 6.2 Bond Dissociation Energies ($\Delta H$) for Some Common Bonds (A—B → A· + ·B)

| Bond | $\Delta H$ (kcal/mol) |
|------|----------------------|
| H—H | +104 |
| F—F | +38 |
| Cl—Cl | +58 |
| Br—Br | +46 |
| I—I | +36 |
| H—OH | +119 |
| H—F | +136 |
| H—Cl | +103 |
| H—Br | +88 |
| H—I | +71 |

## SAMPLE PROBLEM 6.3

Write the equation for the formation of HCl from H and Cl atoms. Classify the reaction as endothermic or exothermic, and give the $\Delta H$ using the values in Table 6.2.

### Analysis

Bond formation is exothermic and $\Delta H$ is (–). The energy released in forming a bond is (–) the bond dissociation energy.

### Solution

Energy is released.

$$H\cdot + \cdot\ddot{C}l: \longrightarrow H—\ddot{C}l: \quad \Delta H = -103 \text{ kcal/mol}$$

Bond formation is **exothermic.**

## PROBLEM 6.5

Using the values in Table 6.2, give $\Delta H$ for each reaction, and classify the reaction as endothermic or exothermic.

a. $H-\ddot{B}r: \longrightarrow H\cdot + \cdot\ddot{B}r:$          c. $H-\ddot{O}H \longrightarrow H\cdot + \cdot\ddot{O}H$

b. $H\cdot + \cdot\ddot{F}: \longrightarrow H-\ddot{F}:$

Bond dissociation energies tell us about bond strength.

- **The *stronger* the bond, the *higher* its bond dissociation energy.**

For example, since the bond dissociation energy for the H—H bond (+104 kcal/mol) is higher than the bond dissociation energy for the Cl—Cl bond (+58 kcal/mol), the H—H bond is stronger.

Bond dissociation energies exhibit periodic trends, much like atomic radius (Section 2.8A) and electronegativity (Section 4.7). In the series, HF, HCl, HBr, and HI, hydrogen is bonded to the first four elements of group 7A (the halogens). According to Table 6.2, the bond dissociation energies of these compounds *decrease* down the column from HF → HCl → HBr → HI. HI has the *weakest* of these four bonds because the valence electrons used by I to form the H—I bond are farther from the nucleus than the valence electrons in Br, Cl, or F. Similarly, HF has the *strongest* of these four bonds because the valence electrons in F are closer to the nucleus than those in Cl, Br, or I. This is a specific example of a general periodic trend.

| highest bond dissociation energy strongest bond | | lowest bond dissociation energy weakest bond | |
|---|---|---|---|
| $H-\ddot{F}:$ | $H-\ddot{C}l:$ | $H-\ddot{B}r:$ | $H-\ddot{I}:$ |
| $\Delta H$ =  +136 kcal/mol | +103 kcal/mol | +88 kcal/mol | +71 kcal/mol |

- **In comparing bonds formed from elements in the same group of the periodic table, bond dissociation energies generally *decrease* going down the column.**

## SAMPLE PROBLEM 6.4

Considering the indicated carbon–halogen bonds, which bond is predicted to have the higher bond dissociation energy? Which bond is stronger?

$$H-\underset{\underset{H}{|}}{\overset{\overset{H}{|}}{C}}-\ddot{F}: \qquad H-\underset{\underset{H}{|}}{\overset{\overset{H}{|}}{C}}-\ddot{C}l:$$

### Analysis

**The higher the bond dissociation energy, the stronger the bond.** In comparing bonds to atoms in the same group of the periodic table, bond dissociation energies and bond strength decrease down a column.

### Solution

Since Cl is below F in the same group of the periodic table, the C—Cl bond is predicted to have the lower bond dissociation energy, thus making it weaker. The actual values for the bond dissociation energies are given and illustrate that the prediction is indeed true.

$$H-\underset{\underset{H}{|}}{\overset{\overset{H}{|}}{C}}-\ddot{F}: \qquad\qquad H-\underset{\underset{H}{|}}{\overset{\overset{H}{|}}{C}}-\ddot{C}l:$$

lower bond dissociation energy
weaker bond

$\Delta H$ = +109 kcal/mol          $\Delta H$ = +84 kcal/mol

PROBLEM 6.6

Which indicated bond in each pair of compounds has the higher bond dissociation energy? Which is the stronger bond?

a. $H-\overset{\overset{\displaystyle H}{|}}{\underset{\underset{\displaystyle H}{|}}{C}}-\ddot{\ddot{I}}:$    or    $H-\overset{\overset{\displaystyle H}{|}}{\underset{\underset{\displaystyle H}{|}}{C}}-\ddot{\ddot{Br}}:$      b. $H-OH$   or   $H-SH$

## 6.2B  Calculations Involving $\Delta H$ Values

The methane produced by decomposing waste material in large landfills is burned to produce energy for heating and generating electricity.

Most reactions involve breaking and forming more than one bond. In these instances, the heat of reaction measures the difference between the energy needed to break bonds in the reactants and the energy released from the bonds formed in the products. In other words, **$\Delta H$ indicates the relative strength of bonds broken and formed in a reaction.**

- When $\Delta H$ is negative, more energy is released in forming bonds than is needed to break bonds. The bonds formed in the products are *stronger* than the bonds broken in the reactants. The reaction is exothermic.

For example, when methane ($CH_4$) burns in the presence of oxygen ($O_2$) to form $CO_2$ and $H_2O$, 213 kcal/mol of energy is released in the form of heat.

Heat is released.

$$CH_4(g) \ + \ 2\,O_2(g) \ \longrightarrow \ CO_2(g) \ + \ 2\,H_2O(l) \quad \Delta H = -213 \text{ kcal/mol}$$

In this reaction energy is released, $\Delta H$ is negative (–), and the reaction is exothermic. The bonds formed are stronger than the bonds broken, since more energy is released in forming the bonds in $CO_2$ and $H_2O$ than is absorbed in breaking the bonds in $CH_4$ and $O_2$. **Since energy is released, the products are *lower* in energy than the reactants.**

The values for $\Delta H$ are reported in kilocalories per mole (kcal/mol). This means that the given amount of energy is released (or absorbed) for the molar quantities shown by the coefficients in the balanced chemical equation. Thus, 213 kcal of energy is released when 1 mol of $CH_4$ reacts with 2 mol of $O_2$ to form 1 mol of $CO_2$ and 2 mol of $H_2O$.

- When $\Delta H$ is positive, more energy is needed to break bonds than is released in forming bonds. The bonds broken in the reactants are *stronger* than the bonds formed in the product. The reaction is endothermic.

For example, in the process of photosynthesis, green plants use chlorophyll to convert $CO_2$ and $H_2O$ to glucose ($C_6H_{12}O_6$, a simple carbohydrate) and $O_2$ and 678 kcal of energy is absorbed.

$$6\,CO_2(g) + 6\,H_2O(l) \longrightarrow C_6H_{12}O_6(aq) + 6\,O_2(g) \quad \Delta H = +678 \text{ kcal/mol}$$

In this reaction energy is absorbed, $\Delta H$ is positive (+), and the reaction is endothermic. The bonds broken are stronger than the bonds formed, since more energy is needed to break the bonds in $CO_2$ and $H_2O$ than is released in forming the bonds in $C_6H_{12}O_6$ and $O_2$. **Since energy is absorbed, the products are *higher* in energy than the reactants.**

Table 6.3 summarizes the characteristics of energy changes in reactions.

Photosynthesis is an endothermic reaction. Energy from sunlight is absorbed in the reaction and stored in the bonds of the products.

PROBLEM 6.7

Answer the following questions using the given equation and $\Delta H$. (a) Is heat absorbed or released? (b) Which bonds are stronger, those in the reactants or those in the products? (c) Are the reactants or products lower in energy? (d) Is the reaction endothermic or exothermic?

$$2\,NH_3(g) \longrightarrow 3\,H_2(g) + N_2(g) \quad \Delta H = +22.0 \text{ kcal/mol}$$

**Table 6.3 Endothermic and Exothermic Reactions**

| Endothermic Reaction | Exothermic Reaction |
|---|---|
| • Heat is absorbed. | • Heat is released. |
| • $\Delta H$ is positive. | • $\Delta H$ is negative. |
| • The bonds broken in the reactants are *stronger* than the bonds formed in the products. | • The bonds formed in the products are *stronger* than the bonds broken in the reactants. |
| • The products are higher in energy than the reactants. | • The products are lower in energy than the reactants. |

Once we know the $\Delta H$ for a balanced chemical reaction, we can use this information to calculate how much energy is absorbed or released for any given amount of reactant or product. A value for $\Delta H$ and the coefficients of the balanced equation are used to set up conversion factors, as shown in Sample Problem 6.5. To convert the number of grams of a reactant to the number of kilocalories released, we must use the molar mass, as shown in Sample Problem 6.6.

### SAMPLE PROBLEM 6.5

The combustion of propane ($C_3H_8$) with $O_2$ according to the given balanced chemical equation releases 531 kcal/mol. How many kilocalories of energy are released when 0.750 mol of propane is burned?

$$C_3H_8(g) + 5\ O_2(g) \longrightarrow 3\ CO_2(g) + 4\ H_2O(l) \quad\quad \Delta H = -531\ \text{kcal/mol}$$
$$\text{propane}$$

### Analysis

Use the given value of $\Delta H$ to set up a conversion factor that relates the kcal of energy released to the number of moles of $C_3H_8$.

### Solution

The given $\Delta H$ value is the amount of energy released when 1 mol of $C_3H_8$ reacts with 5 mol of $O_2$. Set up a conversion factor that relates kilocalories to moles of $C_3H_8$, with moles in the denominator to cancel this unwanted unit.

$$
\boxed{\begin{array}{c}\text{kcal–mol}\\\text{conversion factor}\end{array}}
$$

$$0.750\ \text{mol } C_3H_8 \quad\times\quad \frac{531\ \text{kcal}}{1\ \text{mol } C_3H_8} \quad=\quad 398\ \text{kcal of energy released}$$

$$\text{Moles cancel.} \quad\quad\quad\quad\quad\quad\quad\quad \textbf{Answer}$$

### PROBLEM 6.8

Given the $\Delta H$ and balanced equation in Sample Problem 6.5, how many kilocalories of energy are released when 1.00 mol of $O_2$ reacts with propane?

### SAMPLE PROBLEM 6.6

Using the $\Delta H$ and balanced equation for the combustion of propane ($C_3H_8$) with $O_2$ shown in Sample Problem 6.5, how many kilocalories of energy are released when 20.0 g of propane is burned?

### Analysis

To relate the number of grams of propane to the number of kilocalories of energy released on combustion, two operations are needed: [1] Convert the number of grams to the number of moles using the molar mass. [2] Convert the number of moles to the number of kilocalories using $\Delta H$ (kcal/mol) and the coefficients of the balanced chemical equation.

Solution

**[1] Convert the number of grams of propane to the number of moles of propane.**

- Use the molar mass of the reactant ($C_3H_8$, molar mass 44.09 g/mol) to write a conversion factor. Multiply the number of grams of propane by the conversion factor to give the number of moles of propane.

$$20.0 \ \cancel{g} \ C_3H_8 \quad \times \quad \frac{1 \ mol \ C_3H_8}{44.09 \ \cancel{g} \ C_3H_8} \quad = \quad 0.454 \ mol \ C_3H_8$$

Grams cancel.

**[2] Convert the number of moles of propane to the number of kilocalories using a kcal–mole conversion factor.**

- Use the $\Delta H$ and the number of moles of propane in the balanced chemical equation to write a kcal–mole conversion factor—one mole of propane ($C_3H_8$) releases 531 kcal of energy. Multiply the number of moles of propane by the conversion factor to give the number of kilocalories of energy released. This process was illustrated in Sample Problem 6.5.

kcal–mol
conversion factor

$$0.454 \ mol \ C_3H_8 \quad \times \quad \frac{531 \ kcal}{1 \ mol \ C_3H_8} \quad = \quad 241 \ kcal \ of \ energy \ released$$

Moles cancel.                                                    **Answer**

PROBLEM 6.9

Answer the following questions about the fermentation of glucose ($C_6H_{12}O_6$, molar mass 180.2 g/mol) to ethanol ($C_2H_6O$) and $CO_2$.

$$C_6H_{12}O_6(s) \longrightarrow 2 \ C_2H_6O(l) + 2 \ CO_2(g) \qquad \Delta H = -16 \ kcal/mol$$
glucose                    ethanol

a. How many kilocalories of energy are released from 6.0 mol of glucose?
b. How many kilocalories of energy are released when 1.0 mol of ethanol is formed?
c. How many kilocalories of energy are released from 20.0 g of glucose?

## 6.3  Energy Diagrams

On a molecular level, what happens when a reaction occurs? In order for two molecules to react, they must collide, and in the collision, the kinetic energy they possess is used to break bonds. Not every collision between two molecules, however, leads to a reaction. Collisions must have the proper orientation and enough energy for the reaction to occur.

How does the orientation of a collision affect a reaction? Consider a general reaction between two starting materials, **A—B** and **C** in which the **A—B** bond is broken and a new **B—C** bond is formed.

This bond breaks.                                                    This bond forms.

Since **C** forms a new bond with **B,** a reaction occurs only when **C** collides with **B.** If **C** collides with **A,** no bond breaking or bond making can occur, and a reaction does not take place. Since molecular collisions are random events, many collisions are ineffective because they do not place the reacting atoms close to each other.

| proper orientation | improper orientation |
|---|---|
| **C** collides with **B,** so a new **B—C** bond can form. | **C** collides with **A,** so a new **B—C** bond cannot form. |

The energy of the reacting molecules also determines whether a particular collision will lead to a reaction. In any given sample, molecules possess a wide range of kinetic energies. Some are fast moving and thus possess more kinetic energy than others that are slow moving. Since the kinetic energy of the reacting molecules **A—B** and **C** provides the energy to break the **A—B** bond, reaction occurs only when the reactants possess sufficient energy.

> • **Thus, only collisions that have sufficient energy and proper orientation lead to a reaction.**

The energy changes in a reaction are often illustrated on an **energy diagram,** which plots energy on the vertical axis, and the progress of the reaction—the **reaction coordinate**—on the horizontal axis. The reactants are written on the left side and the products on the right side, and a smooth curve that illustrates how energy changes with time connects them. Let's assume that the products, **A** and **B—C,** are lower in energy than the reactants, **A—B** and **C.**

**Energy Diagram**

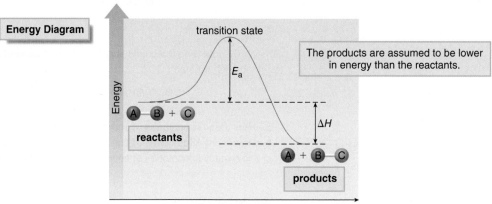

When the reactants **A—B** and **C** approach each other, their electron clouds feel some repulsion, causing an increase in energy until a maximum value is reached. This point is called the **transition state.** In the transition state, the bond between **A** and **B** is partially broken and the bond between **B** and **C** is partially formed. The transition state is located at the top of the energy hill that separates reactants from products. To draw a transition state, we use dashed lines for any bond that is broken or formed.

**Transition state**

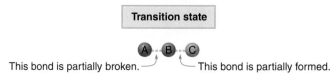

At the transition state, the bond between **A** and **B** can re-form to regenerate reactants, or the bond between **B** and **C** can form to generate products. As the bond forms between **B** and **C,** the energy decreases until some stable energy minimum is reached. The products are drawn lower in energy than the reactants to reflect the initial assumption about their relative energies.

> • **The difference in energy between the reactants and the transition state is called the *energy of activation*, symbolized by $E_a$.**

**Figure 6.1**

Energy Diagram for an
Endothermic Reaction

$E_a$ is the energy difference between the reactants and the transition state. $\Delta H$ is the difference
in energy between the reactants and products. Since the products are higher in energy than the
reactants, $\Delta H$ is positive (+) and the reaction is endothermic.

**The energy of activation is the minimum amount of energy needed for a reaction to occur.**
It represents the amount of energy that the reactants must possess for the reaction to take place.
The energy of activation is often called the **energy barrier** that must be crossed. The height of
the energy barrier—the magnitude of the energy of activation—determines the **reaction rate,
how fast the reaction occurs.**

- When the energy of activation is *high,* few molecules have enough energy to cross the energy
  barrier and the reaction is *slow.*
- When the energy of activation is *low,* many molecules have enough energy to cross the
  energy barrier and the reaction is *fast.*

**The difference in energy between the reactants and products is the $\Delta H$,** which is also labeled
on the energy diagram. When the products are lower in energy than the reactants, as is the case
here, the bonds in the product are stronger than the bonds in the reactants. $\Delta H$ is negative (−), and
the reaction is exothermic.

Energy diagrams can be drawn for any reaction. In the endothermic reaction shown in Figure 6.1,
the products are higher in energy than the reactants.

An energy diagram is a visual tool that helps to illustrate both the rate of a reaction (by the height
of the energy barrier), and the energy difference between the reactants and the products. Keep
in mind that these two quantities are independent. A large $E_a$ does not tell us anything about the
relative energies of the reactants and products.

- The size of $E_a$ determines the rate of a reaction.
- The sign of $\Delta H$ determines whether the products or reactants are lower in energy. Reactions
  are favored in which $\Delta H$ is negative and the products are lower in energy, making them more
  stable than the reactants.

**SAMPLE PROBLEM 6.7**

Draw an energy diagram for a reaction with a low energy of activation and a $\Delta H$ of −10 kcal/mol. Label
the axes, reactants, products, transition state, $E_a$, and $\Delta H$.

**Analysis**

A low energy of activation means a low energy barrier and a small hill that separates reactants and
products. When $\Delta H$ is (−), the products are lower in energy than the reactants.

Solution

PROBLEM 6.10

Draw an energy diagram for a reaction with a high $E_a$ and a $\Delta H$ = +20 kcal/mol.

PROBLEM 6.11

Draw an energy diagram for the following reaction: $H_2O + HCl \longrightarrow H_3O^+ + Cl^-$. Assume the energy of activation is low and the products are lower in energy than the reactants. Clearly label the reactants and products on the energy diagram.

## 6.4 Reaction Rates

Gasoline can be safely handled in the air because its reaction with $O_2$ is slow unless there is a spark to provide energy to initiate the reaction.

Even though we may not realize it, the rate of chemical processes affects many facets of our lives. Aspirin is an effective pain reliever because it rapidly blocks the synthesis of pain-causing molecules. Butter turns rancid with time because its fat molecules are slowly oxidized by oxygen in the air to undesirable by-products. DDT is a persistent environmental pollutant because it does not react appreciably with water, oxygen, or any other chemical with which it comes into contact. All of these processes occur at different rates, resulting in beneficial or harmful effects.

The energy of activation, the minimum amount of energy needed for a reaction to occur, is a fundamental characteristic of a reaction. Some reactions are fast because they have low energies of activation. Other reactions are slow because the energy of activation is high. Even reactions that form products that are lower in energy than the reactants can have high energies of activation. The combustion of gasoline to form $CO_2$ and $H_2O$ releases a great deal of energy, but it is a very slow reaction without a spark or flame to initiate the reaction.

### 6.4A   How Concentration and Temperature Affect Reaction Rate

As we learned in Section 6.3, chemical reactions occur when molecules collide. The rate of a reaction depends on the number of collisions and the effectiveness of each collision. How do changes in concentration and temperature affect the reaction rate?

- Increasing the concentration of the reactants increases the number of collisions, so the reaction rate increases.
- Increasing the temperature increases the reaction rate.

Increasing the temperature increases the reaction rate for two reasons. First, increasing the temperature increases the kinetic energy, which increases the number of collisions. Second, increasing the temperature increases the *average* kinetic energy of the reactants. Because the kinetic energy of colliding molecules is used for bond cleavage, more molecules have sufficient energy to cause

We store food in a cold refrigerator to slow the reactions that cause food to spoil.

bond breaking, and the reaction rate increases. As a general rule, a reaction rate *doubles* for each 10 °C the temperature is *raised*. Similarly, a reaction rate is generally *halved* for each 10 °C the temperature is *lowered*.

## PROBLEM 6.12

Consider the reaction of ozone ($O_3$) with nitrogen monoxide (NO), which occurs in smog. What effect would each of the following changes have on the rate of this reaction?

$$O_3(g) + NO(g) \longrightarrow O_2(g) + NO_2(g)$$

a. increasing the concentration of $O_3$
b. decreasing the concentration of NO

c. increasing the temperature
d. decreasing the temperature

## 6.4B  Catalysts

Some reactions do not occur in a reasonable period of time unless a **catalyst** is added.

- A *catalyst* is a substance that speeds up the rate of a reaction. A catalyst is recovered unchanged in a reaction, and it does not appear in the product.

**Catalysts accelerate a reaction by lowering the energy of activation** (Figure 6.2). They have no effect on the energies of the reactants and products. Thus, the addition of a catalyst lowers $E_a$ but does not affect $\Delta H$.

Metals are often used as catalysts in reactions. For example, ethylene ($CH_2=CH_2$) does not react appreciably with hydrogen ($H_2$), but in the presence of palladium (Pd) a rapid reaction occurs and ethane ($C_2H_6$) is formed as the product. The metal serves as a surface that brings together both reactants, facilitating the reaction. This reaction, called **hydrogenation,** is used in the food industry to prepare margarine, peanut butter, and many other consumer products that contain vegetable oils (Section 13.7).

## Figure 6.2   The Effect of a Catalyst on a Reaction

A catalyst lowers the energy of activation, thus increasing the rate of the catalyzed reaction. The energy of the reactants and products is the same in both the uncatalyzed and catalyzed reactions.

## 6.4C  FOCUS ON THE HUMAN BODY
### Lactase, a Biological Catalyst

The catalysts that synthesize and break down biological molecules in living organisms are governed by the same principles as the metals in organic reactions. The catalysts in living organisms, however, are protein molecules called **enzymes.**

> • *Enzymes* are biological catalysts held together in a very specific three-dimensional shape.

Enzymes are discussed in greater detail in Section 21.9.

An enzyme contains a region called its **active site** that binds a reactant, which then undergoes a very specific reaction with an enhanced rate. For example, **lactase** is the enzyme that binds **lactose,** the principal carbohydrate in milk (Figure 6.3). Once bound, lactose is converted into two simpler sugars, glucose and galactose. When individuals lack adequate amounts of this enzyme, they are unable to digest lactose, and this causes abdominal cramping and diarrhea.

**Figure 6.3**   Lactase, an Example of a Biological Catalyst

The enzyme lactase binds the carbohydrate lactose ($C_{12}H_{22}O_{11}$) in its active site in step [1]. Lactose then reacts with water to break a bond and form two simpler sugars, galactose and glucose, in step [2]. This process is the first step in digesting lactose, the principal carbohydrate in milk. Without the enzyme, individuals are unable to convert lactose to galactose and glucose, lactose cannot be metabolized, and digestive problems result.

There is a direct link between the poor air quality in large metropolitan areas like Los Angeles and an increase in respiratory diseases.

### PROBLEM 6.13

The reaction of acetic acid ($C_2H_4O_2$) and ethanol ($C_2H_6O$) to form ethyl acetate ($C_4H_8O_2$) and water occurs at an appreciable rate only when a small amount of sulfuric acid ($H_2SO_4$) is added. Is $H_2SO_4$ a catalyst for this reaction? What effect does $H_2SO_4$ have on the relative energies of the reactants and products?

## 6.4D FOCUS ON THE ENVIRONMENT
### Catalytic Converters

The combustion of gasoline with oxygen provides a great deal of energy, much like the oxidation reactions of methane and propane discussed in Section 6.2B, and this energy is used to power vehicles. As the number of automobiles increased in the twentieth century, the air pollution they were responsible for became a major problem, especially in congested urban areas.

One problem with the auto engines of the 1970s centered on the carbon- and nitrogen-containing by-products emitted in engine exhaust. In addition to $CO_2$ and $H_2O$ formed during combustion, auto exhaust also contained unreacted gasoline molecules (general formula $C_xH_y$), the toxic gas carbon monoxide (CO, Section 5.5), and nitrogen monoxide (NO, Section 5.5, a contributing component of acid rain). **Catalytic converters** were devised to clean up these polluting automobile emissions.

The newest catalytic converters, called three-way catalytic converters, use a metal as a surface to catalyze three reactions, as shown in Figure 6.4. Both the unreacted gasoline molecules and carbon monoxide (CO) are oxidized to $CO_2$ and $H_2O$. Nitrogen monoxide is also converted to oxygen and nitrogen. In this way, three molecules that contribute to unhealthy smog levels are removed, and the only materials in the engine exhaust are $CO_2$, $H_2O$, $N_2$, and $O_2$.

**Figure 6.4** How a Catalytic Converter Works

A catalytic converter uses a metal catalyst—rhodium, platinum, or palladium—to catalyze three reactions that clean up the exhaust from an auto engine.

## 6.5  Equilibrium

Thus far in discussing reactions we have assumed that the reactants are completely converted to products. A reaction of this sort is said to **go to completion.** Sometimes, however, a reaction is **reversible;** that is, reactants can come together and form products, and products can come together to re-form reactants.

> • A *reversible reaction* can occur in either direction, from reactants to products or from products to reactants.

Consider the reversible reaction of carbon monoxide (CO) with water to form carbon dioxide ($CO_2$) and hydrogen. Two full-headed arrows ($\rightleftharpoons$) are used to show that the reaction can proceed from left to right and right to left as written.

The **forward** reaction proceeds to the *right.*

$$CO(g) \; + \; H_2O(g) \; \rightleftharpoons \; CO_2(g) \; + \; H_2(g)$$

The **reverse** reaction proceeds to the *left.*

> • The *forward* reaction proceeds from left to right as drawn.
> • The *reverse* reaction proceeds from right to left as drawn.

When CO and $H_2O$ are mixed together they react to form $CO_2$ and $H_2$ by the forward reaction. Once $CO_2$ and $H_2$ are formed, they can react together to form CO and $H_2O$ by the reverse reaction. The rate of the forward reaction is rapid at first, and then decreases as the concentration of reactants decreases. The rate of the reverse reaction is slow at first, but speeds up as the concentration of the products increases.

> • When the rate of the forward reaction equals the rate of the reverse reaction, the net concentrations of all species do not change and the system is at *equilibrium.*

The forward and reverse reactions do not stop once equilibrium has been reached. The reactants and products continue to react. Since the rates of the forward and reverse reactions are equal, however, the **net concentrations of all reactants and products do *not* change.** Molecular art in Figure 6.5 shows how the reversible reaction A $\rightleftharpoons$ B reaches equilibrium.

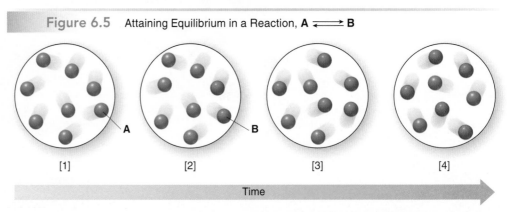

Figure 6.5    Attaining Equilibrium in a Reaction, A $\rightleftharpoons$ B

[1]            [2]            [3]            [4]

Time

The conversion of **A** (shown in blue spheres) to **B** (shown in red spheres) is a reversible reaction. Initially, the reaction contains only **A** (diagram [1]). As **A** reacts to form **B,** the amount of **B** increases (diagram [2]). As **B** is formed, it can be re-converted to **A.** At equilibrium (diagrams [3] and [4]), the amounts of **A** and **B** do not change, but the conversion of **A** to **B** and the conversion of **B** to **A** still occur.

**PROBLEM 6.14**

Identify the forward and reverse reactions in each of the following reversible reactions.

   a. $2 SO_2(g) + O_2(g) \rightleftharpoons 2 SO_3(g)$
   b. $N_2(g) + O_2(g) \rightleftharpoons 2 NO(g)$
   c. $C_2H_4O_2 + CH_4O \rightleftharpoons C_3H_6O_2 + H_2O$

## 6.5A The Equilibrium Constant

Because the net concentrations of the reactants and products do not change at equilibrium, they are used to define an expression, the **equilibrium constant, $K$,** which has a characteristic value for a reaction at a given temperature. When discussing equilibrium it is not the absolute number of moles that is the important quantity, but rather it is the *concentration,* **the number of moles in a given volume.** Brackets, [ ], are used to symbolize concentration, which is reported in moles per liter (mol/L).

Consider the following general reaction, where **A** and **B** represent reactants, **C** and **D** represent products, and *a, b, c,* and *d* represent the coefficients in the balanced chemical equation.

$$a\,\mathbf{A} + b\,\mathbf{B} \rightleftharpoons c\,\mathbf{C} + d\,\mathbf{D}$$

The equilibrium constant $K$ is the ratio of the concentrations of the products (**C** and **D**) multiplied together, to the concentrations of the reactants (**A** and **B**) multiplied together. Each concentration term is raised to a power equal to the coefficient in the balanced chemical equation.

concentration of each product (mol/L)

$$\text{Equilibrium constant} = K = \frac{[\text{products}]}{[\text{reactants}]}$$

concentration of each reactant (mol/L)

$$K = \frac{[C]^c[D]^d}{[A]^a[B]^b}$$

The expression for the equilibrium constant for any reaction can be written from a balanced equation, as shown for the reaction of $N_2$ and $O_2$ to form NO.

above the division line

Balanced equation:    $N_2(g) + O_2(g) \rightleftharpoons 2 NO(g)$

below the division line

The coefficient becomes the exponent.

$$\text{Equilibrium constant} = K = \frac{[NO]^2}{[N_2][O_2]}$$

**SAMPLE PROBLEM 6.8**

Write the expression for the equilibrium constant for the following balanced equation.

$$2 CO(g) + O_2(g) \rightleftharpoons 2 CO_2(g)$$

**Analysis**

To write an expression for the equilibrium constant, multiply the concentration of the products together and divide this number by the product of the concentrations of the reactants. Each concentration term must be raised to a power equal to the coefficient in the balanced chemical equation.

### Solution

The concentration of the sole product, $CO_2$, is placed in the numerator and raised to the second power since this term has the coefficient "2." The denominator contains concentration terms for the two reactants, CO and $O_2$, multiplied together. Since the coefficient preceding CO in the balanced equation is "2," this concentration term has an exponent of "2."

$$\text{Equilibrium constant} = K = \frac{[CO_2]^2}{[CO]^2[O_2]}$$

### PROBLEM 6.15

Write the expression for the equilibrium constant for each equation.

a. $PCl_3(g) + Cl_2(g) \rightleftharpoons PCl_5(g)$
b. $2\,SO_2(g) + O_2(g) \rightleftharpoons 2\,SO_3(g)$
c. $H_2(g) + Br_2(g) \rightleftharpoons 2\,HBr(g)$
d. $CH_4(g) + 3\,Cl_2(g) \rightleftharpoons CHCl_3(g) + 3\,HCl(g)$

## 6.5B  The Magnitude of the Equilibrium Constant

The magnitude of the equilibrium constant tells us whether the products or reactants are favored once equilibrium is reached.

- When the equilibrium constant is much greater than one ($K > 1$), the concentration of the products is larger than the concentration of the reactants. We say equilibrium lies to the *right* and favors the *products.*

When $K$ is greater than 1: $\dfrac{[products]}{[reactants]}$   The numerator is larger.
($K > 1$)                                          Equilibrium favors the **products.**

- When the equilibrium constant is much less than one ($K < 1$), the concentration of the reactants is larger than the concentration of the products. We say equilibrium lies to the *left* and favors the *reactants.*

When $K$ is less than 1: $\dfrac{[products]}{[reactants]}$   The denominator is larger.
($K < 1$)                                        Equilibrium favors the **reactants.**

- When the equilibrium constant is around 1, anywhere in the range of 0.01–100, both reactants and products are present at equilibrium.

When $K$ is approximately equal to 1: $\dfrac{[products]}{[reactants]}$   Both reactants and products are present.
($K \approx 1$)

For example, the equilibrium constant for the reaction of $H_2$ and $O_2$ to form water is much greater than one, so the product, $H_2O$, is highly favored at equilibrium. A reaction with such a large $K$ essentially goes to completion, with little or no reactants left.

$$2\,H_2(g) \;+\; O_2(g) \;\rightleftharpoons\; 2\,H_2O(g) \qquad K \;=\; 2.9 \times 10^{82}$$

- The product is highly favored since $K > 1$.
- Equilibrium lies to the right.

In contrast, the equilibrium constant for the conversion of $O_2$ to $O_3$ is much less than one, so the reactant, $O_2$, is highly favored at equilibrium, and almost no product, $O_3$, is formed. The relationship between the equilibrium constant and the direction of equilibrium is summarized in Table 6.4.

$$3\ O_2(g) \rightleftharpoons 2\ O_3(g) \qquad K = 2.7 \times 10^{-29}$$

• The reactant is highly favored since $K < 1$.
• Equilibrium lies to the left.

Generally there is a relationship between the equilibrium constant $K$ and the $\Delta H$ of a reaction.

> • The products of a reaction are favored when $K$ is much greater than one ($K > 1$), and $\Delta H$ is negative. In other words, equilibrium favors the products when they are lower in energy than the reactants.

There is, however, no relationship between $K$ and the reaction rate. Some reactions with very large equilibrium constants are still very slow. Moreover, a catalyst may speed up a reaction, but it does not affect the size of $K$. With a catalyst, equilibrium is reached more quickly, but the relative concentrations of reactants and products do not change.

### Table 6.4  How the Magnitude of $K$ Relates to the Direction of Equilibrium

| Value of $K$ | Position of Equilibrium |
| --- | --- |
| $K > 1$ | Equilibrium favors the products.<br>Equilibrium lies to the right. |
| $K < 1$ | Equilibrium favors the reactants.<br>Equilibrium lies to the left. |
| $K \approx 1$ | Both the reactants and products are present at equilibrium. |

### SAMPLE PROBLEM 6.9

Consider the reversible reaction $\mathbf{A} \rightleftharpoons \mathbf{B}$, with $K = 10$. Assume the reaction begins with only $\mathbf{A}$, and draw a representation for the reaction mixture at equilibrium.

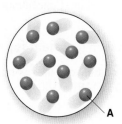

A

### Analysis

Write the expression for the equilibrium constant, and use the value of $K$ to determine the relative amounts of product ($\mathbf{B}$) and reactant ($\mathbf{A}$).

### Solution

In this reaction, $K = [\mathbf{B}]/[\mathbf{A}] = 10$. Since the concentration of the product is in the numerator, this means that there is 10 times as much product ($\mathbf{B}$) as reactant ($\mathbf{A}$) at equilibrium.

$$\text{For } K = 10: \qquad K = \frac{[\mathbf{B}]}{[\mathbf{A}]} = \frac{10}{1} \qquad \text{10 times as much } \mathbf{B} \text{ as } \mathbf{A}$$

To represent equilibrium in this reaction using molecular art, draw 10 times as many **B** spheres (in red) as **A** spheres (in blue).

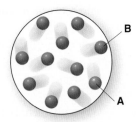

## PROBLEM 6.16

Consider the reversible reaction **A** ⇌ **B,** with $K = 1$. Assuming the reaction begins with only **A,** draw a representation using molecular art for the reaction mixture at equilibrium. Use blue spheres for **A** and red spheres for **B.**

## PROBLEM 6.17

Given each equilibrium constant, state whether the reactants are favored, the products are favored, or both the reactants and products are present at equilibrium.

   a. $5.0 \times 10^{-4}$       b. $4.4 \times 10^{5}$       c. 350       d. 0.35

## PROBLEM 6.18

Predict whether the reactions with the equilibrium constants in Problem 6.17 are endothermic or exothermic.

## PROBLEM 6.19

Consider the following reaction: $2\,H_2(g) + S_2(g) \longrightarrow 2\,H_2S(g)$ with $K = 1.1 \times 10^{7}$. (a) Write the expression for the equilibrium constant for this reaction. (b) Are the reactants or products favored at equilibrium? (c) Would you predict $\Delta H$ to be positive or negative? (d) Are the reactants or products lower in energy? (e) Would you predict this reaction to be fast or slow? Explain your choice.

## 6.5C   Calculating the Equilibrium Constant

The equilibrium constant for a reaction is an experimentally determined value, and thus it can be calculated if the concentrations of all substances involved in a reaction are measured at equilibrium. Concentrations are reported in moles per liter (mol/L), symbolized as M.

---

### *How To*  Calculate the Equilibrium Constant for a Reaction

**Example:**  Calculate $K$ for the reaction between the general reactants $A_2$ and $B_2$. The equilibrium concentrations are as follows: $[A_2] = 0.25$ M; $[B_2] = 0.25$ M; $[AB] = 0.50$ M.

$$A_2 + B_2 \rightleftharpoons 2\,AB$$

**Step [1]**  **Write the expression for the equilibrium constant from the balanced chemical equation, using the coefficients as exponents for the concentration terms.**

$$\text{Equilibrium constant} = K = \frac{[AB]^2}{[A_2][B_2]}$$

**Step [2]**  **Substitute the given concentrations in the equilibrium expression and calculate $K$.**

- Since the concentration is always reported in mol/L (M), these units are omitted during the calculation.

$$K = \frac{[AB]^2}{[A_2][B_2]} = \frac{[0.50]^2}{[0.25][0.25]} = \frac{(0.50) \times (0.50)}{0.0625}$$

$$= \frac{0.25}{0.0625} = 4.0$$

**Answer**

The conversion of nitrogen and hydrogen to ammonia (Sample Problem 6.10) is an exceedingly important reaction since it converts molecular nitrogen from the air to a nitrogen compound ($NH_3$) that can be used as a fertilizer for plants. In the early twentieth century, German chemist Fritz Haber developed a catalyst that enabled this reaction to proceed quickly to afford favorable yields of $NH_3$. This process paved the way for large-scale agriculture, which provides food for the world's growing population.

## SAMPLE PROBLEM 6.10

Calculate $K$ for the reaction of $N_2$ and $H_2$ to form $NH_3$, with the given balanced equation and the following equilibrium concentrations: $[N_2] = 0.12$ M; $[H_2] = 0.36$ M; $[NH_3] = 1.1$ M.

$$N_2(g) + 3\,H_2(g) \rightleftharpoons 2\,NH_3(g)$$

### Analysis

Write an expression for $K$ using the balanced equation and substitute the equilibrium concentrations of all substances in the expression.

### Solution

$$K = \frac{[NH_3]^2}{[N_2][H_2]^3} = \frac{(1.1)^2}{(0.12)(0.36)^3} = \frac{1.1 \times 1.1}{0.12 \times 0.36 \times 0.36 \times 0.36}$$

$$= \frac{1.21}{0.0056} = 216 \text{ rounded to } 220$$

**Answer**

## PROBLEM 6.20

Calculate the equilibrium constant for each reaction using the balanced chemical equations and the concentrations of the substances at equilibrium.

a. $CO(g) + H_2O(g) \rightleftharpoons CO_2(g) + H_2(g)$    $[CO] = 0.0236$ M; $[H_2O] = 0.00240$ M; $[CO_2] = 0.0164$ M; $[H_2] = 0.0164$ M

b. $2\,NO_2(g) \rightleftharpoons N_2O_4(g)$    $[NO_2] = 0.0760$ M; $[N_2O_4] = 1.26$ M

# 6.6 Le Châtelier's Principle

What happens when a reaction is at equilibrium and something changes? For example, what happens when the temperature is increased or some additional reactant is added? **Le Châtelier's principle** is a general rule used to explain the effect of a change in reaction conditions on equilibrium. Le Châtelier's principle states:

> • If a chemical system at equilibrium is disturbed or stressed, the system will react in the direction that counteracts the disturbance or relieves the stress.

Let's examine the effect of changes in concentration, temperature, and pressure on equilibrium.

## 6.6A Concentration Changes

Consider the reaction of carbon monoxide (CO) with oxygen ($O_2$) to form carbon dioxide ($CO_2$).

$$2\,CO(g) + O_2(g) \rightleftharpoons 2\,CO_2(g)$$

If the reactants and products are at equilibrium, what happens if the concentration of CO is increased? Now the equilibrium is disturbed and, as a result, the rate of the forward reaction increases to produce more $CO_2$. We can think of **added reactant as driving the equilibrium to the *right*.**

Adding more reactant…

$$2\,CO(g) \quad + \quad O_2(g) \rightleftharpoons 2\,CO_2(g)$$

…drives the reaction to the right.

When the system reaches equilibrium once again, the concentrations of $CO_2$ and $CO$ are both higher. Since $O_2$ reacted with the additional $CO$, its new value at equilibrium is lower. Even though the concentrations of reactants and products are different, the value of $K$ is the same.

If CO is added…

$$2\ CO(g)\ +\ O_2(g)\ \rightleftharpoons\ 2\ CO_2(g)$$

…this decreases…     …and this increases.

What happens, instead, if the concentration of $CO_2$ is increased? Now the equilibrium is disturbed but there is more product than there should be. As a result, the rate of the reverse reaction increases to produce more of both reactants, $CO$ and $O_2$. We can think of **added product as driving the equilibrium to the** *left.*

Adding more product…

$$2\ CO(g)\ +\ O_2(g)\ \rightleftharpoons\ 2\ CO_2(g)$$

…drives the reaction to the left.

When the system reaches equilibrium once again, the concentrations of $CO$, $O_2$, and $CO_2$ are all higher. Even though the concentrations of reactants and products are different, the value of $K$ is the same.

If $CO_2$ is added…

$$2\ CO(g)\ +\ O_2(g)\ \rightleftharpoons\ 2\ CO_2(g)$$

…this increases…     …and this increases.

Similar arguments can be made about the effect of decreasing the concentration of a reactant or product. Sometimes, when $K < 1$ and the amount of product at equilibrium is not high, a product is removed from the reaction mixture as it is formed. For example, ethanol ($C_2H_6O$) can be converted to ethylene ($CH_2{=}CH_2$) and water in the presence of a small amount of acid, but equilibrium does not favor the products.

ethanol

Removing a product…

…drives the reaction to the right.

In this case, water can be removed from the reaction as it is formed. A decrease in concentration of one product results in more of the forward reaction to form more product. **This process drives the equilibrium to the right.** If water is continuously removed, essentially all of the starting material can be converted to product.

## SAMPLE PROBLEM 6.11

In which direction is the equilibrium shifted with each of the following concentration changes for the given reaction: (a) increase [$SO_2$]; (b) increase [$SO_3$]; (c) decrease [$O_2$]; (d) decrease [$SO_3$]?

$$2\ SO_2(g)\ +\ O_2(g)\ \rightleftharpoons\ 2\ SO_3(g)$$

### Analysis

Use Le Châtelier's principle to predict the effect of a change in concentration on equilibrium. Adding more reactant or removing product drives the equilibrium to the right. Adding more product or removing reactant drives the equilibrium to the left.

### Solution

a. Increasing [SO$_2$], a reactant, drives the equilibrium to the right to form more product.
b. Increasing [SO$_3$], a product, drives the equilibrium to the left to form more reactants.
c. Decreasing [O$_2$], a reactant, drives the equilibrium to the left to form more reactants.
d. Decreasing [SO$_3$], a product, drives the equilibrium to the right to form more product.

### PROBLEM 6.21

In which direction is the equilibrium shifted with each of the following concentration changes for the given reaction: (a) increase [H$_2$]; (b) increase [HCl]; (c) decrease [Cl$_2$]; (d) decrease [HCl]?

$$H_2(g) + Cl_2(g) \rightleftharpoons 2\ HCl(g)$$

## 6.6B Temperature Changes

In order to predict what effect a change of temperature has on a reaction, we must know if a reaction is endothermic or exothermic.

- **When temperature is increased, the reaction that removes heat is favored.**
- **When temperature is decreased, the reaction that adds heat is favored.**

For example, the reaction of N$_2$ and O$_2$ to form NO is an endothermic reaction ($\Delta H$ = +43 kcal/mol). **Since an endothermic reaction absorbs heat, increasing the temperature increases the rate of the *forward* reaction to form more product.** The equilibrium shifts to the right.

In the exothermic reaction of N$_2$ and H$_2$ to form NH$_3$ ($\Delta H$ = –22 kcal/mol), **increasing the temperature increases the rate of the *reverse* reaction to form more reactants.** When temperature is increased, the reaction that absorbs heat, in this case the reverse reaction, predominates and the equilibrium shifts to the left.

### SAMPLE PROBLEM 6.12

The reaction of SO$_2$ with O$_2$ to form SO$_3$ is an exothermic reaction. In which direction is the equilibrium shifted when the temperature is (a) increased; (b) decreased?

### Analysis

When temperature is increased, the reaction that removes heat is favored. When temperature is decreased, the reaction that adds heat is favored.

### Solution

In an exothermic reaction, the forward reaction releases heat and the reverse reaction absorbs heat. (a) When the temperature is increased, the reverse reaction is favored because it removes heat, so the equilibrium shifts to the reactants (to the left). (b) When the temperature is decreased, the forward reaction is favored because it adds heat, so the equilibrium shifts to the products (to the right).

Pressure, the force per unit area, is discussed in greater detail in Chapter 7.

### PROBLEM 6.22

The conversion of $H_2O$ to $H_2$ and $O_2$ is an endothermic reaction. In which direction is the equilibrium shifted when the temperature is (a) increased; (b) decreased?

### PROBLEM 6.23

The reaction of $O_3$ with NO to form $NO_2$ and $O_2$ is an exothermic reaction. In which direction is the equilibrium shifted when the temperature is (a) increased; (b) decreased?

## 6.6C   Pressure Changes

When the substances involved in a reaction are gases and the total number of moles of reactants and products differs, a change in pressure has an effect on equilibrium.

- When pressure *increases,* equilibrium shifts in the direction that *decreases* the number of moles in order to decrease pressure.
- When pressure *decreases,* equilibrium shifts in the direction that *increases* the number of moles in order to increase pressure.

In the reaction of $N_2$ and $H_2$ to form $NH_3$, there are four moles of reactants but only two moles of product. When the pressure of the system is increased, the equilibrium shifts to the right since there are fewer moles of product.

Increasing pressure…

$$N_2(g) \;+\; 3\,H_2(g) \;\rightleftharpoons\; 2\,NH_3(g)$$

4 moles          2 moles

This side has fewer moles.

…drives the reaction to the right.

In contrast, when the pressure of the system is decreased, the equilibrium shifts to the left since there are more moles of reactants.

$$N_2(g) \;+\; 3\,H_2(g) \;\rightleftharpoons\; 2\,NH_3(g)$$

This side has more moles.      4 moles      2 moles

Decreasing pressure…

…drives the reaction to the left.

### SAMPLE PROBLEM 6.13

In which direction is the equilibrium shifted in the following reaction when the pressure is (a) increased; (b) decreased?

$$H{-}C{\equiv}C{-}H(g) + 2\,H_2(g) \;\rightleftharpoons\; C_2H_6(g)$$

#### Analysis

When pressure is increased, the equilibrium shifts in the direction that decreases the number of moles. When pressure is decreased, the equilibrium shifts in the direction that increases the number of moles.

#### Solution

In this reaction, there are three moles of reactants and only one mole of product. (a) Increasing the pressure shifts the equilibrium to the right, to the side of fewer moles. (b) Decreasing the pressure shifts the equilibrium to the left, to the side of more moles.

Table 6.5 summarizes the effects of changes in reaction conditions on the direction of an equilibrium.

### PROBLEM 6.24

In which direction is the equilibrium shifted in the following reaction when the pressure is
(a) increased; (b) decreased?

$$C_2H_4(g) + Cl_2(g) \rightleftharpoons C_2H_4Cl_2(g)$$

**Table 6.5 The Effects of Changes in Conditions on Equilibrium**

| Change | Effect on Equilibrium |
|---|---|
| **Concentration** | |
| • Adding reactant | Equilibrium favors the products. |
| • Removing reactant | Equilibrium favors the reactants. |
| • Adding product | Equilibrium favors the reactants. |
| • Removing product | Equilibrium favors the products. |
| **Temperature** | |
| • Increasing temperature | In an endothermic reaction, equilibrium favors the products. In an exothermic reaction, equilibrium favors the reactants. |
| • Decreasing temperature | In an endothermic reaction, equilibrium favors the reactants. In an exothermic reaction, equilibrium favors the products. |
| **Pressure** | |
| • Increasing pressure | Equilibrium favors the side that has fewer moles. |
| • Decreasing pressure | Equilibrium favors the side that has more moles. |

## 6.7 FOCUS ON THE HUMAN BODY
### Body Temperature

The human body is an enormously complex organism that illustrates important features of energy and reaction rates. At any moment, millions of reactions occur in the body, when nutrients are metabolized and new cell materials are synthesized.

Normal body temperature, 37 °C, reflects a delicate balance between the amount of heat absorbed and released in all of the reactions and other processes. Since reaction rate increases with increasing temperature, it is crucial to maintain the right temperature for proper body function. When temperature increases, reactions proceed at a faster rate. An individual must breathe more rapidly and the heart must pump harder to supply oxygen for the faster metabolic processes. When temperature decreases, reactions slow down, less heat is generated in exothermic reactions, and it becomes harder and harder to maintain an adequate body temperature.

**Thermoregulation**—regulating temperature—is a complex mechanism that involves the brain, the circulatory system, and the skin (Figure 6.6). Temperature sensors in the skin and body core signal when there is a temperature change. The hypothalamus region of the brain, in turn, responds to changes in its environment in a process that is reminiscent of Le Châtelier's principle.

When the temperature increases, the body must somehow rid itself of excess heat. Blood vessels near the surface of the skin are dilated to release more heat. Sweat glands are stimulated so the body can be cooled by the evaporation of water from the skin's surface.

When the temperature decreases, the body must generate more heat as well as slow down the loss of heat to the surroundings. Blood vessels constrict to reduce heat loss from the skin and muscles shiver to generate more heat.

**Figure 6.6** Temperature Regulation in the Body

hypothalamus—the temperature controller

hair

skin

Sweat glands are stimulated when temperature increases to cool the body by evaporation.

Blood vessels dilate to release more heat or constrict to release less heat as temperature changes.

sensory nerve ending

sweat gland

capillaries

nerve

When the temperature in the environment around the body changes, the body works to counteract the change, in a method similar to Le Châtelier's principle. The hypothalamus acts as a thermostat, which signals the body to respond to temperature changes. When the temperature increases, the body must dissipate excess heat by dilating blood vessels and sweating. When the temperature decreases, blood vessels constrict and the body shivers.

An infection in the body is often accompanied by a fever; that is, the temperature in the body increases. A fever is part of the body's response to increase the rates of defensive reactions that kill bacteria. The respiratory rate and heart rate increase to supply more oxygen needed for faster reactions.

# CHAPTER HIGHLIGHTS

## KEY TERMS

Active site (6.4)
Bond dissociation energy (6.2)
Calorie (6.1)
Catalyst (6.4)
Endothermic reaction (6.2)
Energy (6.1)
Energy diagram (6.3)
Energy of activation (6.3)

Enthalpy change (6.2)
Enzyme (6.4)
Equilibrium (6.5)
Equilibrium constant (6.5)
Exothermic reaction (6.2)
Forward reaction (6.5)
Heat of reaction (6.2)
Joule (6.1)

Kinetic energy (6.1)
Law of conservation of energy (6.1)
Le Châtelier's principle (6.6)
Potential energy (6.1)
Reaction rate (6.3)
Reverse reaction (6.5)
Reversible reaction (6.5)
Transition state (6.3)

# KEY CONCEPTS

**❶ What is energy and what units are used to measure energy? (6.1)**

- Energy is the capacity to do work. Kinetic energy is the energy of motion, whereas potential energy is stored energy.
- Energy is measured in calories (cal) or joules (J), where 1 cal = 4.184 J.
- One nutritional calorie (Cal) = 1 kcal = 1,000 cal.

**❷ Define bond dissociation energy and describe its relationship to bond strength. (6.2)**

- The bond dissociation energy is the energy needed to break a covalent bond by equally dividing the electrons between the two atoms in the bond.
- The higher the bond dissociation energy, the stronger the bond.

**❸ What is the heat of reaction and what is the difference between an endothermic and an exothermic reaction? (6.2)**

- The heat of reaction, also called the enthalpy change and symbolized by $\Delta H$, is the energy absorbed or released in a reaction.
- In an endothermic reaction, energy is absorbed, $\Delta H$ is positive (+), and the products are higher in energy than the reactants. The bonds in the reactants are stronger than the bonds in the products.
- In an exothermic reaction, energy is released, $\Delta H$ is negative (–), and the reactants are higher in energy than the products. The bonds in the products are stronger than the bonds in the reactants.

**❹ What are the important features of an energy diagram? (6.3)**

- An energy diagram illustrates the energy changes that occur during the course of a reaction. Energy is plotted on the vertical axis and reaction coordinate is plotted on the horizontal axis. The transition state is located at the top of the energy barrier that separates the reactants and products.
- The energy of activation is the energy difference between the reactants and the transition state. The higher the energy of activation, the slower the reaction.
- The difference in energy between the reactants and products is the $\Delta H$.

**❺ How do temperature, concentration, and catalysts affect the rate of a reaction? (6.4)**

- Increasing the temperature and concentration increases the reaction rate.
- A catalyst speeds up the rate of a reaction without affecting the energies of the reactants and products. Enzymes are biological catalysts that increase the rate of reactions in living organisms. Catalytic converters use a catalyst to convert automobile engine exhaust to environmentally cleaner products.

**❻ What are the basic features of equilibrium? (6.5)**

- At equilibrium, the rates of the forward and reverse reactions in a reversible reaction are equal and the net concentrations of all substances do not change.
- The equilibrium constant for a reaction $aA + bB \rightleftharpoons cC + dD$ is written as $K = ([C]^c[D]^d)/([A]^a[B]^b)$.
- The magnitude of $K$ tells the relative amount of reactants and products. When $K > 1$, the products are favored; when $K < 1$, the reactants are favored; when $K \approx 1$, both reactants and products are present at equilibrium.

**❼ How does Le Châtelier's principle predict what happens when equilibrium is disturbed? (6.6)**

- Le Châtelier's principle states that a system at equilibrium reacts in such a way as to counteract any disturbance to the equilibrium. How changes in concentration, temperature, and pressure affect equilibrium are summarized in Table 6.5.
- Catalysts increase the rate at which equilibrium is reached, but do not alter the amount of any substance involved in the reaction.

**❽ How can the principles that describe equilibrium and reaction rates be used to understand the regulation of body temperature? (6.7)**

- Increasing temperature increases the rates of the reactions in the body.
- When temperature is increased, the body dissipates excess heat by dilating blood vessels and sweating. When temperature is decreased, blood vessels constrict to conserve heat, and the body shivers to generate more heat.

# PROBLEMS

Selected in-chapter and odd-numbered end-of-chapter problems have brief answers in Appendix B. The *Student Study Guide and Solutions Manual* contains detailed solutions to all in-chapter and odd-numbered end-of-chapter problems, as well as additional worked examples and a chapter self-test.

## Energy

**6.25** What is the difference between kinetic energy and potential energy? Give an example of each type.

**6.26** What is the difference between a calorie and a Calorie?

**6.27** Riding a bicycle at 12–13 miles per hour uses 563 Calories in an hour. Convert this value to (a) calories; (b) kilocalories; (c) joules; (d) kilojoules.

**6.28** Running at a rate of 6 mi/h uses 704 Calories in an hour. Convert this value to (a) calories; (b) kilocalories; (c) joules; (d) kilojoules.

**6.29** Carry out each of the following conversions.
  a. 50 cal to kcal
  b. 56 cal to kJ
  c. 0.96 kJ to cal
  d. 4,230 kJ to cal

**6.30** Carry out each of the following conversions.
- a. 5 kcal to cal
- b. 2,560 cal to kJ
- c. 1.22 kJ to cal
- d. 4,230 J to kcal

**6.31** Estimate the number of Calories in two tablespoons of peanut butter, which contains 16 g of protein, 7 g of carbohydrates, and 16 g of fat.

**6.32** Estimate the number of Calories in a serving of oatmeal that has 4 g of protein, 19 g of carbohydrates, and 2 g of fat.

**6.33** A can of soda contains 120 Calories, and no protein or fat. How many grams of carbohydrates are present in each can?

**6.34** Alcohol releases 29.7 kJ/g when it burns. Convert this value to the number of Calories per gram.

**6.35** Which food has more Calories: 3 oz of salmon, which contains 17 g of protein and 5 g of fat, or 3 oz of chicken, which contains 20 g of protein and 3 g of fat?

**6.36** Which food has more Calories: one egg, which contains 6 g of protein and 6 g of fat, or 1 cup of nonfat milk, which contains 9 g of protein and 12 g of carbohydrates?

## Bond Dissociation Energy and $\Delta H$

**6.37** What is the difference between an endothermic reaction and an exothermic reaction?

**6.38** What is the difference between $\Delta H$ and the bond dissociation energy?

**6.39** Based on the location of the elements in the periodic table, which species in each pair has the stronger bond?
- a. $Br_2$ or $Cl_2$
- b. $Cl_2$ or $I_2$
- c. HF or HBr

**6.40** Using the given bond dissociation energies, rank the indicated bonds in order of increasing strength.

$$
\begin{array}{ccc}
\text{H} & \text{H H} & \\
\text{H—C—H} & \text{H—C—C—H} & \text{H—C}\equiv\text{C—H} \\
\text{H} & \text{H H} & \\
\Delta H = +104 \text{ kcal/mol} & \Delta H = +98 \text{ kcal/mol} & \Delta H = +125 \text{ kcal/mol}
\end{array}
$$

**6.41** Do each of the following statements describe an endothermic or exothermic reaction?
- a. $\Delta H$ is a negative value.
- b. The energy of the reactants is lower than the energy of the products.
- c. Energy is absorbed in the reaction.
- d. The bonds in the products are stronger than the bonds in the reactants.

**6.42** Do each of the following statements describe an endothermic or exothermic reaction?
- a. $\Delta H$ is a positive value.
- b. The energy of the products is lower than the energy of the reactants.
- c. Energy is released in the reaction.
- d. The bonds in the reactants are stronger than the bonds in the products.

**6.43** The combustion of coal with oxygen forms $CO_2$ and releases 94 kcal of energy.

$$C(s) + O_2(g) \longrightarrow CO_2(g)$$

- a. How much energy is released when 2.5 mol of C reacts?
- b. How much energy is released when 3.0 mol of $O_2$ reacts?
- c. How much energy is released when 25.0 g of C reacts?

**6.44** Ammonia ($NH_3$) decomposes to hydrogen and nitrogen and 22.0 kcal/mol of energy is absorbed.

$$2\,NH_3(g) \longrightarrow 3\,H_2(g) + N_2(g)$$

- a. How much energy is absorbed when 1 mol of $N_2$ is formed?
- b. How much energy is absorbed when 1 mol of $NH_3$ reacts?
- c. How much energy is absorbed when 3.50 g of $NH_3$ reacts?

**6.45** The metabolism of glucose (molar mass 180.2 g/mol) with oxygen forms $CO_2$ and $H_2O$ and releases 678 kcal/mol of energy.

$$\underset{\text{glucose}}{C_6H_{12}O_6(aq)} + 6\,O_2(g) \rightleftharpoons 6\,CO_2(g) + 6\,H_2O(l)$$

- a. Are the bonds formed in the products stronger or weaker than the bonds broken in the reactants?
- b. How much energy is released when 4.00 mol of glucose is metabolized?
- c. How much energy is released when 3.00 mol of $O_2$ reacts?
- d. How much energy is released when 10.0 g of glucose reacts?

**6.46** Ethanol ($C_2H_6O$), a gasoline additive, is formed by the reaction of ethylene ($CH_2$=$CH_2$) with water. The $\Delta H$ for this reaction is –9.0 kcal/mol.

$$
\underset{\text{ethylene}}{
\begin{array}{c}
\text{H} \quad\quad \text{H} \\
\text{C=C} \\
\text{H} \quad\quad \text{H}
\end{array}}
\;+\; H_2O \;\rightleftharpoons\; \underset{\text{ethanol}}{C_2H_6O}
$$

- a. How much energy is released when 3.5 mol of ethylene reacts?
- b. How much energy is released when 0.50 mol of $H_2O$ reacts?
- c. How much energy is released when 15.0 g of ethylene reacts?
- d. How much energy is released when 2.5 g of ethanol is formed?

## Energy Diagrams

**6.47** What is the difference between the energy of activation and the transition state?

**6.48** What is the difference between $E_a$ and $\Delta H$?

**6.49** Consider the energy diagram drawn below.

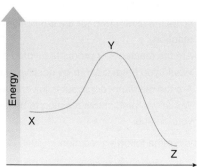

a. Which point on the graph corresponds to reactants?
b. Which point on the graph corresponds to products?
c. Which point on the graph corresponds to the transition state?
d. The difference in energy between which two points equals the energy of activation?
e. The difference in energy between which two points equals the $\Delta H$?
f. Which point is highest in energy?
g. Which point is lowest in energy?

**6.50** Compound **A** can be converted to either **B** or **C**. The energy diagrams for both processes are drawn on the graph below.

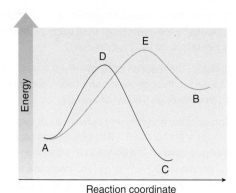

a. Label each reaction as endothermic or exothermic.
b. Which reaction is faster?
c. Which reaction generates the product lower in energy?
d. Which points on the graphs correspond to transition states?
e. Label the energy of activation for each reaction.
f. Label the $\Delta H$ for each reaction.

**6.51** Draw an energy diagram that fits each description.
a. an endothermic reaction with a high $E_a$
b. a reaction that has a low $E_a$ and $\Delta H$ is negative
c. a slow reaction in which the products are at a lower energy than the reactants

**6.52** Draw an energy diagram that fits each description.
a. an exothermic reaction with a high $E_a$
b. a reaction with a low $E_a$ and a positive value of $\Delta H$
c. a fast reaction in which the products are at a lower energy than the reactants

**6.53** Draw an energy diagram for the following reaction in which $\Delta H = -12$ kcal/mol and $E_a = 5$ kcal: $A_2 + B_2 \longrightarrow 2\ AB$. Label the axes, reactants, products, transition state, $E_a$, and $\Delta H$. Is the reaction endothermic or exothermic?

**6.54** Draw an energy diagram for the following reaction in which $\Delta H = +13$ kcal/mol and $E_a = 21$ kcal: $A + B \longrightarrow C$. Label the axes, reactants, products, transition state, $E_a$, and $\Delta H$. Are the products or reactants higher in energy?

## Reaction Rates

**6.55** How does collision orientation affect the rate of a reaction?

**6.56** Explain why a high energy of activation causes a reaction to be slow.

**6.57** State two reasons why increasing temperature increases reaction rate.

**6.58** Why does decreasing concentration decrease the rate of a chemical reaction?

**6.59** Which value (if any) in each pair corresponds to a faster reaction? Explain your choice.
a. $E_a = 10$ kcal or $E_a = 1$ kcal
b. $K = 10$ or $K = 100$
c. $\Delta H = -2$ kcal/mol or $\Delta H = +2$ kcal/mol

**6.60** Which value (if any) in each pair corresponds to a faster reaction? Explain your choice.
a. $E_a = 0.10$ kcal or $E_a = 1$ kcal
b. $K = 10$ or $K = 0.001$
c. $\Delta H = -25$ kcal/mol or $\Delta H = -2$ kcal/mol

**6.61** Which of the following affect the rate of a reaction: (a) $K$; (b) $E_a$; (c) temperature?

**6.62** Which of the following affect the rate of a reaction: (a) concentration; (b) $\Delta H$; (c) energy difference between the reactants and the transition state?

**6.63** How does a catalyst affect each of the following: (a) reaction rate; (b) $\Delta H$; (c) $E_a$; (d) $K$; (e) relative energy of the reactants and products?

**6.64** What is the difference between a catalyst and an enzyme?

## Equilibrium

**6.65** What is the difference between the forward and reverse reactions?

**6.66** What is the difference between a reversible reaction and the reverse reaction?

**6.67** Given each value of the equilibrium constant, are the reactants or products favored at equilibrium?
a. $K = 5.2 \times 10^3$          c. $K = 0.002$
b. $\Delta H = -27$ kcal/mol      d. $\Delta H = +2$ kcal/mol

**6.68** Given each value of the equilibrium constant, are the reactants or products favored at equilibrium?
a. $K = 5.2 \times 10^{-6}$       c. $K = 10,000$
b. $\Delta H = +16$ kcal/mol      d. $\Delta H = -21$ kcal/mol

**6.69** How is the magnitude of $K$ related to the sign of $\Delta H$?

**6.70** How are the sign and magnitude of $\Delta H$ affected by the presence of a catalyst?

**6.71** Consider the reversible reaction $A \rightleftharpoons B$, and assume the reaction begins with pure **A**. Using red spheres for **A** and blue spheres for **B**, match each representation to one of the following equilibrium constants: [1] $K = 5$; [2] $K = 1$; [3] $K = 0.5$.

a.                           b.                           c.

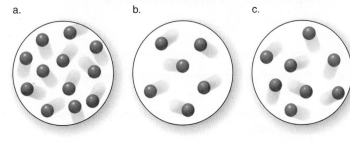

**6.72** Consider the reversible reaction $A \rightleftharpoons B$, with $K = 0.1$. Assume the reaction begins with only **A**, and draw a representation using molecular art for the reaction mixture at equilibrium. Use red spheres for **A** and blue spheres for **B**.

**6.73** Write an expression for the equilibrium constant for each reaction.
  a. $2\,NO(g) + O_2(g) \rightleftharpoons 2\,NO_2(g)$
  b. $CH_4(g) + 2\,Br_2(g) \rightleftharpoons CH_2Br_2(g) + 2\,HBr(g)$

**6.74** Write an expression for the equilibrium constant for each reaction.
  a. $HBr + H_2O \rightleftharpoons H_3O^+ + Br^-$
  b. $2\,HCl(g) \rightleftharpoons H_2(g) + Cl_2(g)$

**6.75** Use each expression for the equilibrium constant to write a chemical equation.
  a. $K = \dfrac{[A_2]}{[A]^2}$        b. $K = \dfrac{[AB_3]^2}{[A_2][B_2]^3}$

**6.76** Use each expression for the equilibrium constant to write a chemical equation.
  a. $K = \dfrac{[AB_2]^2}{[A_2][B_2]^2}$        b. $K = \dfrac{[A_2B_3]}{[A]^2[B]^3}$

**6.77** Consider the following reaction: $2\,HBr(g) \rightleftharpoons H_2(g) + Br_2(g)$ with $K = 5.3 \times 10^{-20}$.
  a. Write the expression for the equilibrium constant for this reaction.
  b. Are the reactants or products favored at equilibrium?
  c. Would you predict $\Delta H$ to be positive or negative?
  d. Are the reactants or products lower in energy?
  e. Would you predict this reaction to be fast or slow? Explain your choice.

**6.78** Consider the following reaction: $CO(g) + Cl_2(g) \rightleftharpoons COCl_2(g)$ with $K = 6.6 \times 10^{11}$.
  a. Write the expression for the equilibrium constant for this reaction.
  b. Are the reactants or products favored at equilibrium?
  c. Would you predict $\Delta H$ to be positive or negative?
  d. Are the reactants or products lower in energy?
  e. Would you predict this reaction to be fast or slow? Explain your choice.

**6.79** Consider the following reaction.

$$CO(g) + H_2O(g) \rightleftharpoons CO_2(g) + H_2(g)$$

  a. Write the expression for the equilibrium constant.
  b. Calculate $K$ using the following concentrations of each substance at equilibrium: [CO] = 0.090 M; [$H_2O$] = 0.12 M; [$CO_2$] = 0.15 M; [$H_2$] = 0.30 M.

**6.80** Consider the following reaction.

$$H_2(g) + I_2(g) \rightleftharpoons 2\,HI(g)$$

  a. Write the expression for the equilibrium constant.
  b. Calculate $K$ using the following concentrations of each substance at equilibrium: [$H_2$] = 0.95 M; [$I_2$] = 0.78 M; [HI] = 0.27 M.

## Le Châtelier's Principle

**6.81** Consider the reaction of $N_2(g) + O_2(g) \rightleftharpoons 2\,NO(g)$. What happens to the concentration of each substance when (a) [$O_2$] is increased; (b) [NO] is increased?

**6.82** Consider the reaction of $H_2(g) + F_2(g) \rightleftharpoons 2\,HF(g)$. What happens to the concentration of each substance when (a) [$H_2$] is decreased; (b) [HF] is increased?

**6.83** Consider the endothermic conversion of oxygen to ozone: $3\,O_2(g) \rightleftharpoons 2\,O_3(g)$. What effect does each of the following changes have on the direction of equilibrium?
  a. decrease [$O_3$]                 d. decrease temperature
  b. decrease [$O_2$]                 e. add a catalyst
  c. increase [$O_3$]                  f. increase pressure

**6.84** Consider the exothermic reaction: $H_2(g) + I_2(g) \rightleftharpoons 2\,HI(g)$. What effect does each of the following changes have on the direction of equilibrium?
  a. decrease [HI]                   d. increase temperature
  b. increase [$H_2$]                 e. decrease temperature
  c. decrease [$I_2$]                  f. increase pressure

**6.85** Consider the exothermic reaction: $C_2H_4(g) + Cl_2(g) \rightleftharpoons C_2H_4Cl_2(g)$. What effect does each of the following changes have on the direction of equilibrium?
  a. increase [$C_2H_4$]              d. decrease pressure
  b. decrease [$Cl_2$]                 e. increase temperature
  c. decrease [$C_2H_4Cl_2$]         f. decrease temperature

**6.86** Consider the endothermic reaction: $2\ NH_3(g) \rightleftharpoons$
$3\ H_2(g) + N_2(g)$. What effect does each of the following
changes have on the direction of equilibrium?

   a. increase $[NH_3]$       d. increase temperature

   b. decrease $[N_2]$        e. decrease temperature

   c. increase $[H_2]$        f. increase pressure

## General Problems

**6.87** Consider the gas-phase reaction of ethylene ($CH_2{=}CH_2$) with
hydrogen to form ethane ($C_2H_6$), which occurs in the presence
of a palladium catalyst (Section 6.4B).

   a. Write the expression for the equilibrium constant for this
reaction.

   b. If $\Delta H = -28$ kcal/mol, are the products or reactants higher
in energy?

   c. Which is likely to be true about the equilibrium constant
for the reaction: $K > 1$ or $K < 1$?

   d. How much energy is released when 20.0 g of ethylene
reacts?

   e. What happens to the rate of the reaction if the
concentration of ethylene is increased?

   f. What happens to the equilibrium when each of the
following changes occurs: [1] an increase in $[H_2]$; [2] a
decrease in $[C_2H_6]$; [3] an increase in temperature; [4] an
increase in pressure; [5] removal of the palladium catalyst?

**6.88** Methanol ($CH_4O$), which is used as a fuel in race cars, burns in
oxygen ($O_2$) to form $CO_2$ and $H_2O$.

   a. Write a balanced equation for this reaction.

   b. Write the expression for the equilibrium constant for this
reaction.

   c. If $\Delta H = -174$ kcal/mol, are the products or reactants higher
in energy?

   d. How much energy is released when 10.0 g of methanol is
burned?

   e. Although this reaction is exothermic, the reaction is very
slow unless a spark or flame initiates the reaction. Explain
how this can be possible.

## Applications

**6.89** What is the role of lactase and why is it important in the
human body?

**6.90** How does a catalytic converter clean up automobile
emissions?

**6.91** A patient receives 2,000 mL of a glucose solution that
contains 5 g of glucose in 100 mL. How many Calories does
the glucose, a simple carbohydrate, contain?

**6.92** The reaction of salicylic acid with acetic acid yields aspirin
and water according to the given balanced equation. Since
the equilibrium constant for this reaction is close to one,
both reactants and products are present at equilibrium. If the
reaction has a small negative value of $\Delta H$, suggest ways that
this equilibrium could be driven to the right to favor products.

$$C_7H_6O_3 \ + \ C_2H_4O_2 \ \rightleftharpoons \ C_9H_8O_4 \ + \ H_2O$$

  salicylic acid    acetic acid        aspirin

**6.93** Walking at a brisk pace burns off about 280 Cal/h. How long
would you have to walk to burn off the Calories obtained from
eating a cheeseburger that contained 32 g of protein, 29 g of
fat, and 34 g of carbohydrates?

**6.94** How many kilocalories does a runner expend when he runs
for 4.5 h and uses 710 Cal/h? How many pieces of pizza
that each contain 12 g of protein, 11 g of fat, and 30 g of
carbohydrates could be eaten after the race to replenish these
Calories?

**6.95** The amount of energy released when a fuel burns is called
its heat content. The heat content of fuels is often reported in
kcal/g not kcal/mol so that fuels with different molar masses
can be compared on a mass basis. The heat content of
propane ($C_3H_8$), used as the fuel in gas grills, is 531 kcal/mol,
while the heat content of butane ($C_4H_{10}$), used in lighters, is
688 kcal/mol. Show that the heat content of these two fuels is
similar when converted to kcal/g.

**6.96** One mole of ethanol ($C_2H_6O$) releases 327 kcal when
burned, whereas one mole of hydrogen ($H_2$) releases only
68.4 kcal/mol. How many kcal/g are released when each
of these fuels is burned? On a per gram basis, which
substance would be a better source of energy?

# CHALLENGE PROBLEMS

**6.97** Let's assume that a gallon of gasoline contains pure octane
($C_8H_{18}$) and has a density of 0.700 g/mL. When octane is
burned, it releases 1,303 kcal/mol of energy. How many
kilocalories of energy are released from burning one gallon of
gasoline?

**6.98** An energy bar contains 4 g of fat, 12 g of protein, and 24 g of
carbohydrates. How many kilojoules of energy are obtained
from eating two bars per day for a month? Write the answer in
scientific notation.

# 7

Scuba divers must carefully plan the depth and duration of their dives to avoid "the bends," a dangerous condition caused by the formation of nitrogen gas bubbles in the bloodstream.

# Gases, Liquids, and Solids

## CHAPTER GOALS

*In this chapter you will learn how to:*

1. Measure pressure and convert one unit of pressure to another
2. Describe the relationship between the pressure, volume, and temperature of a gas using gas laws
3. Describe the relationship between the volume and number of moles of a gas
4. Write the equation for the ideal gas law and use it in calculations
5. Use Dalton's law to determine the partial pressure and total pressure of a gas mixture
6. Determine the types of intermolecular forces in a compound, and how these forces determine a compound's boiling point and melting point
7. Describe the properties of a liquid, including vapor pressure, viscosity, and surface tension
8. Describe the features of different types of solids
9. Describe the energy changes that accompany changes of state
10. Interpret the changes depicted in heating and cooling curves

In Chapter 7 we study the properties of gases, liquids, and solids. Why is air pulled into the lungs when we expand our rib cage and diaphragm? Why does a lid pop off a container of food when it is heated in the microwave? Why does sweating cool down the body? To answer questions of this sort, we must understand the properties of the three states of matter, as well as the energy changes involved when one state is converted to another.

## 7.1   The Three States of Matter

As we first learned in Section 1.2, matter exists in three common states—**gas, liquid,** and **solid.**

- A gas consists of particles that are far apart and move rapidly and independently from each other.
- A liquid consists of particles that are much closer together but are still somewhat disorganized since they can move about. The particles in a liquid are close enough that they exert a force of attraction on each other.
- A solid consists of particles—atoms, molecules, or ions—that are close to each other and are often highly organized. The particles in a solid have little freedom of motion and are held together by attractive forces.

As shown in Figure 7.1, air is composed largely of $N_2$ and $O_2$ molecules, along with small amounts of argon (Ar), carbon dioxide ($CO_2$), and water molecules that move about rapidly. Liquid water is composed of $H_2O$ molecules that have no particular organization. Sand is a solid composed of $SiO_2$, which contains a network of covalent silicon–oxygen bonds.

**Figure 7.1**   The Three States of Matter—Solid, Liquid, and Gas

solid $SiO_2$          liquid $H_2O$          $N_2$ and $O_2$ gases

Most sand is composed of silicon dioxide ($SiO_2$), which forms a three-dimensional network of covalent bonds. Liquid water is composed of $H_2O$ molecules, which can move past each other but are held close together by a force of attraction (Section 7.7). Air contains primarily $N_2$ and $O_2$ molecules that move rapidly with no force of attraction for each other.

**Whether a substance exists as a gas, liquid, or solid depends on the balance between the kinetic energy of its particles and the strength of the interactions between the particles.** In a gas, the kinetic energy of motion is high and the particles are far apart from each other. As a result, the attractive forces between the molecules are negligible and gas molecules move freely. In a liquid, attractive forces hold the molecules much more closely together, so the distance between molecules and the kinetic energy is much less than the gas. In a solid, the attractive forces between molecules are even stronger, so the distance between individual particles is small and there is little freedom of motion. The properties of gases, liquids, and solids are summarized in Table 7.1.

**Table 7.1 Properties of Gases, Liquids, and Solids**

| Property | Gas | Liquid | Solid |
|---|---|---|---|
| **Shape and Volume** | Expands to fill its container | A fixed volume that takes the shape of the container it occupies | A definite shape and volume |
| **Arrangement of Particles** | Randomly arranged, disorganized, and far apart | Randomly arranged but close | Fixed arrangement of very close particles |
| **Density** | Low (< 0.01 g/mL) | High (~1 g/mL)[a] | High (1–10 g/mL) |
| **Particle Movement** | Very fast | Moderate | Slow |
| **Interaction Between Particles** | None | Strong | Very strong |

[a]The symbol "~" means approximately.

**PROBLEM 7.1**

How do gaseous, liquid, and solid methanol ($CH_4O$) compare in each of the following features: (a) density; (b) the space between the molecules; (c) the attractive force between the molecules?

## 7.2 Gases and Pressure

Anyone who has ridden a bike against the wind knows that even though we can't see the gas molecules of the air, we can feel them as we move through them.

Simple gases in the atmosphere—oxygen ($O_2$), carbon dioxide ($CO_2$), and ozone ($O_3$)—are vital to life. Oxygen, which constitutes 21% of the earth's atmosphere, is needed for metabolic processes that convert carbohydrates to energy. Green plants use carbon dioxide, a minor component of the atmosphere, to store the energy of the sun in the bonds of carbohydrate molecules during photosynthesis. Ozone forms a protective shield in the upper atmosphere to filter out harmful radiation from the sun, thus keeping it from the surface of the earth.

### 7.2A Properties of Gases

Helium, a noble gas composed of He atoms, and oxygen, a gas composed of diatomic $O_2$ molecules, behave differently in chemical reactions. Many of their properties, however, and the properties of all gases, can be explained by the **kinetic-molecular theory of gases,** a set of principles based on the following assumptions:

## Figure 7.2

A Barometer—A Device for Measuring Atmospheric Pressure

vacuum

atmospheric pressure

760 mm

mercury-filled dish

A barometer measures atmospheric pressure. Air pressure on the Hg in the dish pushes Hg up a sealed glass tube to a height that equals the atmospheric pressure.

- A gas consists of particles—atoms or molecules—that move randomly and rapidly.
- The size of gas particles is small compared to the space between the particles.
- Because the space between gas particles is large, gas particles exert no attractive forces on each other.
- The kinetic energy of gas particles increases with increasing temperature.
- When gas particles collide with each other, they rebound and travel in new directions. When gas particles collide with the walls of a container, they exert a pressure.

Because gas particles move rapidly, two gases mix together quickly. Moreover, when a gas is added to a container, the particles rapidly move to fill the entire container.

### 7.2B Gas Pressure

When many gas molecules strike a surface, they exert a measurable pressure. **Pressure ($P$) is the force ($F$) exerted per unit area ($A$).**

$$\text{Pressure} = \frac{\text{Force}}{\text{Area}} = \frac{F}{A}$$

All of the gases in the atmosphere collectively exert **atmospheric pressure** on the surface of the earth. The value of the atmospheric pressure varies with location, decreasing with increasing altitude. Atmospheric pressure also varies slightly from day to day, depending on the weather.

Atmospheric pressure is measured with a **barometer** (Figure 7.2). A barometer consists of a column of mercury (Hg) sealed at one end and inverted in a dish of mercury. The downward pressure exerted by the mercury in the column equals the atmospheric pressure on the mercury in the dish. Thus, the height of the mercury in the column measures the atmospheric pressure. Atmospheric pressure at sea level corresponds to a column of mercury 760. mm in height.

Many different units are used for pressure. The two most common units are the **atmosphere (atm),** and **millimeters of mercury (mm Hg),** where **1 atm = 760. mm Hg.** One millimeter of mercury is also called one **torr.** In the United States, the common pressure unit is **pounds per square inch (psi),** where **1 atm = 14.7 psi.** Pressure can also be measured in pascals (Pa), where 1 mm Hg = 133.32 Pa.

$$
\begin{aligned}
1 \text{ atm} &= 760. \text{ mm Hg} \\
&= 760. \text{ torr} \\
&= 14.7 \text{ psi} \\
&= 101{,}325 \text{ Pa}
\end{aligned}
$$

To convert a value from one pressure unit to another, set up conversion factors and use the method in Sample Problem 7.1.

### SAMPLE PROBLEM 7.1

A scuba diver typically begins a dive with a compressed air tank at 3,000. psi. Convert this value to (a) atmospheres; (b) mm Hg.

### Analysis

To solve each part, set up conversion factors that relate the two units under consideration. Use conversion factors that place the unwanted unit, psi, in the denominator to cancel.

In part (a), the conversion factor must relate psi and atm:

psi–atm conversion factor

$$\frac{1 \text{ atm}}{14.7 \text{ psi}}$$

unwanted unit

In part (b), the conversion factor must relate psi and mm Hg:

psi–mm Hg conversion factor

$$\frac{760. \text{ mm Hg}}{14.7 \text{ psi}}$$

unwanted unit

A scuba diver's pressure gauge shows the amount of air (usually measured in psi) in his tank before and during a dive.

### Solution

a. Convert the original unit (3,000. psi) to the desired unit (atm) using the conversion factor:

$$3000.\ \cancel{psi} \times \frac{1\ atm}{14.7\ \cancel{psi}} = 204\ atm$$

**Answer**

Psi cancels.

b. Convert the original unit (3,000. psi) to the desired unit (mm Hg) using the conversion factor:

$$3000.\ \cancel{psi} \times \frac{760.\ mm\ Hg}{14.7\ \cancel{psi}} = 155,000\ mm\ Hg$$

**Answer**

Psi cancels.

### PROBLEM 7.2

Typical atmospheric pressure in Denver is 630 mm Hg. Convert this value to (a) atmospheres; (b) psi.

### PROBLEM 7.3

Convert each pressure unit to the indicated unit.

    a. 3.0 atm to mm Hg          b. 720 mm Hg to psi          c. 424 mm Hg to atm

## 7.2C FOCUS ON HEALTH & MEDICINE
### Blood Pressure

Taking a patient's blood pressure is an important part of most physical examinations. Blood pressure measures the pressure in an artery of the upper arm using a device called a **sphygmomanometer.** A blood pressure reading consists of two numbers such as 120/80, where both values represent pressures in mm Hg. The higher number is the systolic pressure and refers to the maximum pressure in the artery right after the heart contracts. The lower number is the diastolic pressure and represents the minimum pressure when the heart muscle relaxes. A desirable systolic pressure is in the range of 100–120 mm Hg. A desirable diastolic pressure is in the range of 60–80 mm Hg. Figure 7.3 illustrates how a sphygmomanometer records pressure in a blood vessel.

**Figure 7.3**    Measuring Blood Pressure

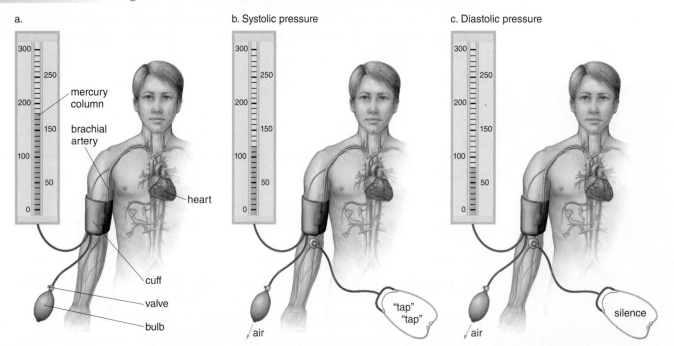

(a) To measure blood pressure, a cuff is inflated around the upper arm and a stethoscope is used to listen to the sound of blood flowing through the brachial artery. When the pressure in the cuff is high, it constricts the artery, so that no blood can flow to the lower arm. (b) Slowly the pressure in the cuff is decreased, and when it gets to the point that blood begins to spurt into the artery, a tapping sound is heard in the stethoscope. This value corresponds to the systolic blood pressure. (c) When the pressure in the cuff is further decreased, so that blood once again flows freely in the artery, the tapping sound disappears and the diastolic pressure is recorded.

When a patient's systolic pressure is routinely 140 mm Hg or greater or diastolic pressure is 90 mm Hg or greater, an individual is said to have **hypertension**—that is, high blood pressure. Consistently high blood pressure leads to increased risk of stroke and heart attacks. Many forms of hypertension can be controlled with medications such as propranolol (trade name Inderal, Problem 15.12).

### PROBLEM 7.4

Convert both values in the blood pressure reading 120/80 to atmospheres.

## 7.3 Gas Laws That Relate Pressure, Volume, and Temperature

Four variables are important in discussing the behavior of gases—pressure ($P$), volume ($V$), temperature ($T$), and number of moles ($n$). The relationship of these variables is described by equations called **gas laws** that predict the behavior of all gases as conditions change. Three gas laws illustrate the interrelationship of pressure, volume, and temperature.

- Boyle's law relates pressure and volume.
- Charles's law relates volume and temperature.
- Gay–Lussac's law relates pressure and temperature.

### 7.3A Boyle's Law—How the Pressure and Volume of a Gas Are Related

**Boyle's law** describes how the volume of a gas changes as the pressure is changed.

- Boyle's law: For a fixed amount of gas at constant temperature, the pressure and volume of a gas are inversely related.

When two quantities are *inversely* related, one quantity *increases* as the other *decreases*. **The product of the two quantities, however, is a *constant*, symbolized by $k$.**

When pressure increases...

Pressure × Volume = constant

...volume decreases.

$$PV = k$$

Thus, if the volume of a cylinder of gas is halved, the pressure of the gas inside the cylinder doubles. **The same number of gas particles occupies half the volume and exerts two times the pressure.**

$P = 1$ atm    Decrease volume.    $P = 2$ atm

$V = 2$ L        $V = 1$ L    Pressure increases.

If we know the pressure and volume under an initial set of conditions ($P_1$ and $V_1$), we can calculate the pressure or volume under a different set of conditions ($P_2$ and $V_2$), since the product of pressure and volume is a constant.

$$P_1V_1 \quad = \quad P_2V_2$$

initial conditions    new conditions

## How To  Use Boyle's Law to Calculate a New Gas Volume or Pressure

**Example:** If a 4.0-L container of helium gas has a pressure of 10.0 atm, what pressure does the gas exert if the volume is increased to 6.0 L?

**Step [1]  Identify the known quantities and the desired quantity.**

- To solve an equation using Boyle's law, we must know three quantities and solve for one quantity. In this case $P_1$, $V_1$, and $V_2$ are known and the final pressure, $P_2$, must be determined.

$$P_1 = 10.0 \text{ atm}$$

$$V_1 = 4.0 \text{ L} \qquad V_2 = 6.0 \text{ L} \qquad\qquad P_2 = ?$$

known quantities                        desired quantity

**Step [2]  Write the equation and rearrange it to isolate the desired quantity on one side.**

- Rearrange the equation for Boyle's law so that the unknown quantity, $P_2$, is present alone on one side.

$$P_1V_1 \quad = \quad P_2V_2 \qquad \text{Solve for } P_2 \text{ by dividing both sides by } V_2.$$

$$\frac{P_1V_1}{V_2} \quad = \quad P_2$$

**Step [3]  Solve the problem.**

- Substitute the known quantities into the equation and solve for $P_2$. Identical units must be used for two similar quantities (liters in this case) so that the units cancel.

$$P_2 \quad = \quad \frac{P_1V_1}{V_2} \quad = \quad \frac{(10.0 \text{ atm})(4.0\ \cancel{L})}{6.0\ \cancel{L}} \quad = \quad 6.7 \text{ atm}$$

Liters cancel.    **Answer**

- In this example, the volume increased so the pressure decreased.

### SAMPLE PROBLEM 7.2

A tank of compressed air for scuba diving contains 8.5 L of gas at 204 atm pressure. What volume of air does this gas occupy at 1.0 atm?

#### Analysis

Boyle's law can be used to solve this problem since an initial pressure and volume ($P_1$ and $V_1$) and a final pressure ($P_2$) are known, and a final volume ($V_2$) must be determined.

#### Solution

**[1]  Identify the known quantities and the desired quantity.**

$$P_1 = 204 \text{ atm} \qquad P_2 = 1.0 \text{ atm}$$

$$V_1 = 8.5 \text{ L} \qquad\qquad\qquad\qquad\qquad V_2 = ?$$

known quantities                        desired quantity

**[2]  Write the equation and rearrange it to isolate the desired quantity, $V_2$, on one side.**

$$P_1V_1 \quad = \quad P_2V_2 \qquad \text{Solve for } V_2 \text{ by dividing both sides by } P_2.$$

$$\frac{P_1V_1}{P_2} \quad = \quad V_2$$

**[3] Solve the problem.**

- Substitute the three known quantities into the equation and solve for $V_2$.

$$V_2 = \frac{P_1V_1}{P_2} = \frac{(204 \text{ atm})(8.5 \text{ L})}{1.0 \text{ atm}} = 1,734 \text{ rounded to } 1,700 \text{ L}$$

**Answer**

Atm cancels.

- Thus, the volume increased because the pressure decreased.

### PROBLEM 7.5

A sample of helium gas has a volume of 2.0 L at a pressure of 4.0 atm. What is the volume of gas at each of the following pressures?

  a. 5.0 atm        b. 2.5 atm        c. 10.0 atm        d. 380 mm Hg

### PROBLEM 7.6

A sample of nitrogen gas has a volume of 15.0 mL at a pressure of 0.50 atm. What is the pressure exerted by the gas if the volume is changed to each of the following values?

  a. 30.0 mL        b. 5.0 mL        c. 100. mL        d. 1.0 L

Boyle's law explains how air is brought into or expelled from the lungs as the rib cage and diaphragm expand and contract when we breathe (Figure 7.4).

**Figure 7.4**    Focus on the Human Body: Boyle's Law and Breathing

a.

b.

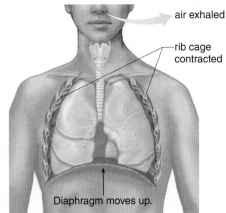

a. When an individual inhales, the rib cage expands and the diaphragm is lowered, thus increasing the volume of the lungs. According to Boyle's law, increasing the volume of the lungs decreases the pressure inside the lungs. The decrease in pressure draws air into the lungs.

b. When an individual exhales, the rib cage contracts and the diaphragm is raised, thus decreasing the volume of the lungs. Since the volume is now decreased, the pressure inside the lungs increases, causing air to be expelled into the surroundings.

## 7.3B   Charles's Law—How the Volume and Temperature of a Gas Are Related

**All gases expand when they are heated and contract when they are cooled. Charles's law** describes how the volume of a gas changes as the Kelvin temperature is changed.

- **Charles's law:** For a fixed amount of gas at constant pressure, the volume of a gas is proportional to its Kelvin temperature.

A hot air balloon illustrates Charles's law. Heating the air inside the balloon causes it to expand and fill the balloon. When the air inside the balloon becomes less dense than the surrounding air, the balloon rises.

Equations for converting one temperature unit to another are given in Section 1.9.

**Volume and temperature are** *proportional;* that is, as one quantity *increases,* the other *increases* as well. Thus, **dividing volume by temperature is a constant ($k$).**

$$\frac{V}{T} = k$$

Increasing the temperature increases the kinetic energy of the gas particles, and they move faster and spread out, thus occupying a larger volume. Note that **Kelvin temperature** must be used in calculations involving gas laws. Any temperature reported in °C or °F must be converted to kelvins (K) prior to carrying out the calculation.

Since dividing the volume of a gas by the temperature gives a constant, knowing the volume and temperature under an initial set of conditions ($V_1$ and $T_1$) means we can calculate the volume or temperature under another set of conditions ($V_2$ and $T_2$) when either volume or temperature is changed.

$$\frac{V_1}{T_1} = \frac{V_2}{T_2}$$

initial conditions     new conditions

To solve a problem of this sort, we follow the same three steps listed in the *How To* outlined in Section 7.3A, except we use the equation for Charles's law in step [2] in place of the equation for Boyle's law. This procedure is illustrated in Sample Problem 7.3.

### SAMPLE PROBLEM 7.3

A balloon that contains 0.50 L of air at 25 °C is cooled to –196 °C. What volume does the balloon now occupy?

#### Analysis

Since this question deals with volume and temperature, Charles's law is used to determine a final volume because three quantities are known—the initial volume and temperature ($V_1$ and $T_1$), and the final temperature ($T_2$).

#### Solution

**[1] Identify the known quantities and the desired quantity.**

$$V_1 = 0.50 \text{ L}$$

$$T_1 = 25 \text{ °C} \qquad T_2 = -196 \text{ °C} \qquad\qquad V_2 = ?$$

known quantities          desired quantity

- Both temperatures must be converted to Kelvin temperatures using the equation
  **K = °C + 273.**
- $T_1 = 25 \text{ °C} + 273 = 298 \text{ K}$
- $T_2 = -196 \text{ °C} + 273 = 77 \text{ K}$

**[2] Write the equation and rearrange it to isolate the desired quantity, $V_2$, on one side.**

- Use Charles's law.

$$\frac{V_1}{T_1} = \frac{V_2}{T_2} \qquad \text{Solve for } V_2 \text{ by multiplying both sides by } T_2.$$

$$\frac{V_1 T_2}{T_1} = V_2$$

**[3] Solve the problem.**

- Substitute the three known quantities into the equation and solve for $V_2$.

$$V_2 = \frac{V_1 T_2}{T_1} = \frac{(0.50\ \text{L})(77\ \cancel{K})}{298\ \cancel{K}} = 0.13\ \text{L}$$

Kelvins cancel.            **Answer**

- Since the temperature has decreased, the volume of gas must decrease as well.

## PROBLEM 7.7

A volume of 0.50 L of air at 37 °C is expelled from the lungs into cold surroundings at 0.0 °C. What volume does the expelled air occupy at this temperature?

## PROBLEM 7.8

(a) A volume (25.0 L) of gas at 45 K is heated to 450 K. What volume does the gas now occupy? (b) A volume (50.0 mL) of gas at 400. °C is cooled to 50. °C. What volume does the gas now occupy?

Charles's law can be used to explain how wind currents form at the beach (Figure 7.5). The air above land heats up faster than the air above water. As the temperature of the air above the land increases, the volume that it occupies increases; that is, the air expands, and as a result, its density decreases. This warmer, less dense air then rises, and the cooler denser air above the water moves toward the land as wind, filling the space left vacant by the warm, rising air.

**Figure 7.5**    Focus on the Environment: How Charles's Law Explains Wind Currents

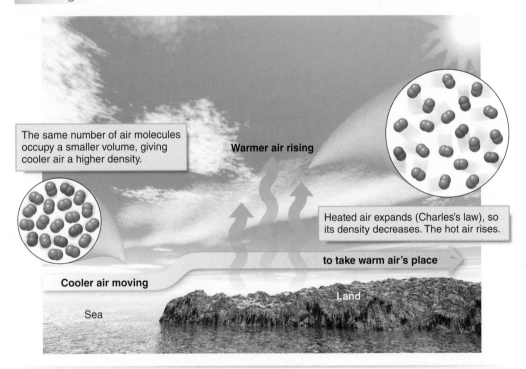

The same number of air molecules occupy a smaller volume, giving cooler air a higher density.

Warmer air rising

Heated air expands (Charles's law), so its density decreases. The hot air rises.

to take warm air's place

Cooler air moving

Land

Sea

## 7.3C  Gay–Lussac's Law—How the Pressure and Temperature of a Gas Are Related

Gay–Lussac's law describes how the pressure of a gas changes as the Kelvin temperature is changed.

- **Gay–Lussac's law: For a fixed amount of gas at constant volume, the pressure of a gas is proportional to its Kelvin temperature.**

**Pressure and temperature are *proportional;* that is, as one quantity *increases,* the other *increases.*** Thus, **dividing the pressure by the temperature is a constant (*k*).**

$$\frac{P}{T} = k$$

Increasing the temperature increases the kinetic energy of the gas particles, and if the volume is kept constant, the pressure exerted by the particles increases.

$P = 1$ atm

Increase temperature.

$P = 2$ atm

Pressure increases.

$V = 2$ L                $V = 2$ L

Since dividing the pressure of a gas by the temperature gives a constant, knowing the pressure and Kelvin temperature under an initial set of conditions ($P_1$ and $T_1$) means we can calculate the pressure or temperature under another set of conditions ($P_2$ and $T_2$) when either pressure or temperature is changed.

$$\frac{P_1}{T_1} = \frac{P_2}{T_2}$$

initial conditions      new conditions

We solve this type of problem by following the same three steps in the *How To* in Section 7.3A, using the equation for Gay–Lussac's law in step [2].

## SAMPLE PROBLEM 7.4

The tire on a bicycle stored in a cool garage at 18 °C had a pressure of 80. psi. What is the pressure inside the tire after riding the bike at 43 °C?

### Analysis

Since this question deals with pressure and temperature, Gay–Lussac's law is used to determine a final pressure because three quantities are known—the initial pressure and temperature ($P_1$ and $T_1$), and the final temperature ($T_2$).

### Solution

**[1] Identify the known quantities and the desired quantity.**

$$P_1 = 80. \text{ psi}$$

$$T_1 = 18 °C \qquad T_2 = 43 °C \qquad\qquad P_2 = ?$$

known quantities                desired quantity

- Both temperatures must be converted to Kelvin temperatures.
- $T_1 = °C + 273 = 18 °C + 273 = 291$ K
- $T_2 = °C + 273 = 43 °C + 273 = 316$ K

**[2] Write the equation and rearrange it to isolate the desired quantity, $P_2$, on one side.**

- Use Gay–Lussac's law. Since the initial pressure is reported in psi, the final pressure will be calculated in psi.

$$\frac{P_1}{T_1} = \frac{P_2}{T_2} \qquad \text{Solve for } P_2 \text{ by multiplying both sides by } T_2.$$

$$\frac{P_1 T_2}{T_1} = P_2$$

**[3]  Solve the problem.**

- Substitute the three known quantities into the equation and solve for $P_2$.

$$P_2 = \frac{P_1 T_2}{T_1} = \frac{(80. \text{ psi})(316 \text{ K})}{291 \text{ K}} = 87 \text{ psi}$$

Kelvins cancel.  **Answer**

- Since the temperature has increased, the pressure of the gas must increase as well.

### PROBLEM 7.9

A pressure cooker is used to cook food in a closed pot. By heating the contents of a pressure cooker at constant volume, the pressure increases. If the steam inside the pressure cooker is initially at 100. °C and 1.00 atm, what is the final temperature of the steam if the pressure is increased to 1.05 atm?

### PROBLEM 7.10

The temperature of a 0.50-L gas sample at 25 °C and 1.00 atm is changed to each of the following temperatures. What is the final pressure of the system?

   a.  310. K       b.  150. K       c.  50. °C       d.  200. °C

### PROBLEM 7.11

Use Gay–Lussac's law to answer the question posed at the beginning of the chapter: Why does a lid pop off a container of food when it is heated in a microwave?

Food cooks faster in a pressure cooker because the reactions involved in cooking occur at a faster rate at a higher temperature.

## 7.3D    The Combined Gas Law

All three gas laws—Boyle's, Charles's, and Gay–Lussac's laws—can be combined in a single equation, the **combined gas law,** that relates pressure, volume, and temperature.

$$\frac{P_1 V_1}{T_1} = \frac{P_2 V_2}{T_2}$$

initial conditions    new conditions

The combined gas law contains six terms that relate the pressure, volume, and temperature of an initial and final state of a gas. It can be used to calculate one quantity when the other five are known, as long as the number of moles of gas ($n$) is constant. The combined gas law is used for determining the effect of changing two factors—such as pressure and temperature—on the third factor, volume.

We solve this type of problem by following the same three steps in the *How To* in Section 7.3A, using the equation for the combined gas law in step [2]. Sample Problem 7.5 shows how this is done. Table 7.2 summarizes the equations for the gas laws presented in Section 7.3.

### SAMPLE PROBLEM 7.5

A weather balloon contains 222 L of helium at 20. °C and 760 mm Hg. What is the volume of the balloon when it ascends to an altitude where the temperature is –40. °C and the pressure is 540 mm Hg?

### Analysis

Since this question deals with pressure, volume, and temperature, the combined gas law is used to determine a final volume ($V_2$) because five quantities are known—the initial pressure, volume, and temperature ($P_1$, $V_1$, and $T_1$), and the final pressure and temperature ($P_2$ and $T_2$).

### Solution

**[1]  Identify the known quantities and the desired quantity.**

$$P_1 = 760 \text{ mm Hg} \qquad P_2 = 540 \text{ mm Hg}$$
$$T_1 = 20. \text{ °C} \qquad\qquad T_2 = -40. \text{ °C}$$
$$V_1 = 222 \text{ L} \qquad\qquad\qquad\qquad\qquad\qquad V_2 = ?$$

known quantities                desired quantity

- Both temperatures must be converted to Kelvin temperatures.
- $T_1 = °C + 273 = 20. °C + 273 = 293$ K
- $T_2 = °C + 273 = -40. °C + 273 = 233$ K

**[2] Write the equation and rearrange it to isolate the desired quantity, $V_2$, on one side.**

- Use the combined gas law.

$$\frac{P_1V_1}{T_1} = \frac{P_2V_2}{T_2} \qquad \text{Solve for } V_2 \text{ by multiplying both sides by } \frac{T_2}{P_2}.$$

$$\frac{P_1V_1T_2}{T_1P_2} = V_2$$

**[3] Solve the problem.**

- Substitute the five known quantities into the equation and solve for $V_2$.

$$V_2 = \frac{P_1V_1T_2}{T_1P_2} = \frac{(760 \text{ mm Hg})(222 \text{ L})(233 \text{ K})}{(293 \text{ K})(540 \text{ mm Hg})} = 248.5 \text{ L rounded to 250 L}$$

**Answer**

Kelvins and mm Hg cancel.

### PROBLEM 7.12

The pressure inside a 1.0-L balloon at 25 °C was 750 mm Hg. What is the pressure inside the balloon when it is cooled to −40. °C and expands to 2.0 L in volume?

**Table 7.2  Summary of the Gas Laws That Relate Pressure, Volume, and Temperature**

| Law | Equation | Relationship |
|---|---|---|
| Boyle's law | $P_1V_1 = P_2V_2$ | As $P$ increases, $V$ decreases for constant $T$ and $n$. |
| Charles's law | $\dfrac{V_1}{T_1} = \dfrac{V_2}{T_2}$ | As $T$ increases, $V$ increases for constant $P$ and $n$. |
| Gay–Lussac's law | $\dfrac{P_1}{T_1} = \dfrac{P_2}{T_2}$ | As $T$ increases, $P$ increases for constant $V$ and $n$. |
| Combined gas law | $\dfrac{P_1V_1}{T_1} = \dfrac{P_2V_2}{T_2}$ | The combined gas law shows the relationship of $P$, $V$, and $T$ when two quantities are changed and the number of moles ($n$) is constant. |

## 7.4  Avogadro's Law—How Volume and Moles Are Related

Each equation in Section 7.3 was written for a constant amount of gas; that is, the number of moles ($n$) did not change. **Avogadro's law** describes the relationship between the number of moles of a gas and its volume.

- Avogadro's law: When the pressure and temperature are held constant, the volume of a gas is proportional to the number of moles present.

As the number of moles of a gas *increases*, its volume *increases* as well. Thus, dividing the volume by the number of moles is a constant ($k$). **The value of $k$ is the same regardless of the identity of the gas.**

$$\frac{V}{n} = k$$

A balloon inflates when someone blows into it because the volume increases with an increased number of moles of air.

Thus, if the pressure and temperature of a system are held constant, **increasing the number of moles increases the volume of a gas.**

Since dividing the volume of a gas by the number of moles is a constant, knowing the volume and number of moles initially ($V_1$ and $n_1$) means we can calculate a new volume or number of moles ($V_2$ and $n_2$) when one of these quantities is changed.

$$\frac{V_1}{n_1} = \frac{V_2}{n_2}$$

initial conditions     new conditions

To solve a problem of this sort, we follow the same three steps listed in the *How To* outlined in Section 7.3A, using Avogadro's law in step [2].

### SAMPLE PROBLEM 7.6

The lungs of an average male hold 0.25 mol of air in a volume of 5.8 L. How many moles of air do the lungs of an average female hold if the volume is 4.6 L?

#### Analysis

This question deals with volume and number of moles, so Avogadro's law is used to determine a final number of moles when three quantities are known—the initial volume and number of moles ($V_1$ and $n_1$), and the final volume ($V_2$).

#### Solution

**[1] Identify the known quantities and the desired quantity.**

$$V_1 = 5.8 \text{ L} \qquad\qquad V_2 = 4.6 \text{ L}$$
$$n_1 = 0.25 \text{ mol} \qquad\qquad\qquad n_2 = ?$$

known quantities         desired quantity

**[2] Write the equation and rearrange it to isolate the desired quantity, $n_2$, on one side.**

- Use Avogadro's law. To solve for $n_2$, we must invert the numerator and denominator on *both* sides of the equation, and then multiply by $V_2$.

$$\boxed{\frac{V_1}{n_1} = \frac{V_2}{n_2}} \xrightarrow[\text{on both sides.}]{\text{Switch } V \text{ and } n} \frac{n_1}{V_1} = \frac{n_2}{V_2} \quad \text{Solve for } n_2 \text{ by multiplying both sides by } V_2.$$

$$\frac{n_1 V_2}{V_1} = n_2$$

**[3] Solve the problem.**

- Substitute the three known quantities into the equation and solve for $n_2$.

$$n_2 = \frac{n_1 V_2}{V_1} = \frac{(0.25 \text{ mol})(4.6 \, \cancel{L})}{(5.8 \, \cancel{L})} = 0.20 \text{ mol}$$

Liters cancel. **Answer**

### PROBLEM 7.13

A sample of nitrogen gas contains 5.0 mol in a volume of 3.5 L. Calculate the new volume of the container if the pressure and temperature are kept constant but the number of moles of nitrogen is changed to each of the following values: (a) 2.5 mol; (b) 3.65 mol; (c) 21.5 mol.

Avogadro's law allows us to compare the amounts of any two gases by comparing their volumes. Often amounts of gas are compared at a set of **standard conditions of temperature and pressure,** abbreviated as **STP.**

- STP conditions are:    1 atm (760 mm Hg) for pressure
                         273 K (0 °C) for temperature
- At STP, one mole of any gas has the same volume, 22.4 L, called the *standard molar volume.*

Under STP conditions, one mole of nitrogen gas and one mole of helium gas each contain $6.02 \times 10^{23}$ molecules of gas and occupy a volume of 22.4 L at 0 °C and 1 atm pressure. Since the molar masses of nitrogen and helium are different (28.0 g for $N_2$ compared to 4.0 g for He), one mole of each substance has a *different* mass.

The standard molar volume can be used to set up conversion factors that relate the volume and number of moles of a gas at STP, as shown in the following stepwise procedure.

---

## How To  Convert Moles of Gas to Volume at STP

**Example:** How many moles are contained in 2.0 L of $N_2$ at standard temperature and pressure?

### Step [1]  Identify the known quantities and the desired quantity.

$$2.0 \text{ L of } N_2 \qquad ? \text{ moles of } N_2$$

original quantity        desired quantity

### Step [2]  Write out the conversion factors.

- Set up conversion factors that relate the number of moles of a gas to volume at STP. Choose the conversion factor that places the unwanted unit, liters, in the denominator so that the units cancel.

$$\frac{22.4 \text{ L}}{1 \text{ mol}} \quad \text{or} \quad \boxed{\frac{1 \text{ mol}}{22.4 \text{ L}}}$$

Choose this conversion factor to cancel L.

### Step [3]  Solve the problem.

- Multiply the original quantity by the conversion factor to obtain the desired quantity.

$$2.0 \, \cancel{L} \quad \times \quad \frac{1 \text{ mol}}{22.4 \, \cancel{L}} \quad = \quad 0.089 \text{ mol of } N_2$$

Liters cancel.                                **Answer**

By using the molar mass of a gas, we can determine the volume of a gas from a given number of grams, as shown in Sample Problem 7.7.

### SAMPLE PROBLEM 7.7

Burning one mole of propane in a gas grill adds 132 g of carbon dioxide ($CO_2$) to the atmosphere. What volume of $CO_2$ does this correspond to at STP?

#### Analysis

To solve this problem, we must convert the number of grams of $CO_2$ to moles using the molar mass. The number of moles of $CO_2$ can then be converted to its volume using a mole–volume conversion factor (1 mol/22.4 L).

#### Solution

**[1] Identify the known quantities and the desired quantity.**

$$132 \text{ g } CO_2 \qquad\qquad ? \text{ L } CO_2$$

known quantity          desired quantity

**[2] Convert the number of grams of $CO_2$ to the number of moles of $CO_2$ using the molar mass.**

molar mass
conversion factor

$$132 \text{ g } CO_2 \quad\times\quad \frac{1 \text{ mol } CO_2}{44.01 \text{ g } CO_2} \quad=\quad 3.00 \text{ mol } CO_2$$

Grams cancel.

**[3] Convert the number of moles of $CO_2$ to the volume of $CO_2$ using a mole–volume conversion factor.**

mole–volume
conversion factor

$$3.00 \text{ mol } CO_2 \quad\times\quad \frac{22.4 \text{ L}}{1 \text{ mol}} \quad=\quad 67.2 \text{ L } CO_2$$

Moles cancel.                          **Answer**

### PROBLEM 7.14

How many liters does each of the following quantities of $O_2$ occupy at STP: (a) 4.5 mol; (b) 0.35 mol; (c) 18.0 g?

### PROBLEM 7.15

How many moles are contained in the following volumes of air at STP: (a) 1.5 L; (b) 8.5 L; (c) 25 mL?

## 7.5   The Ideal Gas Law

All four properties of gases—pressure, volume, temperature, and number of moles—can be combined into a single equation called the **ideal gas law.** The product of pressure and volume divided by the product of moles and Kelvin temperature is a constant, called the **universal gas constant** and symbolized by **R.**

$$\frac{PV}{nT} \quad=\quad R \qquad \text{universal gas constant}$$

More often the equation is rearranged and written in the following way:

$$PV = nRT$$

Ideal gas law

For atm: $R = 0.0821 \dfrac{L \cdot atm}{mol \cdot K}$

For mm Hg: $R = 62.4 \dfrac{L \cdot mm\,Hg}{mol \cdot K}$

The value of the universal gas constant $R$ depends on its units. The two most common values of $R$ are given using atmospheres or mm Hg for pressure, liters for volume, and kelvins for temperature. **Be careful to use the correct value of $R$ for the pressure units in the problem you are solving.**

The ideal gas law can be used to find any value—$P$, $V$, $n$, or $T$—as long as three of the quantities are known. Solving a problem using the ideal gas law is shown in the stepwise *How To* procedure and in Sample Problem 7.8. Although the ideal gas law gives exact answers only for a perfectly "ideal" gas, it gives a good approximation for most real gases, such as the oxygen and carbon dioxide in breathing, as well (Figure 7.6).

**Figure 7.6** Focus on the Human Body: The Lungs

- Humans have two lungs that contain a vast system of air passages, allowing gases to be exchanged between the atmosphere and with the bloodstream. The lungs contain about 1,500 miles of airways that have a total surface area about the size of a tennis court.

- The total air volume of the lungs is large compared to the tidal volume, the amount of air taken in or expelled with each breath. This large reserve explains why people can smoke for years without noticing any significant change in normal breathing.

- In individuals with asthma, small airways are constricted and inflamed, making it difficult to breathe.

trachea

average lung capacity—4–6 L

average tidal volume—0.5 L

right lung with its three lobes

left lung with its two lobes

heart

pulmonary artery

pulmonary vein

alveolus

section of alveoli cut open

Blood in pulmonary arteries gives up waste $CO_2$ to the lungs so that it can be expelled to the air.

Blood in pulmonary veins picks up $O_2$ in the lungs so that it can be pumped by the heart to the body.

## How To Carry Out Calculations with the Ideal Gas Law

**Example:** How many moles of gas are contained in a typical human breath that takes in 0.50 L of air at 1.0 atm pressure and 37 °C?

**Step [1]** Identify the known quantities and the desired quantity.

$$P = 1.0 \text{ atm}$$

$$V = 0.50 \text{ L}$$

$$T = 37 \text{ °C} \qquad\qquad n = ? \text{ mol}$$

known quantities          desired quantity

**Step [2]** Convert all values to proper units and choose the value of $R$ that contains these units.
- Convert °C to K. $K = °C + 273 = 37 \text{ °C} + 273 = 310. \text{ K}$
- Use the value of $R$ in atm since the pressure is given in atm; that is, $R = 0.0821 \text{ L} \cdot \text{atm/(mol} \cdot \text{K)}$.

**Step [3]** Write the equation and rearrange it to isolate the desired quantity on one side.
- Use the ideal gas law and solve for $n$ by dividing both sides by $RT$.

$$PV = nRT \qquad \text{Solve for } n \text{ by dividing both sides by } RT.$$

$$\frac{PV}{RT} = n$$

**Step [4]** Solve the problem.
- Substitute the known quantities into the equation and solve for $n$.

$$n = \frac{PV}{RT} = \frac{(1.0 \text{ atm})(0.50 \text{ L})}{\left(0.0821 \dfrac{\text{L} \cdot \text{atm}}{\text{mol} \cdot \text{K}}\right)(310. \text{ K})} = 0.0196 \text{ rounded to } 0.020 \text{ mol}$$

**Answer**

---

### SAMPLE PROBLEM 7.8

If a person exhales 25.0 g of $CO_2$ in an hour, what volume does this amount occupy at 1.00 atm and 37 °C?

#### Analysis

Use the ideal gas law to calculate $V$, since $P$ and $T$ are known and $n$ can be determined by using the molar mass of $CO_2$ (44.01 g/mol).

#### Solution

**[1]** Identify the known quantities and the desired quantity.

$$P = 1.00 \text{ atm}$$

$$T = 37 \text{ °C} \qquad 25.0 \text{ g } CO_2 \qquad\qquad V = ? \text{ L}$$

known quantities          desired quantity

**[2]** Convert all values to proper units and choose the value of $R$ that contains these units.
- Convert °C to K. $K = °C + 273 = 37 \text{ °C} + 273 = 310. \text{ K}$
- Use the value of $R$ with atm since the pressure is given in atm; that is, $R = 0.0821 \text{ L} \cdot \text{atm/(mol} \cdot \text{K)}$.
- Convert the number of grams of $CO_2$ to the number of moles of $CO_2$ using the molar mass (44.01 g/mol).

molar mass conversion factor

$$25.0 \text{ g } CO_2 \times \frac{1 \text{ mol } CO_2}{44.01 \text{ g } CO_2} = 0.568 \text{ mol } CO_2$$

Grams cancel.

**[3] Write the equation and rearrange it to isolate the desired quantity, _V_, on one side.**
- Use the ideal gas law and solve for _V_ by dividing both sides by _P_.

$$PV = nRT \qquad \text{Solve for } V \text{ by dividing both sides by } P.$$

$$V = \frac{nRT}{P}$$

**[4] Solve the problem.**
- Substitute the three known quantities into the equation and solve for _V_.

$$V = \frac{nRT}{P} = \frac{(0.568 \text{ mol})\left(0.0821 \dfrac{\text{L} \cdot \text{atm}}{\text{mol} \cdot \text{K}}\right)(310. \text{ K})}{1.0 \text{ atm}} = 14.5 \text{ L}$$

**Answer**

## PROBLEM 7.16

How many moles of oxygen ($O_2$) are contained in a 5.0-L cylinder that has a pressure of 175 atm and a temperature of 20. °C?

## PROBLEM 7.17

Determine the pressure of $N_2$ under each of the following conditions.

a. 0.45 mol at 25 °C in 10.0 L          b. 10.0 g at 20. °C in 5.0 L

# 7.6  Dalton's Law and Partial Pressures

Since gas particles are very far apart compared to the size of an individual particle, gas particles behave independently. As a result, the identity of the components of a gas mixture does not matter, and **a mixture of gases behaves like a pure gas.** Each component of a gas mixture is said to exert a pressure called its **partial pressure. Dalton's law** describes the relationship between the partial pressures of the components and the total pressure of a gas mixture.

Since the partial pressure of $O_2$ is low at very high altitudes, most mountain climbers use supplemental $O_2$ tanks above about 24,000 ft.

- **Dalton's law:** The *total pressure* ($P_{total}$) of a gas mixture is the sum of the partial pressures of its component gases.

Thus, if a mixture has two gases (**A** and **B**) with partial pressures $P_A$ and $P_B$, respectively, the total pressure of the system ($P_{total}$) is the sum of the two partial pressures. The partial pressure of a component of a mixture is the same pressure that the gas would exert if it were a pure gas.

| | | |
|:---:|:---:|:---:|
| $P_A = 5$ atm | $P_B = 3$ atm | $P_{total} = 8$ atm |
| $P_A$ | $+$ $P_B$ | $=$ $P_{total}$ |
| partial pressure of **A** | partial pressure of **B** | total pressure |

### SAMPLE PROBLEM 7.9

A sample of exhaled air from the lungs contains four gases with the following partial pressures: $N_2$ (563 mm Hg), $O_2$ (118 mm Hg), $CO_2$ (30. mm Hg), and $H_2O$ (50. mm Hg). What is the total pressure of the sample?

#### Analysis

Using Dalton's law, the total pressure is the sum of the partial pressures.

#### Solution

Adding up the four partial pressures gives the total:

$$563 + 118 + 30. + 50. = 761 \text{ mm Hg (total pressure)}$$

### PROBLEM 7.18

$CO_2$ was added to a cylinder containing 2.5 atm of $O_2$ to give a total pressure of 4.0 atm of gas. What is the partial pressure of $O_2$ and $CO_2$ in the final mixture?

We can also calculate the partial pressure of each gas in a mixture if two quantities are known— [1] the total pressure and [2] the percent of each component—as shown in Sample Problem 7.10.

### SAMPLE PROBLEM 7.10

Air is a mixture of 21% $O_2$, 78% $N_2$, and 1% argon by volume. What is the partial pressure of each gas at sea level, where the total pressure is 760 mm Hg?

#### Analysis

Convert each percent to a decimal by moving the decimal point two places to the left. Multiply each decimal by the total pressure to obtain the partial pressure for each component.

#### Solution

|  |  | **Partial pressure** |
|---|---|---|
| Fraction $O_2$: | 21% = 0.21 | 0.21 × 760 mm Hg = 160 mm Hg ($O_2$) |
| Fraction $N_2$: | 78% = 0.78 | 0.78 × 760 mm Hg = 590 mm Hg ($N_2$) |
| Fraction Ar: | 1% = 0.01 | 0.01 × 760 mm Hg = ___8 mm Hg (Ar)___ |
|  |  | 758 rounded to 760 mm Hg |

### PROBLEM 7.19

A sample of natural gas at 750 mm Hg contains 85% methane, 10.% ethane, and 5.0% propane. What are the partial pressures of each gas in this mixture?

The high pressures of a hyperbaric chamber can be used to treat patients fighting infections and scuba divers suffering from the bends.

The composition of the atmosphere does not change with location, even though the total atmospheric pressure decreases with increasing altitude. At high altitudes, therefore, the partial pressure of oxygen is much lower than it is at sea level, making breathing difficult. This is why mountain climbers use supplemental oxygen at altitudes above 8,000 meters.

In contrast, a hyperbaric chamber is a device that maintains air pressure two to three times higher than normal. Hyperbaric chambers have many uses. At this higher pressure the partial pressure of $O_2$ is higher. For burn patients, the higher pressure of $O_2$ increases the amount of $O_2$ in the blood, where it can be used by the body for reactions that fight infections.

When a scuba diver surfaces too quickly, the $N_2$ dissolved in the blood can form microscopic bubbles that cause pain in joints and can occlude small blood vessels, causing organ injury. This condition, called the bends, is treated by placing a diver in a hyperbaric chamber, where the elevated pressure decreases the size of the $N_2$ bubbles, which are then eliminated as $N_2$ gas from the lungs as the pressure is slowly decreased.

### PROBLEM 7.20

In which hyperbaric chamber is the pressure due to $O_2$ higher: chamber **A** with pure $O_2$ at 2.5 atm pressure, or chamber **B**, which has a total pressure of 5.5 atm and contains 40.% $O_2$?

## 7.7 Intermolecular Forces, Boiling Point, and Melting Point

Unlike gases, the behavior of liquids and solids cannot be described by a set of laws that can be applied regardless of the identity of the substance. Since liquids and solids are composed of particles that are much closer together, **a force of attraction exists between them.**

Ionic compounds are composed of extensive arrays of oppositely charged ions that are held together by strong electrostatic interactions. These ionic interactions are much stronger than the forces between covalent molecules, so it takes a great deal of energy to separate ions from each other (Section 3.5).

In covalent compounds, the nature and strength of the attraction between individual molecules depend on the identity of the atoms.

- Intermolecular forces are the attractive forces that exist *between* molecules.

There are three different types of intermolecular forces in covalent molecules, presented in order of *increasing strength:*

- London dispersion forces
- Dipole–dipole interactions
- Hydrogen bonding

The strength of the intermolecular forces determines whether a compound has a high or low melting point and boiling point, and thus if the compound is a solid, liquid, or gas at a given temperature.

### 7.7A London Dispersion Forces

**London dispersion forces** can also be called **van der Waals forces.**

- London dispersion forces are very weak interactions due to the momentary changes in electron density in a molecule.

For example, although a nonpolar methane molecule ($CH_4$) has no net dipole, at any one instant its electron density may not be completely symmetrical. If more electron density is present in one region of the molecule, less electron density must be present some place else, and this creates a *temporary* dipole. A temporary dipole in one $CH_4$ molecule induces a temporary dipole in another $CH_4$ molecule, with the partial positive and negative charges arranged close to each other. **The weak interaction between these temporary dipoles constitutes London dispersion forces.**

Although any single interaction is weak, a large number of London dispersion forces creates a strong force. For example, geckos stick to walls and ceilings by London dispersion forces between the surfaces and the 500,000 tiny hairs on each foot.

London dispersion force between two $CH_4$ molecules

More electron density in one region creates a partial negative charge ($\delta^-$).

Less electron density in one region creates a partial positive charge ($\delta^+$).

***All* covalent compounds exhibit London dispersion forces.** These intermolecular forces are the only intermolecular forces present in nonpolar compounds. The strength of these forces is related to the size of the molecule.

- The larger the molecule, the larger the attractive force between two molecules, and the stronger the intermolecular forces.

### PROBLEM 7.21

Which of the following compounds exhibit London dispersion forces: (a) $NH_3$; (b) $H_2O$; (c) HCl; (d) ethane ($C_2H_6$)?

## 7.7B    Dipole–Dipole Interactions

How to determine whether a molecule is polar is shown in Section 4.8.

- Dipole–dipole interactions are the attractive forces between the permanent dipoles of two polar molecules.

For example, the carbon–oxygen bond in formaldehyde, $H_2C{=}O$, is polar because oxygen is more electronegative than carbon. This polar bond gives formaldehyde a permanent dipole, making it a polar molecule. The dipoles in adjacent formaldehyde molecules can align so that the partial positive and partial negative charges are close to each other. These attractive forces due to permanent dipoles are much stronger than London dispersion forces.

formaldehyde

### PROBLEM 7.22

Draw the individual dipoles of two H—Cl molecules and show how the dipoles are aligned in a dipole–dipole interaction.

## 7.7C    Hydrogen Bonding

- Hydrogen bonding occurs when a hydrogen atom bonded to O, N, or F is electrostatically attracted to an O, N, or F atom in another molecule.

covalent O–H bond

hydrogen bond between two $H_2O$ molecules

Hydrogen bonding is only possible between two molecules that contain a hydrogen atom bonded to a very electronegative atom—that is, oxygen, nitrogen, or fluorine. For example, two $H_2O$ molecules can hydrogen bond to each other: a hydrogen atom is covalently bonded to oxygen in one water molecule, and hydrogen bonded to an oxygen atom in another water molecule. **Hydrogen bonds are the strongest of the three types of intermolecular forces.** Table 7.3 summarizes the three types of intermolecular forces.

Hydrogen bonding is important in many biological molecules, including proteins and DNA. DNA, which is contained in the chromosomes of the nucleus of a cell, is responsible for the storage of all genetic information. DNA is composed of two long strands of atoms that are held together by hydrogen bonding as shown in Figure 7.7. A detailed discussion of DNA appears in Chapter 22.

Table 7.3 Summary of the Types of Intermolecular Forces

| Type of Force | Relative Strength | Exhibited by | Example |
|---|---|---|---|
| London dispersion | Weak | All molecules | $CH_4$, $H_2CO$, $H_2O$ |
| Dipole–dipole | Moderate | Molecules with a net dipole | $H_2CO$, $H_2O$ |
| Hydrogen bonding | Strong | Molecules with an O—H, N—H, or H—F bond | $H_2O$ |

Figure 7.7

Hydrogen Bonding and DNA

DNA double helix

Hydrogen-bonding interactions are shown as dashed red lines.

DNA is composed of two long strands of atoms that wind around each other in an arrangement called a double helix. The two strands are held together by an extensive network of hydrogen bonds. In each hydrogen bond, an H atom of an N—H bond on one chain is intermolecularly hydrogen bonded to an oxygen or nitrogen atom on an adjacent chain. Five hydrogen bonds are indicated.

## SAMPLE PROBLEM 7.11

What types of intermolecular forces are present in each compound: (a) HCl; (b) $C_2H_6$ (ethane); (c) $NH_3$?

### Analysis

- London dispersion forces are present in all covalent compounds.
- Dipole–dipole interactions are present only in polar compounds with a permanent dipole.
- Hydrogen bonding occurs only in compounds that contain an O—H, N—H, or H—F bond.

### Solution

a.

polar bond

$\overset{\delta^+}{H}—\overset{\delta^-}{Cl}$

- HCl has London forces like all covalent compounds.
- HCl has a polar bond, so it exhibits dipole–dipole interactions.
- HCl has no H atom on an O, N, or F, so it has no intermolecular hydrogen bonding.

b.

nonpolar molecule

- $C_2H_6$ is a nonpolar molecule since it has only nonpolar C—C and C—H bonds. Thus, it exhibits only London forces.

c.

net dipole

- $NH_3$ has London forces like all covalent compounds.
- $NH_3$ has a net dipole from its three polar bonds (Section 4.8), so it exhibits dipole–dipole interactions.
- $NH_3$ has a H atom bonded to N, so it exhibits intermolecular hydrogen bonding.

## PROBLEM 7.23

What types of intermolecular forces are present in each molecule?

a. $Cl_2$     b. HCN     c. HF     d. $CH_3Cl$     e. $H_2$

## PROBLEM 7.24

Which of the compounds in each pair has stronger intermolecular forces?

a. $CO_2$ or $H_2O$     b. $CO_2$ or HBr     c. HBr or $H_2O$     d. $CH_4$ or $C_2H_6$

## 7.7D Boiling Point and Melting Point

The **boiling point (bp)** of a compound is the temperature at which a liquid is converted to the gas phase, while the **melting point (mp)** is the temperature at which a solid is converted to the liquid phase. The strength of the intermolecular forces determines the boiling point and melting point of compounds.

- The *stronger* the intermolecular forces, the *higher* the boiling point and melting point.

In boiling, energy must be supplied to overcome the attractive forces of the liquid state and separate the molecules to the gas phase. Similarly, in melting, energy must be supplied to overcome the highly ordered solid state and convert it to the less ordered liquid phase. A stronger force of attraction between molecules means that more energy must be supplied to overcome those intermolecular forces, increasing the boiling point and melting point.

In comparing compounds of similar size, the following trend is observed:

Methane ($CH_4$) and water ($H_2O$) are both small molecules with hydrogen atoms bonded to a second-row element, so you might expect them to have similar melting points and boiling points. Methane, however, is a nonpolar molecule that exhibits only London dispersion forces, whereas water is a polar molecule that can form intermolecular hydrogen bonds. As a result, the melting point and boiling point of water are *much higher* than those of methane. In fact, the hydrogen bonds in water are so strong that it is a liquid at room temperature, whereas methane is a gas.

methane

London forces only
bp = −162 °C
mp = −183 °C

water

hydrogen bonding
bp = 100 °C
mp = 0 °C

stronger forces
higher bp and mp

In comparing two compounds with similar types of intermolecular forces, the higher molecular weight compound generally has more surface area and therefore a larger force of attraction, giving it the higher boiling point and melting point. Thus, propane ($C_3H_8$) and butane ($C_4H_{10}$) have only nonpolar bonds and London forces, but butane is larger and therefore has the higher boiling point and melting point.

propane

bp = −42 °C
mp = −190 °C

butane

bp = −0.5 °C
mp = −138 °C

larger molecule
stronger forces
higher bp and mp

## SAMPLE PROBLEM 7.12

(a) Which compound, **A** or **B**, has the higher boiling point? (b) Which compound, **C** or **D**, has the higher melting point?

$NH_3$

ammonia

**A**

$CH_4$

methane

**B**

methanol

**C**

chloromethane

**D**

### Analysis

Determine the types of intermolecular forces in each compound. The compound with the stronger forces has the higher boiling point or melting point.

### Solution

a. $NH_3$ (**A**) has an N—H bond, so it exhibits intermolecular hydrogen bonding. $CH_4$ (**B**) has only London forces since it has only nonpolar C—H bonds. $NH_3$ has stronger forces and the higher boiling point.

b. Methanol (**C**) has an O—H bond, so it can intermolecularly hydrogen bond. Chloromethane (**D**) has a polar C—Cl bond, so it has dipole–dipole interactions, but it cannot hydrogen bond. **C** has stronger forces, so **C** has the higher melting point.

## PROBLEM 7.25

Which compound in each pair has the higher boiling point? Which compound in each pair has the higher melting point?

a. $CH_4$ or $C_2H_6$      b. $C_2H_6$ or $CH_3OH$      c. HBr or HCl      d. $C_2H_6$ or $CH_3Br$

## PROBLEM 7.26

Explain why $CO_2$ is a gas at room temperature but $H_2O$ is a liquid.

## 7.8  The Liquid State

Since liquid molecules are much closer together than gas molecules, many properties of a liquid are determined by the strength of its intermolecular forces. The molecules in a liquid are still much more mobile than those of a solid, though, making liquids fluid and giving them no definite shape. Some liquid molecules move fast enough that they escape the liquid phase altogether and become gas molecules that are very far apart from each other.

Chloroethane ($CH_3CH_2Cl$), commonly called ethyl chloride, is a local anesthetic. When chloroethane is sprayed on a wound it quickly evaporates, causing a cooling sensation that numbs the site of an injury.

## 7.8A Vapor Pressure

When a liquid is placed in an open container, liquid molecules near the surface that have enough kinetic energy to overcome the intermolecular forces escape to the gas phase. This process, **evaporation,** will continue until all of the liquid has become gas. A puddle of water formed after a rainstorm evaporates as all of the liquid water is converted to gas molecules called water **vapor.** **Evaporation is an** *endothermic* **process**—it absorbs heat from the surroundings. This explains why the skin is cooled as sweat evaporates.

evaporation

In a closed container, some liquid molecules evaporate from the surface and enter the gas phase. As more molecules accumulate in the gas phase, some molecules re-enter the liquid phase in the process of **condensation. Condensation is an** *exothermic* **process**—it gives off heat to the surroundings. At equilibrium, the rate of evaporation and the rate of condensation are equal.

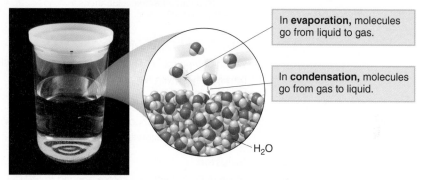

In **evaporation,** molecules go from liquid to gas.

In **condensation,** molecules go from gas to liquid.

liquid in a closed container

The gas laws we have already learned can describe the behavior of the gas molecules above a liquid. In particular, these gas molecules exert pressure, called **vapor pressure.**

- Vapor pressure is the pressure exerted by gas molecules in equilibrium with the liquid phase.

The vapor pressure exerted by a particular liquid depends on the identity of the liquid and the temperature. As the temperature is increased, the kinetic energy of the molecules increases and more molecules escape into the gas phase.

- Vapor pressure increases with increasing temperature.

When the temperature is high enough that the vapor pressure above the liquid equals the atmospheric pressure, even molecules below the surface of the liquid have enough kinetic energy to enter the gas phase and the liquid boils. **The** *normal boiling point* **of a liquid is the temperature at which its vapor pressure equals 760 mm Hg.**

The boiling point depends on the atmospheric pressure. At the lower atmospheric pressure of higher altitudes, a liquid has a lower boiling point because the vapor pressure above the liquid equals the atmospheric pressure at a lower temperature. In Denver, Colorado (elevation 1,609 m or 5,280 ft), where atmospheric pressure is typically 630 mm Hg, water boils at 93 °C.

How is the strength of the intermolecular forces related to the vapor pressure? The stronger the intermolecular forces, the less readily a compound escapes from the liquid to the gas phase. Thus,

• **The stronger the intermolecular forces, the lower the vapor pressure at a given temperature.**

Compounds with strong intermolecular forces have high boiling points and low vapor pressures at a given temperature. In Section 7.7 we learned that water has a *higher* boiling point than methane ($CH_4$) because water can hydrogen bond while methane cannot. At any given temperature, water has a *lower* vapor pressure because its molecules are held more tightly and remain in the liquid phase.

$H_2O$

Stronger intermolecular forces
keep the $H_2O$ molecules as a liquid.

$CH_4$

Weaker intermolecular forces allow more
$CH_4$ molecules to escape to the gas phase.

### SAMPLE PROBLEM 7.13

Which compound, $H_2O$ or $H_2S$, has the higher boiling point? Which compound has the higher vapor pressure at a given temperature?

#### Analysis

Determine which compound has the stronger intermolecular forces. Stronger forces mean a higher boiling point and a lower vapor pressure.

#### Solution

Since $H_2O$ contains an O atom bonded to H, $H_2O$ exhibits hydrogen bonding, the strongest of the intermolecular forces. $H_2S$ has no hydrogen bonding since it has no hydrogen bonded to O, N, or F. The stronger intermolecular forces in $H_2O$ give it a higher boiling point. The weaker intermolecular forces in $H_2S$ mean that the molecules escape into the gas phase more readily, giving $H_2S$ the higher vapor pressure.

### PROBLEM 7.27

Which molecule in each pair has the higher vapor pressure at a given temperature?

  a. $CH_4$ or $NH_3$         b. $CH_4$ or $C_2H_6$         c. $C_2H_6$ or $CH_3OH$

### PROBLEM 7.28

Explain why you feel cool when you get out of a swimming pool, even when the air temperature is quite warm. Then explain why the water feels warmer when you get back into the swimming pool.

## 7.8B  Viscosity and Surface Tension

Viscosity and surface tension are two more properties of liquids that can be explained at least in part by the strength of the intermolecular forces.

***Viscosity* is a measure of a fluid's resistance to flow freely.** A viscous liquid is one that feels "thicker." Compounds with stronger intermolecular forces tend to be more viscous than

**Figure 7.8** Surface Tension

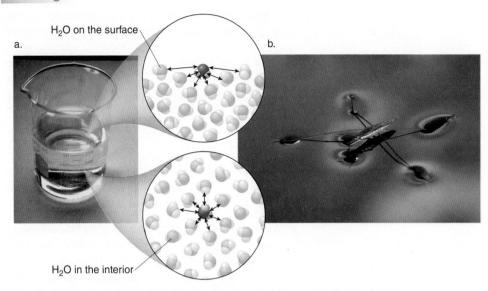

(a) Interior molecules experience intermolecular forces (shown with double-headed arrows) evenly in all directions, whereas surface molecules experience uneven interactions and are pulled downward towards the interior. (b) Water's high surface tension allows a water strider to walk on the surface.

compounds with weaker forces. Thus water is more viscous than gasoline, which is composed of nonpolar molecules with weak intermolecular forces. The size of molecules also plays a role. Large molecules do not slide past each other as freely, so substances composed of large molecules tend to be more viscous. Olive oil, for example, is more viscous than water because olive oil is composed of compounds with three long floppy chains that contain more than 50 atoms in each chain.

*Surface tension* **is a measure of the resistance of a liquid to spread out.** Molecules in the interior of a liquid are surrounded by intermolecular forces on all sides, making them more stable than surface molecules that only experience intermolecular forces from neighbors on the side and below [Figure 7.8a]. This makes surface molecules less stable. **The *stronger* the intermolecular forces, the stronger surface molecules are pulled down toward the interior of a liquid and the *higher* the surface tension.** Because water has strong intermolecular hydrogen bonding, its surface tension is high. This explains why water striders can walk across the surface [Figure 7.8b], and why a paper clip can "float" on water.

## PROBLEM 7.29

Explain why benzene is less viscous than water, but ethylene glycol is more viscous than water.

benzene             ethylene glycol

## PROBLEM 7.30

Would you predict the surface tension of gasoline, composed of molecules containing only carbon and hydrogen atoms, to be higher or lower than the surface tension of water?

## 7.9   The Solid State

When a liquid is cooled so that the intermolecular forces are stronger than the kinetic energy of the particles, a solid is formed. Solids can be either **crystalline** or **amorphous.**

- A crystalline solid has a regular arrangement of particles—atoms, molecules, or ions—with a repeating structure.
- An amorphous solid has no regular arrangement of its closely packed particles.

There are four different types of crystalline solids—**ionic, molecular, network,** and **metallic**—as shown in Figure 7.9.

An **ionic solid** is composed of oppositely charged ions. For example, sodium chloride, NaCl, is composed of $Na^+$ cations and $Cl^-$ anions, arranged so that each $Na^+$ cation is surrounded by six $Cl^-$ anions and each $Cl^-$ anion is surrounded by six $Na^+$ cations.

A **molecular solid** is composed of individual molecules arranged regularly. Ice, for example, contains a hexagonal arrangement of water molecules that are extensively hydrogen bonded to each other. In fact, the crystalline structure of water accounts for one of its unique properties. Water is one of the few substances whose solid phase is *less* dense than its liquid phase. As a result, solid ice floats on liquid water. A sheet of ice freezes on top of a lake, allowing plant and animal life to survive beneath the surface.

A **network solid** is composed of a vast number of atoms covalently bonded together, forming sheets or three-dimensional arrays. Quartz sand, $SiO_2$, contains an infinite network of silicon and oxygen atoms. Each silicon atom is bonded to four oxygen atoms and each oxygen is bonded to two silicon atoms, so that there are twice as many oxygen atoms as silicon. Other examples include diamond and graphite, two elemental forms of carbon, whose structures appeared in Figure 2.6.

Since metals are atoms that readily give up their electrons, a **metallic solid** such as copper or silver can be thought of as a lattice of metal cations surrounded by a cloud of electrons that move freely. Because of their loosely held, delocalized electrons, metals conduct electricity and heat.

**Figure 7.9**    Four Examples of Crystalline Solids

a. Table salt (NaCl)      b. Ice ($H_2O$ molecules)      c. Sand ($SiO_2$)      d. Copper (Cu)

$Na^+$

$Cl^-$

$H_2O$ molecule

O

Si

Cu atom

(a) Sodium chloride, NaCl, an ionic solid; (b) ice, a molecular solid composed of $H_2O$ molecules arranged in a hexagonal pattern; (c) silicon dioxide, $SiO_2$, a network solid that comprises sand; (d) metallic copper.

A polycarbonate helmet, polyethylene water bottle, and rubber tires are all examples of amorphous solids.

In contrast to crystalline solids, **amorphous solids have no regular arrangement of particles.** Amorphous solids can be formed when a liquid cools too quickly to allow the regular crystalline pattern to form. Substances composed of very large strands of covalent molecules also tend to form amorphous solids, because the chains can become folded and intertwined, making an organized regular arrangement impossible. Examples of amorphous solids include rubber, glass, and most plastics.

### PROBLEM 7.31

Which type of crystalline solid is formed by each substance: (a) $CaCl_2$; (b) Fe (iron); (c) sugar $(C_{12}H_{22}O_{11})$; (d) $NH_3(s)$?

## 7.10 Energy and Phase Changes

In Section 7.7 we learned how the strength of intermolecular forces in a liquid and solid affect a compound's boiling point and melting point. Let's now look in more detail at the energy changes that occur during phase changes.

### 7.10A Converting a Solid to a Liquid

**Converting a solid to a liquid is called *melting*.** Melting is an *endothermic* process. Energy must be absorbed to overcome some of the attractive intermolecular forces that hold the organized solid molecules together to form the more random liquid phase. The amount of energy needed to melt 1 g of a substance is called its **heat of fusion.**

When an ice cube is added to a liquid at room temperature, the ice cube melts. The energy needed for melting is "pulled" from the warmer liquid molecules and the liquid cools down.

Freezing is the opposite of melting; that is, *freezing* **converts a liquid to a solid.** Freezing is an *exothermic* process because energy is released as the faster moving liquid molecules form an organized solid in which particles have little freedom of motion. For a given mass of a particular substance, the amount of energy released in freezing is the same as the amount of energy absorbed during melting.

Heats of fusion are reported in calories per gram (cal/g). A heat of fusion can be used as a conversion factor to determine how much energy is absorbed when a particular amount of a substance melts, as shown in Sample Problem 7.14.

### SAMPLE PROBLEM 7.14

How much energy in calories is absorbed when 50.0 g of ice cubes melt? The heat of fusion of $H_2O$ is 79.7 cal/g.

#### Analysis

Use the heat of fusion as a conversion factor to determine the amount of energy absorbed in melting.

#### Solution

**[1] Identify the original quantity and the desired quantity.**

|  |  |
|---|---|
| 50.0 g | ? calories |
| original quantity | desired quantity |

**[2] Write out the conversion factors.**

- Use the heat of fusion as a conversion factor to convert grams to calories.

g–cal conversion factors

$$\frac{1\ g}{79.7\ cal} \quad or \quad \boxed{\frac{79.7\ cal}{1\ g}}$$

Choose this conversion factor
to cancel the unwanted unit, g.

**[3] Solve the problem.**

$$50.0\ \cancel{g} \quad \times \quad \frac{79.7\ cal}{1\ \cancel{g}} \quad = \quad 3{,}985\ cal\ rounded\ to\ 3{,}990\ cal$$

Grams cancel.

**Answer**

### PROBLEM 7.32

Use the heat of fusion of water from Sample Problem 7.14 to answer each question.

 a. How much energy in calories is released when 50.0 g of water freezes?
 b. How much energy in calories is absorbed when 35.0 g of water melts?
 c. How much energy in kilocalories is absorbed when 35.0 g of water melts?
 d. How much energy in calories is absorbed when 1.00 mol of water melts?

## 7.10B   Converting a Liquid to a Gas

**Converting a liquid to a gas is called *vaporization*.** Vaporization is an *endothermic* process. Energy must be absorbed to overcome the attractive intermolecular forces of the liquid phase to form gas molecules. The amount of energy needed to vaporize 1 g of a substance is called its **heat of vaporization.**

liquid water                                                                 steam

Condensation is the opposite of vaporization; that is, **condensation converts a gas to a liquid.** Condensation is an *exothermic* process because energy is released as the faster moving gas molecules form the more organized liquid phase. For a given mass of a particular substance, the amount of energy released in condensation equals the amount of energy absorbed during vaporization.

Heats of vaporization are reported in calories per gram (cal/g). A high heat of vaporization means that a substance absorbs a great deal of energy as it is converted from a liquid to a gas. **Water has a high heat of vaporization.** As a result, the evaporation of sweat from the skin is a very effective cooling mechanism for the body. The heat of vaporization can be used as a conversion factor to determine how much energy is absorbed when a particular amount of a substance vaporizes, as shown in Sample Problem 7.15.

### SAMPLE PROBLEM 7.15

How much heat in kilocalories is absorbed when 22.0 g of 2-propanol, rubbing alcohol, evaporates after being rubbed on the skin? The heat of vaporization of 2-propanol is 159 cal/g.

## Analysis

Use the heat of vaporization to convert grams to an energy unit, calories. Calories must also be converted to kilocalories using a cal–kcal conversion factor.

## Solution

**[1] Identify the original quantity and the desired quantity.**

22.0 g          ? kilocalories

original quantity     desired quantity

**[2] Write out the conversion factors.**

- We have no conversion factor that relates grams and kilocalories directly. We do know, however, how to relate grams to calories using the heat of vaporization, and calories to kilocalories.

g–cal conversion factors           cal–kcal conversion factors

$$\frac{1\ g}{159\ cal} \quad \text{or} \quad \boxed{\frac{159\ cal}{1\ g}} \qquad\qquad \frac{1000\ cal}{1\ kcal} \quad \text{or} \quad \boxed{\frac{1\ kcal}{1000\ cal}}$$

Choose the conversion factors with the unwanted units—g and cal—in the denominator.

**[3] Solve the problem.**

$$22.0\ \cancel{g} \quad \times \quad \frac{159\ \cancel{cal}}{1\ \cancel{g}} \quad \times \quad \frac{1\ kcal}{1000\ \cancel{cal}} \quad = \quad 3.50\ kcal$$

**Answer**

Grams cancel.        Calories cancel.

### PROBLEM 7.33

Answer the following questions about water, which has a heat of vaporization of 540 cal/g.

a. How much energy in calories is absorbed when 42 g of water is vaporized?
b. How much energy in calories is released when 42 g of water is condensed?
c. How much energy in kilocalories is absorbed when 1.00 mol of water is vaporized?
d. How much energy in kilocalories is absorbed when 3.5 mol of water is vaporized?

## 7.10C   Converting a Solid to a Gas

Occasionally a solid phase forms a gas phase without passing through the liquid state. This process is called **sublimation.** The reverse process, conversion of a gas directly to a solid, is called **deposition.** Carbon dioxide is called *dry ice* because solid carbon dioxide ($CO_2$) sublimes to gaseous $CO_2$ without forming liquid $CO_2$.

Freeze-drying removes water from foods by the process of sublimation. These products can be stored almost indefinitely, since bacteria cannot grow in them without water.

endothermic

**sublimation**

**deposition**

exothermic

$CO_2(s)$                             $CO_2(g)$

Carbon dioxide is a good example of a solid that undergoes this process at atmospheric pressure. At reduced pressure other substances sublime. For example, freeze-dried foods are prepared by subliming water from a food product at low pressure.

Table 7.4 summarizes the phase changes in Section 7.10.

### Table 7.4  Summary of Energy and Phase Changes

| Process | Phases | Energy Change |
|---|---|---|
| Melting | Solid ⟶ liquid | Endothermic process—Energy is absorbed. |
| Freezing | Liquid ⟶ solid | Exothermic process—Energy is released. |
| Vaporization | Liquid ⟶ gas | Endothermic process—Energy is absorbed. |
| Condensation | Gas ⟶ liquid | Exothermic process—Energy is released. |
| Sublimation | Solid ⟶ gas | Endothermic process—Energy is absorbed. |
| Deposition | Gas ⟶ solid | Exothermic process—Energy is released. |

### SAMPLE PROBLEM 7.16

Is the process depicted in the molecular art endothermic or exothermic?

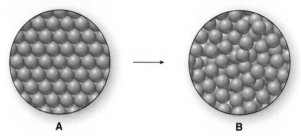

A                                    B

### Analysis

Identify the phase by the distance between the spheres and their level of organization. A solid has closely packed spheres that are well organized; a liquid has closely packed but randomly arranged spheres; a gas has randomly arranged spheres that are far apart. Then, classify the transformation as melting, freezing, vaporization, condensation, sublimation, or deposition, depending on the phases depicted.

### Solution

**A** represents a solid and **B** represents a liquid, so the molecular art represents melting. Melting is an endothermic process because energy must be absorbed to convert the more ordered solid state to the less ordered liquid state.

### PROBLEM 7.34

Is the process depicted in the molecular art endothermic or exothermic?

## 7.11   Heating and Cooling Curves

The changes of state described in Section 7.10 can be illustrated on a single graph called a **heating curve.** A heating curve shows how the temperature of a substance (plotted on the vertical axis) changes as heat is *added*. A general heating curve is shown in Figure 7.10.

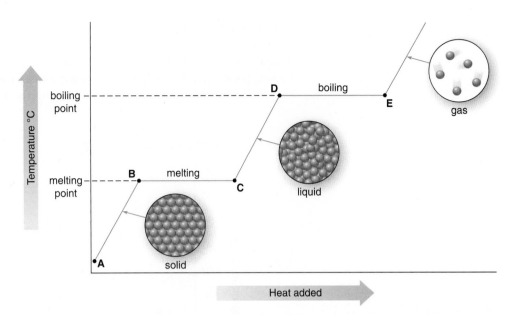

**Figure 7.10**

Heating Curve

A heating curve shows how the temperature of a substance changes as heat is added. The plateau **B** ⟶ **C** occurs at the melting point, while the plateau **D** ⟶ **E** occurs at the boiling point.

A solid is present at point **A.** As the solid is heated it increases in temperature until its melting point is reached at **B.** More heat causes the solid to melt to a liquid, without increasing its temperature (the plateau from **B** ⟶ **C**). Added heat increases the temperature of the liquid until its boiling point is reached at **D.** More heat causes the liquid to boil to form a gas, without increasing its temperature (the plateau from **D** ⟶ **E**). Additional heat then increases the temperature of the gas. Each diagonal line corresponds to the presence of a single phase—solid, liquid, or gas—while horizontal lines correspond to phase changes—solid to liquid or liquid to gas.

A **cooling curve** illustrates how the temperature of a substance (plotted on the vertical axis) changes as heat is *removed*. A cooling curve for water is shown in Figure 7.11.

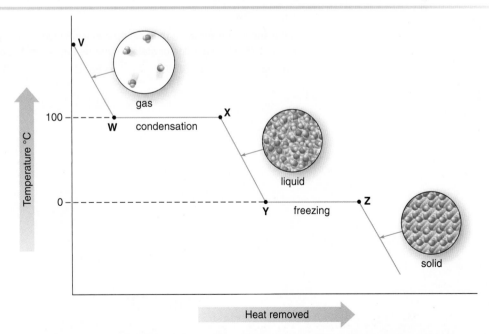

**Figure 7.11**

Cooling Curve for Water

The cooling curve shows how the temperature of water changes as heat is removed. The plateau **W** ⟶ **X** occurs at the boiling point, while the plateau **Y** ⟶ **Z** occurs at the freezing point.

Gaseous water is present at point **V.** As the gas is cooled it decreases in temperature until its boiling point is reached at **W.** Condensation at 100 °C forms liquid water, represented by the plateau from **W → X.** Further cooling of the liquid water takes place until its freezing point (melting point) is reached at **Y.** Freezing water forms ice at 0 °C, represented by the plateau from **Y → Z.** Cooling the ice further decreases its temperature below its freezing point.

### PROBLEM 7.35

Answer the following questions about the graph.

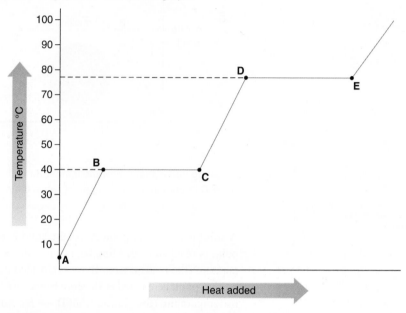

a. Does the graph illustrate a heating curve or a cooling curve?
b. What is the melting point of the substance?
c. What is the boiling point of the substance?
d. What phase(s) are present at plateau **B → C?**
e. What phase(s) are present along the diagonal **C → D?**

### PROBLEM 7.36

If the substance shown in the heating curve in Figure 7.10 has a melting point of 50 °C and a boiling point of 75 °C, what state or states of matter are present at each temperature?

a. 85 °C          b. 50 °C          c. 65 °C          d. 10 °C          e. 75 °C

# CHAPTER HIGHLIGHTS

## KEY TERMS

Amorphous solid (7.9)
Atmosphere (7.2)
Avogadro's law (7.4)
Barometer (7.2)
Boiling point (bp, 7.7)
Boyle's law (7.3)
Charles's law (7.3)
Combined gas law (7.3)
Condensation (7.8, 7.10)
Cooling curve (7.11)
Crystalline solid (7.9)
Dalton's law (7.6)
Deposition (7.10)
Dipole–dipole interactions (7.7)
Evaporation (7.8)

Freezing (7.10)
Gas laws (7.3)
Gay–Lussac's law (7.3)
Heating curve (7.11)
Heat of fusion (7.10)
Heat of vaporization (7.10)
Hydrogen bonding (7.7)
Ideal gas law (7.5)
Intermolecular forces (7.7)
Ionic solid (7.9)
Kinetic-molecular theory (7.2)
London dispersion forces (7.7)
Melting (7.10)
Melting point (mp, 7.7)
Metallic solid (7.9)

Millimeters of mercury (7.2)
Molecular solid (7.9)
Network solid (7.9)
Normal boiling point (7.8)
Partial pressure (7.6)
Pressure (7.2)
Standard molar volume (7.4)
STP (7.4)
Sublimation (7.10)
Surface tension (7.8)
Universal gas constant (7.5)
Vapor (7.8)
Vapor pressure (7.8)
Vaporization (7.10)
Viscosity (7.8)

## KEY CONCEPTS

**❶ What is pressure and what units are used to measure it? (7.2)**

- Pressure is the force per unit area. The pressure of a gas is the force exerted when gas particles strike a surface. Pressure is measured by a barometer and recorded in atmospheres (atm), millimeters of mercury (mm Hg), or pounds per square inch (psi).
- 1 atm = 760 mm Hg = 14.7 psi.

**❷ What are gas laws and how are they used to describe the relationship between the pressure, volume, and temperature of a gas? (7.3)**

- Because gas particles are far apart and behave independently, a set of gas laws describes the behavior of all gases regardless of their identity. Three gas laws—Boyle's law, Charles's law, and Gay–Lussac's law—describe the relationship between the pressure, volume, and temperature of a gas. These gas laws are summarized in "Key Equations— The Gas Laws" on page 234.
- For a constant amount of gas, the following relationships exist.
  - The pressure and volume of a gas are inversely related, so increasing the pressure decreases the volume at constant temperature.
  - The volume of a gas is proportional to its Kelvin temperature, so increasing the temperature increases the volume at constant pressure.
  - The pressure of a gas is proportional to its Kelvin temperature, so increasing the temperature increases the pressure at constant volume.

**❸ Describe the relationship between the volume and number of moles of a gas. (7.4)**

- Avogadro's law states that when temperature and pressure are held constant, the volume of a gas is proportional to its number of moles.
- One mole of any gas has the same volume, the standard molar volume of 22.4 L, at 1 atm and 273 K (STP).

**❹ What is the ideal gas law? (7.5)**

- The ideal gas law is an equation that relates the pressure ($P$), volume ($V$), temperature ($T$), and number of moles ($n$) of a gas; $PV = nRT$, where $R$ is the universal gas constant. The ideal gas law can be used to calculate any one of the four variables, as long as the other three variables are known.

**❺ What is Dalton's law and how is it used to relate partial pressures and the total pressure of a gas mixture? (7.6)**

- Dalton's law states that the total pressure of a gas mixture is the sum of the partial pressures of its component gases. The partial pressure is the pressure exerted by each component of a mixture.

**❻ What types of intermolecular forces exist and how do they determine a compound's boiling point and melting point? (7.7)**

- Intermolecular forces are the forces of attraction between molecules. Three types of intermolecular forces exist in covalent compounds. London dispersion forces are due to momentary changes in electron density in a molecule. Dipole–dipole interactions are due to permanent dipoles. Hydrogen bonding, the strongest intermolecular force, results when a H atom bonded to an O, N, or F, is attracted to an O, N, or F atom in another molecule.
- The stronger the intermolecular forces, the higher the boiling point and melting point of a compound.

**7** Describe three features of the liquid state—vapor pressure, viscosity, and surface tension. (7.8)

- Vapor pressure is the pressure exerted by gas molecules in equilibrium with the liquid phase. Vapor pressure increases with increasing temperature. The higher the vapor pressure at a given temperature, the lower the boiling point of a compound.
- Viscosity measures a liquid's resistance to flow. More viscous compounds tend to have stronger intermolecular forces or they have high molecular weights.
- Surface tension measures a liquid's resistance to spreading out. The stronger the intermolecular forces, the higher the surface tension.

**8** Describe the features of different types of solids. (7.9)

- Solids can be amorphous or crystalline. An amorphous solid has no regular arrangement of particles. A crystalline solid has a regular arrangement of particles in a repeating pattern. There are four types of crystalline solids. Ionic solids are composed of ions. Molecular solids are composed of individual molecules. Network solids are composed of vast repeating arrays of covalently bonded atoms in a regular three-dimensional arrangement. Metallic solids are composed of metal cations with a cloud of delocalized electrons.

**9** Describe the energy changes that accompany changes of state. (7.10)

- A phase change converts one state to another. Energy is absorbed when a more organized state is converted to a less organized state. Thus, energy is absorbed when a solid melts to form a liquid, or when a liquid vaporizes to form a gas.
- Energy is released when a less organized state is converted to a more organized state. Thus, energy is released when a gas condenses to form a liquid, or a liquid freezes to form a solid.
- The heat of fusion is the energy needed to melt 1 g of a substance, while the heat of vaporization is the energy needed to vaporize 1 g of a substance.

**10** What changes are depicted on heating and cooling curves? (7.11)

- A heating curve shows how the temperature of a substance changes as heat is added. Diagonal lines show the temperature increase of a single phase. Horizontal lines correspond to phase changes—solid to liquid or liquid to gas.
- A cooling curve shows how the temperature of a substance changes as heat is removed. Diagonal lines show the temperature decrease of a single phase. Horizontal lines correspond to phase changes—gas to liquid or liquid to solid.

## KEY EQUATIONS—THE GAS LAWS

| Name | Equation | Variables Related | Constant Terms |
| --- | --- | --- | --- |
| Boyle's law | $P_1V_1 = P_2V_2$ | $P, V$ | $T, n$ |
| Charles's law | $\dfrac{V_1}{T_1} = \dfrac{V_2}{T_2}$ | $V, T$ | $P, n$ |
| Gay–Lussac's law | $\dfrac{P_1}{T_1} = \dfrac{P_2}{T_2}$ | $P, T$ | $V, n$ |
| Combined gas law | $\dfrac{P_1V_1}{T_1} = \dfrac{P_2V_2}{T_2}$ | $P, V, T$ | $n$ |
| Avogadro's law | $\dfrac{V_1}{n_1} = \dfrac{V_2}{n_2}$ | $V, n$ | $P, T$ |
| Ideal gas law | $PV = nRT$ | $P, V, T, n$ | $R$ |

## PROBLEMS

Selected in-chapter and odd-numbered end-of-chapter problems have brief answers in Appendix B. The *Student Study Guide and Solutions Manual* contains detailed solutions to all in-chapter and odd-numbered end-of-chapter problems, as well as additional worked examples and a chapter self-test.

### Pressure

**7.37** The highest atmospheric pressure ever measured is 814.3 mm Hg, recorded in Mongolia in December, 2001. Convert this value to atmospheres.

**7.38** The lowest atmospheric pressure ever measured is 652.5 mm Hg, recorded during Typhoon Tip on October 12, 1979. Convert this value to atmospheres.

**7.39** Convert each quantity to the indicated unit.
   a. 2.8 atm to psi            c. 20.0 atm to torr
   b. 520 mm Hg to atm          d. 100. mm Hg to Pa

**7.40** The compressed air tank of a scuba diver reads 3,200 psi at the beginning of a dive and 825 psi at the end of a dive. Convert each of these values to atm and mm Hg.

## General Gas Law Problems

**7.41** **X** consists of a flexible container with eight particles of a gas as shown. What happens to the pressure of the system when **X** is converted to the representations in parts (a), (b), and (c)?

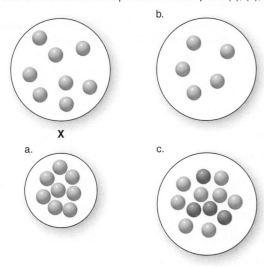

**7.42** Suppose **A** represents a balloon that can expand or contract. **A** contains 10 particles of a gas as shown. Draw a diagram that shows the volume of **A** when each change occurs.

a. The volume is halved and the temperature and number of particles remain the same.

b. The pressure is doubled and the temperature and number of particles remain the same.

c. The temperature is increased and the pressure and number of particles remain the same.

d. The number of particles is doubled and the pressure and temperature remain the same.

**7.43** Draw a picture that represents the given balloon when each of the following changes occurs.

a. The balloon is inflated outside on a cold winter day and then taken inside a building at 75 °F.

b. The balloon is taken to the top of Mauna Kea, Hawaii (elevation 13,796 ft). Assume the temperature is constant.

c. The balloon is taken inside an airplane pressurized at 0.8 atm.

**7.44** Which representation ([1], [2], or [3]) shows what balloon **Z** resembles after each change occurs?

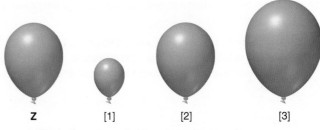

a. The balloon is cooled to a lower temperature.

b. Some gas leaks out.

c. The balloon is allowed to rise to a higher altitude.

**7.45** A balloon is filled with helium at sea level. What happens to the volume of the balloon in each instance? Explain each answer.

a. The balloon floats to a higher altitude.

b. The balloon is placed in a bath of liquid nitrogen at −196 °C.

c. The balloon is placed inside a hyperbaric chamber at a pressure of 2.5 atm.

d. The balloon is heated inside a microwave.

**7.46** Suppose you have a fixed amount of gas in a container with a movable piston, as drawn. Re-draw the container and piston to illustrate what it looks like after each of the following changes takes place.

a. The temperature is held constant and the pressure is doubled.

b. The pressure is held constant and the Kelvin temperature is doubled.

c. The pressure is halved and the Kelvin temperature is halved.

## Boyle's Law

**7.47** Assuming a fixed amount of gas at constant temperature, complete the following table.

|    | $P_1$ | $V_1$ | $P_2$ | $V_2$ |
|----|-------|-------|-------|-------|
| a. | 2.0 atm | 3.0 L | 8.0 atm | ? |
| b. | 55 mm Hg | 0.35 L | 18 mm Hg | ? |
| c. | 705 mm Hg | 215 mL | ? | 1.52 L |

**7.48** Assuming a fixed amount of gas at constant temperature, complete the following table.

|    | $P_1$ | $V_1$ | $P_2$ | $V_2$ |
|----|-------|-------|-------|-------|
| a. | 2.5 atm | 1.5 L | 3.8 atm | ? |
| b. | 2.0 atm | 350 mL | 750 mm Hg | ? |
| c. | 75 mm Hg | 9.1 mL | ? | 890 mL |

**7.49** If a scuba diver releases a 10.-mL air bubble below the surface where the pressure is 3.5 atm, what is the volume of the bubble when it rises to the surface and the pressure is 1.0 atm?

**7.50** If someone takes a breath and the lungs expand from 4.5 L to 5.6 L in volume, and the initial pressure was 756 mm Hg, what is the pressure inside the lungs before any additional air is pulled in?

## Charles's Law

**7.51** Assuming a fixed amount of gas at constant pressure, complete the following table.

|   | $V_1$ | $T_1$ | $V_2$ | $T_2$ |
|---|-------|-------|-------|-------|
| a. | 5.0 L | 310 K | ? | 250 K |
| b. | 150 mL | 45 K | ? | 45 °C |
| c. | 60.0 L | 0.0 °C | 180 L | ? |

**7.52** Assuming a fixed amount of gas at constant pressure, complete the following table.

|   | $V_1$ | $T_1$ | $V_2$ | $T_2$ |
|---|-------|-------|-------|-------|
| a. | 10.0 mL | 210 K | ? | 450 K |
| b. | 255 mL | 55 °C | ? | 150 K |
| c. | 13 L | −150 °C | 52 L | ? |

**7.53** If a balloon containing 2.2 L of gas at 25 °C is cooled to −78 °C, what is its new volume?

**7.54** How hot must the air in a balloon be heated if initially it has a volume of 750. L at 20 °C and the final volume must be 1,000. L?

## Gay–Lussac's Law

**7.55** Assuming a fixed amount of gas at constant volume, complete the following table.

|   | $P_1$ | $T_1$ | $P_2$ | $T_2$ |
|---|-------|-------|-------|-------|
| a. | 3.25 atm | 298 K | ? | 398 K |
| b. | 550 mm Hg | 273 K | ? | −100. °C |
| c. | 0.50 atm | 250 °C | 955 mm Hg | ? |

**7.56** Assuming a fixed amount of gas at constant volume, complete the following table.

|   | $P_1$ | $T_1$ | $P_2$ | $T_2$ |
|---|-------|-------|-------|-------|
| a. | 1.74 atm | 120 °C | ? | 20. °C |
| b. | 220 mm Hg | 150 °C | ? | 300. K |
| c. | 0.75 atm | 198 °C | 220 mm Hg | ? |

**7.57** An autoclave is a pressurized container used to sterilize medical equipment by heating it to a high temperature under pressure. If an autoclave containing steam at 100. °C and 1.0 atm pressure is then heated to 150. °C, what is the pressure inside it?

**7.58** If a plastic container at 1.0 °C and 750. mm Hg is heated in a microwave oven to 80. °C, what is the pressure inside the container?

## Combined Gas Law

**7.59** Assuming a fixed amount of gas, complete the following table.

|   | $P_1$ | $V_1$ | $T_1$ | $P_2$ | $V_2$ | $T_2$ |
|---|-------|-------|-------|-------|-------|-------|
| a. | 0.90 atm | 4.0 L | 265 K | ? | 3.0 L | 310 K |
| b. | 1.2 atm | 75 L | 5.0 °C | 700. mm Hg | ? | 50 °C |
| c. | 200. mm Hg | 125 mL | 298 K | 100. mm Hg | 0.62 L | ? |

**7.60** Assuming a fixed amount of gas, complete the following table.

|   | $P_1$ | $V_1$ | $T_1$ | $P_2$ | $V_2$ | $T_2$ |
|---|-------|-------|-------|-------|-------|-------|
| a. | 0.55 atm | 1.1 L | 340 K | ? | 3.0 L | 298 K |
| b. | 735 mm Hg | 1.2 L | 298 K | 1.1 atm | ? | 0.0 °C |
| c. | 7.5 atm | 230 mL | −120 °C | 15 atm | 0.45 L | ? |

**7.61** If a compressed air cylinder for scuba diving contains 6.0 L of gas at 18 °C and 200. atm pressure, what volume does the gas occupy at 1.0 atm and 25 °C?

**7.62** What happens to the pressure of a sample with each of the following changes?
   a. Double the volume and halve the Kelvin temperature.
   b. Double the volume and double the Kelvin temperature.
   c. Halve the volume and double the Kelvin temperature.

## Avogadro's Law

**7.63** What is the difference between STP and standard molar volume?

**7.64** Given the same number of moles of two gases at STP conditions, how do the volumes of two gases compare? How do the masses of the two gas samples compare?

**7.65** How many moles of helium are contained in each volume at STP: (a) 5.0 L; (b) 11.2 L; (c) 50.0 mL?

**7.66** How many moles of argon are contained in each volume at STP: (a) 4.0 L; (b) 31.2 L; (c) 120 mL?

**7.67** Calculate the volume of each substance at STP.
   a. 4.2 mol Ar       b. 3.5 g $CO_2$       c. 2.1 g $N_2$

**7.68** What volume does $3.01 \times 10^{21}$ molecules of $N_2$ occupy at STP?

## Ideal Gas Law

**7.69** How many moles of gas are contained in a human breath that occupies 0.45 L and has a pressure of 747 mm Hg at 37 °C?

**7.70** How many moles of gas are contained in a compressed air tank for scuba diving that has a volume of 7.0 L and a pressure of 210 atm at 25 °C?

**7.71** How many moles of air are present in the lungs if they occupy a volume of 5.0 L at 37 °C and 740 mm Hg? How many molecules of air does this correspond to?

**7.72** If a cylinder contains 10.0 g of $CO_2$ in 10.0 L at 325 K, what is the pressure?

**7.73** Which sample contains more moles: 2.0 L of $O_2$ at 273 K and 500. mm Hg, or 1.5 L of $N_2$ at 298 K and 650 mm Hg? Which sample has more mass?

**7.74** An unknown amount of gas occupies 30.0 L at 2.1 atm and 298 K. How many moles does the sample contain? What is the mass if the gas is helium? What is the mass if the gas is argon?

## Dalton's Law and Partial Pressure

**7.75** The molecular art shows a closed container with two gases, **A** (red spheres) and **B** (blue spheres) at a pressure of 630 mm Hg. What is the partial pressure of **A** and **B?**

**7.76** If the pressure due to the red spheres in the molecular art is 480 mm Hg, what is the pressure due to the blue spheres? What is the total pressure of the system?

**7.77** Air pressure on the top of Mauna Loa, a 13,000-ft mountain in Hawaii, is 460 mm Hg. What are the partial pressures of $O_2$ and $N_2$, which compose 21% and 78% of the atmosphere, respectively?

**7.78** If air contains 21% $O_2$, what is the partial pressure of $O_2$ in a cylinder of compressed air at 175 atm?

**7.79** The partial pressure of $N_2$ in the air is 593 mm Hg at 1 atm. What is the partial pressure of $N_2$ in a bubble of air a scuba diver breathes when he is 66 ft below the surface of the water where the pressure is 3 atm?

**7.80** If $N_2$ is added to a balloon that contains $O_2$ (partial pressure 450 mm Hg) and $CO_2$ (partial pressure 150 mm Hg) to give a total pressure of 850 mm Hg, what is the partial pressure of each gas in the final mixture?

## Intermolecular Forces

**7.81** Why is $H_2O$ a liquid at room temperature, but $H_2S$, which has a higher molecular weight and a larger surface area, is a gas at room temperature?

**7.82** Why is $Cl_2$ a gas, $Br_2$ a liquid, and $I_2$ a solid at room temperature?

**7.83** What types of intermolecular forces are exhibited by each compound? Chloroethane is a local anesthetic and cyclopropane is a general anesthetic.

a. 
$$\begin{array}{c} \text{H} \quad \text{H} \\ | \quad | \\ \text{H—C—C—Cl} \\ | \quad | \\ \text{H} \quad \text{H} \end{array}$$
chloroethane

b. 
$$\begin{array}{c} \text{H} \quad \text{H} \\ \diagdown \text{C} \diagup \\ \text{H—C——C—H} \\ | \quad | \\ \text{H} \quad \text{H} \end{array}$$
cyclopropane

**7.84** What types of intermolecular forces are exhibited by each compound? Acetaldehyde is formed when ethanol, the alcohol in alcoholic beverages, is metabolized, and acetic acid gives vinegar its biting odor and taste.

a. 
$$\begin{array}{c} \text{H} \quad \text{O} \\ | \quad \| \\ \text{H—C—C—H} \\ | \\ \text{H} \end{array}$$
acetaldehyde

b. 
$$\begin{array}{c} \text{H} \quad \text{O} \\ | \quad \| \\ \text{H—C—C—O—H} \\ | \\ \text{H} \end{array}$$
acetic acid

**7.85** Which molecules are capable of intermolecular hydrogen bonding?

a. H—C≡C—H    b. $CO_2$    c. $Br_2$    d. 
$$\begin{array}{c} \text{H} \quad \text{H} \\ | \quad | \\ \text{H—C—N—H} \\ | \\ \text{H} \end{array}$$

**7.86** Which molecules are capable of intermolecular hydrogen bonding?

a. $N_2$    b. 
$$\begin{array}{c} \text{H} \\ | \\ \text{H—C—F} \\ | \\ \text{H} \end{array}$$    c. HI    d. 
$$\begin{array}{c} \text{H} \\ | \\ \text{H—C—O—H} \\ | \\ \text{H} \end{array}$$

**7.87** Can two molecules of formaldehyde ($H_2C$=O) intermolecularly hydrogen bond to each other? Explain why or why not.

**7.88** Why is the melting point of NaCl (801 °C) much higher than the melting point of water (0 °C)?

**7.89** Ethylene and methanol have approximately the same molar mass.

ethylene                                methanol

a. What types of intermolecular forces are present in each compound?
b. Which compound has the higher boiling point?
c. Which compound has the higher vapor pressure at a given temperature?

**7.90** Ethanol and dimethyl ether have the same molecular formula.

ethanol                              dimethyl ether

a. What types of intermolecular forces are present in each compound?
b. Which compound has the higher boiling point?
c. Which compound has the higher vapor pressure at a given temperature?

## Liquids and Solids

**7.91** Given the following vapor pressures at 20 °C, arrange the compounds in order of increasing boiling point: butane, 1,650 mm Hg; acetaldehyde, 740 mm Hg; Freon-113, 284 mm Hg.

**7.92** Using the given boiling points, predict which compound has the higher vapor pressure at a given temperature.
a. ethanol ($C_2H_6O$, bp 78 °C) or 1-propanol ($C_3H_8O$, bp 97 °C)
b. hexane ($C_6H_{14}$, bp 69 °C) or octane ($C_8H_{18}$, bp 125 °C)

**7.93** Explain why glycerol is *more* viscous than water, but acetone is *less* viscous than water. Glycerol is a component of skin lotions and creams. Acetone is the main ingredient in nail polish remover.

glycerol                                  acetone

**7.94** Explain the following observation. When a needle is carefully placed on the surface of water, it floats, yet when its tip is pushed below the surface, it sinks to the bottom.

**7.95** Classify each solid as amorphous, ionic, molecular, network, or metallic.
a. KI
b. $CO_2$
c. bronze, an alloy of Cu and Sn
d. diamond
e. the plastic polyethylene

**7.96** Classify each solid as amorphous, ionic, molecular, network, or metallic.
a. $CaCO_3$
b. $CH_3COOH$ (acetic acid)
c. Ag
d. graphite
e. the plastic polypropylene

## Energy and Phase Changes

**7.97** What is the difference between evaporation and condensation?

**7.98** What is the difference between sublimation and deposition?

**7.99** What phase change is shown in the accompanying molecular art? Is energy absorbed or released during the process?

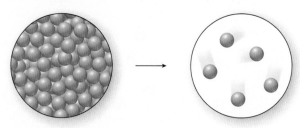

**7.100** What phase change is shown in the accompanying molecular art? Is energy absorbed or released during the process?

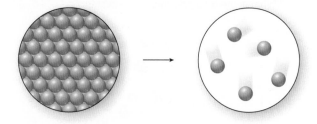

**7.101** Indicate whether heat is absorbed or released in each process.
a. melting 100 g of ice
b. freezing 25 g of water
c. condensing 20 g of steam
d. vaporizing 30 g of water

**7.102** What is the difference between the heat of fusion and the heat of vaporization?

**7.103** Which process requires more energy, melting 250 g of ice or vaporizing 50.0 g of water? The heat of fusion of water is 79.7 cal/g and the heat of vaporization is 540 cal/g.

**7.104** How much energy in kilocalories is needed to vaporize 255 g of water? The heat of vaporization of water is 540 cal/g.

## Heating and Cooling Curves

**7.105** Consider the cooling curve drawn below.

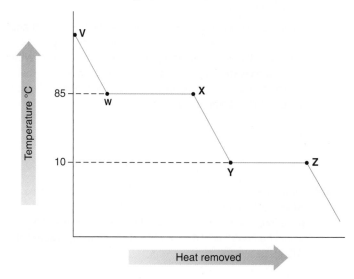

a. Which line segment corresponds to the following changes of state?

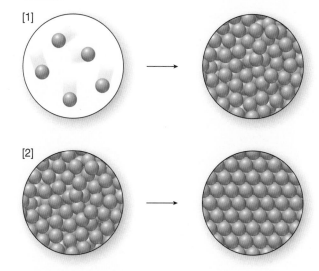

[1]

[2]

b. What is the melting point of the substance?
c. What is the boiling point of the substance?

**7.106** Which line segments on the cooling curve in Problem 7.105 correspond to each of the following physical states?

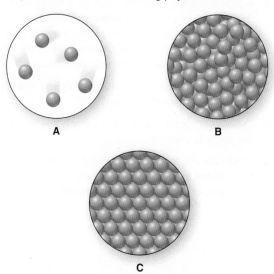

A          B

C

**7.107** Draw the heating curve that is observed when octane is warmed from –70 °C to 130 °C. Octane, a component of gasoline, has a melting point of –57 °C and a boiling point of 126 °C.

**7.108** Draw the heating curve that is observed when ice is warmed from –20 °C to 120 °C. Which sections of the curve correspond to the molecular art in **A, B,** and **C?**

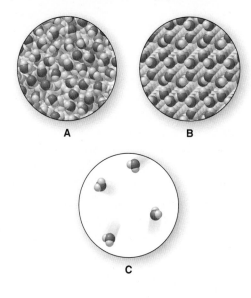

A          B

C

## Applications

**7.109** If you pack a bag of potato chips for a snack on a plane ride, the bag appears to have inflated when you take it out to open. Explain why this occurs. If the initial volume of air in the bag was 250 mL at 760 mm Hg, and the plane is pressurized at 650 mm Hg, what is the final volume of the bag?

**7.110** Why does a bubble at the bottom of a glass of a soft drink get larger as it rises to the surface?

**7.111** Explain why cooling a full glass water bottle to –10 °C causes the bottle to crack.

**7.112** What happens to the density of a gas if the temperature is increased but the pressure is held constant? Use this information to explain how wind currents arise.

**7.113** A common laboratory test for a patient is to measure blood gases—that is, the partial pressures of $O_2$ and $CO_2$ in oxygenated blood. Normal values are 100 mm Hg for $O_2$ and 40 mm Hg for $CO_2$. A high or low level of one or both readings has some underlying cause. Offer an explanation for each of the following situations.

 a. If a patient comes in agitated and hyperventilating—breathing very rapidly—the partial pressure of $O_2$ is normal but the partial pressure of $CO_2$ is 22 mm Hg.

 b. A patient with chronic lung disease has a partial pressure of $O_2$ of 60 mm Hg and a partial pressure of $CO_2$ of 60 mm Hg.

**7.114** If a scuba diver inhales 0.50 L of air at a depth of 100. ft and 4.0 atm pressure, what volume does this air occupy at the surface of the water, assuming air pressure is 1.0 atm? When a scuba diver must make a rapid ascent to the surface, he is told to exhale slowly as he ascends. How does your result support this recommendation?

## CHALLENGE PROBLEMS

**7.115** A gas (4.0 g) occupies 11.2 L at 2 atm and 273 K. What is the molar mass of the gas? What is the identity of the gas?

**7.116** As we learned in Chapter 5, an automobile airbag inflates when $NaN_3$ is converted to Na and $N_2$ according to the equation, $2\ NaN_3 \longrightarrow 2\ Na + 3\ N_2$. What volume of $N_2$ would be produced if 100. g of $NaN_3$ completely reacted at STP?

A sports drink is a solution of dissolved ions and carbohydrates, used to provide energy and hydration during strenuous exercise.

# Solutions

## CHAPTER GOALS

*In this chapter you will learn how to:*

1. Describe the fundamental properties of a solution
2. Predict whether a substance is soluble in water or a nonpolar solvent
3. Predict the effect of temperature and pressure on solubility
4. Calculate the concentration of a solution
5. Prepare a dilute solution from a more concentrated solution
6. Describe the effect of dissolved particles on the boiling point and melting point of a solution
7. Describe the process of osmosis and how it relates to biological membranes and dialysis

A pepperoni pizza is a heterogeneous mixture, while a soft drink is a homogeneous solution.

The particles in a colloid are typically between 1 and 1,000 nm in diameter.

I n Chapter 8 we study **solutions**—homogeneous mixtures of two or more substances. Why are table salt (NaCl) and sugar (sucrose) soluble in water but vegetable oil and gasoline are not? How does a healthcare professional take a drug as supplied by the manufacturer and prepare a dilute solution to administer a proper dose to a patient? An understanding of solubility and concentration is needed to explain each of these phenomena.

## 8.1   Introduction

Thus far we have concentrated primarily on **pure substances**—elements, covalent compounds, and ionic compounds. Most matter with which we come into contact, however, is a **mixture** composed of two or more pure substances. The air we breathe is composed of nitrogen and oxygen, together with small amounts of argon, water vapor, carbon dioxide, and other gases. Seawater is composed largely of sodium chloride and water. A mixture may be **heterogeneous** or **homogeneous.**

- A *heterogeneous* mixture does not have a uniform composition throughout a sample.
- A *homogeneous* mixture has a uniform composition throughout a sample.

Homogeneous mixtures are either **solutions** or **colloids.**

- A *solution* is a homogeneous mixture that contains small particles. Liquid solutions are transparent.
- A *colloid* is a homogeneous mixture with larger particles, often having an opaque appearance.

A cup of hot coffee, vinegar, and gasoline are transparent solutions, whereas milk is an opaque colloid that contains undissolved particles of fat and proteins. Any phase of matter can form a solution (Figure 8.1). Air is a solution of gases. An intravenous saline solution contains solid sodium chloride (NaCl) in liquid water. A dental filling contains liquid mercury (Hg) in solid silver.

**Figure 8.1**   Three Different Types of Solutions

a. Air: Two (or more) gases        b. Saline solution: A solid in a liquid        c. Dental filling: A liquid in a solid

a. Air is a solution of gases, primarily $N_2$ and $O_2$. The lungs contain significant amounts of $H_2O$ and $CO_2$ as well.

b. An IV saline solution contains solid sodium chloride (NaCl) dissolved in liquid water.

c. A dental filling contains a liquid, mercury (Hg), dissolved in solid silver (Ag).

When two substances form a solution, the substance present in the lesser amount is called the **solute,** and the substance present in the larger amount is the **solvent.** A solution with water as the solvent is called an **aqueous solution.**

Although a solution can be separated into its pure components, one component of a solution cannot be filtered away from the other component. For a particular solute and solvent, solutions having different compositions are possible. For example, 1.0 g of NaCl can be mixed with 50.0 g of water or 10.0 g of NaCl can be mixed with 50.0 g of water.

An aqueous solution that contains ions conducts electricity, whereas one that contains only neutral molecules does not. Thus, an aqueous solution of sodium chloride, NaCl, contains $Na^+$ cations and $Cl^-$ anions and conducts electricity. An aqueous solution of hydrogen peroxide, $H_2O_2$, contains only neutral $H_2O_2$ molecules in $H_2O$, so it does not conduct electricity.

- A substance that conducts an electric current in water is called an *electrolyte.* NaCl is an electrolyte.
- A substance that does not conduct an electric current in water is called a *nonelectrolyte.* $H_2O_2$ is a nonelectrolyte.

Figure 8.2 summarizes the classification of matter.

PROBLEM 8.1

Classify each substance as a heterogeneous mixture, solution, or colloid: (a) Cherry Garcia ice cream (cherry ice cream + chocolate bits + cherries); (b) mayonnaise; (c) seltzer water; (d) nail polish remover; (e) brass (an alloy of Cu and Zn).

PROBLEM 8.2

Classify each solution as an electrolyte or nonelectrolyte: (a) KCl in $H_2O$; (b) sucrose ($C_{12}H_{22}O_{11}$) in $H_2O$; (c) KI in $H_2O$.

Figure 8.2 Classification of Matter

## 8.2 Solubility—General Features

**Solubility is the amount of solute that dissolves in a given amount of solvent,** usually reported in grams of solute per 100 mL of solution (g/100 mL). A solution that has less than the maximum number of grams of solute is said to be **unsaturated.** A solution that has the maximum number of grams of solute that can dissolve is said to be **saturated.** If we added more solute to a saturated solution, the additional solute would remain undissolved in the flask.

### 8.2A Basic Principles

What determines if a compound dissolves in a particular solvent? Whether a compound is soluble in a given solvent depends on the strength of the interactions between the compound and the solvent. As a result, compounds are soluble in solvents to which they are strongly attracted. Solubility is often summed up in three words: **"Like dissolves like."**

- Most ionic and polar covalent compounds are soluble in water, a polar solvent.
- Nonpolar compounds are soluble in nonpolar solvents.

**Water-soluble compounds are ionic or are small polar molecules that can hydrogen bond with the water solvent.** For example, solid sodium chloride (NaCl) is held together by very strong electrostatic interactions of the oppositely charged ions. When it is mixed with water, the $Na^+$ and $Cl^-$ ions are separated from each other and surrounded by polar water molecules (Figure 8.3). Each $Na^+$ is surrounded by water molecules arranged with their O atoms (which bear a partial negative charge) in close proximity to the positive charge of the cation. Each $Cl^-$ is surrounded by water molecules arranged with their H atoms (which bear a partial positive charge) in close proximity to the negative charge of the anion.

- The attraction of an ion with a dipole in a molecule is called an ion–dipole interaction.

### Figure 8.3    Dissolving Sodium Chloride in Water

When ionic NaCl dissolves in water, the $Na^+$ and $Cl^-$ interactions of the crystal are replaced by new interactions of $Na^+$ and $Cl^-$ ions with the solvent. Each ion is surrounded by a loose shell of water molecules arranged so that oppositely charged species are close to each other.

The ion–dipole interactions between $Na^+$, $Cl^-$, and water provide the energy needed to break apart the ions from the crystal lattice. The water molecules form a loose shell of solvent around each ion. The process of surrounding particles of a solute with solvent molecules is called **solvation.**

Small neutral molecules that can hydrogen bond with water are also soluble. Thus, ethanol ($C_2H_5OH$), which is present in alcoholic beverages, dissolves in water because hydrogen bonding occurs between the OH group in ethanol and the OH group of water.

Ethanol can hydrogen bond with water.

The basic principles of solubility explain why some vitamins are fat soluble while others are water soluble, as discussed in Chapter 11.

**Water solubility for neutral molecules occurs only with small polar molecules or those with many O or N atoms that can hydrogen bond to water.** Thus, stearic acid ($C_{18}H_{36}O_2$), a component of animal fats, is *insoluble* in water because its nonpolar part (C—C and C—H bonds) is large compared to its polar part (C—O and O—H bonds). On the other hand, glucose ($C_6H_{12}O_6$), a simple carbohydrate, is *soluble* in water because it has many OH groups and thus many opportunities for hydrogen bonding with water.

**Stearic acid–Water insoluble**

many nonpolar C–C and C–H bonds

Most of the molecule is nonpolar, so it is not attracted to a polar solvent like $H_2O$.

polar C–O and O–H bonds

**Glucose–Water soluble**

many O–H bonds for hydrogen bonding to $H_2O$

**Nonpolar compounds are soluble in nonpolar solvents.** As a result, octane ($C_8H_{18}$), a component of gasoline, dissolves in the nonpolar solvent carbon tetrachloride ($CCl_4$), as shown in Figure 8.4. Animal fat and vegetable oils, which are composed largely of nonpolar C—C and C—H bonds, are soluble in $CCl_4$, but are insoluble in a polar solvent like water. These solubility properties explain why "oil and water don't mix."

Dissolving a solute in a solvent is a physical process that is accompanied by an energy change. Breaking up the particles of the solute requires energy, and forming new attractive forces between the solute and the solvent releases energy.

**Figure 8.4**    Solubility—A Nonpolar Compound in a Nonpolar Solvent

$CCl_4$

octane

octane in $CCl_4$

Octane ($C_8H_{18}$) dissolves in $CCl_4$ because both are nonpolar liquids that exhibit only London dispersion forces.

- When solvation releases more energy than that required to separate particles, the overall process is exothermic (heat is released).
- When the separation of particles requires more energy than is released during solvation, the process is endothermic (heat is absorbed).

These energy changes are used to an advantage in commercially available hot packs and cold packs. A hot pack, sometimes used for pain relief of sore muscles, contains calcium chloride ($CaCl_2$) or magnesium sulfate ($MgSO_4$) and water. Breaking the seal that separates them allows the salt to dissolve in the water, releasing heat, and the pouch gets warm. In contrast, ammonium nitrate ($NH_4NO_3$) absorbs heat on mixing with water, so this salt is found in instant cold packs used to reduce swelling.

### SAMPLE PROBLEM 8.1

Predict the water solubility of each compound: (a) KCl; (b) methanol ($CH_3OH$); (c) hexane ($C_6H_{14}$).

### Analysis

Use the general solubility rule—"like dissolves like." Generally, ionic and small polar compounds that can hydrogen bond are soluble in water. Nonpolar compounds are soluble in nonpolar solvents.

### Solution

a. KCl is an ionic compound, so it dissolves in water, a polar solvent.
b. $CH_3OH$ is a small polar molecule that contains an OH group. As a result, it can hydrogen bond to water, making it soluble.
c. Hexane ($C_6H_{14}$) has only nonpolar C—C and C—H bonds, making it a nonpolar molecule that is therefore water insoluble.

### PROBLEM 8.3

Which compounds are water soluble?

a. $NaNO_3$    b. $CH_4$    c. $HO-\overset{\overset{\displaystyle H}{|}}{\underset{\underset{\displaystyle H}{|}}{C}}-\overset{\overset{\displaystyle H}{|}}{\underset{\underset{\displaystyle H}{|}}{C}}-OH$    d. KBr    e. $NH_2OH$

### PROBLEM 8.4

Which pairs of compounds will form a solution?

a. benzene ($C_6H_6$) and hexane ($C_6H_{14}$)          c. NaCl and hexane ($C_6H_{14}$)
b. $Na_2SO_4$ and $H_2O$                                    d. $H_2O$ and $CCl_4$

## 8.2B    Ionic Compounds—Additional Principles

Although ionic compounds are generally water soluble, some are not. If the attraction between the ions in a crystalline solid is stronger than the forces of attraction between the ions and water, the ionic compound does not dissolve. The identity of the cation and anion in the ionic compound determines its water solubility. Two rules can be used to predict water solubility.

### General Rules for the Solubility of Ionic Compounds

**Rule [1]**    A compound is soluble if it contains one of the following cations:
- Group 1A cations: $Li^+$, $Na^+$, $K^+$, $Rb^+$, $Cs^+$
- Ammonium, $NH_4^+$

**Rule [2]**    A compound is soluble if it contains one of the following anions:
- Halide: $Cl^-$, $Br^-$, $I^-$, except for salts with $Ag^+$, $Hg_2^{2+}$, and $Pb^{2+}$
- Nitrate, $NO_3^-$
- Acetate, $CH_3CO_2^-$
- Sulfate, $SO_4^{2-}$, except for salts with $Ba^{2+}$, $Hg_2^{2+}$, and $Pb^{2+}$

Thus, $Na_2CO_3$ is water soluble because it contains a $Na^+$ cation (rule [1]), but $CaCO_3$ is water insoluble because it contains none of the ions listed in rules [1] and [2]. In dealing with the solubility of ionic compounds in this text, we will assume the compound to be water soluble unless specifically asked to consider the solubility rules just mentioned.

## SAMPLE PROBLEM 8.2

Use the solubility rules to predict whether the following ionic compounds are soluble in water:
(a) $Na_3PO_4$; (b) $Mg_3(PO_4)_2$; (c) KOH.

### Analysis

Identify the cation and anion and use the solubility rules to predict if the ionic compound is water soluble.

### Solution

a. $Na_3PO_4$ contains a $Na^+$ cation, and all $Na^+$ salts are soluble regardless of the anion.
b. $Mg_3(PO_4)_2$ contains none of the cations or anions listed under the solubility rules, so it is water insoluble.
c. KOH contains a $K^+$ cation, and all $K^+$ salts are soluble regardless of the anion.

## PROBLEM 8.5

Use the solubility rules to predict whether the following ionic compounds are soluble in water:
(a) $Li_2CO_3$; (b) $MgCO_3$; (c) KBr; (d) $PbSO_4$; (e) $CaCl_2$; (f) $MgCl_2$.

## PROBLEM 8.6

Use the solubility rules for ionic compounds to explain why milk of magnesia, which contains $Mg(OH)_2$ and water, is a heterogeneous mixture rather than a solution.

# 8.3 Solubility—Effects of Temperature and Pressure

Both temperature and pressure can affect solubility.

## 8.3A Temperature Effects

**For most ionic and molecular solids, solubility generally increases as temperature increases.** Thus, sugar is much more soluble in a cup of hot coffee than in a glass of iced tea. If a solid is dissolved in a solvent at high temperature and then the solution is slowly cooled, the solubility of the solute decreases and it precipitates from the solution. Sometimes, however, if cooling is very slow, the solution becomes **supersaturated** with solute; that is, the solution contains more than the predicted maximum amount of solute at a given temperature. Such a solution is unstable, and when it is disturbed, the solute precipitates rapidly.

In contrast, **the solubility of gases *decreases* with increasing temperature.** Because increasing temperature increases the kinetic energy, more gas particles escape into the gas phase and fewer remain in solution. Increasing temperature decreases the solubility of oxygen in lakes and streams. In cases where industrial plants operating near lakes or streams have raised water temperature, marine life dies from lack of sufficient oxygen in solution.

## PROBLEM 8.7

Why does a soft drink become "flat" faster when it is left open at room temperature compared to when it is left open in the refrigerator?

**Figure 8.5** Henry's Law and Carbonated Beverages

higher pressure of $CO_2$

Closed can of soda

Open can of soda

lower pressure of $CO_2$

$H_2O$

higher concentration of $CO_2$ in solution

$H_2O$

lower concentration of $CO_2$ in solution

The air pressure in a closed can of soda is approximately 2 atm. When the can is opened, the pressure above the liquid in the can decreases to 1 atm, so the $CO_2$ concentration in the soda decreases as well, and the gas fizzes from the soda.

## 8.3B Pressure Effects

Pressure changes do not affect the solubility of liquids and solids, but pressure affects the solubility of gases a great deal. **Henry's law** describes the effect of pressure on gas solubility.

- Henry's law: The solubility of a gas in a liquid is proportional to the partial pressure of the gas above the liquid.

Thus, the **higher the pressure, the higher the solubility of a gas in a solvent.** A practical demonstration of Henry's law occurs whenever we open a carbonated soft drink. Soft drinks containing dissolved $CO_2$ are sealed under greater than 1 atm pressure. When a can is opened, the pressure above the liquid decreases to 1 atm, so the solubility of the $CO_2$ in the soda decreases as well and some of the dissolved $CO_2$ fizzes out of solution (Figure 8.5).

As we learned in Section 7.6, increasing gas solubility affects scuba divers because more $N_2$ is dissolved in the blood under the higher pressures experienced under water. Divers must ascend slowly to avoid forming bubbles of $N_2$ in joints and small blood vessels. If a diver ascends slowly, the external pressure around the diver slowly decreases and by Henry's law, the solubility of the gas in the diver's blood slowly decreases as well.

Scuba divers often hold onto a rope so that they ascend to the surface slowly after a dive, in order to avoid forming bubbles of nitrogen gas in joints and blood vessels.

### PROBLEM 8.8

Predict the effect each change has on the solubility of [1] $Na_2CO_3(s)$; [2] $N_2(g)$.

a. increasing the temperature
b. decreasing the temperature

c. increasing the pressure
d. decreasing the pressure

## 8.4 Concentration Units—Percent Concentration

In using a solution in the laboratory or in administering the proper dose of a liquid medication, we must know its *concentration—how much solute is dissolved in a given amount of solution.* Concentration can be measured in several different ways that use mass, volume, or moles. Two useful measures of concentration are reported as percentages—that is, the number of grams or milliliters of solute per 100 mL of solution.

Mouthwash, sore throat spray, and many other over-the-counter medications contain ingredients whose concentrations are reported in (w/v)%.

## 8.4A  Weight/Volume Percent

One of the most common measures of concentration is **weight/volume percent concentration, (w/v)%—that is, the number of grams of solute dissolved in 100 mL of solution.** Mathematically, weight/volume percent is calculated by dividing the number of grams of solute in a given number of milliliters of solution, and multiplying by 100%.

$$
\boxed{\text{Weight/volume percent concentration}} \quad (\text{w/v})\% = \frac{\text{mass of solute (g)}}{\text{volume of solution (mL)}} \times 100\%
$$

For example, vinegar contains 5 g of acetic acid dissolved in 100 mL of solution, so the acetic acid concentration is 5% (w/v).

$$
(\text{w/v})\% = \frac{5 \text{ g acetic acid}}{100 \text{ mL vinegar solution}} \times 100\% = 5\% \text{ (w/v) acetic acid}
$$

Note that the volume used to calculate concentration is the *final* volume of the solution, not the volume of solvent added to make the solution. A special flask called a **volumetric flask** is used to make a solution of a given concentration (Figure 8.6). The solute is placed in the flask and then enough solvent is added to dissolve the solute by mixing. Next, additional solvent is added until it reaches a calibrated line that measures the final volume of the solution.

**Figure 8.6**  Making a Solution with a Particular Concentration

a. Add the solute.

b. Add the solvent.

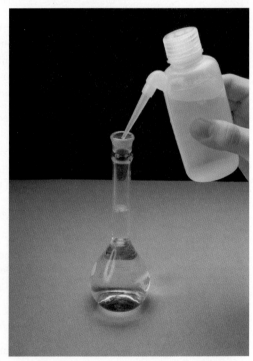

To make a solution of a given concentration, (a) add a measured number of grams of solute to a volumetric flask; (b) then add solvent to dissolve the solid, bringing the level of the solvent to the calibrated mark on the neck of the flask.

## SAMPLE PROBLEM 8.3

Chloraseptic sore throat spray contains 0.35 g of the antiseptic phenol dissolved in 25 mL of solution. What is the weight/volume percent concentration of phenol?

### Analysis

Use the formula (w/v)% = (grams of solute)/(mL of solution) × 100%.

### Solution

$$(w/v)\% = \frac{0.35 \text{ g phenol}}{25 \text{ mL solution}} \times 100\% = 1.4\% \text{ (w/v) phenol}$$

**Answer**

## PROBLEM 8.9

Pepto-Bismol, an over-the-counter medication used for upset stomach and diarrhea, contains 525 mg of bismuth subsalicylate in each 15-mL tablespoon. What is the weight/volume percent concentration of bismuth subsalicylate?

## PROBLEM 8.10

A commercial mouthwash contains 4.3 g of ethanol and 0.021 g of antiseptic in each 30.-mL portion. Calculate the weight/volume percent concentration of each component.

## 8.4B   Volume/Volume Percent

When the solute in a solution is a liquid, its concentration is often reported using **volume/volume percent concentration, (v/v)%—that is, the number of milliliters of solute dissolved in 100 mL of solution.** Mathematically, volume/volume percent is calculated by dividing the number of milliliters of solute in a given number of milliliters of solution, and multiplying by 100%.

| **Volume/volume percent concentration** | $(v/v)\% = \dfrac{\text{volume of solute (mL)}}{\text{volume of solution (mL)}} \times 100\%$ |
|---|---|

For example, a bottle of rubbing alcohol that contains 70 mL of 2-propanol in 100 mL of solution has a 70% (v/v) concentration of 2-propanol.

$$(v/v)\% = \frac{70 \text{ mL 2-propanol}}{100 \text{ mL rubbing alcohol}} \times 100\% = 70\% \text{ (v/v) 2-propanol}$$

## SAMPLE PROBLEM 8.4

A 750-mL bottle of wine contains 101 mL of ethanol. What is the volume/volume percent concentration of ethanol?

### Analysis

Use the formula (v/v)% = (mL of solute)/(mL of solution) × 100%.

### Solution

$$(v/v)\% = \frac{101 \text{ mL ethanol}}{750 \text{ mL wine}} \times 100\% = 14\% \text{ (v/v) ethanol}$$

**Answer**

## PROBLEM 8.11

A 250-mL bottle of mouthwash contains 21 mL of ethanol. What is the volume/volume percent concentration of ethanol?

The alcohol (ethanol) content of wine, beer, and other alcoholic beverages is reported using volume/volume percent concentration. Wines typically contain 10–13% (v/v) ethanol, whereas beer usually contains 3–5%.

## 8.4C   Using a Percent Concentration as a Conversion Factor

Percent concentration can be used as a conversion factor to relate the amount of solute (either grams or milliliters) to the amount of solution. For example, ketamine, an anesthetic especially useful for children, is supplied as a 5.0% (w/v) solution, meaning that 5.0 g of ketamine are present in 100 mL of solution. Two conversion factors derived from the percent concentration can be written.

$$5.0\% \text{ (w/v) ketamine} \qquad \frac{5.0 \text{ g ketamine}}{100 \text{ mL solution}} \quad \text{or} \quad \frac{100 \text{ mL solution}}{5.0 \text{ g ketamine}}$$

weight/volume
percent concentration

We can use these conversion factors to determine the amount of solute contained in a given volume of solution (Sample Problem 8.5), or to determine how much solution contains a given number of grams of solute (Sample Problem 8.6).

### SAMPLE PROBLEM 8.5

A saline solution used in intravenous drips for patients who cannot take oral fluids contains 0.92% (w/v) NaCl in water. How many grams of NaCl are contained in 250 mL of this solution?

### Analysis and Solution

**[1]  Identify the known quantities and the desired quantity.**

0.92% (w/v) NaCl solution

250 mL                                  ? g NaCl

known quantities                   desired quantity

**[2]  Write out the conversion factors.**

- Set up conversion factors that relate grams of NaCl to the volume of the solution using the weight/volume percent concentration.

$$\frac{100 \text{ mL solution}}{0.92 \text{ g NaCl}} \quad \text{or} \quad \boxed{\frac{0.92 \text{ g NaCl}}{100 \text{ mL solution}}} \quad \begin{array}{l} \text{Choose this conversion} \\ \text{factor to cancel mL.} \end{array}$$

**[3]  Solve the problem.**

- Multiply the original quantity by the conversion factor to obtain the desired quantity.

$$250 \text{ mL} \times \frac{0.92 \text{ g NaCl}}{100 \text{ mL solution}} = 2.3 \text{ g NaCl}$$

**Answer**

### SAMPLE PROBLEM 8.6

What volume of a 5.0% (w/v) solution of ketamine contains 75 mg?

### Analysis and Solution

**[1]  Identify the known quantities and the desired quantity.**

5.0% (w/v) ketamine solution

75 mg                                  ? mL ketamine

known quantities                   desired quantity

**[2]  Write out the conversion factors.**

- Use the weight/volume percent concentration to set up conversion factors that relate grams of ketamine to mL of solution. Since percent concentration is expressed in grams, a mg–g conversion factor is needed as well.

mg–g conversion factors                                    g–mL solution conversion factors

$$\dfrac{1000 \text{ mg}}{1 \text{ g}} \quad \text{or} \quad \boxed{\dfrac{1 \text{ g}}{1000 \text{ mg}}} \qquad\qquad \dfrac{5.0 \text{ g ketamine}}{100 \text{ mL solution}} \quad \text{or} \quad \boxed{\dfrac{100 \text{ mL solution}}{5.0 \text{ g ketamine}}}$$

Choose the conversion factors with the unwanted
units—mg and g—in the denominator.

**[3] Solve the problem.**

- Multiply the original quantity by the conversion factors to obtain the desired quantity.

$$75 \text{ mg ketamine} \times \dfrac{1 \text{ g}}{1000 \text{ mg}} \times \dfrac{100 \text{ mL solution}}{5.0 \text{ g ketamine}} = 1.5 \text{ mL solution}$$

**Answer**

### PROBLEM 8.12

How many mL of ethanol are contained in a 30.-mL portion of a mouthwash that has 8.0% (v/v) of ethanol?

### PROBLEM 8.13

A drink sold in a health food store contains 0.50% (w/v) of vitamin C. What volume would you have to ingest to obtain 1,000. mg of vitamin C?

### PROBLEM 8.14

A cough medicine contains 0.20% (w/v) dextromethorphan, a cough suppressant, and 2.0% (w/v) guaifenisin, an expectorant. How many milligrams of each drug would you obtain from 3.0 tsp of cough syrup? (1 tsp = 5 mL.)

## 8.4D Parts Per Million

Seabirds such as osprey that feed on fish contaminated with the pesticide DDT accumulate an average of 25 parts per million of DDT in their fatty tissues. When DDT concentration is high, mother osprey produce eggs with very thin shells that are easily crushed, so fewer osprey chicks hatch.

When a solution contains a very small concentration of solute, concentration is often expressed in **parts per million (ppm).** Whereas percent concentration is the number of "parts"—grams or milliliters—in 100 parts (100 mL) of solution, parts per million is the number of "parts" in 1,000,000 parts of solution. The "parts" may be expressed in either mass or volume units as long as the *same* unit is used for both the numerator and denominator.

$$\boxed{\textbf{Parts per million}} \qquad \text{ppm} = \dfrac{\text{mass of solute (g)}}{\text{mass of solution (g)}} \times 10^6$$

or

$$\text{ppm} = \dfrac{\text{volume of solute (mL)}}{\text{volume of solution (mL)}} \times 10^6$$

A sample of seawater that contains 1.3 g of magnesium ions in $10^6$ g of solution contains 1.3 ppm of magnesium.

$$\text{ppm} = \dfrac{1.3 \text{ g magnesium}}{10^6 \text{ g seawater}} \times 10^6 = 1.3 \text{ ppm magnesium}$$

Parts per million is used as a concentration unit for very dilute solutions. When water is the solvent, the density of the solution is close to the density of pure water, which is 1.0 g/mL at room temperature. In this case, the numerical value of the denominator is the same no matter if the unit is grams or milliliters. Thus, an aqueous solution that contains 2 ppm of MTBE, a gasoline additive and environmental pollutant, can be written in the following ways:

$$\dfrac{2 \text{ g MTBE}}{10^6 \text{ g solution}} \times 10^6 = \dfrac{2 \text{ g MTBE}}{10^6 \text{ mL solution}} \times 10^6 = 2 \text{ ppm MTBE}$$

$10^6$ mL has a mass of $10^6$ g.

## SAMPLE PROBLEM 8.7

What is the concentration in parts per million of DDT in the tissues of a seabird that contains 50. mg of DDT in 1,900 g of tissue? DDT, a nonbiodegradable pesticide that is a persistent environmental pollutant, has been banned from use in the United States since 1973.

### Analysis

Use the formula ppm = (g of solute)/(g of solution) $\times 10^6$.

### Solution

**[1] Convert milligrams of DDT to grams of DDT so that both the solute and solution have the same unit.**

$$50. \text{ mg DDT} \times \frac{1 \text{ g}}{1000 \text{ mg}} = 0.050 \text{ g DDT}$$

**[2] Use the formula to calculate parts per million.**

$$\frac{0.050 \text{ g DDT}}{1900 \text{ g tissue}} \times 10^6 = 26 \text{ ppm DDT}$$

**Answer**

## PROBLEM 8.15

What is the concentration in parts per million of DDT in each of the following?

a. 0.042 mg in 1,400 g plankton
b. $5 \times 10^{-4}$ g in 1.0 kg minnow tissue
c. 2.0 mg in 1.0 kg needlefish tissue
d. 225 µg in 1.0 kg breast milk

# 8.5  Concentration Units—Molarity

The most common measure of concentration in the laboratory is *molarity*—**the number of moles of solute per liter of solution,** abbreviated as M.

$$\text{Molarity} = \text{M} = \frac{\text{moles of solute (mol)}}{\text{liter of solution (L)}}$$

A solution that is formed from 1.00 mol (58.4 g) of NaCl in enough water to give 1.00 L of solution has a molarity of 1.00 M. A solution that is formed from 2.50 mol (146 g) of NaCl in enough water to give 2.50 L of solution is also a 1.00 M solution. Both solutions contain the *same number of moles per unit volume.*

$$\text{M} = \frac{\text{moles of solute (mol)}}{V \text{ (L)}} = \frac{1.00 \text{ mol NaCl}}{1.00 \text{ L solution}} = 1.00 \text{ M}$$

$$\text{M} = \frac{\text{moles of solute (mol)}}{V \text{ (L)}} = \frac{2.50 \text{ mol NaCl}}{2.50 \text{ L solution}} = 1.00 \text{ M}$$

same concentration
same number of moles per unit volume (*V*)

Since quantities in the laboratory are weighed on a balance, we must learn how to determine molarity beginning with a particular number of grams of a substance, as shown in the accompanying stepwise procedure.

## How To Calculate Molarity from a Given Number of Grams of Solute

**Example:** Calculate the molarity of a solution made from 20.0 g of NaOH in 250 mL of solution.

**Step [1]** **Identify the known quantities and the desired quantity.**

20.0 g NaOH

250 mL solution       ? M (mol/L)

known quantities     desired quantity

**Step [2]** **Convert the number of grams of solute to the number of moles. Convert the volume of the solution to liters, if necessary.**

- Use the molar mass to convert grams of NaOH to moles of NaOH (molar mass 40.00 g/mol).

molar mass
conversion factor

$$20.0 \text{ g NaOH} \quad \times \quad \frac{1 \text{ mol}}{40.00 \text{ g NaOH}} \quad = \quad 0.500 \text{ mol NaOH}$$

Grams cancel.

- Convert milliliters of solution to liters of solution using a mL–L conversion factor.

mL–L
conversion factor

$$250 \text{ mL solution} \quad \times \quad \frac{1 \text{ L}}{1000 \text{ mL}} \quad = \quad 0.25 \text{ L solution}$$

Milliliters cancel.

**Step [3]** **Divide the number of moles of solute by the number of liters of solution to obtain the molarity.**

$$M \quad = \quad \frac{\text{moles of solute (mol)}}{V \text{ (L)}} \quad = \quad \frac{0.500 \text{ mol NaOH}}{0.25 \text{ L solution}} \quad = \quad 2.0 \text{ M}$$

molarity                                 **Answer**

### SAMPLE PROBLEM 8.8

What is the molarity of an intravenous glucose solution prepared from 108 g of glucose in 2.0 L of solution?

#### Analysis and Solution

**[1] Identify the known quantities and the desired quantity.**

108 g glucose

2.0 L solution       ? M (mol/L)

known quantities     desired quantity

**[2] Convert the number of grams of glucose to the number of moles using the molar mass (180.2 g/mol).**

$$108 \text{ g glucose} \quad \times \quad \frac{1 \text{ mol}}{180.2 \text{ g}} \quad = \quad 0.599 \text{ mol glucose}$$

Grams cancel.

- Since the volume of the solution is given in liters, no conversion is necessary for volume.

**[3] Divide the number of moles of solute by the number of liters of solution to obtain the molarity.**

$$M = \frac{\text{moles of solute (mol)}}{V\ (\text{L})} = \frac{0.599\ \text{mol glucose}}{2.0\ \text{L solution}} = 0.30\ \text{M}$$

molarity                                                                 **Answer**

## PROBLEM 8.16

Calculate the molarity of each aqueous solution with the given amount of NaCl (molar mass 58.44 g/mol) and final volume.

a. 1.0 mol in 0.50 L          c. 0.050 mol in 5.0 mL          e. 24.4 g in 350 mL
b. 2.0 mol in 250 mL          d. 12.0 g in 2.0 L              f. 60.0 g in 750 mL

## PROBLEM 8.17

Which solution has the higher concentration, one prepared from 10.0 g of NaOH in a final volume of 150 mL, or one prepared from 15.0 g of NaOH in a final volume of 250 mL of solution?

**Molarity is a conversion factor that relates the number of moles of solute to the volume of solution it occupies.** Thus, if we know the molarity and volume of a solution, we can calculate the number of moles it contains. If we know the molarity and number of moles, we can calculate the volume in liters.

To calculate the moles of solute...                    ...rearrange the equation for molarity (M):

$$\frac{\text{moles of solute (mol)}}{V\ (\text{L})} = M$$                $$\boxed{\text{moles of solute (mol)} = M \times V\ (\text{L})}$$

To calculate the volume of solution...                 ...rearrange the equation for molarity (M):

$$\frac{\text{moles of solute (mol)}}{V\ (\text{L})} = M$$                $$\boxed{V\ (\text{L}) = \frac{\text{moles of solute (mol)}}{M}}$$

## SAMPLE PROBLEM 8.9

What volume in milliliters of a 0.30 M solution of glucose contains 0.025 mol of glucose?

### Analysis

Use the equation, $V$ = (moles of solute)/M, to find the volume in liters, and then convert the liters to milliliters.

### Solution

**[1] Identify the known quantities and the desired quantity.**

0.30 M                          ? $V$ (mL) solution
0.025 mol glucose
known quantities                desired quantity

**[2] Divide the number of moles by molarity to obtain the volume in liters.**

$$V\ (\text{L}) = \frac{\text{moles of solute (mol)}}{M}$$

$$= \frac{0.025\ \text{mol glucose}}{0.30\ \text{mol/L}} = 0.083\ \text{L solution}$$

**[3] Use a mL–L conversion factor to convert liters to milliliters.**

$$0.083\ \cancel{\text{L}}\ \text{solution} \times \frac{1000\ \text{mL}}{1\ \cancel{\text{L}}} = 83\ \text{mL glucose solution}$$

Liters cancel.                                         **Answer**

## PROBLEM 8.18

How many milliliters of a 1.5 M glucose solution contain each of the following number of moles?

a. 0.15 mol  b. 0.020 mol  c. 0.0030 mol  d. 3.0 mol

## PROBLEM 8.19

How many moles of NaCl are contained in each volume of aqueous NaCl solution?

a. 2.0 L of a 2.0 M solution  c. 25 mL of a 2.0 M solution
b. 2.5 L of a 0.25 M solution  d. 250 mL of a 0.25 M solution

Since the number of grams and moles of a substance is related by the molar mass, we can convert a given volume of solution to the number of grams of solute it contains by carrying out the step-wise calculation shown in Sample Problem 8.10.

## SAMPLE PROBLEM 8.10

How many grams of aspirin are contained in 50.0 mL of a 0.050 M solution?

### Analysis

Use the molarity to convert the volume of the solution to moles of solute. Then use the molar mass to convert moles to grams.

### Solution

**[1] Identify the known quantities and the desired quantity.**

$$0.050 \text{ M}$$

| 50.0 mL solution | ? g aspirin |
|---|---|
| known quantities | desired quantity |

**[2] Determine the number of moles of aspirin using the molarity.**

$$50.0 \text{ mL solution} \times \frac{0.050 \text{ mol aspirin}}{1 \text{ L}} \times \frac{1 \text{ L}}{1000 \text{ mL}} = 0.0025 \text{ mol aspirin}$$

**[3] Convert the number of moles of aspirin to grams using the molar mass (180.2 g/mol).**

molar mass conversion factor

$$0.0025 \text{ mol aspirin} \times \frac{180.2 \text{ g aspirin}}{1 \text{ mol aspirin}} = 0.45 \text{ g aspirin}$$

Moles cancel. **Answer**

## PROBLEM 8.20

How many grams of NaCl are contained in each of the following volumes of a 1.25 M solution?

a. 0.10 L  b. 2.0 L  c. 0.55 L  d. 50. mL

## PROBLEM 8.21

How many milliliters of a 0.25 M sucrose solution contain each of the following number of grams? The molar mass of sucrose ($C_{12}H_{22}O_{11}$) is 342.3 g/mol.

a. 0.500 g  b. 2.0 g  c. 1.25 g  d. 50.0 mg

## 8.6 Dilution

Some cleaning products are sold as concentrated solutions, which are then diluted prior to use.

Sometimes a solution has a higher concentration than is needed. *Dilution* **is the addition of solvent to decrease the concentration of the solution.** For example, a stock solution of a drug is often supplied in a concentrated form to take up less space on a pharmacy shelf, and then it is diluted so that it can be administered in a reasonable volume and lower concentration that allows for more accurate dosing.

A key fact to keep in mind is that the **amount of solute is** *constant.* Only the volume of the solution is changed by adding solvent.

Dilute with more solvent.

The diluted solution contains the same number of molecules in a larger volume.

initial solution                    diluted solution

In using molarity as a measure of concentration in Section 8.5, we learned that the number of moles of solute can be calculated from the molarity and volume of a solution.

moles of solute  =  molarity  ×  volume

$$mol = MV$$

Thus, if we have initial values for the molarity and volume ($M_1$ and $V_1$), we can calculate a new value for the molarity or volume ($M_2$ or $V_2$), since the product of the molarity and volume equals the number of moles, a constant.

$$\underset{\text{initial values}}{M_1 V_1} = \underset{\text{final values}}{M_2 V_2}$$

Although molarity is the most common concentration measure in the laboratory, the same facts hold in diluting solutions reported in other concentration units—percent concentration and parts per million—as well. In general, therefore, if we have initial values for the concentration and volume ($C_1$ and $V_1$), we can calculate a new value for the concentration or volume ($C_2$ or $V_2$), since the product of the concentration and volume is a constant.

$$\underset{\text{initial values}}{C_1 V_1} = \underset{\text{final values}}{C_2 V_2}$$

### SAMPLE PROBLEM 8.11

What is the concentration of a solution formed by diluting 5.0 mL of a 3.2 M glucose solution to 40.0 mL?

### Analysis

Since we know an initial molarity and volume ($M_1$ and $V_1$) and a final volume ($V_2$), we can calculate a new molarity ($M_2$) using the equation $M_1 V_1 = M_2 V_2$.

### Solution

**[1] Identify the known quantities and the desired quantity.**

$$M_1 = 3.2 \text{ M}$$

$$\underset{\text{known quantities}}{V_1 = 5.0 \text{ mL} \qquad V_2 = 40.0 \text{ mL}} \qquad \underset{\text{desired quantity}}{M_2 = ?}$$

**[2] Write the equation and rearrange it to isolate the desired quantity, M₂, on one side.**

$$M_1V_1 = M_2V_2 \quad \text{Solve for } M_2 \text{ by dividing both sides by } V_2.$$

$$\frac{M_1V_1}{V_2} = M_2$$

**[3] Solve the problem.**

- Substitute the three known quantities into the equation and solve for $M_2$.

$$M_2 = \frac{M_1V_1}{V_2} = \frac{(3.2\ M)(5.0\ \text{mL})}{(40.0\ \text{mL})} = 0.40\ M \text{ glucose solution}$$

**Answer**

## PROBLEM 8.22

What is the concentration of a solution formed by diluting 25.0 mL of a 3.8 M glucose solution to 275 mL?

## SAMPLE PROBLEM 8.12

Dopamine is a potent drug administered intravenously to increase blood pressure in seriously ill patients. How many milliliters of a 4.0% (w/v) solution must be used to prepare 250 mL of a 0.080% (w/v) solution?

### Analysis

Since we know an initial concentration ($C_1$), a final concentration ($C_2$), and a final volume ($V_2$), we can calculate the volume ($V_1$) of the initial solution that must be used with the equation, $C_1V_1 = C_2V_2$.

### Solution

**[1] Identify the known quantities and the desired quantity.**

$$C_1 = 4.0\% \text{ (w/v)} \quad C_2 = 0.080\% \text{ (w/v)}$$
$$V_2 = 250\ \text{mL} \qquad\qquad V_1 = ?$$

known quantities          desired quantity

**[2] Write the equation and rearrange it to isolate the desired quantity, V₁, on one side.**

$$C_1V_1 = C_2V_2 \quad \text{Solve for } V_1 \text{ by dividing both sides by } C_1.$$

$$V_1 = \frac{C_2V_2}{C_1}$$

**[3] Solve the problem.**

- Substitute the three known quantities into the equation and solve for $V_1$.

$$V_1 = \frac{(0.080\%)(250\ \text{mL})}{4.0\%} = 5.0\ \text{mL dopamine solution}$$

**Answer**

## PROBLEM 8.23

How many milliliters of a 6.0 M NaOH solution would be needed to prepare each solution?

a. 525 mL of a 2.5 M solution          c. 450 mL of a 0.10 M solution
b. 750 mL of a 4.0 M solution          d. 25 mL of a 3.5 M solution

## PROBLEM 8.24

Ketamine, an anesthetic, is supplied in a solution of 100. mg/mL. If 2.0 mL of this solution is diluted to a volume of 10.0 mL, how much of the diluted solution should be administered to supply a dose of 75 mg?

## 8.7  Colligative Properties

Although many properties of a solution are similar to those of a pure solvent, the boiling point and melting point of a solution differ from the boiling point and melting point of the solvent used to make it.

> • *Colligative properties* are properties of a solution that depend on the concentration of the solute but not its identity.

Thus, the *number* of dissolved particles of solute affects the properties of the solution, but the identity of the solute does not. In this section we examine how a dissolved solute increases the boiling point and decreases the melting point of a solution. In Section 8.8, we look at **osmosis,** a process that involves the diffusion of solvent across a semipermeable membrane.

### 8.7A  Boiling Point Elevation

A solute in a solution can be **volatile** or **nonvolatile.**

> • A volatile solute readily escapes into the vapor phase.
> • A nonvolatile solute does not readily escape into the vapor phase, and thus it has a negligible vapor pressure at a given temperature.

Figure 8.7 compares the vapor pressure above a pure liquid (water) with the vapor pressure above a solution made by dissolving a nonvolatile solute in water. The vapor pressure of a solution composed of a nonvolatile solute and a liquid solvent consists solely of gas molecules derived from the solvent. Since there are fewer solvent molecules in the solution than there are in the pure liquid, there are fewer molecules in the gas phase as well. **As a result, the vapor pressure above the solution is *lower* than the vapor pressure of the pure solvent.**

What effect does this lower vapor pressure have on the boiling point of the solution? The boiling point is the temperature at which the vapor pressure equals the atmospheric pressure. A lower vapor pressure means that the solution must be heated to a higher temperature to get the vapor pressure to equal the atmospheric pressure. This results in **boiling point elevation.**

> • A liquid solution that contains a nonvolatile solute has a higher boiling point than the solvent alone.

**The amount that the boiling point increases depends only on the number of dissolved particles.** For example,

> • One mole of any nonvolatile solute raises the boiling point of one kilogram of water by 0.51 °C.

**Figure 8.7**

Vapor Pressure Above a Liquid Solution

H₂O          pure liquid          solution          solute          H₂O

When a nonvolatile solute is added to a solvent, there are fewer molecules of solvent in the gas phase, so the vapor pressure of the solution above the solvent is lower.

Thus, one mole of glucose molecules raises the boiling point of 1 kg of water by 0.51 °C, to 100.51 °C. Since NaCl contains two particles—Na$^+$ cations and Cl$^-$ anions—per mole, one mole of NaCl raises the boiling point of 1 kg of water by 2 × 0.51 °C or 1.02 °C, to 101.02 °C, rounded to 101.0 °C.

### SAMPLE PROBLEM 8.13

What is the boiling point of a solution that contains 0.45 mol of KCl in 1.00 kg of water?

#### Analysis

Determine the number of "particles" contained in the solute. Use 0.51 °C/mol as a conversion factor to relate the temperature change to the number of moles of solute particles.

#### Solution

Each KCl provides two "particles," K$^+$ and Cl$^-$.

$$\text{temperature increase} = \frac{0.51\ °C}{\text{mol particles}} \times 0.45\ \text{mol KCl} \times \frac{2\ \text{mol particles}}{\text{mol KCl}} = 0.46\ °C$$

The boiling point of the solution is 100.0 °C + 0.46 °C = 100.46 °C, rounded to 100.5 °C.

### PROBLEM 8.25

What is the boiling point of a solution prepared from the given quantity of solute in 1.00 kg of water?

a. 2.0 mol of sucrose molecules

b. 2.0 mol of KNO$_3$

c. 2.0 mol of CaCl$_2$

d. 20.0 g of NaCl

## 8.7B Freezing Point Depression

In a similar manner, a dissolved solute lowers the freezing point of a solvent. The presence of solute molecules makes it harder for solvent molecules to form an organized crystalline solid, thus lowering the temperature at which the liquid phase becomes solid. This results in **freezing point depression.**

- A liquid solution that contains a nonvolatile solute has a lower freezing point than the solvent alone.

**The amount of freezing point depression depends only on the number of dissolved particles.** For example,

- One mole of any nonvolatile solute lowers the freezing point of one kilogram of water by 1.86 °C.

Thus, one mole of glucose molecules lowers the freezing point of 1 kg of water to –1.86 °C. Since NaCl contains two particles—Na$^+$ cations and Cl$^-$ anions—per mole, one mole of NaCl lowers the freezing point of 1 kg of water by 2 × (–1.86 °C) or –3.72 °C.

Airplane wings are de-iced with a solution that contains ethylene glycol, which lowers the freezing point, so the ice melts.

Several practical applications exploit freezing point depression. Antifreeze, which contains nonvolatile ethylene glycol, is added to automobile radiators to lower the freezing point of the water in the cooling system, so it does not freeze in cold climates. Fish that inhabit cold environments produce large amounts of glycerol, $C_3H_8O_3$, which lowers the freezing point of their blood, thus allowing it to remain fluid in very cold water.

$H_2O$

$C_3H_8O_3$
glycerol

### SAMPLE PROBLEM 8.14

What is the melting point of a solution that contains 3.00 mol of $CaCl_2$ dissolved in 1.00 kg of water? $CaCl_2$ is used in rock salt to melt ice and snow on highways and sidewalks in the winter.

#### Analysis

Determine the number of "particles" contained in the solute. Use 1.86 °C/mol as a conversion factor to relate the temperature change to the number of moles of solute particles.

#### Solution

Each $CaCl_2$ provides three "particles," $Ca^+$ and 2 $Cl^-$.

$$\text{temperature decrease} = \frac{1.86 \text{ °C}}{\text{mol particles}} \times 3.00 \text{ mol } CaCl_2 \times \frac{3 \text{ mol particles}}{\text{mol } CaCl_2} = 16.7 \text{ °C}$$

The melting point of the solution is 0.0 °C + −16.7 °C = −16.7 °C.

### PROBLEM 8.26

What is the melting point of a solution prepared from the given quantity of solute in 1.00 kg of water?

   a. 2.0 mol of sucrose molecules             c. 2.0 mol of $CaCl_2$
   b. 2.0 mol of $KNO_3$                      d. 20.0 g of NaCl

### PROBLEM 8.27

What is the melting point of a solution that is formed when 250 g of ethylene glycol ($C_2H_6O_2$) is dissolved in 1.00 kg of water?

## 8.8 Osmosis and Dialysis

The membrane that surrounds living cells is an example of a **semipermeable membrane**—a membrane that allows water and small molecules to pass across, but ions and large molecules cannot.

semipermeable membrane

$H_2O$

solute

$H_2O$

solute + solvent        solvent only

- *Osmosis* is the passage of solvent, usually water, across a semipermeable membrane from a solution of low solute concentration to a solution of higher solute concentration.

### 8.8A Osmotic Pressure

What happens when water and an aqueous glucose solution are separated by a semipermeable membrane? Water flows back and forth across the membrane, but more water flows from the side that has pure solvent towards the side that has dissolved glucose. This decreases the volume of pure solvent on one side of the membrane and increases the volume of the glucose solution on the other side.

More H₂O molecules diffuse into the glucose solution, where the concentration of H₂O is lower.

The increased volume of the glucose solution creates increased pressure on one side of the membrane. When the increased pressure gets to a certain point, it prevents more water movement to further dilute the glucose solution. Water continues to diffuse back and forth across the membrane, but the level of the two liquids does not change any further.

- *Osmotic pressure* is the pressure that prevents the flow of additional solvent into a solution on one side of a semipermeable membrane.

Osmotic pressure is a colligative property, so it depends only on the number of particles in a solution. **The greater the number of dissolved particles, the greater the osmotic pressure.** A 0.1 M NaCl solution has twice the osmotic pressure as a 0.1 M glucose solution, since each NaCl is composed of two particles, $Na^+$ cations and $Cl^-$ anions.

If, instead of having pure water on one side of the membrane, there were two solutions of different concentrations, water would flow from the side of the *less* concentrated solution to dilute the *more* concentrated solution.

### SAMPLE PROBLEM 8.15

A 0.1 M glucose solution is separated from a 0.2 M glucose solution by a semipermeable membrane. (a) Which solution exerts the greater osmotic pressure? (b) In which direction will water flow between the two solutions? (c) Describe the level of the two solutions when equilibrium is reached.

### Analysis

The solvent (water) flows from the less concentrated solution to the more concentrated solution.

### Solution

a. The greater the number of dissolved particles, the higher the osmotic pressure, so the 0.2 M glucose solution exerts the greater pressure.

b. Water will flow from the less concentrated solution (0.1 M) to the more concentrated solution (0.2 M).

c. Since water flows into the 0.2 M solution, its height will increase, and the height of the 0.1 M glucose solution will decrease.

## PROBLEM 8.28

Which solution in each pair exerts the greater osmotic pressure?

   a. 1.0% sugar solution or 5.0% sugar solution

   b. 3.0 M NaCl solution or a 4.0 M NaCl solution

   c. 1.0 M glucose solution or a 0.75 M NaCl solution

## PROBLEM 8.29

Describe the process that occurs when a 1.0 M NaCl solution is separated from a 1.5 M NaCl solution by a semipermeable membrane in terms of each of the following: (a) the identity of the substances that flow across the membrane; (b) the direction of flow before and after equilibrium is achieved; (c) the height of the solutions after equilibrium is achieved.

## 8.8B  FOCUS ON THE HUMAN BODY
### Osmosis and Biological Membranes

Since cell membranes are semipermeable and biological fluids contain dissolved ions and molecules, osmosis is an ongoing phenomenon in living cells. Fluids on both sides of a cell membrane must have the same osmotic pressure to avoid pressure buildup inside or outside the cell. Any intravenous solution given to a patient, therefore, must have the same osmotic pressure as the fluids in the body.

> • Two solutions with the same osmotic pressure are said to be *isotonic.*

Isotonic solutions used in hospitals include 0.92% (w/v) NaCl solution (or 0.15 M NaCl solution) and 5.0% (w/v) glucose solution. Although these solutions do not contain exactly the same ions or molecules present in body fluids, they exert the same osmotic pressure. *Remember:* **With a colligative property the concentration of particles is important, but not the identity of those particles.**

If a red blood cell is placed in an isotonic NaCl solution, called physiological saline solution, the red blood cells retain their same size and shape because the osmotic pressure inside and outside the cell is the same (Figure 8.8a). What happens if a red blood cell is placed in a solution having a different osmotic pressure?

> • A *hypotonic* solution has a lower osmotic pressure than body fluids.
> • A *hypertonic* solution has a higher osmotic pressure than body fluids.

In a hypotonic solution, the concentration of particles outside the cell is lower than the concentration of particles inside the cell. In other words, the concentration of water outside the cell is *higher* than the concentration of water inside the cell, so water diffuses inside (Figure 8.8b). As a result, the cell swells and eventually bursts. This swelling and rupture of red blood cells is called **hemolysis.**

In a hypertonic solution, the concentration of particles outside the cell is higher than the concentration of particles inside the cell. In other words, the concentration of water inside the cell is *higher* than the concentration of water outside the cell, so water diffuses out of the cell (Figure 8.8c). As a result, the cell shrinks. This process is called **crenation.**

## PROBLEM 8.30

What happens to a red blood cell when it is placed in each of the following solutions: (a) 3% (w/v) glucose solution; (b) 0.15 M KCl solution; (c) 0.15 M $Na_2CO_3$ solution?

**Figure 8.8**

The Effect of Osmotic Pressure Differences on Red Blood Cells

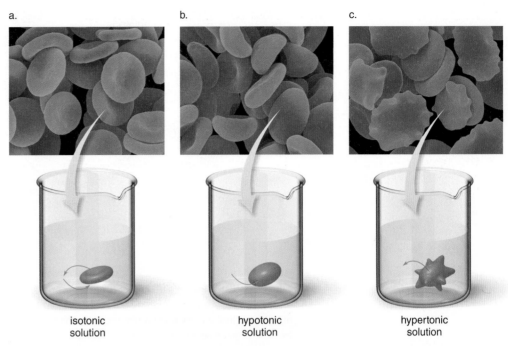

| isotonic solution | hypotonic solution | hypertonic solution |

(a) In an isotonic solution, the movement of water into and out of the red blood cell occurs to an equal extent and the red blood cell keeps its normal volume. (b) In a hypotonic solution, more water moves into the cell than diffuses out, so the cell swells and eventually it can rupture (hemolysis). (c) In a hypertonic solution, more water moves out of the cell than diffuses in, so the cell shrivels (crenation).

## 8.8C  FOCUS ON HEALTH & MEDICINE
### Dialysis

**Dialysis** is also a process that involves the selective passage of substances across a semipermeable membrane, called a dialyzing membrane. In dialysis, however, water, small molecules, and ions can travel across the membrane; only large biological molecules like proteins and starch cannot.

In the human body, blood is filtered through the kidneys by the process of dialysis (Figure 8.9). Each kidney contains over a million nephrons, tubelike structures with filtration membranes.

**Figure 8.9**

Dialysis of Body Fluids by the Kidneys

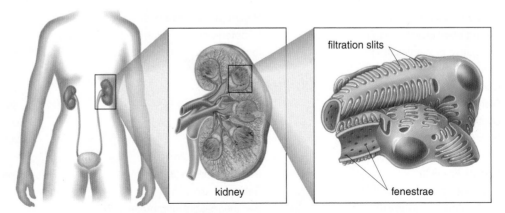

Body fluids are dialyzed by passage through the kidneys, which contain more than a million nephrons that filter out small molecules and ions from the blood. Useful materials are then reabsorbed while urea and other waste products are eliminated in urine.

Figure 8.10   Hemodialysis

When a patient's kidneys no longer function properly, periodic dialysis treatments are used to remove waste products from the blood. Blood is passed through a dialyzer, which contains a membrane that allows small molecules to pass through, thus acting as an artificial kidney. Each treatment takes several hours. Patients usually require two to three treatments per week.

These membranes filter small molecules—glucose, amino acids, urea, ions, and water—from the blood. Useful materials are then reabsorbed, but urea and other waste products are eliminated in urine.

When an individual's kidneys are incapable of removing waste products from the blood, **hemodialysis** is used (Figure 8.10). A patient's blood flows through a long tube connected to a cellophane membrane suspended in an isotonic solution that contains NaCl, KCl, NaHCO$_3$, and glucose. Small molecules like urea cross the membrane into the solution, thus removing them from the blood. Red blood cells and large molecules are not removed from the blood because they are too big to cross the dialyzing membrane.

# CHAPTER HIGHLIGHTS

## KEY TERMS

Aqueous solution (8.1)

Boiling point elevation (8.7)

Colligative properties (8.7)

Colloid (8.1)

Concentration (8.4)

Dialysis (8.8)

Dilution (8.6)

Electrolyte (8.1)

Freezing point depression (8.7)

Henry's law (8.3)

Heterogeneous mixture (8.1)

Homogeneous mixture (8.1)

Hypertonic solution (8.8)

Hypotonic solution (8.8)

Ion–dipole interaction (8.2)

Isotonic solution (8.8)

Molarity (8.5)

Nonelectrolyte (8.1)

Nonvolatile (8.7)

Osmosis (8.8)

Osmotic pressure (8.8)

Parts per million (8.4)

Saturated solution (8.2)

Semipermeable membrane (8.8)

Solubility (8.2)

Solute (8.1)

Solution (8.1)

Solvation (8.2)

Solvent (8.1)

Supersaturated solution (8.3)

Unsaturated solution (8.2)

Volatile (8.7)

Volume/volume percent concentration (8.4)

Weight/volume percent concentration (8.4)

# KEY CONCEPTS

**①** **What are the fundamental features of a solution? (8.1)**
- A solution is a homogeneous mixture that contains small dissolved particles. Any phase of matter can form solutions. The substance present in the lesser amount is called the solute, and the substance present in the larger amount is the solvent.
- A solution conducts electricity if it contains dissolved ions, but does not conduct electricity if it contains atoms or neutral molecules.

**②** **What determines whether a substance is soluble in water or a nonpolar solvent? (8.2)**
- One rule summarizes solubility: "Like dissolves like."
- Most ionic compounds are soluble in water. If the attractive forces between the ions and water are stronger than the attraction between the ions in the crystal, an ionic compound dissolves in water.
- Small polar compounds that can hydrogen bond are soluble in water.
- Nonpolar compounds are soluble in nonpolar solvents. Compounds with many nonpolar $C-C$ and $C-H$ bonds are soluble in nonpolar solvents.

**③** **What effect do temperature and pressure have on solubility? (8.3)**
- The solubility of solids in a liquid solvent generally increases with increasing temperature. The solubility of gases decreases with increasing temperature.
- Increasing pressure increases the solubility of a gas in a solvent. Pressure changes do not affect the solubility of liquids and solids.

**④** **How is the concentration of a solution expressed? (8.4, 8.5)**
- Concentration is a measure of how much solute is dissolved in a given amount of solution, and can be measured using mass, volume, or moles.

- Weight/volume (w/v) percent concentration is the number of grams of solute dissolved in 100 mL of solution.
- Volume/volume (v/v) percent concentration is the number of milliliters of solute dissolved in 100 mL of solution.
- Parts per million (ppm) is the number of parts of solute in 1,000,000 parts of solution, where the units for both the solute and the solution are the same.
- Molarity (M) is the number of moles of solute per liter of solution.

**⑤** **How are dilutions performed? (8.6)**
- Dilution is the addition of solvent to decrease the concentration of a solute. Since the number of moles of solute is constant in carrying out a dilution, a new molarity or volume ($M_2$ and $V_2$) can be calculated from a given molarity and volume ($M_1$ and $V_1$) using the equation $M_1V_1 = M_2V_2$, as long as three of the four quantities are known.

**⑥** **How do dissolved particles affect the boiling point and melting point of a solution? (8.7)**
- A nonvolatile solute lowers the vapor pressure above a solution, thus increasing its boiling point.
- A nonvolatile solute makes it harder for solvent molecules to form a crystalline solid, thus decreasing its melting point.

**⑦** **What is osmosis? (8.8)**
- Osmosis is the passage of solvent, usually water, across a semipermeable membrane. Solvent always moves from the less concentrated solution to the more concentrated solution, until the osmotic pressure prevents additional flow of solvent.
- Since living cells contain and are surrounded by biological solutions separated by a semipermeable membrane, the osmotic pressure must be the same on both sides of the membrane. Dialysis is similar to osmosis in that it involves the selective passage of several substances—water, small molecules, and ions—across a dialyzing membrane.

# KEY EQUATIONS—CONCENTRATION

**Weight/volume percent concentration**

$$(\text{w/v})\% = \frac{\text{mass of solute (g)}}{\text{volume of solution (mL)}} \times 100\%$$

**Volume/volume percent concentration**

$$(\text{v/v})\% = \frac{\text{volume of solute (mL)}}{\text{volume of solution (mL)}} \times 100\%$$

**Parts per million**

$$\text{ppm} = \frac{\text{parts of solute (g or mL)}}{\text{parts of solution (g or mL)}} \times 10^6$$

**Molarity**

$$M = \frac{\text{moles of solute (mol)}}{\text{liter of solution (L)}}$$

# PROBLEMS

Selected in-chapter and odd-numbered end-of-chapter problems have brief answers in Appendix B. The *Student Study Guide and Solutions Manual* contains detailed solutions to all in-chapter and odd-numbered end-of-chapter problems, as well as additional worked examples and a chapter self-test.

## Mixtures and Solutions

**8.31** Which representation of molecular art better shows a solution of KI dissolved in water? Explain your choice. Will this solution conduct an electric current?

A    B

**8.32** Which representation of molecular art better shows a solution of NaF dissolved in water? Explain your choice. Will this solution conduct an electric current?

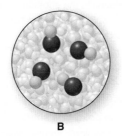

A    B

**8.33** Classify each of the following as a heterogeneous mixture, a solution, or a colloid.
  a. bronze (an alloy of Sn and Cu)
  b. diet soda
  c. orange juice with pulp
  d. household ammonia
  e. gasoline
  f. fog

**8.34** Classify each of the following as a heterogeneous mixture, a solution, or a colloid.
  a. soft drink  c. wine   e. bleach
  b. cream   d. lava rock  f. apple juice

## Solubility

**8.35** If the solubility of KCl in 100 mL of $H_2O$ is 34 g at 20 °C and 43 g at 50 °C, label each of the following solutions as unsaturated, saturated, or supersaturated. If more solid is added than can dissolve in the solvent, assume that undissolved solid remains at the bottom of the flask.
  a. adding 30 g to 100 mL of $H_2O$ at 20 °C
  b. adding 65 g to 100 mL of $H_2O$ at 50 °C
  c. adding 20 g to 50 mL of $H_2O$ at 20 °C
  d. adding 42 g to 100 mL of $H_2O$ at 50 °C and slowly cooling to 20 °C to give a clear solution with no precipitate

**8.36** If the solubility of sucrose in 100 mL of $H_2O$ is 204 g at 20 °C and 260 g at 50 °C, label each of the following solutions as unsaturated, saturated, or supersaturated. If more solid is added than can dissolve in the solvent, assume that undissolved solid remains at the bottom of the flask.
  a. adding 200 g to 100 mL of $H_2O$ at 20 °C
  b. adding 245 g to 100 mL of $H_2O$ at 50 °C
  c. adding 110 g to 50 mL of $H_2O$ at 20 °C
  d. adding 220 g to 100 mL of $H_2O$ at 50 °C and slowly cooling to 20 °C to give a clear solution with no precipitate

**8.37** Which compounds are soluble in water?

  a. LiCl

  b.

  d. $Na_3PO_4$

**8.38** Which compounds are soluble in water?

  a. $C_5H_{12}$  b. $CaCl_2$  c.      d. $CH_3Br$

**8.39** Using the ball-and-stick model for methanol ($CH_3OH$), draw a representation for the solution that results when methanol is dissolved in water.

**8.40** Using the ball-and-stick model for dimethyl ether [$(CH_3)_2O$], draw a representation for the solution that results when dimethyl ether is dissolved in water.

**8.41** Explain the statement, "Oil and water don't mix."

**8.42** Explain why a bottle of salad dressing that contains oil and vinegar has two layers.

**8.43** Predict the solubility of solid $I_2$ in water and in $CCl_4$. Explain your choices.

**8.44** Glycine is a covalent compound that contains two charged atoms. Explain why glycine, an amino acid used to make proteins, is soluble in water.

glycine

**8.45** Explain why cholesterol, a compound with molecular formula $C_{27}H_{46}O$ and one OH group, is soluble in $CCl_4$ but insoluble in water.

**8.46** Which of the following pairs of compounds form a solution?
a. KCl and $CCl_4$
b. 1-propanol ($C_3H_8O$) and $H_2O$
c. cyclodecanone ($C_{10}H_{18}O$) and $H_2O$
d. pentane ($C_5H_{12}$) and hexane ($C_6H_{14}$)

**8.47** The molecular art represents $O_2$ molecules dissolved in water at 25 °C. Draw a representation for the solution that results (a) after heating to 50 °C; (b) after cooling to 10 °C.

**8.48** The molecular art represents NaCl dissolved in water at 25 °C. Assume that this solution is saturated in NaCl and that solid NaCl remains at the bottom of the flask in which the solution is stored. Draw a representation for the solution that results (a) after heating to 50 °C; (b) after cooling to 10 °C.

**8.49** How is the solubility of solid NaCl in water affected by each of the following changes?
a. increasing the temperature from 25 °C to 50 °C
b. decreasing the temperature from 25 °C to 0 °C
c. increasing the pressure from 1 atm to 2 atm
d. decreasing the pressure from 5 atm to 1 atm

**8.50** How is the solubility of helium gas in water affected by each of the following changes?
a. increasing the temperature from 25 °C to 50 °C
b. decreasing the temperature from 25 °C to 0 °C
c. increasing the pressure from 1 atm to 2 atm
d. decreasing the pressure from 5 atm to 1 atm

**8.51** Explain the effect of a decrease in temperature on the solubility of each type of solute in a liquid solvent: (a) gas; (b) solid.

**8.52** Explain the effect of a decrease in pressure on the solubility of each type of solute in a liquid solvent: (a) gas; (b) solid.

**8.53** Explain why many ionic compounds are soluble in water.

**8.54** Explain why some ionic compounds are insoluble in water.

**8.55** Use the solubility rules listed in Section 8.2B to predict whether each of the following ionic compounds is soluble in water.
a. $K_2SO_4$
b. $MgSO_4$
c. $ZnCO_3$
d. KI
e. $Fe(NO_3)_3$
f. $PbCl_2$
g. CsCl
h. $Ni(HCO_3)_2$

**8.56** Use the solubility rules listed in Section 8.2B to predict whether each of the following ionic compounds is soluble in water.
a. $Al(NO_3)_3$
b. $NaHCO_3$
c. $Cr(OH)_2$
d. LiOH
e. $CuCO_3$
f. $(NH_4)_2SO_4$
g. $Fe(OH)_3$
h. $(NH_4)_3PO_4$

## Concentration

**8.57** Write two conversion factors for each concentration.
a. 5% (w/v)   b. 6.0 M   c. 10 ppm

**8.58** Write two conversion factors for each concentration.
a. 15% (v/v)   b. 12.0 M   c. 15 ppm

**8.59** What is the weight/volume percent concentration using the given amount of solute and total volume of solution?
a. 10.0 g of LiCl in 750 mL of solution
b. 25 g of $NaNO_3$ in 150 mL of solution
c. 40.0 g of NaOH in 500. mL of solution

**8.60** What is the weight/volume percent concentration using the given amount of solute and total volume of solution?
a. 5.5 g of LiCl in 550 mL of solution
b. 12.5 g of $NaNO_3$ in 250 mL of solution
c. 20.0 g of NaOH in 400. mL of solution

**8.61** What is the volume/volume percent concentration of a solution prepared from 25 mL of ethyl acetate in 150 mL of solution?

**8.62** What is the volume/volume percent concentration of a solution prepared from 75 mL of acetone in 250 mL of solution?

**8.63** What is the molarity of a solution prepared using the given amount of solute and total volume of solution?
a. 3.5 mol of KCl in 1.50 L of solution
b. 0.44 mol of $NaNO_3$ in 855 mL of solution
c. 25.0 g of NaCl in 650 mL of solution
d. 10.0 g of $NaHCO_3$ in 3.3 L of solution

**8.64** What is the molarity of a solution prepared using the given amount of solute and total volume of solution?
a. 2.4 mol of NaOH in 1.50 L of solution
b. 0.48 mol of $KNO_3$ in 750 mL of solution
c. 25.0 g of KCl in 650 mL of solution
d. 10.0 g of $Na_2CO_3$ in 3.8 L of solution

**8.65** How would you use a 250-mL volumetric flask to prepare each of the following solutions?
a. 4.8% (w/v) acetic acid in water
b. 22% (v/v) ethyl acetate in water
c. 2.5 M NaCl solution

**8.66** How would you use a 250-mL volumetric flask to prepare each of the following solutions?

    a. 2.0% (w/v) KCl in water

    b. 34% (v/v) ethanol in water

    c. 4.0 M NaCl solution

**8.67** How many moles of solute are contained in each solution?

    a. 150 mL of a 0.25 M $NaNO_3$ solution

    b. 45 mL of a 2.0 M $HNO_3$ solution

    c. 2.5 L of a 1.5 M HCl solution

**8.68** How many moles of solute are contained in each solution?

    a. 250 mL of a 0.55 M $NaNO_3$ solution

    b. 145 mL of a 4.0 M $HNO_3$ solution

    c. 6.5 L of a 2.5 M HCl solution

**8.69** How many grams of solute are contained in each solution in Problem 8.67?

**8.70** How many grams of solute are contained in each solution in Problem 8.68?

**8.71** How many mL of ethanol are contained in a 750-mL bottle of wine that contains 11.0% (v/v) of ethanol?

**8.72** What is the molarity of a 20.0% (v/v) aqueous ethanol solution? The density of ethanol ($C_2H_6O$, molar mass 46.07 g/mol) is 0.790 g/mL.

**8.73** A 1.89-L bottle of vinegar contains 5.0% (w/v) of acetic acid ($C_2H_4O_2$, molar mass 60.05 g/mol) in water.

    a. How many grams of acetic acid are present in the container?

    b. How many moles of acetic acid are present in the container?

    c. Convert the weight/volume percent concentration to molarity.

**8.74** What is the molarity of a 15% (w/v) glucose solution?

**8.75** The maximum safe level of each compound in drinking water is given below. Convert each value to parts per million.

    a. chloroform ($CHCl_3$, a solvent), 80 μg/kg

    b. glyphosate (a pesticide), 700 μg/kg

**8.76** The maximum safe level of each metal in drinking water is given below. Convert each value to parts per million.

    a. copper, 1,300 μg/kg

    b. arsenic, 10 μg/kg

    c. chromium, 100 μg/kg

## Dilution

**8.77** If the solution in **X** is diluted, which representation (**A–C**) represents the final solution?

    **X**          **A**          **B**          **C**

**8.78** Consider solutions **A, B,** and **C** in Problem 8.77. If the volumes of **A** and **B** are twice the volume of **C,** which solution is most concentrated? Which solution is least concentrated?

**8.79** (a) If **A** represents a 0.1 M aqueous NaCl solution, what is the concentration of **B,** a solution formed by dilution of **A** with water? (b) If the volume of **A** is 50.0 mL, how much water is added to form **B?**

          Add $H_2O$.

    **A**                         **B**

**8.80** (a) If **C** represents a 2.0 M aqueous NaCl solution, what is the concentration of **D,** a solution formed by dilution of **C** with water? (b) If the volume of **C** is 100. mL, how much water is added to form **D?**

          Add $H_2O$.

    **C**                         **D**

**8.81** How are the concepts of concentration and dilution related?

**8.82** Explain why it is impossible to prepare 200 mL of a 5.0 M NaOH solution by diluting a 2.5 M NaOH solution.

**8.83** What is the weight/volume percent concentration of a 30.0% (w/v) solution of vitamin C after each of the following dilutions?

    a. 100. mL diluted to 200. mL

    b. 100. mL diluted to 500. mL

    c. 250 mL diluted to 1.5 L

    d. 0.35 L diluted to 750 mL

**8.84** One gram (1.00 g) of vitamin $B_3$ (niacin) is dissolved in water to give 10.0 mL of solution. (a) What is the weight/volume percent concentration of this solution? (b) What is the concentration of a solution formed by diluting 1.0 mL of this solution to each of the following volumes: [1] 10.0 mL; [2] 2.5 mL; [3] 50.0 mL; [4] 120 mL?

**8.85** What is the concentration of a solution formed by diluting 125 mL of 12.0 M HCl solution to 850 mL?

**8.86** What is the concentration of a solution formed by diluting 250 mL of 6.0 M NaOH solution to 0.45 L?

**8.87** How many milliliters of a 2.5 M NaCl solution would be needed to prepare each solution?

    a. 25 mL of a 1.0 M solution

    b. 1.5 L of a 0.75 M solution

    c. 15 mL of a 0.25 M solution

    d. 250 mL of a 0.025 M solution

**8.88** How many milliliters of a 5.0 M sucrose solution would be needed to prepare each solution?
  a. 45 mL of a 4.0 M solution
  b. 150 mL of a 0.5 M solution
  c. 1.2 L of a 0.025 M solution
  d. 750 mL of a 1.0 M solution

## Colligative Properties

**8.89** Why is the boiling point of ocean water higher than the boiling point of tap water?

**8.90** Does pure water have osmotic pressure? Explain why or why not.

**8.91** What is the boiling point of a solution that contains each of the following quantities of solute in 1.00 kg of water?
  a. 3.0 mol of fructose molecules
  b. 1.2 mol of KI
  c. 1.5 mol of $Na_3PO_4$

**8.92** What is the freezing point of each solution in Problem 8.91?

**8.93** If 150 g of ethylene glycol ($C_2H_6O_2$) is added to 1,000. g of water, what is the freezing point?

**8.94** How many grams of ethylene glycol must be added to 1,000. g of water to form a solution that has a freezing point of –10. °C?

**8.95** In comparing a 1.0 M NaCl solution and a 1.0 M glucose solution, which solution has the higher: (a) boiling point; (b) melting point; (c) osmotic pressure; (d) vapor pressure at a given temperature?

**8.96** In comparing a 1.0 M NaCl solution and a 1.0 M $CaCl_2$ solution, which solution has the higher: (a) boiling point; (b) melting point; (c) osmotic pressure; (d) vapor pressure at a given temperature?

**8.97** Which solution in each pair has the higher melting point?
  a. 0.10 M NaOH or 0.10 M glucose
  b. 0.20 M NaCl or 0.15 M $CaCl_2$
  c. 0.10 M $Na_2SO_4$ or 0.10 M $Na_3PO_4$
  d. 0.10 M glucose or 0.20 M glucose

**8.98** Which solution in each pair in Problem 8.97 has the higher boiling point?

## Osmosis

**8.99** A flask contains two compartments (**A** and **B**) with equal volumes of solution separated by a semipermeable membrane. Describe the final level of the liquids when **A** and **B** contain each of the following solutions.

| | **A** | **B** |
|---|---|---|
| a. | 1% (w/v) glucose solution | pure water |
| b. | 0.10 M glucose solution | 0.20 M glucose solution |
| c. | 0.10 M NaCl solution | 0.10 M NaI solution |
| d. | 0.10 M $CaCl_2$ solution | 0.10 M NaCl solution |
| e. | 0.20 M glucose solution | 0.10 M NaCl solution |

**8.100** A flask contains two compartments (**A** and **B**) with equal volumes of solution separated by a semipermeable membrane. Which diagram represents the final level of the liquids when **A** and **B** contain each of the following solutions?

[1]   [2]   [3]

| | **A** | **B** |
|---|---|---|
| a. | 10% (w/v) glucose | 20% (w/v) glucose |
| b. | 0.20 M NaCl | 0.30 M glucose |
| c. | pure water | 5% (w/v) glucose |
| d. | 2.0 M NaCl | pure water |
| e. | 3% (w/v) sucrose | 1% (w/v) sucrose |

## Applications

**8.101** Explain why opening a warm can of soda causes a louder "whoosh" and more fizzing than opening a cold can of soda.

**8.102** Explain why more sugar dissolves in a cup of hot coffee than a glass of iced coffee.

**8.103** If the concentration of glucose in the blood is 90 mg/100 mL, what is the weight/volume percent concentration of glucose? What is the molarity of glucose (molar mass 180.2 g/mol) in the blood?

**8.104** If the human body contains 5.0 L of blood, how many grams of glucose are present in the blood if the concentration is 90. mg/100. mL?

**8.105** Mannitol, a carbohydrate, is supplied as a 25% (w/v) solution. This hypertonic solution is given to patients who have sustained a head injury with associated brain swelling. (a) What volume should be given to provide a dose of 70. g? (b) How does the hypertonic mannitol benefit brain swelling?

**8.106** A patient receives 750 mL of a 10.% (w/v) aqueous glucose solution. (a) How many grams of glucose does the patient receive? (b) How many moles of glucose (molar mass 180.2 g/mol) does the patient receive?

**8.107** Explain why a cucumber placed in a concentrated salt solution shrivels.

**8.108** Explain why a raisin placed in water swells.

**8.109** Explain why the solution contained in a dialyzer used in hemodialysis contains NaCl, KCl, and glucose dissolved in water.

**8.110** Explain why pure water is not used in the solution contained in a dialyzer during hemodialysis.

**8.111** A sports drink contains 15 g of soluble complex carbohydrates in 8.0 oz (1 fl oz = 29.6 mL). What weight/volume percent concentration does this represent?

**8.112** A sports drink contains 25 mg of magnesium in an 8.0-oz portion (1 fl oz = 29.6 mL). How many parts per million does this represent? Assume that the mass of 1.0 mL of the solution is 1.0 g.

**8.113** Each day, the stomach produces 2.0 L of gastric juice that contains 0.10 M HCl. How many grams of HCl does this correspond to?

**8.114** Describe what happens when a red blood cell is placed in pure water.

**8.115** An individual is legally intoxicated with a blood alcohol level of 0.08% (w/v) of ethanol. How many milligrams of ethanol are contained in 5.0 L of blood with this level?

**8.116** A bottle of vodka labeled "80 proof" contains 40.% (v/v) ethanol in water. How many mL of ethanol are contained in 250 mL of vodka?

## CHALLENGE PROBLEMS

**8.117** The therapeutic concentration—the concentration needed to be effective—of acetaminophen ($C_8H_9NO_2$, molar mass 151.2 g/mol) is 10–20 µg/mL. Assume that the density of blood is 1.0 g/mL.

  a. If the concentration of acetaminophen in the blood was measured at 15 ppm, is this concentration in the therapeutic range?

  b. How many moles of acetaminophen are present at this concentration in 5.0 L of blood?

**8.118** One individual was told that his total blood cholesterol concentration should be less than 200. mg/dL and another individual was told that his total cholesterol should be less than $5.2 \times 10^{-3}$ M. Are these two values equivalent? If the values differ, which number represents the higher value?

Many over-the-counter medications are acids or bases. The pain reliever aspirin—acetylsalicylic *acid*—is an acid, and the antacids Maalox, Mylanta, and Rolaids all contain a base as their active ingredient.

# Acids and Bases

## CHAPTER GOALS

*In this chapter you will learn how to:*

1 Identify acids and bases and describe their characteristics

2 Write equations for acid–base reactions

3 Relate acid strength to the direction of equilibrium of an acid–base reaction

4 Define the acid dissociation constant and relate its magnitude to acid strength

5 Define the ion–product of water and use it to calculate hydronium or hydroxide ion concentration

6 Calculate pH

7 Draw the products of common acid–base reactions

8 Determine whether a salt solution is acidic, basic, or neutral

9 Use a titration to determine the concentration of an acid or a base

10 Describe the fundamental features of a buffer

11 Understand the importance of buffers in maintaining pH in the body

Chemical terms such as *anion* and *cation* may be unfamiliar to most nonscientists, but **acid** has found a place in everyday language. Commercials advertise the latest remedy for the heartburn caused by excess stomach *acid*. The nightly news may report the latest environmental impact of *acid* rain. Wine lovers often know that wine sours because its alcohol has turned to *acid*. *Acid* comes from the Latin word *acidus*, meaning sour, because when tasting compounds was a routine method of identification, these compounds were found to be sour. Acids commonly react with **bases,** and many products, including antacid tablets, glass cleaners, and drain cleaners, all contain bases. In Chapter 9 we learn about the characteristics of acids and bases and the reactions they undergo.

## 9.1 Introduction to Acids and Bases

The earliest definition of acids and bases was suggested by Swedish chemist Svante Arrhenius in the late nineteenth century. According to Arrhenius,

- An *acid* contains a hydrogen atom and dissolves in water to form a hydrogen ion, $H^+$.
- A *base* contains hydroxide and dissolves in water to form $OH^-$.

By this definition, hydrogen chloride (HCl) is an acid because it forms aqueous $H^+$ and $Cl^-$ when it dissolves in water. Sodium hydroxide (NaOH) is a base because it contains $OH^-$ and forms solvated $Na^+$ and $OH^-$ ions when it dissolves in water.

$H^+$ is formed from HCl.

$$HCl(g) \longrightarrow H^+(aq) + Cl^-(aq)$$
acid

$$NaOH(s) \longrightarrow Na^+(aq) + OH^-(aq)$$
base

$OH^-$ is formed from NaOH.

$H^+(aq)$ and $H_3O^+(aq)$ are sometimes used interchangeably by chemists. Keep in mind, however, that $H^+(aq)$ does not really exist in aqueous solution.

While the Arrhenius definition correctly predicts the behavior of many acids and bases, this definition is limited and sometimes inaccurate. We now know, for example, that the hydrogen ion, $H^+$, does *not* exist in water. $H^+$ is a naked proton with no electrons, and this concentrated positive charge reacts rapidly with a molecule of $H_2O$ to form the **hydronium ion, $H_3O^+$.** Although $H^+(aq)$ will sometimes be written in an equation for emphasis, $H_3O^+(aq)$ is actually the reacting species.

actually present in aqueous solution

$$H^+(aq) + H_2O(l) \longrightarrow H_3O^+(aq)$$
hydrogen ion          hydronium ion

does not really exist
in aqueous solution

Moreover, several compounds contain no hydroxide anions, yet they still exhibit the characteristic properties of a base. Examples include the neutral molecule ammonia ($NH_3$) and the salt sodium carbonate ($Na_2CO_3$). As a result, a more general definition of acids and bases, proposed by Johannes **Brønsted** and Thomas **Lowry** in the early twentieth century, is widely used today.

In the Brønsted–Lowry definition, acids and bases are classified according to whether they can donate or accept a **proton**—a positively charged hydrogen ion, $H^+$.

- A Brønsted–Lowry acid is a *proton donor.*
- A Brønsted–Lowry base is a *proton acceptor.*

Consider what happens when HCl is dissolved in water.

This proton is donated.          $H_2O$ accepts a proton.

$$HCl(g) + H_2O(l) \longrightarrow H_3O^+(aq) + Cl^-(aq)$$
**Brønsted–Lowry**  **Brønsted–Lowry**
**acid**          **base**

- HCl is a Brønsted–Lowry *acid* because it *donates* a proton to the solvent water.
- $H_2O$ is a Brønsted–Lowry *base* because it *accepts* a proton from HCl.

Before we learn more about the details of this process, we must first learn about the characteristics of Brønsted–Lowry acids and bases.

### 9.1A Brønsted–Lowry Acids

**A Brønsted–Lowry acid must contain a hydrogen atom.** HCl is a Brønsted–Lowry acid because it *donates* a proton ($H^+$) to water when it dissolves, forming the hydronium ion ($H_3O^+$) and chloride ($Cl^-$).

This proton is donated to $H_2O$.

$$HCl(g) \ + \ H_2O(l) \ \longrightarrow \ H_3O^+(aq) \ + \ Cl^-(aq)$$

**Brønsted–Lowry acid**

Although hydrogen chloride, HCl, is a covalent molecule and a gas at room temperature, when it dissolves in water it reacts to form two ions, $H_3O^+$ and $Cl^-$. An aqueous solution of hydrogen chloride is called **hydrochloric acid.**

| HCl gas | liquid $H_2O$ | hydrochloric acid |

Because a Brønsted–Lowry acid contains a hydrogen atom, a general Brønsted–Lowry acid is often written as **HA. A** can be a single atom such as Cl or Br. Thus, HCl and HBr are Brønsted–Lowry acids. **A** can also be a polyatomic ion. Sulfuric acid ($H_2SO_4$) and nitric acid ($HNO_3$) are Brønsted–Lowry acids, as well. **Carboxylic acids** are a group of Brønsted–Lowry acids that contain the atoms COOH arranged so that the carbon atom is doubly bonded to one O atom and singly bonded to another. Acetic acid, $CH_3COOH$, is a simple carboxylic acid. Although carboxylic acids may contain several hydrogen atoms, the **H atom of the OH group is the acidic proton that is donated.**

| **Common Brønsted–Lowry Acids** | HCl<br>hydrochloric acid | $H_2SO_4$<br>sulfuric acid | acidic H atom |
| | HBr<br>hydrobromic acid | $HNO_3$<br>nitric acid | acetic acid<br>a carboxylic acid |

**Figure 9.1**    Examples of Brønsted–Lowry Acids in Food Products

| acetic acid | citric acid | carbonic acid |
| $CH_3COOH$ | $C_6H_8O_7$ | $H_2CO_3$ |

a. Acetic acid is the sour-tasting component of vinegar. The air oxidation of ethanol to acetic acid is the process that makes "bad" wine taste sour.

b. Citric acid imparts a sour taste to oranges, lemons, and other citrus fruits.

c. Carbonated beverages contain carbonic acid, $H_2CO_3$.

A Brønsted–Lowry acid may contain one or more protons that can be donated.

- A monoprotic acid contains *one* acidic proton. HCl is a monoprotic acid.
- A diprotic acid contains *two* acidic protons. $H_2SO_4$ is a diprotic acid.
- A triprotic acid contains *three* acidic protons. $H_3PO_4$ is a triprotic acid.

Although a Brønsted–Lowry acid must contain a hydrogen atom, **it may be a neutral molecule or contain a net positive or negative charge.** Thus, $H_3O^+$, HCl, and $HSO_4^-$ are all Brønsted–Lowry acids even though their net charges are +1, 0, and –1, respectively. Vinegar, citrus fruits, and carbonated soft drinks all contain Brønsted–Lowry acids, as shown in Figure 9.1.

### SAMPLE PROBLEM 9.1

Which of the following species can be Brønsted–Lowry acids: (a) HF; (b) $HSO_3^-$; (c) $Cl_2$?

### Analysis

A Brønsted–Lowry acid must contain a hydrogen atom, but it may be neutral or contain a net positive or negative charge.

### Solution

a. HF is a Brønsted–Lowry acid since it contains a H.

b. $HSO_3^-$ is a Brønsted–Lowry acid since it contains a H.

c. $Cl_2$ is not a Brønsted–Lowry acid because it does not contain a H.

### PROBLEM 9.1

Which of the following species can be Brønsted–Lowry acids: (a) HI; (b) $SO_4^{2-}$; (c) $H_2PO_4^-$; (d) $Cl^-$?

## 9.1B Brønsted–Lowry Bases

**A Brønsted–Lowry base is a proton acceptor** and as such, it must be able to form a bond to a proton. Because a proton has no electrons, **a base must contain a lone pair of electrons** that can be donated to form a new bond. Thus, ammonia ($NH_3$) is a Brønsted–Lowry base because it contains a nitrogen atom with a lone pair of electrons. When $NH_3$ is dissolved in water, its N atom accepts a proton from $H_2O$, forming ammonium ($NH_4^+$) and hydroxide ($OH^-$).

This electron pair forms a new bond to a H from $H_2O$.

$$H-\overset{\cdot\cdot}{\underset{|}{N}}-H \;+\; H_2O(l) \longrightarrow \left[ H-\overset{H}{\underset{H}{\overset{|}{N}}}-H \right]^+ \;+\; OH^-(aq)$$

**Brønsted–Lowry base**

A general Brønsted–Lowry base is often written as **B:** to emphasize that the base must contain a lone pair of electrons to bond to a proton. A base may be neutral or, more commonly, have a net negative charge. Hydroxide ($OH^-$), which contains an oxygen atom with three lone pairs of electrons, is the most common Brønsted–Lowry base. The source of hydroxide anions can be a variety of metal salts, including NaOH, KOH, $Mg(OH)_2$, and $Ca(OH)_2$. Ammonia ($NH_3$) and water ($H_2O$) are both Brønsted–Lowry bases because each contains an atom with a lone pair of electrons.

| Common Brønsted–Lowry Bases | | |
|---|---|---|
| NaOH<br>sodium hydroxide | $Mg(OH)_2$<br>magnesium hydroxide | $\overset{\cdot\cdot}{N}H_3$<br>ammonia |
| KOH<br>potassium hydroxide | $Ca(OH)_2$<br>calcium hydroxide | $H_2\overset{\cdot\cdot}{\underset{\cdot\cdot}{O}}$<br>water |

$OH^-$ is the base in each metal salt.

Lone pairs make these neutral compounds bases.

Many consumer products contain Brønsted–Lowry bases, as shown in Figure 9.2.

**Figure 9.2**    Examples of Brønsted–Lowry Bases in Consumer Products

a.                    b.                    c.

OH⁻
NH₄⁺
NH₃
$CO_3^{2-}$
$Ca^{2+}$
$H_2O$
solid $CaCO_3$

OH⁻
Na⁺
$H_2O$
solid NaOH

a. Calcium carbonate ($CaCO_3$), a base, is the active ingredient in the antacid Rolaids.
b. Windex and other household cleaners contain ammonia ($NH_3$) dissolved in water, forming $NH_4^+$ cations and $OH^-$ anions.
c. Drain cleaners contain pellets of solid sodium hydroxide (NaOH), which form $Na^+$ cations and $OH^-$ anions when mixed with water.

## SAMPLE PROBLEM 9.2

Which of the following species can be Brønsted–Lowry bases: (a) LiOH; (b) Cl⁻; (c) CH₄?

### Analysis

A Brønsted–Lowry base must contain a lone pair of electrons, but it may be neutral or have a net negative charge.

### Solution

a. LiOH is a base since it contains hydroxide, OH⁻, which has three lone pairs on its O atom.

b. Cl⁻ is a base since it has four lone pairs.

c. CH₄ is not a base since it has no lone pairs.

## PROBLEM 9.2

Which of the following species can be Brønsted–Lowry bases: (a) $Al(OH)_3$; (b) Br⁻; (c) $NH_4^+$; (d) CN⁻?

## SAMPLE PROBLEM 9.3

Classify each reactant as a Brønsted–Lowry acid or base.

a. $HF(g) + H_2O(l) \longrightarrow F^-(aq) + H_3O^+(aq)$

b. $SO_4^{2-}(aq) + H_2O(l) \longrightarrow HSO_4^-(aq) + OH^-(aq)$

### Analysis

In each equation, the Brønsted–Lowry acid is the species that loses a proton and the Brønsted–Lowry base is the species that gains a proton.

### Solution

a. HF is the acid since it loses a proton (H⁺) to form F⁻, and $H_2O$ is the base since it gains a proton to form $H_3O^+$.

$$\text{gain of } H^+$$

$$HF(g) \quad + \quad H_2O(l) \longrightarrow F^-(aq) \quad + \quad H_3O^+(aq)$$
$$\text{acid} \qquad\qquad \text{base}$$

$$\text{loss of } H^+$$

b. $H_2O$ is the acid since it loses a proton (H⁺) to form OH⁻, and $SO_4^{2-}$ is the base since it gains a proton to form $HSO_4^-$.

$$\text{gain of } H^+$$

$$SO_4^{2-}(aq) \quad + \quad H_2O(l) \longrightarrow HSO_4^-(aq) \quad + \quad OH^-(aq)$$
$$\text{base} \qquad\qquad \text{acid}$$

$$\text{loss of } H^+$$

## PROBLEM 9.3

Classify each reactant as a Brønsted–Lowry acid or base.

a. $HCl(g) + NH_3(g) \longrightarrow Cl^-(aq) + NH_4^+(aq)$

b. $CH_3COOH(l) + H_2O(l) \longrightarrow CH_3COO^-(aq) + H_3O^+(aq)$

c. $OH^-(aq) + HSO_4^-(aq) \longrightarrow H_2O(l) + SO_4^{2-}(aq)$

## 9.2 The Reaction of a Brønsted–Lowry Acid with a Brønsted–Lowry Base

When a Brønsted–Lowry acid reacts with a Brønsted–Lowry base, a proton is *transferred* from the acid to the base. **The Brønsted–Lowry acid donates a proton to the Brønsted–Lowry base, which accepts it.**

Consider, for example, the reaction of the general acid H—A with the general base B:. **In an acid–base reaction, one bond is broken and one bond is formed.** The electron pair of the base B: forms a new bond to the proton of the acid, forming H—B$^+$. The acid H—A loses a proton, leaving the electron pair in the H—A bond on A, forming A:$^-$.

- The product formed by loss of a proton from an acid is called its *conjugate base*.
- The product formed by gain of a proton by a base is called its *conjugate acid*.

Thus, the conjugate base of the acid HA is A:$^-$. The conjugate acid of the base B: is HB$^+$.

- Two species that differ by the presence of a proton are called a conjugate acid–base pair.

Thus, in an acid–base reaction, the acid and the base on the left side of the equation (HA and B:) form two products that are also an acid and a base (HB$^+$ and A:$^-$). Equilibrium arrows ($\rightleftarrows$) are often used to separate reactants and products because the reaction can proceed in either the forward or the reverse directions. In some reactions, the products are greatly favored, as discussed in Section 9.3.

When HBr is dissolved in water, for example, the acid HBr loses a proton to form its conjugate base Br$^-$, and the base $H_2O$ gains a proton to form $H_3O^+$.

$$\text{gain of H}^+$$

$$\underset{\text{acid}}{\text{H—Br}} \quad + \quad \underset{\text{base}}{H_2O} \quad \rightleftarrows \quad \underset{\text{conjugate base}}{Br^-} \quad + \quad \underset{\text{conjugate acid}}{H_3O^+}$$

$$\text{loss of H}^+$$

Thus, HBr and Br$^-$ are a conjugate acid–base pair since these two species differ by the presence of a proton (H$^+$). $H_2O$ and $H_3O^+$ are also a conjugate acid–base pair because these two species differ by the presence of a proton as well.

**The net charge must be the same on both sides of the equation.** In this example, the two reactants are neutral (zero net charge), and the sum of the −1 and +1 charges in the products is also zero.

Take particular note of what happens to the charges in each conjugate acid–base pair. **When a species gains a proton (H$^+$), it gains a +1 charge.** Thus, if a reactant is neutral to begin with, it ends up with a +1 charge. **When a species loses a proton (H$^+$), it effectively gains a −1 charge** since the product has one fewer proton (+1 charge) than it started with. Thus, if a reactant is neutral to begin with, it ends up with a −1 charge.

0 charge → $\underset{\text{base}}{H_2O}$ $\xrightarrow{\text{add H}^+}$ $H_3O^+$ +1 charge

0 charge → $\underset{\text{acid}}{\text{H—Br}}$ $\xrightarrow{\text{lose H}^+}$ $Br^-$ −1 charge

Take away +1 charge.

When HCl donates a proton to $NH_3$ in the absence of water, $NH_4^+$ and $Cl^-$ are formed, which combine to form solid ammonium chloride, $NH_4Cl$.

The reaction of ammonia ($NH_3$) with HCl is also a Brønsted–Lowry acid–base reaction. In this example, $NH_3$ is the base since it gains a proton to form its conjugate acid, $NH_4^+$. HCl is the acid since it donates a proton, forming its conjugate base, $Cl^-$.

$$\text{gain of } H^+$$

$$\underset{\text{base}}{H-\overset{\cdot\cdot}{\underset{\displaystyle H}{N}}-H} \;+\; \underset{\text{acid}}{HCl(g)} \;\rightleftharpoons\; \underset{\text{conjugate acid}}{\left[H-\overset{\displaystyle H}{\underset{\displaystyle H}{N}}-H\right]^+} \;+\; \underset{\text{conjugate base}}{Cl^-(aq)}$$

$$\text{loss of } H^+$$

- **A Brønsted–Lowry acid–base reaction is a *proton transfer reaction* since it always results in the transfer of a proton from an acid to a base.**

The ability to identify and draw a conjugate acid or base from a given starting material is a necessary skill, illustrated in Sample Problems 9.4 and 9.5.

### SAMPLE PROBLEM 9.4

Determine the conjugate acid of each base: (a) $F^-$; (b) $NO_3^-$.

### Analysis

Conjugate acid–base pairs differ by the presence of a proton. To draw a conjugate acid from a base, *add* a proton, $H^+$. This adds +1 to the charge of the base to give the charge on the conjugate acid.

### Solution

a. $F^- + H^+$ gives HF as the conjugate acid. HF has no charge since a proton with a +1 charge is added to an anion with a –1 charge.

b. $NO_3^- + H^+$ gives $HNO_3$ (nitric acid) as the conjugate acid. $HNO_3$ has no charge since a proton with a +1 charge is added to an anion with a –1 charge.

### PROBLEM 9.4

Determine the conjugate acid of each species: (a) $H_2O$; (b) $I^-$; (c) $HCO_3^-$.

### SAMPLE PROBLEM 9.5

Determine the conjugate base of each acid: (a) $H_2O$; (b) $HCO_3^-$.

### Analysis

Conjugate acid–base pairs differ by the presence of a proton. To draw a conjugate base from an acid, *remove* a proton, $H^+$. This adds –1 to the charge of the acid to give the charge on the conjugate base.

### Solution

a. Remove $H^+$ from $H_2O$ to form $OH^-$, the conjugate base. $OH^-$ has a –1 charge since –1 is added to a molecule that was neutral to begin with.

b. Remove $H^+$ from $HCO_3^-$ to form $CO_3^{2-}$, the conjugate base. $CO_3^{2-}$ has a –2 charge since –1 is added to an anion that had a –1 charge to begin with.

### PROBLEM 9.5

Determine the conjugate base of each species: (a) $H_2S$; (b) HCN; (c) $HSO_4^-$.

**A compound that contains both a hydrogen atom and a lone pair of electrons can be either an acid or a base,** depending on the particular reaction. Such a compound is said to be **amphoteric.** For example, when $H_2O$ acts as a base it gains a proton, forming $H_3O^+$. Thus, $H_2O$ and $H_3O^+$ are a conjugate acid–base pair. When $H_2O$ acts as an acid it loses a proton, forming $OH^-$. $H_2O$ and $OH^-$ are also a conjugate acid–base pair.

$$H_2O \text{ as a base} \quad H-\ddot{O}-H \xrightarrow{\text{add } H^+} \left[ H-\underset{|}{\overset{H}{O}}-H \right]^+$$

base        conjugate acid

$$H_2O \text{ as an acid} \quad H-\ddot{O}-H \xrightarrow{\text{remove } H^+} \left[ H-\ddot{\ddot{O}}: \right]^-$$

acid        conjugate base

## SAMPLE PROBLEM 9.6

Label the acid and the base and the conjugate acid and the conjugate base in the following reaction.

$$NH_4^+(aq) + OH^-(aq) \rightleftharpoons NH_3(g) + H_2O(l)$$

### Analysis

The Brønsted–Lowry acid loses a proton to form its conjugate base. The Brønsted–Lowry base gains a proton to form its conjugate acid.

### Solution

$NH_4^+$ is the acid since it loses a proton to form $NH_3$, its conjugate base. $OH^-$ is the base since it gains a proton to form its conjugate acid, $H_2O$.

gain of $H^+$

$$NH_4^+(aq) \quad + \quad OH^-(aq) \rightleftharpoons NH_3(g) \quad + \quad H_2O(l)$$

acid      base      conjugate base    conjugate acid

loss of $H^+$

## PROBLEM 9.6

Label the acid and the base and the conjugate acid and the conjugate base in each reaction.

a. $H_2O(l) + HI(g) \rightleftharpoons I^-(aq) + H_3O^+(aq)$
b. $CH_3COOH(l) + NH_3(g) \rightleftharpoons CH_3COO^-(aq) + NH_4^+(aq)$
c. $Br^-(aq) + HNO_3(aq) \rightleftharpoons HBr(aq) + NO_3^-(aq)$

## PROBLEM 9.7

Ammonia, $NH_3$, is amphoteric. (a) Draw the conjugate acid of $NH_3$. (b) Draw the conjugate base of $NH_3$.

# 9.3 Acid and Base Strength

Although all Brønsted–Lowry acids contain protons, some acids readily donate protons while others do not. Similarly, some Brønsted–Lowry bases accept a proton much more readily than others. How readily proton transfer occurs is determined by the strength of the acid and base.

## 9.3A Relating Acid and Base Strength

When an acid dissolves in water, proton transfer forms $H_3O^+$ and an anion. The splitting apart of a covalent molecule (or an ionic compound) into individual ions is called **dissociation.** Acids differ in their tendency to donate a proton; that is, acids differ in the extent to which they *dissociate* in water.

- A strong acid readily donates a proton. When a strong acid dissolves in water, 100% of the acid dissociates into ions.
- A weak acid less readily donates a proton. When a weak acid dissolves in water, only a small fraction of the acid dissociates into ions.

Common strong acids include **HI, HBr, HCl, H₂SO₄,** and **HNO₃** (Table 9.1). When each acid is dissolved in water, 100% of the acid dissociates, forming $H_3O^+$ and the conjugate base, as shown for HCl and $H_2SO_4$.

> • Use a single reaction arrow.
> • The product is greatly favored at equilibrium.

$$\text{HCl}(g) \ + \ \text{H}_2\text{O}(l) \ \longrightarrow \ \text{H}_3\text{O}^+(aq) \ + \ \text{Cl}^-(aq)$$
strong acid                             conjugate base

$$\text{H}_2\text{SO}_4(l) \ + \ \text{H}_2\text{O}(l) \ \longrightarrow \ \text{H}_3\text{O}^+(aq) \ + \ \text{HSO}_4^-(aq)$$
strong acid                             conjugate base

**HCl,** hydrochloric acid, is secreted by the stomach to digest food (Figure 9.3), and **H₂SO₄,** sulfuric acid, is an important industrial starting material in the synthesis of phosphate fertilizers. A single reaction arrow ($\longrightarrow$) is drawn to show that essentially all of the reactants are converted to products.

Acetic acid, **CH₃COOH,** is a weak acid. When acetic acid dissolves in water, only a small fraction of acetic acid molecules donate a proton to water to form $H_3O^+$ and the conjugate base, $CH_3COO^-$. The major species at equilibrium is the undissociated acid, $CH_3COOH$. Equilibrium arrows that are unequal in length ($\rightleftharpoons$) are used to show that the equilibrium lies to the left. Other weak acids and their conjugate bases are listed in Table 9.1.

> • Use unequal reaction arrows.
> • The reactants are favored at equilibrium.

$$\text{CH}_3\text{COOH}(l) \ + \ \text{H}_2\text{O}(l) \ \rightleftharpoons \ \text{H}_3\text{O}^+(aq) \ + \ \text{CH}_3\text{COO}^-(aq)$$
weak acid                               conjugate base

Figure 9.4 illustrates the difference between an aqueous solution of a strong acid that is completely dissociated and a weak acid that contains much undissociated acid. Sample Problem 9.7 illustrates how the extent of dissociation and acid strength are related.

**Figure 9.3**    Focus on the Human Body: Hydrochloric Acid in the Stomach

The thick mucous layer protects the stomach lining.

Although HCl is a corrosive acid secreted in the stomach, a thick layer of mucus covering the stomach wall protects it from damage by the strong acid. The strong acid HCl is completely dissociated to $H_3O^+$ and $Cl^-$.

## Table 9.1  Relative Strength of Acids and Their Conjugate Bases

| Acid | | Conjugate Base | |
|---|---|---|---|
| **Strong Acids** | | | |
| Hydroiodic acid | HI | $I^-$ | Iodide ion |
| Hydrobromic acid | HBr | $Br^-$ | Bromide ion |
| Hydrochloric acid | HCl | $Cl^-$ | Chloride ion |
| Sulfuric acid | $H_2SO_4$ | $HSO_4^-$ | Hydrogen sulfate ion |
| Nitric acid | $HNO_3$ | $NO_3^-$ | Nitrate ion |
| **Hydronium ion** | **$H_3O^+$** | **$H_2O$** | **Water** |
| **Weak Acids** | | | |
| Phosphoric acid | $H_3PO_4$ | $H_2PO_4^-$ | Dihydrogen phosphate ion |
| Hydrofluoric acid | HF | $F^-$ | Fluoride ion |
| Acetic acid | $CH_3COOH$ | $CH_3COO^-$ | Acetate ion |
| Carbonic acid | $H_2CO_3$ | $HCO_3^-$ | Bicarbonate ion |
| Ammonium ion | $NH_4^+$ | $NH_3$ | Ammonia |
| Hydrocyanic acid | HCN | $CN^-$ | Cyanide ion |
| Water | $H_2O$ | $OH^-$ | Hydroxide ion |

*Increasing acid strength* ↑     ↓ *Increasing base strength*

## Figure 9.4  A Strong and Weak Acid Dissolved in Water

hydrochloric acid

$Cl^-$
$H_3O^+$

A strong acid is
completely dissociated.

vinegar

$CH_3COO^-$
$H_3O^+$
$CH_3COOH$

A weak acid contains mostly
undissociated acid, $CH_3COOH$.

- The strong acid HCl completely dissociates into $H_3O^+$ and $Cl^-$ in water.

- Vinegar contains $CH_3COOH$ dissolved in $H_2O$. The weak acid $CH_3COOH$ is only slightly dissociated into $H_3O^+$ and $CH_3COO^-$, so mostly $CH_3COOH$ is present at equilibrium.

## SAMPLE PROBLEM 9.7

Diagrams **A–C** represent three acids (HA) dissolved in water. Which representation shows the strongest acid? Which representation shows the weakest acid?

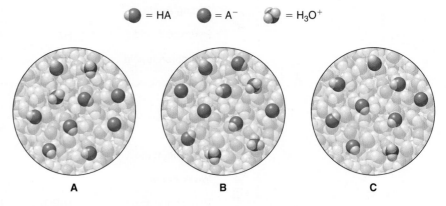

### Analysis

The stronger the acid, the more readily it dissociates to form its conjugate base $A^-$ and $H_3O^+$. In molecular art, the strongest acid has the most $A^-$ and $H_3O^+$ ions, and the fewest molecules of undissociated HA.

### Solution

**B** is the strongest acid since it contains the largest number of $A^-$ and $H_3O^+$ ions (three each), and the smallest number (five) of undissociated HA molecules. **C** is the weakest acid since it contains the smallest number of $A^-$ and $H_3O^+$ ions (one each), and the largest number (seven) of undissociated HA molecules.

## PROBLEM 9.8

Diagrams **D–F** represent three acids (HA) dissolved in water. Rank the three acids (**D–F**) in order of increasing acidity.

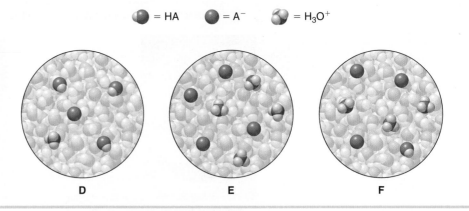

Bases also differ in their ability to accept a proton.

- A strong base readily accepts a proton. When a strong base dissolves in water, 100% of the base dissociates into ions.
- A weak base less readily accepts a proton. When a weak base dissolves in water, only a small fraction of the base forms ions.

The most common strong base is hydroxide, **$OH^-$**, used as a variety of metal salts, including NaOH and KOH. Solid NaOH dissolves in water to form solvated $Na^+$ cations and $OH^-$ anions. In contrast, when **$NH_3$**, a weak base, dissolves in water, only a small fraction of $NH_3$ molecules react to form $NH_4^+$ and $OH^-$. The major species at equilibrium is the undissociated molecule, $NH_3$.

**Figure 9.5**    A Strong and Weak Base Dissolved in Water

sodium hydroxide

$Na^+$

$OH^-$

A strong base is
completely dissociated.

ammonia

$NH_3$

$NH_4^+$

$OH^-$

A weak base contains mostly
undissociated base, $NH_3$.

- The strong base NaOH completely dissociates into $Na^+$ and $OH^-$ in water.

- The weak base $NH_3$ is only slightly dissociated into $NH_4^+$ and $OH^-$, so mostly $NH_3$ is present at equilibrium.

Figure 9.5 illustrates the difference between aqueous solutions of strong and weak bases. Table 9.1 lists common bases.

- Use a single reaction arrow.
- The products are greatly favored at equilibrium.

$$NaOH(s) \ + \ H_2O(l) \ \longrightarrow \ Na^+(aq) \ + \ OH^-(aq)$$
strong base

$$NH_3(g) \ + \ H_2O(l) \ \rightleftharpoons \ NH_4^+(aq) \ + \ OH^-(aq)$$
weak base

- Use unequal reaction arrows.
- The reactants are favored at equilibrium.

An inverse relationship exists between acid and base strength.

- A strong acid readily donates a proton, forming a *weak* conjugate base.
- A strong base readily accepts a proton, forming a *weak* conjugate acid.

Why does this inverse relationship exist? Since a strong acid readily donates a proton, it forms a conjugate base that has little ability to accept a proton. Since a strong base readily accepts a proton, it forms a conjugate acid that tightly holds onto its proton, making it a weak acid.

Thus, a *strong* acid like HCl forms a *weak* conjugate base ($Cl^-$), and a *strong* base like $OH^-$ forms a *weak* conjugate acid ($H_2O$). The entries in Table 9.1 are arranged in order of *decreasing* acid strength. This means that Table 9.1 is also arranged in order of *increasing* strength of the resulting conjugate bases. Knowing the relative strength of two acids makes it possible to predict the relative strength of their conjugate bases.

## SAMPLE PROBLEM 9.8

Using Table 9.1: (a) Is $H_3PO_4$ or HF the stronger acid? (b) Draw the conjugate base of each acid and predict which base is stronger.

### Analysis

The stronger the acid, the weaker the conjugate base.

### Solution

a. $H_3PO_4$ is located above HF in Table 9.1, making it the stronger acid.

b. To draw each conjugate base, remove a proton ($H^+$). Since each acid is neutral, both conjugate bases have a −1 charge. Since HF is the weaker acid, $F^-$ is the stronger conjugate base.

## PROBLEM 9.9

Label the stronger acid in each pair. Which acid has the stronger conjugate base?

a. $H_2SO_4$ or $H_3PO_4$      b. HF or HCl      c. $H_2CO_3$ or $NH_4^+$      d. HCN or HF

## PROBLEM 9.10

(a) Draw the conjugate acids of $NO_2^-$ and $NO_3^-$. (b) If $NO_2^-$ is the stronger base, which acid is stronger?

## 9.3B   Using Acid Strength to Predict the Direction of Equilibrium

A Brønsted–Lowry acid–base reaction represents an equilibrium. Since an acid donates a proton to a base, forming a conjugate acid and conjugate base, there are always two acids and two bases in the reaction mixture. Which pair of acids and bases is favored at equilibrium? **The position of the equilibrium depends upon the strength of the acids and bases.**

> • The stronger acid reacts with the stronger base to form the weaker acid and weaker base.

Since a strong acid readily donates a proton and a strong base readily accepts one, these two species react to form a weaker conjugate acid and base that do not donate or accept a proton as readily. Thus, **when the stronger acid and base are the reactants on the left side, the reaction readily occurs and the reaction proceeds to the** *right.*

On the other hand, **if an acid–base reaction would form the stronger acid and base, equilibrium favors the reactants and little product forms.**

Predicting the direction of equilibrium using the information in Table 9.1 is illustrated in the accompanying stepwise *How To* procedure.

---

### How To  Predict the Direction of Equilibrium in an Acid–Base Reaction

**Example:** Are the reactants or products favored in the following acid–base reaction?

$$HCN(g) + OH^-(aq) \rightleftharpoons CN^-(aq) + H_2O(l)$$

**Step [1]  Identify the acid in the reactants and the conjugate acid in the products.**

gain of H$^+$

$$HCN(g) \quad + \quad OH^-(aq) \quad \rightleftharpoons \quad CN^-(aq) \quad + \quad H_2O(l)$$

acid        base        conjugate base    conjugate acid

loss of H$^+$

- HCN is the acid since it donates a proton.
- H$_2$O is the conjugate acid formed from the hydroxide base.

**Step [2]  Determine the relative strength of the acid and the conjugate acid.**
- According to Table 9.1, HCN is a stronger acid than H$_2$O.

**Step [3]  Equilibrium favors the formation of the weaker acid.**
- Since the stronger acid HCN is a reactant, the reaction *proceeds to the right* as written, to form the weaker acid, H$_2$O. Unequal equilibrium arrows should be drawn with the larger arrow pointing towards the product side on the right.

$$HCN(g) \quad + \quad OH^-(aq) \quad \rightleftharpoons \quad CN^-(aq) \quad + \quad H_2O(l)$$

stronger acid                       weaker acid

Products are favored.

---

**HEALTH NOTE**

Lactic acid accumulates in tissues during vigorous exercise, making muscles feel tired and sore. The formation of lactic acid is discussed in greater detail in Section 24.4.

### PROBLEM 9.11

Are the reactants or products favored at equilibrium in each reaction?

a. $HF(g) + OH^-(aq) \rightleftharpoons F^-(aq) + H_2O(l)$
b. $NH_4^+(aq) + Cl^-(aq) \rightleftharpoons NH_3(g) + HCl(aq)$
c. $HCO_3^-(aq) + H_3O^+(aq) \rightleftharpoons H_2CO_3(aq) + H_2O(l)$

### PROBLEM 9.12

If lactic acid is similar in strength to acetic acid (Table 9.1), predict whether reactants or products are favored in each reaction.

$$CH_3-\underset{\underset{OH}{|}}{\overset{\overset{H}{|}}{C}}-\underset{OH}{\overset{O}{\overset{\|}{C}}}$$

$C_3H_6O_3$
lactic acid

a. $C_3H_6O_3(aq)$ + $H_2O(l)$ $\rightleftharpoons$ $C_3H_5O_3^-(aq)$ + $H_3O^+(aq)$
    lactic acid

b. $C_3H_6O_3(aq)$ + $HCO_3^-(aq)$ $\rightleftharpoons$ $C_3H_5O_3^-(aq)$ + $H_2CO_3(aq)$
    lactic acid

## 9.4  Equilibrium and Acid Dissociation Constants

Like all equilibria, we can write an expression for the equilibrium constant for the acid–base reaction that takes place when an acid HA dissolves in water. The equilibrium constant ($K$) shows the ratio of the concentrations of the products to the concentrations of the reactants.

**Reaction**      $HA(aq) + H_2O(l) \rightleftharpoons H_3O^+(aq) + A:^-$

**Equilibrium constant**    $K = \dfrac{[H_3O^+][A:^-]}{[HA][H_2O]}$    concentrations of the products / concentrations of the reactants

Water serves as both the base and the solvent. Since water is a liquid and its concentration is essentially constant, the equation can be rearranged by multiplying both sides by $[H_2O]$. This forms a new constant called the **acid dissociation constant, $K_a$.**

$$K_a = K[H_2O] = \frac{[H_3O^+][A:^-]}{[HA]}$$

**acid dissociation constant**

How is $K_a$ related to acid strength? The stronger the acid, the higher the concentration of the products of an acid–base reaction, and the larger the numerator in the expression for $K_a$. As a result:

- **The stronger the acid, the larger the value of $K_a$.**

The strong acids listed in Table 9.1 all have $K_a$ values much greater than 1. Weak acids have $K_a$ values less than 1. The $K_a$'s for several weak acids are listed in Table 9.2.

**Table 9.2** Acid Dissociation Constants ($K_a$) for Common Weak Acids

| Acid | Structure | $K_a$ |
|------|-----------|-------|
| Hydrogen sulfate ion | $HSO_4^-$ | $1.2 \times 10^{-2}$ |
| Phosphoric acid | $H_3PO_4$ | $7.5 \times 10^{-3}$ |
| Hydrofluoric acid | $HF$ | $7.2 \times 10^{-4}$ |
| Acetic acid | $CH_3COOH$ | $1.8 \times 10^{-5}$ |
| Carbonic acid | $H_2CO_3$ | $4.3 \times 10^{-7}$ |
| Dihydrogen phosphate ion | $H_2PO_4^-$ | $6.2 \times 10^{-8}$ |
| Ammonium ion | $NH_4^+$ | $5.6 \times 10^{-10}$ |
| Hydrocyanic acid | $HCN$ | $4.9 \times 10^{-10}$ |
| Bicarbonate ion | $HCO_3^-$ | $5.6 \times 10^{-11}$ |
| Hydrogen phosphate ion | $HPO_4^{2-}$ | $2.2 \times 10^{-13}$ |

*Increasing acidity* (arrow pointing upward along left side of table)

## SAMPLE PROBLEM 9.9

Which acid in each pair is stronger: (a) HCN or $HSO_4^-$; (b) $CH_3COOH$ or $NH_4^+$?

### Analysis

Use Table 9.2 to find the $K_a$ for each acid. The acid with the larger $K_a$ is the stronger acid.

### Solution

a.
| HCN | $HSO_4^-$ |
|-----|-----------|
| $K_a = 4.9 \times 10^{-10}$ | $K_a = 1.2 \times 10^{-2}$ |
| | larger $K_a$ |
| | **stronger acid** |

b.
| $CH_3COOH$ | $NH_4^+$ |
|------------|----------|
| $1.8 \times 10^{-5}$ | $5.6 \times 10^{-10}$ |
| larger $K_a$ | |
| **stronger acid** | |

## PROBLEM 9.13

Rank the acids in each group in order of increasing acid strength.

a. $H_3PO_4$, $H_2PO_4^-$, $HPO_4^{2-}$          b. HCN, HF, $CH_3COOH$

### PROBLEM 9.14

(a) Which compound is the stronger acid, $H_3PO_4$ or $CH_3COOH$? (b) Draw the conjugate base of each compound and predict which base is stronger.

Because $K_a$ values tell us the relative strength of two acids, we can use $K_a$'s to predict the direction of equilibrium in an acid–base reaction, as shown in Sample Problem 9.10.

- Equilibrium favors the formation of the weaker acid—that is, the acid with the *smaller* $K_a$ value.

### SAMPLE PROBLEM 9.10

Citrus fruits (oranges, grapefruit, and lemons) are well known sources of vitamin C (ascorbic acid, Sample Problem 9.10), but guava, kiwifruit, and rose hips are excellent sources, too.

Ascorbic acid, vitamin C, is needed for the formation of collagen, a common protein in connective tissues in muscles and blood vessels. If vitamin C has a $K_a$ of $7.9 \times 10^{-5}$, are the reactants or products favored in the following acid–base reaction?

$$C_6H_8O_6(aq) + NH_3(aq) \rightleftharpoons C_6H_7O_6^-(aq) + NH_4^+(aq)$$

vitamin C — conjugate base of vitamin C

vitamin C
ascorbic acid
$C_6H_8O_6$

#### Analysis

To determine the direction of equilibrium, we must identify the acid in the reactants and the conjugate acid in the products. Then compare their $K_a$'s. **Equilibrium favors the formation of the acid with the smaller $K_a$ value.**

#### Solution

Vitamin C is the acid and $NH_3$ is the base on the reactant side. $NH_3$ gains a proton to form its conjugate acid, $NH_4^+$, which has a $K_a$ of $5.6 \times 10^{-10}$ (Table 9.2). The conjugate acid, therefore, has a *smaller* $K_a$ than vitamin C ($7.9 \times 10^{-5}$), making it the *weaker acid*. Thus, the products are favored at equilibrium.

products favored

$$C_6H_8O_6(aq) + NH_3(aq) \rightleftharpoons C_6H_7O_6^-(aq) + NH_4^+(aq)$$

| vitamin C | | conjugate acid |
|---|---|---|
| $K_a = 7.9 \times 10^{-5}$ | | $K_a = 5.6 \times 10^{-10}$ |
| larger $K_a$ | | smaller $K_a$ |
| **stronger acid** | | **weaker acid** |

### PROBLEM 9.15

Use the acid dissociation constants in Table 9.2 to determine whether the reactants or products are favored in the following reaction.

$$HCO_3^-(aq) + NH_3(aq) \rightleftharpoons CO_3^{2-}(aq) + NH_4^+(aq)$$

### PROBLEM 9.16

Consider the weak acids, HCN and $H_2CO_3$.

a. Which acid has the larger $K_a$?
b. Which acid is stronger?
c. Which acid has the stronger conjugate base?
d. Which acid has the weaker conjugate base?
e. When each acid is dissolved in water, for which acid does the equilibrium lie further to the right?

## 9.5  Dissociation of Water

In Section 9.2 we learned that water can behave as *both* a Brønsted–Lowry acid and a Brønsted–Lowry base. As a result, two molecules of water can react together in an acid–base reaction.

- One molecule of $H_2O$ donates a proton ($H^+$), forming its conjugate base $OH^-$.
- One molecule of $H_2O$ accepts a proton, forming its conjugate acid $H_3O^+$.

Equilibrium favors the starting materials in this reaction, since the reactant acid, $H_2O$, is much weaker than the conjugate acid, $H_3O^+$. Thus, pure water contains an exceedingly low concentration of ions, $H_3O^+$ and $OH^-$.

As usual, an expression for the equilibrium constant can be written that shows the ratio of the concentrations of the products, $H_3O^+$ and $OH^-$, to the concentration of the reactants, two molecules of $H_2O$. Since water is a liquid and its concentration is essentially constant, this equation can be rearranged by multiplying by $[H_2O]^2$ to afford a new equilibrium constant, $K_w$, **the ion–product constant** for water.

$$K = \frac{[H_3O^+][OH^-]}{[H_2O][H_2O]} = \frac{[H_3O^+][OH^-]}{[H_2O]^2} \quad \text{Multiply both sides by } [H_2O]^2.$$

$$K_w = K[H_2O]^2 = [H_3O^+][OH^-]$$

**ion–product constant**

$$\boxed{K_w = [H_3O^+][OH^-]}$$

Since one $H_3O^+$ ion and one $OH^-$ ion are formed in each reaction, the concentrations of $H_3O^+$ and $OH^-$ are equal in pure water. Experimentally it can be shown that the $[H_3O^+] = [OH^-] = 1.0 \times 10^{-7}$ M at 25 °C. Thus,

$$K_w = [H_3O^+][OH^-]$$
$$K_w = (1.0 \times 10^{-7}) \times (1.0 \times 10^{-7})$$
$$K_w = 1.0 \times 10^{-14}$$

- The product, $[H_3O^+][OH^-]$, is a constant, $1.0 \times 10^{-14}$, for all aqueous solutions at 25 °C.

Thus, **the value of $K_w$ applies to any aqueous solution,** not just pure water. If we know the concentration of one ion, $H_3O^+$ or $OH^-$, we can find the concentration of the other by rearranging the expression for $K_w$.

To calculate $[OH^-]$ when $[H_3O^+]$ is known:

$$K_w = [H_3O^+][OH^-]$$

$$[OH^-] = \frac{K_w}{[H_3O^+]}$$

$$[OH^-] = \frac{1.0 \times 10^{-14}}{[H_3O^+]}$$

To calculate $[H_3O^+]$ when $[OH^-]$ is known:

$$K_w = [H_3O^+][OH^-]$$

$$[H_3O^+] = \frac{K_w}{[OH^-]}$$

$$[H_3O^+] = \frac{1.0 \times 10^{-14}}{[OH^-]}$$

How to write numbers in scientific notation was presented in Section 1.6. Multiplying and dividing numbers written in scientific notation was described in Section 5.3.

Coffee is an *acidic* solution since the concentration of $H_3O^+$ is *greater* than the concentration of $OH^-$.

Thus, if the concentration of $H_3O^+$ in a cup of coffee is $1.0 \times 10^{-5}$ M, we can use this value to calculate $[OH^-]$.

$$[OH^-] = \frac{K_w}{[H_3O^+]} = \frac{1.0 \times 10^{-14}}{1.0 \times 10^{-5}}$$

$$[OH^-] = 1.0 \times 10^{-9} \text{ M}$$

hydroxide ion concentration
in a cup of coffee

In a cup of coffee, therefore, the concentration of $H_3O^+$ ions is greater than the concentration of $OH^-$ ions, but the product of these concentrations, $1.0 \times 10^{-14}$, is a constant, $K_w$.

**Pure water and any solution that has an equal concentration of $H_3O^+$ and $OH^-$ ions $(1.0 \times 10^{-7})$ is said to be *neutral*.** Other solutions are classified as **acidic** or **basic**, depending on which ion is present in a higher concentration.

- In an *acidic* solution, $[H_3O^+] > [OH^-]$; thus, $[H_3O^+] > 10^{-7}$ M.
- In a *basic* solution, $[OH^-] > [H_3O^+]$; thus, $[OH^-] > 10^{-7}$ M.

In an acidic solution, the concentration of the acid $H_3O^+$ is greater than the concentration of the base $OH^-$. In a basic solution, the concentration of the base $OH^-$ is greater than the concentration of the acid $H_3O^+$. Table 9.3 summarizes information about neutral, acidic, and basic solutions.

### Table 9.3  Neutral, Acidic, and Basic Solutions

| Type | $[H_3O^+]$ and $[OH^-]$ | $[H_3O^+]$ | $[OH^-]$ |
|---|---|---|---|
| Neutral | $[H_3O^+] = [OH^-]$ | $10^{-7}$ M | $10^{-7}$ M |
| Acidic | $[H_3O^+] > [OH^-]$ | $> 10^{-7}$ M | $< 10^{-7}$ M |
| Basic | $[H_3O^+] < [OH^-]$ | $< 10^{-7}$ M | $> 10^{-7}$ M |

### SAMPLE PROBLEM 9.11

If $[H_3O^+]$ in blood is $4.0 \times 10^{-8}$ M, what is the value of $[OH^-]$? Is blood acidic, basic, or neutral?

#### Analysis

Use the equation $[OH^-] = K_w/[H_3O^+]$ to calculate the hydroxide ion concentration.

#### Solution

Substitute the given value of $[H_3O^+]$ in the equation to find $[OH^-]$.

$$[OH^-] = \frac{K_w}{[H_3O^+]} = \frac{1.0 \times 10^{-14}}{4.0 \times 10^{-8}} = 2.5 \times 10^{-7} \text{ M}$$

hydroxide ion concentration
in the blood

Since $[OH^-] > [H_3O^+]$, blood is a basic solution.

### PROBLEM 9.17

Calculate the value of $[OH^-]$ from the given $[H_3O^+]$ in each solution and label the solution as acidic or basic: (a) $[H_3O^+] = 10^{-3}$ M; (b) $[H_3O^+] = 10^{-11}$ M; (c) $[H_3O^+] = 2.8 \times 10^{-10}$ M; (d) $[H_3O^+] = 5.6 \times 10^{-4}$ M.

### PROBLEM 9.18

Calculate the value of $[H_3O^+]$ from the given $[OH^-]$ in each solution and label the solution as acidic or basic: (a) $[OH^-] = 10^{-6}$ M; (b) $[OH^-] = 10^{-9}$ M; (c) $[OH^-] = 5.2 \times 10^{-11}$ M; (d) $[OH^-] = 7.3 \times 10^{-4}$ M.

Since a strong acid like HCl is completely dissociated in aqueous solution, the concentration of the acid tells us the concentration of hydronium ions present. Thus, a 0.1 M HCl solution completely dissociates, so the concentration of $H_3O^+$ is 0.1 M. This value can then be used to calculate the hydroxide ion concentration. Similarly, a strong base like NaOH completely dissociates, so the concentration of the base gives the concentration of hydroxide ions present. Thus, the concentration of $OH^-$ in a 0.1 M NaOH solution is 0.1 M.

In 0.1 M HCl solution:       $[H_3O^+] = 0.1 \text{ M} = 1 \times 10^{-1} \text{ M}$
strong acid

In 0.1 M NaOH solution:       $[OH^-] = 0.1 \text{ M} = 1 \times 10^{-1} \text{ M}$
strong base

## SAMPLE PROBLEM 9.12

Calculate the value of $[H_3O^+]$ and $[OH^-]$ in a 0.01 M NaOH solution.

### Analysis

Since NaOH is a strong base that completely dissociates to form $Na^+$ and $OH^-$, the concentration of NaOH gives the concentration of $OH^-$ ions. The $[OH^-]$ can then be used to calculate $[H_3O^+]$ from the expression for $K_w$.

### Solution

The value of $[OH^-]$ in a 0.01 M NaOH solution is 0.01 M = $1 \times 10^{-2}$ M.

$$[H_3O^+] \quad = \quad \frac{K_w}{[OH^-]} \quad = \quad \frac{1 \times 10^{-14}}{1 \times 10^{-2}} \quad = \quad 1 \times 10^{-12} \text{ M}$$
concentration of $H_3O^+$

concentration of $OH^-$

## PROBLEM 9.19

Calculate the value of $[H_3O^+]$ and $[OH^-]$ in each solution: (a) 0.001 M NaOH; (b) 0.001 M HCl; (c) 1.5 M HCl; (d) 0.30 M NaOH.

## 9.6 The pH Scale

Knowing the hydronium ion concentration is necessary in many different instances. The blood must have an $H_3O^+$ concentration in a very narrow range for an individual's good health. Plants thrive in soil that is not too acidic or too basic. The $H_3O^+$ concentration in a swimming pool must be measured and adjusted to keep the water clean and free from bacteria and algae.

## 9.6A Calculating pH

Since values for the hydronium ion concentration are very small, with negative powers of ten, the **pH scale** is used to more conveniently report $[H_3O^+]$. The pH of a solution is a number generally between 0 and 14, defined in terms of the *logarithm* (log) of the $H_3O^+$ concentration.

$$\text{pH} = -\log [H_3O^+]$$

**A logarithm is an exponent of a power of ten.**

The log is the exponent.

$\log(10^5) \quad = \quad 5$          $\log(10^{-10}) \quad = \quad -10$          $\log(0.001) = \log(10^{-3}) \quad = \quad -3$

The log is the exponent.          Convert to scientific notation.

Apple juice has a pH of about 4, so it is an acidic solution.

In calculating pH, first consider an $H_3O^+$ concentration that has a coefficient of *one* when the number is written in scientific notation. For example, the value of $[H_3O^+]$ in apple juice is about $1 \times 10^{-4}$, or $10^{-4}$ written without the coefficient. The pH of this solution is calculated as follows:

$$pH = -\log [H_3O^+] = -\log(10^{-4})$$
$$= -(-4) \qquad = 4$$

pH of apple juice

Since pH is defined as the *negative* logarithm of $[H_3O^+]$ and these concentrations have *negative* exponents ($10^{-x}$), pH values are *positive* numbers.

Whether a solution is acidic, neutral, or basic can now be defined in terms of its pH.

- Acidic solution:  pH < 7 ⟶ $[H_3O^+] > 1 \times 10^{-7}$
- Neutral solution:  pH = 7 ⟶ $[H_3O^+] = 1 \times 10^{-7}$
- Basic solution:  pH > 7 ⟶ $[H_3O^+] < 1 \times 10^{-7}$

Note the relationship between $[H_3O^+]$ and pH.

- The *lower* the pH, the *higher* the concentration of $H_3O^+$.

Since pH is measured on a *logarithmic* scale, **a small difference in pH translates to a large change in $H_3O^+$ concentration.** For example, a difference of one pH unit means a ten-fold difference in $H_3O^+$ concentration. A difference of three pH units means a thousand-fold difference in $H_3O^+$ concentration.

A difference of one pH unit...

pH = 2    $[H_3O^+] = 1 \times 10^{-2}$
pH = 3    $[H_3O^+] = 1 \times 10^{-3}$

...means the $[H_3O^+]$ differs by a factor of 10.

A difference of three pH units...

pH = 2    $[H_3O^+] = 1 \times 10^{-2}$
pH = 5    $[H_3O^+] = 1 \times 10^{-5}$

...means the $[H_3O^+]$ differs by a factor of 1,000.

The pH of a solution can be measured using a pH meter as shown in Figure 9.6. Approximate pH values are determined using pH paper or indicators that turn different colors depending on the pH of the solution. The pH of various substances is shown in Figure 9.7.

**Figure 9.6** Measuring pH

a.

b.

c.

a. A pH meter is a small electronic device that measures pH when an electrode is dipped into a solution.

b. Paper strips called pH paper change color corresponding to a particular pH, when a drop of an aqueous solution is applied to them.

c. An acid–base indicator can be used to give an approximate pH. The indicator is a dye that changes color depending on the pH of the solution.

**Figure 9.7** The pH of Some Common Substances

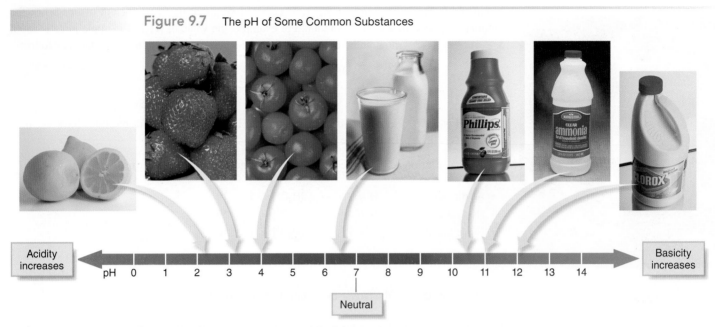

The pH of many fruits is less than 7, making them acidic. Many cleaning agents, such as household ammonia and bleach, are basic (pH > 7).

Converting a given $H_3O^+$ concentration to a pH value is shown in Sample Problem 9.13. The reverse process, converting a pH value to an $H_3O^+$ concentration, is shown in Sample Problem 9.14.

### SAMPLE PROBLEM 9.13

What is the pH of a urine sample that has an $H_3O^+$ concentration of $1 \times 10^{-5}$ M? Classify the solution as acidic, basic, or neutral.

#### Analysis

Use the formula pH = $-\log [H_3O^+]$. When the coefficient of a number written in scientific notation is one, the pH equals the value $x$ in $10^{-x}$.

#### Solution

$$pH = -\log [H_3O^+] = -\log(10^{-5})$$
$$= -(-5) = 5 \quad \text{pH of urine sample}$$
**Answer**

The urine sample is acidic since the pH < 7.

### PROBLEM 9.20

Convert each $H_3O^+$ concentration to a pH value.

  a. $1 \times 10^{-6}$ M      b. $1 \times 10^{-12}$ M      c. 0.000 01 M      d. 0.000 000 000 01 M

### SAMPLE PROBLEM 9.14

What is the $H_3O^+$ concentration in lemon juice that has a pH of about 2? Classify the solution as acidic, basic, or neutral.

#### Analysis

To find $[H_3O^+]$ from a pH, which is a logarithm, we must determine what number corresponds to the given logarithm. When the pH is a whole number $x$, the value of $x$ becomes the exponent in the expression $1 \times 10^{-x} = [H_3O^+]$.

#### Solution

If the pH of lemon juice is 2, $[H_3O^+] = 1 \times 10^{-2}$ M. Since the pH is less than 7, the lemon juice is acidic.

Determining logarithms and anti-
logarithms using an electronic
calculator is shown in Appendix A.

### PROBLEM 9.21

What $H_3O^+$ concentration corresponds to each pH value: (a) 13; (b) 7; (c) 3? Label each solution as acidic, basic, or neutral.

## 9.6B  Calculating pH Using a Calculator

To calculate the pH of a solution in which the hydronium ion concentration has a coefficient in scientific notation that is *not* equal to one—as in $2.0 \times 10^{-3}$—you need a calculator that has a log function. How the keys are labeled and the order of the steps depend on your particular calculator.

Enter this number on your calculator.

$$pH = -\log [H_3O^+] \quad = \quad -\log(2.0 \times 10^{-3})$$
$$= \quad -(-2.70) \quad = \quad 2.70$$

Similarly, when a reported pH is *not* a whole number—as in the pH = 8.50 for a sample of seawater—you need a calculator to calculate an *antilogarithm*—that is, the number that has a logarithm of 8.50. To make sure your calculation is correct, note that since the pH of seawater is between 8 and 9, the $H_3O^+$ concentration must be between $10^{-8}$ and $10^{-9}$.

$$[H_3O^+] = \text{antilog}(-pH) = \text{antilog}(-8.50)$$
$$= 3.2 \times 10^{-9} \text{ M}$$

Care must be taken in keeping track of significant figures when using logarithms.

- A logarithm has the same number of digits to the right of the decimal point as are contained in the coefficient of the original number.

$$[H_3O^+] \quad = \quad 3.2 \times 10^{-9} \text{ M} \qquad pH = 8.50 \quad \text{two digits after the decimal point}$$

two significant figures

Because seawater contains dissolved salts, its pH is 8.50, making it slightly basic, not neutral like pure water.

### SAMPLE PROBLEM 9.15

What is the pH of wine that has an $H_3O^+$ concentration of $3.2 \times 10^{-4}$ M?

#### Analysis

Use a calculator to determine the logarithm of a number that contains a coefficient in scientific notation that is not a whole number; $pH = -\log [H_3O^+]$.

#### Solution

The order of the steps in using an electronic calculator, as well as the labels on the calculator buttons, vary. In some cases it is possible to calculate the pH by following three steps: enter the number ($H_3O^+$ concentration); press the *log* button; and press the change sign key. Consult your calculator manual if these steps do not give the desired value. Because the coefficient in the original number had two significant figures, the pH must have two digits to the right of the decimal point.

two significant figures

$$pH = -\log [H_3O^+] \quad = \quad -\log(3.2 \times 10^{-4})$$
$$= \quad -(-3.49) \quad = \quad 3.49 \quad \text{two digits to the right of the decimal point}$$

### PROBLEM 9.22

What $H_3O^+$ concentration corresponds to each pH value: (a) 10.2; (b) 7.8; (c) 4.3?

### SAMPLE PROBLEM 9.16

What is the $H_3O^+$ concentration in sweat that has a pH of 5.8?

#### Analysis

Use a calculator to determine the antilogarithm of the negative of the pH; $[H_3O^+] = \text{antilog}(-pH)$.

## Solution

The order of the steps in using an electronic calculator, as well as the labels on the calculator buttons, vary. In some cases it is possible to calculate $[H_3O^+]$ by the following steps: enter the pH value; press the change sign key; and press the *2nd + log* buttons. Since the pH has only one number to the right of the decimal point, the $H_3O^+$ concentration must have only one significant figure in its coefficient.

one digit to the right of the decimal point

$$[H_3O^+] \ = \ antilog(-pH) \ = \ antilog(-5.8)$$
$$[H_3O^+] \ = \ 2 \times 10^{-6} \ M$$

one significant figure

### PROBLEM 9.23

Convert each $H_3O^+$ concentration to a pH value.

a. $1.8 \times 10^{-6}$ M     b. $9.21 \times 10^{-12}$ M     c. 0.000 088 M     d. 0.000 000 000 076 2 M

## 9.6C  FOCUS ON THE HUMAN BODY
### The pH of Body Fluids

The human body contains fluids that vary in pH as shown in Figure 9.8. While saliva is slightly acidic, the gastric juice in the stomach has the lowest pH found in the body. The strongly acidic environment of the stomach aids in the digestion of food. It also kills many types of bacteria that might be inadvertently consumed along with food and drink. When food leaves the stomach, it passes to the basic environment of the small intestines. Bases in the small intestines react with acid from the stomach.

**Figure 9.8**    Variation in pH Values in the Human Body

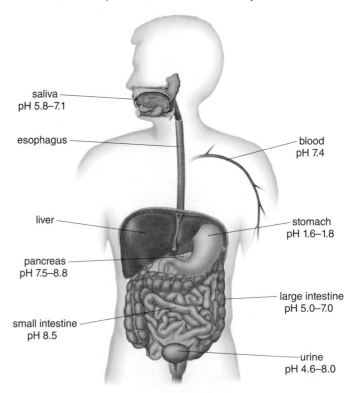

saliva
pH 5.8–7.1

esophagus

blood
pH 7.4

liver

stomach
pH 1.6–1.8

pancreas
pH 7.5–8.8

large intestine
pH 5.0–7.0

small intestine
pH 8.5

urine
pH 4.6–8.0

The pH of some body fluids must occupy a very narrow range. For example, a healthy individual has a blood pH in the range of 7.35–7.45. Maintaining this pH is accomplished by a complex mechanism described in Section 9.11. The pH of other fluids can be more variable. Urine has a pH anywhere from 4.6–8.0, depending on an individual's recent diet and exercise.

### PROBLEM 9.24

Label each organ or fluid in Figure 9.8 as being acidic, basic, or neutral.

## 9.7 Common Acid–Base Reactions

Although we have already seen a variety of acid–base reactions in Sections 9.2–9.4, two common reactions deserve additional attention—reaction of acids with hydroxide bases ($OH^-$), and reaction of acids with bicarbonate ($HCO_3^-$) or carbonate ($CO_3^{2-}$).

### 9.7A Reaction of Acids with Hydroxide Bases

The reaction of a Brønsted–Lowry acid (HA) with the metal salt of a hydroxide base (MOH) is an example of a *neutralization* reaction—**an acid–base reaction that produces a salt and water as products.**

$$HA(aq) + MOH(aq) \longrightarrow H-OH(l) + MA(aq)$$
$$\text{acid} \qquad \text{base} \qquad\qquad \text{water} \qquad \text{salt}$$

- The acid HA donates a proton ($H^+$) to the $OH^-$ base to form $H_2O$.
- The anion $A^-$ from the acid combines with the cation $M^+$ from the base to form the salt MA.

For example, hydrochloric acid, HCl, reacts with sodium hydroxide, NaOH, to form water and sodium chloride, NaCl. A single reaction arrow is drawn between reactants and products because equilibrium greatly favors the products.

$$HCl(aq) + NaOH(aq) \longrightarrow H-OH(l) + NaCl(aq)$$
$$\text{acid} \qquad \text{base} \qquad\qquad \text{water} \qquad \text{salt}$$

The important reacting species in this reaction are $H^+$ from the acid HCl and $OH^-$ from the base NaOH. To more clearly see the acid–base reaction, we can write an equation that contains only the species that are actually involved in the reaction. Such an equation is called a **net ionic equation.**

- A *net ionic equation* contains only the species involved in a reaction.

To write a net ionic equation for an acid–base reaction, we first write the acid, base, and salt as individual ions in solution. This process is simplified if we use $H^+$ (not $H_3O^+$) as the reacting species of the acid, since it is the $H^+$ ion that is transferred to the base. The reaction of HCl with NaOH using individual ions is then drawn as:

$$H^+(aq) + Cl^-(aq) + Na^+(aq) + OH^-(aq) \longrightarrow H-OH(l) + Na^+(aq) + Cl^-(aq)$$

Writing the equation in this manner shows that the $Na^+$ and $Cl^-$ ions are unchanged in the reaction. Ions that appear on both sides of an equation but undergo no change in a reaction are called **spectator ions.** Removing the spectator ions from the equation gives the net ionic equation.

$$H^+(aq) + Cl^-(aq) + Na^+(aq) + OH^-(aq) \longrightarrow H-OH(l) + Na^+(aq) + Cl^-(aq)$$

Omit the spectator ions.            Omit the spectator ions.

**Net ionic equation**     $H^+(aq) + OH^-(aq) \longrightarrow H-OH(l)$

- Whenever a strong acid and strong base react, the net ionic equation is always the same—$H^+$ reacts with $OH^-$ to form $H_2O$.

To draw the products of these neutralization reactions, keep in mind that **two products are always formed—water and a metal salt.** Balancing an acid–base equation can be done with the stepwise procedure for balancing a general reaction outlined in Section 5.2. The coefficients in a balanced chemical equation illustrate that one $H^+$ ion is always needed to react with each $OH^-$ anion.

---

**How To** Draw a Balanced Equation for a Neutralization Reaction Between HA and MOH

**Example:** Write a balanced equation for the reaction of $Mg(OH)_2$, an active ingredient in the antacid product Maalox, with the hydrochloric acid (HCl) in the stomach.

**Step [1] Identify the acid and base in the reactants and draw $H_2O$ as one product.**

- HCl is the acid and $Mg(OH)_2$ is the base. $H^+$ from the acid reacts with $OH^-$ from the base to form $H_2O$.

$$HCl(aq) + Mg(OH)_2(aq) \longrightarrow H_2O(l) + salt$$
$$\text{acid} \qquad\qquad \text{base}$$

**Step [2] Determine the structure of the salt formed as product.**

- The salt is formed from the elements of the acid and base that are *not* used to form $H_2O$. The anion of the salt comes from the acid and the cation of the salt comes from the base.
- In this case, $Cl^-$ (from HCl) and $Mg^{2+}$ [from $Mg(OH)_2$] combine to form the salt $MgCl_2$.

**Step [3] Balance the equation.**

- Follow the procedure in Section 5.2 to balance an equation. The balanced equation shows that *two* moles of HCl are needed for *each* mole of $Mg(OH)_2$, since each mole of $Mg(OH)_2$ contains two moles of $OH^-$.

Place a 2 to balance H and O.

$$2\ HCl(aq) + Mg(OH)_2(aq) \longrightarrow 2\ H_2O(l) + MgCl_2$$

Place a 2 to balance Cl.

---

The antacid products Maalox and Mylanta both contain two bases—$Mg(OH)_2$ and $Al(OH)_3$—that react with excess stomach acid. A combination of bases is used so that the constipating effect of the aluminum salt is counteracted by the laxative effect of the magnesium salt.

**PROBLEM 9.25**

Write a balanced equation for each acid–base reaction.

a. $HNO_3(aq) + NaOH(aq) \longrightarrow$

b. $H_2SO_4(aq) + KOH(aq) \longrightarrow$

**PROBLEM 9.26**

Write the net ionic equation for each reaction in Problem 9.25.

## 9.7B   Reaction of Acids with Bicarbonate and Carbonate

Acids react with the bases bicarbonate ($HCO_3^-$) and carbonate ($CO_3^{2-}$). A bicarbonate base reacts with *one* proton to form carbonic acid, $H_2CO_3$. A carbonate base reacts with *two* protons. The carbonic acid formed in these reactions is unstable and decomposes to form $CO_2$ and $H_2O$. Thus, when an acid reacts with either base, bubbles of $CO_2$ gas are given off.

$$H^+(aq) + HCO_3^-(aq) \longrightarrow \left[H_2CO_3(aq)\right] \longrightarrow H_2O(l) + CO_2(g)$$
1 $H^+$ needed    bicarbonate               bubbles of $CO_2$

$$2\ H^+(aq) + CO_3^{2-}(aq) \longrightarrow \left[H_2CO_3(aq)\right] \longrightarrow H_2O(l) + CO_2(g)$$
2 $H^+$ needed    carbonate

Sodium bicarbonate ($NaHCO_3$), an ingredient in the over-the-counter antacid Alka-Seltzer, is the metal salt of a bicarbonate base that reacts with excess stomach acid, releasing $CO_2$. Like the

Like taking other over-the-counter medications, care must be exercised when using antacids. Ingestion of large amounts of $CaCO_3$ can increase the incidence of kidney stones.

neutralization reactions in Section 9.7A, a salt, NaCl, is formed in which the cation ($Na^+$) comes from the base and the anion ($Cl^-$) comes from the acid.

$$HCl(aq) \quad + \quad NaHCO_3(aq) \quad \longrightarrow \quad NaCl(aq) \quad + \quad H_2CO_3(aq)$$
$$\text{acid} \qquad\qquad \text{base} \qquad\qquad\qquad \text{salt} \qquad\qquad \longrightarrow H_2O(l) \quad + \quad CO_2(g)$$

Calcium carbonate ($CaCO_3$), a calcium supplement and antacid in Tums, also reacts with excess stomach acid with release of $CO_2$. Since each carbonate ion reacts with two protons, the balanced equation shows a 2:1 ratio of HCl to $CaCO_3$.

$$2\,HCl(aq) \quad + \quad CaCO_3(aq) \quad \longrightarrow \quad CaCl_2(aq) \quad + \quad H_2CO_3(aq)$$
$$\text{acid} \qquad\qquad \text{base} \qquad\qquad\qquad \text{salt} \qquad\qquad \longrightarrow H_2O(l) \quad + \quad CO_2(g)$$

### SAMPLE PROBLEM 9.17

Write a balanced equation for the reaction of $H_2SO_4$ with $NaHCO_3$.

### Analysis

The acid and base react to form a salt and carbonic acid ($H_2CO_3$), which decomposes to $CO_2$ and $H_2O$.

### Solution

$H_2SO_4$ is the acid and $NaHCO_3$ is the base. $H^+$ from the acid reacts with $HCO_3^-$ from the base to give $H_2CO_3$, which decomposes to $H_2O$ and $CO_2$. A salt ($Na_2SO_4$) is also formed from the cation of the base ($Na^+$) and the anion of the acid ($SO_4^{2-}$).

$$\text{Unbalanced equation:} \quad H_2SO_4(aq) \quad + \quad NaHCO_3(aq) \quad \longrightarrow \quad Na_2SO_4(aq) \quad + \quad H_2O(l) \quad + \quad CO_2(g)$$
$$\text{acid} \qquad\qquad \text{base} \qquad\qquad\qquad \text{salt} \qquad\qquad\qquad \text{from } H_2CO_3$$

To balance the equation, place coefficients so the number of atoms on both sides of the arrow is the same.

Place a 2 to balance Na…

$$H_2SO_4(aq) \quad + \quad 2\,NaHCO_3(aq) \quad \longrightarrow \quad Na_2SO_4(aq) \quad + \quad 2\,H_2O(l) \quad + \quad 2\,CO_2(g)$$
$$\text{acid} \qquad\qquad \text{base} \qquad\qquad\qquad \text{salt}$$

…then place 2's to balance C, H, and O.

### PROBLEM 9.27

The acid in acid rain is generally sulfuric acid ($H_2SO_4$). When this rainwater falls on statues composed of marble ($CaCO_3$), the $H_2SO_4$ slowly dissolves the $CaCO_3$. Write a balanced equation for this acid–base reaction.

### PROBLEM 9.28

Write a balanced equation for the reaction of nitric acid ($HNO_3$) with each base: (a) $NaHCO_3$; (b) $MgCO_3$.

## 9.8 The Acidity and Basicity of Salt Solutions

Thus far we have discussed what occurs when an acid or a base dissolves in water. What happens to the pH of water when a salt is dissolved? A salt is the product of a neutralization reaction (Section 9.7A). Does this mean that a salt dissolved in water forms a neutral solution with a pH of 7?

- A salt can form an acidic, basic, or neutral solution depending on whether its cation and anion are derived from a strong or weak acid and base.

Let's first examine what acid and base are used to form a salt $M^+A^-$.

- The cation $M^+$ comes from the base.
- The anion $A^-$ comes from the acid HA.

Thus, we consider NaCl to be a salt formed when the strong base NaOH and the strong acid HCl react together. On the other hand, $NaHCO_3$ is formed from the strong base NaOH and the weak acid $H_2CO_3$, and $NH_4Cl$ is formed from the weak base $NH_3$ and the strong acid HCl.

| NaCl | NaHCO₃ | NH₄Cl |
| --- | --- | --- |
| Na⁺   Cl⁻ | Na⁺   HCO₃⁻ | NH₄⁺   Cl⁻ |
| from NaOH   from HCl | from NaOH   from H₂CO₃ | from NH₃   from HCl |
| strong base   strong acid | strong base   weak acid | weak base   strong acid |

**A salt derived from a strong base and a strong acid forms a neutral solution (pH = 7).** When one ion of a salt is derived from a weak acid or base, one principle is followed: **the ion derived from the *stronger* acid or base determines whether the solution is acidic or basic.**

- A salt derived from a *strong base* and a weak acid forms a *basic* solution (pH > 7).
- A salt derived from a weak base and a *strong acid* forms an *acidic* solution (pH < 7).

For example, when $NaHCO_3$ dissolves in water, it forms $Na^+(aq)$ and $HCO_3^-(aq)$. Alkali metal cations like $Na^+$ do not react with $H_2O$, but $HCO_3^-$ reacts with $H_2O$ to form $OH^-$. Thus, **$NaHCO_3$, a salt derived from a *strong* base and a weak acid, forms a *basic* solution.**

$$HCO_3^-(aq) \; + \; H_2O(l) \; \rightleftharpoons \; H_2CO_3(aq) \; + \; \boxed{OH^-(aq)}$$

Hydroxide makes the solution basic,
so the pH > 7.

When $NH_4Cl$ dissolves in water it forms $NH_4^+(aq)$ and $Cl^-(aq)$. Halide anions like $Cl^-$ do not react with $H_2O$, but $NH_4^+$ reacts with $H_2O$ to form $H_3O^+$. Thus, **$NH_4Cl$, a salt derived from a *strong* acid and a weak base, forms an *acidic* solution.**

$$NH_4^+(aq) \; + \; H_2O(l) \; \rightleftharpoons \; NH_3(aq) \; + \; \boxed{H_3O^+(aq)}$$

$H_3O^+$ makes the solution acidic,
so the pH < 7.

When NaCl dissolves in water it forms $Na^+(aq)$ and $Cl^-(aq)$. Neither ion reacts with water. Since no acid–base reaction occurs, the solution remains neutral. Thus, **NaCl, a salt derived from a strong acid and strong base, forms a neutral solution.** The acidity and basicity of salt solutions is summarized in Table 9.4.

### Table 9.4 The Acidity and Basicity of Salt Solutions

| Cation Derived from | Anion Derived from | Solution | pH | Examples |
| --- | --- | --- | --- | --- |
| Strong base | Strong acid | neutral | 7 | NaCl, KBr, NaNO₃ |
| Strong base | Weak acid | basic | > 7 | NaHCO₃, KCN, CaF₂ |
| Weak base | Strong acid | acidic | < 7 | NH₄Cl, NH₄NO₃ |

### SAMPLE PROBLEM 9.18

Determine whether each salt forms an acidic, basic, or neutral solution when dissolved in water:
(a) NaF; (b) $KNO_3$; (c) $NH_4Br$.

### Analysis

Determine what type of acid and base (strong or weak) are used to form the salt. When the ions in the salt come from a strong acid and strong base, the solution is neutral. When the ions come from acids and bases of different strength, the ion derived from the stronger reactant determines the acidity.

Solution

a.

NaF

$\overset{\frown}{Na^+}$ $\overset{\frown}{F^-}$

from NaOH   from HF
**strong base**   weak acid

**basic** solution

b.

$KNO_3$

$\overset{\frown}{K^+}$ $\overset{\frown}{NO_3^-}$

from KOH   from $HNO_3$
**strong base**  **strong acid**

**neutral** solution

c.

$NH_4Br$

$\overset{\frown}{NH_4^+}$ $\overset{\frown}{Br^-}$

from $NH_3$   from HBr
weak base  **strong acid**

**acidic** solution

### PROBLEM 9.29

Determine whether each salt forms an acidic, basic, or neutral solution when dissolved in water:
(a) KI; (b) $K_2CO_3$; (c) $Ca(NO_3)_2$; (d) $NH_4I$; (e) $BaCl_2$; (f) $Na_3PO_4$.

### PROBLEM 9.30

Which of the following salts forms an aqueous solution that has a pH > 7: (a) LiCl; (b) $K_2CO_3$;
(c) $NH_4Br$; (d) $MgCO_3$?

## 9.9 Titration

Sometimes it is necessary to know the exact concentration of acid or base in a solution. To determine the molarity of a solution, we carry out a **titration.** A titration uses a *buret,* a calibrated tube with a stopcock at the bottom that allows a solution of known molarity to be added in small quantities to a solution of unknown molarity. The procedure for determining the total acid concentration of a solution of HCl is illustrated in Figure 9.9.

**Figure 9.9**   Titration of an Acid with a Base of Known Concentration

a.

b.

c.

Steps in determining the molarity of a solution of HCl:

a. Add a measured volume of HCl solution to a flask. Add an acid–base indicator, often phenolphthalein, which is colorless in acid but turns bright pink in base.

b. Fill a buret with an NaOH solution of known molarity and slowly add it to the HCl solution.

c. Add NaOH solution until the *end point* is reached, the point at which the indicator changes color. At the end point, the **number of moles of NaOH added equals the number of moles of HCl** in the flask. In other words, all of the HCl has reacted with NaOH and the solution is no longer acidic. Read the volume of NaOH solution added from the buret. Using the known volume and molarity of the NaOH solution and the known volume of HCl solution, the molarity of the HCl solution can be calculated.

How does a titration tell us the concentration of an HCl solution? A titration is based on the acid–base reaction that occurs between the acid in the flask (HCl) and the base that is added (NaOH). **When the number of moles of base added equals the number of moles of acid in the flask, the acid is *neutralized*, forming a salt and water.**

At the end point, the number of moles of the acid ($H^+$) and the base ($OH^-$) are equal.

$$HCl(aq) \ + \ NaOH(aq) \ \rightleftharpoons \ NaCl(aq) \ + \ H_2O(l)$$

To determine an unknown molarity from titration data requires three operations.

First, we determine the number of moles of base added using its known molarity and volume. Then we use coefficients in the balanced acid–base equation to tell us the number of moles of acid that react with the base. Finally, we determine the molarity of the acid from the calculated number of moles and the known volume of the acid.

## How To  Determine the Molarity of an Acid Solution from a Titration

**Example:** What is the molarity of an HCl solution if 22.5 mL of a 0.100 M NaOH solution are needed to titrate a 25.0 mL sample of the acid?

**Step [1]**  **Determine the number of moles of base used to neutralize the acid.**

- Convert milliliters to liters of base using a mL–L conversion factor. Use the molarity (M) and volume (V) of the base to calculate the number of moles (mol = MV).

| volume of NaOH | mL–L conversion factor | M (mol/L) conversion factor |
|---|---|---|

$$22.5 \ \text{m}\cancel{\text{L}} \ \text{NaOH} \ \times \ \frac{1 \ \cancel{\text{L}}}{1000 \ \text{m}\cancel{\text{L}}} \ \times \ \frac{0.100 \ \text{mol NaOH}}{1 \ \cancel{\text{L}}} \ = \ 0.002 \ 25 \ \text{mol NaOH}$$

**Step [2]**  **Determine the number of moles of acid that react from the balanced chemical equation.**

- In this reaction, one mole of HCl reacts with one mole of NaOH, so the number of moles of NaOH equals the number of moles of HCl at the end point.

$$HCl(aq) \ + \ NaOH(aq) \ \longrightarrow \ NaCl(aq) \ + \ H_2O(l)$$

  0.002 25 mol  0.002 25 mol

**Step [3]**  **Determine the molarity of the acid from the number of moles and known volume.**

- Convert milliliters to liters of acid using a mL–L conversion factor. Use the number of moles and known volume of the acid to calculate the molarity (M = mol/L).

| mL–L conversion factor |
|---|

$$M \ = \ \frac{\text{mol}}{\text{L}} \ = \ \frac{0.002 \ 25 \ \text{mol HCl}}{25.0 \ \text{m}\cancel{\text{L}} \ \text{solution}} \ \times \ \frac{1000 \ \text{m}\cancel{\text{L}}}{1 \ \text{L}} \ = \ 0.0900 \ \text{M HCl}$$

molarity

Sample Problem 9.19 illustrates a calculation for a titration in which the ratio of acid to base in the balanced acid–base equation is something other than 1:1.

### SAMPLE PROBLEM 9.19

Acid rain is rainwater with a lower-than-normal pH, caused by the presence of dissolved acids such as $H_2SO_4$. What is the molarity of $H_2SO_4$ in rainwater if 5.22 mL of a 0.20 M NaOH solution are needed to titrate 125 mL of the sample? The balanced equation for this acid–base reaction is given.

$$H_2SO_4(aq) + 2\ NaOH(aq) \longrightarrow Na_2SO_4(aq) + 2\ H_2O(l)$$

### Analysis and Solution

**[1] Determine the number of moles of base used to neutralize the acid.**

- Use the molarity (M) and volume (V) of the base to calculate the number of moles (mol = MV).

$$5.22\ \cancel{mL}\ NaOH \times \frac{1\ \cancel{L}}{1000\ \cancel{mL}} \times \frac{0.20\ mol\ NaOH}{1\ \cancel{L}} = 0.0010\ mol\ NaOH$$

**[2] Determine the number of moles of acid that react from the balanced chemical equation.**

- Since each $H_2SO_4$ molecule contains two protons, *one* mole of the acid $H_2SO_4$ reacts with *two* moles of the base NaOH in the neutralization reaction. The coefficients in the balanced equation form a mole ratio to calculate the number of moles of acid that react.

$$0.0010\ mol\ NaOH \times \frac{1\ mol\ H_2SO_4}{2\ mol\ NaOH} = 0.000\ 50\ mol\ H_2SO_4$$

**[3] Determine the molarity of the acid from the number of moles and known volume.**

$$M = \frac{mol}{L} = \frac{0.000\ 50\ mol\ H_2SO_4}{125\ \cancel{mL}\ solution} \times \frac{1000\ \cancel{mL}}{1\ L} = 0.0040\ M\ H_2SO_4$$

molarity                                                         **Answer**

### PROBLEM 9.31

What is the molarity of an HCl solution if 25.5 mL of a 0.24 M NaOH solution are needed to neutralize 15.0 mL of the sample?

### PROBLEM 9.32

How many milliliters of 2.0 M NaOH are needed to neutralize 5.0 mL of a 6.0 M $H_2SO_4$ solution?

## 9.10 Buffers

**A *buffer* is a solution whose pH changes very little when acid or base is added.** Most buffers are solutions composed of approximately equal amounts of a weak acid and the salt of its conjugate base.

- **The weak acid of the buffer reacts with added base, OH⁻.**
- **The conjugate base of the buffer reacts with added acid, $H_3O^+$.**

### 9.10A General Characteristics of a Buffer

The effect of a buffer can be illustrated by comparing the pH change that occurs when a small amount of strong acid or strong base is added to water, compared to the pH change that occurs when the same amount of strong acid or strong base is added to a buffer, as shown in Figure 9.10. When 0.020 mol of HCl is added to 1.0 L of water, the pH changes from 7 to 1.7, and when 0.020 mol of NaOH is added to 1.0 L of water, the pH changes from 7 to 12.3. In this example, addition of a small quantity of a strong acid or strong base to neutral water changes the pH by over 5 pH units.

The sulfur oxides formed when sulfur-containing fuel is burned form $H_2SO_4$, which acidifies rainwater. This acid rain destroys forest vegetation and makes lakes and streams too acidic for fish and shellfish to survive.

**Figure 9.10**   The Effect of a Buffer on pH Changes

a.

a. The pH of pure water changes drastically when a small amount of strong acid or strong base is added.

b. The pH of a buffer changes very little when the same amount of strong acid or strong base is added.

b.

In contrast, a buffer prepared from 0.50 M acetic acid ($CH_3COOH$) and 0.50 M sodium acetate ($NaCH_3COO$) has a pH of 4.74. Addition of the same quantity of acid, 0.020 mol HCl, changes the pH to 4.70, and addition of the same quantity of base, 0.020 mol of NaOH, changes the pH to 4.77. In this example, the change of pH in the presence of the buffer is no more than 0.04 pH units!

Why is a buffer able to absorb acid or base with very little pH change? Let's use as an example a buffer that contains equal concentrations of acetic acid ($CH_3COOH$), and the sodium salt of its conjugate base, sodium acetate ($NaCH_3COO$). $CH_3COOH$ is a weak acid, so when it dissolves in water, only a small fraction dissociates to form its conjugate base $CH_3COO^-$. In the buffer solution, however, the sodium acetate provides an equal amount of the conjugate base.

$$CH_3COOH(aq) \quad + \quad H_2O(l) \quad \rightleftharpoons \quad H_3O^+(aq) \quad + \quad CH_3COO^-(aq)$$

approximately equal amounts

In Section 9.4, we learned how to write the expression for the acid dissociation constant $K_a$ for this reaction. Rearranging this expression to solve for $[H_3O^+]$ then illustrates why a buffer does not change pH much when acid or base is added.

$$\text{Expression for } K_a: \quad K_a = \frac{[H_3O^+][CH_3COO^-]}{[CH_3COOH]}$$

$$\text{Rearranging the expression:} \quad [H_3O^+] = K_a \times \frac{[CH_3COOH]}{[CH_3COO^-]}$$

If this ratio does not change much, then $[H_3O^+]$ does not change much.

The $H_3O^+$ concentration depends on two terms—$K_a$, which is a constant, and the ratio of the concentrations of the weak acid and its conjugate base. If these concentrations do not change much, then the concentration of $H_3O^+$ and therefore the pH do not change much.

Suppose a small amount of strong acid is added to the buffer. Added $H_3O^+$ reacts with $CH_3COO^-$ to form $CH_3COOH$, so that $[CH_3COO^-]$ decreases slightly and $[CH_3COOH]$ increases slightly. However, the ratio of these two concentrations is not altered significantly, so the $[H_3O^+]$ and therefore the pH change only slightly.

On the other hand, if a small amount of strong base is added to the buffer, $OH^-$ reacts with $CH_3COOH$ to form $CH_3COO^-$, so that $[CH_3COOH]$ decreases slightly and $[CH_3COO^-]$ increases slightly. However, the ratio of these two concentrations is not altered significantly, so the $[H_3O^+]$ and therefore the pH change only slightly.

For a buffer to be effective, the amount of added acid or base must be small compared to the amount of buffer present. When a large amount of acid or base is added to a buffer, the concentrations of the weak acid and its conjugate base change a great deal, so the $H_3O^+$ concentration changes a great deal as well. Some common buffers are listed in Table 9.5.

### Table 9.5 Common Buffers

| Buffer | Weak Acid | Conjugate Base | $K_a$ |
|---|---|---|---|
| Acetic acid/acetate | $CH_3COOH$ | $CH_3COO^-$ | $1.8 \times 10^{-5}$ |
| Bicarbonate/carbonate | $HCO_3^-$ | $CO_3^{2-}$ | $5.6 \times 10^{-11}$ |
| Dihydrogen phosphate/hydrogen phosphate | $H_2PO_4^-$ | $HPO_4^{2-}$ | $6.2 \times 10^{-8}$ |
| Hydrogen phosphate/phosphate | $HPO_4^{2-}$ | $PO_4^{3-}$ | $2.2 \times 10^{-13}$ |

### PROBLEM 9.33

Determine whether a solution containing each of the following substances is a buffer. Explain your reasoning.

a. HBr and NaBr        b. HF and KF        c. $CH_3COOH$ alone

### PROBLEM 9.34

Consider a buffer prepared from the weak acid $HCO_3^-$ and its conjugate base $CO_3^{2-}$.

$$HCO_3^-(aq) + H_2O(l) \rightleftharpoons CO_3^{2-}(aq) + H_3O^+(aq)$$

a. Explain why both $HCO_3^-$ and $CO_3^{2-}$ are needed to prepare the buffer.
b. What happens to the concentrations of $HCO_3^-$ and $CO_3^{2-}$ when a small amount of acid is added to the buffer?
c. What happens to the concentrations of $HCO_3^-$ and $CO_3^{2-}$ when a small amount of base is added to the buffer?

## 9.10B Calculating the pH of a Buffer

The effective pH range of a buffer depends on its $K_a$. The pH of a buffer can be calculated from the $K_a$ of the weak acid (HA), and the concentrations of the weak acid (HA) and conjugate base (A:$^-$) used to prepare it, as shown in Sample Problem 9.20.

Acid dissociation constant $K_a$ for the general acid HA:

$$K_a = \frac{[H_3O^+][A:^-]}{[HA]}$$

Rearranging the expression to solve for $[H_3O^+]$:

$$[H_3O^+] = K_a \times \frac{[HA]}{[A:^-]}$$

determines the buffer pH

### SAMPLE PROBLEM 9.20

What is the pH of a buffer that contains 0.20 M $CH_3COOH$ and 0.20 M $NaCH_3COO$?

#### Analysis

Use the $K_a$ of the weak acid of the buffer in Table 9.5 and the expression $[H_3O^+] = K_a([HA]/[A:^-])$ to calculate $[H_3O^+]$. Calculate the pH using the expression, pH = $-\log [H_3O^+]$.

#### Solution

[1] Substitute the given concentrations of $CH_3COOH$ and $CH_3COO^-$ for [HA] and [A:$^-$], respectively. $K_a$ for $CH_3COOH$ is $1.8 \times 10^{-5}$.

$$[H_3O^+] = K_a \times \frac{[CH_3COOH]}{[CH_3COO^-]} = (1.8 \times 10^{-5}) \times \frac{[0.20 \text{ M}]}{[0.20 \text{ M}]}$$

$$[H_3O^+] = 1.8 \times 10^{-5} \text{ M}$$

[2] Use an electronic calculator to convert the $H_3O^+$ concentration to pH, as in Sample Problem 9.15.

$$pH = -\log [H_3O^+] = -\log(1.8 \times 10^{-5})$$
$$pH = 4.74$$

### PROBLEM 9.35

Calculate the pH of a dihydrogen phosphate/hydrogen phosphate buffer prepared with each of the following concentrations. What do you conclude about the pH of a buffer when equal concentrations of the weak acid and conjugate base are used to prepare it?

a. 0.10 M $NaH_2PO_4$ and 0.10 M $Na_2HPO_4$
b. 1.0 M $NaH_2PO_4$ and 1.0 M $Na_2HPO_4$
c. 0.50 M $NaH_2PO_4$ and 0.50 M $Na_2HPO_4$

### PROBLEM 9.36

What is the pH of a buffer that contains 0.20 M $CH_3COOH$ and 0.15 M $NaCH_3COO$?

## 9.10C  FOCUS ON THE ENVIRONMENT
### Acid Rain and a Naturally Buffered Lake

Unpolluted rainwater is not a neutral solution with a pH of 7; rather, because it contains dissolved carbon dioxide, it is slightly acidic with a pH of about 5.6.

$$CO_2(g) \quad + \quad 2\,H_2O(l) \quad \rightleftharpoons \quad H_3O^+(aq) \quad + \quad HCO_3^-(aq)$$

carbon dioxide
from the air

A low concentration of $H_3O^+$ gives rainwater a pH < 7.

Rainwater that contains dissolved $H_2SO_4$ (or $HNO_3$) from burning fossil fuels has a pH lower than 5.6. In some parts of the United States, rainwater often has a pH range of 4–5, and readings as low as pH = 1.8 have been recorded. When the rain in a region consistently has a lower-than-normal pH, this acid rain can have a devastating effect on plant and animal life.

The pH of some lakes changes drastically as the result of acid rain, whereas the pH of other lakes does not. In fact, the ability of some lakes to absorb acid rain without much pH change is entirely due to buffers (Figure 9.11). Lakes that are surrounded by limestone-rich soil are in contact with

Figure 9.11    Acid Rain and a Naturally Buffered Lake

Acid precipitation contains $H_2SO_4$ and $HNO_3$ dissolved in rain and snow.

$CO_3^{2-}$

$HCO_3^-$

lake surrounded by limestone ($CaCO_3$)

lake with no natural buffer

Acid rain adds $H_3O^+$ to the water, decreasing the pH.

The lake contains a natural buffer of $CO_3^{2-}$ and $HCO_3^-$. $H_3O^+$ from rain reacts with dissolved $CO_3^{2-}$, forming more $HCO_3^-$. Since the concentrations of $CO_3^{2-}$ and $HCO_3^-$ do not change by much, the pH changes only slightly.

solid calcium carbonate, $CaCO_3$. As a result, the lake contains a natural carbonate/bicarbonate buffer. When acid precipitation falls on the lake, the dissolved carbonate ($CO_3^{2-}$) reacts with the acid to form bicarbonate ($HCO_3^-$).

The buffer reacts with added acid from rain.

$$CO_3^{2-}(aq) \ + \ H_3O^+(aq) \ \rightleftharpoons \ HCO_3^-(aq) \ + \ H_2O(l)$$

A lake surrounded by limestone contains a natural $CO_3^{2-}/HCO_3^-$ buffer.

The carbonate/bicarbonate buffer thus allows the lake to resist large pH changes when acid is added. In some areas acidic lakes have been treated with limestone, thus adding calcium carbonate to neutralize the acid and restore the natural pH. This procedure is expensive and temporary because with time and more acid rain, the pH of the lakes decreases again.

## 9.11 FOCUS ON THE HUMAN BODY
### Buffers in the Blood

The normal blood pH of a healthy individual is in the range of 7.35 to 7.45. A pH above or below this range is generally indicative of an imbalance in respiratory or metabolic processes. The body is able to maintain a very stable pH because the blood and other tissues are buffered. The principal buffer in the blood is carbonic acid/bicarbonate ($H_2CO_3/HCO_3^-$).

In examining the carbonic acid/bicarbonate buffer system in the blood, two equilibria are important. First of all, carbonic acid ($H_2CO_3$) is in equilibrium with $CO_2$ dissolved in the bloodstream (Section 9.7). Second, since carbonic acid is a weak acid, it is also dissociated in water to form its conjugate base, bicarbonate ($HCO_3^-$). Bicarbonate is also generated in the kidneys.

$$CO_2(g) \ + \ H_2O(l) \ \rightleftharpoons \ \underset{\text{carbonic acid}}{H_2CO_3(aq)} \ \overset{H_2O}{\rightleftharpoons} \ H_3O^+(aq) \ + \ \underset{\text{bicarbonate}}{HCO_3^-(aq)}$$

principal buffer in the blood

$CO_2$ is constantly produced by metabolic processes in the body and then transported to the lungs to be eliminated. Thus, the amount of $CO_2$ dissolved in the blood is directly related to the $H_3O^+$ concentration and therefore the pH of the blood. If the pH of the blood is lower than 7.35, the blood is more acidic than normal, and the condition is called **acidosis.** If the pH of the blood is higher than 7.45, the blood is more basic than normal, and the condition is called **alkalosis.**

Le Châtelier's principle explains the effect of increasing or decreasing the level of dissolved $CO_2$ on the pH of the blood. A higher-than-normal $CO_2$ concentration shifts the equilibrium to the right, increasing the $H_3O^+$ concentration and lowering the pH. **Respiratory acidosis** results when the body fails to eliminate adequate amounts of $CO_2$ through the lungs. This may occur in patients with advanced lung disease or respiratory failure.

A lower respiratory rate increases [$CO_2$].

$$CO_2(g) \ + \ 2 H_2O(g) \ \rightleftharpoons \ H_3O^+(aq) \ + \ HCO_3^-(aq)$$

This drives the reaction to the right, increasing [$H_3O^+$].
Blood has a higher [$H_3O^+$] $\longrightarrow$ lower pH

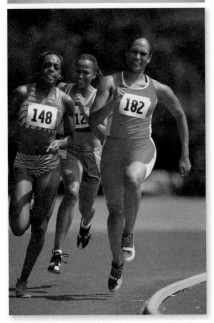

During strenuous exercise, the lungs expel more $CO_2$ than usual and the pH of the blood increases.

A lower-than-normal $CO_2$ concentration shifts the equilibria to the left, decreasing the $H_3O^+$ concentration and raising the pH. **Respiratory alkalosis** is caused by hyperventilation, very rapid breathing that occurs when an individual experiences excitement or panic.

$$CO_2(g) \;+\; 2\,H_2O(g) \;\rightleftharpoons\; H_3O^+(aq) \;+\; HCO_3^-(aq)$$

A faster respiratory rate decreases $[CO_2]$.

This drives the reaction to the left, decreasing $[H_3O^+]$.
Blood has a lower $[H_3O^+]$ $\longrightarrow$ higher pH

The pH of the blood may also be altered when the metabolic processes of the body are not in balance. **Metabolic acidosis** results when excessive amounts of acid are produced and the blood pH falls. This may be observed in patients with severe infections (sepsis) when a large amount of lactic acid accumulates. It may also occur in poorly controlled diabetes when keto acid levels rise (Chapter 24). **Metabolic alkalosis** may occur when recurrent vomiting decreases the amount of acid in the stomach, thus causing a rise in pH.

# CHAPTER HIGHLIGHTS

## KEY TERMS

Acid (9.1)
Acid dissociation constant ($K_a$, 9.4)
Acidic solution (9.5)
Amphoteric (9.2)
Base (9.1)
Basic solution (9.5)
Brønsted–Lowry acid (9.1)
Brønsted–Lowry base (9.1)

Buffer (9.10)
Conjugate acid (9.2)
Conjugate acid–base pair (9.2)
Conjugate base (9.2)
Diprotic acid (9.1)
Dissociation (9.3)
Ion–product constant ($K_w$, 9.5)
Monoprotic acid (9.1)

Net ionic equation (9.7)
Neutral solution (9.5)
Neutralization reaction (9.7)
pH scale (9.6)
Proton transfer reaction (9.2)
Spectator ion (9.7)
Titration (9.9)
Triprotic acid (9.1)

## KEY CONCEPTS

**❶ Describe the principal features of acids and bases. (9.1)**
- A Brønsted–Lowry acid is a proton donor, often symbolized by HA. A Brønsted–Lowry acid must contain one or more hydrogen atoms.
- A Brønsted–Lowry base is a proton acceptor, often symbolized by B:. To form a bond to a proton, a Brønsted–Lowry base must contain a lone pair of electrons.

**❷ What are the principal features of an acid–base reaction? (9.2)**
- In a Brønsted–Lowry acid–base reaction, a proton is transferred from the acid (HA) to the base (B:). In this reaction, the acid loses a proton to form its conjugate base ($A:^-$) and the base gains a proton to form its conjugate acid ($HB^+$).

**❸ How is acid strength related to the direction of equilibrium in an acid–base reaction? (9.3)**
- A strong acid readily donates a proton, and when dissolved in water, 100% of the acid dissociates into ions. A strong base readily accepts a proton, and when dissolved in water, 100% of the base dissociates into ions.
- An inverse relationship exists between acid and base strength. A strong acid forms a weak conjugate base, whereas a weak acid forms a strong conjugate base.
- In an acid–base reaction, the stronger acid reacts with the stronger base to form the weaker acid and the weaker base.

**4** **What is the acid dissociation constant and how is it related to acid strength? (9.4)**

- For a general acid HA, the acid dissociation constant $K_a$ is defined by the equation:

$$K_a = \frac{[H_3O^+][A:^-]}{[HA]}$$

- The stronger the acid, the larger the $K_a$. Equilibrium in an acid–base reaction favors formation of the acid with the smaller $K_a$ value.

**5** **What is the ion–product of water and how is it used to calculate hydronium or hydroxide ion concentration? (9.5)**

- The ion–product of water, $K_w$, is a constant for all aqueous solutions; $K_w = [H_3O^+][OH^-] = 1.0 \times 10^{-14}$ at 25 °C. If either $[H_3O^+]$ or $[OH^-]$ is known, the other value can be calculated from $K_w$.

**6** **What is pH? (9.6)**

- The pH of a solution measures the concentration of $H_3O^+$; $pH = -\log [H_3O^+]$.
- A pH = 7 means $[H_3O^+] = [OH^-]$ and the solution is neutral.
- A pH < 7 means $[H_3O^+] > [OH^-]$ and the solution is acidic.
- A pH > 7 means $[H_3O^+] < [OH^-]$ and the solution is basic.

**7** **Draw the products of some common acid–base reactions. (9.7)**

- In a Brønsted–Lowry acid–base reaction with hydroxide bases (MOH), the acid HA donates a proton to $OH^-$ to form $H_2O$. The anion from the acid HA combines with the cation $M^+$ of the base to form the salt MA. This reaction is called a neutralization reaction.
- In acid–base reactions with bicarbonate ($HCO_3^-$) or carbonate ($CO_3^{2-}$) bases, carbonic acid ($H_2CO_3$) is formed, which decomposes to form $H_2O$ and $CO_2$.

**8** **What happens to the pH of an aqueous solution when a salt is dissolved? (9.8)**

- A salt can form an acidic, basic, or neutral solution depending on whether its cation and anion are derived from strong or weak acids and bases. A salt derived from a strong acid and strong base forms a neutral solution with pH = 7. When one ion of a salt is derived from a weak acid or base, the ion derived from the stronger acid or base determines whether the solution is acidic or basic.

**9** **How is a titration used to determine the concentration of an acid or base? (9.9)**

- A titration is a procedure that uses a base (or acid) of known volume and molarity to react with a known volume of acid (or base) of unknown molarity. The volume and molarity of the base are used to calculate the number of moles of base that react, and from this value, the molarity of the acid can be determined.

**10** **What is a buffer? (9.10)**

- A buffer is a solution whose pH changes very little when acid or base is added. Most buffers are composed of approximately equal amounts of a weak acid and the salt of its conjugate base.

**11** **What is the principal buffer present in the blood? (9.11)**

- The principal buffer in the blood is carbonic acid/bicarbonate. Since carbonic acid ($H_2CO_3$) is in equilibrium with dissolved $CO_2$, the amount of $CO_2$ in the blood affects its pH, which is normally maintained in the range of 7.35–7.45. When the $CO_2$ concentration in the blood is higher than normal, the acid–base equilibrium shifts to form more $H_3O^+$ and the pH decreases. When the $CO_2$ concentration in the blood is lower than normal, the acid–base equilibrium shifts to consume $[H_3O^+]$, so $[H_3O^+]$ decreases, and the pH increases.

## PROBLEMS

Selected in-chapter and odd-numbered end-of-chapter problems have brief answers in Appendix B. The *Student Study Guide and Solutions Manual* contains detailed solutions to all in-chapter and odd-numbered end-of-chapter problems, as well as additional worked examples and a chapter self-test.

### Acids and Bases

**9.37** Which of the following species can be Brønsted–Lowry acids?

| | | |
|---|---|---|
| a. HBr | c. $AlCl_3$ | e. $NO_2^-$ |
| b. $Br_2$ | d. HCOOH | f. $HNO_2$ |

**9.38** Which of the following species can be Brønsted–Lowry acids?

| | | |
|---|---|---|
| a. $H_2O$ | c. HOCl | e. $CH_3CH_2COOH$ |
| b. $I^-$ | d. $FeBr_3$ | f. $CO_2$ |

**9.39** Which of the following species can be Brønsted–Lowry bases?

| | | |
|---|---|---|
| a. $OH^-$ | c. $C_2H_6$ | e. $OCl^-$ |
| b. $Ca^{2+}$ | d. $PO_4^{3-}$ | f. $MgCO_3$ |

**9.40** Which of the following species can be Brønsted–Lowry bases?

| | | |
|---|---|---|
| a. $Cl^-$ | c. $H_2O$ | e. $Ca(OH)_2$ |
| b. $BH_3$ | d. $Na^+$ | f. $HCOO^-$ |

**9.41** Draw the conjugate acid of each base.

a. $HS^-$    b. $CO_3^{2-}$    c. $NO_2^-$    d. $H-\overset{\overset{\displaystyle H}{|}}{\underset{\underset{\displaystyle H}{|}}{C}}-\overset{..}{\underset{\underset{\displaystyle H}{|}}{N}}-H$

**9.42** Draw the conjugate acid of each base.

a. $Br^-$    b. $HPO_4^{2-}$    c. $CH_3COO^-$    d. $H-\overset{\overset{\displaystyle H}{|}}{\underset{\underset{\displaystyle H}{|}}{C}}-\overset{..}{\underset{..}{O}}-H$

**9.43** Draw the conjugate base of each acid.

a. $HNO_2$    b. $NH_4^+$    c. $H_2O_2$

**9.44** Draw the conjugate base of each acid.

a. $H_3O^+$    b. $H_2Se$    c. $HSO_4^-$

**9.45** Identify the acid, base, conjugate acid, and conjugate base in each diagram. Gray spheres correspond to H atoms.

a. ⬤ + ⬤ ⟶ ⬤ + ⬤

b. ⬤ + ⬤ ⟶ ⬤ + ⬤

**9.46** Use the given representations for $H_2Z$, $HZ^-$, and $Z^{2-}$, as well as the space-filling structures of $H_2O$, $H_3O^+$, and $OH^-$ that appear in Chapter 9, to depict each equation. Label the acid, base, conjugate acid, and conjugate base in each equation.

⬤ = $H_2Z$    ⬤ = $HZ^-$    ⬤ = $Z^{2-}$

a. $H_2Z + H_2O \longrightarrow HZ^- + H_3O^+$
b. $HZ^- + OH^- \longrightarrow Z^{2-} + H_2O$

**9.47** Label the conjugate acid–base pairs in each equation.

a. $HI(g) + NH_3(g) \rightleftharpoons NH_4^+(aq) + I^-(aq)$
b. $HCOOH(l) + H_2O(l) \rightleftharpoons H_3O^+(aq) + HCOO^-(aq)$
c. $HSO_4^-(aq) + H_2O(l) \rightleftharpoons H_2SO_4(aq) + OH^-(aq)$

**9.48** Label the conjugate acid–base pairs in each equation.

a. $Cl^-(aq) + HSO_4^-(aq) \rightleftharpoons HCl(aq) + SO_4^{2-}(aq)$
b. $HPO_4^{2-}(aq) + OH^-(aq) \rightleftharpoons PO_4^{3-}(aq) + H_2O(l)$
c. $NH_3(g) + HF(g) \rightleftharpoons NH_4^+(aq) + F^-(aq)$

**9.49** Like $H_2O$, $HCO_3^-$ is amphoteric. (a) Draw the conjugate acid of $HCO_3^-$. (b) Draw the conjugate base of $HCO_3^-$.

**9.50** Like $H_2O$, $H_2PO_4^-$ is amphoteric. (a) Draw the conjugate acid of $H_2PO_4^-$. (b) Draw the conjugate base of $H_2PO_4^-$.

**9.51** Write the equation for the acid–base reaction that takes place when nitric acid ($HNO_3$) dissolves in $H_2O$.

**9.52** Write the equation for the acid–base reaction that takes place when formic acid (HCOOH) dissolves in $H_2O$.

## Acid and Base Strength

**9.53** Which diagram represents an aqueous solution of HF and which represents HCl? Explain your choice.

A

B

**9.54** Which diagram represents what happens when HCN dissolves in water? Explain your choice.

A

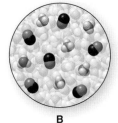

B

**9.55** (a) Which of the following represents a strong acid HZ dissolved in water? (b) Which represents a weak acid HZ dissolved in water?

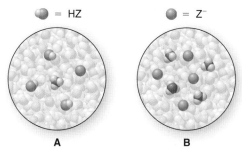

⬤ = HZ    ⬤ = $Z^-$

A          B

**9.56** (a) Using molecular art, draw a diagram that represents an aqueous solution of a strong acid $H_2Z$. (b) Using molecular art, draw a diagram that represents an aqueous solution of a weak acid $H_2Z$.

⬤ = $H_2Z$    ⬤ = $HZ^-$

**9.57** Use the data in Tables 9.1 and 9.2 to label the stronger acid in each pair.

a. $H_2O$ or $CH_3COOH$
b. $H_3PO_4$ or $HCO_3^-$
c. $H_2SO_4$ or $HSO_4^-$

**9.58** Use the data in Tables 9.1 and 9.2 to label the stronger acid in each pair.

a. $HPO_4^{2-}$ or HCN
b. $HSO_4^-$ or $NH_4^+$
c. $H_2O$ or HF

**9.59** Which acid in each pair in Problem 9.57 has the stronger conjugate base?

**9.60** Which acid in each pair in Problem 9.58 has the stronger conjugate base?

**9.61** Which acid, **A** or **B,** is stronger in each part?

a. **A** dissociates to a greater extent in water.
b. **A** has a smaller $K_a$.
c. The conjugate base of **A** is stronger than the conjugate base of **B.**

**9.62** Which acid, **A** or **B,** is stronger in each part?

a. **B** dissociates to a greater extent in water.
b. **A** has a larger $K_a$.
c. The conjugate base of **B** is stronger than the conjugate base of **A.**

## Equilibrium and Acid Dissociation Constants

**9.63** For each pair of acids: [1] Label the stronger acid. [2] Draw the conjugate bases. [3] Label the stronger conjugate base.

a.     $HSO_4^-$         or         $H_2PO_4^-$
       bisulfate                    dihydrogen phosphate
   $K_a = 1.2 \times 10^{-2}$      $K_a = 6.2 \times 10^{-8}$

b.    $CH_3CH_2COOH$     or        $CH_3COOH$
       propanoic acid               acetic acid
   $K_a = 1.3 \times 10^{-5}$      $K_a = 1.8 \times 10^{-5}$

**9.64** For each pair of acids: [1] Label the stronger acid. [2] Draw the conjugate bases. [3] Label the stronger conjugate base.

a.       $H_3PO_4$      or        HCOOH
        phosphoric acid          formic acid
        $K_a = 7.5 \times 10^{-3}$       $K_a = 1.8 \times 10^{-4}$

b.       HCOOH      or       $C_6H_5COOH$
        formic acid          benzoic acid
        $K_a = 1.8 \times 10^{-4}$      $K_a = 6.5 \times 10^{-5}$

**9.65** (a) Which diagram illustrates the stronger acid? (b) Which diagram represents the acid with the larger $K_a$?

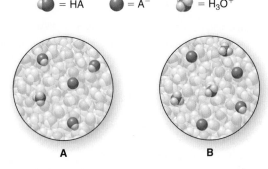

         ● = HA      ● = A⁻      ⬤ = $H_3O^+$

        **A**                **B**

**9.66** Which diagram in Problem 9.65 contains the stronger conjugate base? Explain your choice.

**9.67** Label the acid in the reactants and the conjugate acid in the products in each reaction. Use the data in Tables 9.1 and 9.2 to determine whether the reactants or products are favored at equilibrium. Explain your reasoning.

a. $H_3PO_4(aq) + CN^-(aq) \rightleftarrows H_2PO_4^-(aq) + HCN(aq)$
b. $Br^-(aq) + HSO_4^-(aq) \rightleftarrows SO_4^{2-}(aq) + HBr(aq)$
c. $CH_3COO^-(aq) + H_2CO_3(aq) \rightleftarrows$
                         $CH_3COOH(aq) + HCO_3^-(aq)$

**9.68** Label the acid in the reactants and the conjugate acid in the products in each reaction. Use the data in Tables 9.1 and 9.2 to determine whether the reactants or products are favored at equilibrium. Explain your reasoning.

a. $HF(g) + NH_3(g) \rightleftarrows NH_4^+(aq) + F^-(aq)$
b. $Br^-(aq) + H_2O(l) \rightleftarrows HBr(aq) + OH^-(aq)$
c. $HCN(aq) + HCO_3^-(aq) \rightleftarrows H_2CO_3(aq) + CN^-(aq)$

## Water and the pH Scale

**9.69** Calculate the value of [OH⁻] from the given [$H_3O^+$] and label the solution as acidic or basic.

a. $10^{-8}$ M          c. $3.0 \times 10^{-4}$ M
b. $10^{-10}$ M         d. $2.5 \times 10^{-11}$ M

**9.70** Calculate the value of [OH⁻] from the given [$H_3O^+$] and label the solution as acidic or basic.

a. $10^{-1}$ M          c. $2.6 \times 10^{-7}$ M
b. $10^{-13}$ M         d. $1.2 \times 10^{-12}$ M

**9.71** Calculate the value of [$H_3O^+$] from the given [OH⁻] and label the solution as acidic or basic.

a. $10^{-2}$ M          c. $6.2 \times 10^{-7}$ M
b. $4.0 \times 10^{-8}$ M     d. $8.5 \times 10^{-13}$ M

**9.72** Calculate the value of [$H_3O^+$] from the given [OH⁻] and label the solution as acidic or basic.

a. $10^{-12}$ M         c. $6.0 \times 10^{-4}$ M
b. $5.0 \times 10^{-10}$ M    d. $8.9 \times 10^{-11}$ M

**9.73** Calculate the pH from each $H_3O^+$ concentration determined in Problem 9.71.

**9.74** Calculate the pH from each $H_3O^+$ concentration determined in Problem 9.72.

**9.75** Complete the following table with the needed [$H_3O^+$], [OH⁻], and pH, and classify the solution as acidic, basic, or neutral.

| [$H_3O^+$] | [OH⁻] | pH | Classification |
|---|---|---|---|
| $5.3 \times 10^{-3}$ | | | |
| | $2.0 \times 10^{-8}$ | | |
| | | 4.4 | |
| | $6.8 \times 10^{-10}$ | | |

**9.76** Complete the following table with the needed [$H_3O^+$], [OH⁻], and pH, and classify the solution as acidic, basic, or neutral.

| [$H_3O^+$] | [OH⁻] | pH | Classification |
|---|---|---|---|
| $6.3 \times 10^{-4}$ | | | |
| | $2.5 \times 10^{-9}$ | | |
| | | 9.4 | |
| | $6.8 \times 10^{-4}$ | | |

**9.77** Calculate the $H_3O^+$ concentration from each pH: (a) 12; (b) 1; (c) 1.80; (d) 8.90.

**9.78** Calculate the $H_3O^+$ concentration from each pH: (a) 4; (b) 8; (c) 2.60; (d) 11.30.

**9.79** If a urine sample has a pH of 5.90, calculate the concentrations of $H_3O^+$ and $OH^-$ in the sample.

**9.80** If pancreatic fluids have a pH of 8.2, calculate the concentrations of $H_3O^+$ and $OH^-$ in the pancreas.

**9.81** What are the concentrations of $H_3O^+$ and $OH^-$ in tomatoes that have a pH of 4.10?

**9.82** What are the concentrations of $H_3O^+$ and $OH^-$ in a cola beverage that has a pH of 3.15?

**9.83** Calculate the pH of each aqueous solution: (a) 0.0025 M HCl; (b) 0.015 M KOH.

**9.84** Calculate the pH of each aqueous solution: (a) 0.015 M $HNO_3$; (b) 0.0025 M NaOH.

**9.85** Why is the pH of 0.10 M HCl lower than the pH of 0.10 M $CH_3COOH$ solution (1.0 vs. 2.88)?

**9.86** Why is the pH of 0.0050 M $CH_3COOH$ solution higher than the pH of 0.0050 M HCl solution (3.5 vs. 2.3)?

## Acid–Base Reactions

**9.87** Write a balanced equation for each reaction.
a. $HBr(aq) + KOH(aq) \longrightarrow$
b. $HNO_3(aq) + Ca(OH)_2(aq) \longrightarrow$
c. $HCl(aq) + NaHCO_3(aq) \longrightarrow$
d. $H_2SO_4(aq) + Mg(OH)_2(aq) \longrightarrow$

**9.88** Write a balanced equation for each reaction.
a. $HNO_3(aq) + LiOH(aq) \longrightarrow$
b. $H_2SO_4(aq) + NaOH(aq) \longrightarrow$
c. $K_2CO_3(aq) + HCl(aq) \longrightarrow$
d. $HI(aq) + NaHCO_3(aq) \longrightarrow$

**9.89** Marble statues, which are composed of calcium carbonate $(CaCO_3)$, are slowly eaten away by the nitric acid $(HNO_3)$ in acid rain. Write a balanced equation for the reaction of $CaCO_3$ with $HNO_3$.

**9.90** Some liquid antacids contain suspensions of aluminum hydroxide $[Al(OH)_3]$. Write a balanced equation for the reaction of $Al(OH)_3$ with the HCl in stomach acid.

## Salt Solutions

**9.91** Determine whether each salt forms an acidic, basic, or neutral solution when it dissolves in water.
a. NaI               c. $NH_4NO_3$          e. $MgBr_2$
b. LiF               d. $KHCO_3$            f. $NaH_2PO_4$

**9.92** Determine whether each salt forms an acidic, basic, or neutral solution when it dissolves in water.
a. NaBr              c. $KCH_3COO$          e. $CaBr_2$
b. NaCN              d. CsF                f. $K_3PO_4$

## Titration

**9.93** What is the molarity of an HCl solution if 35.5 mL of 0.10 M NaOH are needed to neutralize 25.0 mL of the sample?

**9.94** What is the molarity of an HCl solution if 17.2 mL of 0.15 M NaOH are needed to neutralize 5.00 mL of the sample?

**9.95** What is the molarity of an acetic acid $(CH_3COOH)$ solution if 15.5 mL of 0.20 M NaOH are needed to neutralize 25.0 mL of the sample?

**9.96** What is the molarity of an $H_2SO_4$ solution if 18.5 mL of 0.18 M NaOH are needed to neutralize 25.0 mL of the sample?

**9.97** How many milliliters of 1.0 M NaOH solution are needed to neutralize 10.0 mL of 2.5 M $CH_3COOH$ solution?

**9.98** How many milliliters of 2.0 M NaOH solution are needed to neutralize 8.0 mL of 3.5 M $H_2SO_4$ solution?

## Buffers

**9.99** Consider a weak acid $H_2A$ and its conjugate base $HA^-$. Which diagram represents a buffer? Explain your choice.

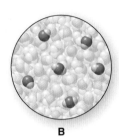

A                                    B

**9.100** Consider a weak acid $H_2A$ and its conjugate base $HA^-$. Which diagram represents a buffer? Explain your choice.

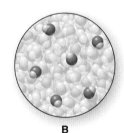

A                                    B

**9.101** Why is a buffer most effective at minimizing pH changes when the concentrations of the weak acid and its conjugate base are equal?

**9.102** Although most buffers are prepared from a weak acid and its conjugate base, explain why a buffer can also be prepared from a weak base such as $NH_3$ and its conjugate acid $NH_4^+$.

**9.103** Can a buffer be prepared from equal amounts of NaCN and HCN? Explain why or why not.

**9.104** Can a buffer be prepared from equal amounts of $HNO_3$ and $KNO_3$? Explain why or why not.

**9.105** Consider a buffer prepared from the weak acid $HNO_2$ and its conjugate base $NO_2^-$.

$$HNO_2(aq) + H_2O(l) \rightleftharpoons NO_2^-(aq) + H_3O^+(aq)$$

a. Explain why both $HNO_2$ and $NO_2^-$ are needed to prepare the buffer.
b. What happens to the concentrations of $HNO_2$ and $NO_2^-$ when a small amount of acid is added to the buffer?
c. What happens to the concentrations of $HNO_2$ and $NO_2^-$ when a small amount of base is added to the buffer?

**9.106** Consider a buffer prepared from the weak acid HF and its conjugate base F⁻.

$$HF(aq) + H_2O(l) \rightleftharpoons F^-(aq) + H_3O^+(aq)$$

a. Explain why both HF and F⁻ are needed to prepare the buffer.

b. What happens to the concentrations of HF and F⁻ when a small amount of acid is added to the buffer?

c. What happens to the concentrations of HF and F⁻ when a small amount of base is added to the buffer?

**9.107** Using the $K_a$ values in Table 9.5, calculate the pH of a buffer that contains the given concentrations of a weak acid and its conjugate base.

a. 0.10 M $Na_2HPO_4$ and 0.10 M $Na_3PO_4$

b. 0.22 M $NaHCO_3$ and 0.22 M $Na_2CO_3$

**9.108** Using the $K_a$ values in Table 9.5, calculate the pH of a buffer that contains the given concentrations of a weak acid and its conjugate base.

a. 0.55 M $CH_3COOH$ and 0.55 M $NaCH_3COO$

b. 0.15 M $NaH_2PO_4$ and 0.15 M $Na_2HPO_4$

**9.109** Calculate the pH of an acetic acid/acetate buffer in which the concentration of acetic acid is always 0.20 M, but the concentration of sodium acetate ($NaCH_3COO$) corresponds to each of the following values: (a) 0.20 M; (b) 0.40 M; (c) 0.10 M.

**9.110** Calculate the pH of a bicarbonate/carbonate buffer in which the concentration of sodium bicarbonate ($NaHCO_3$) is always 0.20 M, but the concentration of sodium carbonate ($Na_2CO_3$) corresponds to each of the following values: (a) 0.20 M; (b) 0.40 M; (c) 0.10 M.

## Applications

**9.111** Why is the pH of unpolluted rainwater lower than the pH of pure water?

**9.112** Why is the pH of acid rain lower than the pH of rainwater?

**9.113** The optimum pH of a swimming pool is 7.50. Calculate the value of $[H_3O^+]$ and $[OH^-]$ at this pH.

**9.114** A sample of rainwater has a pH of 4.18. (a) Calculate the $H_3O^+$ concentration in the sample. (b) Suggest a reason why this pH differs from the pH of unpolluted rainwater (5.6).

**9.115** When an individual hyperventilates, he is told to blow into a paper bag held over his mouth. What effect should this process have on the $CO_2$ concentration and pH of the blood?

**9.116** What is the difference between respiratory acidosis and respiratory alkalosis?

**9.117** How is $CO_2$ concentration related to the pH of the blood?

**9.118** Explain why a lake on a bed of limestone is naturally buffered against the effects of acid rain.

## CHALLENGE PROBLEMS

**9.119** Calcium hypochlorite $[Ca(OCl)_2]$ is used to chlorinate swimming pools. $Ca(OCl)_2$ acts as a source of the weak acid hypochlorous acid, HOCl, a disinfectant that kills bacteria. Write the acid–base reaction that occurs when OCl⁻ dissolves in water and explain why this reaction makes a swimming pool more basic.

**9.120** Most buffer solutions are prepared using a weak acid and a salt of its conjugate base. Explain how the following combination can also form a buffer solution: 0.20 M $H_3PO_4$ and 0.10 M NaOH.

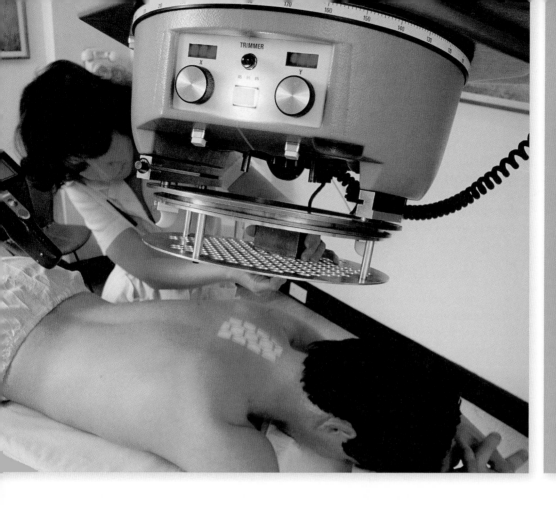

Radiation produced by cobalt-60 and other radioactive isotopes is used to treat many different forms of cancer.

# Nuclear Chemistry

## CHAPTER OUTLINE

## CHAPTER GOALS

*In this chapter you will learn how to:*

1. Describe the different types of radiation emitted by a radioactive nucleus

2. Write equations for nuclear reactions

3. Define half-life

4. Recognize the units used for measuring radioactivity

5. Give examples of common radioisotopes used in medical diagnosis and treatment

6. Describe the general features of nuclear fission and nuclear fusion

7. Describe the features of medical imaging techniques that do not use radioactivity

Thus far our study of reactions has concentrated on processes that involve the valence electrons of atoms. In these reactions, bonds that join atoms are broken and new bonds between atoms are formed, but the identity of the atoms does not change. In Chapter 10, we turn our attention to **nuclear reactions,** processes that involve changes in the nucleus of atoms. While certainly much less common than chemical reactions that occur with electrons, nuclear reactions form a useful group of processes with a wide range of applications. Nuclear medicine labs in hospitals use radioactive isotopes to diagnose disease, visualize organs, and treat tumors. Generating energy in nuclear power plants, dating archaeological objects using the isotope carbon-14, and designing a simple and reliable smoke detector all utilize the concepts of nuclear chemistry discussed here in Chapter 10.

## 10.1    Introduction

Although most reactions involve valence electrons, a small but significant group of reactions, **nuclear reactions,** involves the subatomic particles of the nucleus. To understand nuclear reactions we must first review facts presented in Chapter 2 regarding isotopes and the characteristics of the nucleus.

### 10.1A    Isotopes

The nucleus of an atom is composed of protons and neutrons.

> • The atomic number (Z) = the number of protons in the nucleus.
> • The mass number (A) = the number of protons and neutrons in the nucleus.

Atoms of the same type of element have the same atomic number, but the number of neutrons may vary.

> • Isotopes are atoms of the same element having a different number of neutrons.

As a result, isotopes have the same atomic number (Z) but different mass numbers (A). Carbon, for example, has three naturally occurring isotopes. Each isotope has six protons in the nucleus (i.e., Z = 6), but the number of neutrons may be six, seven, or eight. Thus, the mass numbers (A) of these isotopes are 12, 13, and 14, respectively. As we learned in Chapter 2, we can refer to these isotopes as carbon-12, carbon-13, and carbon-14. Isotopes are also written with the mass number to the upper left of the element symbol and the atomic number to the lower left.

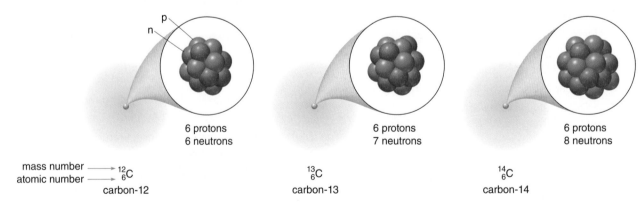

6 protons
6 neutrons

6 protons
7 neutrons

6 protons
8 neutrons

mass number $\longrightarrow$ $^{12}_{6}C$

atomic number $\longrightarrow$

carbon-12

$^{13}_{6}C$

carbon-13

$^{14}_{6}C$

carbon-14

Many isotopes are stable, but a larger number are not.

> • A *radioactive isotope,* called a *radioisotope,* is unstable and spontaneously emits energy to form a more stable nucleus.

*Radioactivity* **is the nuclear radiation emitted spontaneously by an unstable radioactive isotope.** Of the known isotopes of all the elements, 264 are stable and 300 are naturally occurring but unstable. An even larger number of radioactive isotopes, called **artificial isotopes,** have been produced in the laboratory. Both carbon-12 and carbon-13 are stable isotopes and occur in higher natural abundance than carbon-14, a radioactive isotope.

## SAMPLE PROBLEM 10.1

Iodine-123 and iodine-131 are radioactive isotopes used for the diagnosis or treatment of thyroid disease. Complete the following table for both isotopes.

|  | Atomic Number | Mass Number | Number of Protons | Number of Neutrons | Isotope Symbol |
|---|---|---|---|---|---|
| Iodine-123 |  |  |  |  |  |
| Iodine-131 |  |  |  |  |  |

### Analysis

- The atomic number = the number of protons.
- The mass number = the number of protons + the number of neutrons.
- Isotopes are written with the mass number to the upper left of the element symbol and the atomic number to the lower left.

### Solution

|  | Atomic Number | Mass Number | Number of Protons | Number of Neutrons | Isotope Symbol |
|---|---|---|---|---|---|
| Iodine-123 | 53 | 123 | 53 | $123 - 53 = 70$ | $^{123}_{53}\text{I}$ |
| Iodine-131 | 53 | 131 | 53 | $131 - 53 = 78$ | $^{131}_{53}\text{I}$ |

## PROBLEM 10.1

Complete the following table for two isotopes of cobalt. Cobalt-60 is commonly used in cancer therapy.

|  | Atomic Number | Mass Number | Number of Protons | Number of Neutrons | Isotope Symbol |
|---|---|---|---|---|---|
| Cobalt-59 |  |  |  |  |  |
| Cobalt-60 |  |  |  |  |  |

## PROBLEM 10.2

Each of the following radioisotopes is used in medicine. For each isotope give its: [1] atomic number; [2] mass number; [3] number of protons; [4] number of neutrons.

a. $^{85}_{38}\text{Sr}$
used in bone scans

b. $^{67}_{31}\text{Ga}$
used in abdominal scans

c. selenium-75
used in pancreas scans

## 10.1B  Types of Radiation

Different forms of radiation are emitted when a radioactive nucleus is converted to a more stable nucleus, including **alpha particles, beta particles, positrons,** and **gamma radiation.**

- An *alpha particle* is a high-energy particle that contains two protons and two neutrons.

alpha particle:  $\alpha$  or  $^{4}_{2}\text{He}$

An alpha particle, symbolized by the Greek letter **alpha ($\alpha$)** or the element symbol for helium, has a +2 charge and a mass number of 4.

- A *beta particle* is a high-energy electron.

$$\text{beta particle:} \quad \beta \quad \text{or} \quad {}_{-1}^{0}e$$

An electron has a $-1$ charge and a negligible mass compared to a proton. A beta particle, symbolized by the Greek letter **beta ($\beta$),** is also drawn with the symbol for an electron, **e,** with a mass number of 0 in the upper left corner and a charge of $-1$ in the lower left corner. A $\beta$ particle is formed when a neutron (n) is converted to a proton (p) and an electron.

$$\overbrace{\qquad}^{\text{mass = 1 amu}}$$
$${}_{0}^{1}\text{n} \longrightarrow {}_{1}^{1}\text{p} \quad + \quad {}_{-1}^{0}\text{e}$$

neutron           proton    $\beta$ particle

- A *positron* is called an *antiparticle* of a $\beta$ particle, since their charges are different but their masses are the same.

Thus, a **positron** has a negligible mass like a $\beta$ particle, but is opposite in charge, $+1$. A positron, symbolized as $\beta^{+}$, is also drawn with the symbol for an electron, **e,** with a mass number of 0 in the upper left corner and a charge of $+1$ in the lower left corner. A positron, which can be thought of as a "positive electron," is formed when a proton is converted to a neutron.

**Symbol:** ${}_{+1}^{0}\text{e}$ or $\beta^{+}$    **Formation:** ${}_{1}^{1}\text{p} \longrightarrow {}_{0}^{1}\text{n} + {}_{+1}^{0}\text{e}$

positron                              proton      neutron positron

- *Gamma rays* are high-energy radiation released from a radioactive nucleus.

Gamma rays, symbolized by the Greek letter **gamma ($\gamma$),** are a form of energy and thus they have no mass or charge. Table 10.1 summarizes the properties of some of the different types of radiation.

$$\text{gamma ray:} \quad \gamma$$

### Table 10.1 Types of Radiation

| Type of Radiation | Symbol | Charge | Mass |
| --- | --- | --- | --- |
| Alpha particle | $\alpha$ or ${}_{2}^{4}\text{He}$ | $+2$ | 4 |
| Beta particle | $\beta$ or ${}_{-1}^{0}\text{e}$ | $-1$ | 0 |
| Positron | $\beta^{+}$ or ${}_{+1}^{0}\text{e}$ | $+1$ | 0 |
| Gamma ray | $\gamma$ | 0 | 0 |

### PROBLEM 10.3

What is the difference between an $\alpha$ particle and a helium atom?

### PROBLEM 10.4

Identify Q in each of the following symbols.

a. ${}_{-1}^{0}\text{Q}$        b. ${}_{2}^{4}\text{Q}$        c. ${}_{+1}^{0}\text{Q}$

### 10.1C  FOCUS ON HEALTH & MEDICINE
The Effects of Radioactivity

Radioactivity cannot be seen, smelled, tasted, heard, or felt, and yet it can have powerful effects. Because it is high in energy, nuclear radiation penetrates the surface of an object or living organism, where it can damage or kill cells. The cells that are most sensitive to radiation are those that undergo rapid cell division, such as those in bone marrow, reproductive organs, skin, and the intestinal tract. Since cancer cells also rapidly divide, they are also particularly sensitive to radiation, a fact that makes radiation an effective method of cancer treatment (Section 10.5).

Alpha ($\alpha$) particles, $\beta$ particles, and $\gamma$ rays differ in the extent to which they can penetrate a surface. Alpha particles are the heaviest of the radioactive particles, and as a result they move the slowest and penetrate the least. Individuals who work with radioisotopes that emit $\alpha$ particles wear lab coats and gloves that provide a layer of sufficient protection. Beta particles move much faster since they have negligible mass, and they can penetrate into body tissue. Lab workers and health professionals must wear heavy lab coats and gloves when working with substances that give off $\beta$ particles. Gamma rays travel the fastest and readily penetrate body tissue. Working with substances that emit $\gamma$ rays is extremely hazardous, and a thick lead shield is required to halt their penetration.

That $\gamma$ rays kill cells is used to an advantage in the food industry. To decrease the incidence of harmful bacteria in foods, certain fruits and vegetables are irradiated with $\gamma$ rays that kill any bacteria contained in them. **Foods do not come into contact with radioisotopes and the food is not radioactive after irradiation.** Gamma rays merely penetrate the food and destroy any live organism, and often as a result, the food product has a considerably longer shelf life.

A lab worker must use protective equipment when working with radioactive substances.

**CONSUMER NOTE**

Strawberries that have been irradiated (on left) show no mold growth after two weeks, compared to strawberries that have not been irradiated (on right), which are moldy.

## 10.2  Nuclear Reactions

*Radioactive decay* **is the process by which an unstable radioactive nucleus emits radiation, forming a nucleus of new composition.** A nuclear equation can be written for this process, which contains the original nucleus, the new nucleus, and the radiation emitted. Unlike a chemical equation that balances atoms, in a nuclear equation the mass numbers and the atomic numbers of the nuclei must be balanced.

- The sum of the mass numbers ($A$) must be equal on both sides of a nuclear equation.
- The sum of the atomic numbers ($Z$) must be equal on both sides of a nuclear equation.

### 10.2A  Alpha Emission

*Alpha emission* **is the decay of a nucleus by emitting an $\alpha$ particle.** For example, uranium-238 decays to thorium-234 by loss of an $\alpha$ particle.

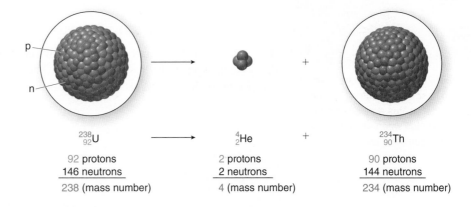

| $^{238}_{92}\text{U}$ | $^{4}_{2}\text{He}$ | $^{234}_{90}\text{Th}$ |
|---|---|---|
| 92 protons | 2 protons | 90 protons |
| 146 neutrons | 2 neutrons | 144 neutrons |
| 238 (mass number) | 4 (mass number) | 234 (mass number) |

Since an α particle has two protons, **the new nucleus has *two fewer protons* than the original nucleus.** Because it has a *different* number of protons, **the new nucleus represents a *different* element.** Uranium-238 has 92 protons, so loss of two protons forms the element thorium with 90 protons. The thorium nucleus has a mass number that is four fewer than the original—234—because it has been formed by loss of an α particle with a mass number of four.

As a result, the sum of the mass numbers is equal on both sides of the equation—238 = 4 + 234. The sum of the atomic numbers is also equal on both sides of the equation—92 = 2 + 90.

---

*How To* **Balance an Equation for a Nuclear Reaction**

Example: Write a balanced nuclear equation showing how americium-241, a radioactive element used in smoke detectors, decays to form an α particle.

Step [1] **Write an incomplete equation with the original nucleus on the left and the particle emitted on the right.**
- Include the mass number and atomic number (from the periodic table) in the equation.

$$^{241}_{95}\text{Am} \longrightarrow {}^{4}_{2}\text{He} + \text{?}$$

Step [2] **Calculate the mass number and atomic number of the newly formed nucleus on the right.**
- Mass number: Subtract the mass of an α particle (4) to obtain the mass of the new nucleus; 241 – 4 = 237.
- Atomic number: Subtract the two protons of an α particle to obtain the atomic number of the new nucleus; 95 – 2 = 93.

Step [3] **Use the atomic number to identify the new nucleus and complete the equation.**
- From the periodic table, the element with an atomic number of 93 is neptunium, Np.
- Write the mass number and the atomic number with the element symbol to complete the equation.

$$241 = 4 + 237$$
$$95 = 2 + 93$$
$$^{241}_{95}\text{Am} \longrightarrow {}^{4}_{2}\text{He} + {}^{237}_{93}\text{Np}$$

---

Americium-241 is a radioactive element contained in smoke detectors. The decay of α particles creates an electric current that is interrupted when smoke enters the detector, sounding an alarm.

**PROBLEM 10.5**

Radon, a radioactive gas formed in the soil, can cause lung cancers when inhaled in high concentrations for a long period of time. Write a balanced nuclear equation for the decay of radon-222, which emits an α particle.

**PROBLEM 10.6**

Radon (Problem 10.5) is formed in the soil as a product of radioactive decay that produces an α particle. Write a balanced nuclear equation for the formation of radon-222 and an α particle.

**PROBLEM 10.7**

Write a balanced equation showing how each nucleus decays to form a new element after releasing an α particle: (a) polonium-218; (b) thorium-230; (c) Es-252.

## 10.2B Beta Emission

***Beta emission* is the decay of a nucleus by emitting a β particle.** For example, carbon-14 decays to nitrogen-14 by loss of a β particle. The decay of carbon-14 is used to date archaeological specimens (Section 10.3).

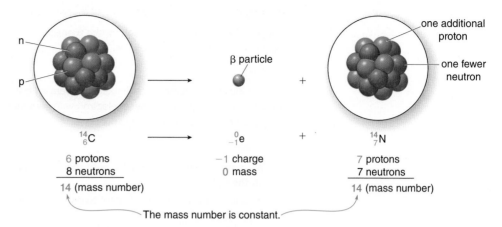

The mass number is constant.

In β emission, one neutron of the original nucleus decays to a β particle and a proton. As a result, the **new nucleus has *one more proton*** and ***one fewer neutron*** **than the original nucleus.** In this example, a carbon atom with six protons decays to a nitrogen atom with seven protons. Since the total number of particles in the nucleus does not change, the **mass number is constant.**

The subscripts that represent the atomic numbers are balanced because the β particle has a charge of −1. Seven protons on the right side plus a −1 charge for the β particle gives a total "charge" of +6, the atomic number of carbon on the left. The mass numbers are also balanced since a β particle has zero mass, and both the original nucleus and the new nucleus contain 14 subatomic particles (protons + neutrons).

Radioactive elements that emit β radiation are widely used in medicine. Since β radiation is composed of high-energy, rapidly moving electrons that penetrate tissue in a small, localized region, radioactive elements situated in close contact with tumor cells kill them. Although both healthy and diseased cells are destroyed by this internal radiation therapy, rapidly dividing tumor cells are more sensitive to its effects and therefore their growth and replication are affected the most.

Iodine-131, a radioactive element that emits β radiation, is used to treat hyperthyroidism, a condition resulting from an overactive thyroid gland (Figure 10.1). When iodine-131 is administered, it is incorporated into thyroxine, an iodine-containing hormone that is concentrated in the thyroid gland. The β radiation emitted by the iodine-131 kills some of the thyroid tissue, so that the gland is no longer overactive.

**Figure 10.1**    The Use of Iodine-131 to Treat Hyperthyroidism

Iodine-131 is incorporated into the thyroid hormone thyroxine. Beta radiation emitted by the radioactive isotope destroys nearby thyroid cells, thus decreasing the activity of the thyroid gland and bringing the disease under control.

### SAMPLE PROBLEM 10.2

Write a balanced nuclear equation for the β emission of phosphorus-32, a radioisotope used to treat leukemia and other blood disorders.

#### Analysis

Balance the atomic numbers and mass numbers on both sides of a nuclear equation. With β emission, treat the β particle as an electron with zero mass in balancing mass numbers, and a –1 charge when balancing the atomic numbers.

#### Solution

**[1] Write an incomplete equation with the original nucleus on the left and the particle emitted on the right.**

- Use the identity of the element to determine the atomic number; phosphorus has an atomic number of 15.

$$^{32}_{15}P \longrightarrow \ ^{\ 0}_{-1}e \ + \ ?$$

**[2] Calculate the mass number and the atomic number of the newly formed nucleus on the right.**

- Mass number: Since a β particle has no mass, the masses of the new particle and the original particle are the same, 32.
- Atomic number: Since β emission converts a neutron into a proton, the new nucleus has one more proton than the original nucleus; $15 = -1 + ?$. Thus the new nucleus has an atomic number of 16.

**[3] Use the atomic number to identify the new nucleus and complete the equation.**

- From the periodic table, the element with an atomic number of 16 is sulfur, S.
- Write the mass number and the atomic number with the element symbol to complete the equation.

$$^{32}_{15}P \longrightarrow \ ^{\ 0}_{-1}e \ + \ ^{32}_{16}S$$

### PROBLEM 10.8

Write a balanced nuclear equation for the β emission of iodine-131.

### PROBLEM 10.9

Write a balanced nuclear equation for the β emission of each of the following isotopes.

a. $^{20}_{9}F$          b. $^{92}_{38}Sr$          c. chromium-55

## 10.2C   Positron Emission

***Positron emission* is the decay of a nucleus by emitting a positron (β⁺).** For example, carbon-11, an artificial radioactive isotope of carbon, decays to boron-11 by loss of a β⁺ particle. Positron emitters are used in a relatively new diagnostic technique, positron emission tomography (PET), described in Section 10.5.

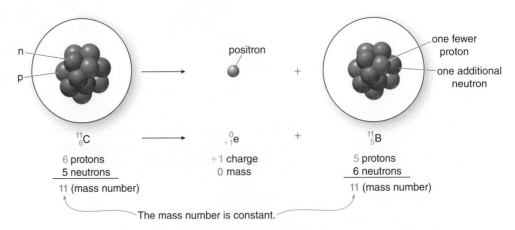

In positron emission, one proton of the original nucleus decays to a $\beta^+$ particle and a neutron. As a result, the **new nucleus has *one fewer proton* and *one more neutron* than the original nucleus.** In this example, a carbon atom with six protons decays to a boron atom with five protons. Since the total number of particles in the nucleus does not change, the **mass number is constant.**

### SAMPLE PROBLEM 10.3

Write a balanced nuclear equation for the positron emission of fluorine-18, a radioisotope used for imaging in PET scans.

#### Analysis

Balance the atomic numbers and mass numbers on both sides of a nuclear equation. With $\beta^+$ emission, treat the positron as a particle with zero mass when balancing mass numbers, and a +1 charge when balancing the atomic numbers.

#### Solution

**[1] Write an incomplete equation with the original nucleus on the left and the particle emitted on the right.**

- Use the identity of the element to determine the atomic number; fluorine has an atomic number of 9.

$$^{18}_{9}\text{F} \longrightarrow \ ^{0}_{+1}\text{e} \ + \ ?$$

**[2] Calculate the mass number and the atomic number of the newly formed nucleus on the right.**

- Mass number: Since a $\beta^+$ particle has no mass, the masses of the new particle and the original particle are the same, 18.
- Atomic number: Since $\beta^+$ emission converts a proton into a neutron, the new nucleus has one fewer proton than the original nucleus; $9 - 1 = 8$. Thus, the new nucleus has an atomic number of 8.

**[3] Use the atomic number to identify the new nucleus and complete the equation.**

- From the periodic table, the element with an atomic number of 8 is oxygen, O.
- Write the mass number and the atomic number with the element symbol to complete the equation.

$$^{18}_{9}\text{F} \longrightarrow \ ^{0}_{+1}\text{e} \ + \ ^{18}_{8}\text{O}$$

### PROBLEM 10.10

Write a balanced nuclear equation for the positron emission of each of the following nuclei:
(a) arsenic-74; (b) oxygen-15.

## 10.2D  Gamma Emission

*Gamma emission* is the decay of a nucleus by emitting $\gamma$ radiation. Since $\gamma$ rays are simply a form of energy, their emission causes **no change in the atomic number or mass number** of a radioactive nucleus. Gamma emission sometimes occurs alone. For example, one form of technetium-99, written as technetium-99m, is an energetic form of the technetium nucleus that decays with emission of $\gamma$ rays to technetium-99, a more stable but still radioactive element.

$$^{99m}_{43}\text{Tc} \longrightarrow \ ^{99}_{43}\text{Tc} \ + \ \gamma$$

The mass number and atomic number are the same.

The *m* in technetium-99m stands for *metastable.* This designation is meant to indicate that the isotope decays to a more stable form of the same isotope.

Technetium-99m is a widely used radioisotope in medical imaging. Because it emits high-energy $\gamma$ rays but decays in a short period of time, it is used to image the brain, thyroid, lungs, liver, skeleton, and many other organs. It has also been used to detect ulcers in the gastrointestinal system, and combined with other compounds, it is used to map the circulatory system and gauge damage after a heart attack.

More commonly, γ emission accompanies α or β emission. For example, cobalt-60 decays with both β and γ emission. Because a β particle is formed, decay generates an element with the *same* mass but a *different* number of protons, and thus a new element, nickel-60.

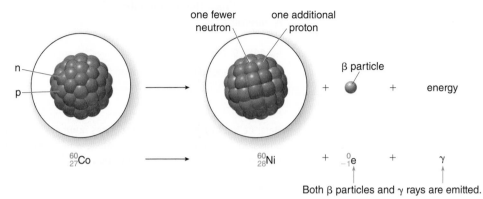

Both β particles and γ rays are emitted.

Cobalt-60 is used in external radiation treatment for cancer. Radiation generated by cobalt-60 decay is focused on a specific site in the body that contains cancerous cells (Figure 10.2). By directing the radiation on the tumor, damage to surrounding healthy tissues is minimized.

### PROBLEM 10.11

Write a nuclear equation for the decay of iridium-192 with β and γ emission. Iridium implants have been used to treat breast cancer. After the correct dose is administered, the iridium source is removed.

### PROBLEM 10.12

Complete each nuclear equation.

a. $^{11}_{5}B \longrightarrow ? + \gamma$       b. $^{40}_{19}K \longrightarrow ? + ^{0}_{-1}e + \gamma$

**Figure 10.2**    Focus on Health & Medicine: External Radiation Treatment for Tumors

a.                                                      b.                                          c.

a. Gamma radiation from the decay of cobalt-60 is used to treat a variety of tumors, especially those that cannot be surgically removed.

b. A tumor (bright area in circle) before radiation treatment

c. A tumor (bright area in circle) that has decreased in size after six months of radiation treatment

## 10.3  Half-Life

How fast do radioactive isotopes decay? It depends on the isotope.

> • The *half-life* ($t_{1/2}$) of a radioactive isotope is the time it takes for one-half of the sample to decay.

### 10.3A  General Features

Suppose we have a sample that contains 16 g of phosphorus-32, a radioactive isotope that decays to sulfur-32 by β emission (Sample Problem 10.2). Phosphorus-32 has a half-life of approximately 14 days. Thus, after 14 days, the sample contains only half the amount of P-32—8.0 g. After another 14 days (a total of two half-lives), the 8.0 g of P-32 is again halved to 4.0 g. After another 14 days (a total of three half-lives), the 4.0 g of P-32 is halved to 2.0 g, and so on. Every 14 days, half of the P-32 decays.

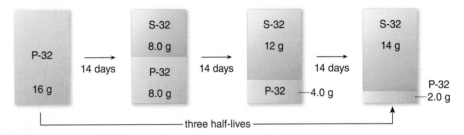

Many naturally occurring isotopes have long half-lives. Examples include carbon-14 (5,730 years) and uranium-235 ($7.0 \times 10^8$ years). Radioisotopes that are used for diagnosis and imaging in medicine have short half-lives so they do not linger in the body. Examples include technetium-99m (6.0 hours) and iodine-131 (8.0 days). The half-lives of several elements are given in Table 10.2.

**The half-life of a radioactive isotope is a property of a given isotope and is independent of the amount of sample, temperature, and pressure.** Thus, if the half-life and amount of a sample are known, it is possible to predict how much of the radioactive isotope will remain after a period of time.

### Table 10.2  Half-Lives of Some Common Radioisotopes

| Radioisotope | Symbol | Half-Life | Use |
|---|---|---|---|
| Carbon-14 | $^{14}_{6}C$ | 5,730 years | Archaeological dating |
| Cobalt-60 | $^{60}_{27}Co$ | 5.3 years | Cancer therapy |
| Iodine-131 | $^{131}_{53}I$ | 8.0 days | Thyroid therapy |
| Potassium-40 | $^{40}_{19}K$ | $1.3 \times 10^9$ years | Geological dating |
| Phosphorus-32 | $^{32}_{15}P$ | 14.3 days | Leukemia treatment |
| Technetium-99m | $^{99m}_{43}Tc$ | 6.0 hours | Organ imaging |
| Uranium-235 | $^{235}_{92}U$ | $7.0 \times 10^8$ years | Nuclear reactors |

## How To  Use a Half-Life to Determine the Amount of Radioisotope Present

**Example:** If the half-life of iodine-131 is 8.0 days, how much of a 100. mg sample of iodine-131 remains after 32 days?

**Step [1]** **Determine how many half-lives occur in the given amount of time.**

- Use the half-life of iodine-131 as a conversion factor to convert the number of days to the number of half-lives.

$$32 \text{ days} \times \frac{1 \text{ half-life}}{8.0 \text{ days}} = 4.0 \text{ half-lives}$$

**Step [2]** **For each half-life, multiply the initial mass by one-half to obtain the final mass.**

- Since 32 days corresponds to *four* half-lives, multiply the initial mass by ½ *four* times to obtain the final mass. After four half-lives, 6.25 mg of iodine-131 remains.

$$\underbrace{100. \text{ mg}}_{\text{initial mass}} \times \underbrace{\frac{1}{2} \times \frac{1}{2} \times \frac{1}{2} \times \frac{1}{2}}_{\text{The mass is halved four times.}} = 6.25 \text{ mg of iodine-131 remains.}$$

---

### PROBLEM 10.13

How much phosphorus-32 remains from a 1.00 g sample after each of the following number of half-lives: (a) 2; (b) 4; (c) 8; (d) 20?

### PROBLEM 10.14

If a 160. mg sample of technetium-99m is used for a diagnostic procedure, how much Tc-99m remains after each interval: (a) 6.0 h; (b) 18.0 h; (c) 24.0 h; (d) 2 days?

## 10.3B  Archaeological Dating

Archaeologists use the half-life of carbon-14 to determine the age of carbon-containing material derived from plants or animals. The technique, **radiocarbon dating,** is based on the fact that the ratio of radioactive carbon-14 to stable carbon-12 is a constant value in a living organism that is constantly taking in $CO_2$ and other carbon-containing nutrients from its surroundings. Once the organism dies, however, the radioactive isotope (C-14) decays (Section 10.2B) without being replenished, thus decreasing its concentration, while the stable isotope of carbon (C-12) remains at a constant value. By comparing the ratio of C-14 to C-12 in an artifact to the ratio of C-14 to C-12 in organisms today, the age of the artifact can be determined. Radiocarbon dating can be used to give the approximate age of wood, cloth, bone, charcoal, and many other substances that contain carbon.

The half-life of carbon-14 is 5,730 years, so half of the C-14 has decayed after about 6,000 years. Thus, a 6,000-year-old object has a ratio of C-14 to C-12 that has decreased by a factor of two, a 12,000-year-old object has a ratio of C-14 to C-12 that has decreased by a factor of four, and so forth.

This isotope decays, so its concentration decreases.     $\frac{1}{2}$ (original amount)     $\frac{1}{4}$ (original amount)

$$\frac{\text{carbon-14}}{\text{carbon-12}} \xrightarrow[\text{5,730 years}]{\text{1}^{\text{st}} \text{ half-life}} \frac{\text{carbon-14}}{\text{carbon-12}} \xrightarrow[\text{5,730 years}]{\text{2}^{\text{nd}} \text{ half-life}} \frac{\text{carbon-14}}{\text{carbon-12}}$$

This isotope does not decay, so its concentration remains the same.

Using this technique, archaeologists have determined the age of the paintings on cave walls in Algeria to be about 8,000 years old (Figure 10.3). Because the amount of carbon-14 decreases with time, artifacts older than about 20,000 years have too little carbon-14 to accurately estimate their age.

Figure 10.3    Radiocarbon Dating

Radiocarbon dating has been used to estimate the age of this Algerian cave painting at about 8,000 years.

A Geiger counter is a device used to detect radiation.

Individuals who work with radioactivity wear badges to monitor radiation levels.

### PROBLEM 10.15

Estimate the age of an artifact that has 1/8 of the amount of C-14 (relative to C-12) compared to living organisms.

## 10.4    Detecting and Measuring Radioactivity

We all receive a miniscule daily dose of radiation from cosmic rays and radioactive substances in the soil. Additional radiation exposure comes from television sets, dental X-rays, and other man-made sources. Moreover, we are still exposed to nuclear fallout, residual radiation resulting from the testing of nuclear weapons in the atmosphere decades ago.

Although this background radiation is unavoidable and minute, higher levels can be harmful and life-threatening because radiation is composed of high-energy particles and waves that damage cells and disrupt key biological processes, often causing cell death. How can radiation be detected and measured when it can't be directly observed by any of the senses?

A **Geiger counter** is a small portable device used for measuring radioactivity. It consists of a tube filled with argon gas that is ionized when it comes into contact with nuclear radiation. This in turn generates an electric current that produces a clicking sound or registers on a meter. Geiger counters are used to locate a radiation source or a site that has become contaminated by radioactivity.

Individuals who work with radioactivity wear protective clothing (Section 10.1) as well as radiation badges. A radiation badge contains photographic film that fogs when it comes into contact with radioactivity. These badges are regularly monitored to assure that these individuals are not exposed to unhealthy levels of harmful radiation.

## 10.4A   Measuring the Radioactivity in a Sample

**The amount of radioactivity in a sample is measured by the number of nuclei that decay per unit time—disintegrations per second.** The most common unit is the **curie** (Ci), and smaller units derived from it, the **millicurie** (mCi) and the **microcurie** ($\mu$Ci). One curie equals $3.7 \times 10^{10}$ disintegrations/second, which corresponds to the decay rate of 1 g of the element radium.

1 Ci = $3.7 \times 10^{10}$ disintegrations/second

1 Ci = 1,000 mCi

1 Ci = 1,000,000 $\mu$Ci

The **becquerel** (Bq), an SI unit, is also used to measure radioactivity; 1 Bq = 1 disintegration/second. Since each nuclear decay corresponds to one becquerel, 1 Ci = $3.7 \times 10^{10}$ Bq. Radioactivity units are summarized in Table 10.3.

Often a dose of radiation is measured in the number of millicuries that must be administered. For example, a diagnostic test for thyroid activity uses sodium iodide that contains iodine-131—that is, Na$^{131}$I. The radioisotope is purchased with a known amount of radioactivity per milliliter, such as 3.5 mCi/mL. By knowing the amount of radioactivity a patient must be given, as well as the concentration of radioactivity in the sample, one can calculate the volume of radioactive isotope that must be administered (Sample Problem 10.4).

### SAMPLE PROBLEM 10.4

A patient must be given a 4.5-mCi dose of iodine-131, which is available as a solution that contains 3.5 mCi/mL. What volume of solution must be administered?

### Analysis

Use the amount of radioactivity (mCi/mL) as a conversion factor to convert the dose of radioactivity from millicuries to a volume in milliliters.

### Solution

The dose of radioactivity is known in millicuries, and the amount of radioactivity per unit volume (3.5 mCi/mL) is also known. Use 3.5 mCi/mL as a millicurie–milliliter conversion factor.

mCi–mL
conversion factor

4.5 m̶C̶i̶ dose   $\times$   $\dfrac{1\ \text{mL}}{3.5\ \text{m̶C̶i̶}}$   =   1.3 mL dose

Millicuries cancel.         **Answer**

### PROBLEM 10.16

To treat a thyroid tumor, a patient must be given a 110-mCi dose of iodine-131, supplied in a vial containing 25 mCi/mL. What volume of solution must be administered?

## 10.4B   Measuring Human Exposure to Radioactivity

Several units are used to measure the amount of radiation *absorbed* by an organism.

- The **rad**—radiation absorbed dose—is the amount of radiation absorbed by one gram of a substance. The amount of energy absorbed varies with both the nature of the substance and the type of radiation.
- The **rem**—radiation equivalent for man—is the amount of radiation that also factors in its energy and potential to damage tissue. Using rem as a measure of radiation, 1 rem of any type of radiation produces the same amount of tissue damage.

Other units to measure absorbed radiation include the **gray** (1 Gy = 100 rad) and the **sievert** (1 Sv = 100 rem).

---

**Table 10.3 Units Used to Measure Radioactivity**

| |
|---|
| 1 Ci = $3.7 \times 10^{10}$ disintegrations/s |
| 1 Ci = $3.7 \times 10^{10}$ Bq |
| 1 Ci = 1,000 mCi |
| 1 Ci = 1,000,000 $\mu$Ci |

The curie is named for Polish chemist Marie Skłodowska Curie who discovered the radioactive elements polonium and radium, and received Nobel Prizes for both Chemistry and Physics in the early twentieth century.

Although background radiation varies with location, the average radiation dose per year for an individual is estimated at 0.27 rem. Generally, no detectable biological effects are noticed when the dose of radiation is less than 25 rem. A single dose of 25–100 rem causes a temporary decrease in white blood cell count. The symptoms of radiation sickness—nausea, vomiting, fatigue, and prolonged decrease in white blood cell count—are visible at a dose of more than 100 rem.

Death results at still higher doses of radiation. The **LD$_{50}$—the lethal dose that kills 50% of a population**—is 500 rem in humans, and exposure to 600 rem of radiation is fatal for an entire population.

### PROBLEM 10.17

The unit millirem (1 rem = 1,000 mrem) is often used to measure the amount of radiation absorbed. (a) The average yearly dose of radiation from radon gas is 200 mrem. How many rem does this correspond to? (b) If a thyroid scan exposes a patient to 0.014 rem of radiation, how many mrem does this correspond to? (c) Which represents the larger dose?

## 10.5 FOCUS ON HEALTH & MEDICINE
### Medical Uses of Radioisotopes

Radioactive isotopes are used for both diagnostic and therapeutic procedures in medicine. In a diagnostic test to measure the function of an organ or to locate a tumor, low doses of radioactivity are generally given. When the purpose of using radiation is therapeutic, such as to kill diseased cells or cancerous tissue, a much higher dose of radiation is required.

### 10.5A Radioisotopes Used in Diagnosis

Radioisotopes are routinely used to determine if an organ is functioning properly or to detect the presence of a tumor. The isotope is ingested or injected and the radiation it emits can be used to produce a scan. Sometimes the isotope is an atom or ion that is not part of a larger molecule. Examples include iodine-131, which is administered as the salt sodium iodide (Na$^{131}$I), and xenon-133, which is a gas containing radioactive xenon atoms. At other times the radioactive atom is bonded to a larger molecule that targets a specific organ. An organ that has increased or decreased uptake of the radioactive element can indicate disease, the presence of a tumor, or other conditions.

A HIDA scan (hepatobiliary iminodiacetic acid scan) uses a technetium-99m-labeled molecule to evaluate the functioning of the gall bladder and bile ducts (Figure 10.4). After injection, the technetium-99m travels through the bloodstream and into the liver, gall bladder, and bile ducts, where, in a healthy individual, the organs are all clearly visible on a scan. When the gall bladder is inflamed or the bile ducts are obstructed by gallstones, uptake of the radioisotope does not occur and these organs are not visualized because they do not contain the radioisotope.

Red blood cells tagged with technetium-99m are used to identify the site of internal bleeding in an individual. Bone scans performed with technetium-99m can show the location of metastatic cancer, so that specific sites can be targeted for radiation therapy (Figure 10.5).

Thallium-201 is used in stress tests to diagnose coronary artery disease. Thallium injected into a vein crosses cell membranes into normal heart muscle. Little radioactive thallium is found in areas of the heart that have a poor blood supply. This technique is used to identify individuals who may need bypass surgery or other interventions because of blocked coronary arteries.

### PROBLEM 10.18

The half-life of thallium-201 is three days. What fraction of thallium-201 is still present in an individual after nine days?

**Figure 10.4** HIDA Scan Using Technetium-99m

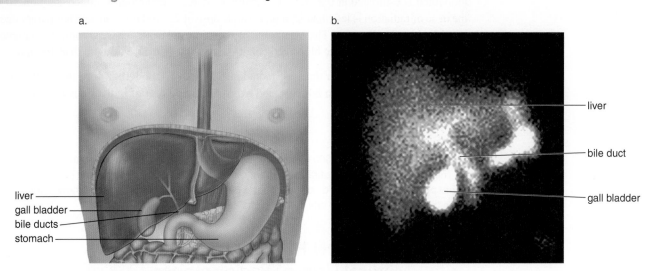

a.

b.

liver
gall bladder
bile ducts
stomach

liver
bile duct
gall bladder

a. Schematic showing the location of the liver, gall bladder, and bile ducts

b. A scan using technetium-99m showing bright areas for the liver, gall bladder, and bile ducts, indicating normal function

**Figure 10.5** Bone Scan Using Technetium-99m

a.

b.

kidneys

bladder

The bone scan of a patient whose lung cancer has spread to other organs. The anterior view [from the front in (a)] shows the spread of disease to the ribs, while the posterior view [from the back in (b)] shows spread of disease to the ribs and spine. The bright areas in the mid-torso and lower pelvis are due to a collection of radioisotope in the kidneys and bladder, before it is eliminated in the urine.

## 10.5B Radioisotopes Used in Treatment

The high-energy radiation emitted by radioisotopes can be used to kill rapidly dividing tumor cells. Two techniques are used. Sometimes the radiation source is external to the body. For example, a beam of radiation produced by decaying cobalt-60 can be focused at a tumor. Such a radiation source must have a much longer half-life—5.3 years in this case—than radioisotopes that are ingested for diagnostic purposes. With this method some destruction of healthy tissue often occurs, and a patient may experience some signs of radiation sickness, including vomiting, fatigue, and hair loss.

Figure 10.6    Common Radioisotopes Used in Medicine

**Xenon-133**
lung function

**Iodine-131**
hyperthyroidism
and thyroid tumors

**Technetium-99m**
bone scan

**Phosphorus-32**
treating leukemia
and lymphomas

**Technetium-99m**
gall bladder function

**Iridium-192**
cancers of
the breast

**Technetium-99m**
visualizing gastrointestinal
bleeding

**Thallium-201**
heart function

A more selective approach to cancer treatment involves using a radioactive isotope internally at the site of the tumor within the body. Using iodine-131 to treat hyperthyroidism has already been discussed (Section 10.1). Other examples include using radioactive "seeds" or wire that can be implanted close to a tumor. Iodine-125 seeds are used to treat prostate cancer and iridium-192 wire is used to treat some cancers of the breast.

Figure 10.6 illustrates radioisotopes that are used for diagnosis or treatment.

## 10.5C   Positron Emission Tomography—PET Scans

**Positron emission tomography (PET)** scans use radioisotopes that emit positrons when the nucleus decays. Once formed, a positron combines with an electron to form two γ rays, which create a scan of an organ.

Carbon-11, oxygen-15, nitrogen-13, and fluorine-18 are common radioactive isotopes used in PET scans. For example, a carbon-11 or fluorine-18 isotope can be incorporated in a glucose molecule. When this radioactive molecule is taken internally, its concentration becomes highest in areas in the body that continually use glucose. A healthy brain shows a high level of radioactivity from labeled glucose. When an individual suffers a stroke or has Alzheimer's disease, brain activity is significantly decreased and radioactivity levels are decreased.

PET scans are also used to detect tumors and coronary artery disease, and determine whether cancer has spread to other organs of the body. A PET scan is also a noninvasive method of monitoring whether cancer treatment has been successful (Figure 10.7).

HEALTH NOTE

Quadramet is the trade name of a medication that contains radioactive samarium-153. Quadramet is administered to relieve pain in patients whose cancer has spread to the bone.

### PROBLEM 10.19

Samarium-153, a radioactive isotope with a half-life of approximately 48 hours, is used to treat cancers lodged in the bone. (a) How many protons, neutrons, and electrons does samarium-153 contain? (b) Write a balanced nuclear equation for the emission of a β particle from samarium-153. (c) If a vial with an activity of 150 mCi is purchased, what is the activity of the solution after eight days?

**Figure 10.7** PET Scans

a.    b.    c.

a. The PET scan shows cancer of the lymph nodes in the neck and abdomen, as well as scattered areas of tumor in the bone marrow of the arms and spine before treatment.

b. The schematic of selected organs in the torso and pelvis

c. The PET scan shows significant clearing of disease after chemotherapy by the decrease in intensity of the radioisotope. The dark regions in the kidneys (in the torso) and bladder (in the lower pelvis) are due to the concentration of the radioisotope before elimination in the urine.

**PROBLEM 10.20**

Write a nuclear equation for the emission of a positron from nitrogen-13.

## 10.6   Nuclear Fission and Nuclear Fusion

The nuclear reactions used in nuclear power plants occur by a process called *nuclear fission,* whereas the nuclear reactions that take place in the sun occur by a process called *nuclear fusion.*

- *Nuclear fission* is the splitting apart of a heavy nucleus into lighter nuclei and neutrons.
- *Nuclear fusion* is the joining together of two light nuclei to form a larger nucleus.

### 10.6A   Nuclear Fission

When uranium-235 is bombarded by a neutron, it undergoes **nuclear fission** and splits apart into two lighter nuclei. Several different fission products have been identified. One common nuclear reaction is the fission of uranium-235 into krypton-91 and barium-142.

$$^{235}_{92}\text{U} + {}^{1}_{0}\text{n} \longrightarrow {}^{91}_{36}\text{Kr} + {}^{142}_{56}\text{Ba} + 3\,{}^{1}_{0}\text{n}$$

Each neutron can react with more uranium-235.

More fission products and more neutrons are formed.

Three high-energy neutrons are also produced in the reaction as well as a great deal of energy. Whereas burning 1 g of methane in natural gas releases 13 kcal of energy, fission of 1 g of uranium-235 releases $3.4 \times 10^8$ kcal. Each neutron produced during fission can go on to bombard three other uranium-235 nuclei to produce more nuclei and more neutrons. Such a process is called a **chain reaction.**

In order to sustain a chain reaction there must be a sufficient amount of uranium-235. When that amount—the **critical mass**—is present, the chain reaction occurs over and over again and an atomic explosion occurs. When less than the critical mass of uranium-235 is present, there is a more controlled production of energy, as is the case in a nuclear power plant.

A nuclear power plant utilizes the tremendous amount of energy produced by fission of the uranium-235 nucleus to heat water to steam, which powers a generator to produce electricity (Figure 10.8). While nuclear energy accounts for a small but significant fraction of the electricity needs in the United States, most of the electricity generated in some European countries comes from nuclear power.

Two problems that surround nuclear power generation are the possibility of radiation leaks and the disposal of nuclear waste. Plants are designed and monitored to contain the radioactive materials within the nuclear reactor. The reactor core itself is located in a containment facility with thick walls, so that should a leak occur, the radiation should in principle be kept within the building. The nuclear reactor in Chernobyl, Russia, was built without a containment facility and in 1986 it exploded, releasing high levels of radioactivity to the immediate environment and sending a cloud of radioactivity over much of Europe.

The products of nuclear fission are radioactive nuclei with long half-lives, often hundreds or even thousands of years. As a result, nuclear fission generates radioactive waste that must be stored in a secure facility so that it does not pose a hazard to the immediate surroundings. Burying waste far underground is currently considered the best option, but this issue is still unresolved.

Figure 10.8    A Nuclear Power Plant

a.

b.

a. Nuclear power plant with steam rising from a cooling tower

b. Fission occurs in a nuclear reactor core that is housed in a containment facility. Water surrounding the reactor is heated by the energy released during fission, and this energy drives a turbine, which produces electricity. Once the steam has been used to drive the turbine, it is cooled and re-circulated around the core of the reactor. To prevent the loss of any radioactive material to the environment, the water that surrounds the reactor core never leaves the containment building.

## SAMPLE PROBLEM 10.5

Write a nuclear equation for the fission of uranium-235 by neutron bombardment to form strontium-90, an isotope of xenon, and three neutrons.

### Analysis

Balance the atomic numbers and mass numbers on both sides of the nuclear equation. In fission reactions, include the neutron used for bombardment on the left and the high-energy neutrons produced on the right. Each neutron has a mass of one and zero charge.

### Solution

**[1] Write an incomplete equation with the original nucleus and neutron used for bombardment on the left, and the particles formed on the right.**

- Use the identity of each element to determine its atomic number. Uranium has an atomic number of 92, and xenon has an atomic number of 54.
- Include one neutron on the left side. In this reaction, three high-energy neutrons are formed, so include three neutrons on the right side.

$$^{235}_{92}U \ + \ ^{1}_{0}n \ \longrightarrow \ ^{90}_{38}Sr \ + \ ^{?}_{54}Xe \ + \ 3^{1}_{0}n$$

**[2] Calculate the mass numbers and atomic numbers of all newly formed nuclei on the right.**

- Atomic number: In this problem all atomic numbers are known from the identity of the elements.
- Mass number: Balance mass numbers by taking into account the mass of the neutrons used or produced in the reaction. On the left side, the total mass of the particles (the uranium nucleus and one neutron) is 236 (235 + 1). On the right side, the sum of the masses of Sr-90, xenon, and three neutrons (total mass of three) must also equal 236.

$$236 = 90 + ? + 3(1) \qquad \text{three neutrons}$$
$$236 = 93 + ? \qquad \text{one mass unit from each neutron}$$
$$143 = ?$$

The mass number of xenon is 143.

**[3] Write the complete equation.**

$$^{235}_{92}U \ + \ ^{1}_{0}n \ \longrightarrow \ ^{90}_{38}Sr \ + \ ^{143}_{54}Xe \ + \ 3^{1}_{0}n$$

## PROBLEM 10.21

Write a nuclear equation for the fission of uranium-235 by neutron bombardment to form antimony-133, three neutrons, and one other isotope.

## 10.6B  Nuclear Fusion

**Nuclear fusion** occurs when two light nuclei join together to form a larger nucleus. For example, fusion of a deuterium nucleus with a tritium nucleus forms helium and a neutron. Recall from Section 2.3 that deuterium is an isotope of hydrogen that contains one proton and one neutron in its nucleus, while tritium is an isotope of hydrogen that contains one proton and two neutrons in its nucleus.

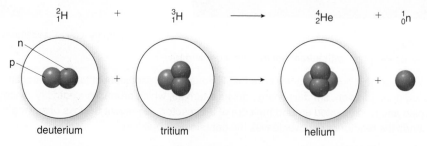

Like fission, fusion also releases a great deal of energy—namely, $5.3 \times 10^8$ kcal/mol of helium produced. The light and heat of the sun and other stars result from nuclear fusion.

One limitation of using fusion to provide energy for mankind is the extreme experimental conditions needed to produce it. Because it takes a considerable amount of energy to overcome the repulsive forces of the like charges of two nuclei, fusion can only be accomplished at high temperatures (greater than 100,000,000 °C) and pressures (greater than 100,000 atm). Since these conditions are not easily achieved, using controlled nuclear fusion as an energy source has yet to become a reality.

Controlled nuclear fusion has the potential of providing cheap and clean power. It is not plagued by the nuclear waste issues of fission reactors, and the needed reactants are readily available.

### PROBLEM 10.22

Nuclear fusion in the stars occurs by a series of reactions. Identify **X, Y,** and **Z** in the following nuclear reactions that ultimately convert hydrogen into helium.

a. $^1_1\text{H} + \textbf{X} \longrightarrow {}^2_1\text{H} + {}^0_{+1}\text{e}$

b. $^1_1\text{H} + {}^2_1\text{H} \longrightarrow \textbf{Y}$

c. $^1_1\text{H} + {}^3_2\text{He} \longrightarrow {}^4_2\text{He} + \textbf{Z}$

## 10.7 FOCUS ON HEALTH & MEDICINE
### Medical Imaging Without Radioactivity

**X-rays, CT scans,** and **MRIs** are also techniques that provide an image of an organ or extremity that is used for diagnosis of a medical condition. Unlike PET scans and other procedures discussed thus far, however, **these procedures are *not* based on nuclear reactions and they do *not* utilize radioactivity.** In each technique, an energy source is directed towards a specific region in the body, and a scan is produced that is analyzed by a trained medical professional.

**X-rays** are a high-energy type of radiation called electromagnetic radiation. Tissues of different density interact differently with an X-ray beam, and so a map of bone and internal organs is created on an X-ray film. Dense bone is clearly visible in an X-ray, making it a good diagnostic

**Figure 10.9**    Imaging the Human Body

a.

b.

c.

herniated disc

a. X-ray of a broken humerus in a patient's arm

b. A color-enhanced CT scan of the head showing the site of a stroke

c. MRI of the spinal cord showing spinal compression from a herniated disc technique for finding fractures (Figure 10.9a). Although X-rays are a form of high-energy radiation, they are lower in energy than the γ rays produced in nuclear reactions. Nonetheless, X-rays still cause adverse biological effects on the cells with which they come in contact, and the exposure of both the patient and X-ray technician must be limited.

**CT** (computed tomography) scans, which also use X-rays, provide high resolution images of "slices" of the body. Historically, CT images have shown a slice of tissue perpendicular to the long axis of the body. Modern CT scanners can now provide a three-dimensional view of the body's organs. CT scans of the head are used to diagnose bleeding and tumors in the brain (Figure 10.9b).

**MRI** (magnetic resonance imaging) uses low-energy radio waves to visualize internal organs. Unlike methods that use high-energy radiation, MRIs do not damage cells. An MRI is a good diagnostic method for visualizing soft tissue (Figure 10.9c), and thus it complements X-ray techniques.

# CHAPTER HIGHLIGHTS

## KEY TERMS

Alpha (α) particle (10.1)
Becquerel (10.4)
Beta (β) particle (10.1)
Chain reaction (10.6)
Critical mass (10.6)
Curie (10.4)
Gamma (γ) ray (10.1)
Geiger counter (10.4)

Gray (10.4)
Half-life (10.3)
$LD_{50}$ (10.4)
Nuclear fission (10.6)
Nuclear fusion (10.6)
Nuclear reaction (10.1)
Positron (10.1)
Rad (10.4)

Radioactive decay (10.2)
Radioactive isotope (10.1)
Radioactivity (10.1)
Radiocarbon dating (10.3)
Rem (10.4)
Sievert (10.4)
X-ray (10.7)

## KEY CONCEPTS

**❶ Describe the different types of radiation emitted by a radioactive nucleus. (10.1)**

- A radioactive nucleus can emit α particles, β particles, positrons, or γ rays.
- An α particle is a high-energy nucleus that contains two protons and two neutrons.
- A β particle is a high-energy electron that has a –1 charge and negligible mass.
- A positron is an antiparticle of a β particle. A positron has a +1 charge and negligible mass.
- A γ ray is high-energy radiation with no mass or charge.

**❷ How are equations for nuclear reactions written? (10.2)**

- In an equation for a nuclear reaction, the sum of the mass numbers (A) must be equal on both sides of the equation. The sum of the atomic numbers (Z) must be equal on both sides of the equation as well.

**❸ What is the half-life of a radioactive isotope? (10.3)**

- The half-life ($t_{1/2}$) is the time it takes for one-half of a radioactive sample to decay. Knowing the half-life and the amount of a radioactive substance, one can calculate how much sample remains after a period of time.

**❹ What units are used to measure radioactivity? (10.4)**

- Radiation in a sample is measured by the number of disintegrations per second, most often using the curie (Ci); 1 Ci = $3.7 \times 10^{10}$ disintegrations/s. The becquerel (Bq) is also used; 1 Bq = 1 disintegration/s; 1 Ci = $3.7 \times 10^{10}$ Bq.
- The exposure of a substance to radioactivity is measured with the rad (radiation absorbed dose) or the rem (radiation equivalent for man).

**❺ Give examples of common radioisotopes used in medicine. (10.5)**

- Iodine-131 is used to diagnose and treat thyroid disease.
- Technetium-99m is used to evaluate the functioning of the gall bladder and bile ducts, and in bone scans to evaluate the spread of cancer.
- Red blood cells tagged with technetium-99m are used to find the site of a gastrointestinal bleed.
- Thallium-201 is used to diagnose coronary artery disease.
- Cobalt-60 is used as an external source of radiation for cancer treatment.
- Iodine-125 and iridium-192 are used in internal radiation treatment of prostate cancer and breast cancer, respectively.
- Carbon-11, oxygen-15, nitrogen-13, and fluorine-18 are used in positron emission tomography.

**6** **What are nuclear fission and nuclear fusion? (10.6)**
- Nuclear fission is the splitting apart of a heavy nucleus into lighter nuclei and neutrons.
- Nuclear fusion is the joining together of two light nuclei to form a larger nucleus.
- Both nuclear fission and nuclear fusion release a great deal of energy. Nuclear fission is used in nuclear power plants to generate electricity. Nuclear fusion occurs in stars.

**7** **What medical imaging techniques do not use radioactivity? (10.7)**
- X-rays and CT scans both use X-rays, a high-energy form of electromagnetic radiation.
- MRIs use low-energy radio waves to image soft tissue.

# PROBLEMS

Selected in-chapter and odd-numbered end-of-chapter problems have brief answers in Appendix B. The *Student Study Guide and Solutions Manual* contains detailed solutions to all in-chapter and odd-numbered end-of-chapter problems, as well as additional worked examples and a chapter self-test.

## Isotopes and Radiation

**10.23** Compare fluorine-18 and fluorine-19 with regard to each of the following: (a) atomic number; (b) number of protons; (c) number of neutrons; (d) mass number. Give the isotope symbol for each isotope. F-19 is a stable nucleus and F-18 is used in PET scans.

**10.24** Compare nitrogen-13 and nitrogen-14 with regard to each of the following: (a) atomic number; (b) number of protons; (c) number of neutrons; (d) mass number. Give the isotope symbol for each isotope. N-14 is a stable nucleus and N-13 is used in PET scans.

**10.25** Complete the table of isotopes, each of which has found use in medicine.

| | Atomic Number | Mass Number | Number of Protons | Number of Neutrons | Isotope Symbol |
|---|---|---|---|---|---|
| a. Chromium-51 | | | | | |
| b. | 46 | 103 | | | |
| c. | | | 19 | 23 | |
| d. | | 133 | 54 | | |

**10.26** Complete the table of isotopes, each of which has found use in medicine.

| | Atomic Number | Mass Number | Number of Protons | Number of Neutrons | Isotope Symbol |
|---|---|---|---|---|---|
| a. Sodium-24 | | | | | |
| b. | | 89 | | 51 | |
| c. | | 59 | 26 | | |
| d. Samarium-153 | | | | | |

**10.27** How much does the mass and charge of a nucleus change when each type of radiation is emitted: (a) $\alpha$ particle; (b) $\beta$ particle; (c) $\gamma$ ray; (d) positron?

**10.28** Compare $\alpha$ particles, $\beta$ particles, and $\gamma$ rays with regard to each of the following: (a) speed the radiation travels; (b) penetrating power; (c) protective equipment that must be worn when handling.

**10.29** What is the mass and charge of radiation that has each of the following symbols: (a) $\alpha$; (b) n; (c) $\gamma$; (d) $\beta$?

**10.30** What is the mass and charge of radiation that has each of the following symbols?
a. $_{-1}^{0}e$   b. $_{+1}^{0}e$   c. $_{2}^{4}He$   d. $\beta^{+}$

## Nuclear Reactions

**10.31** Complete the nuclear equation by drawing the nucleus of the missing atom. Give the symbol for each atom and type of radiation. (The blue spheres represent protons and the red spheres represent neutrons.)

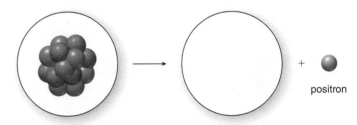

positron

**10.32** Complete the nuclear equation by drawing the nucleus of the missing atom. Give the symbol for each atom and type of radiation. (The blue spheres represent protons and the red spheres represent neutrons.)

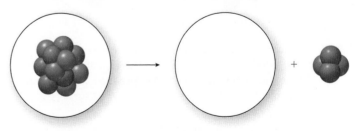

**10.33** Complete each nuclear equation.
a. $_{26}^{59}Fe \longrightarrow ? + _{-1}^{0}e$   c. $_{80}^{178}Hg \longrightarrow ? + _{+1}^{0}e$
b. $_{78}^{190}Pt \longrightarrow ? + _{2}^{4}He$

**10.34** Complete each nuclear equation.

a. $^{77}_{37}\text{Rb} \longrightarrow ? + ^{0}_{+1}e$     c. $^{66}_{29}\text{Cu} \longrightarrow ? + ^{0}_{-1}e$

b. $^{251}_{102}\text{No} \longrightarrow ? + ^{4}_{2}\text{He}$

**10.35** Complete each nuclear equation.

a. $^{90}_{39}\text{Y} \longrightarrow ^{90}_{40}\text{Zr} + ?$     c. $^{210}_{83}\text{Bi} \longrightarrow ? + ^{4}_{2}\text{He}$

b. $? \longrightarrow ^{135}_{59}\text{Pr} + ^{0}_{+1}e$

**10.36** Complete each nuclear equation.

a. $? \longrightarrow ^{90}_{39}\text{Y} + ^{0}_{-1}e$     c. $^{214}_{84}\text{Po} \longrightarrow ? + ^{4}_{2}\text{He}$

b. $^{29}_{15}\text{P} \longrightarrow ^{29}_{14}\text{Si} + ?$

**10.37** Bismuth-214 can decay to form either polonium-214 or thallium-210, depending on what type of radiation is emitted. Write a balanced nuclear equation for each process.

**10.38** Lead-210 can be formed by the decay of either thallium-210 or polonium-214, depending on what type of radiation is emitted. Write a balanced nuclear equation for each process.

**10.39** Write a balanced nuclear equation for each reaction.
  a. decay of thorium-232 by α emission
  b. decay of sodium-25 by β emission
  c. decay of xenon-118 by positron emission
  d. decay of curium-243 by α emission

**10.40** Write a balanced nuclear equation for each reaction.
  a. decay of sulfur-35 by β emission
  b. decay of thorium-225 by α emission
  c. decay of rhodium-93 by positron emission
  d. decay of silver-114 by β emission

## Half-Life

**10.41** A radioactive element (shown with blue spheres) forms a decay product (shown with green spheres) with a half-life of three days. How many half-lives have elapsed in diagram **A?**

initial sample                          **A**

**10.42** A radioactive element (shown with blue spheres) forms a decay product (shown with green spheres) with a half-life of 10 min. How many minutes have elapsed to form the sample in diagram **B?**

initial sample                          **B**

**10.43** If the amount of a radioactive element decreases from 2.4 g to 0.30 g in 12 days, what is its half-life?

**10.44** If the amount of a radioactive element decreases from 0.36 g to 90. mg in 22 min, what is its half-life?

**10.45** Radioactive iodine-131 ($t_{1/2}$ = 8.0 days) decays to form xenon-131 by emission of a β particle. How much of each isotope is present after each time interval if 64 mg of iodine-131 was present initially: (a) 8.0 days; (b) 16 days; (c) 24 days; (d) 32 days?

**10.46** Radioactive phosphorus-32 decays to form sulfur-32 by emission of a β particle. Estimating the half-life to be 14 days, how much of each isotope is present after each time interval if 124 mg of phosphorus-32 was present initially: (a) 14 days; (b) 28 days; (c) 42 days; (d) 56 days?

**10.47** If the half-life of an isotope is 24 hours, has all the isotope decayed in 48 hours?

**10.48** Explain how the half-life of carbon-14 is used to date objects.

**10.49** Why can't radiocarbon dating be used to determine the age of an artifact that is over 50,000 years old?

**10.50** Why can't radiocarbon dating be used to estimate the age of rocks?

**10.51** A patient is injected with a sample of technetium-99m ($t_{1/2}$ = 6.0 h), which has an activity of 20 mCi. What activity is observed after each interval: (a) 6 h; (b) 12 h; (c) 24 h?

**10.52** A sample of iodine-131 ($t_{1/2}$ = 8.0 days) has an activity of 200. mCi. What activity is observed after each interval: (a) 8.0 days; (b) 24 days; (c) 48 days?

## Measuring Radioactivity

**10.53** If a radioactive sample had an activity of 5.0 mCi, how many disintegrations per second does this correspond to?

**10.54** Why is the average amount of background radiation generally higher at higher elevations?

**10.55** A patient must be administered a 28-mCi dose of technetium-99m, which is supplied in a vial containing a solution with an activity of 12 mCi/mL. What volume of solution must be given?

**10.56** A radioactive isotope used for imaging is supplied in an 8.0-mL vial containing a solution with an activity of 108 mCi. What volume must be given to a patient who needs a 12-mCi dose?

**10.57** Radioactive sodium-24, administered as $^{24}\text{NaCl}$, is given to treat leukemia. If a patient must receive 190 μCi/kg and the isotope is supplied as a solution that contains 5.0 mCi/mL, what volume is needed for a 68-kg patient?

**10.58** Radioactive phosphorus-32, administered as sodium phosphate ($\text{Na}_3{}^{32}\text{PO}_4$), is used to treat chronic leukemia. The activity of an intravenous solution is 670 μCi/mL. What volume of solution must be used to supply a dose of 15 mCi?

**10.59** The units chosen to report radiation amounts give us different information. What is measured using the curie compared to the rad?

**10.60** The units chosen to report radiation amounts give us different information. What is measured using the millicurie compared to the rem?

**10.61** The initial responders to the Chernobyl nuclear disaster were exposed to 20 Sv of radiation. Convert this value to rem. Did these individuals receive a fatal dose of radiation?

**10.62** Many individuals who fought fires at the Chernobyl nuclear disaster site were exposed to 0.25 Sv of radiation. Convert this value to rem. Did these individuals receive a fatal dose of radiation? Would you expect any of these individuals to have shown ill health effects?

## Nuclear Fission and Nuclear Fusion

**10.63** What is the difference between nuclear fission and nuclear fusion?

**10.64** What is the difference between the nuclear fission process that takes place in a nuclear reactor and the nuclear fission that occurs in an atomic bomb?

**10.65** For which process does each statement apply—nuclear fission, nuclear fusion, both fission and fusion?
  a. The reaction occurs in the sun.
  b. A neutron is used to bombard a nucleus.
  c. A large amount of energy is released.
  d. Very high temperatures are required.

**10.66** For which process does each statement apply—nuclear fission, nuclear fusion, both fission and fusion?
  a. The reaction splits a nucleus into lighter nuclei.
  b. The reaction joins two lighter nuclei into a heavier nucleus.
  c. The reaction is used to generate energy in a nuclear power plant.
  d. The reaction generates radioactive waste with a long half-life.

**10.67** Complete each nuclear fission equation.
  a. $^{235}_{92}U + ^{1}_{0}n \longrightarrow ? + ^{97}_{42}Mo + 2\,^{1}_{0}n$
  b. $^{235}_{92}U + ^{1}_{0}n \longrightarrow ? + ^{140}_{56}Ba + 3\,^{1}_{0}n$

**10.68** Complete each nuclear fission equation.
  a. $^{235}_{92}U + ^{1}_{0}n \longrightarrow ? + ^{139}_{57}La + 2\,^{1}_{0}n$
  b. $^{235}_{92}U + ^{1}_{0}n \longrightarrow ? + ^{140}_{58}Ce + 2\,^{1}_{0}n + 6\,^{0}_{-1}e$

**10.69** Complete the nuclear fusion equation by drawing in the nucleus of the missing atom. Blue spheres represent protons and red spheres represent neutrons.

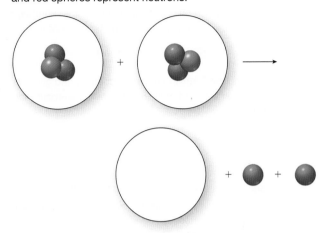

**10.70** Complete the nuclear fusion equation by drawing in the nucleus of the missing atom. Blue spheres represent protons and red spheres represent neutrons.

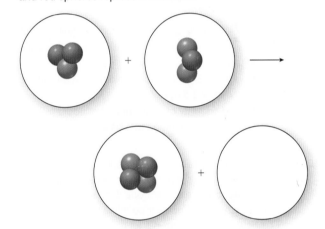

**10.71** The fusion of two deuterium nuclei (hydrogen-2) forms a hydrogen nucleus (hydrogen-1) as one product. What other product is formed?

**10.72** Fill in the missing product in the following nuclear fusion reaction.
$$^{3}_{2}He + ^{3}_{2}He \longrightarrow ? + 2\,^{1}_{1}H$$

**10.73** Discuss two problems that surround the generation of electricity from a nuclear power plant.

**10.74** Why are there as yet no nuclear power plants that use nuclear fusion to generate electricity?

**10.75** All nuclei with atomic numbers around 100 or larger do not exist naturally; rather they have been synthesized by fusing two lighter-weight nuclei together. Complete the following nuclear equation by giving the name, atomic number, and mass number of the element made by this reaction.

$$^{209}_{83}\text{Bi} + {}^{58}_{26}\text{Fe} \longrightarrow \text{?} + {}^{1}_{0}\text{n}$$

**10.76** Complete the following nuclear equation, and give the name, atomic number, and mass number of the element made by this reaction.

$$^{235}_{92}\text{U} + {}^{14}_{7}\text{N} \longrightarrow \text{?} + 5\,{}^{1}_{0}\text{n}$$

## General Questions

**10.77** Arsenic-74 is a radioisotope used for locating brain tumors.
   a. Write a balanced nuclear equation for the positron emission of arsenic-74.
   b. If $t_{1/2}$ for As-74 is 18 days, how much of a 120-mg sample remains after 90 days?
   c. If the radioactivity of a 2.0-mL vial of arsenic-74 is 10.0 mCi, what volume must be administered to give a 7.5-mCi dose?

**10.78** Sodium-24 is a radioisotope used for examining circulation.
   a. Write a balanced nuclear equation for the β decay of sodium-24.
   b. If $t_{1/2}$ for Na-24 is 15 h, how much of an 84-mg sample remains after 2.5 days?
   c. If the radioactivity of a 5.0-mL vial of sodium-24 is 10.0 mCi, what volume must be administered to give a 6.5-mCi dose?

**10.79** Strontium-89 is a radioactive isotope ($t_{1/2}$ = 50. days) used to reduce the pain of prostate and bone cancer. (a) How many protons, neutrons, and electrons does strontium-89 contain? (b) Write a balanced nuclear equation for the emission of a β particle from strontium-89. (c) If a vial contains 10.0 μg of strontium-89, how much of the radioisotope remains after 200. days?

**10.80** Rhenium-186 is a radioactive isotope ($t_{1/2}$ = 4.0 days) used for pain relief in bone cancer. (a) How many protons, neutrons, and electrons does rhenium-186 contain? (b) Write a balanced nuclear equation for the emission of a β particle from rhenium-186. (c) If a vial contains 200. μg of rhenium-186, how much of the radioisotope remains after 16 days?

## Applications

**10.81** Explain how each isotope is used in medicine.
   a. iodine-131
   b. iridium-192
   c. thallium-201

**10.82** Explain how each isotope is used in medicine.
   a. iodine-125
   b. technetium-99m
   c. cobalt-60

**10.83** How does the half-life of each of the following isotopes of iodine affect the manner in which it is administered to a patient: (a) iodine-125, $t_{1/2}$ = 60 days; (b) iodine-131, $t_{1/2}$ = 8 days?

**10.84** Explain why food is irradiated with γ rays.

**10.85** A mammogram is an X-ray of the breast. Why does an X-ray technician leave the room or go behind a shield when a mammogram is performed on a patient?

**10.86** Why is a lead apron placed over a patient's body when dental X-rays are taken?

**10.87** One of the radioactive isotopes that contaminated the area around Chernobyl after the nuclear accident in 1986 was iodine-131. Suggest a reason why individuals in the affected region were given doses of NaI that contained the stable iodine-127 isotope.

**10.88** The element strontium has similar properties to calcium. Suggest a reason why exposure to strontium-90, a product of nuclear testing in the atmosphere, is especially hazardous for children.

## CHALLENGE PROBLEMS

**10.89** An article states that the fission of 1.0 g of uranium-235 releases $3.4 \times 10^8$ kcal, the same amount of energy as burning one ton (2,000 lb) of coal. If this report is accurate, how much energy is released when 1.0 g of coal is burned?

**10.90** Radioactive isotopes with high atomic numbers often decay to form isotopes that are themselves radioactive, and once formed, decay to form new isotopes. Sometimes a series of such decays occurs over many steps until a stable nucleus is formed. The following series of decays occurs: Polonium-218 decays with emission of an α particle to form **X,** which emits a β particle to form **Y,** which emits an α particle to form **Z.** Identify **X, Y,** and **Z.**

**11**

**Vitamin A,** a key component of the vision receptors in the eye, is synthesized in the body from β-carotene, the orange pigment found in carrots.

# Introduction to Organic Molecules and Functional Groups

## CHAPTER GOALS

*In this chapter you will learn how to:*

1. Recognize the characteristic features of organic compounds
2. Predict the shape around atoms in organic molecules
3. Use shorthand methods to draw organic molecules
4. Recognize the common functional groups and understand their importance
5. Distinguish organic compounds from ionic inorganic compounds
6. Determine whether an organic compound is polar or nonpolar
7. Determine solubility properties of organic compounds
8. Determine whether a vitamin is fat soluble or water soluble

Consider for a moment the activities that occupied your past 24 hours. You likely showered with soap, drank a caffeinated beverage and ate a few meals, read a newspaper, listened to a CD, and traveled in a vehicle that had rubber tires and was powered by fossil fuels. If you did any *one* of these, your life was touched by organic chemistry. In Chapter 11, we learn about the characteristic features of organic molecules.

## 11.1   Introduction to Organic Chemistry

What is organic chemistry?

- **Organic chemistry is the study of compounds that contain the element carbon.**

While it may seem odd that an entire discipline is devoted to the study of a single element in the periodic table, millions of organic compounds are known, far more than the inorganic compounds discussed in Chapters 1–10. **These organic chemicals affect virtually every facet of our lives, and for this reason, it is important and useful to know something about them.**

Clothes, foods, medicines, gasoline, refrigerants, and soaps are composed almost solely of organic compounds. Some, like cotton, wool, or silk are naturally occurring; that is, they can be isolated directly from natural sources. Others, such as nylon and polyester are synthetic, meaning they are produced by chemists in the laboratory. By studying the principles and concepts of organic chemistry, you can learn more about compounds such as these and how they affect the world around you. Figure 11.1 illustrates some common products of organic chemistry used in medicine.

### PROBLEM 11.1

Which chemical formulas represent organic compounds and which represent inorganic compounds?

| | | |
|---|---|---|
| a. $C_6H_{12}$ | c. KI | e. $CH_4O$ |
| b. $H_2O$ | d. $MgSO_4$ | f. NaOH |

**Figure 11.1**    Some Common Products of Organic Chemistry Used in Medicine

a. Oral contraceptives      b. Plastic syringes      c. Antibiotics      d. Synthetic heart valves

Organic chemistry has given us contraceptives, plastics, antibiotics, synthetic heart valves, and a myriad of other materials. Our lives would be vastly different today without these products of organic chemistry.

## 11.2 Characteristic Features of Organic Compounds

Perhaps the best way to appreciate the variety of organic molecules is to look at a few. Simple organic compounds that contain just one or two carbon atoms, respectively, are methane and ethanol.

methane ethanol

**Methane,** the main component of natural gas, burns in the presence of oxygen. The natural gas we use today was formed by the decomposition of organic material millions of years ago. **Ethanol,** the alcohol present in wine and other alcoholic beverages, is formed by the fermentation of sugar. Ethanol can also be made in the lab by a totally different process. **Ethanol produced in the lab is identical to the ethanol produced by fermentation.**

Two more complex organic molecules are capsaicin and caffeine. **Capsaicin,** the compound responsible for the characteristic spiciness of hot peppers, is the active ingredient in several topical creams for pain relief. **Caffeine** is the bitter-tasting stimulant found in coffee, tea, cola beverages, and chocolate.

capsaicin

caffeine

What are the common features of these organic compounds?

> **[1] All organic compounds contain carbon atoms and most contain hydrogen atoms. Carbon always forms four covalent bonds, and hydrogen forms one covalent bond.**

Carbon is located in group 4A of the periodic table, so a carbon atom has four valence electrons available for bonding (Section 4.1). Since hydrogen has a single valence electron, methane ($CH_4$) consists of four single bonds, each formed from one electron from a hydrogen atom and one electron from carbon.

methane

> **[2] Carbon forms single, double, and triple bonds to other carbon atoms.**

When a compound contains two or more carbon atoms, the type of bonding is determined by the number of atoms around carbon. Consider the three compounds drawn below:

| Each C forms four single bonds. | A double bond contains four electrons. | A triple bond contains six electrons. |

ethane              ethylene              acetylene

- **A C atom surrounded by four atoms forms four single bonds.** In ethane ($C_2H_6$), each carbon atom is bonded to three hydrogen atoms and one carbon atom. All bonds are single bonds.
- **A C atom surrounded by three atoms forms one double bond.** In ethylene ($C_2H_4$), each carbon atom is surrounded by three atoms (two hydrogens and one carbon); thus, each C forms a single bond to each hydrogen atom and a double bond to carbon.
- **A C atom surrounded by two atoms generally forms one triple bond.** In acetylene ($C_2H_2$), each carbon atom is surrounded by two atoms (one hydrogen and one carbon); thus, each C forms a single bond to hydrogen and a triple bond to carbon.

> **[3] Some compounds have chains of atoms and some compounds have rings.**

For example, three carbon atoms can bond in a row to form propane, or form a ring called cyclopropane. Propane is the fuel burned in gas grills, and cyclopropane is an anesthetic.

propane
$C_3H_8$

cyclopropane
$C_3H_6$

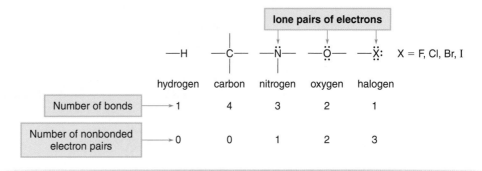

Figure 11.2    Common Bonding Patterns for Atoms in Organic Compounds

[4] Organic compounds may also contain elements other than carbon and hydrogen. Any atom that is not carbon or hydrogen is called a *heteroatom.*

The most common heteroatoms are nitrogen, oxygen, and the halogens (F, Cl, Br, and I).

- Each heteroatom forms a characteristic number of bonds, determined by its location in the periodic table.
- The common heteroatoms also have nonbonding, lone pairs of electrons, so that each atom is surrounded by eight electrons.

The number of bonds formed by common elements was first discussed in Section 4.1.

Thus, nitrogen forms three bonds and has one lone pair of electrons, while oxygen forms two bonds and has two additional lone pairs. The halogens form one bond and have three additional lone pairs. Common bonding patterns for atoms in organic compounds are summarized in Figure 11.2. Except for hydrogen, these common elements in organic compounds follow one rule in bonding:

$$\boxed{\text{Number of bonds}} \;+\; \boxed{\text{Number of lone pairs}} \;=\; \boxed{4}$$

Oxygen and nitrogen form both single and multiple bonds to carbon. **The most common multiple bond between carbon and a heteroatom is a carbon–oxygen double bond ($C=O$).** The bonding patterns remain the same even when an atom is part of a multiple bond, as shown with methanol ($CH_3OH$) and formaldehyde ($H_2C=O$, a preservative).

These features explain why there are so many organic compounds: **Carbon forms four strong bonds with itself and other elements. Carbon atoms combine together to form rings and chains.**

## SAMPLE PROBLEM 11.1

Draw in all H's and lone pairs in each compound.

  a.  C—C—Cl                    b.  C—C=O                    c.  C—C≡N

### Analysis

**Each C and heteroatom must be surrounded by eight electrons.** Use the common bonding patterns in Figure 11.2 to fill in the needed H's and lone pairs. C needs four bonds; Cl needs one bond and three lone pairs; O needs two bonds and two lone pairs; N needs three bonds and one lone pair.

Solution

a.

Cl needs three lone pairs.

$$H-\underset{\underset{H}{\overset{H}{|}}}{C}-\underset{\underset{H}{\overset{H}{|}}}{C}-\ddot{\underset{..}{Cl}}:$$

C needs 3 H's to have four bonds.

c.

N needs one lone pair.

$$H-\underset{\underset{H}{\overset{H}{|}}}{C}-C{\equiv}N:$$

C already has four bonds.

b.

O needs two lone pairs.

$$H-\underset{\underset{H}{\overset{H}{|}}}{C}-\underset{\underset{H}{\overset{}{|}}}{C}=\ddot{O}:$$

C needs 1 H to have four bonds.

## PROBLEM 11.2

Fill in all H's and lone pairs in each compound.

a. C—C≡C—C  b. C—Ċ—C  c. C—Ċ—C  d. C—Ċ—N—C  e. $\underset{C}{\overset{C}{\diagup}}O$

where b is $C{-}\underset{\overset{\|}{O}}{C}{-}C$ , c is $C{-}\underset{\overset{\|}{O}}{C}{-}C$ , d is $C{-}\underset{\overset{\|}{O}}{C}{-}N{-}C$

Because acetylene produces a very hot flame on burning, it is often used in welding torches.

Ethylene is an important starting material in the preparation of the plastic polyethylene. Polyethylene is a synthetic plastic first produced in the 1930s, initially used as insulating material for radar during World War II. It is now a plastic in milk containers, sandwich bags, and plastic wrapping. Over 100 billion pounds of polyethylene are manufactured each year.

## 11.3 Shapes of Organic Molecules

The shape around atoms in organic molecules is determined by counting groups using the principles of VSEPR theory (Section 4.6). Recall that a group is either another atom or a lone pair of electrons. **The most stable arrangement keeps these groups as far away from each other as possible.**

- **An atom surrounded by two groups is linear and has a bond angle of 180°.**

Each carbon in acetylene (HC≡CH) is surrounded by two atoms and no lone pairs. Thus, each H—C—C bond angle is 180°, making all four atoms of acetylene linear.

$$\overset{180°}{H-C{\equiv}C-H}$$
$$\underset{180°}{}$$

=

two atoms around each C

acetylene
ball-and-stick model

- **An atom surrounded by three groups is trigonal planar and has a bond angle of 120°.**

Each carbon in ethylene ($CH_2{=}CH_2$) is surrounded by three atoms and no lone pairs. Thus, each H—C—C bond angle is 120°, and all six atoms of ethylene lie in one plane.

$$\underset{H}{\overset{H}{\diagdown}}C{=}C\underset{H}{\overset{H}{\diagup}}\,120°$$

=

three atoms around each C

ethylene

- An atom surrounded by four groups places these four groups at the corners of a tetrahedron, giving bond angles of approximately 109.5°.

The carbon atom in methane ($CH_4$) is bonded to four hydrogen atoms, pointing to the corners of a tetrahedron.

tetrahedral carbon

To draw the three-dimensional tetrahedron on a two-dimensional page, place two of the bonds in the plane of the page, one bond in front, and one bond behind. Then, use the drawing conventions first presented in Section 4.6:

- A solid line is used for bonds in the plane.
- A wedge is used for a bond in front of the plane.
- A dashed line is used for a bond behind the plane.

bonds **in the plane**

bond **behind**

bond **in front**

methane
ball-and-stick model

**All carbons having four single bonds are tetrahedral.** For example, each carbon of ethane is tetrahedral and can be drawn with two bonds in the plane, one in front on a wedge, and one behind on a dashed line.

ethane

tetrahedral C's

**Don't forget about the lone pairs of electrons on nitrogen and oxygen when determining the shape around these atoms.** The N atom in methylamine ($CH_3NH_2$) is surrounded by three atoms and one lone pair—four groups. To keep these four groups as far apart as possible, each of these groups occupies the corner of a tetrahedron. In this way, the N atom of methylamine resembles the N atom of ammonia ($NH_3$) discussed in Section 4.6. The H—N—C bond angle of 112° is close to the tetrahedral bond angle of 109.5°. This molecular shape is referred to as a **trigonal pyramid,** because one of the groups around the N is a lone pair, not another atom.

One corner of the tetrahedron has an **electron pair**, not a bond.

**four** groups around N
- three atoms
- one lone pair

methylamine

trigonal pyramid

Ethane is a constituent of natural gas.

Similarly, the O atom in methanol ($CH_3OH$) is surrounded by two atoms and two lone pairs—four groups. To keep these groups as far apart as possible, each of these groups occupies the corner of a tetrahedron. In this way the O atom of methanol resembles the O atom of water ($H_2O$) discussed in Section 4.6. The C—O—H bond angle of 109° is close to the tetrahedral bond angle of 109.5°. Methanol has a bent molecular shape around O because two of the groups around oxygen are lone pairs. Table 11.1 summarizes the possible shapes around atoms in organic compounds.

methanol

bent shape

Table 11.1  Molecular Shape Around Atoms in Organic Compounds

| Total Number of Groups | Number of Atoms | Number of Lone Pairs | Shape Around an Atom (A) | Approximate Bond Angle (°) |
|---|---|---|---|---|
| 2 | 2 | 0 | linear | 180 |
| 3 | 3 | 0 | trigonal planar | 120 |
| 4 | 4 | 0 | tetrahedral | 109.5 |
| 4 | 3 | 1 | trigonal pyramidal | ~109.5[a] |
| 4 | 2 | 2 | bent | ~109.5[a] |

[a]The symbol "~" means approximately.

## SAMPLE PROBLEM 11.2

Determine the shape around each atom in dimethyl ether.

dimethyl ether

### Analysis

First, draw in all lone pairs on the heteroatom. A heteroatom needs eight electrons around it, so add two lone pairs to O. Then count groups to determine the molecular shape.

### Solution

- Each C is surrounded by four atoms (3 H's and 1 O), making each C tetrahedral.
- The O atom is surrounded by 2 C's and two lone pairs (four groups), giving it a bent shape.
- This results in the following three-dimensional shape:

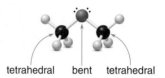

tetrahedral    bent    tetrahedral

### PROBLEM 11.3

Determine the shape around the indicated atoms in each compound. Don't forget to add electron pairs to heteroatoms before determining the shape.

a. (1) (2) shown above H—C=C—Br with H H below

c. H—C—O—H with O double-bonded above, (1) (2) below

b. (1) (3) H—C≡C—C—O—H with H above and (2) H below

d. phenol ring structure H—C ring C—C—C≡N with (1) and (2) labels

### PROBLEM 11.4

Predict the indicated bond angles in each compound.

a. halothane (general anesthetic) — F—C—C—Br structure with (1) (2) (3) labels

b. propene (petroleum product) — H—C—C=C—H structure with (1) (2) (3) labels

c. phenol (antiseptic) — ring structure C=C / C—O—H with (1) (2) (3) labels

### PROBLEM 11.5

Draw the structure of each compound using solid lines, wedges, and dashes to indicate the three-dimensional shape around each carbon.

a. H—C—Cl with H above, below, and Cl

b. H—C—C—Br with H's

Don't let the size or complexity of an organic molecule intimidate you! Using the principles described in Section 11.3, you can predict the shape around any atom in any molecule no matter how complex it might be.

**SAMPLE PROBLEM 11.3**

L-Dopa is a drug used to treat Parkinson's disease. Give the shape around each indicated atom.

L-dopa

### Analysis

First, add lone pairs of electrons to each heteroatom so that it is surrounded by eight electrons. Each O gets two lone pairs and N gets one. Then count groups to predict shape.

### Solution

Adding electron pairs around O and N:

L-dopa

three atoms ⟶ **trigonal planar**

four atoms ⟶ **tetrahedral**

three atoms ⟶ **trigonal planar**

three atoms + one lone pair **trigonal pyramidal**

two atoms + two lone pairs **bent**

Pay special attention to the O and N atoms, and note the importance of adding the lone pairs before determining shape. O atoms are surrounded by *four* groups—two atoms *and* two electron pairs— giving them a bent shape. O atoms are *never* surrounded by two groups, making them linear.

**PROBLEM 11.6**

Enanthotoxin is a poisonous compound isolated from a common variety of hemlock grown in England. Predict the shape around the indicated atoms in enanthotoxin.

Hemlock is the source of the poison enanthotoxin.

enanthotoxin

## 11.4 Drawing Organic Molecules

Because organic molecules often contain many atoms, we need shorthand methods to simplify their structures. The two main types of shorthand representations used for organic compounds are **condensed structures** and **skeletal structures.**

### 11.4A Condensed Structures

Condensed structures are most often used for a compound having a chain of atoms bonded together, rather than a ring. The following conventions are used.

- All of the atoms are drawn in, but the two-electron bond lines are generally omitted.
- Lone pairs on heteroatoms are omitted.

To interpret a condensed formula, it is usually best to start at the *left side* of the molecule and remember that the **carbon atoms must have four bonds.**

- A carbon bonded to 3 H's becomes $CH_3$.
- A carbon bonded to 2 H's becomes $CH_2$.
- A carbon bonded to 1 H becomes CH.

$$= CH_3CH_2CH_2CH_3$$

$$= CH_3CHCH_2CH_3$$

Keep the vertical bond line to show where the $CH_3$ group is bonded.

Sometimes these structures are further simplified by using parentheses around like groups. Two $CH_2$ groups bonded together become $(CH_2)_2$. Two $CH_3$ groups bonded to the same carbon become $(CH_3)_2C$.

| two $CH_2$ groups bonded together | two $CH_3$ groups bonded to the same C |
|---|---|
| $CH_3CH_2CH_2CH_3 = CH_3(CH_2)_2CH_3$ | $CH_3CHCH_2CH_3 = (CH_3)_2CHCH_2CH_3$ |

### SAMPLE PROBLEM 11.4

Convert each compound into a condensed structure.

### Analysis

Start at the left and proceed to the right, making sure that each carbon has four bonds. Omit lone pairs on the heteroatoms O and Cl. When like groups are bonded together or bonded to the same atom, use parentheses to further simplify the structure.

### Solution

| | Condensed structure | Further simplified |
|---|---|---|

a. $= CH_3CHCH_2CHCH_3 \quad = (CH_3)_2CHCH_2CH(CH_3)_2$

with $CH_3 \quad CH_3$

Use parentheses to show 2 $CH_3$ groups on one C.

b. $= CH_3CH_2CH_2OCH_2Cl \quad = CH_3(CH_2)_2OCH_2Cl$

PROBLEM 11.7

Convert each compound to a condensed formula.

a. H—C—C—C—C—C—H

b. :Br—C—C—Br:

c. H—C—C—Ö—C—C—Ö—H

d. H—C—C—C—C—H

PROBLEM 11.8

Convert each condensed formula to a complete structure.

a. $CH_3(CH_2)_8CH_3$
b. $CH_3(CH_2)_4OH$

c. $CH_3CCl_3$
d. $CH_3(CH_2)_4CH(CH_3)_2$

e. $(CH_3)_2CHCH_2NH_2$

## 11.4B   Skeletal Structures

Skeletal structures are used for organic compounds containing both rings and chains of atoms. Three important rules are used in drawing them.

- Assume there is a carbon atom at the junction of any two lines or at the end of any line.
- Assume there are enough hydrogens around each carbon to give it four bonds.
- Draw in all heteroatoms and the hydrogens directly bonded to them.

Rings are drawn as polygons with a carbon atom "understood" at each vertex, as shown for cyclohexane and cyclopentanol. All carbons and hydrogens in these molecules are understood, except for H's bonded to heteroatoms.

Each C has 2 H's bonded to it.

Draw in the H on O.

cyclohexane          skeletal structure                    cyclopentanol                    skeletal structure

SAMPLE PROBLEM 11.5

Convert each skeletal structure to a complete structure with all C's and H's drawn in.

a. 

b. —$CH_3$

Analysis

To draw each complete structure, place a C atom at the corner of each polygon and add H's to give carbon four bonds.

## Solution

a. ☐ =

Each C needs 2 H's.

b. ▷—CH₃ =

This C needs only 1 H.

## PROBLEM 11.9

Convert each skeletal structure to a complete structure with all C's and H's drawn in. Add lone pairs on all heteroatoms.

a.

cyclooctane

b. 

lindane
(an insecticide)

c. $CH_3$—⬡—$CH(CH_3)_2$

menthol
(isolated from peppermint)

## SAMPLE PROBLEM 11.6

Shorthand structures for more complex organic compounds are drawn with the same principles used for simpler structures. Answer the following questions about estradiol, a female sex hormone that controls the development of secondary sex characteristics.

estradiol
(female sex hormone)

a. How many C atoms are present in estradiol?

b. How many H atoms are bonded to C1? C2? C3?

c. Draw a complete structure for estradiol, including all lone pairs on O atoms.

## Analysis

Place a C atom at each corner of all polygons. Add enough H's to give each C four bonds. Each O needs two lone pairs to have eight electrons around it.

## Solution

a. Since each corner of a polygon represents a C, estradiol has a total of 18 C's.

b. C1, labeled in red (below), needs 2 H's to give it four bonds. C2, labeled in blue, needs 1 H to give it four bonds. C3, labeled in green, needs 1 H to give it four bonds.

c.

estradiol
(female sex hormone)

**PROBLEM 11.10**

How many H's are bonded to each indicated carbon (C1–C5) in the following drugs?

ibuprofen
(anti-inflammatory agent)

fentanyl
(narcotic pain reliever)

## 11.5   Functional Groups

In addition to strong C—C and C—H bonds, organic molecules may have other structural features as well. Although over 20 million organic compounds are currently known, only a limited number of common structural features, called **functional groups,** are found in these molecules.

- A *functional group* is an atom or a group of atoms with characteristic chemical and physical properties.
- A functional group contains a heteroatom, a multiple bond, or sometimes both a heteroatom *and* a multiple bond.

A functional group determines a molecule's shape, properties, and the type of reactions it undergoes. A functional group behaves the same whether it is bonded to a carbon backbone having as few as two or as many as 20 carbons. For this reason, we often abbreviate the carbon and hydrogen portion of the molecule by a capital letter **R,** and draw the **R** bonded to a particular functional group.

R—Functional group

Carbon backbone…   bonded to…   a particular functional group.

Ethanol ($CH_3CH_2OH$), for example, has two carbons and five hydrogens in its carbon backbone, as well as an OH group, a functional group called a **hydroxyl** group. The hydroxyl group determines the physical properties of ethanol as well as the type of reactions it undergoes. Moreover, any organic molecule containing a hydroxyl group has properties similar to ethanol. Compounds that contain a hydroxyl group are called **alcohols.**

hydroxyl group

carbon backbone

ethanol

The most common functional groups can be subdivided into three types.

- Hydrocarbons
- Compounds containing a single bond to a heteroatom
- Compounds containing a C=O group

## 11.5A   Hydrocarbons

*Hydrocarbons* **are compounds that contain only the elements of carbon and hydrogen,** as shown in Table 11.2.

- *Alkanes* have only C—C single bonds and no functional group. Ethane, $CH_3CH_3$, is a simple alkane.
- *Alkenes* have a C—C double bond as their functional group. Ethylene, $CH_2{=}CH_2$, is a simple alkene.
- *Alkynes* have a C—C triple bond as their functional group. Acetylene, $HC{\equiv}CH$, is a simple alkyne.
- *Aromatic compounds* contain a benzene ring, a six-membered ring with three double bonds.

All hydrocarbons other than alkanes contain multiple bonds. Alkanes, which have no functional groups and therefore no reactive sites, are notoriously unreactive except under very drastic conditions. For example, **polyethylene** is a synthetic plastic and high molecular weight alkane, consisting of long chains of —$CH_2$— groups bonded together, hundreds or even thousands of atoms long. Because it has no reactive sites, it is a very stable compound that does not readily degrade and thus persists for years in landfills.

polyethylene

The chain continues in both directions.

## Table 11.2   Hydrocarbons

| Type of Compound | General Structure | Example | 3-D Structure | Functional Group |
|---|---|---|---|---|
| **Alkane** | R—H | $CH_3CH_3$ | | — |
| **Alkene** | C=C | C=C (with H atoms) | | Carbon–carbon double bond |
| **Alkyne** | —C≡C— | H—C≡C—H | | Carbon–carbon triple bond |
| **Aromatic compound** | (benzene ring) | (benzene ring) | | Benzene ring |

## 11.5B Compounds Containing a Single Bond to a Heteroatom

Several types of functional groups contain a carbon atom singly bonded to a heteroatom. Common examples include alkyl halides, alcohols, ethers, and amines, as shown in Table 11.3.

Several simple compounds in this category are widely used. Bromomethane ($CH_3Br$) is an alkyl halide that has been used to control the spread of the destructive Asian long-horned beetle to the United States. Chloroethane ($CH_3CH_2Cl$, commonly called ethyl chloride) is an alkyl halide used as a local anesthetic. When chloroethane is sprayed on a wound it quickly evaporates, causing a cooling sensation that numbs the site of injury.

Molecules containing these functional groups may be simple or very complex. It doesn't matter what else is present in other parts of the molecule. **Always dissect it into small pieces to identify the functional groups.** For example, diethyl ether, the first general anesthetic, is an ether because it has an O atom bonded to two C's. Tetrahydrocannabinol (THC), the active component in marijuana, is also an ether because it contains an O atom bonded to two carbon atoms. In this case the O atom is also part of a ring.

diethyl ether

tetrahydrocannabinol
(THC)

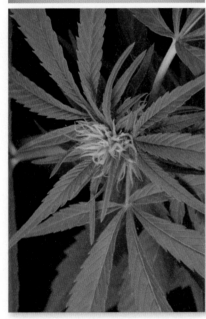

Tetrahydrocannabinol (THC) is the primary active constituent in marijuana. Although the recreational use of cannabis is illegal in the United States, THC can be used legally in some states for medical purposes.

### PROBLEM 11.11

Identify the functional groups in each compound. Some compounds contain more than one functional group.

a.
  OH
  |
CH₃CHCH₃

2-propanol
(disinfectant in
rubbing alcohol)

b.  ⬡—CH=CH₂

styrene
(starting material used
to synthesize Styrofoam)

c. $H_2NCH_2CH_2CH_2CH_2NH_2$

putrescine
(putrid odor of rotting fish)

## 11.5C Compounds Containing a C=O Group

Many different kinds of compounds contain a carbon–oxygen double bond (**C=O, carbonyl group**), as shown in Table 11.4. Carbonyl compounds include aldehydes, ketones, carboxylic acids, esters, and amides. The type of atom bonded to the carbonyl carbon—hydrogen, carbon, or a heteroatom—determines the specific class of carbonyl compound.

carbonyl group

Take special note of the condensed structures used to draw aldehydes, carboxylic acids, and esters.

## Table 11.3 Compounds Containing a Carbon–Heteroatom Single Bond

| Type of Compound | General Structure | Example | 3-D Structure | Functional Group |
|---|---|---|---|---|
| **Alkyl halide** | R—Ẍ: <br> (X = F, Cl, Br, I) | $CH_3$—Br̈: | | —X |
| **Alcohol** | R—ÖH | $CH_3$—ÖH | | —OH <br> hydroxyl group |
| **Ether** | R—Ö—R | $CH_3$—Ö—$CH_3$ | | —OR |
| **Amine** | R—N̈H₂ or <br> R₂N̈H or R₃N̈ | $CH_3$—N̈H₂ | | —NH₂ <br> amino group |

## Table 11.4 Compounds Containing a C=O Group

| Type of Compound | General Structure | Example | 3-D Structure | Functional Group |
|---|---|---|---|---|
| **Aldehyde** | :O: ‖ R—C—H | :O: ‖ $CH_3$—C—H | | :O: ‖ —C—H |
| **Ketone** | :O: ‖ R—C—R | :O: ‖ $CH_3$—C—$CH_3$ | | :O: ‖ —C— |
| **Carboxylic acid** | :O: ‖ R—C—ÖH | :O: ‖ $CH_3$—C—ÖH | | :O: ‖ —C—ÖH <br> carboxyl group |
| **Ester** | :O: ‖ R—C—ÖR | :O: ‖ $CH_3$—C—Ö$CH_3$ | | :O: ‖ —C—ÖR |
| **Amide** | :O: ‖ R—C—N̈—H (or R) ‖ H (or R) | :O: ‖ $CH_3$—C—N̈H₂ | | :O: ‖ —C—N̈— |

- An aldehyde has a hydrogen atom bonded directly to the carbonyl carbon.

acetaldehyde

= CH₃CHO | C is bonded to both H and O.

condensed structure

- A carboxylic acid contains an OH group bonded directly to the carbonyl carbon.

acetic acid

= CH₃COOH   or   CH₃CO₂H | C is bonded to both O atoms.

condensed structures

- An ester contains an OR group bonded directly to the carbonyl carbon.

ethyl acetate

= CH₃COOCH₂CH₃   or   CH₃CO₂CH₂CH₃

condensed structures | C is bonded to both O atoms.

Carbonyl compounds occur widely in nature, and many are responsible for the characteristic odor or flavor of the fruits shown in Figure 11.3.

## SAMPLE PROBLEM 11.7

Identify the functional group in each compound.

a.   A          b.   B          c.   C

### Analysis

Concentrate on the multiple bonds and heteroatoms and refer to Tables 11.2, 11.3, and 11.4.

### Solution

a.   A          b.   B          c.   C          C's on both sides of the C=O

**A** is a hydrocarbon with a carbon–carbon double bond, making it an alkene.

**B** has a carbon atom bonded to a hydroxyl group (OH), making it an alcohol.

**C** contains a C=O. Since the carbonyl carbon is bonded to two other carbons in the ring, **C** is a ketone.

## PROBLEM 11.12

For each compound: [1] Identify the functional group; [2] draw out the complete compound, including lone pairs on heteroatoms.

a. [cyclohexane]—CHO          c. [cyclohexane]=O          e. [cyclopentane structure with C(=O)NHCH₃]

b. CH₃CH₂CH₂CO₂H          d. CH₃CH₂CO₂CH₂CH₃

Figure 11.3    What We Eat—Naturally Occurring Carbonyl Compounds in Fruit

benzaldehyde
(aroma of cherries
and almonds)

$CH_3CO_2CH_2CH_2CH(CH_3)_2$
isoamyl acetate
(odor of banana)

citric acid
(responsible for the tartness
of citrus fruits)

$CH_3CH_2CH_2CO_2CH_2CH_3$
ethyl butanoate
(odor of pineapple)

In addition to water, fruits (and other foods) contain a variety of organic compounds that give them taste, odor, texture, and nutritional value. Although one organic compound might be the major component in a food's flavor or odor, what we taste and smell is often a complex mixture of compounds. When even one of these components is missing, the odor and flavor can be somewhat different. This explains why artificial flavors and colors mimic, but don't really replace, the natural flavor.

Many useful organic compounds contain complex structures with two or more functional groups. Sample Problem 11.8 illustrates an example of identifying several functional groups in a single molecule.

### SAMPLE PROBLEM 11.8

Tamiflu is the trade name for oseltamivir, an antiviral drug used to treat influenza.

Tamiflu is an antiviral drug effective against avian influenza. Identify all of the functional groups in Tamiflu.

Tamiflu

### Analysis

To identify functional groups, look for multiple bonds and heteroatoms. With functional groups that contain O atoms, look at what is bonded to the O's to decide if the group is an alcohol, ether, or other group. With carbonyl-containing groups, look at what is bonded to the carbonyl carbon.

### Solution

Re-draw Tamiflu to further clarify the functional groups:

- Tamiflu contains a total of five functional groups: a carbon–carbon double bond (an alkene), ether, ester, amide, and amine.
- Note the difference between an amine and an amide. **An amine contains a N atom but no C=O. An amide contains a N atom bonded directly to a C=O.**

### PROBLEM 11.13

Identify all of the functional groups in atenolol, an antihypertensive agent; that is, it is used to treat high blood pressure.

atenolol

### SAMPLE PROBLEM 11.9

Convert each ball-and-stick model to a condensed or skeletal structure and identify the functional groups.

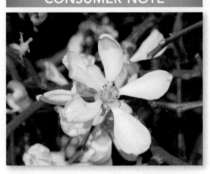
a.

*cis*-2-butene

b.

methyl anthranilate

### Analysis

Use the common element colors shown on the inside back cover to convert the ball-and-stick model to a shorthand representation. Look for multiple bonds and heteroatoms to locate the functional groups, and refer to Tables 11.2, 11.3, and 11.4.

### Solution

a.

*cis*-2-butene

$$CH_3 \qquad CH_3$$
$$= \quad \underset{H}{\overset{}{C}} = \underset{H}{\overset{}{C}} \quad \longleftarrow \text{carbon–carbon double bond (an alkene)}$$

b.

methyl anthranilate

benzene ring

OCH₃ — ester

NH₂ — amine

### PROBLEM 11.14

Convert each ball-and-stick model to a condensed or skeletal structure and identify the functional groups.

a.

b.

The kernel of the fruit of the nutmeg tree contains elemicin (Problem 11.15) and several other organic compounds responsible for its characteristic flavor and fragrance.

**PROBLEM 11.15**

Convert the ball-and-stick model of elemicin, a component of nutmeg, to a skeletal structure and identify the functional groups.

elemicin

## 11.6 Properties of Organic Compounds

Because organic compounds are composed of covalent bonds, their properties differ a great deal from those of ionic inorganic compounds.

The intermolecular forces in covalent compounds were discussed in Section 7.7.

- Organic compounds exist as discrete molecules with much weaker intermolecular forces—the forces that exist *between* molecules—than those seen in ionic compounds, which are held together by very strong interactions of oppositely charged ions.

As a result, organic compounds resemble other covalent compounds in that they have much lower melting points and boiling points than ionic compounds. While ionic compounds are generally solids at room temperature, many organic compounds are liquids and some are even gases. Table 11.5 compares these and other properties of a typical organic compound (butane, $CH_3CH_2CH_2CH_3$) and a typical ionic inorganic compound (sodium chloride, NaCl).

### 11.6A Polarity

Review Sections 4.6 and 4.7 on electronegativity, bond polarity, and polar molecules. Recall that **electronegativity** measures how much a particular atom "wants" the electron density in a bond.

Are organic compounds polar or nonpolar? That depends. Like other covalent compounds, the polarity of an organic compound is determined by two factors: the polarity of the individual bonds and the overall shape of the molecule. **The polarity of an individual bond depends on the electronegativity of the atoms that form it.**

- A covalent bond is *nonpolar* when two atoms of identical or similar electronegativity are joined together. Thus, C—C and C—H bonds are nonpolar bonds.
- A covalent bond is *polar* when atoms of different electronegativity are joined together. Thus, bonds between carbon and common heteroatoms (N, O, and the halogens) are polar bonds.

Since the common heteroatoms are *more* electronegative than carbon, these atoms pull electron density away from carbon, making it partially positive and the heteroatom partially negative.

$$\overset{\delta^+}{C}-\overset{\delta^-}{\ddot{O}}- \qquad \overset{\delta^+}{C}-\overset{\delta^-}{\ddot{N}}- \qquad \overset{\delta^+}{C}-\overset{\delta^-}{\ddot{X}}:$$

X = halogen

- The symbol $\delta^+$ is given to the less electronegative atom (usually C or H).
- The symbol $\delta^-$ is given to the more electronegative atom (usually N, O, or a halogen).

**Table 11.5**  Comparing the Properties of an Organic Compound ($CH_3CH_2CH_2CH_3$) and an Ionic Inorganic Compound (NaCl)

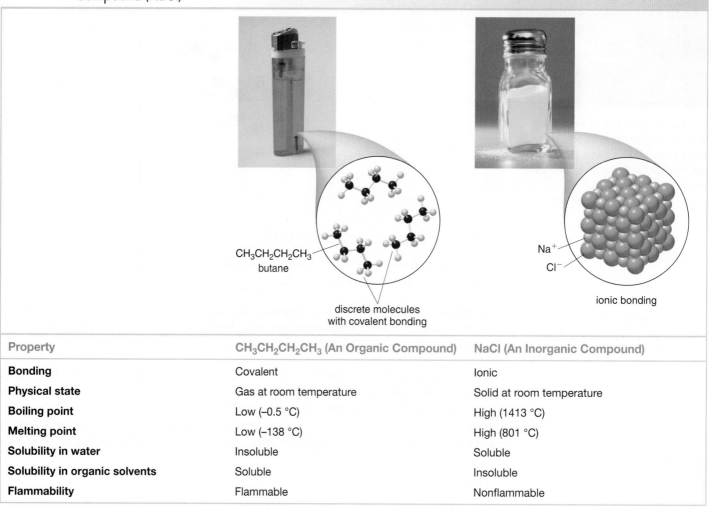

CH₃CH₂CH₂CH₃
butane

discrete molecules
with covalent bonding

Na⁺

Cl⁻

ionic bonding

| Property | $CH_3CH_2CH_2CH_3$ (An Organic Compound) | NaCl (An Inorganic Compound) |
| --- | --- | --- |
| **Bonding** | Covalent | Ionic |
| **Physical state** | Gas at room temperature | Solid at room temperature |
| **Boiling point** | Low (–0.5 °C) | High (1413 °C) |
| **Melting point** | Low (–138 °C) | High (801 °C) |
| **Solubility in water** | Insoluble | Soluble |
| **Solubility in organic solvents** | Soluble | Insoluble |
| **Flammability** | Flammable | Nonflammable |

**PROBLEM 11.16**

Indicate the polar bonds in each compound. Label the bonds with $\delta^+$ and $\delta^-$.

a.

$$\begin{array}{c} Cl \\ | \\ Cl-C-H \\ | \\ Cl \end{array}$$

chloroform
(once used as an anesthetic)

c.   H$-$C$-$O$-$C$-$C$-$F  (with F, F, H above and F, F, Cl below)

enflurane
(anesthetic)

b.

$$\begin{array}{c} H \\ \diagdown \\ C=O \\ \diagup \\ H \end{array}$$

formaldehyde
(preservative)

d.   $-$C$-$C$-$N$-$CH₃  (with H, H, H above and H, CH₃ below; ring on left)

methamphetamine
(illegal, addictive stimulant)

Hydrocarbons contain only nonpolar C—C and C—H bonds, so **hydrocarbons are nonpolar molecules.** In contrast, when an organic compound contains a *single* polar bond, as in the alkyl halide $CH_3CH_2Cl$, the molecule contains a net dipole, and is therefore a polar molecule.

ethane

no polar bonds
nonpolar molecule

chloroethane

one polar bond
polar molecule

With organic compounds that have more than one polar bond, **the shape of the molecule determines the overall polarity.**

- If the individual bond dipoles cancel in a molecule, the molecule is nonpolar.
- If the individual bond dipoles do not cancel, the molecule is polar.

A bond dipole can be indicated by an arrow with the head of the arrow pointing towards the more electronegative element, and a perpendicular line drawn through the tail of the arrow (⊢——→). Thus, dichloroacetylene (ClC≡CCl) is a linear molecule with two polar C—Cl bonds, but the individual bond dipoles are equal in magnitude and opposite in direction. As a result, dichloroacetylene is a *nonpolar* molecule. In contrast, methanol, $CH_3OH$, has two polar bonds (C—O and O—H), and a bent shape around oxygen (Section 11.3). The individual bond dipoles do *not* cancel, so $CH_3OH$ is a *polar* molecule.

| Two bond dipoles cancel. | Two bond dipoles do *not* cancel. |

dichloroacetylene
nonpolar molecule

methanol
polar molecule

### SAMPLE PROBLEM 11.10

Explain why dichloromethane ($CH_2Cl_2$), a solvent used in paint remover, is a polar molecule.

### Analysis

$CH_2Cl_2$ has two polar C—Cl bonds. We must determine the shape of the molecule around the carbon atom and check whether the two bond dipoles cancel or reinforce.

### Solution

Since the C atom in $CH_2Cl_2$ is surrounded by four atoms, it is tetrahedral. The two bond dipoles do not cancel, and **$CH_2Cl_2$ is a polar molecule.**

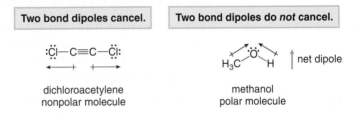

| Draw $CH_2Cl_2$ as a tetrahedron to see that the bond dipoles do not cancel. | Do *not* draw $CH_2Cl_2$ as: |

**polar molecule**

In this drawing it appears as if the bond dipoles cancel, but in reality they do *not*.

**PROBLEM 11.17**

Label each molecule as polar or nonpolar and explain your choice.

a. △

b.
$$CH_3$$
$$C{=}O$$
$$CH_3$$

c. $CCl_4$

d. $CH_3CH_2CH_2NH_2$

**PROBLEM 11.18**

Explain why dimethyl ether ($CH_3OCH_3$) is a polar molecule.

## 11.6B   Solubility

Review the general principles of solubility in Section 8.2.

Understanding the solubility properties of organic compounds allows us to learn about many interesting phenomena. One rule governs solubility: **"Like dissolves like."** Three facts can then be used to explain the solubility of organic compounds.

- Most organic compounds are soluble in organic solvents.
- Hydrocarbons and other nonpolar organic compounds are not soluble in water.
- Polar organic compounds are water soluble only if they are small and contain a nitrogen or oxygen atom that can hydrogen bond with water.

Three compounds—hexane, ethanol, and cholesterol—illustrate these principles. All of these compounds are organic and therefore soluble in an organic solvent like diethyl ether ($CH_3CH_2OCH_2CH_3$). Their water solubility depends on their polarity and size.

Since hexane ($CH_3CH_2CH_2CH_2CH_2CH_3$) is a nonpolar hydrocarbon, it is insoluble in water. Ethanol ($CH_3CH_2OH$), on the other hand, is water soluble because it is small and contains a polar OH group. The ethanol in gin dissolves in the water of tonic water, resulting in the alcoholic beverage called a "gin and tonic."

Cholesterol has 27 carbon atoms and only one OH group. Its nonpolar hydrocarbon part is too large to dissolve in water, making it water insoluble. As a result, cholesterol can't dissolve in the aqueous medium of the blood. When it must be transported through the body in the bloodstream, cholesterol is bound to other substances that are water soluble.

$CH_3CH_2{-}OH$
ethanol

**H₂O soluble**

cholesterol

There are too many nonpolar C—C and C—H bonds for cholesterol to be soluble in water.

**H₂O insoluble**

Table 11.6 summarizes the solubility characteristics of hexane, ethanol, and cholesterol.

Table 11.6 The Solubility Characteristics of Three Representative
Organic Molecules

| Compound | Solubility in an Organic Solvent | Solubility in Water |
|---|---|---|
| $CH_3CH_2CH_2CH_2CH_2CH_3$<br>Hexane | Soluble | Insoluble |
| $CH_3CH_2OH$<br>Ethanol | Soluble | Soluble |
| Cholesterol | Soluble | Insoluble |

PROBLEM 11.19

Predict the water solubility of each compound.

a. $CH_3(CH_2)_6CH_3$

octane
(gasoline component)

b.

$$CH_3 \overset{\overset{\displaystyle O}{\|}}{C} CH_3$$

acetone
(solvent)

c. $CH_3(CH_2)_{16}CO_2H$

stearic acid
(a fatty acid)

## 11.6C FOCUS ON THE ENVIRONMENT
### Environmental Pollutants

MTBE (*tert*-butyl methyl ether) and 4,4'–dichlorobiphenyl (a PCB, polychlorinated biphenyl) demonstrate that solubility properties can help to determine the fate of organic pollutants in the environment.

$$CH_3 - O - C(CH_3)_3$$

MTBE
*tert*-butyl methyl ether

4,4'-dichlorobiphenyl
(a PCB)

**MTBE** is a small polar organic molecule that has been used as a high-octane additive in unleaded gasoline. The use of MTBE, however, has now also caused environmental concern. Although MTBE is not toxic or carcinogenic, it has a distinctive, nauseating odor, and **it is water soluble.** Small amounts of MTBE have contaminated the drinking water in several California communities, making it unfit for consumption. As a result, the use of MTBE as a gasoline additive has declined in the United States.

4,4'-Dichlorobiphenyl is one of a group of compounds called **PCB**s, which have been used in the manufacture of polystyrene coffee cups and other products. They have been released into the environment during production, use, storage, and disposal, making them one of the most widespread organic pollutants. **PCBs are insoluble in $H_2O$, but very soluble in organic media,** so they are soluble in fatty tissue, including that found in all types of fish and birds around the world. Although not acutely toxic, ingesting large quantities of fish contaminated with PCBs has been shown to retard growth and memory retention in children.

**PROBLEM 11.20**

DDT is a persistent environmental pollutant once widely used as an insecticide. Using solubility principles, explain why shore birds that populate areas sprayed with DDT are found to have a high concentration of DDT in their tissues.

DDT

# 11.7 FOCUS ON HEALTH & MEDICINE
## Vitamins

*Vitamins* **are organic compounds needed in small amounts for normal cell function.** Our bodies cannot synthesize these compounds, so they must be obtained in our diet. Most vitamins are identified by a letter, such as A, C, D, E, and K. There are several different B vitamins, though, so a subscript is added to distinguish them—for example, $B_1$, $B_2$, and $B_{12}$.

Vitamins are classified on the basis of their solubility properties.

- A *fat-soluble vitamin* dissolves in an organic solvent but is insoluble in water. Fat-soluble vitamins have many nonpolar C—C and C—H bonds and few polar functional groups.
- A *water-soluble vitamin* dissolves in water. Water-soluble vitamins have many polar bonds.

Whether a vitamin is fat soluble or water soluble can be determined by applying the solubility principles discussed in Section 11.6. Vitamins A and C illustrate the differences between fat-soluble and water-soluble vitamins.

## 11.7A  Vitamin A

**Vitamin A,** or **retinol,** is an essential component of the vision receptors in the eyes. It also helps to maintain the health of mucous membranes and the skin, so many anti-aging creams contain vitamin A. A deficiency of this vitamin leads to a loss of night vision.

vitamin A

Vitamin A contains 20 carbons and a single OH group, making it **water insoluble.** Because it is organic, it is **soluble in any organic medium.** To understand the consequences of these solubility characteristics, we must learn about the chemical environment of the body.

About 70% of the body is composed of water. Fluids such as blood, gastric juices in the stomach, and urine are largely water with dissolved ions such as $Na^+$ and $K^+$. Vitamin A is insoluble in these fluids. There are also fat cells composed of organic compounds having C—C and C—H bonds. Vitamin A is soluble in this organic environment, and thus it is readily stored in these fat cells, particularly in the liver.

The name **vitamin** was first used in 1912 by the Polish chemist Casimir Funk, who called them *vitamines,* since he thought that they all contained an *amine* functional group. Later the word was shortened to vitamin, because some are amines but others, like vitamins A and C, are not.

**CONSUMER NOTE**

Some anti-aging creams contain vitamin A.

In addition to obtaining vitamin A directly from the diet, β-carotene, the orange pigment found in many plants including carrots, is readily converted to vitamin A in our bodies.

β-carotene
(orange pigment in carrots)

vitamin A

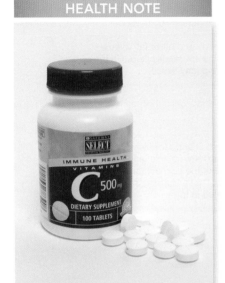
Eating too many carrots does not result in storing an excess of vitamin A. If you consume more β-carotene in carrots than you need, the body stores this precursor until it needs more vitamin A. Some of the stored β-carotene reaches the surface tissues of the skin, giving it an orange color. This phenomenon is harmless and reversible. When stored β-carotene is converted to vitamin A and is no longer in excess, these tissues will return to their normal hue.

Ingesting a moderate excess of vitamin A doesn't cause any harm, but a large excess causes headaches, loss of appetite, and even death. Early Arctic explorers who ate polar bear livers that contain an unusually large amount of vitamin A, are thought to have died from consuming too much vitamin A.

## 11.7B  Vitamin C

Although most animal species can synthesize vitamin C, humans, the Indian fruit bat, and the bulbul bird must obtain this vitamin from dietary sources. Citrus fruits, strawberries, tomatoes, and sweet potatoes are all excellent sources of vitamin C.

**Vitamin C,** or **ascorbic acid,** is important in the formation of collagen, a protein that forms the connective tissues of skin, muscle, and blood vessels. A deficiency of vitamin C causes scurvy, a common disease of sailors in the 1600s who had no access to fresh fruits on long voyages.

vitamin C
(ascorbic acid)

Vitamin C has six carbon atoms and six oxygen atoms, making it **water soluble.** Vitamin C thus dissolves in urine. Although it has been acclaimed as a deterrent for all kinds of diseases, from the common cold to cancer, the benefits of taking large amounts of vitamin C are not really known, since an excess of the minimum daily requirement is excreted unchanged in the urine.

The solubility characteristics of vitamins A and C are shown in Figure 11.4.

**Figure 11.4    Solubility Characteristics of Vitamins A and C**

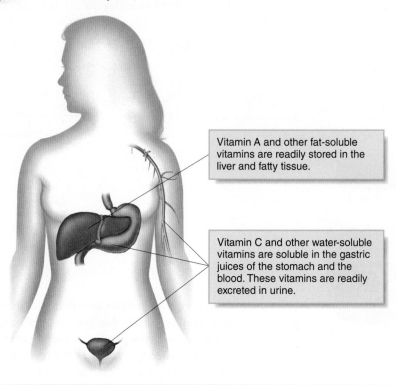

Vitamin A and other fat-soluble vitamins are readily stored in the liver and fatty tissue.

Vitamin C and other water-soluble vitamins are soluble in the gastric juices of the stomach and the blood. These vitamins are readily excreted in urine.

**PROBLEM 11.21**

Predict the solubility of vitamin $B_3$ in water.

vitamin $B_3$
(niacin)

**PROBLEM 11.22**

Predict the solubility of vitamin $K_1$ in water and in organic solvents.

vitamin $K_1$
(phylloquinone)

# CHAPTER HIGHLIGHTS

## KEY TERMS

Alcohol (11.5)

Aldehyde (11.5)

Alkane (11.5)

Alkene (11.5)

Alkyl halide (11.5)

Alkyne (11.5)

Amide (11.5)

Amine (11.5)

Amino group (11.5)

Aromatic compound (11.5)

Carbonyl group (11.5)

Carboxyl group (11.5)

Carboxylic acid (11.5)

Condensed structure (11.4)

Ester (11.5)

Ether (11.5)

Fat-soluble vitamin (11.7)

Functional group (11.5)

Heteroatom (11.2)

Hydrocarbon (11.5)

Hydroxyl group (11.5)

Ketone (11.5)

"Like dissolves like" (11.6)

Nonpolar molecule (11.6)

Organic chemistry (11.1)

Polar molecule (11.6)

Skeletal structure (11.4)

Vitamin (11.7)

Water-soluble vitamin (11.7)

## KEY CONCEPTS

**❶ What are the characteristic features of organic compounds? (11.2)**

- Organic compounds contain carbon atoms and most contain hydrogen atoms. Carbon forms four bonds.
- Carbon forms single, double, and triple bonds to itself and other atoms.
- Carbon atoms can bond to form chains or rings.
- Organic compounds often contain heteroatoms, commonly N, O, and the halogens.

**❷ How can we predict the shape around an atom in an organic molecule? (11.3)**

- The shape around an atom is determined by counting groups, and then arranging them to keep them as far away from each other as possible.

| Number of Groups | Number of Atoms | Number of Lone Pairs | Shape | Bond Angle | Example |
|---|---|---|---|---|---|
| 2 | 2 | 0 | Linear | 180° | $HC{\equiv}CH$ |
| 3 | 3 | 0 | Trigonal planar | 120° | $CH_2{=}CH_2$ |
| 4 | 4 | 0 | Tetrahedral | 109.5° | $CH_3CH_3$ |
| 4 | 3 | 1 | Trigonal pyramidal | ~109.5° | $CH_3NH_2$ (N atom) |
| 4 | 2 | 2 | Bent | ~109.5° | $CH_3OH$ (O atom) |

**❸ What shorthand methods are used to draw organic molecules? (11.4)**

- In condensed structures, atoms are drawn in but the two-electron bonds are generally omitted. Lone pairs are omitted as well. Parentheses are used around like groups bonded together or to the same atom.
- Three assumptions are used in drawing skeletal structures: [1] There is a carbon at the intersection of two lines or at the end of any line. [2] Each carbon has enough hydrogens to give it four bonds. [3] Heteroatoms and the hydrogens bonded to them are drawn in.

**❹ What is a functional group and why are functional groups important? (11.5)**

- A functional group is an atom or a group of atoms with characteristic chemical and physical properties.
- A functional group determines all of the properties of a molecule—its shape, physical properties, and the type of reactions it undergoes.

**❺ How do organic compounds differ from ionic inorganic compounds? (11.6)**

- The main difference between organic compounds and ionic inorganic compounds is their bonding. Organic compounds are composed of discrete molecules with covalent bonds. Ionic inorganic compounds are composed of cations and anions held together by the strong attraction of oppositely charged ions. Other properties that are consequences of these bonding differences are summarized in Table 11.5.

**❻ How can we determine if an organic molecule is polar or nonpolar? (11.6A)**

- A nonpolar molecule has either no polar bonds or two or more bond dipoles that cancel.
- A polar molecule has either one polar bond, or two or more bond dipoles that do not cancel.

**❼ What are the solubility properties of organic compounds? (11.6B)**

- Most organic molecules are soluble in organic solvents.
- Hydrocarbons and other nonpolar organic molecules are not soluble in water.
- Polar organic molecules are water soluble only if they are small and contain a nitrogen or oxygen atom that can hydrogen bond with water.

**❽ What are vitamins and when is a vitamin fat soluble or water soluble? (11.7)**

- A vitamin is an organic compound that cannot be synthesized by the body but is needed in small amounts for cell function.
- A fat-soluble vitamin has many nonpolar C—C and C—H bonds and few polar bonds, making it insoluble in water.
- A water-soluble vitamin has many polar bonds, so it dissolves in water.

# PROBLEMS

Selected in-chapter and odd-numbered end-of-chapter problems have brief answers in Appendix B. The *Student Study Guide and Solutions Manual* contains detailed solutions to all in-chapter and odd-numbered end-of-chapter problems, as well as additional worked examples and a chapter self-test.

## General Characteristics of Organic Molecules

**11.23** Which chemical formulas represent organic compounds and which represent inorganic compounds: (a) $H_2SO_4$; (b) $Br_2$; (c) $C_5H_{12}$?

**11.24** Which chemical formulas represent organic compounds and which represent inorganic compounds: (a) LiBr; (b) HCl; (c) $CH_5N$?

**11.25** Complete each structure by filling in all H's and lone pairs.

a. $C-C=C-C\equiv C$

b. $C=C-C-O$

c. $C\equiv C-C-C$
with Cl

d. $C\equiv C-C-C-N$ with O

**11.26** Complete each structure by filling in all H's and lone pairs.

a. $C-C-C=O$ (O, O)

glyceraldehyde
(simple carbohydrate)

b. $C-C-C=O$ (O, O)

lactic acid
(product of carbohydrate metabolism)

c. $N-C-C-O$ (O, C)

alanine
(amino acid in proteins)

d. $O-C-C-C-O$ (O)

dihydroxyacetone
(ingredient in artificial tanning agents)

## Predicting Shape and Bond Angles

**11.27** Determine the shape around the indicated atoms in each compound. Don't forget to add lone pairs to heteroatoms before determining the shape around them.

a. (1) (2)
$H-C=C-C\equiv N$ with H H

acrylonitrile
(used to prepare Orlon fibers)

b. (1) (2) (3)
$CH_3-O-C(CH_3)_3$

MTBE
(gasoline additive)

**11.28** Ethambutol is a drug used to treat tuberculosis. Determine the shape around the indicated atoms in ethambutol. Don't forget to add lone pairs to heteroatoms before determining the shape around them.

$H-O-CH_2-C-N-CH_2CH_2-N-C-CH_2-O-H$
with $CH_2CH_3$, H, H, H, H, $CH_2CH_3$

ethambutol

**11.29** Predict the indicated bond angles in each compound.

a. $CH_3-C\equiv C-Cl$ (1)(2)

b. $CH_2=C-Cl$ with H (2), (1)

c. $CH_3-C-Cl$ with H (1)(2), H

**11.30** Predict the indicated bond angles in each compound. Don't forget to add lone pairs to heteroatoms before determining the shape around them.

a. $CH_3(CH_2)_7-C=C-(CH_2)_7-C-O-H$ with H H and O

oleic acid
(fatty acid in vegetable oil)

b. $H-N-C-(CH_2)_5NH_2$ with H, H, H

1,6-diaminohexane
(used to synthesize nylon)

**11.31** "Ecstasy" is a widely used illegal stimulant. Determine the shape around each indicated atom.

(1) (2) (3)
$-CH_2CHNCH_3$ with H and $CH_3$ (4)

MDMA
"Ecstasy"

**11.32** Fenfluramine is one component of the appetite suppressant Fen–Phen, which was withdrawn from the market in 1997 after it was shown to damage the heart valves in some patients. Determine the shape around each indicated atom.

$CF_3$
$-CH_2CHNCH_2CH_3$ with H and $CH_3$

fenfluramine

**11.33** Explain why each C—C—C bond angle in benzene (Table 11.2) is 120°.

**11.34** Hexachloroethane ($Cl_3C-CCl_3$), an alkyl chloride with a camphor-like odor, is a derivative of ethane ($CH_3CH_3$), formed by replacing each H by a Cl atom. Draw the structure of hexachloroethane using solid lines, wedges, and dashes to indicate the three-dimensional shape around each atom.

## Drawing Organic Molecules

**11.35** Convert each compound to a condensed structure.

a.

b.

c.

d.

**11.36** Convert each compound to a condensed structure.

a.

b.

c.

d.

**11.37** Convert each compound to a skeletal structure.

a.

b.

**11.38** Convert each compound to a skeletal structure.

a.

b.

**11.39** Convert each shorthand structure to a complete structure with all atoms and lone pairs drawn in.

a. $(CH_3)_2CH(CH_2)_6CH_3$

b. $(CH_3)_3COH$

c. $CH_3CO_2(CH_2)_3CH_3$

d.

**11.40** Convert each shorthand structure to a complete structure with all atoms and lone pairs drawn in.

a. $(CH_3)_2CHO(CH_2)_4CH_3$

b. $(CH_3)_3C(CH_2)_3CBr_3$

c. $(CH_3)_2CHCONH_2$

d.

**11.41** What is wrong in each of the following shorthand structures?

a. $(CH_3)_3CHCH_2CH_3$

b. $CH_3(CH_2)_4CH_3OH$

c. $(CH_3)_2C=CH_3$

d.

e.

**11.42** What is wrong in each of the following shorthand structures?

a. $HC\equiv CCH_2C=CH_2$

b. $CH_3C\equiv C(CH_3)_2$

c. $HC\equiv CCH_2C(CH_3)_2$

d.

e.

**11.43** Convert the shorthand structure of tyrosine to a complete structure with all atoms and lone pairs drawn in. Tyrosine is one of the 20 amino acids used for protein synthesis.

$$HO\!-\!\!\bigcirc\!\!-\!CH_2CHCO_2H$$
$$|$$
$$NH_2$$

tyrosine

**11.44** Albuterol (trade names: Proventil and Ventolin) is a bronchodilator, a drug that widens airways, thus making it an effective treatment for individuals suffering from asthma. Draw a complete structure for albuterol with all atoms and lone pairs.

$$HO\!-\!\!\bigcirc\!\!-\!\overset{OH}{\underset{}{CHCH_2NHC(CH_3)_3}}$$

HOCH$_2$          albuterol

## Functional Groups

**11.45** Identify the functional groups in each molecule.

a. isoprene
(emitted by plants)

b. 2-heptanone
(from blue cheese)

$$CH_3\!-\!\overset{O}{\overset{\|}{C}}\!-\!(CH_2)_4CH_3$$

c. propyl acetate
(from pears)

$$CH_3\!-\!\overset{O}{\overset{\|}{C}}\!-\!OCH_2CH_2CH_3$$

**11.46** Identify the functional groups in each molecule.

a. tartaric acid
(from grapes)

b. butanedione
(component of butter flavor)

$$CH_3\!-\!\overset{O}{\overset{\|}{C}}\!-\!\overset{O}{\overset{\|}{C}}\!-\!CH_3$$

c. dimethylformamide
(solvent)

$$H\!-\!\overset{O}{\overset{\|}{C}}\!-\!N(CH_3)_2$$

**11.47** Identify the functional groups in each molecule.

a. isobutyl formate
(odor of raspberries)

$$H\!-\!\overset{O}{\overset{\|}{C}}\!-\!OCH_2CH(CH_3)_2$$

b. $CH_2\!=\!CHCHCH_2\!-\!C\!\equiv\!C\!-\!C\!\equiv\!C\!-\!CH_2CH\!=\!CH(CH_2)_5CH_3$
     $|$
     OH

carotatoxin
(neurotoxin from carrots)

c. vanillin
(isolated from vanilla beans)

**11.48** Identify the functional groups in each drug.

a. pseudoephedrine
(nasal decongestant)

b. acetaminophen
(analgesic in Tylenol)

c. ketoprofen
(analgesic)

**11.49** Dopamine, a molecule synthesized by nerve cells in the brain, affects movement, emotions, and pleasure. When dopamine-producing nerve cells die, Parkinson's disease results. Identify the functional groups in dopamine.

dopamine

**11.50** GHB is an addictive, illegal recreational drug that depresses the central nervous system and results in intoxication. Identify the functional groups in GHB.

GHB

**11.51** Convert the ball-and-stick model of neral, a compound isolated from lemons and limes, to a condensed or skeletal structure and identify the functional groups.

neral

**11.52** Convert the ball-and-stick model of estragole, a compound isolated from tarragon, to a skeletal structure and identify the functional groups.

estragole

**11.53** Describe how the functional groups in a carboxylic acid and an ester differ. Give an example of a carboxylic acid with three carbons and an ester with three carbons.

**11.54** Describe how the functional groups in an amine and an amide differ. Give an example of an amine with two carbons and an amide with two carbons.

**11.55** Draw an organic compound that fits each of the following criteria.
a. a hydrocarbon having molecular formula $C_3H_4$ that contains a triple bond
b. an alcohol containing three carbons
c. an aldehyde containing three carbons
d. a ketone having molecular formula $C_4H_8O$

**11.56** Draw an organic compound that fits each of the following criteria.
a. an amine containing two $CH_3$ groups bonded to the N atom
b. an alkene that has the double bond in a ring
c. an ether having two different R groups bonded to the ether oxygen
d. an amide that has molecular formula $C_3H_7NO$

**11.57** Draw the structure of an alkane, an alkene, and an alkyne, each having five carbon atoms. What is the molecular formula for each compound?

**11.58** Aspartame (trade name: NutraSweet) is a widely used substitute sweetener, 180 times sweeter than table sugar. Identify the functional groups in aspartame.

aspartame

## Properties of Organic Compounds

**11.59** You are given two unlabeled bottles of solids, one containing sodium chloride (NaCl) and one containing cholesterol ($C_{27}H_{46}O$, Section 11.6B). You are also given two labeled bottles of liquids, one containing water and one containing dichloromethane ($CH_2Cl_2$). How can you determine which solid is sodium chloride and which solid is cholesterol?

**11.60** State how potassium iodide (KI) and pentane ($CH_3CH_2CH_2CH_2CH_3$) differ with regards to each of the following properties: (a) type of bonding; (b) solubility in water; (c) solubility in an organic solvent; (d) melting point; (e) boiling point.

**11.61** Why do we need to know the shape of a molecule with polar bonds before deciding if the molecule is polar or nonpolar?

**11.62** 1,1-Dichloroethylene ($CH_2{=}CCl_2$) is a starting material used to prepare the plastic packaging material Saran wrap. Your friend thinks that 1,1-dichloroethylene is a nonpolar molecule because the dipoles in the two C—Cl bonds cancel. Draw out the proper three-dimensional structure of 1,1-dichloroethylene, and then explain why your friend is correct or incorrect.

**11.63** Indicate the polar bonds in each molecule. Label the bonds with $\delta^+$ and $\delta^-$.

a.

$$F{-}\overset{\overset{\displaystyle Cl}{|}}{\underset{\underset{\displaystyle Cl}{|}}{C}}{-}Cl$$

trichlorofluoromethane
(responsible for atmospheric ozone destruction)

b.

$$HOCH_2\overset{\overset{\displaystyle OH}{|}}{C}HCH_2OH$$

glycerol
(used in cosmetics)

**11.64** Indicate the polar bonds in each molecule. Label the bonds with $\delta^+$ and $\delta^-$.

a.

$$\underset{\underset{\displaystyle H}{}}{\overset{\overset{\displaystyle H}{}}{C}}{=}\underset{\underset{\displaystyle Cl}{}}{\overset{\overset{\displaystyle H}{}}{C}}$$

vinyl chloride

b.

—OCH₃

anisole

**11.65** Classify each molecule as polar or nonpolar.

a. (cyclopentane structure)

b. $CH_3CH_2\overset{\overset{\displaystyle O}{\|}}{C}CH_2CH_3$

c. $CH_2Br_2$

**11.66** Classify each molecule as polar or nonpolar.

    a. $CH_3OCH_2CH_3$     b. $(CH_3CH_2)_2NH$     c.

**11.67** Which molecule is more water soluble? Explain.

      butane          ethylene glycol

**11.68** Explain why pantothenic acid, vitamin $B_5$, is water soluble.

vitamin $B_5$

**11.69** Sucrose (table sugar) and 1-dodecanol [$(CH_3(CH_2)_{11}OH$] both contain 12 carbon atoms and hydroxyl groups. Explain why sucrose is water soluble, but 1-dodecanol is not water soluble.

sucrose

**11.70** Acetic acid ($CH_3CO_2H$) and palmitic acid [$CH_3(CH_2)_{14}CO_2H$] are both carboxylic acids. Acetic acid is the water-soluble carboxylic acid in vinegar, while palmitic acid is a water-insoluble fatty acid. Give a reason for this solubility difference.

**11.71** Spermaceti wax [$CH_3(CH_2)_{14}CO_2(CH_2)_{15}CH_3$], a compound isolated from sperm whales, was once a common ingredient in cosmetics. Its use is now banned to help protect whales. (a) Identify the functional group in spermaceti wax. (b) Predict its solubility properties in water and organic solvents and explain your reasoning.

**11.72** Beeswax has the structure $CH_3(CH_2)_{14}CO_2(CH_2)_{29}CH_3$. Consider its solubility in three different solvents—water, hexane [$CH_3(CH_2)_4CH_3$], and ethanol ($CH_3CH_2OH$). In which solvent is beeswax most soluble? In which solvent is beeswax least soluble? Explain your choices.

## Vitamins

**11.73** Explain why regularly taking a large excess of a fat-soluble vitamin can lead to severe health problems, whereas taking a large excess of a water-soluble vitamin often causes no major health problems.

**11.74** You can obtain the minimum daily requirement of vitamin E by eating leafy greens or by taking vitamin E tablets. As a source of vitamin E, which of these methods is better for an individual?

**11.75** Vitamin E is a natural antioxidant found in fish oil, almonds, hazelnuts, and leafy greens. Predict the solubility of vitamin E in water and in organic solvents.

vitamin E

**11.76** Vitamin $B_6$ is obtained by eating a diet that includes meat, fish, wheat germ, and bananas. A deficiency of vitamin $B_6$ can cause convulsions and anemia. Predict the solubility of vitamin $B_6$ in water and in organic solvents.

vitamin $B_6$
pyridoxine

## General Questions and Applications

**11.77** Can a hydrocarbon have each of the following molecular formulas? Explain why or why not in each case. (a) $C_3H_8$; (b) $C_3H_9$; (c) $C_3H_6$.

**11.78** Can an oxygen-containing organic compound have molecular formula $C_2H_6O$? Explain your reasoning.

**11.79** (a) Draw a condensed structure for an amine having molecular formula $C_4H_{11}N$. (b) Label all polar bonds using the symbols $\delta^+$ and $\delta^-$. (c) Determine the geometry around the N atom. (d) Is the compound you drew polar or nonpolar?

**11.80** (a) Draw a condensed structure for an alcohol having molecular formula $C_4H_{10}O$. (b) Label all polar bonds using the symbols $\delta^+$ and $\delta^-$. (c) Determine the geometry around the O atom. (d) Is the compound you drew polar or nonpolar?

**11.81** Benzocaine is the active ingredient in topical pain relievers such as Orajel and Anbesol.

benzocaine

   a. Give the molecular formula for benzocaine.
   b. Draw in all lone pairs on heteroatoms using a skeletal structure.
   c. How many trigonal planar carbons does benzocaine contain?
   d. Predict the water solubility of benzocaine.
   e. Label all polar bonds.

**11.82** Methyl salicylate is responsible for the characteristic odor of the oil wintergreen.

methyl salicylate

a. Give the molecular formula for methyl salicylate.
b. Draw in all lone pairs on heteroatoms using a skeletal structure.
c. How many trigonal planar carbons does methyl salicylate contain?
d. Predict the water solubility of methyl salicylate.
e. Label all polar bonds.

**11.83** Answer the following questions about aldosterone, a compound that helps to control the absorption of $Na^+$ and $Cl^-$ ions in the kidneys, and as a result, affects water retention.

aldosterone

a. Identify the functional groups.
b. Draw in all lone pairs on O atoms.
c. How many C's does aldosterone contain?

d. How many H's are present at each C labeled with an asterisk (*)?
e. Give the shape around each atom indicated with an arrow.
f. Label all polar bonds.

**11.84** Answer the following questions about levonorgestrel (trade name: Plan B). Levonorgestrel interferes with ovulation, the release of an egg from an ovary, so it prevents pregnancy if taken within a few days of unprotected sex.

levonorgestrel

a. Identify the functional groups.
b. How many C's does levonorgestrel contain?
c. How many H's are present at each C labeled with an asterisk (*)?
d. Give the shape around each atom indicated with an arrow.
e. Label all polar bonds.
f. Is levonorgestrel soluble in an organic solvent?
g. Is levonorgestrel soluble in water?

**11.85** Cabbage leaves are coated with a hydrocarbon of molecular formula $C_{29}H_{60}$. What purpose might this hydrocarbon coating serve?

**11.86** Skin moisturizers come in two types. (a) One type of moisturizer is composed mainly of hydrocarbon material. Suggest a reason as to how a moisturizer of this sort helps to keep the skin from drying out. (b) A second type of moisturizer is composed mainly of propylene glycol [$CH_3CH(OH)CH_2OH$]. Suggest a reason as to how a moisturizer of this sort helps to keep the skin from drying out.

## CHALLENGE PROBLEMS

**11.87** THC is the active component in marijuana (Section 11.5), and ethanol ($CH_3CH_2OH$) is the alcohol in alcoholic beverages. Using the solubility principles in Section 11.6, predict the water solubility of each of these compounds. Then, explain why drug screenings are able to detect the presence of THC but not ethanol weeks after these substances have been introduced into the body.

**11.88** Cocaine is a widely abused, addicting drug. Cocaine is usually obtained as its hydrochloride salt (cocaine hydrochloride, an ionic salt). This salt can be converted to crack (a neutral molecule) by treatment with base.

cocaine (crack)
neutral organic molecule

cocaine hydrochloride
a salt

a. Identify the functional groups in cocaine.
b. Given what you have learned about ionic and covalent bonding, which of the two compounds—crack or cocaine hydrochloride—has a higher boiling point?
c. Which compound is more soluble in water?
d. Can you use the relative solubility to explain why crack is usually smoked but cocaine hydrochloride is injected directly into the bloodstream?

# 12

Crude petroleum spilled into the sea creates an insoluble oil slick. Petroleum is a complex mixture that includes the family of organic compounds called **alkanes.**

# Alkanes

## CHAPTER GOALS

*In this chapter you will learn how to:*

1. Identify and draw acyclic alkanes and cycloalkanes
2. Identify constitutional isomers
3. Name alkanes using the IUPAC system of nomenclature
4. Predict the physical properties of alkanes
5. Write equations for the complete and incomplete combustion of alkanes

$\mathbf{I}$n Chapter 12, we apply the principles of bonding, shape, and physical properties discussed in Chapter 11 to our first family of organic compounds, the **alkanes.** Since alkanes have no functional group, their chemical reactions are limited, and much of Chapter 12 is devoted to learning how to name and draw them. Alkanes do, however, undergo one important reaction, combustion, a process that powers automobiles and heats homes. The combustion of alkanes has also increased the carbon dioxide concentration in the atmosphere over the last 50 years, which may have long-term and far-reaching environmental consequences.

## 12.1   Introduction

*Alkanes* **are hydrocarbons having only C—C and C—H single bonds.** The carbons of an alkane can be joined together to form chains or rings of atoms.

The prefix *a-* means *not,* so an acyclic alkane is *not* cyclic.

- **Alkanes that contain chains of carbon atoms but no rings are called *acyclic alkanes.*** An acyclic alkane has the molecular formula $C_nH_{2n+2}$, where *n* is the number of carbons it contains. Acyclic alkanes are also called **saturated hydrocarbons** because they have the maximum number of hydrogen atoms per carbon.
- ***Cycloalkanes* contain carbons joined in one or more rings.** Since a cycloalkane has two fewer H's than an acyclic alkane with the same number of carbons, its general formula is $C_nH_{2n}$.

Undecane and cyclohexane are examples of two naturally occurring alkanes. Undecane is an acyclic alkane with molecular formula $C_{11}H_{24}$. Undecane is a *pheromone,* **a chemical substance used for communication** in a specific animal species, most commonly an insect population. Secretion of undecane by a cockroach causes other members of the species to aggregate. Cyclohexane, a cycloalkane with molecular formula $C_6H_{12}$, is one component of the mango, the most widely consumed fruit in the world.

$CH_3CH_2CH_2CH_2CH_2CH_2CH_2CH_2CH_2CH_2CH_3$

undecane

cyclohexane

### PROBLEM 12.1

How many hydrogen atoms are present in each compound?

a. an acyclic alkane with three carbons
b. a cycloalkane with four carbons

c. a cycloalkane with nine carbons
d. an acyclic alkane with seven carbons

### PROBLEM 12.2

Which formulas represent acyclic alkanes and which represent cycloalkanes?

a. $C_5H_{12}$        b. $C_4H_8$        c. $C_{12}H_{24}$        d. $C_{10}H_{22}$

## 12.2 Simple Alkanes

We begin our study of alkanes with acyclic alkanes, and then move on to cycloalkanes in Section 12.5.

### 12.2A Acyclic Alkanes Having Fewer Than Five Carbons

The structures for the two simplest acyclic alkanes were given in Chapter 11.

- **Methane, CH₄,** has a single carbon atom surrounded by four hydrogens to give it four bonds.
- **Ethane, CH₃CH₃,** has two carbon atoms joined together by a single bond. Each carbon is also bonded to three hydrogens to give it four bonds total.

Since each carbon in an alkane is surrounded by four atoms, each carbon is **tetrahedral,** and all bond angles are 109.5°.

To draw the structure of an alkane, join the carbon atoms together with single bonds, and add enough H's to give each C four bonds.

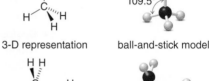

3-D representation     ball-and-stick model

To draw a three-carbon alkane, draw three carbons joined together with single bonds and add enough hydrogens to give each carbon four bonds. This forms **propane, CH₃CH₂CH₃.**

3-D representation     ball-and-stick model

The carbon skeleton in propane and other alkanes can be drawn in a variety of different ways and still represent the same molecule. For example, the three carbons of propane can be drawn in a horizontal row or with a bend. *These representations are equivalent.* **If you follow the carbon chain from one end to the other, you move across the *same* three carbon atoms in both representations.**

3 C's in a row          3 C's with a bend

- The bends in a carbon chain don't matter when it comes to identifying different compounds.

There are two different ways to arrange four carbons, giving two compounds with molecular formula C₄H₁₀.

- **Butane, CH₃CH₂CH₂CH₃,** has four carbon atoms in a row. Butane is a **straight-chain alkane,** an alkane that has all of its carbons in one continuous chain.
- **Isobutane, (CH₃)₃CH,** has three carbon atoms in a row and one carbon bonded to the middle carbon. Isobutane is a **branched-chain alkane,** an alkane that contains one or more carbon branches bonded to a carbon chain.

butane = $CH_3CH_2CH_2CH_3$

4 C's in a row    **straight-chain alkane**

isobutane = $CH_3-\underset{\underset{H}{|}}{\overset{\overset{CH_3}{|}}{C}}-CH_3$

3 C's with a one-carbon branch    **branched-chain alkane**

Butane and isobutane are *isomers,* **two different compounds with the same molecular formula.** They belong to one of the two major classes of isomers called **constitutional isomers.**

> • *Constitutional isomers* differ in the way the atoms are connected to each other.

Constitutional isomers like butane and isobutane belong to the same family of compounds: they are both **alkanes.** This is not always the case. For example, there are two different arrangements of atoms for a compound of molecular formula $C_2H_6O$.

$CH_3CH_2OH$
ethanol

$CH_3OCH_3$
dimethyl ether

Ethanol ($CH_3CH_2OH$) and dimethyl ether ($CH_3OCH_3$) are constitutional isomers with different functional groups: $CH_3CH_2OH$ is an **alcohol** and $CH_3OCH_3$ is an **ether.**

## SAMPLE PROBLEM 12.1

Are the compounds in each pair constitutional isomers or are they not isomers of each other?

a. $CH_3CH_2CH_3$ and $\underset{\underset{H}{\diagup}}{\overset{\overset{H}{\diagup}}{C}}=\underset{\underset{CH_3}{\diagdown}}{\overset{\overset{H}{\diagdown}}{C}}

b. $CH_3CH_2CH_2NH_2$ and $CH_3-\underset{\underset{CH_3}{|}}{N}-CH_3$

### Analysis

First compare molecular formulas; two compounds are isomers only if they have the same molecular formula. Then, check how the atoms are connected to each other. Constitutional isomers have atoms bonded to different atoms.

### Solution

a. $CH_3CH_2CH_3$ and $\underset{\underset{H}{\diagup}}{\overset{\overset{H}{\diagup}}{C}}=\underset{\underset{CH_3}{\diagdown}}{\overset{\overset{H}{\diagdown}}{C}}

molecular formula
$C_3H_8$

molecular formula
$C_3H_6$

The two compounds have the same number of C's but a different number of H's, so they have different molecular formulas. Thus, they are *not* isomers of each other.

b. $CH_3CH_2CH_2NH_2$ and $CH_3-\underset{\underset{CH_3}{|}}{N}-CH_3$

Both compounds have molecular formula $C_3H_9N$. Since one compound has C–C bonds and the other does not, the atoms are connected differently. These compounds are *constitutional isomers.*

PROBLEM 12.3

Are the compounds in each pair isomers or are they not isomers of each other?

a. $CH_3CH_2CH_2CH_3$ and $CH_3CH_2CH_3$

b. $CH_3CH_2CH_2OH$ and $CH_3OCH_2CH_3$

c. and —$CH_3$

## 12.2B　Acyclic Alkanes Having Five or More Carbons

As the number of carbon atoms in an alkane increases, so does the number of isomers. There are three constitutional isomers for the five-carbon alkane, each having molecular formula $C_5H_{12}$: **pentane, isopentane** (or 2-methylbutane), and **neopentane** (or 2,2-dimethylpropane).

$CH_3CH_2CH_2CH_2CH_3$

$$CH_3-\overset{\overset{\displaystyle CH_3}{|}}{\underset{\underset{\displaystyle H}{|}}{C}}-CH_2CH_3$$

$$CH_3-\overset{\overset{\displaystyle CH_3}{|}}{\underset{\underset{\displaystyle CH_3}{|}}{C}}-CH_3$$

pentane

isopentane
(2-methylbutane)

neopentane
(2,2-dimethylpropane)

The suffix -**ane** identifies a molecule as an alk**ane**.

With alkanes having five or more carbons, the names of the straight-chain isomers are derived from Greek roots: *pent*ane for **five** carbons, *hex*ane for **six,** and so on. Table 12.1 lists the names and structures for the straight-chain alkanes having up to 10 carbons. The suffix -**ane** identifies a molecule as an alk**ane**. The remainder of the name—meth-, eth-, prop-, and so forth—indicates the number of carbons in the long chain.

## Table 12.1 Straight-Chain Alkanes

| Number of C's | Molecular Formula | Structure | Name |
|---|---|---|---|
| 1 | $CH_4$ | $CH_4$ | *meth*ane |
| 2 | $C_2H_6$ | $CH_3CH_3$ | *eth*ane |
| 3 | $C_3H_8$ | $CH_3CH_2CH_3$ | *prop*ane |
| 4 | $C_4H_{10}$ | $CH_3CH_2CH_2CH_3$ | *but*ane |
| 5 | $C_5H_{12}$ | $CH_3CH_2CH_2CH_2CH_3$ | *pent*ane |
| 6 | $C_6H_{14}$ | $CH_3CH_2CH_2CH_2CH_2CH_3$ | *hex*ane |
| 7 | $C_7H_{16}$ | $CH_3CH_2CH_2CH_2CH_2CH_2CH_3$ | *hept*ane |
| 8 | $C_8H_{18}$ | $CH_3CH_2CH_2CH_2CH_2CH_2CH_2CH_3$ | *oct*ane |
| 9 | $C_9H_{20}$ | $CH_3CH_2CH_2CH_2CH_2CH_2CH_2CH_2CH_3$ | *non*ane |
| 10 | $C_{10}H_{22}$ | $CH_3CH_2CH_2CH_2CH_2CH_2CH_2CH_2CH_2CH_3$ | *dec*ane |

### SAMPLE PROBLEM 12.2

Draw two isomers with molecular formula $C_6H_{14}$ that have five carbon atoms in the longest chain and a one-carbon branch coming off the chain.

#### Analysis

Since isomers are different compounds with the same molecular formula, we must add a one-carbon branch to two different carbons to form two different products. Then add enough H's to give each C four bonds.

#### Solution

Compounds **A** and **B** are isomers because the $CH_3$ group is bonded to different atoms in the five-carbon chain. Note, too, that we cannot add the one-carbon branch to an *end* carbon because that creates a continuous six-carbon chain. Remember that **bends in the chain don't matter.**

Adding a C to an end C makes a six-carbon chain.

C—C—C—C—C  ----→  C—C—C—C—C  =  C—C—C—C—C—C

**equivalent structures**

### PROBLEM 12.4

Draw two isomers with molecular formula $C_6H_{14}$ that have four carbon atoms in the longest chain and two one-carbon branches coming off the chain.

### PROBLEM 12.5

Which of the following is *not* another representation for isopentane?

a. $CH_3CH_2$—C—$CH_3$ with H on top and $CH_3$ on bottom

b. H—C—$CH_3$ with H on top, $CH_3$—C—$CH_3$, H on bottom

c. $CH_3CH_2CH(CH_3)_2$

d. H—C—C—H with H H on top, $CH_3$—C—H$CH_3$, H on bottom

## 12.2C  Classifying Carbon Atoms

Carbon atoms in alkanes and other organic compounds are classified by the number of other carbons directly bonded to them.

- A *primary carbon* (1° C) is bonded to *one* other C.
- A *secondary carbon* (2° C) is bonded to *two* other C's.
- A *tertiary carbon* (3° C) is bonded to *three* other C's.
- A *quaternary carbon* (4° C) is bonded to *four* other C's.

**Classification of carbon atoms**

1° C        2° C        3° C        4° C

**Example**

SAMPLE PROBLEM 12.3

Classify each carbon atom in the following molecule as 1°, 2°, 3°, or 4°.

$$CH_3-\underset{\underset{CH_3}{|}}{\overset{\overset{CH_3}{|}}{C}}-CH_2CH_2CH_3$$

### Analysis

To classify a carbon atom, count the number of C's bonded to it. Draw a complete structure with all bonds and atoms to clarify the structure if necessary.

### Solution

All C's labeled in red are 1° C's.

PROBLEM 12.6

Classify the carbon atoms in each compound as 1°, 2°, 3°, or 4°.

a. $CH_3CH_2CH_2CH_3$     b. $(CH_3)_3CH$     c. $CH_3-\underset{\underset{H}{|}}{\overset{\overset{CH_3}{|}}{C}}-CH_2CH_3$     d. $CH_3-\underset{\underset{CH_3}{|}}{\overset{\overset{CH_3}{|}}{C}}-CH_3$

PROBLEM 12.7

Draw a condensed structure for an alkane that fits each description.

a. an alkane that contains only 1° and 2° carbons
b. an alkane of molecular formula $C_5H_{12}$ that has one 3° carbon
c. an alkane with two 4° carbons

## 12.2D   Bond Rotation and Skeletal Structures for Acyclic Alkanes

A ball-and-stick model of ethane with two labeled hydrogens reveals an important feature. **Rotation can occur around carbon–carbon single bonds.** This allows the hydrogens on one $CH_3$ group to adopt different orientations relative to the hydrogens on the other $CH_3$ group. This is a characteristic of *all* carbon–carbon single bonds.

rotation

Rotation occurs here.

The location of the two labeled H atoms changes with rotation.

In a similar fashion, each carbon–carbon bond in butane ($CH_3CH_2CH_2CH_3$) undergoes rotation, a process that is rapid at room temperature. As a result, the carbon backbone of butane can be arranged in a variety of ways. The most stable arrangement avoids crowding between nearby carbons, so that the carbon skeleton is extended in a zigzag fashion.

Bond rotation in butane, $CH_3CH_2CH_2CH_3$

rotation here    crowding

rotate

preferred arrangement

Sometimes zigzag skeletal structures are used to represent these extended carbon skeletons. Recall from Section 11.4 that a skeletal structure has a carbon atom at the intersection of any two lines and at the end of each line. Each carbon has enough hydrogens to give it four bonds.

skeletal structure

## PROBLEM 12.8

Draw a skeletal structure for each compound: (a) $CH_3CH_2CH_2CH_2CH_2CH_3$ (hexane); (b) $CH_3(CH_2)_5CH_3$ (heptane).

## PROBLEM 12.9

Convert each skeletal structure to a complete structure with all atoms and bond lines.

a.          b.          c.

## 12.3  An Introduction to Nomenclature

### 12.3A  The IUPAC System of Nomenclature

How are organic compounds named? Long ago, the name of a compound was often based on the plant or animal source from which it was obtained. For example, the name allicin, the principal component of the odor of garlic, is derived from the botanical name for garlic, *Allium sativum*. Other compounds were named by their discoverer for more personal reasons. Adolf von Baeyer supposedly named barbituric acid after a woman named Barbara, although no one knows Barbara's identity—a lover, a Munich waitress, or even St. Barbara.

Garlic has been used in Chinese herbal medicine for over 4,000 years. Today it is sold as a dietary supplement because of its reported health benefits. **Allicin,** the molecule responsible for garlic's odor, is not stored in the garlic bulb, but rather is produced by the action of enzymes when the bulb is crushed or bruised.

$CH_2{=}CHCH_2\overset{\overset{\textstyle O}{\|}}{S}SCH_2CH{=}CH_2$

allicin
(odor of garlic)

barbituric acid
(named for Barbara whom?)

With the isolation and preparation of thousands of new organic compounds it became obvious that each organic compound must have an unambiguous name. A systematic method of naming compounds (a system of **nomenclature**) was developed by the *I*nternational *U*nion of *P*ure and *A*pplied *C*hemistry. It is referred to as the **IUPAC** system of nomenclature, and how it can be used to name alkanes is explained in Section 12.4.

### 12.3B  FOCUS ON HEALTH & MEDICINE
Naming New Drugs

Naming organic compounds has become big business for drug companies. The IUPAC name of an organic compound can be long and complex. As a result, most drugs have three names:

- **Systematic:** The systematic name follows the accepted rules of nomenclature; this is the IUPAC name.
- **Generic:** The generic name is the official, internationally approved name for the drug.
- **Trade:** The trade name for a drug is assigned by the company that manufactures it. Trade names are often "catchy" and easy to remember. Companies hope that the public will continue to purchase a drug with an easily recalled trade name long after a cheaper generic version becomes available.

Consider the world of over-the-counter anti-inflammatory agents. The compound a chemist calls 2-[4-(2-methylpropyl)phenyl]propanoic acid has the generic name ibuprofen. It is marketed under a variety of trade names, including Motrin and Advil.

| | |
|---|---|
| **Systematic name:** | 2-[4-(2-methylpropyl)phenyl]propanoic acid |
| **Generic name:** | ibuprofen |
| **Trade name:** | Motrin or Advil |

## 12.4  Alkane Nomenclature

Although the names of the straight-chain alkanes having 10 carbons or fewer were already given in Table 12.1, we must also learn how to name alkanes that have carbon branches, called **substituents,** bonded to a long chain. The names of these organic molecules have three parts.

- The **parent name** indicates the number of carbons in the longest continuous carbon chain in the molecule.
- The **suffix** indicates what functional group (if any) is present.
- The **prefix** tells us the identity, location, and number of substituents attached to the carbon chain.

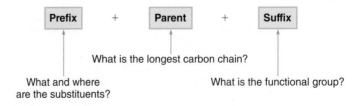

The names of the straight-chain alkanes in Table 12.1 consist of two parts. The suffix *-ane* indicates that the compounds are alkanes. The remainder of the name is the parent name, which indicates the number of carbon atoms in the longest carbon chain. The parent name for **one carbon is *meth-*,** for **two carbons is *eth-*,** and so on. Thus, we are already familiar with two parts of the name of an organic compound.

To determine the third part of a name, the prefix, we must learn how to name the substituents that are bonded to the longest carbon chain.

## 12.4A   Naming Substituents

Carbon substituents bonded to a long carbon chain are called *alkyl groups.*

- An *alkyl group* is formed by removing one hydrogen from an alkane.

An alkyl group is a part of a molecule that is now able to bond to another atom or a functional group. **To name an alkyl group, change the *-ane* ending of the parent alkane to *-yl*.** Thus, methane ($CH_4$) becomes methyl ($CH_3-$) and ethane ($CH_3CH_3$) becomes ethyl ($CH_3CH_2-$).

Removing one hydrogen from an *end* carbon in any straight-chain alkane forms other alkyl groups named in a similar fashion. Thus, propane ($CH_3CH_2CH_3$) becomes propyl ($CH_3CH_2CH_2-$) and butane ($CH_3CH_2CH_2CH_3$) becomes butyl ($CH_3CH_2CH_2CH_2-$). The names of alkyl groups having six carbons or fewer are summarized in Table 12.2.

### Table 12.2  Some Common Alkyl Groups

| Number of C's | Structure | Name |
|---|---|---|
| 1 | $CH_3-$ | methyl |
| 2 | $CH_3CH_2-$ | ethyl |
| 3 | $CH_3CH_2CH_2-$ | propyl |
| 4 | $CH_3CH_2CH_2CH_2-$ | butyl |
| 5 | $CH_3CH_2CH_2CH_2CH_2-$ | pentyl |
| 6 | $CH_3CH_2CH_2CH_2CH_2CH_2-$ | hexyl |

## 12.4B   Naming an Acyclic Alkane

Four steps are needed to name an alkane.

### How To  Name an Alkane Using the IUPAC System

**Step [1]**   Find the parent carbon chain and add the suffix.

- **Find the longest continuous carbon chain,** and name the molecule using the parent name for that number of carbons, given in Table 12.1. To the name of the parent, add the suffix **-ane** for an alkane. Each functional group has its own suffix.

$$CH_3 - \overset{\overset{\displaystyle CH_3}{|}}{CH} - CH_2 - CH_2 - CH_2 - CH_3$$

6 C's in the longest chain

6 C's   ---→   **hexane**

- The longest chain may not be written horizontally across the page. Remember that **it does not matter if the chain is *straight* or has *bends.*** All of the following representations are equivalent.

6 C's in the longest chain of each structure

**Step [2]**   Number the atoms in the carbon chain to give the first substituent the lower number.

| *CORRECT* | *INCORRECT* |
|---|---|

Start numbering here.

$$CH_3 - \overset{\overset{\displaystyle CH_3}{|}}{CH} - CH_2 - CH_2 - CH_2 - CH_3$$
$$\quad 1 \quad\; 2 \quad\; 3 \quad\; 4 \quad\; 5 \quad\; 6$$

**first substituent at C2**

$$CH_3 - \overset{\overset{\displaystyle CH_3}{|}}{CH} - CH_2 - CH_2 - CH_2 - CH_3$$
$$\quad 6 \quad\; 5 \quad\; 4 \quad\; 3 \quad\; 2 \quad\; 1$$

**first substituent at C5**

**Step [3]**   Name and number the substituents.

- Name the substituents as alkyl groups, and use the numbers from step [2] to designate their location.

methyl at C2

longest chain (6 C's)
**hexane**

- Every carbon belongs to *either* the longest chain or a substituent, but *not both.*
- Each substituent needs its *own* number.
- If two or more identical substituents are bonded to the longest chain, use **prefixes** to indicate how many: **di-** for two groups, **tri-** for three groups, **tetra-** for four groups, and so forth. The following compound has two methyl groups so its name contains the prefix di- before methyl → *di*methyl.

methyl at C2

Use the prefix di-.

methyl at C3

*—Continued*

*How To, continued . . .*

Step [4]  **Combine substituent names and numbers + parent + suffix.**
- Precede the name of the parent by the names of the substituents. **Alphabetize** the names of the substituents, ignoring any prefixes like *di-*. For example, triethyl precedes dimethyl because the *e* of **e**thyl comes before the *m* of **m**ethyl in the alphabet.
- Precede the name of each substituent by the number that indicates its location. There must be **one number for each substituent.**
- Separate numbers by commas and separate numbers from letters by dashes.

To help identify which carbons belong to the longest chain and which are substituents, always box in the atoms of the long chain. Every other carbon atom then becomes a substituent that needs its own name as an alkyl group.

methyl at C2

CH₃—CH—CH₂—CH₂—CH₂—CH₃

1   2   longest chain (6 C's)
**hexane**

**Answer: 2-methylhexane**

methyl at C2

CH₃—CH—CH—CH₂—CH₂—CH₃   ← **hexane**
         |
         CH₃   methyl at C3

1   2 3

- Two numbers are needed, one for each methyl group.

**Answer: 2,3-dimethylhexane**

---

## SAMPLE PROBLEM 12.4

Give the IUPAC name for the following compound.

$$CH_3-\underset{\underset{H}{|}}{\overset{\overset{CH_3}{|}}{C}}-CH_2CH_2-\underset{\underset{H}{|}}{\overset{\overset{CH_3CH_2}{|}}{C}}-\underset{\underset{CH_3}{|}}{\overset{\overset{H}{|}}{C}}-CH_2CH_3$$

### Analysis and Solution

**[1] Name the parent and use the suffix -*ane* since the molecule is an alkane.**

$$CH_3-\underset{\underset{H}{|}}{\overset{\overset{CH_3}{|}}{C}}-CH_2CH_2-\underset{\underset{H}{|}}{\overset{\overset{CH_3CH_2}{|}}{C}}-\underset{\underset{CH_3}{|}}{\overset{\overset{H}{|}}{C}}-CH_2CH_3$$

8 C's in the longest chain  - - -→  **octane**

- Box in the atoms of the longest chain to clearly show which carbons are part of the longest chain and which carbons are substituents.

**[2] Number the chain to give the first substituent the lower number.**

$$CH_3-\underset{\underset{H}{|}}{\overset{\overset{CH_3}{|}}{C}}-CH_2CH_2-\underset{\underset{H}{|}}{\overset{\overset{CH_3CH_2}{|}}{C}}-\underset{\underset{CH_3}{|}}{\overset{\overset{H}{|}}{C}}-CH_2CH_3$$

1   2   5   6

- Numbering from left to right puts the first substituent at C2.

**[3] Name and number the substituents.**

methyl at C2      ethyl at C5

$$CH_3-\underset{\underset{H}{|}}{\overset{\overset{CH_3}{|}}{C}}-CH_2CH_2-\underset{\underset{H}{|}}{\overset{\overset{CH_3CH_2}{|}}{C}}-\underset{\underset{CH_3}{|}}{\overset{\overset{H}{|}}{C}}-CH_2CH_3$$

2   5   6   methyl at C6

- This compound has three substituents: two methyl groups at C2 and C6 and an ethyl group at C5.

**[4] Combine the parts.**

- Write the name as one word and use the prefix di- before methyl since there are two methyl groups.
- Alphabetize the *e* of **e**thyl before the *m* of **m**ethyl. The prefix di- is ignored when alphabetizing.

methyl at C2      ethyl at C5

$$CH_3-C-CH_2CH_2-C-C-CH_2CH_3$$ ← octane

methyl at C6

**Answer: 5-ethyl-2,6-dimethyloctane**

## PROBLEM 12.10

Give the IUPAC name for each compound.

a. $CH_3CH_2CHCH_2CH_3$
   |
   $CH_3$

b. $CH_3CH_2CH_2-C-C-CH_2CH_2CH_2CH_3$
   with $CH_3$ $CH_2CH_2CH_3$ above and $H$ $H$ below

c. $H-C-CH_2-CHCH_3$
   with $CH_2CH_3$ above, $CH_3$ and $CH_3$ below

## PROBLEM 12.11

Give the IUPAC name for each compound.

a. $(CH_3)_2CHCH(CH_3)_2$

b. $CH_3CH_2CH_2CHCH_2C-H$
   with $CH_2CH_2CH_2CH_3$ above, $CH_3CH_2$ and $H$ below

c. $CH_3CH_2CH_2CH_2-C-C-CH_2CH_3$
   with $CH_3$ $H$ above, $CH_2$ $CH_3$ below and $CH_3$

You must also know how to derive a structure from a given name. Sample Problem 12.5 demonstrates a stepwise method.

## SAMPLE PROBLEM 12.5

Give the structure with the following IUPAC name: 2,3,3-trimethylpentane.

### Analysis

To derive a structure from a name, first look at the end of the name to find the parent name and suffix. From the parent we know the number of C's in the longest chain, and the suffix tells us the functional group; the suffix -*ane* = an alkane. Then, number the carbon chain from either end and add the substituents. Finally, add enough H's to give each C four bonds.

### Solution

2,3,3-Trimethyl**pentane** has **pentane** (5 C's) as the longest chain and three methyl groups at carbons 2, 3, and 3.

**Answer:**

Draw 5 C's and number the chain:

C—C—C—C—C → Add 3 CH₃ groups → C—C—C—C—C → Add H's → 2,3,3-trimethylpentane
1 2 3 4 5

## PROBLEM 12.12

Give the structure corresponding to each IUPAC name.

a. 3-methylhexane                    c. 3,5,5-trimethyloctane
b. 3,3-dimethylpentane               d. 3-ethyl-4-methylhexane

## PROBLEM 12.13

Give the structure corresponding to each IUPAC name.

a. 2,2-dimethylbutane                c. 4,4,5,5-tetramethylnonane
b. 6-butyl-3-methyldecane            d. 3-ethyl-5-propylnonane

# 12.5  Cycloalkanes

**Cycloalkanes contain carbon atoms arranged in a ring.** Think of a cycloalkane as being formed by removing two H's from the end carbons of a chain, and then bonding the two carbons together.

## 12.5A  Simple Cycloalkanes

Simple cycloalkanes are named by adding the prefix *cyclo-* to the name of the acyclic alkane having the same number of carbons. Cycloalkanes having three to six carbon atoms are shown in the accompanying figure. They are drawn using polygons in skeletal representations (Section 11.4). Each corner of the polygon has a carbon atom with two hydrogen atoms to give it four bonds.

cyclopropane
$C_3H_6$

cyclobutane
$C_4H_8$

cyclopentane
$C_5H_{10}$

cyclohexane
$C_6H_{12}$

Cyclic compounds occur widely in nature and many have interesting and important biological properties. For example, **pyrethrin I,** a naturally occurring insecticide obtained from chrysanthemums, contains both a three- and five-membered ring. **Vitamin D₃,** a fat-soluble vitamin that regulates calcium and phosphorus metabolism, contains six- and five-membered rings. Many foods, particularly milk, are fortified with vitamin $D_3$ so that we get enough of this vital nutrient in our diet.

pyrethrin I

vitamin D₃

Although we draw cycloalkanes as flat polygons, in reality cycloalkanes with more than three carbons are not planar molecules. Cyclohexane, for example, adopts a puckered arrangement called the **chair** form, in which all bond angles are 109.5°.

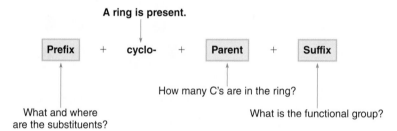

cyclohexane

skeletal structure                    nonplanar cyclohexane                    ball-and-stick model
                                             **chair form**

**PROBLEM 12.14**

Review: Label the functional groups in pyrethrin I.

**PROBLEM 12.15**

Review: Explain why vitamin D₃ is a fat-soluble vitamin.

## 12.5B  Naming Cycloalkanes

Cycloalkanes are named using the rules in Section 12.4, but the prefix *cyclo-* immediately precedes the name of the parent.

**A ring is present.**

**Prefix**  +  **cyclo-**  +  **Parent**  +  **Suffix**

How many C's are in the ring?

What and where                                                        What is the functional group?
are the substituents?

## How To  Name a Cycloalkane Using the IUPAC System

**Step [1]  Find the parent cycloalkane.**

• Count the number of carbon atoms in the ring and use the parent name for that number of carbons. Add the prefix *cyclo-* and the suffix *-ane* to the parent name.

$CH_3$

6 C's in the ring

$CH_2CH_3$

**cyclohexane**

**Step [2]  Name and number the substituents.**

• No number is needed to indicate the location of a **single** substituent.

—$CH_3$                              —$CH_2CH_2CH_2CH_3$

methylcyclohexane                    butylcyclopentane

—*Continued*

- For rings with more than one substituent, begin numbering at one substituent, and then give the **second substituent** the lower number. With two **different** substituents, number the ring to assign the lower number to the substituents **alphabetically.**

- Place $CH_3$ groups at C1 and C3.

**1,3-dimethylcyclohexane**
(*not* 1,5-dimethylcyclohexane)

Earlier letter - - - → lower number

- **e**thyl group at **C1**
- **m**ethyl group at **C3**

**1-ethyl-3-methylcyclohexane**
(*not* 3-ethyl-1-methylcyclohexane)

## SAMPLE PROBLEM 12.6

Give the IUPAC name for the following compound.

### Analysis and Solution

**[1] Name the ring.** The ring has 5 C's so the molecule is named as a cyclopentane.

**[2] Name and number the substituents.**

- There are two substituents: $CH_3CH_2-$ is an ethyl group and $CH_3CH_2CH_2-$ is a propyl group.
- Number to put the two groups at C1 and C2 (not C1 and C5).
- Place the ethyl group at C1 since the *e* of **e**thyl comes before the *p* of **p**ropyl in the alphabet.

Start numbering here.

5 C's - - - → cyclopentane

ethyl at C1

propyl at C2 (not C5)

**Answer: 1-ethyl-2-propylcyclopentane**

## PROBLEM 12.16

Give the IUPAC name for each compound.

a.   b.   c.   d.

## PROBLEM 12.17

Give the structure corresponding to each IUPAC name.

a. propylcyclopentane
b. 1,2-dimethylcyclobutane

c. 1,1,2-trimethylcyclopropane
d. 4-ethyl-1,2-dimethylcyclohexane

## 12.6  FOCUS ON THE ENVIRONMENT
### Fossil Fuels

Many alkanes occur in nature, primarily in natural gas and petroleum. Both of these fossil fuels serve as energy sources, formed long ago by the degradation of organic material.

**Natural gas** is composed largely of **methane** (60–80% depending on its source), with lesser amounts of ethane, propane, and butane. These organic compounds burn in the presence of oxygen, releasing energy for cooking and heating (Section 12.8).

**Petroleum** is a complex mixture of compounds, most of which are hydrocarbons containing 1–40 carbon atoms. Distilling crude petroleum, a process called **refining,** separates it into usable fractions that differ in boiling point (Figure 12.1). Most products of petroleum refining provide fuel for home heating, automobiles, diesel engines, and airplanes. Each fuel type has a different composition of hydrocarbons, as indicated below.

- **Gasoline:** $C_5H_{12}$–$C_{12}H_{26}$
- **Kerosene:** $C_{12}H_{26}$–$C_{16}H_{34}$
- **Diesel fuel:** $C_{15}H_{32}$–$C_{18}H_{38}$

**Figure 12.1**    Refining Crude Petroleum into Usable Fuel and Other Petroleum Products

a.

b.

**An oil refinery.** At an oil refinery, crude petroleum is separated into fractions of similar boiling point.

**A refinery tower.** As crude petroleum is heated, the lower-boiling components come off at the top of the tower, followed by fractions of higher boiling point.

Petroleum provides more than fuel. About 3% of crude oil is used to make plastics and other synthetic compounds, including drugs, fabrics, dyes, and pesticides. These products are responsible for many of the comforts we now take for granted in industrialized countries. Imagine what life would be like without air-conditioning, refrigeration, anesthetics, and pain relievers, all products of the petroleum industry.

**Barrel of crude oil**

petroleum starting materials
for chemical synthesis (1.3 gal)

asphalt and road oil (1.3 gal)

boiler oil (2.9 gal)

lubricants, waxes, solvents (4.2 gal)

jet fuel (4.2 gal)

diesel and home heating oil (8.4 gal)

gasoline (19.7 gal)

1 barrel = 42 gal

products made from petroleum

Energy from petroleum is *nonrenewable,* and the remaining known oil reserves are limited. Given our dependence on petroleum, not only for fuel, but also for the many necessities of modern society, it becomes obvious that we must both conserve what we have and find alternate energy sources.

The high cost of energy and limited petroleum reserves have prompted many ingenious approaches to energy production. Several large cattle farms in the United States use manure digesters to convert animal waste into methane, called "biogas," which in turn is used to generate electricity (Figure 12.2). The manure is pumped into large oxygen-free tanks, where anaerobic bacteria break down the organic material in the manure to form methane. The methane is collected and then combusted to generate electricity. The residue is compressed and used for fertilizer. In this way, a large volume of animal waste is transformed into two useful products—electricity and fertilizer.

**Figure 12.2**   Methane from Manure

digester cover

biogas

to flame for electricity generation

biogas outlet

manure inlet

Bubbles of $CH_4$ gas form and escape from the mixture.

effluent outlet

fertilizer

## 12.7  Physical Properties

**Alkanes contain only nonpolar C—C and C—H bonds,** so they exhibit only **weak intermolecular forces.** As a result, alkanes have low melting points and boiling points. Low molecular weight alkanes are gases at room temperature, and alkanes used in gasoline are all liquids.

The melting points and boiling points of alkanes increase as the number of carbons increases. Increased surface area increases the force of attraction between molecules, thus raising the boiling point and melting point. This is seen in comparing the boiling points of three straight-chain alkanes.

$CH_3CH_2CH_2CH_3$      $CH_3CH_2CH_2CH_2CH_3$      $CH_3CH_2CH_2CH_2CH_2CH_3$
butane                     pentane                        hexane

bp = −0.5 °C              bp = 36 °C                     bp = 69 °C

**Increasing surface area
Increasing boiling point**

Because nonpolar alkanes are water insoluble and less dense than water, crude petroleum spilled into the sea from a ruptured oil tanker creates an insoluble oil slick on the surface. The insoluble hydrocarbon oil poses a special threat to birds whose feathers are coated with natural nonpolar oils for insulation. Because these oils dissolve in the crude petroleum, birds lose their layer of natural protection and many die.

### PROBLEM 12.18

Answer the following questions about pentane ($C_5H_{12}$), heptane ($C_7H_{16}$), and decane ($C_{10}H_{22}$).

a. Which compound has the highest boiling point?
b. Which compound has the lowest boiling point?
c. Which compound has the highest melting point?
d. Which compound has the lowest melting point?

### PROBLEM 12.19

Explain why Vaseline, a complex mixture of hydrocarbons used as a skin lubricant and ointment, is insoluble in water and soluble in dichloromethane ($CH_2Cl_2$).

### PROBLEM 12.20

Polyisobutylene, a synthetic high molecular weight alkane with many properties similar to polyethylene (Section 11.5A), is the principal component of Elastol, a product used to clean up oil spills. Elastol dissolves oil to form a thick mat that can be skimmed or suctioned from the surface. Explain why oil dissolves in Elastol.

$$\text{—CH}_2\text{—}\underset{\underset{CH_3}{|}}{\overset{\overset{CH_3}{|}}{C}}\text{—CH}_2\text{—}\underset{\underset{CH_3}{|}}{\overset{\overset{CH_3}{|}}{C}}\text{—CH}_2\text{—}\underset{\underset{CH_3}{|}}{\overset{\overset{CH_3}{|}}{C}}\text{—}$$

polyisobutylene

## 12.8  FOCUS ON THE ENVIRONMENT
### Combustion

Alkanes are the only family of organic molecules that has no functional group, so **alkanes undergo few reactions.** In this chapter, we consider only one reaction of alkanes—**combustion.** Combustion is an example of an **oxidation–reduction** reaction, a class of reactions first discussed in Section 5.9.

---

Crude oil that leaks into the sea forms an insoluble layer on the surface.

The insolubility of nonpolar oil and very polar water leads to the expression, "Oil and water don't mix."

Vaseline petroleum jelly (Problem 12.19), a skin lubricant often used for chapped lips and diaper rash, is a mixture of high molecular weight alkanes.

To determine if an organic compound undergoes oxidation or reduction, we concentrate on the carbon atoms of the starting material and product, and **compare the relative number of C—H and C—O bonds.**

> * *Oxidation* results in an *increase* in the number of C—O bonds or a *decrease* in the number of C—H bonds.
> * *Reduction* results in a *decrease* in the number of C—O bonds or an *increase* in the number of C—H bonds.

Review Section 5.2 on how to balance a chemical equation.

Alkanes undergo **combustion—that is, they burn in the presence of oxygen to form carbon dioxide ($CO_2$) and water.** This is a practical example of oxidation. Every C—H and C—C bond in the starting material is converted to a C—O bond in the product. Equations are written with two different alkanes.

$$CH_4 \ + \ 2 \, O_2 \ \xrightarrow{\text{flame}} \ CO_2 \ + \ 2 \, H_2O \ + \ \text{energy}$$

methane
(natural gas)

$$2 \, (CH_3)_3CCH_2CH(CH_3)_2 \ + \ 25 \, O_2 \ \xrightarrow{\text{flame}} \ 16 \, CO_2 \ + \ 18 \, H_2O \ + \ \text{energy}$$

isooctane
(high-octane component of gasoline)

Note that the products, **$CO_2$ + $H_2O$,** are the same regardless of the identity of the starting material. Combustion of alkanes in the form of natural gas, gasoline, or heating oil releases energy for heating homes, powering vehicles, and cooking food.

A spark or a flame is needed to initiate combustion. Gasoline, which is composed largely of alkanes, can be safely handled and stored in the air, but the presence of a spark or open flame causes immediate and violent combustion.

The combustion of alkanes and other hydrocarbons obtained from fossil fuels adds a tremendous amount of $CO_2$ to the atmosphere each year. Quantitatively, data show over a 20% increase in the atmospheric concentration of $CO_2$ in the last 52 years (from 315 parts per million in 1958 to 390 parts per million in 2010; Figure 12.3). Although the composition of the atmosphere has changed

**ENVIRONMENTAL NOTE**

Driving an automobile 10,000 miles at 25 miles per gallon releases 10,000 lb of $CO_2$ into the atmosphere.

**Figure 12.3**

The Changing Concentration of $CO_2$ in the Atmosphere

The 2007 Nobel Peace Prize was awarded to former Vice President Al Gore and the Intergovernmental Panel on Climate Change for their roles in focusing attention on the potentially disastrous effects of rapid climate change caused by human activity.

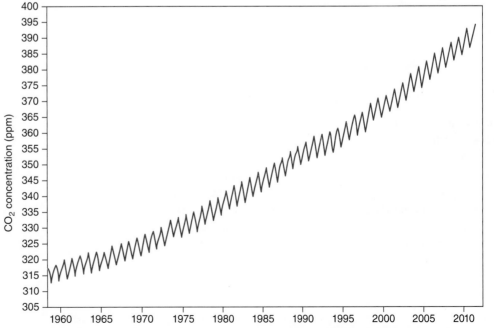

The graph clearly shows the increasing level of $CO_2$ in the atmosphere (1958–2010). Two data points are recorded each year. The sawtooth nature of the graph is due to seasonal variation of $CO_2$ level with the seasonal variation in photosynthesis. (Data recorded at Mauna Loa, Hawaii.)

over the lifetime of the earth, this is likely the first time that the actions of mankind have altered that composition significantly and so quickly.

An increased $CO_2$ concentration in the atmosphere may have long-range and far-reaching effects. $CO_2$ is a **greenhouse gas** because it absorbs thermal energy that normally radiates from the earth's surface, and redirects it back to the surface. Higher levels of $CO_2$ may therefore contribute to an increase in the average temperature of the earth's atmosphere. This **global warming,** as it has been termed, has many consequences—the melting of polar ice caps, the rise in sea level, and drastic global climate changes to name a few.

### PROBLEM 12.21

Write a balanced equation for each combustion reaction.

a. $CH_3CH_2CH_3$ + $O_2$ $\xrightarrow{\text{flame}}$          b. $CH_3CH_2CH_2CH_3$ + $O_2$ $\xrightarrow{\text{flame}}$

   propane                                          butane

When there is not enough oxygen available to completely burn a hydrocarbon, **incomplete combustion** may occur and **carbon monoxide** (CO) is formed instead of carbon dioxide ($CO_2$).

| Incomplete combustion | $2\,CH_4$ + $3\,O_2$ $\xrightarrow{\text{flame}}$ $2\,CO$ + $4\,H_2O$ + energy |

methane          carbon monoxide

Carbon monoxide is a poisonous gas that binds to hemoglobin in the blood, thus reducing the amount of oxygen that can be transported through the bloodstream to cells. CO can be formed whenever hydrocarbons burn. When an automobile engine burns gasoline, unwanted carbon monoxide can be produced. Yearly car inspections measure CO and other pollutant levels and are designed to prevent cars from emitting potentially hazardous substances into ambient air. Carbon monoxide is also formed when cigarettes burn, so heavy smokers have an unhealthy concentration of CO in their bloodstreams.

### PROBLEM 12.22

Write a balanced equation for the incomplete combustion of ethane ($CH_3CH_3$) to form carbon monoxide as one product.

---

**HEALTH NOTE**

Meters that measure CO levels can be purchased, as described in Section 5.5. When wood is burned in a poorly ventilated fireplace situated in a well-insulated room, the CO concentration can reach an unhealthy level.

---

# CHAPTER HIGHLIGHTS
## KEY TERMS

| | | |
|---|---|---|
| Acyclic alkane (12.1) | Incomplete combustion (12.8) | Quaternary carbon, 4° C (12.2) |
| Alkane (12.1) | Isomer (12.2) | Reduction (12.8) |
| Alkyl group (12.4) | IUPAC nomenclature (12.3) | Refining (12.6) |
| Branched-chain alkane (12.2) | Oxidation (12.8) | Saturated hydrocarbon (12.1) |
| Combustion (12.8) | Parent name (12.4) | Secondary carbon, 2° C (12.2) |
| Constitutional isomer (12.2) | Petroleum (12.6) | Straight-chain alkane (12.2) |
| Cycloalkane (12.1) | Pheromone (12.1) | Tertiary carbon, 3° C (12.2) |
| Greenhouse gas (12.8) | Primary carbon, 1° C (12.2) | |

# KEY CONCEPTS

**❶ What are the characteristics of an alkane? (12.1, 12.2)**
- Alkanes are hydrocarbons having only nonpolar C—C and C—H single bonds.
- There are two types of alkanes: Acyclic alkanes ($C_nH_{2n+2}$) have no rings. Cycloalkanes ($C_nH_{2n}$) have one or more rings.
- A carbon is classified as 1°, 2°, 3°, or 4° by the number of carbons bonded to it. A 1° C is bonded to one carbon; a 2° C is bonded to two carbons, and so forth.

**❷ What are constitutional isomers? (12.2)**
- Isomers are different compounds with the same molecular formula.
- Constitutional isomers differ in the way the atoms are connected to each other. $CH_3CH_2CH_2CH_3$ and $HC(CH_3)_3$ are constitutional isomers because they have molecular formula $C_4H_{10}$ but one compound has a chain of four carbons in a row and the other does not.

**❸ How are alkanes named? (12.4, 12.5)**
- Alkanes are named using the IUPAC system of nomenclature. A name has three parts: the parent indicates the number of carbons in the longest chain or the ring; the suffix indicates the functional group (-ane = alkane); the prefix tells the number and location of substituents coming off the chain or ring.

- Alkyl groups are formed by removing one hydrogen from an alkane. Alkyl groups are named by changing the -ane ending of the parent alkane to the suffix -yl.

**❹ Characterize the physical properties of alkanes. (12.7)**
- Alkanes are nonpolar, so they have weak intermolecular forces, low melting points, and low boiling points.
- The melting points and boiling points of alkanes increase as the number of carbons increases due to increased surface area.
- Alkanes are insoluble in water.

**❺ What are the products of the combustion and incomplete combustion of an alkane? (12.8)**
- Alkanes burn in the presence of air. Combustion forms $CO_2$ and $H_2O$ as products. Incomplete combustion forms CO and $H_2O$.
- Alkane combustion has increased the level of $CO_2$, a greenhouse gas, in the atmosphere.
- Incomplete combustion forms carbon monoxide, a toxin and air pollutant.

# PROBLEMS

Selected in-chapter and odd-numbered end-of-chapter problems have brief answers in Appendix B. The *Student Study Guide and Solutions Manual* contains detailed solutions to all in-chapter and odd-numbered end-of-chapter problems, as well as additional worked examples and a chapter self-test.

## Alkanes and Isomers

**12.23** The waxy coating that covers tobacco leaves contains a straight-chain alkane having 31 carbons. How many hydrogens does this alkane contain?

**12.24** The sex attractant of the female tiger moth is an alkane of molecular formula $C_{18}H_{38}$. Is this molecule an acyclic alkane or a cycloalkane?

**12.25** Paraffin wax is a mixture of straight- and branched-chain alkanes having 26–30 carbons. How many hydrogens does each of these alkanes contain?

**12.26** An alkane has 20 hydrogen atoms. How many carbon atoms would it contain if it were (a) a straight-chain alkane; (b) a branched-chain alkane; (c) a cycloalkane?

**12.27** Explain why a cycloalkane has two fewer hydrogen atoms than an acyclic alkane with the same number of carbon atoms.

**12.28** What is the difference between a branched-chain alkane and a cycloalkane?

**12.29** Classify each carbon as 1°, 2°, 3°, or 4°.

a. $CH_3(CH_2)_3CH_3$

b. $CH_3CH_2\underset{\underset{CH_3}{|}}{\overset{\overset{CH_3}{|}}{C}}HCHCH_3$

c. $(CH_3)_3CC(CH_3)_3$

d.

**12.30** Give the structure of an alkane that fits each description.
a. an alkane that contains only 1° and 4° carbons
b. a cycloalkane that contains only 2° carbons
c. an alkane of molecular formula $C_6H_{14}$ that contains a 4° carbon
d. a cycloalkane that contains 2° and 3° carbons

**12.31** Draw the structure of an alkane with molecular formula $C_7H_{16}$ that (a) contains one 4° carbon; (b) contains only 1° and 2° carbons.

**12.32** Is it possible to have an alkane that contains only 1° carbons? Explain why or why not with an example.

**12.33** Label each pair of compounds as constitutional isomers or identical molecules.

a. $CH_3\underset{\underset{CH_2CH_3}{|}}{\overset{\overset{CH_2CH_3}{|}}{C}}HCHCH_3$ and $CH_3CH_2CHCH_2CH(CH_3)_2$ with $\overset{CH_3}{|}$

b. $CH_3CH_2\underset{\underset{CH_3}{|}}{\overset{\overset{CH_3}{|}}{C}}HCHCH_2CH_3$ and $CH_3\underset{\underset{CH_2CH_3}{|}}{\overset{\overset{CH_2CH_3}{|}}{C}}HCHCH_3$

c.  and  ▷—CH$_2$CH$_3$

d. (cyclohexane with two CH$_3$ groups on adjacent carbons) and (cyclohexane with CH$_3$ groups in 1,3 positions)

**12.34** Label each pair of compounds as constitutional isomers, identical molecules, or not isomers of each other.

  a. CH$_3$CH$_2$CH$_2$CH$_3$     and     CH$_3$CH$_2$CH$_2$CH$_2$CH$_3$

  b.
$$\begin{array}{c} CH_2-CH_2 \\ |\qquad\quad| \\ CH_3CH_2\quad CH_2CH_3 \end{array}$$
and     CH$_3$(CH$_2$)$_4$CH$_3$

  c. CH$_3$CH$_2$CH$_2$CH$_2$CH$_3$     and     (cyclopentane)

  d.
$$CH_3-\overset{\displaystyle O}{\overset{\|}{C}}-OCH_3$$
and
$$CH_3CH_2-\overset{\displaystyle O}{\overset{\|}{C}}-OH$$

**12.35** How is each of the following compounds related to (CH$_3$)$_2$CHCH$_2$CH$_2$CH$_3$? Choose from constitutional isomers or identical molecules.

  a. CH$_3$CHCHCH$_3$ with CH$_3$ above and CH$_3$ below

  b. CH$_3$CHCH$_2$CH$_2$ with CH$_3$ above and CH$_3$ below

  c. CH$_3$CHCH$_3$ with CH$_2$CH$_2$CH$_3$ below

  d. CH$_3$CHCH$_2$CH$_3$ with CH$_2$CH$_3$ below

  e. (branched skeletal structure)

**12.36** Consider compounds **A–E** and label each pair of compounds as identical molecules, constitutional isomers, or not isomers of each other: (a) **A** and **B**; (b) **A** and **C**; (c) **B** and **D**; (d) **D** and **E**; (e) **B** and **E**.

**A** (zigzag skeletal structure)

**B** CH$_3$(CH$_2$)$_3$CHCH$_3$ with CH$_3$ below

**C**
$$\begin{array}{c} CH_3 \qquad\qquad H \\ | \qquad\qquad\quad | \\ H-C-CH_2CH_2CH_2-C-H \\ | \qquad\qquad\quad | \\ H \qquad\qquad CH_3 \end{array}$$

**D** CH$_3$CH$_2$CH$_2$CHCH$_2$CH$_3$ with CH$_3$ above

**E** CH$_3$CH$_2$CHCH$_2$CH$_2$CH$_3$ with CH$_3$ below

**12.37** Draw structures that fit the following descriptions:

  a. two cycloalkanes that are constitutional isomers with molecular formula C$_7$H$_{14}$

  b. an ether and an alcohol that are constitutional isomers with molecular formula C$_5$H$_{12}$O

  c. two constitutional isomers of molecular formula C$_3$H$_7$Cl

**12.38** Draw the five constitutional isomers having molecular formula C$_6$H$_{14}$.

**12.39** Draw all constitutional isomers having molecular formula C$_8$H$_{18}$ that contain seven carbons in the longest chain and a single CH$_3$ group bonded to the chain.

**12.40** Draw the five constitutional isomers that have molecular formula C$_5$H$_{10}$ and contain one ring.

**12.41** Draw three constitutional isomers with molecular formula C$_3$H$_6$O. Draw the structure of one alcohol, one ketone, and one cyclic ether.

**12.42** Draw one constitutional isomer of each compound.

  a.
$$CH_3CH_2-\overset{\displaystyle O}{\overset{\|}{C}}-CH_3$$

  b.
$$\begin{array}{c} NH_2 \\ | \\ CH_3CH_2CHCH_3 \end{array}$$

  c.  (cyclohexane with OH)

## Alkane Nomenclature

**12.43** Give the IUPAC name for each of the five constitutional isomers of molecular formula C$_6$H$_{14}$ in Problem 12.38.

**12.44** Give the IUPAC name for each of the five cyclic isomers of molecular formula C$_5$H$_{10}$ in Problem 12.40.

**12.45** Give the IUPAC name for each compound.

  a.

  b.

**12.46** Give the IUPAC name for each compound.

  a.

  b.

**12.47** Give the IUPAC name for each compound.

a. CH₃CH₂CHCH₂CH₂CH₂CH₃
            |
            CH₃

b. CH₃CH₂CHCH₂CHCH₂CH₂CH₃
          |     |
          CH₃  CH₃

c. CH₃CH₂CH₂C(CH₂CH₃)₃

d. CH₃CHCH₂CHCH₂CH₃   (with CH₃ / CH₂CHCH₃ and CH₂CH₃ branches)

e. (CH₃CH₂)₂CHCH₂CH₂CH₂CH(CH₃)₂

f. CH₃CH₂—C—CH₂CH₂ ... CH₃ / CH₂CH₂CH₂—C—CH₃

*(structures as drawn)*

**12.48** Give the IUPAC name for each compound.

a. CH₃—C—CHCH₃   (H, CH₃, CH₂CH₃)

b. CH₃CH₂—C—CH₂CH₂CH₃   (CH₃, CH₃)

c. CH₃CH₂CHCH₂CH₂CH₂CH₃   (CH₂CH₂CH₂CH₃)

d. (CH₃CH₂)₂CHCH(CH₂CH₃)₂

e. CH₃—C—CH₂—C—CH₂CH₃   (CH₃, CH₃ / H, CH₂CH₃)

f. CH₃—C—CH₂CH₂—C—CHCH₂CH₃   (H, CH₃ / CH₂CH₃, H, CH₃)

**12.49** Give the IUPAC name for each cycloalkane.

a. *(cyclooctane drawing)*

b. *(cyclopropane)—CH₃*

c. *(cyclobutane with CH₃, CH₃, CH₃, CH₃)*

d. *(cyclohexane with CH₃CH₂ and CH₂CH₃)*

**12.50** Give the IUPAC name for each cycloalkane.

a. *(cycloheptane)—CH₂CH₃*

b. *(cyclohexane with CH₂CH₂CH₃ and CH₂CH₂CH₂CH₃)*

c. *(cyclopentane with CH₂CH₂CH₃ and CH₂CH₃)*

d. CH₃—*(cyclohexane)*—CH₂CH₂CH₂CH₃   (CH₃CH₂)

**12.51** Give the structure corresponding to each IUPAC name.
a. 3-ethylhexane
b. 3-ethyl-3-methyloctane
c. 2,3,4,5-tetramethyldecane
d. cyclononane
e. 1,1,3-trimethylcyclohexane
f. 1-ethyl-2,3-dimethylcyclopentane

**12.52** Give the structure corresponding to each IUPAC name.
a. 3-ethyl-3-methylhexane
b. 2,2,3,4-tetramethylhexane
c. 4-ethyl-2,2-dimethyloctane
d. 1,3,5-triethylcycloheptane
e. 3-ethyl-3,4-dimethylnonane
f. 2-ethyl-1-methyl-3-propylcyclopentane

**12.53** Each of the following IUPAC names is incorrect. Explain why it is incorrect and give the correct IUPAC name.
a. 3-methylbutane
b. 1-methylcyclopentane
c. 1,3-dimethylbutane
d. 5-ethyl-2-methylhexane
e. 1,5-dimethylcyclohexane
f. 1-propyl-2-ethylcyclopentane

**12.54** Each of the following IUPAC names is incorrect. Explain why it is incorrect and give the correct IUPAC name.
a. 4-methylpentane
b. 2,3,3-trimethylbutane
c. 1,3-dimethylpentane
d. 3-methyl-5-ethylhexane
e. 2-ethyl-2-methylcycloheptane
f. 1,6-diethylcyclohexane

**12.55** Draw three constitutional isomers having molecular formula C₇H₁₄ that contain a five-membered ring and two CH₃ groups bonded to the ring. Give the IUPAC name for each isomer.

**12.56** Draw four constitutional isomers having molecular formula C₆H₁₂ that contain a four-membered ring. Give the IUPAC name for each isomer.

## Drawing Acyclic Alkanes and Cycloalkanes

**12.57** Draw a skeletal structure for each compound.
  a. octane
  b. 1,2-dimethylcyclopentane
  c. $CH_3CHCH_2CH_2CH_2CH_2CH_3$

     |
     $CH_3$

**12.58** Convert each compound to a skeletal structure.
  a. $CH_3(CH_2)_7CH_3$
  b. 1,1-diethylcyclohexane
  c. $(CH_3CH_2)_2CHCH_2CH_2CH_3$

**12.59** Convert each skeletal structure to a complete structure with all atoms drawn in.

  a.                 c.

  b.

**12.60** Convert each skeletal structure to a complete structure with all atoms drawn in.

  a.               c.

  b.

## Physical Properties

**12.61** Which compound in each pair has the higher melting point?

**12.62** Which compound in each pair has the higher boiling point?

**12.63** Branching in an alkane chain decreases surface area. As a result, a branched-chain alkane tends to have a lower boiling point than a straight-chain alkane with the same number of carbons. Keeping this in mind, rank the alkane isomers in each group in order of increasing boiling point.
  a. $CH_3CH_2CH_2CH_2CH_3$, $(CH_3)_2CHCH_2CH_3$, $(CH_3)_4C$
  b. $(CH_3)_2CHCH(CH_3)_2$, $CH_3(CH_2)_4CH_3$, $CH_3CH_2CH_2CH(CH_3)_2$

**12.64** Explain why the boiling points of heptane [$CH_3(CH_2)_5CH_3$] and $H_2O$ are similar even though heptane has a much higher molecular weight and greater surface area.

**12.65** Explain why hexane is more soluble in dichloromethane ($CH_2Cl_2$) than in water.

**12.66** Mineral oil and Vaseline are both mixtures of alkanes, but mineral oil is a liquid at room temperature and Vaseline is a solid. Which product is composed of alkanes that contain a larger number of carbon atoms? Explain your choice.

## Reactions

**12.67** Write a balanced equation for the combustion of each alkane: (a) $CH_3CH_3$; (b) $(CH_3)_2CHCH_2CH_3$.

**12.68** Write a balanced equation for the combustion of each cycloalkane.

  a. ⬡                b. ⬠

**12.69** Write a balanced equation for the incomplete combustion of each alkane: (a) $CH_3CH_2CH_3$; (b) $CH_3CH_2CH_2CH_3$.

**12.70** Benzene ($C_6H_6$) is a fuel additive sometimes used to make gasoline burn more efficiently. Write a balanced equation for the incomplete combustion of benzene.

**12.71** In the body, glucose, a simple carbohydrate with molecular formula $C_6H_{12}O_6$, is oxidized to $CO_2$ and $H_2O$ with the release of a great deal of energy. Thus, the metabolism of glucose provides energy for our bodies, in much the same way as the oxidation of an alkane provides energy to power an automobile. Write a balanced equation for the oxidation of glucose to form $CO_2$ and $H_2O$.

**12.72** Gasohol is a mixture of 90% gasoline and 10% ethanol, $CH_3CH_2OH$. Ethanol is considered an environmentally friendly fuel additive because it can be made from a renewable source—sugarcane. Ethanol burns in air to form $CO_2$ and $H_2O$, and, like the combustion of alkanes, this reaction also releases a great deal of energy. Write a balanced equation for the combustion of ethanol.

## Applications

**12.73** The gasoline industry seasonally changes the composition of gasoline in locations where it gets very hot in the summer and very cold in the winter. Gasoline is refined to contain a larger fraction of higher molecular weight alkanes in warmer weather. In colder weather, it is refined to contain a larger fraction of lower molecular weight alkanes. What is the purpose of producing different types of gasoline for different temperatures?

**12.74** Polyethylene (Section 11.5) is a high molecular weight alkane that contains hundreds or even thousands of carbon atoms, bonded together in long carbon chains. When a new home is built, the concrete foundation is often wrapped with polyethylene (sold under the trade name of Tyvek). What purpose does the polyethylene serve?

**12.75** Mineral oil, a mixture of high molecular weight alkanes, is sometimes used as a laxative. Individuals who use mineral oil for this purpose are advised to avoid taking it at the same time they consume foods rich in fat-soluble vitamins such as vitamin A. Why is this advice given?

**12.76** Explain why having a fire in a fireplace in a poorly ventilated room poses a health hazard.

**12.77** You went running on a newly paved asphalt road, which soiled your sneakers. What solvent might be best for removing asphalt, a mixture of high molecular weight hydrocarbons, from your sneakers: (a) water; (b) nail polish remover, which is mainly acetone [$(CH_3)_2C{=}O$]; (c) paint thinner, which is largely liquid alkanes? Explain your choice.

**12.78** A major component of animal fat is tristearin. (a) Identify the three functional groups in tristearin. (b) Label all the polar bonds. (c) Explain why tristearin will dissolve in an organic solvent like hexane, but is insoluble in water.

$$H_2C{-}O{-}\overset{\displaystyle O}{\overset{\|}{C}}{-}(CH_2)_{16}CH_3$$

$$H{-}\overset{|}{C}{-}O{-}\overset{\displaystyle O}{\overset{\|}{C}}{-}(CH_2)_{16}CH_3$$

$$H_2C{-}O{-}\overset{\displaystyle O}{\overset{\|}{C}}{-}(CH_2)_{16}CH_3$$

tristearin

## General Questions

**12.79** Answer the following questions about the alkane drawn below.

$$CH_3CH_2CH_2{-}\overset{\overset{\displaystyle CH_3}{|}}{\underset{\underset{\displaystyle CH_3}{|}}{C}}{-}\overset{\overset{\displaystyle CH_2CH_3}{|}}{\underset{\underset{\displaystyle H}{|}}{C}}{-}CH_2CH_3$$

a. Give the IUPAC name.
b. Draw one constitutional isomer.
c. Predict the solubility in water.
d. Predict the solubility in an organic solvent.
e. Write a balanced equation for complete combustion.
f. Draw a skeletal structure.

**12.80** Answer the questions in Problem 12.79 for the alkane drawn below.

**12.81** Answer the questions in Problem 12.79 for the cycloalkane depicted in the given ball-and-stick model.

**12.82** Answer the questions in Problem 12.79 for the cycloalkane depicted in the given ball-and-stick model.

## CHALLENGE PROBLEMS

**12.83** What is the molecular formula for a compound with 10 carbons and two rings?

**12.84** Draw the structure of the 12 constitutional isomers that have the molecular formula $C_6H_{12}$ and contain one ring.

**12.85** Cyclopentane has a higher boiling point than pentane even though both compounds have the same number of carbons (49 °C vs. 36 °C). Can you suggest a reason for this phenomenon?

**12.86** Draw the structure of the seven constitutional isomers having molecular formula $C_4H_{10}O$. Each compound is either an ether or an alcohol.

# 13

Vegetable oils obtained from olives, peanuts, and corn are formed from unsaturated organic molecules such as oleic acid and linoleic acid.

# Unsaturated Hydrocarbons

## CHAPTER OUTLINE

## CHAPTER GOALS

*In this chapter you will learn how to:*

1. Identify the three major types of unsaturated hydrocarbons—alkenes, alkynes, and aromatic compounds

2. Name alkenes, alkynes, and substituted benzenes

3. Recognize the difference between constitutional isomers and stereoisomers, as well as identify cis and trans isomers

4. Identify saturated and unsaturated fatty acids and predict their relative melting points

5. Draw the products of addition reactions of alkenes

6. Draw the products of reactions that follow Markovnikov's rule

7. Explain what products are formed when a vegetable oil is partially hydrogenated

8. Draw the structure of polymers formed from alkene monomers

9. Draw the products of substitution reactions of benzene

In Chapter 13 we continue our study of hydrocarbons by examining three families of compounds that contain carbon–carbon multiple bonds. **Alkenes** contain a double bond and **alkynes** contain a triple bond. **Aromatic hydrocarbons** contain a benzene ring, a six-membered ring with three double bonds. These compounds differ from the alkanes of Chapter 12 because they each have a functional group, making them much more reactive. Thousands of biologically active molecules contain these functional groups, and many useful synthetic products result from their reactions.

## 13.1　Alkenes and Alkynes

**Alkenes and alkynes are two families of organic molecules that contain multiple bonds.**

- Alkenes are compounds that contain a carbon–carbon double bond.

The general molecular formula of an alkene is $C_nH_{2n}$, so an alkene has **two** fewer hydrogens than an acyclic alkane, which has a general molecular formula of $C_nH_{2n+2}$. Ethylene ($C_2H_4$) is the simplest alkene. Since each carbon of ethylene is surrounded by three atoms, each carbon is **trigonal planar.** All six atoms of ethylene lie in the same plane, and all bond angles are **120°.**

Ethylene is a hormone that regulates plant growth and fruit ripening. This allows individuals to enjoy bananas, strawberries, and tomatoes that were grown in faraway countries. Fruit can be picked green, and then sprayed with ethylene when ripening is desired upon arrival at its destination.

- Alkynes are compounds that contain a carbon–carbon triple bond.

The general molecular formula for an alkyne is $C_nH_{2n-2}$, so an alkyne has **four** fewer hydrogens than an acyclic alkane. Acetylene ($C_2H_2$) is the simplest alkyne. Each carbon of acetylene is surrounded by two atoms, making each carbon **linear** with bond angles of **180°.**

Because alkenes and alkynes are composed of nonpolar carbon–carbon and carbon–hydrogen bonds, their physical properties are similar to other hydrocarbons. Like alkanes:

- Alkenes and alkynes have low melting points and boiling points and are insoluble in water.

Recall from Chapter 12 that acyclic alkanes are called saturated hydrocarbons, because they contain the maximum number of hydrogen atoms per carbon. In contrast, **alkenes and alkynes are called *unsaturated* hydrocarbons.**

- Unsaturated hydrocarbons are compounds that contain fewer than the maximum number of hydrogen atoms per carbon.

A ripe banana speeds up the ripening of green tomatoes because the banana gives off ethylene, a plant growth hormone.

The multiple bond of an alkene or alkyne is always drawn in a condensed structure. To translate a condensed structure to a complete structure with all bond lines drawn in, make sure that **each carbon of a double bond has three atoms around it, and each carbon of a triple bond has two atoms around it,** as shown in Sample Problem 13.1. Keep in mind that in every structure, each carbon always has four bonds.

## SAMPLE PROBLEM 13.1

Draw a complete structure for each alkene or alkyne.

  a. $CH_2\!=\!CHCH_2CH_3$                    b. $CH_3C\!\equiv\!CCH_2CH_3$

### Analysis

First, draw the multiple bond in each structure. Draw an alkene so that each C of the double bond has three atoms around it. Draw an alkyne so that each C of the triple bond has two atoms around it. All other C's have four single bonds.

### Solution

  a. The C labeled in red has single bonds to 2 H's. The C labeled in blue has single bonds to 1 H and a $CH_2CH_3$ group.

  b. The C labeled in red has a single bond to a $CH_3$ group. The C labeled in blue has a single bond to a $CH_2CH_3$ group.

## PROBLEM 13.1

Convert each condensed structure to a complete structure with all atoms and bond lines drawn in.

  a. $CH_2\!=\!CHCH_2OH$         b. $(CH_3)_2C\!=\!CH(CH_2)_2CH_3$         c. $(CH_3)_2CHC\!\equiv\!CCH_2C(CH_3)_3$

## PROBLEM 13.2

Determine whether each molecular formula corresponds to a saturated hydrocarbon, an alkene, or an alkyne.

  a. $C_3H_6$              b. $C_5H_{12}$              c. $C_8H_{14}$              d. $C_6H_{12}$

Give the molecular formula for each of the following compounds.

    a. an alkene that has four carbons                c. an alkyne that has seven carbons
    b. a saturated hydrocarbon that has six carbons    d. an alkene that has five carbons

## 13.2 Nomenclature of Alkenes and Alkynes

Whenever we encounter a new functional group, we must learn how to use the IUPAC system to name it. There are two new facts to learn: how to name the suffix that identifies the functional group, and how to number the carbon skeleton. In the IUPAC system:

> • An alkene is identified by the suffix *-ene.*
> • An alkyne is identified by the suffix *-yne.*

## *How To* Name an Alkene or an Alkyne

**Example:** Give the IUPAC name of each alkene and alkyne.

a. $CH_2{=}CHCHCH_3$   (with $CH_3$ substituent on C3)

b. $CH_3CH_2CHC{\equiv}CCH_3$   (with $CH_2CH_3$ substituent)

**Step [1]** **Find the longest chain that contains *both* carbon atoms of the double or triple bond.**

a. $CH_2{=}CHCHCH_3$ (with $CH_3$ substituent)

4 C's in the longest chain

but**ane** – – – ➔ but**ene**

- Since the compound is an alkene, change the *-ane* ending of the parent alkane to *-ene.*

b. $CH_3CH_2CHC{\equiv}CCH_3$ (with $CH_2CH_3$ substituent)

6 C's in the longest chain

hex**ane** – – – ➔ hex**yne**

- Since the compound is an alkyne, change the *-ane* ending of the parent alkane to *-yne.*

**Step [2]** **Number the carbon chain from the end that gives the multiple bond the lower number.**

For each compound, number the chain and name the compound using the *first* number assigned to the multiple bond.

Start numbering here.

a. $CH_2{=}CHCHCH_3$ (with $CH_3$ substituent)

  1   2 3 4

1-butene

- Numbering the chain from left to right puts the double bond at C1 (not C3). The alkene is named using the *first* number assigned to the double bond, making it 1-butene.

Start numbering here.

b. $CH_3CH_2CHC{\equiv}CCH_3$ (with $CH_2CH_3$ substituent)

 6  5  4 3  2 1

2-hexyne

- Numbering the chain from right to left puts the triple bond at C2 (not C4). The alkyne is named using the *first* number assigned to the triple bond, making it 2-hexyne.

—Continued

Step [3] **Number and name the substituents, and write the name.**

a.

CH₃ — methyl group at C3

CH₂=CHCHCH₃

1        3

**Answer: 3-methyl-1-butene**

b.

CH₂CH₃ — ethyl group at C4

CH₃CH₂CHC≡CCH₃

4        1

**Answer: 4-ethyl-2-hexyne**

Compounds with two double bonds are called **dienes.** They are named by changing the *-ane* ending of the parent alkane to the suffix *-adiene.* Each double bond gets its own number.

CH₂=CHCH=CH₂

Numbering: 1    2 3    4

Name: **1,3-butadiene**

$CH_3$

CH₃C=CHCH₂CH=CH₂

Numbering: 6  5  4  3  2    1

Name: **5-methyl-1,4-hexadiene**

In naming cycloalkenes, the double bond is located between C1 and C2, and the "1" is usually omitted in the name. The ring is numbered to give the first substituent the lower number.

**1-methylcyclopentene**

**3-methylcycloheptene**

| Number clockwise beginning at the C=C and place the CH₃ at C3. |

**1,6-dimethylcyclohexene**

| Number counterclockwise beginning at the C=C and place the first CH₃ at C1. |

A few simple alkenes and alkynes have names that do not follow the IUPAC system. The simplest alkene, CH₂=CH₂, is called *ethene* in the IUPAC system, but it is commonly called **ethylene.** The simplest alkyne, HC≡CH, is called *ethyne* in the IUPAC system, but it is commonly named **acetylene.** We will use these common names since they are more widely used than their systematic IUPAC names.

## SAMPLE PROBLEM 13.2

Give the IUPAC name for the following compound.

CH₃

CH₃CH₂C=CCH₃

CH₃

### Analysis and Solution

**[1] Find the longest chain containing both carbon atoms of the multiple bond.**

CH₃

CH₃CH₂C=CCH₃

CH₃

5 C's in the longest chain ----→ **pentene**

**[2] Number the chain to give the double bond the lower number.**

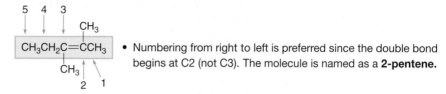

- Numbering from right to left is preferred since the double bond begins at C2 (not C3). The molecule is named as a **2-pentene**.

**[3] Name and number the substituents and write the complete name.**

- The alkene has two methyl groups located at C2 and C3. Use the prefix di- before methyl → 2,3-**di**methyl.

**Answer: 2,3-dimethyl-2-pentene**

## PROBLEM 13.4

Give the IUPAC name for each alkene.

a. $CH_2=CHCHCH_2CH_3$
    $\quad\quad\quad\quad |$
    $\quad\quad\quad\quad CH_3$

b. $(CH_3CH_2)_2C=CHCH_2CH_2CH_3$

c. $CH_3CH_2CH=CHCH=CHCH_3$

d. ⬡ $CH_2CH_3$

## PROBLEM 13.5

Give the IUPAC name for each alkyne.

a. $CH_3CH_2CH_2CH_2CH_2C\equiv CCH(CH_3)_2$

b. $CH_3CH_2-C\equiv C-CH_2-\underset{\underset{CH_3}{|}}{\overset{\overset{CH_2CH_3}{|}}{C}}-CH_3$

## SAMPLE PROBLEM 13.3

Draw the structure corresponding to each IUPAC name: (a) 5,5-dimethyl-3-heptyne; (b) 1,3-dimethylcyclohexene.

### Analysis

First identify the parent name to find the longest carbon chain or ring, and then use the suffix to determine the functional group; the suffix -*ene* = an alkene and -*yne* = an alkyne. Then number the carbon chain or ring and place the functional group at the indicated carbon. Add the substituents and enough hydrogens to give each carbon four bonds.

### Solution

a. 5,5-Dimethyl-3-heptyne has 7 C's as its longest chain (hept-) and a triple bond that begins at C3 (3-heptyne). Two methyl groups are bonded to C5.

Draw 7 C's and number the chain:

**Answer:**

**5,5-dimethyl-3-heptyne**

b. 1,3-Dimethylcyclohexene contains a six-membered ring with a double bond (cyclohexene). Number the ring to put the double bond between C1 and C2, and then add two methyl groups at C1 and C3.

- Draw a 6 C ring.
- Begin numbering at any C.

**Answer:**

1,3-dimethylcyclohexene

---

### PROBLEM 13.6

Give the structure corresponding to each name.

a. 4-methyl-1-hexene

b. 5-ethyl-2-methyl-2-heptene

c. 2,5-dimethyl-3-hexyne

d. 1-propylcyclobutene

e. 1,3-cyclohexadiene

f. 4-ethyl-1-decyne

---

## 13.3   Cis–Trans Isomers

As we learned in Section 12.2 on alkanes, constitutional isomers are possible for alkenes of a given molecular formula. For example, there are three constitutional isomers for an alkene of molecular formula $C_4H_8$—1-butene, 2-butene, and 2-methylpropene.

$$CH_2{=}CHCH_2CH_3 \qquad CH_3CH{=}CHCH_3 \qquad CH_2{=}\overset{\overset{\textstyle CH_3}{|}}{C}CH_3$$

1-butene                    2-butene                2-methylpropene

These compounds are constitutional isomers because the atoms are bonded to each other in different ways. 1-Butene and 2-butene both have a four-carbon chain, but the location of the double bond is different, and 2-methylpropene has a longest chain containing only three carbon atoms.

### 13.3A   Stereoisomers—A New Class of Isomer

2-Butene illustrates another important aspect about alkenes. In contrast to the free rotation observed around carbon–carbon single bonds (Section 12.2D), there is **restricted rotation** around the carbon atoms of a double bond. As a result, the groups on one side of the double bond *cannot* rotate to the other side.

With 2-butene, there are two ways to arrange the atoms on the double bond. The two $CH_3$ groups can be on the *same side* of the double bond or they can be on *opposite sides* of the double bond. These molecules are *different* compounds with the same molecular formula; that is, they are **isomers.**

| General structure | Two possible arrangements |
|---|---|

$CH_3CH{=}CHCH_3$

2-butene

two $CH_3$ groups on the **same** side

**cis** isomer

two $CH_3$ groups on **opposite** sides

**trans** isomer

- When the two $CH_3$ groups are on the *same side* of the double bond, the compound is called the *cis* isomer.
- When the two $CH_3$ groups are on *opposite sides* of the double bond, the compound is called the *trans* isomer.

To give these compounds unique IUPAC names, we use the prefixes *cis* and *trans* before the remainder of the name to indicate the relative location of the two alkyl groups on the double bond. Thus, one isomer is called ***cis*-2-butene,** and the other isomer is called ***trans*-2-butene.**

two $CH_3$ groups on the **same** side

two $CH_3$ groups on **opposite** sides

*cis*-2-butene          *trans*-2-butene

**different compounds**

The cis and trans isomers of 2-butene are a specific example of a general class of isomer that occurs at carbon–carbon double bonds. **Whenever the two groups on *each* end of a C=C are *different from each other,* two isomers are possible.**

These two groups must be **different from each other...**

$$\underset{B}{\overset{A}{C}}=\underset{D}{\overset{C}{C}}$$

***...and* these two groups must also be **different from each other.**

When the two groups on one end of the double bond are identical, there is still restricted rotation, but no cis and trans isomers are possible. With 1-butene, $CH_2=CHCH_2CH_3$, one end of the double bond has two hydrogens, so the ethyl group ($CH_2CH_3$) is always cis to a hydrogen, no matter how the molecule is drawn.

two identical groups

$$\underset{H}{\overset{H}{C}}=\underset{CH_2CH_3}{\overset{H}{C}}$$

- - - ►

$$\underset{H}{\overset{H}{C}}=\underset{H}{\overset{CH_2CH_3}{C}}$$

1-butene          **identical**

No cis and trans isomers are possible.

## SAMPLE PROBLEM 13.4

Draw *cis*- and *trans*-3-hexene.

### Analysis

First, use the parent name to draw the carbon skeleton, and place the double bond at the correct carbon; 3-hexene indicates a 6 C chain with the double bond beginning at C3. Then use the definitions of cis and trans to draw the isomers.

### Solution

Each C of the double bond is bonded to a $CH_3CH_2$ group and a hydrogen. A cis isomer has the $CH_3CH_2$ groups bonded to the same side of the double bond. A trans isomer has the two $CH_3CH_2$ groups bonded to the opposite sides of the double bond.

$$CH_3CH_2CH=CHCH_2CH_3$$
$$1 \quad 2 \quad 3 \quad\quad 4 \ 5 \ 6$$

- - - ►

$$\underset{H}{\overset{CH_3CH_2}{C}}=\underset{H}{\overset{CH_2CH_3}{C}} \quad\quad \underset{H}{\overset{CH_3CH_2}{C}}=\underset{CH_2CH_3}{\overset{H}{C}}$$

3-hexene          *cis*-3-hexene          *trans*-3-hexene

### PROBLEM 13.7

Draw a condensed structure for each compound: (a) *cis*-2-octene; (b) *trans*-3-heptene; (c) *trans*-4-methyl-2-pentene.

### PROBLEM 13.8

For which compounds are cis and trans isomers possible?

a. $CH_3CH_2CH{=}CHCH_3$     b. $CH_2{=}CHCH_2CH_2CH_3$     c.
$$\underset{CH_3}{CH_3C}{=}CHCH_2CH_2CH_3$$

### PROBLEM 13.9

Bombykol is secreted by the female silkworm moth (*Bombyx mori*) to attract mates. Bombykol contains two double bonds, and each double bond must have a particular three-dimensional arrangement of groups around it to be biologically active. Label the double bonds of bombykol as cis or trans.

bombykol

Cis and trans compounds are isomers, but they are *not* constitutional isomers. Each carbon atom of *cis*- and *trans*-2-butene is bonded to the same atoms. The only difference is the three-dimensional arrangement of the groups around the double bond. Isomers of this sort are called **stereoisomers.**

- *Stereoisomers* are isomers that differ *only* in the 3-D arrangement of atoms.

Thus, *cis*-2-butene and *trans*-2-butene are stereoisomers, but each of these compounds is a constitutional isomer of 1-butene, as shown in Figure 13.1.

We have now learned the two major classes of isomers.

- Constitutional isomers differ in the way the atoms are bonded to each other.
- Stereoisomers differ only in the three-dimensional arrangement of atoms.

**Figure 13.1**   Comparing Three Isomers: 1-Butene, *cis*-2-Butene, and *trans*-2-Butene

Linoleic and linolenic acids are **essential fatty acids,** meaning they cannot be synthesized in the human body and must therefore be obtained in the diet. A common source of these essential fatty acids is whole milk. Babies fed a diet of nonfat milk in their early months do not thrive because they do not obtain enough of these essential fatty acids.

**PROBLEM 13.10**

Label each pair of alkenes as constitutional isomers or stereoisomers.

a. $CH_3CH{=}CHCH_2CH_3$   and   $CH_2{=}CHCH_2CH_2CH_3$

b.
$$\begin{array}{c} CH_3CH_2 \quad\quad CH_3 \\ C{=}C \\ H \quad\quad\quad H \end{array} \quad \text{and} \quad \begin{array}{c} CH_3CH_2 \quad\quad H \\ C{=}C \\ H \quad\quad\quad CH_3 \end{array}$$

c.
$$\begin{array}{c} CH_3CH_2 \quad\quad H \\ C{=}C \\ CH_3 \quad\quad\quad H \end{array} \quad \text{and} \quad \begin{array}{c} CH_3CH_2 \quad\quad CH_3 \\ C{=}C \\ H \quad\quad\quad H \end{array}$$

## 13.3B  FOCUS ON HEALTH & MEDICINE
### Saturated and Unsaturated Fatty Acids

Naturally occurring animal fats and vegetable oils are formed from fatty acids. **Fatty acids are carboxylic acids (RCOOH) with long carbon chains of 12–20 carbon atoms.** Because a fatty acid has many nonpolar C—C and C—H bonds and few polar bonds, fatty acids are insoluble in water. There are two types of fatty acids.

- *Saturated* fatty acids have no double bonds in their long hydrocarbon chains.
- *Unsaturated* fatty acids have one or more double bonds in their long hydrocarbon chains.

Table 13.1 lists the structure and melting point of four fatty acids containing 18 carbon atoms. Stearic acid is one of the two most common saturated fatty acids, while oleic and linoleic acids are the most common unsaturated ones.

One structural feature of unsaturated fatty acids is especially noteworthy.

- Generally, double bonds in naturally occurring fatty acids are cis.

**Table 13.1  Common Saturated and Unsaturated Fatty Acids**

| Name | Structure | Mp (°C) |
|---|---|---|
| Stearic acid<br>(0 C=C) | $CH_3CH_2CH_2CH_2CH_2CH_2CH_2CH_2CH_2CH_2CH_2CH_2CH_2CH_2CH_2CH_2CH_2COOH$ | 71 |
| Oleic acid<br>(1 C=C) | $CH_3CH_2CH_2CH_2CH_2CH_2CH_2CH_2$ $\overset{\displaystyle H \quad\quad H}{C{=}C}$ $CH_2CH_2CH_2CH_2CH_2CH_2CH_2COOH$ | 16 |
| Linoleic acid<br>(2 C=C) | $CH_3CH_2CH_2CH_2CH_2$ $\overset{\displaystyle H \quad\quad H}{C{=}C}$ $CH_2$ $\overset{\displaystyle H \quad\quad H}{C{=}C}$ $CH_2CH_2CH_2CH_2CH_2CH_2CH_2COOH$ | −5 |
| Linolenic acid<br>(3 C=C) | $CH_3CH_2$ $\overset{\displaystyle H \quad\quad H}{C{=}C}$ $CH_2$ $\overset{\displaystyle H \quad\quad H}{C{=}C}$ $CH_2$ $\overset{\displaystyle H \quad\quad H}{C{=}C}$ $CH_2CH_2CH_2CH_2CH_2CH_2CH_2COOH$ | −11 |

**Figure 13.2**     The Three-Dimensional Structure of Four Fatty Acids

stearic acid

oleic acid

linoleic acid

linolenic acid

The presence of cis double bonds affects the melting point of these fatty acids greatly.

• **As the number of double bonds in the fatty acid *increases,* the melting point *decreases.***

The cis double bonds introduce kinks in the long hydrocarbon chain, as shown in Figure 13.2. This makes it difficult for the molecules to pack closely together in a solid. **The larger the number of cis double bonds, the more kinks in the hydrocarbon chain, and the lower the melting point.**

Fats and oils are organic molecules synthesized in plant and animal cells from fatty acids. Fats and oils have different physical properties.

• **Fats are solids at room temperature. Fats are generally formed from fatty acids having few double bonds.**
• **Oils are liquids at room temperature. Oils are generally formed from fatty acids having a larger number of double bonds.**

**Saturated fats are typically obtained from animal sources, while unsaturated oils are common in vegetable sources.** Thus, butter and lard are formed from saturated fatty acids, while olive oil and safflower oil are formed from unsaturated fatty acids. An exception to this generalization is coconut oil, which is composed largely of saturated fatty acids.

Considerable evidence suggests that an elevated cholesterol level is linked to increased risk of heart disease. Saturated fats stimulate cholesterol synthesis in the liver, resulting in an increase in cholesterol concentration in the blood. We will learn more about fats and oils in Section 13.7 and Chapter 19.

## PROBLEM 13.11

Draw out a structure of arachidonic acid, indicating the arrangement of groups around the four double bonds.

$$CH_3(CH_2)_4CH=CHCH_2CH=CHCH_2CH=CHCH_2CH=CHCH_2(CH_2)_2CO_2H$$

arachidonic acid

## PROBLEM 13.12

You have two fatty acids, one with a melting point of 63 °C, and one with a melting point of 1 °C. Which structure corresponds to each melting point?

$$CH_3(CH_2)_{14}COOH \qquad CH_3(CH_2)_5CH = CH(CH_2)_7COOH$$

palmitic acid                    palmitoleic acid

## 13.4 Interesting Alkenes in Food and Medicine

In addition to the plant hormone ethylene, $CH_2=CH_2$ (Section 13.1), many useful compounds contain one or more carbon–carbon double bonds.

More examples of antioxidants are given in Section 13.12.

**Lycopene,** the red pigment in tomatoes and watermelon, contains 13 double bonds. Lycopene is an **antioxidant,** a compound that prevents an unwanted oxidation reaction from occurring. Diets that contain a high intake of antioxidants like lycopene have been shown to decrease the risk of heart disease and certain forms of cancer. Unlike other antioxidants that can be destroyed when fresh fruits or vegetables are processed, even foods such as tomato paste, tomato juice, and ketchup are high in lycopene.

lycopene

Lycopene's red color is due to the 11 double bonds that are each separated by one single bond (labeled in red). These double bonds absorb some (but not all) wavelengths of visible light. When a compound absorbs visible light, it takes on the color of those wavelengths of light it does *not* absorb. Since lycopene absorbs blue-green light, it appears red because it does not absorb the red light of the visible spectrum.

Lycopene absorbs this part of the visible region.

visible region

This part of the spectrum is *not* absorbed.

> **Lycopene appears red.**

Processed tomato products contain the antioxidant lycopene.

**Tamoxifen** is a potent anticancer drug that contains a carbon–carbon double bond in addition to other functional groups. Tamoxifen is used widely in the treatment of certain breast cancers that require the female sex hormone estrogen for growth. Tamoxifen binds to estrogen receptors, and in this way it inhibits the growth of breast cancers that are estrogen dependent. Tamoxifen is sold under the trade name of Novaldex.

$OCH_2CH_2N(CH_3)_2$

tamoxifen

$CH_3CH_2$

## PROBLEM 13.13

Identify all of the functional groups in tamoxifen.

## 13.5  FOCUS ON HEALTH & MEDICINE
### Oral Contraceptives

The development of synthetic oral contraceptives in the 1960s revolutionized the ability to control fertility. Prior to that time, women ingested all sorts of substances—iron rust, gunpowder, tree bark, sheep's urine, elephant dung, and others—in the hope of preventing pregnancy.

Synthetic birth control pills are similar in structure to the female sex hormones **estradiol** and **progesterone,** but they also contain a carbon–carbon triple bond. Most oral contraceptives contain two synthetic hormones that are more potent than these natural hormones, so they can be administered in lower doses.

estradiol　　　　　　　　　progesterone

Two common components of birth control pills are **ethynylestradiol** and **norethindrone.** Ethynylestradiol is a synthetic estrogen that resembles the structure and biological activity of estradiol. Norethindrone is a synthetic progesterone that is similar to the natural hormone progesterone. These compounds act by artificially elevating hormone levels in a woman, and this prevents pregnancy, as illustrated in Figure 13.3.

**Figure 13.3**　How Oral Contraceptives Work

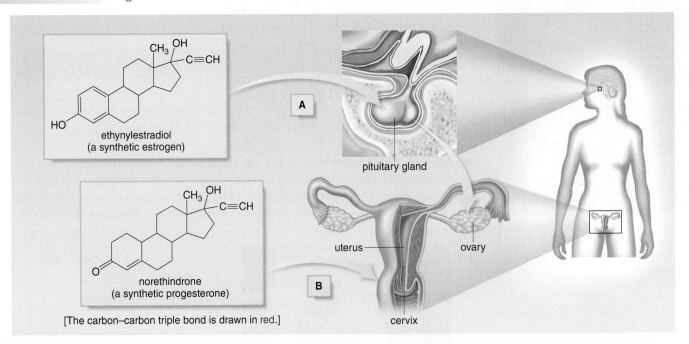

Monthly cycles of hormones from the pituitary gland cause ovulation, the release of an egg from an ovary. To prevent pregnancy, the two synthetic hormones in many oral contraceptives have different effects on the female reproductive system. **A:** The elevated level of **ethynylestradiol,** a synthetic estrogen, "fools" the pituitary gland into thinking a woman is pregnant, so ovulation does not occur. **B:** The elevated level of **norethindrone,** a synthetic progesterone, stimulates the formation of a thick layer of mucus in the cervix, making it difficult for sperm to reach the uterus.

Two other synthetic hormones with triple bonds are **RU 486** and **levonorgestrel.** RU 486 blocks the effects of progesterone, and by this means, prevents implantation of a fertilized egg. RU 486 is used to induce abortions within the first few weeks of pregnancy. Levonorgestrel interferes with ovulation, and thereby prevents pregnancy if taken within a few days of unprotected sex.

RU 486
(Trade name: Mifepristone)

levonorgestrel
(Trade name: Plan B)

[The carbon–carbon triple bond is drawn in red.]

**PROBLEM 13.14**

Identify the functional groups in RU 486 and levonorgestrel.

## 13.6 Reactions of Alkenes

Most families of organic compounds undergo a characteristic type of reaction. **Alkenes undergo addition reactions.** In an addition reaction, new groups X and Y are added to a starting material. One bond of the double bond is broken and two new single bonds are formed.

- Addition is a reaction in which elements are added to a compound.

**Addition**     $\overset{}{\underset{}{C}}=\overset{}{\underset{}{C}}$  +  X—Y  $\longrightarrow$  $-\overset{|}{\underset{X}{C}}-\overset{|}{\underset{Y}{C}}-$

One bond is broken.          Two single bonds are formed.

Why does addition occur? A double bond is composed of one strong bond and one weak bond. In an addition reaction, the weak bond is broken and two new strong single bonds are formed. Alkenes react with hydrogen ($H_2$), halogens ($Cl_2$ and $Br_2$), hydrogen halides (HCl and HBr), and water ($H_2O$). These reactions are illustrated in Figure 13.4 with a single alkene starting material.

**Figure 13.4**

Four Addition Reactions of Alkenes

One bond is broken.

Two single bonds are formed.

cyclohexene

$H_2$ / metal catalyst → Hydrogenation

$X_2$ (X = Cl or Br) → Halogenation

HX (X = Cl or Br) → Hydrohalogenation

$H_2O$ / $H_2SO_4$ → Hydration

## 13.6A Addition of Hydrogen—Hydrogenation

**Hydrogenation is the addition of hydrogen ($H_2$) to an alkene.** Two bonds are broken—one bond of the carbon–carbon double bond and the H—H bond—and two new C—H bonds are formed.

The addition of $H_2$ occurs only in the presence of a **metal catalyst** such as palladium (Pd). The metal provides a surface that binds both the alkene and $H_2$, and this speeds up the rate of reaction. Hydrogenation of an alkene forms an **alkane** since the product has only C—C single bonds.

### SAMPLE PROBLEM 13.5

Draw the product of the following reaction.

$$CH_3CH_2CH_2CH{=}CH_2 \quad + \quad H_2 \xrightarrow{\;Pd\;}$$

### Analysis

To draw the product of a hydrogenation reaction:

- Locate the C=C and mentally break one bond in the double bond.
- Mentally break the H—H bond of the reagent.
- Add one H atom to each C of the C=C, thereby forming two new C—H single bonds.

### Solution

### PROBLEM 13.15

What product is formed when each alkene is treated with $H_2$ and a Pd catalyst?

a. $CH_3CH_2CH{=}CHCH_2CH_3$

## 13.6B Addition of Halogen—Halogenation

**Halogenation is the addition of halogen ($X_2$) to an alkene.** Two bonds are broken—one bond of the carbon–carbon double bond and the X—X bond—and two new C—X bonds are formed.

Halogenation readily occurs with $Cl_2$ and $Br_2$. The product of halogenation is a **dihalide.**

When an alkene is treated with red liquid bromine, the $Br_2$ adds to the carbon–carbon double bond to give a colorless product.

Halogenation with bromine is a simple chemical test used to determine if a double bond is present in an unknown compound. Bromine is a fuming red liquid. When bromine is added to an alkene, the bromine adds to the double bond and the red color disappears. The disappearance of the red color shows that a double bond is present.

### PROBLEM 13.16

Draw the product of each reaction.

a. $CH_3CH_2CH{=}CH_2$  +  $Cl_2$  $\longrightarrow$

b. [structure: cyclohexene with two $CH_3$ groups]  +  $Br_2$  $\longrightarrow$

## 13.6C  Addition of Hydrogen Halides—Hydrohalogenation

**Hydrohalogenation is the addition of HX** (X = Cl or Br) to an alkene. Two bonds are broken—one bond of the carbon–carbon double bond and the H—X bond—and new C—H and C—X bonds are formed.

Hydrohalogenation readily occurs with HCl and HBr. The product of hydrohalogenation is an **alkyl halide.**

There is one important difference in this addition reaction compared to the addition of $H_2$ and $X_2$. In this case, addition puts different atoms—H and X—on the two carbons of the double bond. As a result, HX can add to the double bond to give two constitutional isomers when an unsymmetrical alkene is used as starting material.

only product

For example, the addition of HCl to propene could in theory form two products. If H adds to the end carbon (labeled C1) and Cl adds to the middle carbon (C2), 2-chloropropane is formed. If Cl adds to the end carbon (C1) and H adds to the middle carbon (C2), 1-chloropropane is formed. In fact, **addition forms *only* 2-chloropropane.** This is a specific example of a general trend called **Markovnikov's rule,** named for the Russian chemist who first determined the selectivity of the addition of HX to an alkene.

- In the addition of HX to an unsymmetrical alkene, the H atom bonds to the less substituted carbon atom—that is, the carbon that has more H's to begin with.

The end carbon (C1) of propene has two hydrogens while the middle carbon (C2) has just one hydrogen. Addition puts the H of HCl on C1 since it had more hydrogens (two versus one) to begin with.

## SAMPLE PROBLEM 13.6

What product is formed when 2-methylpropene [(CH$_3$)$_2$C=CH$_2$] is treated with HBr?

### Analysis

Alkenes undergo addition reactions, so the elements of H and Br must be added to the double bond. Since the alkene is unsymmetrical, the H atom of HBr bonds to the carbon that has more H's to begin with.

### Solution

## PROBLEM 13.17

What product is formed in each of the following reactions?

a. CH$_3$CH=CHCH$_3$  +  HBr  ⟶

c. (CH$_3$)$_2$C=CHCH$_3$  +  HCl  ⟶

b.  +  HBr  ⟶

d.  +  HCl  ⟶

## 13.6D   Addition of Water—Hydration

**Hydration is the addition of water** to an alkene. Two bonds are broken—one bond of the carbon–carbon double bond and the H—OH bond—and new C—H and C—OH bonds are formed.

alkene

alcohol ← H$_2$O is added.

Hydration occurs only if a strong acid such as H$_2$SO$_4$ is added to the reaction mixture. The product of hydration is an **alcohol.** For example, hydration of ethylene forms ethanol.

ethylene                                                    ethanol

Gasohol contains 10% ethanol.

**Ethanol** is used as a solvent in many reactions in the laboratory. **Ethanol is also used as a gasoline additive** because, like alkanes, it burns in the presence of oxygen to form CO$_2$ and H$_2$O with the release of a great deal of energy. Although ethanol can also be formed by the fermentation of carbohydrates in grains and potatoes, much of the ethanol currently used in gasoline and solvent comes from the hydration of ethylene.

The hydration of unsymmetrical alkenes follows Markovnikov's rule.

> • In the addition of H$_2$O to an unsymmetrical alkene, the H atom bonds to the less substituted carbon atom—that is, the carbon that has more H's to begin with.

This C has only 1 H so the OH bonds here.

This C has 2 H's so the H bonds here.

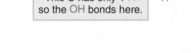

Addition of H$_2$O to propene forms 2-propanol [(CH$_3$)$_2$CHOH], the main component of rubbing alcohol.

## PROBLEM 13.18

What alcohol is formed when each alkene is treated with H$_2$O in the presence of H$_2$SO$_4$?

a.  CH$_3$CH=CHCH$_3$          b.  CH$_3$CH$_2$CH=CH$_2$          c.

## PROBLEM 13.19

What product is formed when 1-pentene (CH$_3$CH$_2$CH$_2$CH=CH$_2$) is treated with each reagent?

a. H$_2$, Pd          c. Br$_2$          e. HCl
b. Cl$_2$          d. HBr          f. H$_2$O, H$_2$SO$_4$

## 13.7 FOCUS ON HEALTH & MEDICINE
### Margarine or Butter?

**One addition reaction of alkenes, hydrogenation, is especially important in the food industry.** It lies at the heart of the debate over which product, butter or margarine, is better for the consumer.

As we learned in Section 13.3, butter is derived from saturated fatty acids like stearic acid [$CH_3(CH_2)_{16}COOH$], compounds with long carbon chains that contain only carbon–carbon single bonds. As a result, butter is a solid at room temperature.

**CONSUMER NOTE**

Margarine produced by the partial hydrogenation of vegetable oil has no color or taste. Several ingredients are added to make margarine more closely resemble butter: orange β-carotene (Section 11.7) is often added for color, salt for flavor, and 2,3-butanedione ($CH_3COCOCH_3$) to mimic the flavor of butter.

**Figure 13.5**    Partial Hydrogenation of the Double Bonds in a Vegetable Oil

- When an oil is *partially* hydrogenated, some double bonds react with $H_2$, while some double bonds remain in the product. Since the product has fewer double bonds, it has a higher melting point. Thus, a liquid oil is converted to a semi-solid.

- Partial hydrogenation decreases the number of carbons bonded to double bonds, making the molecule less easily oxidized, thereby increasing its shelf life.

Peanut butter is a common consumer product that contains partially hydrogenated vegetable oil.

Margarine, on the other hand, is a synthetic product that mimics the taste and texture of butter. It is prepared from vegetable oils derived from unsaturated fatty acids like linoleic acid [$CH_3(CH_2)_4CH=CHCH_2CH=CH(CH_2)_7COOH$]. Margarine is composed mainly of *partially hydrogenated* vegetable oils formed by adding hydrogen to the double bonds in the carbon chain derived from unsaturated fatty acids.

When an unsaturated liquid vegetable oil is treated with hydrogen, some (or all) of the double bonds add $H_2$, as shown in Figure 13.5. This increases the melting point of the oil, thus giving it a semi-solid consistency that more closely resembles butter. This process is called **hardening.**

As we will learn in Section 19.4, unsaturated oils with carbon–carbon double bonds are healthier than saturated fats with no double bonds. Why, then, does the food industry partially hydrogenate oils, thus reducing the number of double bonds? The reasons relate to texture and shelf life. Consumers prefer the semi-solid consistency of margarine to a liquid oil. Imagine pouring vegetable oil on a piece of toast or pancakes!

Furthermore, unsaturated oils are more susceptible than saturated fats to oxidation at the carbons adjacent to the double bond carbons. Oxidation makes the oil rancid and inedible. Hydrogenating the double bonds reduces the number of carbons bonded to double bonds (also illustrated in Figure 13.5), thus reducing the likelihood of oxidation and increasing the shelf life of the food product. This process reflects a delicate balance between providing consumers with healthier food products, while maximizing shelf life to prevent spoilage.

One other fact is worthy of note. During hydrogenation, some of the cis double bonds in vegetable oils are converted to trans double bonds, forming so-called "trans fats." The shape of the resulting fatty acid chain is very different, closely resembling the shape of a *saturated* fatty acid chain. As a result, trans fats are thought to have the same negative effects on blood cholesterol levels as saturated fats; that is, trans fats stimulate cholesterol synthesis in the liver, thus increasing blood cholesterol levels, a factor linked to increased risk of heart disease.

A "trans" fat and a saturated fat have a similar 3-D shape.

trans double bond

a trans fatty acid chain

similar shape

a saturated fatty acid chain

Which should you choose—butter or margarine—and if it's margarine, which of the many varieties is best for you? Margarine can be hard or soft. It can be made from olive oil, corn oil, safflower oil, or even yogurt. One fact remains clear to nutritionists. It is best to limit your intake of both butter (high in saturated fat) and margarine (high in trans fat).

### PROBLEM 13.20

(a) When linolenic acid (Table 13.1) is partially hydrogenated with one equivalent of $H_2$ in the presence of a Pd catalyst, three constitutional isomers are formed. One of them is linoleic acid. Draw the structures of the other two possible products. (b) What product is formed when linolenic acid is completely hydrogenated with three equivalents of $H_2$?

## 13.8 Polymers—The Fabric of Modern Society

*Polymers* **are large molecules made up of repeating units of smaller molecules—called** *monomers*—**covalently bonded together.** Polymers include the naturally occurring proteins that compose hair, tendons, and fingernails. They also include such industrially important plastics as polyethylene, poly(vinyl chloride) (PVC), and polystyrene. Since 1976, the U.S. production of synthetic polymers has exceeded its steel production.

### 13.8A Synthetic Polymers

Many synthetic polymers—that is, those synthesized in the lab—are among the most widely used organic compounds in modern society. Soft drink bottles, plastic bags, food wrap, compact discs, Teflon, and Styrofoam are all made of synthetic polymers. Figure 13.6 illustrates several consumer products and the polymers from which they are made.

To form a polymer from an alkene monomer, the weak bond that joins the two carbons of the double bond is broken and new strong carbon–carbon single bonds join the monomers together. For example, joining **ethylene monomers** together forms the polymer **polyethylene,** a plastic used in milk containers and sandwich bags.

| ethylene monomers | $CH_2=CH_2$ + $CH_2=CH_2$ + $CH_2=CH_2$ |

polymerization ↓

| polyethylene polymer | $-CH_2CH_2-CH_2CH_2-CH_2CH_2-$ | New bonds are shown in red. |

**three monomer units joined together**

- *Polymerization* is the joining together of monomers to make polymers.

Many ethylene derivatives having the general structure $CH_2=CHZ$ are also used as monomers for polymerization. The identity of Z affects the physical properties of the resulting polymer, making some polymers more suitable for one consumer product (e.g., plastic bags or food wrap)

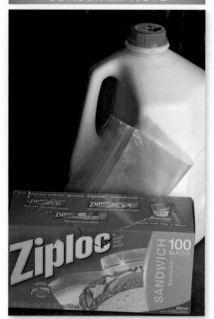

**HDPE** (high-density polyethylene) and **LDPE** (low-density polyethylene) are common types of polyethylene prepared under different reaction conditions and having different physical properties. HDPE is opaque and rigid, and used in milk containers and water jugs. LDPE is less opaque and more flexible, and used in plastic bags and electrical insulation.

**Figure 13.6** Polymers in Some Common Products

poly(vinyl chloride) PVC

polyacrylonitrile

polyisobutylene

polystyrene (Styrofoam)

than another (e.g., soft drink bottles or compact discs). Polymerization of $CH_2=CHZ$ usually yields polymers with the Z groups on every other carbon atom in the chain.

**Three monomer units joined together**

$$CH_2=CHZ \quad + \quad CH_2=CHZ \quad + \quad CH_2=CHZ \quad \longrightarrow$$

Repeating unit: $\left[ CH_2CH \right]_n$ — Many monomers are joined together.

shorthand structure

Polymer structures are often abbreviated by placing the atoms in the repeating unit in brackets, as shown. Table 13.2 lists some common monomers and polymers used in medicine and dentistry.

## Table 13.2 Common Monomers and Polymers Used in Medicine and Dentistry

| Monomer ⟶ | Polymer | Product |
|---|---|---|
| vinyl chloride | poly(vinyl chloride) PVC | PVC blood bags and tubing |
| propene | polypropylene | polypropylene syringes |
| tetrafluoroethylene | polytetrafluoroethylene Teflon | dental floss |

## SAMPLE PROBLEM 13.7

What polymer is formed when $CH_2=CHCO_2CH_3$ (methyl acrylate) is polymerized?

### Analysis

Draw three or more alkene molecules and arrange the carbons of the double bonds next to each other. Break one bond of each double bond, and join the alkenes together with single bonds. With unsymmetrical alkenes, substituents are bonded to every other carbon.

**Solution**

Join these 2 C's.    Join these 2 C's.    **Answer:**

Break one bond that joins each C=C.

[New bonds are drawn in red.]

## PROBLEM 13.21

What polymer is formed when each compound is polymerized?

a. $CH_2=C$ with $CH_3$ and $CH_2CH_3$

b. $CH_2=C$ with $CH_3$ and $CN$

c. $CH_2=C$ with $H$ and a benzene ring with $Cl$

## PROBLEM 13.22

What monomer is used to form poly(vinyl acetate), a polymer used in paints and adhesives?

$$-CH_2C-CH_2C-CH_2C-$$
with O, O, O and $COCH_3$ $COCH_3$ $COCH_3$

poly(vinyl acetate)

## 13.8B   FOCUS ON THE ENVIRONMENT
Polymer Recycling

The same desirable characteristics that make polymers popular materials for consumer products—durability, strength, and lack of reactivity—also contribute to environmental problems. Polymers do not degrade readily, and as a result, billions of pounds of polymers end up in landfills every year. Estimates suggest that synthetic polymers comprise 11% of solid municipal waste, 30% of which comes from packaging materials. Recycling existing polymer types to make new materials is one solution to the waste problem created by polymers.

Although thousands of different synthetic polymers have now been prepared, six compounds, called the **"Big Six,"** account for 76% of the synthetic polymers produced in the United States each year. Each polymer is assigned a recycling code (1–6) that indicates its ease of recycling; **the lower the number, the easier it is to recycle.** Table 13.3 lists these six most common polymers, as well as the type of products made from each recycled polymer.

Recycling begins with sorting plastics by type, shredding into small chips, and washing to remove adhesives and labels. After drying and removing any metal caps or rings, the polymer is melted and molded for reuse.

Of the Big Six, only the polyethylene terephthalate (PET) in soft drink bottles and the high-density polyethylene (HDPE) in milk jugs and juice bottles are recycled to any great extent. Since recycled polymers are often still contaminated with small amounts of adhesives and other materials, these recycled polymers are generally not used for storing food or drink products. Recycled HDPE is converted to Tyvek, an insulating wrap used in new housing construction, and recycled PET is used to make fibers for fleece clothing and carpeting. Currently about 23% of all plastics are recycled in the United States.

**HDPE**

**LDPE**

Table 13.3 Recyclable Polymers

| Recycling Code | Polymer Name | Shorthand Structure | Recycled Product |
|---|---|---|---|
| 1 | PET<br>polyethylene terephthalate | | fleece jackets<br>carpeting<br>plastic bottles |
| 2 | HDPE<br>high-density polyethylene | $-[CH_2CH_2]_n-$ | Tyvek insulation<br>sports clothing |
| 3 | PVC<br>poly(vinyl chloride) | $-[CH_2CH\underset{Cl}{}]_n-$ | floor mats |
| 4 | LDPE<br>low-density polyethylene | $-[CH_2CH_2]_n-$ | trash bags |
| 5 | PP<br>polypropylene | $-[CH_2CH\underset{CH_3}{}]_n-$ | furniture |
| 6 | PS<br>polystyrene | | molded trays<br>trash cans |

## 13.9 Aromatic Compounds

Aromatic compounds represent another example of unsaturated hydrocarbons. Aromatic compounds were originally named because many simple compounds in this family have characteristic odors. Today, the word **aromatic refers to compounds that contain a benzene ring,** or rings that react in a similar fashion to benzene.

**Benzene,** the simplest and most widely known aromatic compound, contains a six-membered ring and three double bonds. Since each carbon of the ring is also bonded to a hydrogen atom, the molecular formula for benzene is $C_6H_6$. Each carbon is surrounded by three groups, making it trigonal planar. Thus, **benzene is a planar molecule,** and all bond angles are **120°.**

benzene
$C_6H_6$

planar molecule

Although benzene is drawn with a six-membered ring and three double bonds, there are two different ways to arrange the double bonds so that they alternate with single bonds around the ring.

This bond is a single bond in one structure and a double bond in the second structure.

Drawing resonance structures was first presented in Section 4.4.

Each of these representations has the same arrangement of atoms. Only the location of the electrons is different. These structures are called **resonance structures.**

- Resonance structures are Lewis structures with the same arrangement of atoms but a different arrangement of electrons.

A **double-headed arrow** indicates that the two structures are resonance structures. In actuality, neither structure represents the true structure of benzene. The true structure of benzene is really a combination of both resonance structures, called a **hybrid.** Because the electron pair in a given double bond in a benzene ring is not really located between two particular carbon atoms, we say that the three electron pairs in the double bonds are *delocalized* in the six-membered ring. This gives benzene added stability compared to other unsaturated hydrocarbons.

Sometimes, a benzene ring is drawn with a circle inside a hexagon in place of the three double bonds.

three equivalent representations of benzene

The circle is meant to show that the six electrons from the three double bonds move freely around the ring. Realize, however, that we can draw benzene using either resonance structure or a benzene ring with a circle inside. Each of these representations is equivalent.

The physical properties of aromatic hydrocarbons are similar to other hydrocarbons—they have low melting points and boiling points and are water insoluble. Their chemical properties, however, are very different. **Aromatic hydrocarbons do not undergo the addition reactions that characterize alkenes.** For example, bromine adds to ethylene to form an addition product with two new C—Br bonds, but benzene does not react under similar conditions.

- Aromatic compounds resemble benzene—they are unsaturated compounds that do not undergo the addition reactions characteristic of alkenes.

## 13.10 Nomenclature of Benzene Derivatives

Many organic molecules contain a benzene ring with one or more substituents, so we must learn how to name them. Many common names are recognized by the IUPAC system, however, so this complicates the nomenclature of benzene derivatives somewhat.

### 13.10A Monosubstituted Benzenes

To name a benzene ring with one substituent, **name the substituent and add the word** *benzene.* Carbon substituents are named as alkyl groups. When a halogen is a substituent, name the halogen by changing the *-ine* ending of the name of the halogen to the suffix *-o*; for example, chlor*ine* → chlor*o*.

ethyl group
ethylbenzene

butyl group
butylbenzene

chloro group
chlorobenzene

Many monosubstituted benzenes, such as those with methyl ($CH_3$–), hydroxyl (–OH), and amino (–$NH_2$) groups, have common names that you must learn, too.

toluene
(methylbenzene)

phenol
(hydroxybenzene)

aniline
(aminobenzene)

## 13.10B   Disubstituted Benzenes

There are three different ways that two groups can be attached to a benzene ring, so a prefix—**ortho, meta,** or **para**—is used to designate the relative position of the two substituents. Ortho, meta, and para are generally abbreviated as *o, m,* and *p,* respectively.

| 1,2-Disubstituted benzene **ortho** isomer | 1,3-Disubstituted benzene **meta** isomer | 1,4-Disubstituted benzene **para** isomer |
|---|---|---|

*o*-diethylbenzene
or
1,2-diethylbenzene

*m*-diethylbenzene
or
1,3-diethylbenzene

*p*-diethylbenzene
or
1,4-diethylbenzene

If the two groups on the benzene ring are different, **alphabetize the name of the substituents** preceding the word benzene. If one of the substituents is part of a **common root,** name the **molecule as a derivative of that monosubstituted benzene.**

**Alphabetize two different substituent names:**

**Use a common root name:**

*o*-bromochloro-
benzene

*m*-**e**thylfluoro-
benzene

toluene
phenol

*p*-bromo**toluene**

*o*-chloro**phenol**

## 13.10C   Polysubstituted Benzenes

For three or more substituents on a benzene ring:

1. Number to give the lowest possible numbers around the ring.
2. Alphabetize the substituent names.
3. When substituents are part of common roots, name the molecule as a derivative of that monosubstituted benzene. The substituent that comprises the common root is located at C1, but the "1" is omitted from the name.

## Examples of naming polysubstituted benzenes

- Assign the lowest set of numbers.
- Alphabetize the names of all the substituents.

**4-chloro-1-ethyl-2-propylbenzene**

- Name the molecule as a derivative of the common root **aniline.**
- Designate the position of the $NH_2$ group as "1," and then assign the lowest possible set of numbers to the other substituents.

**2,5-dichloroaniline**

## 13.10D   Aromatic Compounds with More Than One Ring

Some aromatic compounds contain two or more benzene rings joined together. Naphthalene has two benzene rings joined together. There are two different aromatic hydrocarbons with three benzene rings, named anthracene and phenanthrene.

naphthalene              anthracene              phenanthrene

## SAMPLE PROBLEM 13.8

Name each of the following aromatic compounds.

a.    $CH_3CH_2$⸺⟨ring⟩⸺$CH_2CH_2CH_3$

b.    $CH_3$⸺⟨ring⟩⸺$Cl$ / $Br$

### Analysis

Name the substituents on the benzene ring. With two groups, alphabetize the substituent names and use the prefix ortho, meta, or para to indicate their location. With three substituents, alphabetize the substituent names, and number to give the lowest set of numbers.

### Solution

a.    $CH_3CH_2$⸺⟨ring⟩⸺$CH_2CH_2CH_3$

ethyl group          propyl group

- The two substituents are located 1,3- or **meta** to each other.
- Alphabetize the *e* of **e**thyl before the *p* of **p**ropyl.

**Answer: *m*-ethylpropylbenzene**

b.    $CH_3$⸺⟨ring⟩⸺$Cl$ (3) / $Br$ (4)

toluene

- Since a $CH_3$– group is bonded to the ring, name the molecule as a derivative of toluene.
- Place the $CH_3$ group at the "1" position, and number to give the lowest set of numbers.

**Answer: 4-bromo-3-chlorotoluene**

## PROBLEM 13.23

Give the IUPAC name of each compound.

a.

b.

c. 

d. 

## PROBLEM 13.24

Draw the structure corresponding to each name.

a. pentylbenzene
b. *o*-dichlorobenzene

c. *m*-bromoaniline
d. 4-chloro-1,2-diethylbenzene

## 13.11 FOCUS ON HEALTH & MEDICINE
### Aromatic Drugs, Sunscreens, and Carcinogens

Many widely used drugs contain an aromatic ring. Notable examples include the analgesic acetaminophen, the local anesthetic lidocaine, and the antihistamine loratadine (Figure 13.7). These drugs are better known by their trade names Tylenol, Xylocaine, and Claritin, respectively.

All commercially available sunscreens contain a benzene ring. A sunscreen absorbs ultraviolet radiation and thus shields the skin for a time from its harmful effects. Two sunscreens that have been used for this purpose are *p*-aminobenzoic acid (PABA) and Padimate O.

*p*-aminobenzoic acid
(PABA)

Padimate O

Compounds containing two or more benzene rings that share carbon–carbon bonds are called **polycyclic aromatic hydrocarbons (PAHs). Benzo[*a*]pyrene,** a PAH containing five rings joined together, is a widespread environmental pollutant, produced during the combustion of all types of organic material—gasoline, fuel oil, wood, garbage, and cigarettes.

Commercial sunscreens are given an **SPF** rating (sun protection factor), according to the amount of sunscreen present. The higher the number, the greater the protection.

tobacco plant

benzo[*a*]pyrene
(a polycyclic aromatic hydrocarbon)

**Figure 13.7    Three Drugs That Contain a Benzene Ring**

acetaminophen
(Trade name: Tylenol)

- Acetaminophen reduces fever and pain, but it is not anti-inflammatory. Thus, it is ineffective in treating conditions like arthritis, which have a significant inflammatory component.

lidocaine
(Trade name: Xylocaine)

- Lidocaine is a local anesthetic used to numb the skin when suturing an injury. It is also commonly used by dentists.

loratadine
(Trade name: Claritin)

- Loratadine is an over-the-counter antihistamine used for the treatment of seasonal allergies. Loratadine is an antihistamine that does not cause drowsiness.

When benzo[*a*]pyrene, a nonpolar and water-insoluble hydrocarbon, is inhaled or ingested, it is oxidized in the liver. Oxidation is a common fate of foreign substances that are not useful nutrients for the body. The oxidation products are more polar, making them much more water soluble, and more readily excreted in urine. The oxidation product from benzo[*a*]pyrene is also a potent **carcinogen;** that is, it causes cancer. The carcinogen binds to a needed protein or DNA in the cell and disrupts normal cell function, causing cancer or cell death.

**PROBLEM 13.25**

Which of the following compounds might be an ingredient in a commercial sunscreen? Explain why or why not.

a.

b.

## 13.12 FOCUS ON HEALTH & MEDICINE
### Phenols as Antioxidants

A wide variety of phenols, compounds that contain a hydroxyl group bonded to a benzene ring, occur in nature. **Vanillin** from the vanilla bean and **eugenol** from cloves are both phenols.

vanilla bean

cloves

turmeric

vanillin

eugenol

curcumin

**Curcumin** is a yellow pigment isolated from turmeric, a tropical perennial in the ginger family and a principal ingredient in curry powder. Curcumin has long been used as an anti-inflammatory agent in traditional eastern medicine.

Some phenols are antiseptics and others are irritants. The disinfectant Lysol contains 2-benzyl-4-chlorophenol. The phenol urushiol in poison ivy causes an irritating rash on contact.

2-benzyl-4-chlorophenol
(active ingredient in Lysol)

urushiol
(found in poison ivy)

The purported health benefits of antioxidants have made them a popular component in anti-aging formulations.

Like lycopene (Section 13.4), many **phenols are antioxidants.** Two examples are naturally occurring vitamin E and synthetic BHT. **The OH group on the benzene ring is the key functional group that prevents unwanted oxidation reactions from occurring.**

vitamin E

BHT
(**b**utylated **h**ydroxy **t**oluene)

Nuts are an excellent source of vitamin E.

**Vitamin E** is a natural antioxidant found in fish oil, peanut oil, wheat germ, and leafy greens. Although the molecular details of its function remain obscure, it is thought that vitamin E prevents the unwanted oxidation of unsaturated fatty acid residues in cell membranes. In this way, vitamin E helps retard the aging process.

Synthetic antioxidants such as **BHT**—**b**utylated **h**ydroxy **t**oluene—are added to packaged and prepared foods to prevent oxidation and spoilage. BHT is a common additive in breakfast cereals.

**PROBLEM 13.26**

Which of the following compounds might be antioxidants?

a. CH₃ —⟨⟩— CH(CH₃)₂ with OH
menthol

b. curcumin

c. CH₃ —⟨⟩— CH₃
*p*-xylene
(gasoline additive)

## 13.13   Reactions of Aromatic Compounds

Like the alkenes, aromatic compounds undergo a characteristic type of reaction. In contrast to the alkenes, however, aromatic compounds undergo **substitution** *not* addition.

- Substitution is a reaction in which an atom is *replaced* by another atom or a group of atoms.

**Substitution**    ⟨⟩—H  +  X—Y  ⟶  ⟨⟩—X  +  H—Y

substitution of H by X

Why does substitution occur? **Substitution of H by X keeps the stable aromatic ring intact.** Benzene does *not* undergo addition reactions like other unsaturated hydrocarbons because the product would not contain a benzene ring.

**Addition does *not* occur.**    +  X—Y  ⟶✗

The product is *not* aromatic.

Three specific reactions of benzene are considered: **chlorination, nitration,** and **sulfonation.** In each reaction, one hydrogen atom on the benzene ring is replaced by another atom or group: –Cl, –NO₂, or –SO₃H, respectively.

### 13.13A   Chlorination and the Synthesis of the Pesticide DDT

Benzene reacts with Cl₂ in the presence of an iron catalyst (FeCl₃) to yield chlorobenzene. Chlorobenzene is an **aryl halide,** an organic halide with the halogen bonded directly to the aromatic ring. Reaction with chlorine is called **chlorination.** In chlorination, a Cl atom substitutes for a hydrogen atom on the benzene ring.

Winston Churchill called DDT a "miraculous" chemical in 1945 for the many lives it saved during World War II. Less than 20 years later, as prolonged use of large quantities of this nonspecific pesticide led to harmful environmental effects, Rachel Carson called DDT the "elixir of death" in her book *Silent Spring.* DDT use was banned in the United States in 1973, but given its low cost, it is still widely used to control insect populations in developing countries.

**Chlorination**

The chlorination of benzene is the first step in the two-step synthesis of the pesticide **DDT** (*d*ichloro*d*iphenyl*t*richloroethane).

DDT
(nonbiodegradable pesticide)

DDT is an organic molecule with valuable short-term effects that has caused long-term problems. DDT kills insects that spread diseases such as malaria and typhus, and in controlling insect populations, DDT has saved millions of lives worldwide. DDT is a weakly polar and very stable organic compound, and so it (and compounds like it) persists in the environment for years. Since DDT is soluble in organic media, it accumulates in the fatty tissues of most animals. Most adults in the United States have low concentrations of DDT (or a degradation product of DDT) in them. The long-term effect on humans is not known, but DDT has had a direct harmful effect on the eggshell formation of certain predator birds such as eagles and hawks.

## 13.13B  FOCUS ON HEALTH & MEDICINE
### Nitration and Sulfa Drugs

Benzene reacts with nitric acid ($HNO_3$) in the presence of sulfuric acid ($H_2SO_4$) to yield nitrobenzene. Substitution of a **nitro group** ($NO_2$) for a hydrogen is called **nitration.**

**Nitration**

nitrobenzene

Nitration is a very valuable reaction because nitro groups are readily converted to amino groups, ($NH_2$) with $H_2$ and a palladium catalyst.

aniline

Many of the antibacterial sulfa drugs have $NH_2$ groups bonded to the benzene ring. Examples include sulfanilamide, one of the first antibiotics synthesized in the 1930s, and newer sulfa drugs such as sulfamethoxazole (trade name Bactrim) and sulfisoxazole (trade name Gantrisin), which are used to treat ear and urinary tract infections.

sulfanilamide

sulfamethoxazole
(Trade name: Bactrim)

sulfisoxazole
(Trade name: Gantrisin)

In cells, sulfamethoxazole and sulfisoxazole are both metabolized to sulfanilamide, the active agent. To understand how sulfanilamide functions as an antibacterial agent we must examine **folic acid,** which microorganisms synthesize from *p*-aminobenzoic acid.

*p*-aminobenzoic acid
PABA

folic acid

Sulfanilamide and *p*-aminobenzoic acid are similar in size and shape and have related functional groups. Thus, when sulfanilamide is administered, bacteria attempt to use it in place of *p*-aminobenzoic acid to synthesize folic acid. Derailing folic acid synthesis means that the bacteria cannot grow and reproduce. Sulfanilamide only affects bacterial cells, though, because humans do not synthesize folic acid, and must obtain it from their diets.

sulfanilamide                    *p*-aminobenzoic acid

## 13.13C   Sulfonation and Detergent Synthesis

Benzene reacts with sulfur trioxide ($SO_3$) in the presence of sulfuric acid ($H_2SO_4$) to yield benzenesulfonic acid. Substitution of $SO_3H$ for a hydrogen is called **sulfonation.**

benzenesulfonic acid

Although less widely used than chlorination and nitration, sulfonation is an important step in the synthesis of detergents. Many detergents are sodium salts of sulfonic acids, and are prepared by the two-step sequence shown in Figure 13.8.

### PROBLEM 13.27

What product is formed when *p*-dichlorobenzene is treated with each reagent: (a) $Cl_2$, $FeCl_3$; (b) $HNO_3$, $H_2SO_4$; (c) $SO_3$, $H_2SO_4$?

### PROBLEM 13.28

When toluene (methylbenzene) is treated with $Cl_2$ and $FeCl_3$, a total of three products are possible. Draw the structure of the three products and give their IUPAC names.

**Figure 13.8**   Synthesis of a Detergent Using Sulfonation

a benzenesulfonic acid

sodium salt of
a benzenesulfonic acid

synthetic detergent

# CHAPTER HIGHLIGHTS

## KEY TERMS

Addition reaction (13.6)
Alkene (13.1)
Alkyne (13.1)
Antioxidant (13.4)
Aromatic compound (13.9)
Aryl halide (13.13)
Chlorination (13.13)
Cis isomer (13.3)
Double-headed arrow (13.9)
Fat (13.3)
Fatty acid (13.3)
Halogenation (13.6)

Hardening (13.7)
Hybrid (13.9)
Hydration (13.6)
Hydrogenation (13.6)
Hydrohalogenation (13.6)
Markovnikov's rule (13.6)
Meta isomer (13.10)
Monomer (13.8)
Nitration (13.13)
Nitro group (13.13)
Oil (13.3)
Ortho isomer (13.10)

Para isomer (13.10)
Partial hydrogenation (13.7)
Polycyclic aromatic hydrocarbon
   (PAH, 13.11)
Polymer (13.8)
Polymerization (13.8)
Resonance structure (13.9)
Stereoisomer (13.3)
Substitution reaction (13.13)
Sulfonation (13.13)
Trans isomer (13.3)
Unsaturated hydrocarbon (13.1)

## KEY REACTIONS

[1]   Addition reactions of alkenes (13.6)

a. Hydrogenation (13.6A)

$$CH_2{=}CH_2 \ + \ H_2 \ \xrightarrow{Pd} \ \underset{\underset{H}{|} \quad \underset{H}{|}}{CH_2{-}CH_2}$$

b. Halogenation (13.6B)

$$CH_2{=}CH_2 \ + \ X_2 \ \longrightarrow \ \underset{\underset{X}{|} \quad \underset{X}{|}}{CH_2{-}CH_2} \quad (X = Cl \ or \ Br)$$

c. Hydrohalogenation (13.6C)

$$CH_2{=}CH_2 \ + \ HX \ \longrightarrow \ \underset{\underset{H}{|} \quad \underset{X}{|}}{CH_2{-}CH_2} \quad (X = Cl \ or \ Br)$$

d. Hydration (13.6D)

$$CH_2{=}CH_2 \ + \ H_2O \ \xrightarrow{H_2SO_4} \ \underset{\underset{H}{|} \quad \underset{OH}{|}}{CH_2{-}CH_2}$$

[2]   Substitution reactions of benzene (13.13)

a. Chlorination (13.13A)

benzene + $Cl_2$ $\xrightarrow{FeCl_3}$ chlorobenzene (Cl) + HCl

b. Nitration (13.13B)

benzene + $HNO_3$ $\xrightarrow{H_2SO_4}$ nitrobenzene ($NO_2$) + $H_2O$

c. Sulfonation (13.13C)

benzene + $SO_3$ $\xrightarrow{H_2SO_4}$ benzenesulfonic acid ($SO_3H$)

## KEY CONCEPTS

❶ **What are the characteristics of alkenes, alkynes, and aromatic compounds?**

- Alkenes are unsaturated hydrocarbons that contain a carbon–carbon double bond and have molecular formula $C_nH_{2n}$. Each carbon of the double bond is trigonal planar. (13.1)
- Alkynes are unsaturated hydrocarbons that contain a carbon–carbon triple bond and have molecular formula $C_nH_{2n-2}$. Each carbon of the triple bond is linear. (13.1)
- Benzene, molecular formula $C_6H_6$, is the most common aromatic hydrocarbon. Benzene is a stable hybrid of two resonance structures, each containing a six-membered ring and three double bonds. Each carbon of benzene is trigonal planar. (13.9)

❷ **How are alkenes, alkynes, and substituted benzenes named?**

- An alkene is identified by the suffix -*ene,* and the carbon chain is numbered to give the C=C the lower number. (13.2)
- An alkyne is identified by the suffix -*yne,* and the carbon chain is numbered to give the C≡C the lower number. (13.2)
- Substituted benzenes are named by naming the substituent and adding the word *benzene.* When two substituents are bonded to the ring, the prefixes ortho, meta, and para are used to show the relative positions of the two groups: 1,2-, 1,3- or 1,4-, respectively. With three substituents on a benzene ring, number to give the lowest possible numbers. (13.10)

**❸ What is the difference between constitutional isomers and stereoisomers? How are cis and trans isomers different? (13.3)**

- Constitutional isomers differ in the way the atoms are bonded to each other.
- Stereoisomers differ only in the three-dimensional arrangement of atoms.
- Cis and trans isomers are one type of stereoisomer. A cis alkene has two alkyl groups on the same side of the double bond. A trans alkene has two alkyl groups on opposite sides of the double bond.

**❹ How do saturated and unsaturated fatty acids differ? (13.3B)**

- Fatty acids are carboxylic acids (RCOOH) with long carbon chains. Saturated fatty acids have no double bonds in the carbon chain and unsaturated fatty acids have one or more double bonds in their long carbon chains.
- All double bonds in naturally occurring fatty acids are cis.
- As the number of double bonds in the fatty acid increases, the melting point decreases.

**❺ What types of reactions do alkenes undergo? (13.6)**

- Alkenes undergo addition reactions with reagents X—Y. One bond of the double bond and the X—Y bond break and two new single bonds (C—X and C—Y) are formed.
- Alkenes react with four different reagents—$H_2$ (Pd catalyst), $X_2$ (X = Cl or Br), HX (X = Cl or Br), and $H_2O$ (with $H_2SO_4$).

**❻ What is Markovnikov's rule? (13.6)**

- Markovnikov's rule explains the selectivity observed when an unsymmetrical reagent HX adds to an unsymmetrical alkene like propene ($CH_3CH=CH_2$). The H of HX is added to the end of the C=C that has more H's to begin with, forming $CH_3CH(X)CH_3$.

**❼ What products are formed when a vegetable oil is partially hydrogenated? (13.7)**

- When an unsaturated oil is partially hydrogenated, some but not all of the cis C=C's add $H_2$, reducing the number of double bonds and increasing the melting point.
- Some of the cis double bonds are converted to trans double bonds, forming trans fats, whose shape and properties closely resemble those of saturated fats.

**❽ What are polymers, and how are they formed from alkene monomers? (13.8)**

- Polymers are large molecules made up of repeating smaller molecules called monomers covalently bonded together. When alkenes are polymerized, one bond of the double bond breaks, and two new single bonds join the alkene monomers together in long carbon chains.

**❾ What types of reactions does benzene undergo? (13.13)**

- To keep the stable aromatic ring intact, benzene undergoes substitution, not addition, reactions. One H atom on the ring is replaced by another atom or group of atoms. Reactions include chlorination (substitution by Cl), nitration (substitution by $NO_2$), and sulfonation (substitution by $SO_3H$).

## PROBLEMS

Selected in-chapter and odd-numbered end-of-chapter problems have brief answers in Appendix B. The *Student Study Guide and Solutions Manual* contains detailed solutions to all in-chapter and odd-numbered end-of-chapter problems, as well as additional worked examples and a chapter self-test.

### Alkene, Alkyne, and Benzene Structure

**13.29** Anethole, the major constituent of anise oil, is used in licorice-flavored sweets and flavored brandy. Answer the following questions using the ball-and-stick model of anethole.

anethole

a. What is the molecular formula of anethole?
b. Identify the functional groups.
c. Label the carbon–carbon double bond as cis or trans.
d. Draw the structure of anethole and label each carbon as trigonal planar or tetrahedral.

**13.30** Methyl cinnamate, isolated from red clover flowers, is used in perfumery and as a flavoring agent because of its strawberry-like taste and odor. Answer the following questions using the ball-and-stick model of methyl cinnamate.

methyl cinnamate

a. What is the molecular formula of methyl cinnamate?
b. Identify the functional groups.
c. Label the carbon–carbon double bond as cis or trans.
d. Draw the structure of methyl cinnamate and label each carbon as trigonal planar or tetrahedral.

**13.31** What is the molecular formula for a hydrocarbon with 10 carbons that is (a) completely saturated; (b) an alkene; (c) an alkyne?

**13.32** Draw the structure of a hydrocarbon with molecular formula $C_6H_{10}$ that also contains: (a) a carbon–carbon triple bond; (b) two carbon–carbon double bonds; (c) one ring and one C=C.

**13.33** Draw structures for the three alkynes having molecular formula $C_5H_8$.

**13.34** Draw the structures of the five constitutional isomers of molecular formula $C_5H_{10}$ that contain a double bond.

**13.35** Label each carbon in the following molecules as tetrahedral, trigonal planar, or linear.

a.

c.

b.  —C≡CH

**13.36** Falcarinol is a natural pesticide found in carrots that protects them from fungal diseases. Predict the indicated bond angles in falcarinol.

falcarinol

## Nomenclature of Alkenes and Alkynes

**13.37** Give the IUPAC name for each molecule depicted in the ball-and-stick models.

a.     b.

**13.38** Give the IUPAC name for each molecule depicted in the ball-and-stick models.

a.     b.

**13.39** Give the IUPAC name for each compound.

a. $CH_2$=CHCH$_2$CH$_2$C(CH$_3$)$_3$

b. (CH$_3$CH$_2$)$_2$C=CHCHCH$_2$CHCH$_3$
                    CH$_3$   CH$_3$

c. $CH_2$=CCH$_2$CH$_3$
      CH$_2$CH$_2$CH$_2$CH$_2$CH$_3$

d. CH$_3$C≡CCH$_2$C(CH$_3$)$_3$

e. CH$_3$C≡C—CH$_2$—CH—C—CH$_2$CH$_3$
                     CH$_3$  CH$_3$
                           CH$_2$CH$_3$

                CH$_3$
f. $CH_2$=CHCH$_2$—C—CH=CH$_2$
                CH$_3$

**13.40** Give the IUPAC name for each compound.

a. $CH_2$=CHCH$_2$CHCH$_2$CH$_3$
             CH$_3$

b. (CH$_3$)$_2$C=CHCH$_2$CHCH$_2$CH$_3$
                    CH$_2$CH$_2$CH$_3$

c. CH$_3$C≡CCHCH$_3$
           CH$_2$CH$_2$CH$_3$

d. (CH$_3$)$_3$CC≡CC(CH$_3$)$_3$

e. (CH$_3$CH$_2$CH$_2$CH$_2$)$_2$C=CHCH$_3$

f. (CH$_3$)$_2$C=CHCH$_2$CH$_2$CH$_2$CH=C(CH$_3$)$_2$

**13.41** Give the IUPAC name for each cyclic compound.

a.  —CH$_3$

b.

**13.42** Give the IUPAC name for each cyclic compound.

a.     —CH$_2$CH$_2$CH$_3$     b.

**13.43** Give the structure corresponding to each IUPAC name.
a. 3-methyl-1-octene
b. 1-ethylcyclobutene
c. 2-methyl-3-hexyne
d. 3,5-diethyl-2-methyl-3-heptene
e. 1,3-heptadiene
f. *cis*-7-methyl-2-octene

**13.44** Give the structure corresponding to each IUPAC name.
a. 1,2-dimethylcyclopentene
b. 6-ethyl-2-octyne
c. 3,3-dimethyl-1,4-pentadiene
d. *trans*-5-methyl-2-hexene
e. 5,6-dimethyl-2-heptyne
f. 3,4,5,6-tetramethyl-1-decyne

**13.45** Each of the following IUPAC names is incorrect. Explain why it is incorrect and give the correct IUPAC name.
a. 5-methyl-4-hexene
b. 1-methylbutene
c. 2,3-dimethylcyclohexene
d. 3-butyl-1-butyne

**13.46** Each of the following IUPAC names is incorrect. Explain why it is incorrect and give the correct IUPAC name.
a. *cis*-2-methyl-2-hexene
b. 2-methyl-2,4-pentadiene
c. 2,4-dimethylcyclohexene
d. 1,1-dimethyl-2-cyclohexene

## Isomers

**13.47** Leukotriene $C_4$ is a key compound that causes the constriction of small airways, and in this way contributes to the asthmatic response. Label each double bond in leukotriene $C_4$ as cis or trans.

$$CH_3CH_2CH_2CH_2CH_2$$

leukotriene $C_4$

**13.48** Draw the complete structure of each naturally occurring compound using the proper cis or trans arrangement around the carbon–carbon double bond. Muscalure is the sex attractant of the housefly. Cinnamaldehyde is responsible for the odor of cinnamon.

a. $CH_3(CH_2)_8CH{=}CH(CH_2)_{12}CH_3$

muscalure
(cis double bond)

b.  $-CH{=}CHCHO$

cinnamaldehyde
(trans double bond)

**13.49** Label the carbon–carbon double bond as cis or trans, and give the IUPAC name for the alkene depicted in the ball-and-stick model.

**13.50** Label the carbon–carbon double bond as cis or trans, and give the IUPAC name for the alkene depicted in the ball-and-stick model.

**13.51** Draw the cis and trans isomers for each compound:
(a) 2-nonene; (b) 2-methyl-3-heptene.

**13.52** Draw the cis and trans isomers for each compound:
(a) 3-heptene; (b) 4,4-dimethyl-2-hexene.

**13.53** Explain the difference between a constitutional isomer and a stereoisomer.

**13.54** Draw all of the possible stereoisomers for 2,4-hexadiene $(CH_3CH{=}CH{-}CH{=}CHCH_3)$.

**13.55** How are the compounds in each pair related? Choose from constitutional isomers, stereoisomers, or identical.

a.        and

b.        and

**13.56** How are the compounds in each pair related? Choose from constitutional isomers, stereoisomers, or identical.

a.        and

b.        and

## Reactions of Alkenes

**13.57** What alkane is formed when each alkene is treated with $H_2$ in the presence of a Pd catalyst?

a. $CH_2{=}CHCH_2CH_2CH_2CH_3$

b. $(CH_3)_2C{=}CHCH_2CH_2CH_3$

c.

d.

**13.58** What dihalide is formed when each of the alkenes in Problem 13.57 is treated with $Br_2$?

**13.59** What alkyl halide is formed when each alkene is treated with HCl?

a. ▢

b. $(CH_3)_2C{=}C(CH_3)_2$

c. $CH_2{=}CHCH_2CH(CH_3)_2$

d. ⬡ ${=}CH_2$

**13.60** What alcohol is formed when each alkene in Problem 13.59 is treated with $H_2O$ and $H_2SO_4$?

**13.61** Draw the product formed when 1-ethylcyclohexene is treated with each reagent.

$CH_2CH_3$

a. $H_2$, Pd     d. HCl
b. $Cl_2$         e. HBr
c. $Br_2$         f. $H_2O$, $H_2SO_4$

1-ethylcyclohexene

**13.62** Draw the products formed in each reaction.

a. $CH_3CH=CHCH_3$ + HCl $\longrightarrow$

b. [cyclopentene structure] + $H_2$ $\xrightarrow{Pd}$

c. [cyclohexene with two $CH_3$ groups] + $Cl_2$ $\longrightarrow$

d. $CH_3CH=CHCH_2CH_2CH_3$ + $Br_2$ $\longrightarrow$

e. $(CH_3)_2C=CHCH_2CH_3$ + HBr $\longrightarrow$

f. [cyclopentene with CH_3 groups] + $H_2O$ $\xrightarrow{H_2SO_4}$

**13.63** What alkene is needed as a starting material to prepare each of the following alkyl halides or dihalides. In each case, also indicate what reagent is needed to react with the alkene.

a. $CH_3CH_2Br$

b. [cyclohexane with Cl]

c. [cyclopentane with two Cl and CH_3]

d. $BrCH_2CHCH_2CH(CH_3)_2$ with Br substituent

**13.64** 2-Bromobutane can be formed as the only product of the addition of HBr to two different alkenes. In contrast, 2-bromopentane can be formed as the *only* product of the addition of HBr to just one alkene. Draw the structures of the alkene starting materials and explain the observed results.

$CH_3CHCH_2CH_3$ with Br    $CH_3CHCH_2CH_2CH_3$ with Br

2-bromobutane          2-bromopentane

**13.65** What reagent is needed to convert 2-methylpropene $[(CH_3)_2C=CH_2]$ to each compound?

a. $(CH_3)_3CCl$

b. $(CH_3)_3CH$

c. $(CH_3)_3COH$

d. $(CH_3)_3CBr$

e. $(CH_3)_2CCH_2Br$ with Br

f. $(CH_3)_2CCH_2Cl$ with Cl

**13.66** What chemical test can be used to distinguish between each pair of compounds? Describe what you would visually observe (color changes or no changes in color) for each compound.

a. [cyclohexane] and [cyclohexene]

b. [cyclohexene] and [benzene]

## Polymers

**13.67** Draw the structure of poly(acrylic acid), the polymer formed by polymerizing acrylic acid ($CH_2=CHCOOH$). Poly(acrylic acid) is used in disposable diapers because it can absorb 30 times its weight in water.

**13.68** What polymer is formed when methyl α-methylacrylate $[CH_2=C(CH_3)CO_2CH_3]$ is polymerized? This polymer is used in Lucite and Plexiglas, transparent materials that are lighter but more impact resistant than glass.

**13.69** What polymer is formed when each compound is polymerized?

a. $CH_2=C$ with $CH_2CH_3$ and $H$

b. $CH_2=C$ with $Cl$ and $CN$

c. $CH_2=C$ with $Cl$ and $Cl$

**13.70** What polymer is formed when each compound is polymerized?

a. $CH_2=C$ with $OCH_3$ and $H$

b. $CH_2=C$ with $Cl$ and $CO_2CH_3$

c. $CH_2=C$ with $H$ and $NHCOCH_3$

**13.71** What monomer is used to form the following polymer?

[polymer chain: $-CH_2-C(Br)(Cl)-CH_2-C(Br)(Cl)-CH_2-C(Br)(Cl)-$]

**13.72** What monomer is used to form the following polymer?

[polymer chain: $-CH_2-C(CH_3)-CH_2-C(CH_3)-CH_2-C(CH_3)-$ with $C=O$ and $OCH_2CH_3$ groups]

## Structure and Nomenclature of Benzene

**13.73** Draw two resonance structures for chlorobenzene.

**13.74** Explain why structures **A** and **B** are the same compound, even though **A** has the two Cl atoms on the same double bond and **B** has the two Cl atoms on different double bonds.

[structure A: benzene with two Cl]    [structure B: benzene with two Cl]

**A**          **B**

**13.75** Name each aromatic compound.

a.

b.

**13.76** Name each aromatic compound.

a.   b.

**13.77** Give the IUPAC name for each substituted benzene.

a.   c.

b. $H_2N$—⟨⟩—$NO_2$   d.

**13.78** Give the IUPAC name for each substituted benzene.

a. $CH_3(CH_2)_3$—⟨⟩—$(CH_2)_3CH_3$

b.

c.

d.

**13.79** Draw the structure of the three constitutional isomers that have a Cl atom and an $NH_2$ group bonded to a benzene ring. Name each compound using the IUPAC system.

**13.80** Draw the structure of TNT, the explosive that has the IUPAC name 2,4,6-trinitrotoluene.

**13.81** Give the structure corresponding to each IUPAC name.
  a. *p*-nitropropylbenzene   d. 2-bromo-4-chlorotoluene
  b. *m*-dibutylbenzene   e. 2-chloro-6-iodoaniline
  c. *o*-iodophenol

**13.82** Give the structure corresponding to each IUPAC name.
  a. *m*-ethylnitrobenzene   d. 1,3,5-trinitrobenzene
  b. *o*-difluorobenzene   e. 2,4-dibromophenol
  c. *p*-bromotoluene

## Reactions of Aromatic Compounds

**13.83** What product is formed when *p*-dimethylbenzene (also called *p*-xylene) is treated with each reagent?

$CH_3$—⟨⟩—$CH_3$

*p*-dimethylbenzene

  a. $Cl_2$, $FeCl_3$
  b. $HNO_3$, $H_2SO_4$
  c. $SO_3$, $H_2SO_4$

**13.84** What reagents (**A–D**) are needed to carry out each reaction in the following sequence?

**13.85** When bromobenzene is treated with $HNO_3$ and $H_2SO_4$, three different products are formed. Draw the structures of the three products formed.

**13.86** You have three bottles (labeled **A, B,** and **C**) and each contains one of the *o*-, *m*-, or *p*-dibromobenzene isomers, but you don't know which isomer is in which bottle. When the dibromobenzene isomer in bottle **A** is treated with $Cl_2$ and $FeCl_3$, one product of molecular formula $C_6H_3Br_2Cl$ is obtained. When the dibromobenzene isomer in bottle **B** is treated with $Cl_2$ and $FeCl_3$, three products of molecular formula $C_6H_3Br_2Cl$ are obtained. When the dibromobenzene isomer in bottle **C** is treated with $Cl_2$ and $FeCl_3$, two products of molecular formula $C_6H_3Br_2Cl$ are obtained. Which isomer (ortho, meta, or para) is contained in which bottle (**A, B,** or **C**)?

## Applications

**13.87** The breakfast cereal Cheerios lists vitamin E as one of its ingredients. What function does vitamin E serve?

**13.88** Why is BHA an ingredient in some breakfast cereals and other packaged foods?

BHA
(**b**utylated **h**ydroxy **a**nisole)

**13.89** Although nonpolar compounds tend to dissolve and remain in fatty tissues, polar substances are more water soluble, and more readily excreted into an environment where they may be degraded by other organisms. Explain why methoxychlor is more biodegradable than DDT.

methoxychlor

**13.90** Explain why the pesticide DDT is insoluble in water, but the herbicide 2,4-D is water soluble. 2,4-D is one component of the defoliant Agent Orange used extensively during the Vietnam War.

DDT   2,4-D

**13.91** Kukui nuts contain oil that is high in linoleic acid content (Table 13.1). (a) What two constitutional isomers are formed when linoleic acid is partially hydrogenated with one equivalent of $H_2$? (b) What product is formed when linoleic acid is completely hydrogenated with $H_2$? (c) What product would be formed if, during hydrogenation, one equivalent of $H_2$ is added, *and* one of the cis double bonds is converted to a trans double bond?

**13.92** Eleostearic acid is an unsaturated fatty acid found in tung oil, obtained from the seeds of the tung oil tree (*Aleurites fordii*), a deciduous tree native to China. Eleostearic acid is unusual in that the double bond at C9 is cis, but the other two double bonds are trans. (a) Draw the structure of eleostearic acid, showing the arrangement of groups around each double bond. (b) Draw a stereoisomer of eleostearic acid in which all of the double bonds are trans. (c) Which compound, eleostearic acid or its all-trans isomer, has the higher melting point? Explain your reasoning.

$$CH_3(CH_2)_3CH=CHCH=CHCH=CH(CH_2)_7CO_2H$$
C9

eleostearic acid

**13.93** Which of the following compounds might be an antioxidant?

a. ⬡—$CH_2CH_2CH_2OH$   c. HO—⬡—$OCH_3$

b. ⬡—$OCH_3$

**13.94** Which of the following compounds might be an ingredient in a commercial sunscreen?

a. (structure with $CH_3O$)

b. (structure with $CH_2CH_2CH_3$)

**13.95** When benzene enters the body, it is oxidized to phenol ($C_6H_5OH$). What is the purpose of this oxidation reaction?

**13.96** Explain what a PAH is, and give an example of a PAH mentioned in this chapter, other than benzo[*a*]pyrene.

**13.97** Macadamia nuts have a high concentration of unsaturated oils formed from palmitoleic acid [$CH_3(CH_2)_5CH=CH(CH_2)_7COOH$]. (a) Draw the structure of the naturally occurring fatty acid with a cis double bond. (b) Draw a stereoisomer of palmitoleic acid. (c) Draw a constitutional isomer of palmitoleic acid.

**13.98** What products are formed when polyethylene is completely combusted?

## General Questions

**13.99** Why is the six-membered ring in benzene flat but the six-membered ring in cyclohexane is puckered (not flat)?

**13.100** Explain why *p*-dichlorobenzene is a nonpolar molecule but *o*-dichlorobenzene is a polar molecule.

**13.101** Answer the following questions about compound **A**, represented in the given ball-and-stick model.

(ball-and-stick model)

**A**

a. Convert **A** to a condensed structure and give its IUPAC name.
b. What product is formed when **A** is treated with $H_2$ in the presence of a metal catalyst?
c. What product is formed when **A** is treated with $H_2O$ in the presence of $H_2SO_4$?
d. What polymer is formed when **A** is polymerized?

**13.102** Answer the following questions about compound **B**, represented in the given ball-and-stick model.

(ball-and-stick model)

**B**

a. Convert **B** to a condensed structure and give its IUPAC name.
b. What product is formed when **B** is treated with $H_2$ in the presence of a metal catalyst?
c. What product is formed when **B** is treated with $H_2O$ in the presence of $H_2SO_4$?
d. What polymer is formed when **B** is polymerized?

## CHALLENGE PROBLEMS

**13.103** Are *cis*-2-hexene and *trans*-3-hexene constitutional isomers or stereoisomers? Explain.

**13.104** Some polymers are copolymers, formed from two different alkene monomers joined together. An example is Saran, the polymer used in the well known plastic food wrap. What two alkene monomers combine to form Saran?

Saran

# 14

Ethanol, the alcohol in wine, beer, and other alcoholic beverages, is formed by the fermentation of carbohydrates in grapes, grains, and potatoes.

# Organic Compounds That Contain Oxygen, Halogen, or Sulfur

## CHAPTER OUTLINE

## CHAPTER GOALS

*In this chapter you will learn how to:*

1. Identify alcohols, ethers, alkyl halides, and thiols
2. Classify alcohols and alkyl halides as 1°, 2°, or 3°
3. Determine the properties of alcohols, ethers, alkyl halides, and thiols
4. Name alcohols, ethers, alkyl halides, and thiols
5. Draw the products of the dehydration of alcohols
6. Determine the products of alcohol oxidation
7. Convert thiols to disulfides

Chapter 14 concentrates on four families of organic compounds that contain a carbon singly bonded to a heteroatom—**alcohols** (ROH), **ethers** (ROR), **alkyl halides** (RX, X = F, Cl, Br, or I), and **thiols** (RSH). The polar carbon–heteroatom bond gives these compounds different properties than the hydrocarbons of Chapters 12 and 13. Of the four families, alcohols are the most widely occurring, represented by simple compounds such as ethanol ($CH_3CH_2OH$) and by complex compounds such as starch and cellulose. Ethers are the most common anesthetics in use today, and alkyl halides, widely used as industrial solvents and refrigerants, are responsible for the destruction of the ozone layer. The –SH group of thiols plays an important role in protein chemistry. In Chapter 14, we learn about the properties of these four groups of organic compounds.

## 14.1  Introduction

**Alcohols, ethers, alkyl halides,** and **thiols** are four families of compounds that contain a carbon atom singly bonded to a heteroatom—oxygen, halogen, or sulfur.

**Alcohols** and **ethers** are organic derivatives of $H_2O$, formed by replacing one or two hydrogens on the oxygen by alkyl groups, respectively. *Alcohols* **contain a hydroxyl group (OH group)** bonded to a tetrahedral carbon atom, while *ethers* **have two alkyl groups bonded to an oxygen atom.** The oxygen atom in both compounds has two lone pairs of electrons, so it is surrounded by eight electrons.

**Alkyl halides contain a halogen atom (X = F, Cl, Br, or I)** bonded to a tetrahedral carbon. Each halogen atom forms one bond to carbon and has three lone pairs of electrons. **Thiols contain a sulfhydryl group (SH group)** bonded to a tetrahedral carbon atom. A thiol is a sulfur analogue of an alcohol, formed by replacing the oxygen by sulfur. Like oxygen, the sulfur atom has two lone pairs of electrons around it.

Mercaptomethylfuran (characteristic aroma of coffee), enflurane (a common anesthetic), and taxol (an anticancer drug) are compounds that contain these functional groups.

2-mercaptomethylfuran
(coffee aroma)

enflurane
(Trade name: Ēthrane)

taxol
(Trade name: Paclitaxel)

[The OH, SH, halogen, and ether O atoms are labeled in red.]

Taxol, a complex anticancer agent active against ovarian, breast, and some lung tumors, is especially interesting. Initial biological studies with taxol were carried out with natural material isolated from the bark of the Pacific yew tree, but stripping the bark killed these magnificent trees. Taxol can now be synthesized in the laboratory in four steps from a compound isolated from the needles of the common English yew tree, thus providing ample quantities for patients.

## PROBLEM 14.1

a. Label the hydroxyl groups, sulfhydryl groups, halogens, and ether oxygens in each compound.

b. Which –OH group in salmeterol (**C**) is *not* part of an alcohol? Explain.

**A**
chondrochole A
(isolated from red seaweed,
*Chondrococcus hornemanni*)

**B**
(responsible for the
characteristic flavor of
grapefruit)

**C**
salmeterol
Trade name: Serevent
(dilates airways; used to treat asthma)

## PROBLEM 14.2

Besides its three hydroxyl groups and one ether oxygen, taxol contains 10 other functional groups. Identify each of these functional groups.

## 14.2 Structure and Properties of Alcohols

*Alcohols* contain a **hydroxyl group** (**OH** group) bonded to a tetrahedral carbon atom. Alcohols are classified as **primary (1°), secondary (2°),** or **tertiary (3°)** based on the number of carbon atoms bonded to the carbon with the OH group.

| Alcohol | Classification of alcohols | | |
|---|---|---|---|

$$-\overset{|}{\underset{|}{C}}-\ddot{O}-H$$

hydroxyl group

$$CH_3-\overset{H}{\underset{H}{\overset{|}{C}}}-\ddot{O}H$$
1°

$$CH_3-\overset{CH_3}{\underset{H}{\overset{|}{C}}}-\ddot{O}H$$
2°

$$CH_3-\overset{CH_3}{\underset{CH_3}{\overset{|}{C}}}-\ddot{O}H$$
3°

- A primary (1°) alcohol has an OH group on a carbon bonded to one carbon.
- A secondary (2°) alcohol has an OH group on a carbon bonded to two carbons.
- A tertiary (3°) alcohol has an OH group on a carbon bonded to three carbons.

### SAMPLE PROBLEM 14.1

Classify each alcohol as 1°, 2°, or 3°.

a. ⬡—CH₂CH₂OH

b. ⬡—OH

### Analysis

To determine whether an alcohol is 1°, 2°, or 3°, locate the C with the OH group and count the number of C's bonded to it. A 1° alcohol has the OH group on a C bonded to one C, and so forth.

### Solution

Draw out the structure or add H's to the skeletal structure to clearly see how many C's are bonded to the C bearing the OH group.

a. ⬡—$\overset{H}{\underset{H}{\overset{|}{C}}}$—$\overset{H}{\underset{H}{\overset{|}{C}}}$—OH

This C is bonded to 1 C.
**1° alcohol**

b. ⬡$\overset{OH}{\underset{H}{\diagdown}}$

This C is bonded to 2 C's in the ring.
**2° alcohol**

### PROBLEM 14.3

Classify each alcohol as 1°, 2°, or 3°.

a. $(CH_3)_2C=CHCH_2CH_2-\overset{CH_3}{\underset{OH}{\overset{|}{C}}}-CH=CH_2$

linalool
(isolated from lavender)

b. $(CH_3)_2C=CHCH_2-\overset{CH_2OH}{\underset{H}{\overset{|}{C}}}-C(CH_3)=CH_2$

lavandulol
(isolated from lavender)

c. $CH_3-$⬡$-CH(CH_3)_2$
with OH

menthol

Linalool and lavandulol (Problem 14.3) are two of the over 300 compounds that determine the characteristic fragrance of lavender.

**PROBLEM 14.4**

Classify each hydroxyl group in sorbitol as 1°, 2°, or 3°.

sorbitol

An alcohol contains an oxygen atom surrounded by two atoms and two lone pairs of electrons, giving the oxygen atom a **bent** shape like H₂O. The C—O—H bond angle is similar to the tetrahedral bond angle of 109.5°.

$$CH_3 \overset{\cdot\cdot}{\underset{\cdot\cdot}{O}} H \quad = \quad \text{bent shape} \quad 109.5°$$

methanol       bent shape

Because oxygen is much more electronegative than carbon or hydrogen, the C—O and O—H bonds are polar. Since an alcohol contains two polar bonds and a bent shape, it has a net dipole. **Alcohols are also capable of intermolecular hydrogen bonding,** since they possess a hydrogen atom bonded to an oxygen. This gives alcohols much stronger intermolecular forces than the hydrocarbons of Chapters 12 and 13.

| An alcohol has a net dipole. | Alcohols exhibit intermolecular hydrogen bonding. |

As a result:

- **Alcohols have higher boiling points and melting points than hydrocarbons of comparable size and shape.**

CH₃CH₂CH₂CH₃       CH₃CH₂CH₂OH  ←   **stronger intermolecular forces higher boiling point and melting point**

butane             1-propanol

melting point: –138 °C     melting point: –127 °C
boiling point: –0.5 °C      boiling point: 97 °C

The general rule governing solubility—**"like dissolves like"**—explains the solubility properties of alcohols, as we learned in Section 11.6B.

- **Alcohols are soluble in organic solvents.**
- **Low molecular weight alcohols (those having less than six carbons) are soluble in water.**
- **Higher molecular weight alcohols (those having six carbons or more) are not soluble in water.**

Thus, both ethanol (CH$_3$CH$_2$OH) and 1-octanol [CH$_3$(CH$_2$)$_7$OH] are soluble in organic solvents, but ethanol is water soluble and 1-octanol is not.

CH$_3$CH$_2$OH                                     CH$_3$CH$_2$CH$_2$CH$_2$CH$_2$CH$_2$CH$_2$CH$_2$OH

only 2 C's in the chain                           many nonpolar C–C and C–H bonds
**water soluble**                                 **water insoluble**

## PROBLEM 14.5

Which compound in each pair has the higher boiling point?

a.    [structure with OH]    or    [structure with CH$_3$]          b. (CH$_3$)$_3$C—OH    or    (CH$_3$)$_4$C

## PROBLEM 14.6

Label each compound as water soluble or water insoluble.

a. [bicyclic structure]    b. (CH$_3$)$_3$C—OH    c. CH$_2$=CHCH$_2$CH$_3$    d. [bicyclic structure with OH]

# 14.3  Nomenclature of Alcohols

In the IUPAC system, alcohols are identified by the suffix *-ol.*

## How To  Name an Alcohol Using the IUPAC System

**Example:** Give the IUPAC name of the following alcohol.

$$\underset{\text{CH}_3\text{CHCH}_2\text{CHCH}_2\text{CH}_3}{\overset{\text{CH}_3 \quad\;\; \text{OH}}{}}$$

**Step [1]** Find the longest carbon chain containing the carbon bonded to the OH group.

**6** C's in the longest chain

**hexane**  – – –→ **hexano*l***

• Change the *-e* ending of the parent alkane to the suffix *-ol.*

**Step [2]** Number the carbon chain to give the OH group the lower number, and apply all other rules of nomenclature.

a. **Number** the chain.

6  5  4  3  2  1

• Number the chain to put the OH group at C3, not C4.

3-hexanol

b. **Name** and **number** the substituents.

methyl at C5

5      3

**Answer: 5-methyl-3-hexanol**

When an OH group is bonded to a ring, the **ring is numbered beginning with the OH group,** and the "1" is usually omitted from the name. The ring is then numbered in a clockwise or counterclockwise fashion to give the next substituent the lower number.

**3-methylcyclohexanol**

| The OH group is at C1; the second substituent ($CH_3$) gets the lower number. |

**2-ethylcyclopentanol**

| The OH group is at C1; the second substituent ($CH_3CH_2$) gets the lower number. |

Common names are often used for simple alcohols. To assign a common name:

- Name all the carbon atoms of the molecule as a single alkyl group.
- Add the word *alcohol,* separating the words with a space.

$CH_3CH_2CH_2$—OH   alcohol   - - - →   **propyl alcohol**

propyl group                                      a common name

Compounds with two hydroxyl groups are called **diols** (using the IUPAC system) or **glycols.** Compounds with three hydroxyl groups are called **triols,** and so forth. To name a diol, for example, the suffix *-diol* is added to the name of the parent alkane and numbers are used in the prefix to indicate the location of the two OH groups.

$HOCH_2CH_2OH$

IUPAC name: 1,2-ethanediol
Common name: **ethylene glycol**

**1,2-cyclopentanediol**

## SAMPLE PROBLEM 14.2

Give the IUPAC name of the following alcohol.

$$CH_3CH_2\overset{\overset{\displaystyle CH_3}{|}}{\underset{\underset{\displaystyle CH_3}{|}}{C}}CH_2CH_2OH$$

### Analysis and Solution

**[1] Find the longest carbon chain that contains the carbon bonded to the OH group.**

$$CH_3CH_2\overset{\overset{\displaystyle CH_3}{|}}{\underset{\underset{\displaystyle CH_3}{|}}{C}}CH_2\text{—OH}$$

5 C's in the longest chain  - - - → **pentanol**

- Change the *-e* ending of the parent alkane to the suffix *-ol.*

**[2] Number the carbon chain to give the OH group the lower number, and apply all other rules of nomenclature.**

a. **Number** the chain.

$$CH_3CH_2\overset{\overset{\displaystyle CH_3}{|}}{\underset{\underset{\displaystyle CH_3}{|}}{C}}CH_2CH_2\text{—OH}$$

5       3       1

- Number the chain to put the OH group at C1, not C5.

1-pentanol

b. **Name** and **number** the substituents.

two methyls at C3 ——→ dimethyl

**Answer: 3,3-dimethyl-1-pentanol**

### PROBLEM 14.7

Give the IUPAC name for each compound.

a. $CH_3\overset{\underset{\displaystyle |}{OH}}{CH}(CH_2)_4CH_3$

c.

b. $(CH_3CH_2)_2\overset{\underset{\displaystyle |}{OH}}{CH}CHCH_2CH_3$

d. $CH_3CH_2CH_2\overset{\underset{\displaystyle |}{CH_3}}{CH}CH\overset{\underset{\displaystyle |}{OH}}{CH_2}CHCH_2CH_3$
$\quad\quad\quad\quad\quad\quad\quad\quad\quad\underset{\displaystyle CH_2CH_3}{|}$

### PROBLEM 14.8

Give the structure corresponding to each name.

a. 7,7-dimethyl-4-octanol      c. 2-ethyl-3-methylcyclohexanol

b. 5-methyl-4-propyl-3-heptanol      d. 1,3-cyclohexanediol

## 14.4 Interesting Alcohols

The most well known alcohol is ethanol, $CH_3CH_2OH$. **Ethanol** (Figure 14.1), formed by the fermentation of carbohydrates in grains and grapes, is the alcohol present in alcoholic beverages. Fermentation requires yeast, which provides the needed enzymes for the conversion. Ethanol is likely the first organic compound synthesized by humans, since alcohol has been produced for at least 4,000 years.

Ethanol is also a common laboratory solvent, which is sometimes made unfit to ingest by adding small amounts of benzene or methanol ($CH_3OH$), both of which are toxic. Ethanol is used as a gasoline additive since it readily combusts to form $CO_2$ and $H_2O$ with the release of energy. Other simple alcohols are listed in Figure 14.2.

**Figure 14.1**     Ethanol—The Alcohol in Alcoholic Beverages

**Fermentation**

$C_6H_{12}O_6 \xrightarrow[\text{yeast}]{} 2\ \textbf{CH}_3\textbf{CH}_2\textbf{OH} + 2\ CO_2$
glucose              **ethanol**

$CH_3CH_2OH$
ethanol

Ethanol is the alcohol in red wine, obtained by the fermentation of grapes. All alcoholic beverages are mixtures of ethanol and water in various proportions. Beer has 3–8% ethanol, wines have 10–14% ethanol, and other liquors have 35–90% ethanol.

**Figure 14.2** Some Simple Alcohols

**CH₃OH**

- **Methanol (CH₃OH)** is a useful solvent and starting material for the synthesis of plastics. Methanol is extremely toxic because of the oxidation products formed when metabolized in the liver (Section 14.6A). Ingestion of as little as 15 mL (about half an ounce) causes blindness and 100 mL causes death.

**(CH₃)₂CHOH**

- **2-Propanol [(CH₃)₂CHOH, isopropyl alcohol]** is the major component of rubbing alcohol. When rubbed on the skin it evaporates readily, producing a pleasant cooling sensation. 2-Propanol is used to clean skin before medical procedures and to sterilize medical instruments.

**HOCH₂CHCH₂OH**
          |
          **OH**

- **Glycerol [(HOCH₂)₂CHOH]** is a triol used in lotions, liquid soap, and shaving cream. Since it is sweet tasting and nontoxic, it is also an additive in candy and some prepared foods. Its three OH groups readily hydrogen bond to water, so it helps to retain moisture in these products.

The six-membered rings in starch and cellulose are drawn in the puckered "chair" form mentioned in Section 12.5A.

**Starch** and **cellulose** are two polymers that contain many OH groups and belong to the family of molecules called **carbohydrates.**

**Starch** is the main carbohydrate in the seeds and roots of plants. When humans ingest wheat, rice, and potatoes, for example, they consume starch, which is then hydrolyzed to the simple sugar **glucose. Cellulose,** nature's most abundant organic material, gives rigidity to tree trunks and plant stems. Wood, cotton, and flax are composed largely of cellulose. Complete hydrolysis of cellulose also forms glucose, but unlike starch, humans cannot metabolize cellulose to glucose; that is, humans can digest starch but not cellulose.

## 14.5 Reactions of Alcohols

Alcohols undergo two useful reactions—**dehydration** and **oxidation.**

### 14.5A Dehydration

When an alcohol is treated with a strong acid such as $H_2SO_4$, the elements of water are lost and an alkene is formed as product. **Loss of $H_2O$ from a starting material is called** *dehydration.* Dehydration takes place by breaking bonds on two adjacent atoms—the C—OH bond and an adjacent C—H bond.

Dehydration is an example of a general type of organic reaction called an **elimination reaction.**

- *Elimination* is a reaction in which elements of the starting material are "lost" and a new multiple bond is formed.

For example, dehydration of ethanol ($CH_3CH_2OH$) with $H_2SO_4$ forms ethylene ($CH_2$=$CH_2$), as shown. To draw the product of any dehydration, **remove the elements of H and OH from two adjacent atoms and draw a carbon–carbon double bond in the product.**

Sometimes more than one alkene can be formed as the product of a dehydration reaction, as is the case when 2-butanol [$CH_3CH(OH)CH_2CH_3$] is the starting material. If H and OH are removed from C1 and C2, 1-butene is formed. If H and OH are removed from C3 and C2, 2-butene is formed.

Although both products are formed, **the major product is the alkene with more alkyl groups bonded to the carbons of the double bond.** In this case, therefore, 2-butene is the major product, because its C=C has two alkyl groups (two $CH_3$ groups) bonded to it, whereas the C=C of 1-butene has only one alkyl group (one $CH_2CH_3$ group) bonded to it.

1-butene
**minor product**

2-butene
**major product**

This is a specific example of a general trend called the **Zaitsev rule.**

- **The Zaitsev rule: The major product in elimination is the alkene that has more alkyl groups bonded to it.**

### SAMPLE PROBLEM 14.3

Draw all possible products of dehydration of the following alcohol, and predict which one is the major product.

$$CH_3CHCH_2CH(CH_3)_2$$
$$\overset{|}{OH}$$

#### Analysis

To draw the products of dehydration:

- First find the carbon bonded to the OH group, and then identify all carbons with H's bonded to this carbon.
- Remove the elements of H and OH from two adjacent C's, and draw a double bond between these C's in the product.
- When two different alkenes are formed, the major product has more C's bonded to the C=C.

#### Solution

In this example, there are two different C's bonded to the C with the OH. Elimination of H and OH from C1 and C2 forms 4-methyl-1-pentene. Elimination of H and OH from C3 and C2 forms 4-methyl-2-pentene. The major product is 4-methyl-2-pentene because it has two C's bonded to the C=C, whereas 4-methyl-1-pentene has only one C bonded to the C=C.

4-methyl-1-pentene
(1 C bonded to C=C, labeled in green)

4-methyl-2-pentene
(2 C's bonded to C=C, labeled in green)

**major product**

### PROBLEM 14.9

Draw the products formed when each alcohol is dehydrated with $H_2SO_4$.

## PROBLEM 14.10

What alkenes are formed when each alcohol is treated with $H_2SO_4$? Use the Zaitsev rule to predict the major product.

a. $CH_3CHCH_2CH_2CH_3$
      |
      OH

b. $CH_3-\overset{\overset{\displaystyle CH_3}{|}}{\underset{\underset{\displaystyle OH}{|}}{C}}-CH_2CH_3$

c.

## PROBLEM 14.11

Explain why alcohol **A** readily undergoes dehydration in the presence of acid, while alcohol **B** does not.

**A**          **B**

## 14.5B   Oxidation

Recall from Section 12.8 that to determine if an organic compound has been oxidized, we compare the relative number of C—H and C—O bonds in the starting material and product.

- **Oxidation results in an increase in the number of C—O bonds or a decrease in the number of C—H bonds.**

Thus, an organic compound like $CH_4$ can be oxidized by replacing C—H bonds with C—O bonds, as shown in Figure 14.3. When an alkane like $CH_4$ undergoes complete oxidation, as it does during combustion, all C—H bonds are converted to C—O bonds, forming $CO_2$. Organic chemists use the symbol [O] to indicate oxidation.

Alcohols can be oxidized to a variety of compounds, depending on the type of alcohol and the reagent. **Oxidation occurs by replacing the C—H bonds *on the carbon bearing the OH group* by C—O bonds.** All oxidation products from alcohol starting materials contain a **C=O, a carbonyl group.**

**Alcohol**          **Carbonyl compound**

A new C—O bond is formed.

Two bonds are broken.

A common reagent for alcohol oxidation is potassium dichromate, $K_2Cr_2O_7$, a red-orange solid. During oxidation the reagent is converted to a green $Cr^{3+}$ product. Thus, these oxidations are accompanied by a characteristic color change. Since a variety of reagents can be used, we will write oxidation with the general symbol for oxidation, [O].

**Figure 14.3**

A General Scheme for Oxidizing an Organic Compound

| 4 C—H bonds | 3 C—H bonds | 2 C—H bonds | 1 C—H bond | 0 C—H bonds |
| 0 C—O bonds | 1 C—O bond | 2 C—O bonds | 3 C—O bonds | 4 C—O bonds |

Increasing number of C—O bonds

- Primary (1°) alcohols are first oxidized to aldehydes (RCHO), which are further oxidized to carboxylic acids (RCOOH) by replacing one and then two C—H bonds by C—O bonds.

Thus, oxidation of one C—H bond of ethanol forms acetaldehyde. Since acetaldehyde still contains a hydrogen atom on the carbonyl carbon, converting this C—H bond to a C—O bond forms acetic acid, a carboxylic acid with three C—O bonds.

- Secondary (2°) alcohols are oxidized to ketones (R$_2$CO), by replacing one C—H bond by one C—O bond.

Since 2° alcohols have only one hydrogen atom bonded to the carbon with the OH group, they can be oxidized to only one type of compound, a ketone. Thus, 2-propanol is oxidized to acetone.

- Tertiary 3° alcohols have no H atoms on the carbon with the OH group, so they are not oxidized.

## SAMPLE PROBLEM 14.4

Draw the carbonyl products formed when each alcohol is oxidized with K$_2$Cr$_2$O$_7$.

a.

cyclohexanol

b. CH$_3$CH$_2$CH$_2$CH$_2$OH

1-butanol

### Analysis

Classify the alcohol as 1°, 2°, or 3° by drawing in all of the H atoms on the C with the OH. Then concentrate on the C with the OH group and replace H atoms by bonds to O. Keep in mind:

- $RCH_2OH$ (1° alcohols) are oxidized to RCHO, which are then oxidized to RCOOH.
- $R_2CHOH$ (2° alcohols) are oxidized to $R_2CO$.
- $R_3COH$ (3° alcohols) are not oxidized since they have no H atom on the C with the OH.

### Solution

a. Since cyclohexanol is a 2° alcohol with only one H atom on the C bonded to the OH group, it is oxidized to a ketone, cyclohexanone.

only 1 H atom

cyclohexanol  →[O]→  cyclohexanone
2° alcohol          ketone

b. 1-Butanol is a 1° alcohol with two H atoms on the C bonded to the OH group. Thus, it is first oxidized to an aldehyde and then to a carboxylic acid.

$CH_3CH_2CH_2$—C—H  →[O]→  butanal  →[O]→  butanoic acid

1-butanol              butanal              butanoic acid
1° alcohol             aldehyde             carboxylic acid

2 H atoms

### PROBLEM 14.12

What products are formed when each alcohol is oxidized with $K_2Cr_2O_7$? In some cases, no reaction occurs.

a. $CH_3CHCH_2CH_2CH_3$
   |
   OH

b. $(CH_3)_3CCH_2CH_2OH$

c. [cyclopentyl]—OH

d. [cyclohexyl with $CH_3$ and OH]

## 14.5C FOCUS ON THE HUMAN BODY
### Oxidation and Blood Alcohol Screening

Oxidations with chromium reagents are characterized by a color change, as the **red-orange chromium reagent** is reduced to a **green $Cr^{3+}$ product.** The first devices used to measure blood alcohol content in individuals suspected of "driving under the influence," made use of this color change. Oxidation of $CH_3CH_2OH$, the 1° alcohol in alcoholic beverages, with red-orange $K_2Cr_2O_7$ forms $CH_3COOH$ and green $Cr^{3+}$.

$CH_3CH_2$—OH  +  $K_2Cr_2O_7$ red-orange  ⟶  acetic acid  +  $Cr^{3+}$ green

ethanol
"alcohol"

acetic acid

Blood alcohol level can be determined by having an individual blow into a tube containing $K_2Cr_2O_7$ and an inert solid. The alcohol in the exhaled breath is oxidized by the chromium reagent, which turns green in the tube (Figure 14.4). The higher the concentration of $CH_3CH_2OH$ in the breath, the more chromium reagent is reduced, and the farther the green color extends down the length of the sample tube. This value is then correlated with blood alcohol content to determine if an individual has surpassed the legal blood alcohol limit.

Figure 14.4    Blood Alcohol Screening

- The oxidation of $CH_3CH_2OH$ with $K_2Cr_2O_7$ to form $CH_3COOH$ and $Cr^{3+}$ was the first available method for the routine testing of alcohol concentration in exhaled air. Some consumer products for alcohol screening are still based on this technology.

- A driver is considered "under the influence" in most states with a blood alcohol concentration of 0.08%.

## 14.6    FOCUS ON HEALTH & MEDICINE
### Ethanol, the Most Widely Abused Drug

Throughout history, humans have ingested alcoholic beverages for their pleasant taste and the feeling of euphoria they impart. Although we think of alcohol as a stimulant, largely because small amounts decrease social inhibitions, the ethanol ($CH_3CH_2OH$) in an alcoholic beverage actually depresses the central nervous system. The chronic and excessive consumption of alcoholic beverages has become a major health and social crisis, making ethanol the most widely abused drug in the United States. One estimate suggests that there are 40 times more alcoholics than heroin addicts.

### 14.6A    The Metabolism of Ethanol

When ethanol is consumed, it is quickly absorbed in the stomach and small intestines and then rapidly transported in the bloodstream to other organs. Ethanol is metabolized in the liver, by a two-step oxidation sequence. The body does not use chromium reagents as oxidants. Instead, high molecular weight enzymes, alcohol dehydrogenase and aldehyde dehydrogenase, and a small molecule called a **coenzyme** carry out these oxidations.

The products of the biological oxidation of ethanol are the same as the products formed in the laboratory. When ethanol ($CH_3CH_2OH$, a 1° alcohol) is ingested, it is oxidized in the liver first to $CH_3CHO$ (acetaldehyde), and then to $CH_3COOH$ (acetic acid).

$$CH_3CH_2-OH \xrightarrow[\text{alcohol dehydrogenase}]{[O]} \underset{\text{acetaldehyde}}{CH_3\overset{\displaystyle O}{\underset{}{C}}H} \xrightarrow[\text{aldehyde dehydrogenase}]{[O]} \underset{\text{acetic acid}}{CH_3\overset{\displaystyle O}{\underset{}{C}}OH}$$

ethanol

If more ethanol is ingested than can be metabolized in a given time period, the concentration of acetaldehyde accumulates. This toxic compound is responsible for the feelings associated with a hangover.

Antabuse

**Antabuse,** a drug given to alcoholics to prevent them from consuming alcoholic beverages, acts by interfering with the normal oxidation of ethanol. Antabuse inhibits the oxidation of acetaldehyde to acetic acid. Since the first step in ethanol metabolism occurs but the second does not, the concentration of acetaldehyde rises, causing an individual to become violently ill.

Methanol ($CH_3OH$, Section 14.4) is toxic because of these same oxidation reactions. Methanol is oxidized by enzymes to yield formaldehyde and formic acid. Both of these oxidation products are extremely toxic since they cannot be further metabolized by the body. As a result, the pH of the blood decreases, and blindness and death can follow.

$$CH_3-OH \xrightarrow[\text{alcohol dehydrogenase}]{[O]} \underset{\text{formaldehyde}}{\overset{O}{\underset{H}{\overset{\|}{C}}}\!\!H} \xrightarrow[\text{aldehyde dehydrogenase}]{[O]} \underset{\text{formic acid}}{\overset{O}{\underset{H}{\overset{\|}{C}}}\!\!OH}$$

methanol

Since the enzymes have a higher affinity for ethanol than methanol, methanol poisoning is treated by giving ethanol to an individual. With both methanol and ethanol in a patient's system, the enzymes react more readily with ethanol, allowing the methanol to be excreted unchanged without the formation of methanol's toxic oxidation products.

**PROBLEM 14.13**

Ethylene glycol, $HOCH_2CH_2OH$, is an extremely toxic diol because its oxidation products are also toxic. Draw the oxidation products formed during the metabolism of ethylene glycol.

## 14.6B  Health Effects of Alcohol Consumption

Alcohol consumption has both short-term and long-term effects. In small amounts it can cause dizziness, giddiness, and a decrease in social inhibitions. In larger amounts it decreases coordination and reaction time and causes drowsiness. Intoxicated individuals have exaggerated emotions, slurred speech, amnesia, and a lack of coordination. Coma and death can result at even higher concentrations.

Ethanol affects many organs. It dilates blood vessels, resulting in a flushed appearance. It increases urine production and stimulates the secretion of stomach acid. Chronic excessive alcohol consumption damages the heart and can lead to **cirrhosis of the liver,** an incurable and fatal disorder in which the liver is scarred and loses its ability to function.

The consumption of ethanol during pregnancy is not recommended. The liver of a fetus does not contain the enzymes to metabolize ethanol. As a result, any alcohol consumed by a pregnant woman crosses the placenta and can cause a variety of abnormalities. **Fetal alcohol syndrome** can result in infants of women who chronically consume alcohol during pregnancy. Infants with fetal alcohol syndrome are mentally retarded, grow poorly, and have certain facial abnormalities. Even modest alcohol consumption during pregnancy can negatively affect the fetus. Currently the American Medical Association recommends that a woman completely abstain from alcohol during pregnancy.

While alcohol use is socially acceptable, alcohol-related traffic fatalities are common with irresponsible alcohol consumption. In 2004, almost 40% of all fatalities in car crashes in the United States were alcohol related.

## 14.7   Structure and Properties of Ethers

*Ethers* **are organic compounds that have two alkyl groups bonded to an oxygen atom.** These two alkyl groups can be the same, or they can be different.

$$R-\ddot{O}-R \qquad CH_3CH_2-\ddot{O}-CH_2CH_3 \qquad CH_3-\ddot{O}-CH_2CH_3$$

ether                R groups are the **same.**            R groups are **different.**

The oxygen atom of an ether is surrounded by two carbon atoms and two lone pairs of electrons, giving it a **bent** shape like the oxygen in $H_2O$. The C—O—C bond angle is similar to the tetrahedral bond angle of 109.5°.

$$CH_3 \overset{\displaystyle \ddot{O}}{\diagup \diagdown} CH_3 \; = \;$$

dimethyl ether                    bent shape

The ether oxygen can be contained in a ring. **A ring that contains a heteroatom is called a heterocycle.** When the ether is part of a three-membered ring, the ether is called an *epoxide*.

$$H-\overset{\displaystyle \overset{\ddot{O}}{\diagup\diagdown}}{\underset{\displaystyle H}{C}}-\overset{\displaystyle C}{\underset{\displaystyle H}{}}-H \; = \;$$

epoxide                   a three-membered ring
with an ether O atom

Many compounds that contain ether heterocycles are naturally occurring. **Disparlure,** the sex pheromone of the female gypsy moth, is an epoxide used to control the spread of the gypsy moth caterpillar. This pest has periodically devastated the forests of the northeastern United States by eating the leaves of many shade and fruit-bearing trees. **Hemibrevetoxin B,** a complex neurotoxin with four ether oxygens, is produced by algal blooms referred to as "red tides," because of the color of the ocean waters when these algae proliferate.

$$(CH_3)_2CHCH_2CH_2CH_2CH_2-\overset{\displaystyle \overset{\ddot{O}}{\diagup\diagdown}}{\underset{\displaystyle H}{C}}-\overset{\displaystyle C}{\underset{\displaystyle H}{}}-(CH_2)_9CH_3$$

disparlure

hemibrevetoxin B

[Cyclic ethers are labeled in red.]

## PROBLEM 14.14

Draw the structure of the three constitutional isomers of molecular formula $C_4H_{10}O$ that contain an ether.

## 14.7A Physical Properties

Because oxygen is more electronegative than carbon, the C—O bonds of an ether are both polar. Since an ether contains two polar bonds and a bent shape, it has a **net dipole.** In this way, ethers resemble alcohols.

Ethers do not contain a hydrogen atom bonded to oxygen, so unlike alcohols, two ether molecules *cannot* intermolecularly hydrogen bond to each other. **This gives ethers stronger intermolecular forces than alkanes but weaker intermolecular forces than alcohols.** As a result:

- Ethers have higher melting points and boiling points than hydrocarbons of comparable size and shape.
- Ethers have lower melting points and boiling points than alcohols of comparable size and shape.

| $CH_3CH_2CH_2CH_3$ | $CH_3OCH_2CH_3$ | $CH_3CH_2CH_2OH$ |
|---|---|---|
| butane | ethyl methyl ether | 1-propanol |
| boiling point −0.5 °C | boiling point 11 °C | boiling point 97 °C |

Increasing boiling point →

All ethers are soluble in organic solvents. Like alcohols, **low molecular weight ethers are water soluble,** because the oxygen atom of the ether can hydrogen bond to one of the hydrogens of water. When the alkyl groups of the ether have more than a total of five carbons, the nonpolar portion of the molecule is too large, so the ether is water insoluble.

## SAMPLE PROBLEM 14.5

Rank the following compounds in order of increasing boiling point:

### Analysis

Look at the functional groups to determine the strength of the intermolecular forces—**the stronger the forces, the higher the boiling point.**

### Solution

**B** is an alkane with nonpolar C—C and C—H bonds, so it has the weakest intermolecular forces and therefore the lowest boiling point. **C** is an alcohol capable of intermolecular hydrogen bonding, so it has the strongest intermolecular forces and the highest boiling point. **A** is an ether, so it contains a net dipole but is incapable of intermolecular hydrogen bonding. **A,** therefore, has intermolecular forces of intermediate strength and has a boiling point between the boiling points of **B** and **C.**

**B**                    **A**                    **C**

Increasing intermolecular forces
Increasing boiling point

## PROBLEM 14.15

Which compound in each pair has the higher boiling point?

a. $CH_3(CH_2)_6CH_3$  or  $CH_3(CH_2)_5OCH_3$

c. $CH_3(CH_2)_6OH$   or   $CH_3(CH_2)_5OCH_3$

b. [hexane ring] or [oxane ring with O]

d. $CH_3(CH_2)_5OCH_3$  or  $CH_3OCH_3$

## PROBLEM 14.16

Label each ether as water soluble or water insoluble.

a. $CH_3CH_2-O-CH_3$     b. [cyclohexyl-O-cyclohexyl]     c. [decalin with $OCH_3$]

## 14.7B   Naming Ethers

**Simple ethers** are usually assigned common names. To do so, **name both alkyl groups** bonded to the oxygen, arrange these names alphabetically, and add the word **ether.** For ethers with identical alkyl groups, name the alkyl group and add the prefix **di-.**

$CH_3-O-CH_2CH_3$                    $CH_3CH_2-O-CH_2CH_3$

methyl     ethyl                    ethyl          ethyl

**ethyl methyl ether**                    **diethyl ether**

**More complex ethers** are named using the IUPAC system. One alkyl group is named as a hydrocarbon chain, and the other is named as part of a substituent bonded to that chain.

- Name the simpler alkyl group + O atom as an alkoxy substituent by changing the *-yl* ending of the alkyl group to *-oxy.*

$CH_3O-$          $CH_3CH_2O-$

methoxy          ethoxy

- Name the remaining alkyl group as an alkane, with the alkoxy group as a substituent bonded to this chain.

## SAMPLE PROBLEM 14.6

Give the IUPAC name for the following ether.

### Analysis and Solution

| [1] Name the longer chain as an alkane and the shorter chain as an alkoxy group. | [2] Apply other nomenclature rules to complete the name. |
|---|---|
| CH₃CH₂CH₂CH₂CHCH₂CH₂CH₃<br>ethoxy group — OCH₂CH₃<br><br>8 C's ----→ octane | $\overset{4}{}$ $\overset{1}{}$<br>CH₃CH₂CH₂CH₂CHCH₂CH₂CH₃<br>OCH₂CH₃<br><br>**Answer: 4-ethoxyoctane** |

### PROBLEM 14.17

Name each ether.

a. CH₃—O—CH₂CH₂CH₂CH₃

b.  OCH₃

c. CH₃CH₂CH₂—O—CH₂CH₂CH₃

### PROBLEM 14.18

Draw the structure corresponding to each name.

a. dibutyl ether  
b. ethyl propyl ether

c. 1-methoxypentane  
d. 3-ethoxyhexane

## 14.8 FOCUS ON HEALTH & MEDICINE
### Ethers as Anesthetics

diethyl ether

This painting by Robert Hinckley depicts a public demonstration of the use of diethyl ether as an anesthetic at the Massachusetts General Hospital in Boston, MA in the 1840s.

A general anesthetic is a drug that interferes with nerve transmission in the brain, resulting in a loss of consciousness and the sensation of pain. The discovery that **diethyl ether** (CH₃CH₂OCH₂CH₃) is a general anesthetic revolutionized surgery in the nineteenth century. Early experiments performed by a dentist, Dr. William Morton, resulted in a public demonstration of diethyl ether as an anesthetic in Boston in 1846. Diethyl ether quickly supplanted the crude methods then used for a patient to tolerate the excruciating pain of surgery—making an individual unconscious by excess alcohol intake or by striking a blow to the head.

Diethyl ether is an imperfect anesthetic, but considering the alternatives in the nineteenth century, it was considered revolutionary. It is safe and easy to administer with low patient mortality, but it is highly flammable, and it causes nausea in many patients.

For these reasons, alternatives to diethyl ether are now widely used. Many of these newer general anesthetics, which cause little patient discomfort, are also ethers. These include isoflurane, enflurane, and methoxyflurane. Replacing some of the hydrogen atoms in the ether by halogens results in compounds with similar anesthetic properties but decreased flammability.

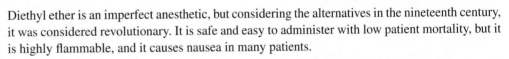

isoflurane (Trade name: Forane)    enflurane (Trade name: Ethrane)    methoxyflurane (Trade name: Penthrane)

### PROBLEM 14.19

Halothane (CF₃CHClBr) is a general anesthetic that is not an ether. Draw a three-dimensional structure for halothane using solid lines, wedges, and dashes (see Section 11.3).

## 14.9  Alkyl Halides

Alkyl halides have the general molecular formula $C_nH_{2n+1}X$, and are formally derived from an alkane by replacing a hydrogen atom with a halogen.

*Alkyl halides* **are organic molecules containing a halogen atom X (X = F, Cl, Br, I) bonded to a tetrahedral carbon atom.** Alkyl halides are classified as **primary (1°), secondary (2°),** or **tertiary (3°)** depending on the number of carbons bonded to the carbon with the halogen.

| Alkyl halide | Classification of alkyl halides | | |
|---|---|---|---|

- A primary (1°) alkyl halide has a halogen on a carbon bonded to one carbon.
- A secondary (2°) alkyl halide has a halogen on a carbon bonded to two carbons.
- A tertiary (3°) alkyl halide has a halogen on a carbon bonded to three carbons.

### PROBLEM 14.20

Classify each alkyl halide as 1°, 2°, or 3°.

a.  $CH_3CH_2CH_2CH_2CH_2—Br$

b.  (cyclohexane with $CH_3$ and $F$)

c.  $CH_3—\overset{\overset{CH_3}{|}}{\underset{\underset{CH_3}{|}}{C}}—\overset{}{\underset{\underset{Cl}{|}}{C}}HCH_3$

### PROBLEM 14.21

Dexamethasone is a halogen-containing steroid used to treat inflammation in rheumatoid arthritis and other conditions. (a) Classify the alkyl halide in dexamethasone as 1°, 2°, or 3°. (b) Classify the hydroxyl groups as 1°, 2°, or 3°.

dexamethasone

NDC 0054-4184-25   100 Tablets
DEXAMETHASONE
Tablets, USP
4 mg
Each tablet contains
4 mg dexamethasone.
$R_x$ only
Boehringer Ingelheim
Roxane Laboratories

Dexamethasone relieves inflammation and is used to treat some forms of arthritis, skin conditions, and asthma.

### 14.9A  Physical Properties

**Alkyl halides contain a polar C—X bond,** but since they have all of their hydrogens bonded to carbon, they are incapable of intermolecular hydrogen bonding. Alkyl halides with one halogen are polar molecules, therefore, because they contain a net dipole. As a result, they have higher melting points and boiling points than alkanes with the same number of carbons.

The size of the alkyl groups and the halogen also affects the physical properties of an alkyl halide.

- The boiling point and melting point of an alkyl halide increase with the size of the alkyl group because of increased surface area.
- The boiling point and melting point of an alkyl halide increase with the size of the halogen.

Thus, $CH_3CH_2CH_2Cl$ has a higher boiling point than $CH_3CH_2Cl$ because it has one more carbon, giving it a larger surface area. $CH_3CH_2CH_2Br$ has a higher boiling point than $CH_3CH_2CH_2Cl$ because Br is further down the column of the periodic table, making it larger than Cl.

| $CH_3CH_2Cl$ | $CH_3CH_2CH_2Cl$ | $CH_3CH_2CH_2Br$ |
|---|---|---|
| chloroethane | 1-chloropropane | 1-bromopropane |
| bp = 12 °C | bp = 47 °C | bp = 71 °C |

Increasing boiling point
Increasing size of the alkyl group
Increasing size of the halogen

Since alkyl halides are incapable of hydrogen bonding, they are insoluble in water regardless of size.

---

**PROBLEM 14.22**

Rank the compounds in each group in order of increasing boiling point.

a. $CH_3CH_2CH_2I$, $CH_3CH_2CH_2Cl$, $CH_3CH_2CH_2F$
b. $CH_3(CH_2)_4CH_3$, $CH_3(CH_2)_5Br$, $CH_3(CH_2)_5Cl$

---

## 14.9B Nomenclature

In the IUPAC system, an alkyl halide is named as an alkane with a halogen substituent—that is, as a *halo alkane.* To name a halogen substituent, change the *-ine* ending of the name of the halogen to the suffix *-o* (e.g., chlor*ine* → chlor*o*).

---

*How To* **Name an Alkyl Halide Using the IUPAC System**

**Example:** Give the IUPAC name of the following alkyl halide.

$$\underset{\text{CH}_3\text{CH}_2\overset{\displaystyle |}{\underset{\displaystyle}{\text{CH}}}\text{CH}_2\text{CH}_2\overset{\displaystyle |}{\underset{\displaystyle}{\text{CH}}}\text{CH}_3}{\overset{\text{CH}_3 \qquad\quad \text{Cl}}{}}$$

**Step [1]** **Find the parent carbon chain containing the halogen.**

7 C's in the longest chain

**7 C's – – – → heptane**

• Name the parent chain as an *alkane,* with the halogen as a substituent bonded to the longest chain.

**Step [2]** **Apply all other rules of nomenclature.**

a. **Number** the chain.

$$\text{CH}_3\text{CH}_2\text{CHCH}_2\text{CH}_2\text{CHCH}_3$$
7  6  5  4  3  2  1

• Begin at the end nearest the first substituent, either alkyl or halogen.

b. **Name** and **number** the substituents.

methyl at C5 — chloro at C2

7  6  5  4  3  2  1

c. Alphabetize: *c* for **c**hloro, then *m* for **m**ethyl.

**ANSWER: 2-chloro-5-methylheptane**

Common names for alkyl halides are used only for simple alkyl halides. To assign a common name, name the carbon atoms as an alkyl group. Then name the halogen by changing the *-ine* ending of the halogen name to the suffix *-ide;* for example, **brom*ine*** → **brom*ide*.**

$$CH_3CH_2-Cl \quad chlor\underline{ine} \longrightarrow chlor\underline{ide}$$

ethyl group

Common name: **ethyl chloride**

### PROBLEM 14.23

Give the IUPAC name for each compound.

a.  $CH_3CHCH_2CH_2CH_2CH_3$
         |
         Br

b.  $(CH_3)_2CHCHCH_2CH_3$
              |
              Cl

c.

### PROBLEM 14.24

Give the structure corresponding to each name.

a. 3-chloro-2-methylhexane

b. 4-ethyl-5-iodo-2,2-dimethyloctane

c. 1,1,3-tribromocyclohexane

d. propyl chloride

## 14.9C   Interesting Alkyl Halides

Many simple alkyl halides make excellent solvents because they are not flammable and they dissolve a wide variety of organic compounds. Two compounds in this category include $CHCl_3$ (chloroform or trichloromethane) and $CCl_4$ (carbon tetrachloride or tetrachloromethane). Large quantities of these solvents are produced industrially each year, but like many chlorinated organic compounds, both chloroform and carbon tetrachloride are toxic if inhaled or ingested. Two other simple alkyl halides are given in Figure 14.5.

**Figure 14.5**   Two Simple Alkyl Halides

$CH_3Cl$

- **Chloromethane ($CH_3Cl$)** is produced by giant kelp and algae and is also found in emissions from volcanoes such as Hawaii's Kilauea. Almost all of the atmospheric chloromethane results from these natural sources.

$CH_2Cl_2$

- **Dichloromethane (or methylene chloride, $CH_2Cl_2$)** is an important solvent, once used to decaffeinate coffee. Coffee is now decaffeinated using liquid $CO_2$ due to concerns over the possible ill effects of trace amounts of residual $CH_2Cl_2$ in the coffee. Subsequent studies on rats have shown, however, that no cancers occurred when animals ingested the equivalent of over 100,000 cups of decaffeinated coffee per day.

## 14.9D   FOCUS ON THE ENVIRONMENT
### Alkyl Halides and the Ozone Layer

While the beneficial effects of many organic halides are undisputed, certain synthetic chlorinated organics, such as the **chlorofluorocarbons,** have caused lasting harm to the environment. **Chlorofluorocarbons (CFCs)** are simple halogen-containing compounds having the general molecular structure $CF_xCl_{4-x}$. CFCs are manufactured under the trade name Freons. Two examples are $CFCl_3$ (Freon 11) and $CF_2Cl_2$ (Freon 12).

The 1995 Nobel Prize in Chemistry was awarded to Professors Mario Molina, Paul Crutzen, and F. Sherwood Rowland for their work in elucidating the interaction of ozone with CFCs. What began as a very fundamental research project turned out to have important implications in the practical world.

### ENVIRONMENTAL NOTE

Propane and butane are now used as propellants in spray cans in place of CFCs.

### ENVIRONMENTAL NOTE

$O_3$ destruction is most severe in the region of the South Pole, where a large ozone hole (shown in purple) is visible with satellite imaging.

**Figure 14.6** CFCs and Ozone Destruction

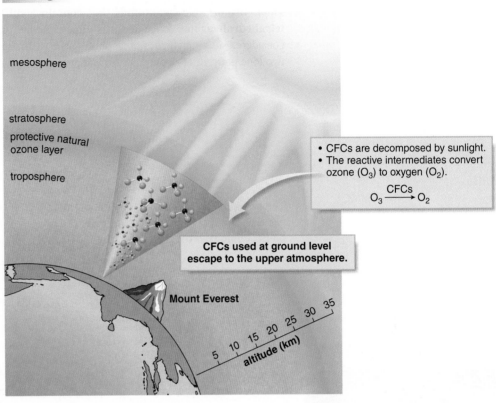

mesosphere

stratosphere

protective natural ozone layer

troposphere

- CFCs are decomposed by sunlight.
- The reactive intermediates convert ozone ($O_3$) to oxygen ($O_2$).

$$O_3 \xrightarrow{\text{CFCs}} O_2$$

**CFCs used at ground level escape to the upper atmosphere.**

**Mount Everest**

5  10  15  20  25  30  35
**altitude (km)**

CFCs are inert and nontoxic, and they have been used as refrigerants, solvents, and aerosol propellants. Because CFCs have low boiling points and are water insoluble, they readily escape into the upper atmosphere. There, CFCs are decomposed by sunlight. This process forms highly reactive intermediates that have been shown to destroy the ozone layer (Figure 14.6).

The ozone ($O_3$) in the upper atmosphere is vital to life: it acts as a shield, protecting the earth's surface from destructive ultraviolet radiation. A decrease in ozone concentration in this protective layer will have some immediate consequences, including an increase in the incidence of skin cancer and eye cataracts. Other long-term effects include a reduced immune response, interference with photosynthesis in plants, and harmful effects on the growth of plankton, the mainstay of the ocean food chain.

These findings led to a ban on the use of CFCs in aerosol propellants in the United States in 1978 and to the phasing out of their use in refrigeration systems. While it is now easy to second-guess the extensive use of CFCs, it is also easy to see why they were used so widely. **CFCs made refrigeration available to the general public.** Would you call your refrigerator a comfort or a necessity?

There are two newer alternatives to CFCs. **Hydrochlorofluorocarbons (HCFCs)** such as $CF_3CHCl_2$ contain the elements of H, Cl, and F bonded to carbon, and **hydrofluorocarbons (HFCs)** such as $FCH_2CF_3$ contain the elements of H and F bonded to carbon. These compounds have many properties in common with CFCs, but they are decomposed more readily before they reach the upper atmosphere, so they are less destructive to the $O_3$ layer.

### PROBLEM 14.25

Classify each compound as a CFC, HCFC, or HFC: (a) $CF_3Cl$; (b) $CHFCl_2$; (c) $CH_2F_2$.

## 14.10 Organic Compounds That Contain Sulfur

*Thiols* **are organic compounds that contain a sulfhydryl group (SH group) bonded to a tetrahedral carbon.** Since sulfur is directly below oxygen in the periodic table, thiols can be considered sulfur analogues of alcohols. Because the sulfur atom is surrounded by two atoms and two lone pairs, thiols have a bent shape around sulfur.

**Thiol**

$$-\overset{|}{\underset{|}{C}}-\overset{..}{\underset{..}{S}}-H \qquad \qquad CH_3CH_2-\overset{..}{\underset{..}{S}}-H \quad =$$

sulfhydryl
group

ethanethiol

bent shape around S

Thiols differ from alcohols in one important way. They contain no O—H bonds, so they are incapable of intermolecular hydrogen bonding. **This gives thiols lower boiling points and melting points compared to alcohols having the same size and shape.**

| Hydrogen bonding can occur. stronger intermolecular forces **higher boiling point** | $CH_3CH_2$—OH | $CH_3CH_2$—SH | Hydrogen bonding is impossible. weaker intermolecular forces **lower boiling point** |
|---|---|---|---|
| | ethanol | ethanethiol | |
| | bp 78 °C | bp 35 °C | |

To name a thiol in the IUPAC system:

- **Name the parent hydrocarbon as an alkane and add the suffix *-thiol.***
- **Number the carbon chain to give the SH group the lower number.**

1-Propanethiol ($CH_3CH_2CH_2SH$) is partly responsible for the characteristic odor of onions.

$$CH_3-SH \qquad CH_3CH_2CH_2-SH \qquad \overset{\displaystyle CH_3}{\underset{\underset{3}{\uparrow}\quad\underset{1}{\uparrow}}{CH_3CHCH_2CH_2-SH}}$$

Begin numbering at this C.

methanethiol        1-propanethiol        3-methyl-1-butanethiol

### SAMPLE PROBLEM 14.7

Give the IUPAC name for the following thiol.

$$\underset{CH_3CH_2CHCH_2CH_2CH_2CHCH_3}{\overset{CH_2CH_3 \qquad\qquad SH}{\phantom{x}}}$$

### Analysis and Solution

**[1] Find the longest carbon chain that contains the carbon bonded to the SH group.**

8 C's in the longest chain - - - → octane

- Name the alkane and add the suffix *-thiol*: **octanethiol.**

**[2] Number the carbon chain to give the SH group the lower number and apply all other rules of nomenclature.**

a. **Number** the chain.

$$\underset{\underset{8}{\uparrow}\quad\underset{6}{\uparrow}\qquad\quad\underset{2}{\uparrow}\,\underset{1}{\uparrow}}{\overset{CH_2CH_3 \qquad\qquad SH}{CH_3CH_2CHCH_2CH_2CH_2CHCH_3}}$$

- Number to put the SH at C2, not C7.

2-octanethiol

b. **Name** and **number** the substituents.

ethyl group at C6

**Answer: 6-ethyl-2-octanethiol**

### PROBLEM 14.26

Give the IUPAC name for each thiol.

a. CH₃CH₂CHCH₂CH₃
        |
        SH

b. [cyclohexane with SH group]

c. (CH₃CH₂)₂CHCH₂CH₂CH₂CH₂SH

### PROBLEM 14.27

Skunk odor contains *trans*-2-butene-1-thiol. Draw the structure of this thiol.

The most obvious physical property of thiols is their distinctive foul odor. For example, 3-methyl-1-butanethiol [(CH₃)₂CHCH₂CH₂SH] is one of the main components of the defensive spray of skunks.

Thiols undergo one important reaction: **thiols are oxidized to disulfides,** compounds that contain a sulfur–sulfur bond. This is an oxidation reaction because two hydrogen atoms are removed in forming the disulfide.

**Oxidation**     2 CH₃CH₂—S—H  $\xrightarrow{[O]}$  CH₃CH₂—S—S—CH₂CH₃     ⌐new S—S bond

                      thiol                          disulfide

Disulfides can also be converted back to thiols with a reducing agent. The symbol for a general reducing agent is **[H],** since hydrogen atoms are often added to a molecule during reduction.

**Reduction**     CH₃CH₂—S—S—CH₂CH₃  $\xrightarrow{[H]}$  2 CH₃CH₂—S—H     ⌐new S—H bond

                      disulfide                          thiol

The chemistry of thiols and disulfides plays an important role in determining the properties and shape of some proteins, as we will learn in Chapter 21. For example, α-keratin, the protein in hair, contains many disulfide bonds. Straight hair can be made curly by cleaving the disulfide bonds in α-keratin, then rearranging and re-forming them, as shown schematically in Figure 14.7.

First, the disulfide bonds in the straight hair are reduced to thiol groups, so the bundles of α-keratin chains are no longer held in their specific "straight" orientation. Then, the hair is wrapped around

**Figure 14.7**     Focus on the Human Body: Making Straight Hair Curly

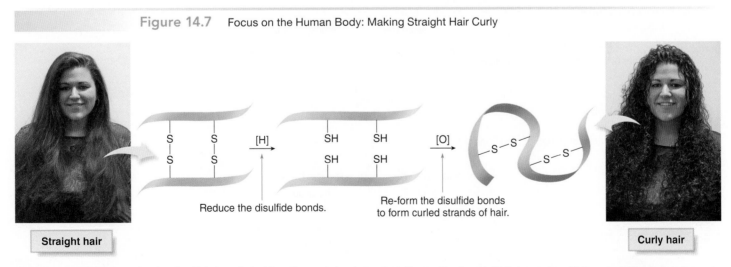

To make straight hair curly, the disulfide bonds holding the protein chains together are reduced. This forms free SH groups. The hair is turned around curlers and then an oxidizing agent is applied. This re-forms the disulfide bonds to the hair, now giving it a curly appearance.

curlers and treated with an oxidizing agent that converts the thiol groups back to disulfide bonds, now with twists and turns in the keratin backbone. This makes the hair look curly and is the chemical basis for a "permanent."

### PROBLEM 14.28

(a) Draw the disulfide formed when $CH_3CH_2CH_2SH$ is oxidized. (b) Draw the product formed when the following disulfide is reduced: $CH_3CH_2CH_2CH_2SSCH_2CH_3$.

# CHAPTER HIGHLIGHTS

## KEY TERMS

Alcohol (14.1)

Alkoxy group (14.7)

Alkyl halide (14.1)

Carbonyl group (14.5)

Chlorofluorocarbon (14.9)

Coenzyme (14.6)

Dehydration (14.5)

Diol (14.3)

Disulfide (14.10)

Elimination (14.5)

Epoxide (14.7)

Ether (14.1)

Glycol (14.3)

Heterocycle (14.7)

Hydrochlorofluorocarbon (14.9)

Hydrofluorocarbon (14.9)

Hydroxyl group (14.1)

Oxidation (14.5)

Primary (1°) alcohol (14.2)

Primary (1°) alkyl halide (14.9)

Secondary (2°) alcohol (14.2)

Secondary (2°) alkyl halide (14.9)

Sulfhydryl group (14.1)

Tertiary (3°) alcohol (14.2)

Tertiary (3°) alkyl halide (14.9)

Thiol (14.1)

Triol (14.3)

Zaitsev rule (14.5)

## KEY REACTIONS

[1] Dehydration of alcohols (14.5A)

$$-\overset{|}{\underset{H}{C}}-\overset{|}{\underset{OH}{C}}- \xrightarrow{H_2SO_4} \enspace \diagdown C=C\diagup \enspace + \enspace H_2O$$

[2] Oxidation of alcohols (14.5B)

  a. Primary (1°) alcohols    $RCH_2OH \xrightarrow{[O]} RCHO \xrightarrow{[O]} RCOOH$
                                     aldehyde     carboxylic acid

  b. Secondary (2°) alcohols  $R_2CHOH \xrightarrow{[O]} R_2CO$
                                         ketone

  c. Tertiary (3°) alcohols    $R_3COH \xrightarrow{[O]}$ No reaction

[3] Oxidation of thiols and reduction of disulfides (14.10)

$$2\ R-S-H \underset{[H]}{\overset{[O]}{\rightleftharpoons}} R-S-S-R$$
$$\text{thiol} \qquad\qquad\qquad \text{disulfide}$$

# KEY CONCEPTS

**❶ What are the characteristics of alcohols, ethers, alkyl halides, and thiols?**

- Alcohols contain a hydroxyl group (OH group) bonded to a tetrahedral carbon. Since the O atom is surrounded by two atoms and two lone pairs, alcohols have a bent shape around O. (14.2)
- Ethers have two alkyl groups bonded to an oxygen atom. Since the O atom is surrounded by two atoms and two lone pairs, ethers have a bent shape around O. (14.7)
- Alkyl halides contain a halogen atom (X = F, Cl, Br, I) singly bonded to a tetrahedral carbon. (14.9)
- Thiols contain a sulfhydryl group (SH group) bonded to a tetrahedral carbon. Since the S atom is surrounded by two atoms and two lone pairs, thiols have a bent shape around S. (14.10)

**❷ How are alcohols and alkyl halides classified?**

- Alcohols and alkyl halides are classified by the number of C's bonded to the C with the functional group.
- $RCH_2OH$ = 1° alcohol; $R_2CHOH$ = 2° alcohol; $R_3COH$ = 3° alcohol. (14.2)
- $RCH_2X$ = 1° alkyl halide; $R_2CHX$ = 2° alkyl halide; $R_3CX$ = 3° alkyl halide. (14.9)

**❸ What are the properties of alcohols, ethers, alkyl halides, and thiols?**

- Alcohols have a bent shape and polar C—O and O—H bonds, so they have a net dipole. Their OH bond allows for intermolecular hydrogen bonding between two alcohol molecules or between an alcohol molecule and water. As a result, alcohols have the strongest intermolecular forces of the four families of molecules in this chapter. (14.2)
- Ethers have a bent shape and two polar C—O bonds, so they have a net dipole. (14.7)

- Alkyl halides with one halogen have one polar bond and a net dipole. (14.9)
- Thiols have a bent shape and lower boiling points than alcohols with the same number of carbons. (14.10)

**❹ How are alcohols, ethers, alkyl halides, and thiols named?**

- Alcohols are identified by the suffix -ol. (14.3)
- Ethers are named in two ways. Simple ethers are named by naming the alkyl groups bonded to the ether oxygen and adding the word *ether.* More complex ethers are named as *alkoxy alkanes;* that is, the simpler alkyl group is named as an alkoxy group (RO) bonded to an alkane. (14.7B)
- Alkyl halides are named as *halo alkanes;* that is, the halogen is named as a substituent (halo group) bonded to an alkane. (14.9B)
- Thiols are identified by the suffix -thiol. (14.10)

**❺ What products are formed when an alcohol undergoes dehydration? (14.5A)**

- Alcohols form alkenes on treatment with strong acid. The elements of H and OH are lost from two adjacent atoms and a new double bond is formed.
- Dehydration follows the Zaitsev rule: When more than one alkene can be formed, the major product of elimination is the alkene that has more alkyl groups bonded to it.

**❻ What products are formed when an alcohol is oxidized? (14.5B)**

- Primary alcohols ($RCH_2OH$) are oxidized to aldehydes (RCHO), which are further oxidized to carboxylic acids ($RCO_2H$).
- Secondary alcohols ($R_2CHOH$) are oxidized to ketones.
- Tertiary alcohols have no C—H bond on the carbon with the OH group, so they are not oxidized.

**❼ What product is formed when a thiol is oxidized? (14.10)**

- Thiols (RSH) are oxidized to disulfides (RSSR).
- Disulfides are reduced to thiols.

# PROBLEMS

Selected in-chapter and odd-numbered end-of-chapter problems have brief answers in Appendix B. The *Student Study Guide and Solutions Manual* contains detailed solutions to all in-chapter and odd-numbered end-of-chapter problems, as well as additional worked examples and a chapter self-test.

## Alcohols, Ethers, Alkyl Halides, and Thiols

**14.29** Classify each alcohol as 1°, 2°, or 3°.

a. $CH_3CH_2CH_2OH$

b. $(CH_3CH_2)_3COH$

c.

d. $CH_3CH_2CHCHCH_3$ with $CH_3$ substituent

**14.30** Classify each alcohol as 1°, 2°, or 3°.

a.

b. $(CH_3)_3CCH_2CH_2OH$

c. $CH_3CH_2CH_2CHOH$ with $CH_3$ substituent

d. $CH_3CH_2CH_2CCH_2OH$ with two $CH_3$ substituents

**14.31** Classify each alkyl halide as 1°, 2°, or 3°.

a. $CH_3(CH_2)_5CHCH_3$ with Cl substituent

b. $CH_3CH_2CCH_2CH_3$ with $CH_3$ and Cl substituents

c.

d. $CH_3CH_2—C—CH_2Br$ with two $CH_3$ substituents

**14.32** Classify each halide in **A** as 1°, 2°, or 3°. **A** is a component of the red seaweed *C. hornemanni* found in Sri Lanka.

$$CH_3 \quad\quad CH_2Br$$
$$CH_3C{=}CHCH_2CH_2CCH{=}CH_2$$
$$\mathbf{A} \quad\quad Cl$$

**14.33** Draw the structure of a molecule that fits each description:
   a. a 2° alcohol of molecular formula $C_6H_{14}O$
   b. an ether with molecular formula $C_6H_{14}O$ that has a methyl group bonded to oxygen
   c. a 3° alkyl halide with molecular formula $C_5H_{11}Br$

**14.34** Draw the structure of a molecule that fits each description:
   a. a 2° alcohol of molecular formula $C_6H_{12}O$
   b. a cyclic ether with molecular formula $C_5H_{10}O$
   c. a 1° alkyl halide with molecular formula $C_5H_{11}Cl$

**14.35** Draw the structure of the six constitutional isomers of molecular formula $C_5H_{12}O$ that contain an ether as functional group.

**14.36** Draw the structure of the four constitutional isomers of molecular formula $C_3H_6Br_2$.

## Nomenclature

**14.37** Name each molecule depicted in the ball-and-stick models.

a.

b.

**14.38** Name each molecule depicted in the ball-and-stick models.

a.

b.

**14.39** Answer each question about alcohol **A**.

**A**

   a. Draw a condensed or skeletal structure for **A**.
   b. Classify the hydroxyl group as 1°, 2°, or 3°.
   c. Give the IUPAC name for **A**.

**14.40** Answer each question about alcohol **B**.

**B**

   a. Draw a skeletal structure for **B**.
   b. Classify the hydroxyl group as 1°, 2°, or 3°.
   c. Give the IUPAC name for **B**.

**14.41** Give the IUPAC name for each alcohol.

$$OH$$
a. $CH_3CHCH_2CH_2CH_3$

$$HO \quad CH_3$$
b. $CH_3CHCCH_2CH_2CH_3$
$$CH_3$$

c. $(CH_3)_2CHCH_2CHCH_2CH_3$
$$CH_2CH_2CH_2OH$$

d.
$$CH_2CH_2CH_2CH_3$$

$$OH$$
e.
$$CH_3$$
$$CH_3$$

$$OH$$
f. $CH_3CH_2$  $CH_2CH_3$

**14.42** Give the IUPAC name for each alcohol.

a. $CH_3CH_2CHCH_2CH_2CH(CH_3)_2$
$$OH$$

$$CH_2OH$$
b. $CH_3CH_2CH_2CHCH_2CH_3$

c. $CH_3(CH_2)_3CHCH_3$
$$CH_2CH_2OH$$

$$OH$$
d. $HOCH_2CHCH_2OH$

$$OH \,\, CH_2CH_3$$
e.
$$CH_3$$

$$HO \quad\quad CH_3$$
f.
$$CH_3$$

**14.43** Give the structure corresponding to each IUPAC name.
   a. 3-hexanol            d. 1,2-butanediol
   b. propyl alcohol       e. 4,4,5-trimethyl-3-heptanol
   c. 2-methylcyclopropanol  f. 3,5-dimethyl-1-heptanol

**14.44** Give the structure corresponding to each IUPAC name.
   a. 3-methyl-3-pentanol          d. 1,3-propanediol
   b. 4-methyl-2-pentanol          e. 3,5-dimethylcyclohexanol
   c. 2,4-dimethyl-2-hexanol       f. 6,6-diethyl-4-nonanol

**14.45** Give an acceptable name (IUPAC or common) for each ether.

   a. $CH_3CH_2OCH_2CH_2CH_2CH_3$         c. [cyclopentyl]—$OCH_2CH_3$

   b. $CH_3CH_2CH_2\overset{\displaystyle OCH_2CH_3}{\underset{\displaystyle |}{CH}}CH_3$

**14.46** Give an acceptable name (IUPAC or common) for each ether.

   a. $CH_3OCH_2CH_2CH_3$                 c. [cyclopropyl]—$OCH_3$

   b. $CH_3O\overset{\displaystyle CH_3}{\underset{\displaystyle |}{CH}}CH_2CH_3$

**14.47** MTBE [$CH_3OC(CH_3)_3$] is a high-octane gasoline additive that has the common name *tert*-butyl methyl ether. What is its IUPAC name?

**14.48** What is the IUPAC name for diethyl ether?

**14.49** Draw the structures and give the IUPAC names for all constitutional isomers of molecular formula $C_7H_{16}O$ that contain an OH group and have seven carbons in the longest chain.

**14.50** Draw structures for the four constitutional isomers of molecular formula $C_4H_{10}O$ that contain an OH group. Give the IUPAC name for each alcohol.

**14.51** Give the IUPAC name for each alkyl halide and thiol.
   a. $(CH_3CH_2CH_2)_2CHBr$         c. $CH_3CH_2CH_2CH_2CH_2SH$

   b.

**14.52** Give the IUPAC name for each alkyl halide and thiol.

   a. $CH_3CH_2\overset{\displaystyle F}{\underset{\displaystyle |}{CH}}CH_2\overset{\displaystyle CH_2CH_3}{\underset{\displaystyle |}{CH}}(CH_2)_4CH_3$         c. $(CH_3)_2CHSH$

   b. [cyclopentane with CH₃CH₂ and Cl substituents]

**14.53** Give the structure corresponding to each IUPAC name.
   a. 2-methoxypropane
   b. cyclobutyl ethyl ether
   c. 1-ethoxy-2-ethylcyclohexane
   d. butyl chloride
   e. 2-methylcyclohexanethiol
   f. 1-ethyl-2-fluorocyclobutane

**14.54** Give the structure corresponding to each IUPAC name.
   a. dicyclohexyl ether
   b. 2-ethoxy-2-methylpropane
   c. propyl iodide
   d. 3-methyl-1-pentanethiol
   e. 1-chloro-2-methylpropane
   f. 2-bromo-3-methylheptane

## Physical Properties

**14.55** Which compound in each pair has the higher boiling point?
   a. $CH_3CH_2CH_2Cl$ or $CH_3CH_2CH_2I$
   b. $CH_3CH_2CH_2OH$ or $HOCH_2CH_2OH$
   c. $CH_3CH_2CH_2OH$ or $CH_3CH_2CH_2F$

**14.56** Rank the compounds in each group in order of increasing boiling point.
   a. $CH_3CH_2OCH_2CH_3$, $CH_3(CH_2)_3CH_3$, $CH_3CH_2CH_2CH_2OH$
   b. $CH_3CH_2CH_2CH_2OH$, $CH_3CH_2CH_2OH$, $CH_3CH_2OH$
   c. $CH_3CH_2CH_2CH_2OH$, $CH_3CH_2CH_2CH_3$, $CH_3CH_2CH_2CH_2Cl$

**14.57** Explain the following observation. Dimethyl ether [$(CH_3)_2O$] and ethanol ($CH_3CH_2OH$) are both water-soluble compounds. The boiling point of ethanol (78 °C), however, is much higher than the boiling point of dimethyl ether (–24 °C).

**14.58** Explain why the boiling point of $CH_3CH_2CH_2CH_2OH$ (118 °C) is higher than the boiling point of $CH_3CH_2CH_2CH_2SH$ (98 °C), even though $CH_3CH_2CH_2CH_2SH$ has a higher molecular weight.

**14.59** Explain why two four-carbon organic molecules have very different solubility properties: 1-butanol ($CH_3CH_2CH_2CH_2OH$) is water soluble but 1-butene ($CH_2{=}CHCH_2CH_3$) is water insoluble.

**14.60** Explain why 1,6-hexanediol [$HO(CH_2)_6OH$] is much more water soluble than 1-hexanol [$CH_3(CH_2)_5OH$].

## Reactions of Alcohols

**14.61** Draw the products formed when each alcohol is dehydrated with $H_2SO_4$. Use the Zaitsev rule to predict the major product when a mixture forms.

   a. [cyclobutane with OH]

   b. [benzene ring]—$\overset{\displaystyle OH}{\underset{\displaystyle |}{CH}}CH_2CH_3$

   c. $CH_3\overset{\displaystyle OH}{\underset{\displaystyle |}{CH}}CH_2CH_2CH_2CH_3$

   d. $CH_3CH_2\overset{\displaystyle OH}{\underset{\displaystyle |}{\underset{\displaystyle |}{\underset{\displaystyle CH_3}{C}}}}CH_2CH_3$

**14.62** Draw the products formed when each alcohol is dehydrated with $H_2SO_4$. Use the Zaitsev rule to predict the major product when a mixture forms.

   a. $(CH_3)_2CHCH_2CH_2CH_2OH$         c. $CH_3CH(CH_2)_5CH_3$

   b. $(CH_3CH_2)_3COH$                  d. [cyclopentane with CH₃ and OH]

**14.63** Dehydration of 3-hexanol [CH$_3$CH$_2$CH(OH)CH$_2$CH$_2$CH$_3$] yields a mixture of two alkenes. (a) Draw the structures of both constitutional isomers formed. (b) Use the Zaitsev rule to explain why both products are formed in equal amounts.

**14.64** Dehydration of 3-methylcyclohexanol yields a mixture of two alkenes. (a) Draw the structures of both constitutional isomers formed. (b) Use the Zaitsev rule to explain why both products are formed in equal amounts.

**14.65** What alcohol is needed to form each alkene as a product of a dehydration reaction?

a. (phenyl)—CH=CH—(phenyl)      b. (cyclooctene ring)

**14.66** What alcohol is needed to form each alkene as the major product of a dehydration reaction?

a. (cyclohexene with two CH$_3$ groups)      b. (CH$_3$)$_2$C=C(CH$_3$)$_2$

**14.67** Propene (CH$_3$CH=CH$_2$) can be formed by dehydrating two different alcohols. Draw the structures of both alcohols.

**14.68** 2-Methylpropene [(CH$_3$)$_2$C=CH$_2$] can be formed by dehydrating two different alcohols. Draw the structures of both alcohols.

**14.69** Draw the products formed when each alcohol is oxidized with K$_2$Cr$_2$O$_7$. In some cases, no reaction occurs.
   a. CH$_3$(CH$_2$)$_6$CH$_2$OH
   b. (CH$_3$CH$_2$)$_2$CHOH
   c. CH$_3$CH$_2$CHCH$_2$OH
          |
          CH$_3$
   d. CH$_3$CH$_2$COH
          |       |
          CH$_3$  CH$_3$

**14.70** Draw the products formed when each alcohol is oxidized with K$_2$Cr$_2$O$_7$. In some cases, no reaction occurs.
   a. (cyclopentane with OH and CH$_3$)
   b. CH$_3$(CH$_2$)$_8$CH$_2$OH
   c. (cyclopentane)—CH$_2$OH
   d. (CH$_3$CH$_2$)$_3$COH

**14.71** Cortisol is an anti-inflammatory agent that also regulates carbohydrate metabolism. What oxidation product is formed when cortisol is treated with K$_2$Cr$_2$O$_7$?

(structure of cortisol)

cortisol

**14.72** Xylitol is a nontoxic compound as sweet as table sugar but with only one-third the calories, so it is often used as a sweetening agent in gum and hard candy.

CH$_2$OH
|
H—C—OH
|
HO—C—H
|
H—C—OH
|
CH$_2$OH

xylitol

   a. Classify the OH groups as 1°, 2°, or 3°.
   b. What product is formed when only the 1° OH groups are oxidized?
   c. What product is formed when all of the OH groups are oxidized?

**14.73** What alcohol starting material is needed to prepare each carbonyl compound as a product of an oxidation reaction?

a. (cycloheptanone)

c. (benzoic acid structure, phenyl—C(=O)—OH)

b. CH$_3$—C—C—CH$_3$
        |   ||
        CH$_3$ O
   (with CH$_3$ below)

**14.74** What alcohol starting material is needed to prepare each carbonyl compound as a product of an oxidation reaction?

a. (methylcyclohexanone)

c. (CH$_3$CH$_2$)$_2$C=O

b. CH$_3$CH$_2$CH$_2$CH$_2$CH$_2$CO$_2$H

**14.75** What products are formed when **X** is treated with each reagent: (a) H$_2$SO$_4$; (b) K$_2$Cr$_2$O$_7$?

**X**

**14.76** What products are formed when **Y** is treated with each reagent: (a) H$_2$SO$_4$; (b) K$_2$Cr$_2$O$_7$?

**Y**

## Reactions of Thiols

**14.77** What disulfide is formed when each thiol is oxidized?

a. (cyclohexyl)—SH    b. $CH_3(CH_2)_4SH$

**14.78** As we will learn in Chapter 21, cysteine is a naturally occurring amino acid that contains a thiol group. What disulfide is formed when cysteine is oxidized?

$$COOH$$
$$H_2N-\underset{\underset{CH_2SH}{|}}{\overset{|}{C}}-H$$

cysteine

**14.79** The smell of fried onions is in part determined by the two disulfides drawn below. What thiols are formed when each disulfide is reduced?

a. $CH_3S—SCH_2CH_2CH_3$    b. $CH_2{=}CHCH_2S—SCH_2CH_2CH_3$

**14.80** Sometimes disulfide bonds occur in a ring. As we will learn in Chapter 21, these disulfide bonds play an important role in determining the shape and properties of proteins. What *di*thiol is formed when the following disulfide is reduced?

$$CH_3CH_2-\overset{\phantom{x}}{\underset{S-S}{\bigcirc}}-CH_2CH_3$$

## Applications

**14.81** Diethyl ether [$(CH_3CH_2)_2O$] is an imperfect anesthetic in part because it readily combusts in air to form $CO_2$ and $H_2O$. Write a balanced equation for the complete combustion of diethyl ether.

**14.82** Methanol ($CH_3OH$) is used as a fuel for some types of race cars, because it readily combusts in air to form $CO_2$ and $H_2O$. Write a balanced equation for the complete combustion of methanol.

**14.83** With reference to the halogenated organic compounds called CFCs, HCFCs, and HFCs: (a) How do these compounds differ in structure? (b) How do these compounds differ in their interaction with ozone?

**14.84** Give an example of a CFC and explain why the widespread use of CFCs has been detrimental to the environment.

**14.85** As we learned in Chapter 13, polymers have very different properties depending (in part) on their functional groups. For example, poly(ethylene glycol) is commonly used in shampoos, where it forms viscous solutions in water. Poly(vinyl chloride), on the other hand, repels water and is used to make pipes and garden hoses. Discuss the water solubility of these polymers, and explain why there is a difference, even though both polymers have several polar bonds.

poly(ethylene glycol)
PEG

poly(vinyl chloride)
PVC

**14.86** Give an example of a halogenated ether commonly used as an anesthetic. Give two reasons why halogenated ethers are now used in place of diethyl ether as anesthetics.

**14.87** Write out the chemical reaction that occurs when a breathalyzer test is carried out. How does this test give an indication of blood alcohol content?

**14.88** 2,3-Butanedione is commonly used to give microwave popcorn a buttery flavor. What diol is needed to prepare 2,3-butanedione by an oxidation reaction?

$$CH_3-\overset{O}{\overset{\|}{C}}-\overset{O}{\underset{\|}{C}}-CH_3$$

2,3-butanedione
(butter flavor)

**14.89** In contrast to ethylene glycol ($HOCH_2CH_2OH$), which is extremely toxic, propylene glycol [$CH_3CH(OH)CH_2OH$] is nontoxic because it is oxidized in the body to a product produced during the metabolism of carbohydrates. What product is formed when propylene glycol is oxidized?

**14.90** Lactic acid [$CH_3CH(OH)CO_2H$] gives sour milk its distinctive taste. What product is formed when lactic acid is oxidized by $K_2Cr_2O_7$?

**14.91** Write out the chemical reactions that occur during the metabolism of ethanol. Explain how Antabuse is used in the treatment of alcoholism.

**14.92** What chemical reactions occur when straight hair is made curly with a "permanent"?

## General Questions

**14.93** An unknown alcohol of molecular formula $C_4H_{10}O$ forms only one alkene when treated with $H_2SO_4$. No reaction is observed when the alcohol is treated with an oxidizing agent. Draw the structure of the alcohol.

**14.94** You have two test tubes, one containing $(CH_3CH_2)_3COH$ and one containing $CH_3(CH_2)_6OH$, but you do not know which alcohol is in which tube. Explain how treating the alcohols with an oxidizing agent like $K_2Cr_2O_7$ can help you to determine which test tube contains which alcohol.

**14.95** Explain why two ether molecules can't hydrogen bond to each other, but an ether molecule can hydrogen bond to a water molecule.

**14.96** When an alcohol hydrogen bonds with water, two different hydrogen bonding interactions are possible. The oxygen atom of the alcohol (ROH) can hydrogen bond with a hydrogen atom of water, or a hydrogen atom of the alcohol can hydrogen bond to the oxygen atom of water. Illustrate both of these possibilities with $CH_3CH_2OH$.

**14.97** Answer the following questions about alcohol **A**.

**A**

- a. Give the IUPAC name.
- b. Classify the alcohol as 1°, 2°, or 3°.
- c. Draw the products formed when **A** is dehydrated with $H_2SO_4$.
- d. What product is formed when **A** is oxidized with $K_2Cr_2O_7$?
- e. Draw a constitutional isomer of **A** that contains an OH group.
- f. Draw a constitutional isomer of **A** that contains an ether.

**14.98** Answer the following questions about alcohol **B**.

**B**

- a. Give the IUPAC name.
- b. Classify the alcohol as 1°, 2°, or 3°.
- c. Draw the products formed when **B** is dehydrated with $H_2SO_4$.
- d. What product is formed when **B** is oxidized with $K_2Cr_2O_7$?
- e. Draw a constitutional isomer of **B** that contains an OH group.
- f. Draw a constitutional isomer of **B** that contains an ether.

## CHALLENGE PROBLEMS

**14.99** 2-Methyl-1-butene can be formed by dehydrating two different alcohols (**A** and **B**) of molecular formula ($C_5H_{12}O$). When **A** undergoes dehydration, 2-methyl-1-butene is formed as the *only* product of dehydration. When alcohol **B** undergoes dehydration, two different alkenes are formed and 2-methyl-1-butene is formed as the *minor* product. (a) Identify the structures of **A** and **B**. (b) What is the major alkene formed when **B** undergoes dehydration?

**14.100** Dehydration of alcohol **C** forms two products of molecular formula $C_{14}H_{12}$ that are isomers, but they are not constitutional isomers. Draw the structures of these two products.

**C**

**Naproxen** is the active ingredient in the widely used pain relievers Naprosyn and Aleve. The three-dimensional arrangement of two atoms on a single carbon atom in naproxen determines its therapeutic properties.

# The Three-Dimensional Shape of Molecules

## CHAPTER GOALS

*In this chapter you will learn how to:*

1 Recognize whether a molecule is chiral or achiral

2 Identify chirality centers

3 Draw two enantiomers in three dimensions around the chirality center

4 Explain why some chiral drugs have very different properties from their mirror images

5 Draw Fischer projection formulas

6 Compare the physical properties of enantiomers

7 Recognize the difference between enantiomers and diastereomers

8 Explain the relationship between the shape and odor of a molecule

Are you left-handed or right-handed? If you're right-handed, you've probably spent little time thinking about your hand preference. If you're left-handed, though, you probably learned at an early age that many objects—like scissors and baseball gloves—"fit" for righties, but are "backwards" for lefties. **Hands, like many objects in the world around us, are mirror images that are *not* identical.** In Chapter 15 we examine the "handedness" of molecules, and ask, "How important is the three-dimensional shape of a molecule?"

## 15.1 Isomers—A Review

Chapter 15 concentrates on *stereochemistry*—**that is, the three-dimensional structure of molecules.** Since an understanding of isomers is needed in the discussion of stereochemistry, let's begin with an overview of isomers. Recall from Section 12.2:

- Isomers are different compounds with the same molecular formula.

There are two major classes of isomers: **constitutional isomers** (Section 12.2) and **stereoisomers** (Section 13.3).

- *Constitutional isomers* differ in the way the atoms are connected to one another.

**Constitutional isomers have atoms bonded to *different* atoms.** As a result, constitutional isomers have different IUPAC names. Constitutional isomers may have the same functional group or they may have different functional groups.

For example, 2-methylpentane and 3-methylpentane are constitutional isomers with molecular formula $C_6H_{14}$. 2-Methylpentane has a $CH_3$ group bonded to the second atom (C2) of a five-carbon chain, while 3-methylpentane has a $CH_3$ group bonded to the middle atom (C3) of a five-carbon chain. Both molecules are alkanes, so they both belong to the same family of organic compounds.

**Constitutional isomers with the same functional group**

$CH_3$ group at C2 — $CH_3CHCH_2CH_2CH_3$ and $CH_3CH_2CHCH_2CH_3$ — $CH_3$ group at C3

2-methylpentane $C_6H_{14}$     3-methylpentane $C_6H_{14}$

Ethanol and dimethyl ether are constitutional isomers with molecular formula $C_2H_6O$. Ethanol contains an O—H bond and dimethyl ether does not. Thus, the atoms are bonded to different atoms and these constitutional isomers have *different* functional groups. Dimethyl ether is an ether and ethanol is an alcohol.

**Constitutional isomers with different functional groups**

$CH_3CH_2$—O—H          $CH_3$—O—$CH_3$

ethanol $C_2H_6O$          dimethyl ether $C_2H_6O$

- *Stereoisomers* differ *only* in the three-dimensional arrangement of atoms.

**Stereoisomers always have the *same* functional group,** since they differ only in the way the atoms are oriented in space. Two stereoisomers need a prefix like cis or trans added to their IUPAC names to distinguish them. The cis and trans isomers of 2-butene are an example of stereoisomers. Each stereoisomer of 2-butene contains the same sequence of atoms. The only difference is the three-dimensional arrangement of the two methyl groups on the double bond.

> **One example of stereoisomers—Isomers at a double bond**
>
> $$CH_3 \quad CH_3 \atop C=C \atop H \quad\quad H$$
> *cis*-2-butene
>
> $$CH_3 \quad H \atop C=C \atop H \quad\quad CH_3$$
> *trans*-2-butene

- The *cis* isomer has the two $CH_3$ groups on the same side of the double bond.
- The *trans* isomer has the two $CH_3$ groups on opposite sides of the double bond.

Cis and trans isomers on a carbon–carbon double bond are one example of stereoisomers. In Section 15.2, we learn about another type of stereoisomer that occurs at a tetrahedral carbon.

### PROBLEM 15.1

Classify each pair of compounds as identical molecules, constitutional isomers, or stereoisomers.

a. $CH_3CH_2\overset{\overset{\textstyle CH_3}{|}}{C}H\overset{\overset{}{}}{C}HCH_3$ and $CH_3\overset{\overset{}{}}{C}HCH_2\overset{\overset{}{}}{C}HCH_3$
  $\qquad\qquad\quad \underset{CH_3}{|} \qquad\qquad\quad \underset{CH_3}{|}\;\; \underset{CH_3}{|}$

b. $$CH_3CH_2 \quad CH_3 \atop C=C \atop H \quad\quad H$$ and $$CH_3CH_2 \quad H \atop C=C \atop H \quad\quad CH_3$$

c. $CH_3CH{=}CHCH_2CH_3$ and $CH_3CH_2CH{=}CHCH_3$

d. ⬚=O and ▷—OH

### PROBLEM 15.2

For *trans*-2-hexene: (a) draw a stereoisomer; (b) draw a constitutional isomer that contains a carbon–carbon double bond; (c) draw a constitutional isomer that does not contain a carbon–carbon double bond.

The dominance of right-handedness over left-handedness occurs in all races and cultures. Despite this fact, even identical twins can exhibit differences in hand preference. Pictured are Zachary (left-handed) and Matthew (right-handed), identical twin sons of the author.

## 15.2 Looking Glass Chemistry— Molecules and Their Mirror Images

To learn more about stereoisomers that occur at tetrahedral carbon atoms, we must turn our attention to molecules and their mirror images. **Everything, including molecules, has a mirror image.** What's important in chemistry is **whether a molecule is *identical* to or *different* from its mirror image.**

## 15.2A  What It Means to Be Chiral or Achiral

Some molecules are like hands. **Left and right hands are mirror images of each other, but they are *not* identical.** If you try to mentally place one hand inside the other hand you can never superimpose either all the fingers, or the tops and palms. To *superimpose* an object on its mirror image means to align *all* parts of the object with its mirror image. With molecules, this means aligning all atoms and all bonds.

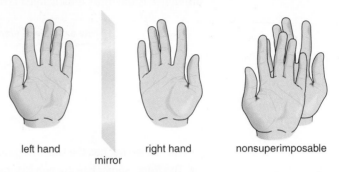

left hand     mirror     right hand     nonsuperimposable

> The adjective *chiral* (pronounced ky-rel) comes from the Greek *cheir,* meaning *hand.* Left and right hands are **chiral:** they are mirror images that do not superimpose on each other.

- A molecule (or object) that is *not* superimposable on its mirror image is said to be *chiral.*

Other molecules are like socks. **Two socks from a pair are mirror images that *are* superimposable.** One sock can fit inside another, aligning toes and heels, and tops and bottoms. A sock and its mirror image are *identical.*

mirror     superimposable

- A molecule (or object) that *is* superimposable on its mirror image is said to be *achiral.*

### PROBLEM 15.3

Classify each object as chiral or achiral: (a) nail; (b) screw; (c) glove; (d) pencil.

## 15.2B  The Chirality of Molecules

Let's determine whether three molecules—$H_2O$, $CH_2BrCl$, and $CHBrClF$—are superimposable on their mirror images; that is, **are $H_2O$, $CH_2BrCl$, and $CHBrClF$ chiral or achiral?**

To test **chirality**—that is, to test whether a molecule and its mirror image are identical or different:

1. Draw the molecule in three dimensions.
2. Draw its mirror image.
3. Try to align all bonds and atoms. To superimpose a molecule and its mirror image you can perform any rotation but **you cannot break bonds.**

Following this procedure, $H_2O$ and $CH_2BrCl$ are both **achiral** molecules: each molecule is superimposable on its mirror image.

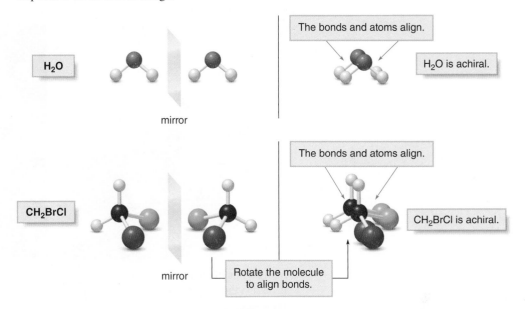

With CHBrClF, the result is different. The molecule (labeled **A**) and its mirror image (labeled **B**) are not superimposable. No matter how you rotate **A** and **B**, all of the atoms never align. **CHBrClF is thus a chiral molecule,** and **A** and **B** are different compounds.

**A** and **B** are **stereoisomers** since they are isomers differing only in the three-dimensional arrangement of substituents. They represent a new type of stereoisomer that occurs at tetrahedral carbon atoms. These stereoisomers are called **enantiomers.**

- Enantiomers are mirror images that are not superimposable.

CHBrClF contains a carbon atom bonded to four different groups. **A carbon atom bonded to four different groups is called a** *chirality center.*

We have now learned two related but different concepts, and it is necessary to distinguish between them.

- A molecule that is not superimposable on its mirror image is a *chiral molecule.*
- A carbon atom surrounded by four different groups is a *chirality center.*

CHBrClF is a chiral molecule because it is not superimposable on its mirror image. CHBrClF contains one chirality center, one carbon atom bonded to four different groups. Molecules can contain zero, one, or more chirality centers.

Naming a carbon atom with four different groups is a topic that currently has no firm agreement among organic chemists. IUPAC recommends the term *chirality center,* and so this is the term used in this text. Other terms in common use are chiral center, chiral carbon, asymmetric carbon, and stereogenic center.

Figure 15.1    Chirality in Nature

a.

b.

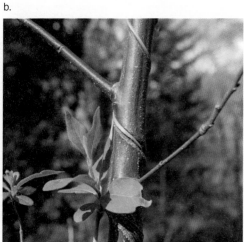

a. Many types of snails possess a chiral, right-handed helical shell. When a right-handed shell is held in the right hand with the thumb pointing towards the wider end, the opening is on the right side.

b. Plants like honeysuckle wind in a chiral left-handed helix.

## 15.2C   Chirality in Nature

Why must we study a topic like stereochemistry that may seem so esoteric? In truth, chirality pervades our existence. On a molecular level, many biological molecules discussed in Chapters 19–22 are chiral. On a macroscopic level, many naturally occurring objects possess handedness. Examples include helical seashells shaped like right-handed screws, and plants such as honeysuckle that wind in a left-handed helix (Figure 15.1). The human body is chiral, and hands, feet, and ears are not superimposable.

### PROBLEM 15.4
Explain the difference between the terms *chiral* and *chirality center.*

## 15.3   Chirality Centers

A necessary skill in studying the three-dimensional structure of molecules is the ability to locate and draw chirality centers—carbon atoms bonded to four different groups.

### 15.3A   Locating Chirality Centers

To locate a chirality center, examine each **tetrahedral** carbon atom in a molecule, and look at the four *groups*—not the four *atoms*—bonded to it. CBrClFI has one chirality center since its carbon atom is bonded to four different elements—Br, Cl, F, and I. 3-Bromohexane also has one chirality center since one carbon is bonded to H, Br, $CH_2CH_3$, and $CH_2CH_2CH_3$. We consider all atoms in a group as a *whole unit,* not just the atom directly bonded to the carbon in question.

This C is bonded to: **H**
**Br**
**CH$_2$CH$_3$**
**CH$_2$CH$_2$CH$_3$**

two *different* alkyl groups

chirality center

chirality center
3-bromohexane

Keep in mind the following:

- A carbon atom bonded to two or more like groups is *never* a chirality center. CH$_2$ and CH$_3$ groups have more than one H atom bonded to the same carbon, so each of these carbons is *never* a chirality center.
- A carbon that is part of a multiple bond does not have four groups around it, so it can *never* be a chirality center.

## SAMPLE PROBLEM 15.1

Locate the chirality center in each drug. Penicillamine is used to treat Wilson's disease, a genetic disorder that leads to a buildup of copper in the liver, kidneys, and the brain. Albuterol is a bronchodilator—that is, it widens air passages—so it is used to treat asthma.

a. penicillamine

b. albuterol

### Analysis

In compounds with many C's, look at each C individually and eliminate those C's that can't be chirality centers. Thus, omit all CH$_2$ and CH$_3$ groups and all multiply bonded C's. Check all remaining C's to see if they are bonded to four different groups.

### Solution

a. The CH$_3$ groups and COOH group in penicillamine are not chirality centers. One C is bonded to two CH$_3$ groups, so it can be eliminated from consideration as well. This leaves one C with four different groups bonded to it.

b. In albuterol, omit all CH$_2$ and CH$_3$ groups and all C's that are part of a double bond. Also omit from consideration the one C bonded to three CH$_3$ groups. This leaves one C with four different groups bonded to it.

a. penicillamine

b. albuterol

## PROBLEM 15.5

Label the chirality center in the given molecules. The compounds contain zero or one chirality center.

a. CH$_3$CHCH$_2$CH$_3$
    |
    Cl

b. (CH$_3$)$_3$CH

c. CH$_2$=CHCHCH$_3$
            |
           OH

d.

## PROBLEM 15.6

Label the chirality center in each drug.

a.

brompheniramine
(antihistamine)

b.

fluoxetine
Trade name: Prozac
(antidepressant)

Larger organic molecules can have two, three, or even hundreds of chirality centers. Tartaric acid, isolated from grapes, and ephedrine, isolated from the herb ma huang (used to treat respiratory ailments in traditional Chinese medicine), each have two chirality centers. Once a popular drug to promote weight loss and enhance athletic performance, ephedrine use has now been linked to episodes of sudden death, heart attack, and stroke.

tartaric acid

ephedrine
(bronchodilator, decongestant)

[Chirality centers are labeled in red.]

## PROBLEM 15.7

Label the chirality centers in each molecule. Compounds may have one or two chirality centers.

a. $CH_3CH_2CH_2$—C—$CH_3$, with H up and OH down

b. $H_2N$—C—H (COOH up), $CH_3$—C—H, $CH_2CH_3$

c. $CH_3CH_2$—C—$CH_2CH_2$—C—$CH_3$ (Br up, H down; Cl up, H down)

Lettuce, spinach, broccoli, and cabbage are all excellent sources of vitamin K.

## PROBLEM 15.8

Label the two chirality centers in vitamin K. Vitamin K is essential to blood clot formation. A deficiency of this vitamin may lead to excessive and often fatal bleeding.

$CH_2CH=CCH_2CH_2CH_2CHCH_2CH_2CH_2CHCH_2CH_2CH_2CH(CH_3)_2$
with $CH_3$ groups

vitamin K

## 15.3B   Drawing a Pair of Enantiomers

How are chirality centers related to chiral molecules?

> • Any molecule with one chirality center is a chiral compound.

Recall from Section 15.2 that a **chiral compound is not superimposable on its mirror image,** and that these mirror image isomers are called **enantiomers.** Let's learn how to draw two enantiomers using 2-butanol [$CH_3CH(OH)CH_2CH_3$], a compound with one chirality center, as an example.

### How To  Draw Two Enantiomers of a Chiral Compound

**Example:** Draw two enantiomers of 2-butanol in three dimensions around the chirality center.

2-butanol

**Step [1]**   Draw one enantiomer by arbitrarily placing the four different groups on any bond to the chirality center.
- Use the convention learned in Section 11.3 for drawing a tetrahedron: **place two bonds in the plane, one in front of the plane on a wedge, and one behind the plane on a dashed line.**
- Arbitrarily place the four groups—H, OH, $CH_3$, and $CH_2CH_3$—on any bond to the chirality center, forming enantiomer **A.**

Draw the bonds:     Add the groups:

**A**

**Step [2]**   Draw a mirror plane and arrange the substituents in the mirror image so that they are a reflection of the groups in the first molecule.
- Place the four groups—H, OH, $CH_3$, and $CH_2CH_3$—on the chirality center in the mirror image to form enantiomer **B.**
- **A** and **B** are mirror images, but no matter how **A** and **B** are rotated their bonds do not align, so **A** and **B** are chiral compounds.

Draw the molecule…then the mirror image.

**A**                    **B**

mirror
not superimposable

**enantiomers**

### PROBLEM 15.9

Locate the chirality center in each compound and draw both enantiomers.

a.  $CH_3CHCH_2CH_3$
         |
         Cl

b.  $CH_3CH_2CHCH_2OH$
              |
              OH

## 15.4 Chirality Centers in Cyclic Compounds

Chirality centers may also occur at carbon atoms that are part of a ring. To find chirality centers on ring carbons, always draw the rings as flat polygons, and look for tetrahedral carbons that are bonded to four different groups, as usual.

### 15.4A Locating Chirality Centers on Ring Carbons

Does methylcyclopentane have a chirality center?

All of the carbon atoms are bonded to two or three hydrogen atoms except for C1, the ring carbon bonded to the methyl group. Next, compare the ring atoms and bonds on both sides the same distance from C1, and continue until a point of difference is reached, or until both sides meet. In this case, there is no point of difference on either side, so C1 is considered to be bonded to identical alkyl groups that happen to be part of a ring. **C1 is therefore *not* a chirality center.**

With 3-methylcyclohexene, the result is different.

All carbon atoms are bonded to two or three hydrogen atoms or are part of a double bond except for C3, the ring carbon bonded to the methyl group. In this case, the atoms equidistant from C3 are different, so C3 is considered to be bonded to *different* alkyl groups in the ring. **C3 is therefore bonded to four different groups, making it a chirality center.**

Since 3-methylcyclohexene has one tetrahedral chirality center, it is a chiral compound, and exists as a pair of enantiomers. Substituents above and below the ring are drawn with wedges and dashes.

### 15.4B FOCUS ON HEALTH & MEDICINE
The Unforgettable Legacy of Thalidomide

Many biologically active compounds contain one or more chirality centers on ring carbons. For example, **thalidomide,** which contains one such chirality center, was once used as a sedative and anti-nausea drug for pregnant women in Europe and Great Britain from 1959–1962.

Although it is a potent teratogen (a substance that causes fetal abnormalities), thalidomide exhibits several beneficial effects, and for this reason, it is now prescribed under strict control for the treatment of Hansen's disease (leprosy). Because it was once thought to be extremely contagious, individuals suffering from Hansen's disease in Hawaii were sent to Kalaupapa, a remote and inaccessible peninsula on the island of Molokai. Hansen's disease is now known to be a treatable bacterial infection completely cured by the sulfa drugs described in Section 13.13.

**Two enantiomers of thalidomide**

chirality center

chirality center

anti-nausea drug

teratogen

Unfortunately, thalidomide was sold as a mixture of its two enantiomers, and each of these stereoisomers has a different biological activity, a property not uncommon to chiral drugs, as we will see in Section 15.5. While one enantiomer has the desired therapeutic effect, the other enantiomer was responsible for thousands of catastrophic birth defects in children born to women who took the drug during pregnancy. Thalidomide was never approved for use in the United States due to the diligence of Frances Oldham Kelsey, a medical reviewing officer for the Food and Drug Administration, who insisted that the safety data on thalidomide were inadequate.

### PROBLEM 15.10

Label the chirality centers in each compound. A molecule may have zero, one, or two chirality centers.

a. (structure: cyclohexene with OH)    b. (structure: benzene with CH₂CH₃ chain)    c. (structure: cyclobutane with two Cl)

### PROBLEM 15.11

Label the two chirality centers in sertraline, the generic name for the antidepressant Zoloft.

CH₃NH (structure of sertraline with Cl, Cl)

sertraline

## 15.5 FOCUS ON HEALTH & MEDICINE
### Chiral Drugs

A living organism is a sea of chiral molecules. Many drugs are chiral, and often they must interact with a chiral receptor to be effective. One enantiomer of a drug may be effective in treating a disease whereas its mirror image may be ineffective.

Why should such a difference in biological activity be observed? For an everyday analogy, consider what happens when you are given a right-handed glove. A glove is a chiral object, and your right and left hands are also chiral—they are mirror images that are not identical. Only your right hand can fit inside a right glove, not your left. Thus, the glove's utility depends on the hand—it either fits or it doesn't fit.

The same phenomenon is observed with drugs that must interact with a chiral receptor in a cell. One enantiomer "fits" the receptor and evokes a specific response. Its mirror image doesn't fit the same receptor, making it ineffective; or if it "fits" another receptor, it can evoke a totally different response. Figure 15.2 schematically illustrates this difference in binding between two enantiomers and a chiral receptor.

**Figure 15.2**    The Interaction of Two Enantiomers With a Chiral Receptor

One enantiomer of the amino acid phenylalanine, labeled **A,** has three groups that can interact with the appropriate binding sites of the chiral receptor. The groups around the chirality center in the mirror image **B,** however, can never be arranged so that all three groups can bind to these same three binding sites. Thus, enantiomer **B** does not "fit" the same receptor, so it does not evoke the same response.

HEALTH NOTE

Ibuprofen is commonly used to relieve headaches, and muscle and joint pain.

## 15.5A   Chiral Pain Relievers

Ibuprofen and naproxen are nonsteroidal anti-inflammatory drugs (NSAIDs) that illustrate how two enantiomers can have different biological activities. Both drugs are common over-the-counter remedies that relieve pain and fever, and reduce inflammation.

Ibuprofen is the generic name for the pain relievers known as Motrin and Advil. Ibuprofen has one chirality center, and thus exists as a pair of enantiomers. Only one enantiomer, labeled **A,** is an active anti-inflammatory agent. Its enantiomer **B** is inactive. **B,** however, is slowly converted to **A** in the body. Ibuprofen is sold as a mixture of both enantiomers. **An equal mixture of two enantiomers is called a** *racemic mixture* (pronounced ra-see′-mik).

**ibuprofen**
active anti-inflammatory agent

inactive enantiomer

One enantiomer of **naproxen,** the pain reliever in Naprosyn and Aleve, is an active anti-inflammatory agent, but its enantiomer is a harmful liver toxin. Changing the orientation of two substituents to form a mirror image can thus alter biological activity to produce an undesirable side effect in the other enantiomer.

**naproxen**
active anti-inflammatory agent

**A**

enantiomer
liver toxin

**B**

These examples illustrate the benefit of marketing a chiral drug as a single active enantiomer. In these instances it should be possible to use smaller doses with fewer side effects, yet many chiral drugs continue to be sold as racemic mixtures, because it is more difficult and therefore more costly to obtain a single enantiomer.

Recent rulings by the Food and Drug Administration have encouraged the development of so-called **racemic switches,** the patenting and marketing of a single enantiomer that was originally sold as a racemic mixture. To obtain a new patent on a single enantiomer, however, a company must show evidence that it provides significant benefit over the racemic mixture.

### PROBLEM 15.12

Propranolol (trade name: Inderal) is used in the treatment of high blood pressure and heart disease. (a) Locate the chirality center in propranolol. (b) Draw both enantiomers of propranolol. Only one of these enantiomers is biologically active. (c) Draw a diagram similar to Figure 15.2 that illustrates how the two enantiomers of propranolol bind differently to a chiral receptor.

$OCH_2CHCH_2NHCH(CH_3)_2$
$OH$

propranolol

### 15.5B  Parkinson's Disease and L-Dopa

L-Dopa was first isolated from the seeds of the broad bean *Vicia faba,* and since 1967 it has been the drug of choice for the treatment of Parkinson's disease. L-Dopa is a chiral molecule with one chirality center. Unlike ibuprofen, which is still marketed as a racemic mixture, L-dopa, also called levodopa, is sold as a single enantiomer. Like many chiral drugs, only one enantiomer is active against Parkinson's disease. The inactive enantiomer is also responsible for neutropenia, a decrease in certain white blood cells that help to fight infection.

L-dopa
active against
Parkinson's disease

D-dopa
enantiomer responsible for
undesired side effects

The broad bean *Vicia faba* produces the drug L-dopa. To meet the large demand for L-dopa today, the commercially available drug is synthesized in the laboratory.

Parkinson's disease, which afflicts 1.5 million individuals in the United States, results from the degeneration of neurons that produce the neurotransmitter dopamine in the brain. Dopamine affects brain processes that control movement and emotions, so proper dopamine levels are needed to maintain an individual's mental and physical health. When the level of dopamine drops, the loss of motor control symptomatic of Parkinson's disease results.

**Figure 15.3**   L-Dopa, Dopamine, and Parkinson's Disease

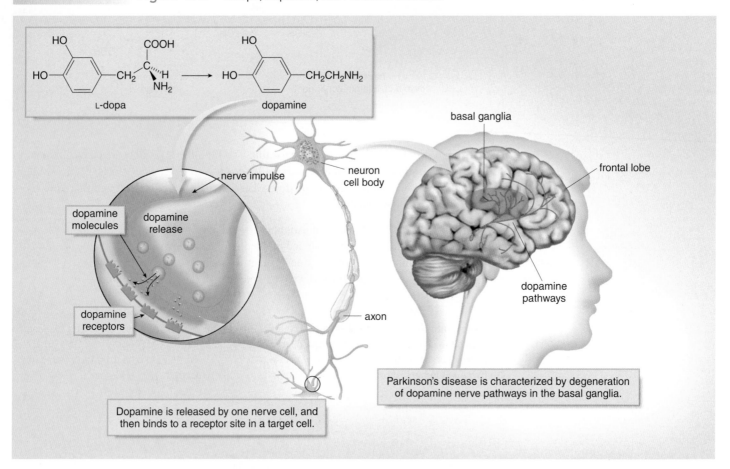

Dopamine is released by one nerve cell, and then binds to a receptor site in a target cell.

Parkinson's disease is characterized by degeneration of dopamine nerve pathways in the basal ganglia.

L-Dopa is an oral medication that is transported to the brain by the bloodstream. In the brain it is converted to dopamine (Figure 15.3). Dopamine itself cannot be given as a medication because it cannot pass from the bloodstream into the brain; that is, it does not cross the blood–brain barrier.

## 15.6 Fischer Projections

The chirality centers in some organic compounds, most notably carbohydrates (Chapter 20), are often drawn using a different convention than is used for other chirality centers.

Instead of drawing a tetrahedron with two bonds in the plane, one in front of the plane, and one behind it, the **tetrahedron is tipped so that both horizontal bonds come forward (drawn on wedges) and both vertical bonds go behind (on dashed lines).** This structure is then abbreviated by a **cross formula,** also called a **Fischer projection formula.** In a Fischer projection formula, therefore,

Draw a tetrahedron as:      Abbreviate it as a cross formula:

Horizontal bonds come forward, on wedges.

$$Z - \overset{\overset{\text{W}}{|}}{\underset{\underset{\text{Y}}{|}}{C}} - X \quad = \quad Z - \overset{\overset{\text{W}}{|}}{\underset{\underset{\text{Y}}{|}}{\quad}} - X$$

Vertical bonds go back, on dashes.

chirality center

Fischer projection formula

- A carbon atom is located at the intersection of the two lines of the cross.
- The horizontal bonds come forward, on wedges.
- The vertical bonds go back, on dashed lines.

For example, to draw the chirality center of 2-butanol [$CH_3CH(OH)CH_2CH_3$, Section 15.3B] using this convention, **draw the tetrahedron with horizontal bonds on wedges and vertical bonds on dashed lines.** Then, **replace the chirality center with a cross** to draw the Fischer projection.

$$CH_3-\overset{\overset{H}{\vdots}}{\underset{\underset{OH}{\vdots}}{C}}-CH_2CH_3 \qquad CH_3CH_2-\overset{\overset{H}{\vdots}}{\underset{\underset{OH}{\vdots}}{C}}-CH_3$$

one enantiomer of 2-butanol                    mirror image

Replace the chirality center with a cross.

$$CH_3-\overset{H}{\underset{OH}{|}}-CH_2CH_3 \qquad CH_3CH_2-\overset{H}{\underset{OH}{|}}-CH_3$$

Fischer projection formulas for both enantiomers of 2-butanol

Sample Problem 15.2 illustrates another example of drawing two enantiomers using this convention.

## SAMPLE PROBLEM 15.2

Draw both enantiomers of glyceraldehyde, a simple carbohydrate, using Fischer projection formulas.

$$HOCH_2\overset{}{\underset{\underset{OH}{|}}{C}}HCHO$$

glyceraldehyde

### Analysis

- Draw the tetrahedron of one enantiomer with the horizontal bonds on wedges, and the vertical bonds on dashed lines. Arrange the four groups on the chirality center—H, OH, CHO, and $CH_2OH$—arbitrarily in the first enantiomer.
- Draw the second enantiomer by arranging the substituents in the mirror image so they are a reflection of the groups in the first molecule.
- Replace the chirality center with a cross to draw the Fischer projections.

### Solution

chirality center

$$HOCH_2\overset{}{\underset{\underset{OH}{|}}{C}}HCHO$$

glyceraldehyde

Draw the compound.

$$\overset{CHO}{\underset{CH_2OH}{\overset{|}{H-C-OH}}}$$

- Horizontal bonds come forward.
- Vertical bonds go back.

$$\overset{CHO}{\underset{CH_2OH}{H-|-OH}}$$

Fischer projection of one enantiomer

Then, draw the mirror image.

$$\overset{CHO}{\underset{CH_2OH}{\overset{|}{HO-C-H}}}$$

$$\overset{CHO}{\underset{CH_2OH}{HO-|-H}}$$

Fischer projection of the second enantiomer

**PROBLEM 15.13**

Convert each molecule into a Fischer projection formula.

a. $H \blacktriangleright \overset{\displaystyle CH_3}{\underset{\displaystyle Cl}{C}} \blacktriangleleft Br$     b. $H \blacktriangleright \overset{\displaystyle COOH}{\underset{\displaystyle CH_2Cl}{C}} \blacktriangleleft OH$

**PROBLEM 15.14**

Convert each Fischer projection formula into a representation that uses wedges and dashes.

a. $CH_3CH_2 \overset{\displaystyle CH_3}{\underset{\displaystyle Cl}{\rule{0.5em}{0.4pt}\vert\rule{0.5em}{0.4pt}}} Br$     b. $CH_3CH_2 \overset{\displaystyle H}{\underset{\displaystyle NH_2}{\rule{0.5em}{0.4pt}\vert\rule{0.5em}{0.4pt}}} CH_3$

**PROBLEM 15.15**

Draw Fischer projections of both enantiomers for each compound.

a. $CH_3\underset{\displaystyle OH}{\overset{\displaystyle |}{C}}HCH_2CH_2CH_3$     b. $CH_3CH_2\underset{\displaystyle Cl}{\overset{\displaystyle |}{C}}HCH_2Cl$

# 15.7   Optical Activity

## 15.7A   The Physical Properties of Enantiomers

How do the physical properties of enantiomers compare?

- Two enantiomers have identical physical properties—melting point, boiling point, and solubility—except for how they interact with plane-polarized light.

What is **plane-polarized light?** Ordinary light consists of waves that oscillate in all planes at right angles to the direction in which the light travels. Passing light through a device called a polarizer allows light in only one plane to come through. This is **plane-polarized light** and it consists of light waves in a single plane.

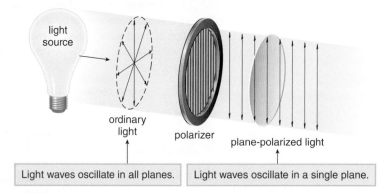

A **polarimeter** is an instrument that allows plane-polarized light to travel through a sample tube containing an organic compound. After the light exits the sample tube, an analyzer slit is rotated to determine the direction of the plane of the polarized light exiting the sample tube.

- An achiral compound does not change the direction of the plane-polarized light and is said to be *optically inactive*.
- A chiral compound rotates the plane of polarized light through an angle α, measured in degrees (°). A compound that rotates plane-polarized light is said to be *optically active*.

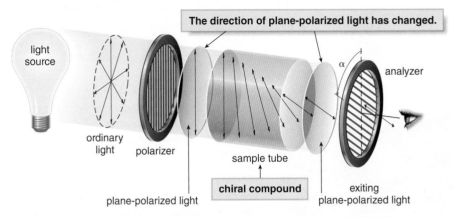

For example, the achiral compound $CH_2BrCl$ is optically *inactive,* whereas a single enantiomer of CHBrClF, a chiral compound, is optically *active.*

The rotation of polarized light can be in the **clockwise** or **counterclockwise** direction.

- If the rotation is *clockwise,* the compound is called *dextrorotatory* and is labeled as the (+)-enantiomer.
- If the rotation is *counterclockwise,* the compound is called *levorotatory* and is labeled as the (−)-enantiomer.

How does the rotation of two enantiomers compare?

- Two enantiomers rotate plane-polarized light *to an equal extent* but in the *opposite* direction.

Thus, if enantiomer **A** rotates polarized light +5°, then the same concentration of enantiomer **B** rotates it −5°. Enantiomer **A** is dextrorotatory, while enantiomer **B** is levorotatory.

PROBLEM 15.16

Label each compound as optically active or optically inactive.

a.  $CH_3(CH_2)_6CH_3$

b.  (structure: central C bonded to COOH, CH₃, H, OH)

c.  (structure: central C bonded to CH₃, CH₃, H, OH)

d.  (hexane ring / cyclohexane structure)

PROBLEM 15.17

Suppose a sample tube contained an equal amount of two enantiomers. Would you expect this solution to be optically active or optically inactive?

## 15.7B  Specific Rotation

The observed rotation of an optically active sample depends on the number of chiral molecules that interact with polarized light. This depends on the concentration of the sample and the length of the sample tube. To standardize data, the quantity **specific rotation** ([α]) is defined using a specific sample tube length (usually 10 cm), concentration (reported in g/mL), temperature (25 °C), and wavelength. A specific rotation is reported as a positive (+) or negative (−) value without units.

For example, naturally occurring (*S*)-glyceraldehyde has a specific rotation of –8.7, while its enantiomer, (*R*)-glyceraldehyde, has a specific rotation of +8.7.

(*S*)-glyceraldehyde
$[\alpha] = -8.7$
levorotatory

(*R*)-glyceraldehyde
$[\alpha] = +8.7$
dextrorotatory

### SAMPLE PROBLEM 15.3

The specific rotation of camphor, an aromatic compound isolated from the wood of the camphor laurel, a large Asian evergreen, is +44. (a) Is camphor a dextrorotatory or levorotatory compound? (b) What is the specific rotation of the enantiomer of camphor? (c) If camphor melts as 174 °C, what is the melting point of its enantiomer?

### Analysis

Two enantiomers have identical melting points, boiling points, and solubility properties. The specific rotation of two enantiomers is the same numerical value, but opposite in sign.

### Solution

a. Camphor is dextrorotatory since its specific rotation is a positive value.

b. The enantiomer has a specific rotation of –44, the same value but opposite in sign to the specific rotation of camphor.

c. Camphor's enantiomer melts at 174 °C, since two enantiomers have identical melting points.

### PROBLEM 15.18

Pure cholesterol has a specific rotation of –32. (a) Is cholesterol a dextrorotatory or levorotatory compound? (b) What is the specific rotation of the enantiomer of cholesterol?

### PROBLEM 15.19

(*S*)-Alanine is an amino acid that is used to synthesize the complex proteins that make up the muscles of the body. (*S*)-Alanine has a melting point of 297 °C and a specific rotation of +8.5.

(*S*)-alanine

a. Draw the enantiomer of (*S*)-alanine, called (*R*)-alanine.

b. What is the melting point of (*R*)-alanine?

c. What is the specific rotation of (*R*)-alanine?

Camphor, a fragrant compound obtained from the wood of camphor laurel, has been utilized for centuries in cooking, ointments, and medicine. Much of the camphor used today is synthesized from petroleum products.

## 15.8 Compounds With Two or More Chirality Centers

Although most chiral compounds we have seen thus far have one chirality center, molecules may have two, three, or hundreds of chirality centers. Two examples—tartaric acid and ephedrine—were shown in Section 15.3.

- A compound with one chirality center has two stereoisomers—a pair of enantiomers.
- A compound with two chirality centers has a maximum of four possible stereoisomers.

Let's examine the four stereoisomers of the amino acid threonine. The two chirality centers in threonine are labeled in the given structure. Threonine is one of the 20 naturally occurring amino acids needed for protein synthesis. Since humans cannot synthesize threonine, it is an essential amino acid, meaning that it must be obtained in the diet.

$$
\begin{array}{c}
CO_2H \\
| \\
H_2N-C-H \\
| \\
H-C-OH \\
| \\
CH_3
\end{array}
$$

[The chirality centers are labeled in red.]

carbon skeleton of the
amino acid threonine

There are four different ways that the groups around two chirality centers can be arranged, shown in structures **A–D.**

**The four stereoisomers of a compound with two chirality centers**

|  A  |  B  |  C  |  D  |
|-----|-----|-----|-----|
| enantiomers | | enantiomers | |

**A** and **B** are mirror images, but they are not superimposable, so they are enantiomers. **C** and **D** are also mirror images, but they are not superimposable, so they are enantiomers as well. In other words, with *two* chirality centers, there can be *two* pairs of enantiomers.

Because these structures are drawn with the horizontal bonds of the chirality centers on wedges and the vertical bonds on dashed lines, Fischer projection formulas can be drawn for each stereoisomer by replacing each chirality center by a cross.

Thus, there are four stereoisomers for threonine: enantiomers **A** and **B,** and enantiomers **C** and **D.** What is the relationship between two stereoisomers like **A** and **C?** **A** and **C** are stereoisomers, but if you arrange a mirror plane between **A** and **C** you can see that they are *not* mirror images of each other. **A** and **C** represent a second broad class of stereoisomers, called **diastereomers.**

- *Diastereomers* are stereoisomers but they are *not* mirror images of each other.

**A** and **B** are diastereomers of **C** and **D,** and vice versa. Naturally occurring threonine is a single stereoisomer corresponding to structure **A.** The other stereoisomers do not occur in nature and cannot be used to synthesize biologically active proteins.

You have now been introduced to all of the possible types of isomers for organic molecules. A flow chart in Figure 15.4 illustrates the relationships among the major classes of isomers.

Figure 15.4    Summary—Types of Isomers

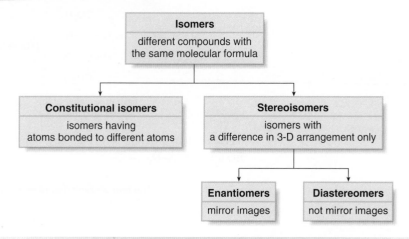

### SAMPLE PROBLEM 15.4

Considering the four stereoisomers of 2,3-pentanediol (**E–H**): (a) Which compound is an enantiomer of **E**? (b) Which compound is an enantiomer of **F**? (c) What two compounds are diastereomers of **G**?

Four stereoisomers
of 2,3-pentanediol:

|            E           |            F           |            G           |            H           |
|------------------------|------------------------|------------------------|------------------------|

### Analysis

Keep in mind the definitions:

- **Enantiomers are stereoisomers that are nonsuperimposable mirror images of each other.** Look for two compounds that when placed side-by-side have the groups on both chirality centers drawn as a *reflection* of each other. A given compound has only one possible enantiomer.
- **Diastereomers are stereoisomers that are *not* mirror images of each other.**

### Solution

a. **E** and **G** are enantiomers because they are mirror images that do not superimpose on each other.

b. **F** and **H** are enantiomers for the same reason.

|      E      |      G      |      F      |      H      |
|-------------|-------------|-------------|-------------|
|  enantiomers  |             |  enantiomers  |             |

c. Any compound that is a stereoisomer of **G** but is not its mirror image is a diastereomer. Thus, **F** and **H** are diastereomers of **G**.

### PROBLEM 15.20

Answer the following questions about the four stereoisomers of 3-bromo-2-chloropentane (**W–Z**).
(a) Which compound is the enantiomer of **W**? (b) Which compound is the enantiomer of **X**? (c) What two compounds are diastereomers of **Y**? (d) What two compounds are diastereomers of **Z**?

Four stereoisomers of
3-bromo-2-chloropentane:

$$
\begin{array}{cccc}
\text{CH}_3 & \text{CH}_3 & \text{CH}_3 & \text{CH}_3 \\
\text{H}{\blacktriangleright}\text{C}{\blacktriangleleft}\text{Cl} & \text{H}{\blacktriangleright}\text{C}{\blacktriangleleft}\text{Cl} & \text{Cl}{\blacktriangleright}\text{C}{\blacktriangleleft}\text{H} & \text{Cl}{\blacktriangleright}\text{C}{\blacktriangleleft}\text{H} \\
\text{H}{\blacktriangleright}\text{C}{\blacktriangleleft}\text{Br} & \text{Br}{\blacktriangleright}\text{C}{\blacktriangleleft}\text{H} & \text{H}{\blacktriangleright}\text{C}{\blacktriangleleft}\text{Br} & \text{Br}{\blacktriangleright}\text{C}{\blacktriangleleft}\text{H} \\
\text{CH}_2 & \text{CH}_2 & \text{CH}_2 & \text{CH}_2 \\
\text{CH}_3 & \text{CH}_3 & \text{CH}_3 & \text{CH}_3 \\
\textbf{W} & \textbf{X} & \textbf{Y} & \textbf{Z}
\end{array}
$$

### PROBLEM 15.21

Convert each stereoisomer (**W–Z**) in Problem 15.20 into a Fischer projection.

## 15.9 FOCUS ON THE HUMAN BODY
### The Sense of Smell

Research suggests that the odor of a particular molecule is determined more by its shape than by the presence of a particular functional group (Figure 15.5). For example, hexachloroethane ($Cl_3CCCl_3$) and cyclooctane have no obvious structural similarities. However, both molecules have a camphor-like odor, a fact attributed to their similar spherical shape, which is readily shown using space-filling models.

cyclooctane     space-filling model          space-filling model     hexachloroethane

**Figure 15.5**   The Shape of Molecules and the Sense of Smell

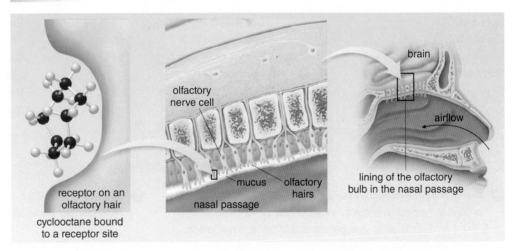

Cyclooctane and other molecules similar in shape bind to a particular olfactory receptor on the nerve cells that lie at the top of the nasal passage. Binding results in a nerve impulse that travels to the brain, which interprets impulses from particular receptors as specific odors.

Since enantiomers interact with chiral smell receptors, some enantiomers have different odors. There are a few well-characterized examples of this phenomenon in nature. For example, one enantiomer of carvone is responsible for the odor of caraway, whereas the other carvone enantiomer is responsible for the odor of spearmint.

caraway seeds

carvone
enantiomer **A**

carvone
enantiomer **B**

spearmint leaves

**A** has the odor of caraway.

**B** has the odor of spearmint.

Thus, the three-dimensional structure of a molecule is important in determining its odor.

### PROBLEM 15.22

Limonene is similar to carvone in that each enantiomer has a different odor; one enantiomer has a citrus fragrance while the other has a turpentine-like odor. Identify the chirality center in limonene and draw both enantiomers of limonene.

limonene

## CHAPTER HIGHLIGHTS

### KEY TERMS

Achiral (15.2)
Chiral (15.2)
Chirality center (15.2)
Constitutional isomer (15.1)
Cross formula (15.6)
Dextrorotatory (15.7)

Diastereomer (15.8)
Enantiomer (15.2)
Fischer projection formula (15.6)
Levorotatory (15.7)
Optically active (15.7)
Optically inactive (15.7)

Plane-polarized light (15.7)
Polarimeter (15.7)
Racemic mixture (15.5)
Specific rotation (15.7)
Stereochemistry (15.1)
Stereoisomer (15.1)

### KEY CONCEPTS

❶ **When is a molecule chiral or achiral? (15.2)**
  • A chiral molecule is not superimposable on its mirror image.
  • An achiral molecule is superimposable on its mirror image.
  • To see whether a molecule is chiral, draw it and its mirror image and see if all of the atoms and bonds align.

❷ **What is a chirality center? (15.2, 15.3)**
  • A chirality center is a carbon with four different groups around it.
  • A molecule with one chirality center is chiral.

**3** **What are enantiomers? (15.2, 15.3)**
- Enantiomers are mirror images that are not superimposable on each other. To draw two enantiomers, draw one molecule in three dimensions around the chirality center. Then draw the mirror image so that the substituents are a reflection of the groups in the first molecule.

**4** **Why do some chiral drugs have different properties from their mirror-image isomers? (15.5)**
- When a chiral drug must interact with a chiral receptor, only one enantiomer fits the receptor properly and evokes a specific response. Ibuprofen, naproxen, and L-dopa are examples of chiral drugs in which the two enantiomers have very different properties.

**5** **What is a Fischer projection? (15.6)**
- A Fischer projection is a specific way of depicting a chirality center. The chirality center is located at the intersection of a cross. The horizontal lines represent bonds that come out of the plane on wedges, and the vertical lines represent bonds that go back on dashed lines.

**6** **How do the physical properties of two enantiomers compare? (15.7)**
- Two enantiomers have identical physical properties except for their interaction with plane-polarized light.
- The specific rotation of two enantiomers is the same numerical value, but opposite in sign.

**7** **What is the difference between an enantiomer and a diastereomer? (15.8)**
- Enantiomers are stereoisomers that are nonsuperimposable mirror images of each other.
- Diastereomers are stereoisomers that are *not* mirror images of each other.

**8** **How is the shape of a molecule related to its odor? (15.9)**
- It is thought that the odor of a molecule is determined more by its shape than the presence of a particular functional group, so compounds of similar shape have similar odors. For an odor to be perceived, a molecule must bind to an olfactory receptor, resulting in a nerve impulse that travels to the brain. Enantiomers may have different odors because they bind with chiral receptors and each enantiomer fits the chiral receptors in a different way.

# PROBLEMS

Selected in-chapter and odd-numbered end-of-chapter problems have brief answers in Appendix B. The *Student Study Guide and Solutions Manual* contains detailed solutions to all in-chapter and odd-numbered end-of-chapter problems, as well as additional worked examples and a chapter self-test.

## Chiral Compounds, Chirality Centers, and Enantiomers

**15.23** Label each of the following objects as chiral or achiral: (a) chalk; (b) shoe; (c) baseball glove; (d) soccer ball.

**15.24** Label each of the following objects as chiral or achiral: (a) boot; (b) index card; (c) scissors; (d) drinking glass.

**15.25** Explain the following statement. Butane ($CH_3CH_2CH_2CH_3$) has a mirror image but it does not have an enantiomer.

**15.26** Explain why the human body is chiral.

**15.27** Draw a mirror image for each compound. Label each compound as chiral or achiral.

a.

halothane
(general anesthetic)

b.

dichloromethane
(common solvent)

**15.28** Draw a mirror image for each compound. Label each compound as chiral or achiral.

a. $CH_3CH_2$—O—$CH_2CH_3$

diethyl ether
(general anesthetic)

b. $HOCH_2$—C—OH
$CH_2OH$ / $H$

glycerol
(triol used in lotions)

**15.29** Consider the ball-and-stick model of **A,** and label **B** and **C** as either identical to **A** or an enantiomer of **A.**

**A**          **B**          **C**

**15.30** Consider the ball-and-stick model of **D,** and label **E** and **F** as either identical to **D** or an enantiomer of **D.**

**D**          **E**          **F**

**15.31** Label the chirality center (if one exists) in each compound. Compounds contain zero or one chirality center.

a. $CH_3CH_2CHCl$
     $|$
     $Cl$

b. $CH_3CHCHCl_2$
     $|$
     $Cl$

c. $CH_3CHCH_3$
     $|$
     $Cl$

d. $CH_3 \quad Cl$
    $| \qquad |$
    $CH_3CCH_2CHCH_3$
    $|$
    $H$

**15.32** Label the chirality center (if one exists) in each compound. Compounds contain zero or one chirality center.

a. $CH_3 \overset{\displaystyle O}{\overset{\|}{C}} CH_2CH_3$

b. $CH_3 \overset{\displaystyle O}{\overset{\|}{C}} CHCH_2CH_3$
    $\qquad\qquad\quad |$
    $\qquad\qquad\quad CH_3$

c. $CH_3CHCHO$
    $\quad\;|$
    $\quad\;CH_3$

d. $CH_3CHCHO$
    $\quad\;|$
    $\quad\;Cl$

**15.33** Label the chirality center (if one exists) in each cyclic compound. Some compounds contain no chirality centers.

a. (cyclohexane with —OH)

b. (cyclohexene with —OH)

c. (cyclopentene with —CH₃)

d. (cyclopentene with —CH₃)

**15.34** Label the chirality center (if one exists) in each cyclic compound. Some compounds contain no chirality centers.

a. (cyclopentane with —CH₃)

b. (cyclohexane with —CHCH₃ and OH)

c. (cyclohexanone, =O)

d. (cyclohexanone with CH₃, =O)

**15.35** Draw the structure of a compound that fits each description:
  a. an alkane of molecular formula $C_7H_{16}$ that contains one chirality center
  b. an alcohol of molecular formula $C_6H_{14}O$ that contains one chirality center

**15.36** Draw the structure of a compound that fits each description:
  a. an alkyl bromide of molecular formula $C_4H_9Br$ that contains one chirality center
  b. a diol of molecular formula $C_5H_{12}O_2$ that contains two chirality centers

**15.37** Explain why a carbonyl carbon can never be a chirality center.

**15.38** Explain why a carbon atom that is part of a triple bond can never be a chirality center.

**15.39** Locate the chirality center(s) in each biologically active compound.

a.

nicotine
(addictive stimulant from tobacco)

b. $HO_2CCH_2\overset{\displaystyle NH_2}{\underset{}{CH}}C\overset{\displaystyle}{\underset{\|}{\underset{O}{}}}NH\overset{\displaystyle CO_2CH_3}{\underset{}{CH}}CH_2$—

aspartame
Trade name: Equal
(synthetic sweetener)

**15.40** Locate the chirality center(s) in each drug.

a.

ketoprofen
(anti-inflammatory agent)

b.

methylphenidate
Trade name: Ritalin
(used for attention deficit hyperactivity disorder)

**15.41** Methamphetamine is an addictive stimulant sold illegally as "speed," "meth," or "crystal meth." Identify the chirality center in methamphetamine, and then draw both enantiomers in three dimensions around the chirality center.

—$CH_2\overset{\displaystyle H}{\underset{}{C}}H N\overset{\displaystyle}{\underset{CH_3}{}}CH_3$

methamphetamine

**15.42** Dobutamine is a heart stimulant used in stress tests to measure cardiac fitness. Identify the chirality center in dobutamine, and then draw both enantiomers in three dimensions around the chirality center.

dobutamine

## Isomers

**15.43** How are the compounds in each pair related? Are they identical molecules or enantiomers?

a.

b.

c.

**15.44** How are the compounds in each pair related? Are they identical molecules or enantiomers?

a.

b.

c.

**15.45** How are the molecules in each pair related? Choose from: identical molecules, constitutional isomers, enantiomers, diastereomers, or not isomers of each other.

a. $CH_3CH_2CH_2OCH_3$   and   $CH_3CH_2OCH_2CH_3$

b.

c.

d.

**15.46** How are the molecules in each pair related? Choose from: identical molecules, constitutional isomers, enantiomers, diastereomers, or not isomers of each other.

a.

b. $CH_3CH_2CH_2CHOH$   and   $CH_3CH_2OCH(CH_3)_2$

   $\qquad\qquad$ | $CH_3$

c. $CH_3CH_2OCH_2CH_3$   and

d.

**15.47** Answer each question with a compound of molecular formula $C_5H_{10}O_2$.
   a. Draw the structure of a compound that contains a COOH group and one chirality center.
   b. Draw the structure of a carboxylic acid that is a constitutional isomer of the compound drawn in part (a).
   c. Draw the structure of a constitutional isomer of the compound drawn in part (a), which contains a different functional group.

**15.48** Answer each question with a compound of molecular formula $C_5H_{12}O$.
   a. Draw the structure of a compound that contains an ether group and one chirality center.
   b. Draw the structure of an ether that is a constitutional isomer of the compound drawn in part (a).
   c. Draw the structure of a constitutional isomer of the compound drawn in part (a), which contains a different functional group.

**15.49** Draw the structure of the four constitutional isomers of molecular formula $C_5H_{10}O$ that contain an aldehyde (—CHO) as a functional group. Label any chirality center present in each compound. Some compounds have no chirality centers.

**15.50** Although there are four constitutional isomers of molecular formula $C_4H_9Cl$, only one contains a chirality center and can therefore exist as a pair of enantiomers. Draw both enantiomers of this alkyl chloride in three dimensions around the chirality center.

## Fischer Projections

**15.51** Convert the given ball-and-stick model to a Fischer projection.

**15.52** Convert the given ball-and-stick model to a Fischer projection.

**15.53** Convert each three-dimensional representation into a Fischer projection.

a. H►C◄OH with CHO above and CH₃ below

b. CH₃►C◄H with OCH₃ above and CH₃►C◄OH / CH₂CH₃ below

**15.54** Convert each three-dimensional representation into a Fischer projection.

a. CH₃►C◄H with OCH₂CH₃ above and N(CH₃)₂ below

b. H►C◄Br with COCH₂CH₃ above and H►C◄OH / CH₃ below

**15.55** Convert each Fischer projection into a three-dimensional representation with wedges and dashed bonds.

a. H——F with CH₃ above and CH(CH₃)₂ below

b. H——NH₂ / CH₃——H with COOH above and CH₂CH₃ below

**15.56** Convert each Fischer projection into a three-dimensional representation with wedges and dashed bonds.

a. HO——CH₃ with CH₂CH₃ above and phenyl below

b. H——Cl / H——Cl with CH₃ above and CH₂Cl below

**15.57** How are the Fischer projection formulas in each pair related to each other? Are they identical or are they enantiomers?

a. Cl——H and H——Cl with CH₃ above and CH₃ below

b. CH₃——OH and HO——CH₃ with COOH above and H below

**15.58** How are the Fischer projection formulas in each pair related to each other? Are they identical or are they enantiomers?

a. H——H and H——H with COOH above and NH₂ below

b. CH₃CH₂——CH₃ and CH₃——CH₂CH₃ with Cl above and Cl below

c. CH₃——OH and HO——CH₃ with CH₂OH above and H below

d. CH₃CH₂——CH₃ and CH₃——CH₂CH₃ with CH₂OCH₃ above and Cl below

(Top right) c. H——NH₂ and H₂N——H with CO₂H above and CH₂OH below

d. (CH₃)₃C——OH and HO——C(CH₃)₃ with C(CH₃)₃ above and H below

## Physical Properties of Enantiomers

**15.59** (a) Define the terms "optically active" and "optically inactive." (b) Give an example of a compound with molecular formula $C_4H_{10}O$ that is optically inactive. (c) Give an example of a compound with molecular formula $C_4H_{10}O$ that is optically active.

**15.60** (a) Draw the structure of a compound with molecular formula $C_5H_{10}O$ that contains an aldehyde and is optically inactive. (b) Draw the structure of a compound with molecular formula $C_5H_{10}O$ that contains an aldehyde and is optically active.

**15.61** Label each compound as optically active or optically inactive.

a. C with CH₃ above, Br and ''''CH₂CH₃, and H below

c. CH₃CH₂CH₂CH₂OH

b. cyclohexane——OH

**15.62** Label each compound as optically active or optically inactive.

a. (CH₃)₂CHCH₂CHO

c. O= cyclohexene with CH₃ wedge

b. cyclohexanone =O

**15.63** Lactose, the major carbohydrate in milk, has a specific rotation of +52 and is water soluble (22 g per 100 mL of $H_2O$).
(a) Is lactose a dextrorotatory or levorotatory compound?
(b) What is the specific rotation of the enantiomer of lactose?
(c) How much of the enantiomer of lactose dissolves in 100 mL of water?

**15.64** The anticancer drug taxol has a specific rotation of –49.
(a) What is the specific rotation of the enantiomer of taxol?
(b) How does the boiling point of taxol compare to the boiling point of its enantiomer? (c) How do the solubility properties of taxol compare to those of its enantiomer?

## Enantiomers and Diastereomers

**15.65** In what way are two enantiomers different from two diastereomers?

**15.66** What are the two major types of stereoisomers? Give an example of each type.

**15.67** Consider the stereoisomers (**A–D**) drawn below. These compounds are four-carbon sugars, as we will learn in Chapter 20.

A    B    C    D

a. How are the compounds in each pair related? Are the compounds enantiomers or diastereomers: [1] **A** and **B**; [2] **A** and **C**; [3] **A** and **D**; [4] **B** and **C**; [5] **B** and **D**; [6] **C** and **D?**
b. Draw a constitutional isomer of **A** that contains a ketone, not an aldehyde.

**15.68** Consider the stereoisomers (**E–H**) drawn below. These compounds are five-carbon sugars, as we will learn in Chapter 20.

E    F    G    H

a. How are the compounds in each pair related? Are the compounds enantiomers or diastereomers: [1] **E** and **F**; [2] **E** and **G**; [3] **E** and **H**; [4] **F** and **G**; [5] **F** and **H**; [6] **G** and **H?**
b. Draw a constitutional isomer of **E** that contains an aldehyde, not a ketone.

**15.69** In Chapter 13 we learned that cis and trans alkenes are stereoisomers. Are *cis*-2-butene and *trans*-2-butene enantiomers or diastereomers? Explain your choice.

**15.70** Are *cis*-2-butene and *trans*-2-butene chiral or achiral compounds? Explain your choice.

## Applications

**15.71** Lactic acid is a product of glucose metabolism. During periods of strenuous exercise, lactic acid forms faster than it can be oxidized, resulting in the aching feeling of tired muscles.

$CH_3CHCO_2H$
|
OH
lactic acid

a. Locate the chirality center in lactic acid.
b. Draw both enantiomers of lactic acid in three dimensions around the chirality center.
c. Draw Fischer projection formulas for both enantiomers of lactic acid.

**15.72** Locate the chirality centers in each vitamin.

a.
vitamin E

b.
vitamin C

**15.73** Hydroxydihydrocitronellal is another example of a compound that has two enantiomers that smell differently. One enantiomer smells minty, and the other smells like lily of the valley.

hydroxydihydrocitronellal

a. Locate the chirality center in this compound.
b. Draw both enantiomers in three dimensions around the chirality center.
c. Draw Fischer projection formulas for both enantiomers.

**15.74** Two enantiomers can sometimes taste very differently. L-Leucine, a naturally occurring amino acid used in protein synthesis, tastes bitter, but its enantiomer, D-leucine, tastes sweet.

leucine

a. Locate the chirality center in leucine.
b. Draw both enantiomers in three dimensions around the chirality center.
c. Draw Fischer projection formulas for both enantiomers.

**15.75** Answer the following questions about the analgesic propoxyphene (trade name: Darvon).

Darvon

a. Label the chirality centers.

b. Draw the enantiomer. Like many of the drugs discussed in Section 15.5, the enantiomer, levopropoxyphene (trade name: Novrad) has different biological properties. Levopropoxyphene is an antitussive agent, meaning it relieves coughs. (Do you notice anything about the trade names Darvon and Novrad?)

c. Draw the structure of one diastereomer.

d. Draw the structure of one constitutional isomer.

e. Convert Darvon to a Fischer projection formula.

**15.76** Plavix, the trade name for the generic drug clopidogrel, is used in the treatment of coronary artery disease. Like many newer drugs, Plavix is sold as a single enantiomer.

clopidogrel
Trade name: Plavix

a. Locate the chirality center.

b. Draw both enantiomers in three dimensions around the chirality center.

c. Convert both enantiomers to Fischer projection formulas.

## CHALLENGE PROBLEMS

**15.77** Identify the nine chirality centers in sucrose, the sweet-tasting carbohydrate we use as table sugar.

sucrose

**15.78** Identify the six chirality centers in the anabolic steroid nandrolone. Nandrolone is used to increase muscle mass in body builders and athletes, although it is not permitted in competitive sports.

nandrolone

**11-*cis*-Retinal** is the light-sensitive aldehyde that plays a key role in the chemistry of vision for all vertebrates, arthropods, and mollusks.

# 16

# Aldehydes and Ketones

## CHAPTER GOALS

*In this chapter you will learn how to:*

1. Identify the characteristics of aldehydes and ketones
2. Name aldehydes and ketones
3. Give examples of useful aldehydes and ketones
4. Draw the products of oxidation reactions of aldehydes
5. Draw the products of reduction reactions of aldehydes and ketones
6. Understand the basic reactions involved in vision
7. Identify and prepare hemiacetals and acetals

C hapter 16 is the first of two chapters that concentrate on compounds that contain a **carbonyl group (C═O),** perhaps the most important functional group in organic chemistry. In this chapter we examine **aldehydes** and **ketones,** compounds that contain a carbonyl carbon bonded to hydrogen or carbon atoms. Aldehydes and ketones occur widely in nature, and also serve as useful starting materials and solvents in industrial processes. All simple carbohydrates contain a carbonyl group, and more complex carbohydrates are derived from reactions discussed in this chapter.

## 16.1   Structure and Bonding

Two broad classes of compounds contain a *carbonyl group.*

**carbonyl group**

1. **Compounds that have only carbon and hydrogen atoms bonded to the carbonyl group**

aldehyde                              ketone

- An *aldehyde* has at least one H atom bonded to the carbonyl group.
- A *ketone* has two alkyl groups bonded to the carbonyl group.

2. **Compounds that contain an electronegative atom bonded to the carbonyl group**

carboxylic acid              ester                     amide

These compounds include **carboxylic acids, esters,** and **amides,** which contain an electronegative oxygen or nitrogen atom bonded directly to the carbonyl carbon. Esters and amides are called **carboxylic acid derivatives,** since they can be prepared from carboxylic acids. Carboxylic acids and their derivatives are discussed in Chapter 17, while aldehydes and ketones are the subject of this chapter.

Two structural features dominate the properties and chemistry of the carbonyl group.

trigonal planar

- The carbonyl carbon atom is trigonal planar, and all bond angles are 120°. In this way the carbonyl carbon resembles the carbons of a carbon–carbon double bond.
- Since oxygen is more electronegative than carbon, a carbonyl group is polar. The carbonyl carbon is electron poor ($\delta^+$) and the oxygen is electron rich ($\delta^-$). In this way the carbonyl carbon is very different from the carbons of a nonpolar carbon–carbon double bond.

As mentioned in Chapter 11, the double bond of a carbonyl group is usually omitted in drawing shorthand structures. An aldehyde is often written as **RCHO**. Remember that the **H atom is bonded to the carbon atom,** not the oxygen. Likewise, a ketone is written as **RCOR,** or if both alkyl groups are the same, **R₂CO**.

Many simple aldehydes and ketones are naturally occurring. For example, octanal, decanal, and piperitone are among the 70 organic compounds that contribute to the flavor and odor of an orange.

### PROBLEM 16.1

Draw out each compound to clearly show what groups are bonded to the carbonyl carbon. Label each compound as a ketone or aldehyde.

a. $CH_3CH_2CHO$     b. $CH_3CH_2COCH_3$     c. $(CH_3)_3CCOCH_3$     d. $(CH_3CH_2)_2CHCHO$

### PROBLEM 16.2

Draw the structure of the three constitutional isomers of molecular formula $C_4H_8O$ that contain a carbonyl group. Label each compound as a ketone or aldehyde.

### PROBLEM 16.3

Label each trigonal planar carbon in 11-*cis*-retinal, the chapter-opening molecule whose chemistry is discussed in Section 16.6.

11-*cis*-retinal

## 16.2 Nomenclature

Both IUPAC and common names are used for aldehydes and ketones.

### 16.2A Naming Aldehydes

- In IUPAC nomenclature, aldehydes are identified by the suffix *-al.*

To name an aldehyde using the IUPAC system:

1. Find the longest chain containing the CHO group, and change the **-e** ending of the parent alkane to the suffix **-al.**
2. Number the chain or ring to put the CHO group at C1, but omit this number from the name. Apply all of the other usual rules of nomenclature.

Simple aldehydes have common names that are widely used. In fact, the common names **formaldehyde, acetaldehyde,** and **benzaldehyde** are virtually always used instead of their IUPAC names. Common names all contain the suffix *-aldehyde.*

formaldehyde
(methanal)

acetaldehyde
(ethanal)

benzaldehyde
(benzenecarbaldehyde)

(IUPAC names are in parentheses.)

### SAMPLE PROBLEM 16.1

Give the IUPAC name for each aldehyde.

### Analysis and Solution

a. [1] Find and name the longest chain containing the CHO.

butane ----→ butanal
(4 C's)

[2] Number and name substituents, making sure the CHO group is at C1.

**Answer: 2,3-dimethylbutanal**

b. [1] Find and name the longest chain containing the CHO.

pentane ----→ pentanal
(5 C's)

[2] Number and name substituents, making sure the CHO group is at C1.

**Answer: 2-ethylpentanal**

## PROBLEM 16.4

Give the IUPAC name for each aldehyde.

a. (CH₃)₂CHCH₂CH₂CH₂CHO     b. (CH₃)₃CC(CH₃)₂CH₂CHO

c. CH₃CHCHCH₂CH₂CHCH₃ with CH₂CH₃ and CHO groups and CH₃ below

## PROBLEM 16.5

Give the structure corresponding to each IUPAC name.

a. 2-chloropropanal
b. 3,4,5-triethylheptanal

c. 3,6-diethylnonanal
d. *o*-ethylbenzaldehyde

## PROBLEM 16.6

Give the IUPAC name for each aldehyde depicted in the ball-and-stick models. Both aldehydes are isolated from yuzu, a citrus fruit extensively cultivated in Japan.

a.     b.

Yuzu is a small citrus fruit used widely in Japanese cooking. Its unusual aroma is partly due to the aldehydes depicted in Problem 16.6.

## 16.2B   Naming Ketones

- **In the IUPAC system, ketones are identified by the suffix *-one*.**

To name an acyclic ketone using IUPAC rules:

1. Find the longest chain containing the carbonyl group, and change the *-e* ending of the parent alkane to the suffix *-one.*
2. Number the carbon chain to give the carbonyl carbon the lower number. Apply all of the other usual rules of nomenclature.

With cyclic ketones, numbering always begins at the carbonyl carbon, but the "1" is usually omitted from the name. The ring is then numbered clockwise or counterclockwise to give the first substituent the lower number.

Most common names for ketones are formed by **naming both alkyl groups** on the carbonyl carbon, **arranging them alphabetically,** and adding the word *ketone.* Using this method, the common name for 2-butanone becomes ethyl methyl ketone.

methyl group      ethyl group

CH₃—C(=O)—CH₂CH₃

IUPAC name: **2-butanone**     |     Common name: **ethyl methyl ketone**

Three widely used common names for some simple ketones do not follow this convention:

acetone          acetophenone          benzophenone

## SAMPLE PROBLEM 16.2

Give IUPAC names for each ketone.

a. $CH_3-\overset{\displaystyle O}{\overset{\|}{C}}-\overset{\displaystyle }{\underset{\underset{\displaystyle CH_3}{|}}{C}}HCH_2CH_3$

b.

### Analysis and Solution

a.  [1] Find and name the longest chain containing the carbonyl group.

$CH_3-\overset{\displaystyle O}{\overset{\|}{C}}-\overset{}{\underset{\underset{\displaystyle CH_3}{|}}{C}}HCH_2CH_3$

pentane  ----→ pentan*one*
(5 C's)

[2] Number and name substituents, making sure the carbonyl carbon has the lowest possible number.

$CH_3-\overset{\displaystyle O}{\overset{\|}{C}}-\overset{}{\underset{\underset{\displaystyle CH_3}{|}}{C}}HCH_2CH_3$

**Answer: 3-methyl-2-pentanone**

b.  [1] Name the ring.

cyclohexane  ----→ cyclohexan*one*
(6 C's)

[2] Number and name substituents, making sure the carbonyl carbon is at C1.

**Answer: 3-ethyl-4-methylcyclohexanone**

## PROBLEM 16.7

Give the IUPAC name for each ketone.

a. $CH_3CH_2\overset{\displaystyle O}{\overset{\|}{C}}\overset{}{\underset{\underset{\displaystyle CH_3}{|}}{C}}HCH_2CH_2CH_3$

b.

c. $(CH_3)_3C\overset{\displaystyle O}{\overset{\|}{C}}CH_2CH_2CH_2CH_3$

## PROBLEM 16.8

Give the structure corresponding to each name.

a. butyl ethyl ketone
b. 2-methyl-3-pentanone

c. *p*-ethylacetophenone
d. 2-propylcyclobutanone

# 16.3   Physical Properties

Because aldehydes and ketones have a polar carbonyl group, they are **polar molecules** with stronger intermolecular forces than the hydrocarbons of Chapters 12 and 13. Since they have no O—H bond, two molecules of RCHO or RCOR are incapable of intermolecular hydrogen bonding, giving them weaker intermolecular forces than alcohols.

CH₃—C(CH₃)=Ö (acetone) polar bond

Oppositely charged ends of the dipoles interact.

As a result:

- Aldehydes and ketones have *higher* boiling points than hydrocarbons of comparable size.
- Aldehydes and ketones have *lower* boiling points than alcohols of comparable size.

| | | |
|---|---|---|
| CH₃CH₂CH₂CH₂CH₃ | CH₃CH₂CH₂CHO | CH₃CH₂CH₂CH₂OH |
| pentane | butanal | 1-butanol |
| bp 36 °C | bp 76 °C | bp 118 °C |

CH₃CH₂COCH₃

2-butanone

bp 80 °C

→ **Increasing strength of intermolecular forces**
**Increasing boiling point**

Based on the general rule governing solubility (i.e., **"like dissolves like,"** Section 8.2), aldehydes and ketones are soluble in organic solvents. Moreover, because aldehydes and ketones contain an oxygen atom with an available lone pair, they can intermolecularly hydrogen bond to water.

CH₃—C(CH₃)=Ö (acetone) · · · hydrogen bond · · · H—Ö:—H

As a result:

- Low molecular weight aldehydes and ketones (those having less than six carbons) are soluble in both organic solvents and water.
- Higher molecular weight aldehydes and ketones (those having six carbons or more) are soluble in organic solvents, but insoluble in water.

## PROBLEM 16.9

Which compound in each pair has the higher boiling point?

a. (cyclohexanone) =O or (methylcyclohexane) —CH₃

c. (cyclohexanone) =O or (cyclohexanol) —OH

b. (CH₃CH₂)₂CO  or  (CH₃CH₂)₂C=CH₂

d. CH₃(CH₂)₆CH₃  or  CH₃(CH₂)₅CHO

**PROBLEM 16.10**

Acetone and progesterone are two ketones that occur naturally in the human body. Discuss the solubility properties of both compounds in water and organic solvents.

acetone

progesterone

## 16.4 FOCUS ON HEALTH & MEDICINE
### Interesting Aldehydes and Ketones

formaldehyde
$CH_2=O$

**Formaldehyde** ($CH_2=O$, the simplest aldehyde) is a starting material for the synthesis of many resins and plastics, and billions of pounds are produced annually in the United States. Formaldehyde is also sold as a 37% aqueous solution called **formalin,** a disinfectant and preservative for biological specimens. As a product of the incomplete combustion of coal and other fossil fuels, formaldehyde is partly responsible for the irritation caused by smoggy air.

acetone
$(CH_3)_2C=O$

**Acetone** [$(CH_3)_2C=O$, the simplest ketone] is an industrial solvent and a starting material in the synthesis of some organic polymers. Acetone is produced naturally in cells during the breakdown of fatty acids. In diabetes, a disease where normal metabolic processes are altered because of the inadequate secretion of insulin, individuals often have unusually high levels of acetone in the bloodstream. The characteristic odor of acetone can be detected on the breath of diabetic patients when their disease is poorly controlled.

Many aldehydes with characteristic odors occur in nature, as shown in Figure 16.1. It is thought that the shape of these molecules is an important factor in determining their odors, as discussed in Section 15.8.

Ketones play an important role in the tanning industry. Dihydroxyacetone is the active ingredient in commercial tanning agents that produce sunless tans. Dihydroxyacetone reacts with proteins in the skin, producing a complex colored pigment that gives the skin a brown hue. In addition, many commercial sunscreens are ketones that have the carbonyl carbon bonded to one or two benzene rings (see also Section 13.11). Examples include avobenzone, oxybenzone, and dioxybenzone.

sunless tanning agent

dihydroxyacetone

avobenzone

oxybenzone            dioxybenzone

sunscreen

[Ketone carbonyls are shown in red.]

## Figure 16.1

Some Naturally Occurring Aldehydes with Characteristic Odors

cinnamaldehyde
(odor of cinnamon)

vanillin
(flavoring agent isolated
from vanilla beans)

[Aldehyde carbonyls are shown in red.]

geranial
(lemony odor,
isolated from lemon grass)

citronellal
(lemony odor, isolated from lemon
grass and citronella grass)

- **Cinnamaldehyde,** the major component of cinnamon bark, is a common flavoring agent.

- **Vanillin** is the primary component of the extract of the vanilla bean. Because natural sources cannot meet the high demand, most vanilla flavoring agents are made synthetically from starting materials derived from petroleum.

- **Geranial** has the lemony odor characteristic of lemon grass. Geranial is used in perfumery and as a starting material for synthesizing vitamin A.

- **Citronellal** gives the distinctive lemon odor to citronella candles, commonly used to repel mosquitoes.

Some naturally occurring compounds do not contain a carbonyl group, but they are converted to aldehydes and ketones by enzymes in cells. One such compound is **amygdalin,** sometimes called **laetrile.**

amygdalin
(laetrile)

enzymes

glucose
(two molecules)

benzaldehyde

+

HCN
hydrogen
cyanide
toxic gas

**Amygdalin** is present in the seeds and pits of apricots, peaches, and wild cherries. In the body, amygdalin is converted to two aldehydes, glucose and benzaldehyde. Also formed as a by-product is hydrogen cyanide, **HCN,** a toxic gas. Amygdalin was once touted as an anticancer drug, and is still available in some countries for this purpose, although its effectiveness is unproven. It appears as if the toxic HCN produced from amygdalin indiscriminately kills cells without targeting cancer cells. Patients in some clinical trials involving amygdalin show signs of cyanide poisoning but not cancer remission.

### PROBLEM 16.11

Acetone [$(CH_3)_2C{=}O$] is a useful solvent because it dissolves a variety of compounds well. For example, both hexane [$CH_3(CH_2)_4CH_3$] and $H_2O$ are soluble in acetone. Explain why these solubility properties are observed.

### PROBLEM 16.12

Which sunscreen—avobenzone, oxybenzone, or dioxybenzone—is probably most soluble in water, and therefore most readily washed off when an individual goes swimming? Explain your choice.

# 16.5   Reactions of Aldehydes and Ketones

## 16.5A   General Considerations

Aldehydes and ketones undergo two general types of reactions.

**1. Aldehydes can be oxidized to carboxylic acids.**

Since aldehydes contain a hydrogen atom bonded to the carbonyl carbon, they can be oxidized to carboxylic acids, as discussed in Section 16.5B.

**2. Aldehydes and ketones undergo addition reactions.**

Like alkenes, aldehydes and ketones contain a multiple bond (the carbonyl group) that is readily broken. As a result, aldehydes and ketones undergo addition reactions with a variety of reagents. In the addition reaction, new groups X and Y are added to the carbonyl group of the starting material. One bond of the double bond is broken and two new single bonds are formed. We examine the addition of $H_2$ in Section 16.6 and the addition of alcohols (ROH) in Section 16.8.

## 16.5B   Oxidation of Aldehydes

**Since aldehydes contain a hydrogen atom bonded directly to the carbonyl carbon, they can be oxidized to carboxylic acids;** that is, the aldehyde C—H bond can be converted to a C—OH bond. Since ketones have no hydrogen atom bonded to the carbonyl group, they are not oxidized under similar reaction conditions.

A common reagent for this oxidation is potassium dichromate, $K_2Cr_2O_7$, a red-orange solid that is converted to a green $Cr^{3+}$ product during oxidation.

Aldehydes are easily oxidized by oxygen in the air. When $CH_3CH_2CH_2CHO$ (butanal) stands at room temperature, it slowly develops the characteristic smell of its oxidation product, $CH_3CH_2CH_2COOH$ (butanoic acid), a compound that contributes to the distinctive odor of human sweat.

As we learned in Section 14.5, $K_2Cr_2O_7$ oxidizes other functional groups (most notably 1° and 2° alcohols), as well. Aldehydes can be oxidized *selectively* in the presence of other functional groups using **silver(I) oxide ($Ag_2O$) in aqueous ammonium hydroxide ($NH_4OH$).** This is called **Tollens reagent.** Only aldehydes react with Tollens reagent; all other functional groups are inert. Oxidation with Tollens reagent provides a distinct color change because the $Ag^+$ reagent is converted to silver metal (Ag), which precipitates out of the reaction mixture as a silver mirror.

Aldehydes are said to give a *positive* Tollens test; that is, they react with $Ag^+$ to form RCOOH and Ag. When the reaction is carried out in a glass flask, a silver mirror is formed on its walls. Other functional groups give a *negative* Tollens test; that is, no silver mirror forms.

### SAMPLE PROBLEM 16.3

What product is formed when each carbonyl compound is treated with $K_2Cr_2O_7$?

a.    b.

### Analysis

Compounds that contain a C—H and C—O bond on the *same* carbon are oxidized with $K_2Cr_2O_7$. Thus:

- Aldehydes (RCHO) are oxidized to $RCO_2H$.
- Ketones ($R_2CO$) are not oxidized with $K_2Cr_2O_7$.

### Solution

The aldehyde in part (a) is oxidized with $K_2Cr_2O_7$ to a carboxylic acid, but the ketone in part (b) is inert to oxidation.

a. 

Replace 1 C—H bond by 1 C—O bond.

b.    No reaction

This C is bonded only to other C's.

### PROBLEM 16.13

What product is formed when each carbonyl compound is treated with $K_2Cr_2O_7$? In some cases, no reaction occurs.

a. $CH_3CH_2CHO$    b. $(CH_3CH_2)_2C=O$    c. $CH_3C=CHCH_2CH_2CHCH_2CHO$ (with $CH_3$ substituents)

### SAMPLE PROBLEM 16.4

What product is formed when each compound is treated with Tollens reagent ($Ag_2O$, $NH_4OH$)?

a.    b. $HOCH_2$—

### Analysis

**Only aldehydes (RCHO) react with Tollens reagent.** Ketones and alcohols are inert to oxidation.

### Solution

The aldehyde in both compounds is oxidized to $RCO_2H$, but the 1° alcohol in part (b) does not react with Tollens reagent.

a.

Replace 1 C—H bond by 1 C—O bond.

b.

Only the aldehyde is oxidized.

---

### PROBLEM 16.14

What product is formed when each compound is treated with Tollens reagent ($Ag_2O$, $NH_4OH$)? In some cases, no reaction occurs.

a. $CH_3(CH_2)_6CHO$     b.     c.     d.

---

## 16.6   Reduction of Aldehydes and Ketones

Recall from Section 12.8 that to determine if an organic compound has been reduced, we compare the number of C—H and C—O bonds. **Reduction is the *opposite* of oxidation.**

- Reduction results in a *decrease* in the number of C—O bonds or an *increase* in the number of C—H bonds.

**The conversion of a carbonyl group (C=O) to an alcohol (C—OH) is a reduction,** since the starting material has more C—O bonds than the product (two versus one). Reduction of a carbonyl is also an **addition reaction,** since the elements of $H_2$ are added across the double bond, forming new C—H and O—H bonds. The symbol **[H]** is often used to represent a general reduction reaction.

## 16.6A Specific Features of Carbonyl Reductions

The identity of the carbonyl starting material determines the type of alcohol formed as product in a reduction reaction.

- Aldehydes (RCHO) are reduced to 1° alcohols (RCH$_2$OH).

aldehyde      1° alcohol

- Ketones (RCOR) are reduced to 2° alcohols (R$_2$CHOH).

ketone      2° alcohol

Many different reagents can be used to reduce an aldehyde or ketone to an alcohol. For example, the addition of H$_2$ to a carbonyl group (C=O) takes place with the same reagents used for the addition of H$_2$ to a C=C—namely, **H$_2$ gas in the presence of palladium (Pd) metal** (Section 13.6). The metal is a catalyst that provides a surface to bind both the carbonyl compound and H$_2$, and this speeds up the rate of reduction. The addition of hydrogen to a multiple bond is called **hydrogenation.**

**Examples**

aldehyde      1° alcohol

ketone      2° alcohol

### SAMPLE PROBLEM 16.5

What alcohol is formed when each aldehyde or ketone is treated with H$_2$ in the presence of a Pd catalyst?

a.

b.

### Analysis

To draw the products of reduction:

- Locate the C=O and mentally break one bond in the double bond.
- Mentally break the H—H bond of the reagent.
- Add one H atom to each atom of the C=O, forming new C—H and O—H single bonds.

## Solution

The aldehyde (RCHO) in part (a) forms a 1° alcohol (RCH$_2$OH) and the ketone in part (b) forms a 2° alcohol (R$_2$CHOH).

Break one bond.

a.

Break the single bond.

1° alcohol

Break one bond.

b.

Break the single bond.

2° alcohol

## PROBLEM 16.15

What alcohol is formed when each compound is treated with H$_2$ and a Pd catalyst?

a. CH$_3$CH$_2$CH$_2$CHO     b.     c. CH$_3$COCH$_2$CH$_3$     d. —CHO

## 16.6B   Examples of Carbonyl Reduction in Organic Synthesis

The reduction of aldehydes and ketones is a common reaction used in the laboratory synthesis of many useful compounds.

Chemists synthesize compounds for many different reasons. Sometimes a naturally occurring compound has useful properties but is produced by an organism in only minute amounts. Chemists then develop a method to prepare this molecule from simpler starting materials to make it more readily available and less expensive. For example, **muscone,** a strongly scented ketone isolated from musk, is an ingredient in many perfumes. Originally isolated from the male musk deer, muscone is now prepared synthetically in the lab. One step in the synthesis involves reducing a ketone to a 2° alcohol.

ketone

2° alcohol

[H]     four steps

muscone
odor of musk
(perfume component)

male musk deer

Sometimes chemists prepare molecules that do not occur in nature because they have useful medicinal properties. For example, **fluoxetine** (trade name: Prozac) is a prescription antidepressant that does not occur in nature. One step in a laboratory synthesis of fluoxetine involves reduction of a ketone to a 2° alcohol. Fluoxetine is widely used because it has excellent medicinal properties, *and* because it is readily available by laboratory synthesis.

## PROBLEM 16.16

What carbonyl starting material is needed to prepare alcohol **A** by a reduction reaction? **A** can be converted to the anti-inflammatory agent ibuprofen in three steps.

$(CH_3)_2CHCH_2$—⟨benzene ring⟩—$\overset{OH}{\underset{}{\overset{|}{C}HCH_3}}$          $(CH_3)_2CHCH_2$—⟨benzene ring⟩—$\overset{COOH}{\underset{}{\overset{|}{C}HCH_3}}$

**A**                                   ibuprofen

**CONSUMER NOTE**

Niacin can be obtained from foods such as soybeans, which contain it naturally, and from breakfast cereals, which are fortified with it.

niacin
vitamin B$_3$

## 16.6C  FOCUS ON THE HUMAN BODY
### Biological Reductions

The reduction of carbonyl groups is common in biological systems. Biological systems do not use $H_2$ and Pd as a reducing agent. Instead, they use the coenzyme **NADH** (nicotinamide adenine dinucleotide, reduced form) in the presence of an enzyme. The enzyme binds both the carbonyl compound and NADH, holding them closely together, and this facilitates the addition of $H_2$ to the carbonyl group, forming an alcohol. The NADH itself is oxidized in the process, forming $NAD^+$. **$NAD^+$,** a biological oxidizing agent, is a coenzyme synthesized from the vitamin niacin, which can be obtained from soybeans, among other dietary sources.

| **Biological reduction** |
|---|

$\overset{O}{\underset{}{\overset{\|}{C}}}$  +  NADH  $\xrightarrow{\text{enzyme}}$  $-\overset{OH}{\underset{H}{\overset{|}{\underset{|}{C}}}}-$  +  $NAD^+$

coenzyme

For example, the reduction of pyruvic acid with NADH, catalyzed by the enzyme lactate dehydrogenase, yields lactic acid. Pyruvic acid is formed during the metabolism of the simple sugar glucose.

$CH_3\overset{O}{\underset{}{\overset{\|}{C}}}COOH$  $\xrightarrow[\text{lactate dehydrogenase}]{\text{NADH}}$  $CH_3-\overset{OH}{\underset{H}{\overset{|}{\underset{|}{C}}}}-COOH$  +  $NAD^+$

pyruvic acid                    lactic acid

## 16.7 FOCUS ON THE HUMAN BODY
### The Chemistry of Vision

The human eye consists of two types of light-sensitive cells—the rod cells, which are responsible for sight in dim light, and the cone cells, which are responsible for color vision and sight in bright light. Animals like pigeons, whose eyes have only cone cells, have color vision but see poorly in dim light, while owls, which have only rod cells, are color blind but see well in dim light.

The chemistry of vision in the rod cells centers around the aldehyde, **11-*cis*-retinal,** the chapter-opening molecule.

11-*cis*-retinal

crowding

light

light

all-*trans*-retinal

+

nerve impulse

The crowding around the double bond is relieved.

Although 11-*cis*-retinal is a stable molecule, the cis geometry around one of the double bonds causes crowding; a hydrogen atom on one double bond is close to the methyl group on an adjacent double bond. In the human retina (Figure 16.2), 11-*cis*-retinal is bonded to the protein opsin, forming rhodopsin or visual purple. When light hits the retina, the 11-cis double bond is isomerized to its more stable trans isomer, and all-*trans*-retinal is formed. This process sends a nerve impulse to the brain, which is then converted into a visual image.

In order for the process to continue, the all-*trans*-retinal must be converted back to 11-*cis*-retinal. This occurs by a series of reactions that involve biological oxidation (Section 14.5) and reduction (Section 16.6). As shown in Figure 16.3, NADH is the coenzyme that reduces the aldehyde in all-*trans*-retinal to all-*trans*-retinol, **vitamin A** (Reaction [1]). NAD$^+$ is the coenzyme that oxidizes 11-*cis*-retinol back to 11-*cis*-retinal (Reaction [3]), so the chemical cycle of vision can continue.

This scheme explains the role of vitamin A (Section 11.7) in vision. Vitamin A can be obtained either directly in the diet or from the orange pigment β-carotene in carrots. Vitamin A, also called all-*trans*-retinol, is converted in two steps to 11-*cis*-retinal, the aldehyde essential for vision in the rod cells. Since the rod cells are responsible for vision in dim light, a deficiency of vitamin A causes night blindness.

### PROBLEM 16.17

How are the compounds in each pair related? Choose from stereoisomers, constitutional isomers, or not isomers of each other.

   a. all-*trans*-retinal and 11-*cis*-retinal            c. vitamin A and 11-*cis*-retinol
   b. all-*trans*-retinal and vitamin A

**Figure 16.2**

Vision

11-*cis*-retinal

rhodopsin

hydrophobic region

disc membrane

rhodopsin in a rod cell

Rhodopsin contains 11-*cis*-retinal bound to the protein opsin.

rod cell in the retina

In the rod cells of the eye, the 11-*cis*-retinal bonded to opsin absorbs light, and the crowded 11-cis double bond is isomerized to the trans isomer. This process generates a nerve impulse that is converted to a visual image by the brain.

**Figure 16.3**    Vitamin A and the Chemistry of Vision

needed for vision

all-*trans*-retinal

11-*cis*-retinal

[1] Reduction    NADH

NAD⁺    [3] Oxidation

all-*trans*-retinol
vitamin A

[2] Isomerization

11-*cis*-retinol

obtained from the diet

- Reaction [1] (reduction): The aldehyde in all-*trans*-retinal (labeled in blue) is reduced to a 1° alcohol using the coenzyme NADH. The product is all-*trans*-retinol.

- Reaction [2] (isomerization): The trans double bond (labeled in red) is isomerized to a cis double bond, forming 11-*cis*-retinol.

- Reaction [3] (oxidation): The 1° alcohol in 11-*cis*-retinol (labeled in blue) is oxidized with the coenzyme NAD⁺ to an aldehyde. This re-forms 11-*cis*-retinal and the chemical cycle of vision continues.

## 16.8   Acetal Formation

**Aldehydes and ketones undergo addition reactions with alcohols (ROH) to form hemi-acetals and acetals.** Acetal formation is done in the presence of sulfuric acid ($H_2SO_4$).

### 16.8A   Acetals and Hemiacetals

Addition of one molecule of alcohol (ROH) to an aldehyde or ketone forms a **hemiacetal.** Like other addition reactions, one bond of the C=O is broken and two new single bonds are formed. Acyclic hemiacetals are unstable. They react with a second molecule of alcohol to form **acetals.**

- A *hemiacetal* contains an OH (hydroxyl) group and an OR (alkoxy) group bonded to the *same* carbon.
- *Acetals* are compounds that contain two OR groups (alkoxy groups) bonded to the *same* carbon.

Two examples of acetal formation using ethanol ($CH_3CH_2OH$) as the alcohol component are given.

### SAMPLE PROBLEM 16.6

Draw the hemiacetal and acetal formed when cyclohexanone is treated with methanol ($CH_3OH$) in the presence of $H_2SO_4$.

## Analysis

To form a hemiacetal and acetal from a carbonyl compound:

- Locate the C=O in the starting material.
- Break one C—O bond and add one equivalent of $CH_3OH$ across the double bond, placing the $OCH_3$ group on the carbonyl carbon. This forms the hemiacetal.
- Replace the OH group of the hemiacetal by $OCH_3$ to form the acetal.

## Solution

## PROBLEM 16.18

Draw the hemiacetal and acetal formed when each carbonyl compound is treated with two equivalents of the given alcohol in the presence of $H_2SO_4$.

a.   +   $CH_3OH$

c.   +   $CH_3CH_2OH$

b. $(CH_3CH_2)_2C=O$   +   $CH_3OH$

**Acetals are *not* ethers,** even though both compounds contain a C—OR bond.

| acetal | ether |
|---|---|
| 2 OR groups on one carbon | 2 C's on a single O atom |

- An acetal contains one carbon atom bonded to *two* OR groups.
- An ether contains only *one* oxygen atom bonded to two carbons.

## SAMPLE PROBLEM 16.7

Identify each compound as an ether, hemiacetal, or acetal.

a. $CH_3CH_2$—O—$CH_2CH_3$

b.

## Analysis

Recall the definitions to identify the functional groups:

- An ether has the general structure ROR.
- A hemiacetal has one C bonded to OH and OR.
- An acetal has one C bonded to two OR groups.

Solution

a.  CH₃CH₂$-$O$-$CH₂CH₃

     2 C's on one O atom

        ether

b.

This C is bonded to 2 O's.

acetal

Note that the acetal in part (b) is part of a ring. It contains one ring carbon bonded to two oxygens, making it an acetal.

### PROBLEM 16.19

Identify each compound as an ether, hemiacetal, or acetal.

a.

c.  CH₃CH₂CH₂CH₂$-$C$-$OCH₃

b.

d.

## 16.8B  Cyclic Hemiacetals

Although acyclic hemiacetals are generally unstable, **cyclic hemiacetals containing five- and six-membered rings are stable compounds** that are readily isolated.

**Hemiacetal General structure**

$$-C-OR$$
OH

One C is bonded to:
• one OH group
• one OR group

**Cyclic hemiacetals**

Each indicated C is bonded to:
• an OH group
• an OR group that is part of a ring

These cyclic hemiacetals are formed by an *intramolecular* reaction of a compound that contains *both* a hydroxyl group and an aldehyde or ketone.

The C$=$O and OH groups react.

HOCH₂CH₂CH₂CH₂$-$C$-$H   —re-draw—→            hemiacetal

5-hydroxypentanal

Cyclic hemiacetals are especially important in carbohydrate chemistry. **The most common simple carbohydrate, glucose, exists predominantly as a cyclic hemiacetal.** Glucose has five OH groups, but only one OH group is bonded to a carbon that is also bonded to another oxygen atom, making it a hemiacetal. All of the other OH groups in glucose are "regular" alcohols. We will learn much more about these stable cyclic hemiacetals in Chapter 20.

HOCH$_2$

hemiacetal

HO

OH

HO OH

glucose
(cyclic hemiacetal form)

**Cyclic hemiacetals are converted to acetals by reaction with another alcohol (ROH).** To draw the structure of the resulting acetal, replace the OH group of the hemiacetal by the OR group of the alcohol.

OH

Replace OH by OCH$_3$.

OCH$_3$

acetal

$+$ CH$_3$O—H $\xrightarrow{\text{H}_2\text{SO}_4}$ $+$ H$_2$O

Many biologically active molecules contain acetals and cyclic hemiacetals. For example, lactose, the principal carbohydrate in milk, contains one acetal and one hemiacetal. Many individuals, mainly of Asian and African descent, lack adequate amounts of lactase, the enzyme needed to digest and absorb lactose. This condition, lactose intolerance, is associated with abdominal cramping and recurrent diarrhea.

HOCH$_2$

acetal

HO

CH$_2$OH

HO HO

HO

hemiacetal

lactose HO OH

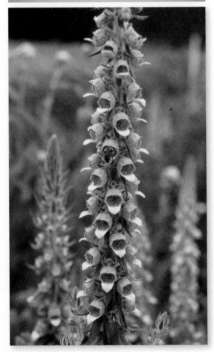

The leaves of the woolly foxglove plant are the source of the potent cardiac drug digoxin.

## SAMPLE PROBLEM 16.8

Identify the three acetals in digoxin, a naturally occurring drug prescribed for patients with congestive heart failure and other heart ailments.

OH CH$_3$

CH$_3$

CH$_3$

O O

CH$_3$ O O

HO O

CH$_3$

OH

HO HO

HO OH

HO O

OH

digoxin

### Analysis

Although the structure of digoxin is complicated, look at each O atom individually and recall that an **acetal has one C bonded to two OR groups.**

## Solution

The acetal carbons in digoxin are indicated with arrows and the oxygen atoms of the acetals are drawn in red.

digoxin

## PROBLEM 16.20

Label the hemiacetal or acetal in each compound. Glucosamine [part (a)] is available in many over-the-counter remedies for the treatment of osteoarthritis, although recent studies cast doubt on its efficacy. Salicin [part (b)] is a naturally occurring pain reliever isolated from the bark of the willow tree.

a.                                                        b.

glucosamine                                              salicin

## PROBLEM 16.21

What acetal is formed in each reaction?

a.    +   $CH_3CH_2OH$   $\xrightarrow{H_2SO_4}$

b.    +     $\xrightarrow{H_2SO_4}$

## 16.8C   Acetal Hydrolysis

Acetals are stable molecules, but they can be converted back to aldehydes and ketones by treatment with acid and water. This reaction is a *hydrolysis,* **since bonds are cleaved by reaction with water.**

### SAMPLE PROBLEM 16.9

What hydrolysis products are formed when the acetal $(CH_3CH_2)_2C(OCH_3)_2$ is treated with $H_2SO_4$ in $H_2O$?

#### Analysis

To draw the products of hydrolysis:

- Locate the two C—OR bonds on the same carbon.
- Replace the two C—O single bonds with a carbonyl group (C=O).
- Each OR group then becomes a molecule of alcohol (ROH) product.

#### Solution

| Break two bonds. | | Form a carbonyl group. |
|---|---|---|

$$CH_3CH_2{-}\underset{\underset{CH_2CH_3}{|}}{\overset{\overset{OCH_3}{|}}{C}}{-}OCH_3 \ + \ H_2O \ \underset{}{\overset{H_2SO_4}{\rightleftharpoons}} \ CH_3CH_2\overset{\overset{O}{\|}}{C}CH_2CH_3 \ + \ 2\ CH_3O{-}H$$

acetal                                      3-pentanone              Two molecules of
                                                                     alcohol are also formed.

### PROBLEM 16.22

What products are formed by hydrolysis of each acetal?

a. $CH_3{-}\underset{\underset{CH_2CH_2CH_3}{|}}{\overset{\overset{OCH_3}{|}}{C}}{-}OCH_3$

b. (cyclohexane with $CH_3CH_2O$ and $OCH_2CH_3$ groups)

c. (cyclohexane with $\underset{\underset{OCH_3}{|}}{\overset{\overset{OCH_3}{|}}{C}}{-}H$)

# CHAPTER HIGHLIGHTS

## KEY TERMS

Acetal (16.8)

Aldehyde (16.1)

Carbonyl group (16.1)

Cyclic hemiacetal (16.8)

Hemiacetal (16.8)

Hydrogenation (16.6)

Hydrolysis (16.8)

Ketone (16.1)

$NAD^+$ (16.6)

NADH (16.6)

Oxidation (16.5)

Reduction (16.6)

Tollens reagent (16.5)

## KEY REACTIONS

[1]  Oxidation of aldehydes (16.5)

$$RCHO \ \xrightarrow[\text{Tollens reagent}]{\overset{K_2Cr_2O_7}{\text{or}}} \ \underset{\text{carboxylic acid}}{RCOOH}$$

**[2]   Reduction (16.6)**

a.   Aldehydes        $RCHO \xrightarrow[\text{Pd}]{H_2} RCH_2OH$

1° alcohol

b.   Ketones          $R_2CO \xrightarrow[\text{Pd}]{H_2} R_2CHOH$

2° alcohol

c.   Biological reduction

**[3]   Acetals and hemiacetals (16.8)**

a.   General reaction

hemiacetal                       acetal

b.   Cyclic hemiacetal       $HOCH_2CH_2CH_2CH_2$

5-hydroxypentanal

cyclic hemiacetal

c.   Cyclic acetals

cyclic hemiacetal                      cyclic acetal

d.   Acetal hydrolysis

## KEY CONCEPTS

**❶  What are the characteristics of aldehydes and ketones?**

- An aldehyde has the general structure RCHO, and contains a carbonyl group (C=O) bonded to at least one hydrogen atom. (16.1)
- A ketone has the general structure RCOR', and contains a carbonyl group (C=O) bonded to two carbon atoms. (16.1)
- The carbonyl carbon is trigonal planar, with bond angles of approximately 120°. (16.1)
- The carbonyl group is polar, giving an aldehyde or ketone stronger intermolecular forces than hydrocarbons. (16.3)
- Aldehydes and ketones have lower boiling points than alcohols, but higher boiling points than hydrocarbons of comparable size. (16.3)
- Aldehydes and ketones are soluble in organic solvents, but those having less than six C's are water soluble, too. (16.3)

**❷  How are aldehydes and ketones named? (16.2)**

- Aldehydes are identified by the suffix -al, and the carbon chain is numbered to put the carbonyl group at C1.
- Ketones are identified by the suffix -one, and the carbon chain is numbered to give the carbonyl group the lower number.

**❸  Give examples of useful aldehydes and ketones. (16.4)**

- Formaldehyde ($CH_2$=O) is an irritant in smoggy air, a preservative, and a disinfectant, and it is a starting material for synthesizing polymers.
- Acetone [$(CH_3)_2$C=O] is an industrial solvent and polymer starting material.
- Several aldehydes—cinnamaldehyde, vanillin, geranial, and citronellal—have characteristic odors and occur naturally in fruits and plants.

- Dihydroxyacetone [$(HOCH_2)_2C=O$] is the active ingredient in artificial tanning agents, and many other ketones are useful sunscreens.
- Amygdalin, a naturally occurring carbonyl derivative, forms toxic HCN on hydrolysis.

**❹ What products are formed when aldehydes are oxidized? (16.5)**
- Aldehydes are oxidized to carboxylic acids (RCOOH) with $K_2Cr_2O_7$ or Tollens reagent.
- Ketones are not oxidized since they contain no H atom on the carbonyl carbon.

**❺ What products are formed when aldehydes and ketones are reduced? (16.6)**
- Aldehydes are reduced to 1° alcohols with $H_2$ and a Pd catalyst.
- Ketones are reduced to 2° alcohols with $H_2$ and a Pd catalyst.
- Biological reduction occurs with the coenzyme NADH.

**❻ What reactions occur during vision? (16.7)**
- When light hits the retina, the crowded C=C in 11-*cis*-retinal is isomerized to a more stable trans double bond, and a nerve impulse is generated. All-*trans*-retinal is converted back to the cis isomer by a three-step sequence—reduction, isomerization, and oxidation.

**❼ What are hemiacetals and acetals, and how are they prepared? (16.8)**
- Hemiacetals contain an OH group and an OR group bonded to the same carbon.
- Acetals contain two OR groups bonded to the same carbon.
- Treatment of an aldehyde or ketone with an alcohol (ROH) first forms an unstable hemiacetal, which reacts with more alcohol to form an acetal.
- Cyclic hemiacetals are stable compounds present in carbohydrates and some drugs.
- Acetals are converted back to aldehydes and ketones by hydrolysis with water and acid.

# PROBLEMS

Selected in-chapter and odd-numbered end-of-chapter problems have brief answers in Appendix B. The *Student Study Guide and Solutions Manual* contains detailed solutions to all in-chapter and odd-numbered end-of-chapter problems, as well as additional worked examples and a chapter self-test.

## Structure and Bonding

**16.23** Draw the structure of a compound that fits each description:
a. an aldehyde of molecular formula $C_8H_{16}O$ that has six carbons in its longest chain
b. a ketone of molecular formula $C_6H_{12}O$ that contains five carbons in its longest chain
c. a ketone of molecular formula $C_5H_8O$ that contains a ring
d. an aldehyde of molecular formula $C_6H_{10}O$ that has the CHO group bonded to a ring

**16.24** Draw the structure of a constitutional isomer of 2-heptanone ($CH_3COCH_2CH_2CH_2CH_2CH_3$) that:
a. contains an aldehyde
b. contains a ketone
c. contains a hydroxyl group (OH)

**16.25** How do a C=O and a C=C compare with regards to the following: (a) geometry; (b) polarity; (c) type of reaction?

**16.26** How do an aldehyde and a ketone compare in (a) structure; (b) geometry; (c) polarity?

**16.27** Can an aldehyde have molecular formula $C_5H_{12}O$? Explain why or why not.

**16.28** Can a ketone have molecular formula $C_4H_{10}O$? Explain why or why not.

## Nomenclature

**16.29** Give an acceptable name for each carbonyl compound depicted in the ball-and-stick models.

a.      b.

**16.30** Give an acceptable name for each carbonyl compound depicted in the ball-and-stick models.

a.      b.

**16.31** Give an acceptable name for each aldehyde.
a. $CH_3CH_2CH_2CHCH_2CHO$
        |
       $CH_3$

   $\phantom{xx}CH_3$
   $\phantom{xx}|$
b. $CH_3CH_2CHCH_2CHCH_2CHO$
              |
             $CH_3$

   $\phantom{xx}CH_2CHO$
   $\phantom{xx}|$
c. $CH_3CH_2CH_2CHCH_2CH_2CH_3$

d. $(CH_3CH_2)_3C(CH_2)_3 - \overset{\overset{\displaystyle CH_3}{|}}{\underset{\underset{\displaystyle CH_3}{|}}{C}} - CHO$

e. $Cl - \overset{\phantom{x}}{\bigcirc} - CHO$

**16.32** Give an acceptable name for each aldehyde.

a. $(CH_3)_3CCH_2CHO$

b. $(CH_3CH_2)_2CHCH_2CH_2CHO$

c. $CH_3CH_2CH_2CH_2\overset{\overset{\displaystyle CH_3}{|}}{CH}CHCH_3$ with $CH_2CHO$ below

d. $(CH_3CH_2CH_2CH_2)_2CHCH_2CHO$

e. $CH_3CH_2 - \bigcirc - CHO$

**16.33** Draw the structure corresponding to each name.

a. 3,3-dichloropentanal
b. 3,4-dimethylhexanal
c. o-bromobenzaldehyde
d. 4-hydroxyheptanal

**16.34** Draw the structure corresponding to each name.

a. 2-bromooctanal
b. 2-propylheptanal
c. 3,4-dimethoxybenzaldehyde
d. 3,4-dihydroxynonanal

**16.35** Give an acceptable name for each ketone.

a. $(CH_3)_2CHCH_2\overset{\overset{\displaystyle O}{\|}}{C}CH_3$

b. $CH_3$ and $CH_3$ cyclohexanone

c. $\bigcirc$ with $\overset{O}{\|}C CH_3$ and $CH_2CH_2CH_2CH_3$

d. $(CH_3)_2CH\overset{\overset{\displaystyle O}{\|}}{C}\overset{\overset{\displaystyle}{}}{CH}CH_2CH_3$ with $CH_3$ below

e. $Cl$ cyclopentanone

**16.36** Give an acceptable name for each ketone.

a. $CH_3CH_2CH_2CH_2CHCH_2CH_3$ with $\overset{O}{\|}C CH_3$

b. cyclobutanone with $Cl$ and $Cl$

c. $CH_3CH_2 \overset{\overset{\displaystyle O}{\|}}{C} (CH_2)_5CH(CH_3)_2$

d. $CH_3CH_2CH\overset{\overset{\displaystyle O}{\|}}{C}CHCH_2CH_3$ with $CH_3$ and $CH_3$ below

e. cyclopentanone with $CH_2CH_3$ and $CH_3$

**16.37** Draw the structure corresponding to each name.

a. 3,3-dimethyl-2-hexanone
b. methyl propyl ketone
c. m-ethylacetophenone
d. 2,4,5-triethylcyclohexanone

**16.38** Draw the structure corresponding to each name.

a. dibutyl ketone
b. 1-chloro-3-pentanone
c. p-bromoacetophenone
d. 3-hydroxycyclopentanone

**16.39** Draw the structure of the four constitutional isomers of molecular formula $C_6H_{12}O$ that contain an aldehyde and four carbons in the longest chain. Give the IUPAC name for each aldehyde.

**16.40** Draw the structure of the three isomeric ketones of molecular formula $C_5H_{10}O$. Give the IUPAC name for each ketone.

**16.41** Each of the following names is incorrect. Draw the structure of the compound and name it correctly.

a. 1-pentanone
b. 4-hexanone
c. 3-propyl-2-butanone
d. 2-methyl-1-octanal

**16.42** Each of the following names is incorrect. Draw the structure of the compound and name it correctly.

a. 6-octanone
b. 1-heptanone
c. 3-propyl-1-cyclopentanone
d. 5-methylcyclohexanone

## Physical Properties and Intermolecular Forces

**16.43** Draw out the structure of benzaldehyde, including any lone pairs on oxygen. Then, show the hydrogen bonding interactions between benzaldehyde and water.

**16.44** Can hydrogen bonding occur between the compounds in each pair? If hydrogen bonding is possible, draw out the compounds and indicate how that interaction would take place.
   a. two molecules of acetaldehyde ($CH_3CHO$)
   b. $CH_3CHO$ and $H_2O$
   c. $CH_3CHO$ and $CH_3OH$

**16.45** Which compound in each pair has the higher boiling point?
   a. $(CH_3)_3CCH_2CH_2CH_3$   or   $(CH_3)_3CCH_2CHO$

   b.

**16.46** Which compound in each pair has the higher boiling point?
   a. $CH_3(CH_2)_6CHO$   or   $CH_3(CH_2)_7OH$
   b. $CH_3(CH_2)_6CHO$   or   $CH_3(CH_2)_2CHO$

**16.47** Rank the following compounds in order of increasing melting point.

**16.48** Menthone and menthol are both isolated from mint. Explain why menthol is a solid at room temperature but menthone is a liquid.

menthone                menthol

**16.49** Label each compound as water soluble or water insoluble.
   a.
   c. $CH_3CH_2CH_2CH_3$

   b.

**16.50** Label each compound as water soluble or water insoluble.
   a.
   c. $CH_3CH_2CH_2OH$

   b. $CH_3CH_2CH_2CHO$

**16.51** Explain why 2,3-butanedione ($CH_3COCOCH_3$) is more soluble in water than acetone [$(CH_3)_2CO$] even though it has more carbon atoms. Would you expect 2,3-butanedione to be soluble in an organic solvent like diethyl ether?

**16.52** Explain why the simplest ketone, acetone, has a much higher boiling point than the simplest aldehyde, formaldehyde.

## Oxidation and Reduction

**16.53** What product is formed when each compound is treated with $K_2Cr_2O_7$? With some compounds, no reaction occurs.
   a. $CH_3(CH_2)_4CHO$
   c.

   b.                     —$CH_2CHO$
   d. $CH_3(CH_2)_4CH_2OH$

**16.54** What product is formed when each compound is treated with $K_2Cr_2O_7$? With some compounds, no reaction occurs.
   a.
   c. $CH_3CHCH_2CH_2CH_3$ with OH

   b. $CH_3(CH_2)_8CHO$
   d.

**16.55** What product is formed when each compound in Problem 16.53 is treated with Tollens reagent ($Ag_2O$, $NH_4OH$)? With some compounds, no reaction occurs.

**16.56** What product is formed when each compound in Problem 16.54 is treated with Tollens reagent ($Ag_2O$, $NH_4OH$)? With some compounds, no reaction occurs.

**16.57** Answer the following questions about the carbohydrate erythrulose, an ingredient in sunless tanning agents.

erythrulose

   a. Does erythrulose contain an aldehyde or ketone?
   b. Classify each hydroxyl group as 1°, 2°, or 3°.
   c. What product is formed when erythrulose is treated with Tollens reagent?
   d. What product is formed when erythrulose is treated with $K_2Cr_2O_7$?

**16.58** Consider the following ball-and-stick model.

   a. Locate the chirality center.
   b. Is the carbonyl group part of an aldehyde or a ketone?
   c. Classify each hydroxyl group as 1°, 2°, or 3°.
   d. What product is formed when this compound is treated with Tollens reagent?

**16.59** What aldehyde is needed to prepare each carboxylic acid by an oxidation reaction?

$\qquad$ CH$_3$
a. CH$_3$CH$_2$CHCH$_2$CO$_2$H

b. CH$_3$—⟨benzene ring⟩—CO$_2$H

c. CH$_3$CH$_2$CHCH$_2$CH$_3$
$\qquad$ CO$_2$H

**16.60** What aldehyde is needed to prepare each carboxylic acid by an oxidation reaction?

a. ⟨cyclopentane ring⟩—CH$_2$CH$_2$CO$_2$H

Br
b. ⟨benzene ring⟩—CO$_2$H

Cl
c. CH$_3$(CH$_2$)$_8$CHCO$_2$H

**16.61** What alcohol is formed when each carbonyl compound is treated with H$_2$ and a Pd catalyst?

a. CH$_3$CH$_2$—⟨benzene ring⟩—CHO

b. ⟨cyclohexanone with CH$_3$⟩
CH$_3$

**16.62** What alcohol is formed when each carbonyl compound is treated with H$_2$ and a Pd catalyst?

O
‖
C
a. CH$_3$CH$_2$$\quad$CH$_2$CH(CH$_3$)$_2$

b. CH$_3$(CH$_2$)$_6$CHO

**16.63** (a) Draw the structure of 6-methyloctanal, a component of yuzu (Section 16.2). (b) Label the chirality center. (c) What product is formed when 6-methyloctanal is treated with H$_2$ and a palladium catalyst?

**16.64** (a) Draw the structure of 2-octanone, a compound partly responsible for the flavor of some mushrooms. (b) What product is formed when 2-octanone is treated with H$_2$ and a palladium catalyst? (c) Label the chirality centers (if any) in the product.

**16.65** What carbonyl compound is needed to make each alcohol by a reduction reaction?

a. CH$_3$CH$_2$CH$_2$CH$_2$CH$_2$OH

OH
b. ⟨cyclohexane ring⟩
CH$_3$

**16.66** What carbonyl compound is needed to make each alcohol by a reduction reaction?

OH
a. CH$_3$CH$_2$CHCH$_2$CH$_2$CH$_3$

b. (CH$_3$)$_2$CHCH$_2$CH$_2$OH

**16.67** Why can't 1-methylcyclohexanol be prepared by the reduction of a carbonyl compound?

⟨cyclohexane ring with⟩ CH$_3$
$\qquad$ OH

1-methylcyclohexanol

**16.68** Why can't (CH$_3$)$_3$COH be prepared by the reduction of a carbonyl compound?

## Hemiacetals and Acetals

**16.69** Draw the structure of a compound of molecular formula C$_5$H$_{12}$O$_2$ that fits each description.
  a. a compound that contains an acetal
  b. a compound that contains a hemiacetal
  c. a compound that contains two ethers
  d. a compound that contains an alcohol and an ether, but is not a hemiacetal

**16.70** Locate the two acetals in amygdalin (Section 16.4).

**16.71** Label each functional group as an alcohol, ether, acetal, or hemiacetal.

OCH$_3$
a. CH$_3$—C—H
OCH$_3$

OCH$_2$CH$_3$
b. CH$_3$—C—H
OH

OCH$_3$
c. HOCH$_2$CHCH$_2$CH$_3$

d. ⟨tetrahydropyran ring with O⟩

**16.72** Label each functional group as an alcohol, ether, acetal, or hemiacetal.

a. ⟨cyclohexane ring with⟩ OCH$_3$ / OCH$_3$

OH
b. CH$_3$—C—OCH$_2$CH$_2$CH$_3$
CH$_3$

c. ⟨pyran ring with O⟩—OCH$_2$CH$_2$CH$_3$

d. ⟨dioxane ring with two O⟩

**16.73** What acetal is formed when each aldehyde or ketone is treated with two equivalents of methanol (CH$_3$OH) in the presence of H$_2$SO$_4$?

CH$_3$
a. ⟨cyclopentanone ring with two CH$_3$⟩=O
CH$_3$

b. CH$_2$=O

O
‖
C
c. CH$_3$$\quad$CH$_2$CH$_2$CH$_3$

d. ⟨benzene ring⟩—CH$_2$CHO

**16.74** What acetal is formed when each aldehyde or ketone is treated with two equivalents of ethanol (CH₃CH₂OH) in the presence of $H_2SO_4$?

a. $CH_3CH_2CH_2\overset{\displaystyle O}{\overset{\|}{C}}CH_2CH_3$ c. $(CH_3)_2CHCH_2CH_2CHO$

b. [cyclohexanone with CH₃ substituent]

d. $CH_3CH_2CHO$

**16.75** (a) What hemiacetal is formed when acetone [(CH₃)₂CO] is treated with one equivalent of cyclopentanol? (b) What acetal is formed when acetone is treated with two equivalents of cyclopentanol in the presence of $H_2SO_4$?

**16.76** (a) What hemiacetal is formed when benzaldehyde (C₆H₅CHO) is treated with one equivalent of cyclohexanol? (b) What acetal is formed when benzaldehyde is treated with two equivalents of cyclohexanol in the presence of $H_2SO_4$?

**16.77** [structure: tetrahydrofuran ring with OH]

**A**

a. Identify the hemiacetal carbon in compound **A**.
b. What hydroxy aldehyde would form this hemiacetal in a cyclization reaction?
c. What product is formed when **A** is treated with CH₃OH and $H_2SO_4$?

**16.78** [structure: pyran ring with two CH₃ and OH]

**B**

a. Identify the hemiacetal carbon in compound **B**.
b. What hydroxy aldehyde would form this hemiacetal in a cyclization reaction?
c. What product is formed when **B** is treated with CH₃CH₂OH and $H_2SO_4$?

**16.79** What hemiacetal is formed when hydroxy aldehyde **C** is cyclized?

$HOCH_2CH_2CH_2\overset{\displaystyle}{\underset{\displaystyle CH_3}{CH}}\overset{\displaystyle O}{\overset{\|}{C}}H$

**C**

**16.80** What hemiacetal is formed when hydroxy aldehyde **D** is cyclized?

$HO\overset{\displaystyle}{\underset{\displaystyle CH_3}{CH}}CH_2CH_2CH_2\overset{\displaystyle O}{\overset{\|}{C}}H$

**D**

**16.81** What products are formed when each acetal is hydrolyzed with water and sulfuric acid?

a. [cyclohexane ring with $OCH_2CH_2CH_3$ and $OCH_2CH_2CH_3$]

b. $H-\overset{\displaystyle OCH_3}{\underset{\displaystyle OCH_3}{C}}-CH_2CH_2CH_3$

**16.82** What products are formed when each acetal is hydrolyzed with water and sulfuric acid?

a. $CH_3CH_2-\overset{\displaystyle OCH_2CH_3}{\underset{\displaystyle OCH_2CH_3}{C}}-CH_2CH_3$

b. $CH_3O-$ [cyclohexane ring with $OCH_3$ and $OCH_3$]

## General Reactions

**16.83** Answer each question about carbonyl compound **A**, depicted in the ball-and-stick model, and one of the many components of the mango.

**A**

a. Draw a skeletal structure for **A**.
b. Give an acceptable name for **A**.
c. How many trigonal planar carbons are present in **A**?
d. What product is formed when **A** is treated with two equivalents of CH₃OH in the presence of acid?

**16.84** Answer each question about phenylacetaldehyde, depicted in the ball-and-stick model, and one of the components responsible for the fragrance of the plumeria flower.

phenylacetaldehyde

a. Draw a skeletal structure for phenylacetaldehyde.
b. How many trigonal planar carbons are present in phenylacetaldehyde?
c. What product is formed when phenylacetaldehyde is treated with two equivalents of CH₃OH in the presence of acid?
d. What product is formed when phenylacetaldehyde is treated with one equivalent of hydrogen gas in the presence of a metal catalyst?

**16.85** Benzaldehyde is the compound principally responsible for the odor of almonds. What products are formed when benzaldehyde is treated with each reagent?

benzaldehyde

a. $H_2$, Pd
b. $K_2Cr_2O_7$
c. $Ag_2O$, $NH_4OH$
d. $CH_3OH$ (2 equivalents), $H_2SO_4$
e. $CH_3CH_2OH$ (2 equivalents), $H_2SO_4$
f. Product in (e), then $H_2O$, $H_2SO_4$

**16.86** Anisaldehyde is a component of anise, a spice with a licorice odor used in cooking and aromatherapy. What products are formed when anisaldehyde is treated with each reagent?

anisaldehyde

a. $H_2$, Pd
b. $K_2Cr_2O_7$
c. $Ag_2O$, $NH_4OH$
d. $CH_3OH$ (2 equivalents), $H_2SO_4$
e. $CH_3CH_2OH$ (2 equivalents), $H_2SO_4$
f. Product in (e), then $H_2O$, $H_2SO_4$

**16.87** 2-Heptanone is an alarm pheromone of the bee. What products are formed when 2-heptanone is treated with each reagent? With some reagents, no reaction occurs.

2-heptanone

a. $H_2$, Pd
b. $K_2Cr_2O_7$
c. $Ag_2O$, $NH_4OH$
d. $CH_3OH$ (2 equivalents), $H_2SO_4$
e. $CH_3CH_2OH$ (2 equivalents), $H_2SO_4$
f. Product in (e), then $H_2O$, $H_2SO_4$

**16.88** 2,6-Dimethyl-3-heptanone is a communication pheromone of the bee. What products are formed when 2,6-dimethyl-3-heptanone is treated with each reagent? With some reagents, no reaction occurs.

2,6-dimethyl-3-heptanone

a. $H_2$, Pd
b. $K_2Cr_2O_7$
c. $Ag_2O$, $NH_4OH$
d. $CH_3OH$ (2 equivalents), $H_2SO_4$
e. $CH_3CH_2OH$ (2 equivalents), $H_2SO_4$
f. Product in (e), then $H_2O$, $H_2SO_4$

**16.89** Three constitutional isomers of molecular formula $C_5H_8O$ can be converted to 1-pentanol ($CH_3CH_2CH_2CH_2CH_2OH$) on treatment with two equivalents of $H_2$ in the presence of a Pd catalyst. Draw the structures of the three possible compounds, all of which contain a carbonyl group.

**16.90** Identify **A–C** in the following reaction sequence.

$$A \xrightarrow[\text{Pd}]{H_2} B \xrightarrow{H_2SO_4}$$
$$C_5H_8O \qquad C_5H_{10}O$$

$$C \xrightarrow[\text{Pd}]{H_2}$$
$$C_5H_8$$

## Applications

**16.91** Androsterone is a male sex hormone that controls the development of secondary sex characteristics in males. Draw the organic products formed when androsterone is treated with each reagent.

androsterone

a. $H_2$, Pd
b. $K_2Cr_2O_7$
c. $CH_3OH$ (2 equivalents), $H_2SO_4$
d. $CH_3CH_2OH$ (2 equivalents), $H_2SO_4$

**16.92** Salmeterol (trade name: Serevent) is a drug that dilates airways and is used to treat asthma. It can be formed by the reduction of a dicarbonyl compound **X** with excess $H_2$ and a Pd catalyst.

X

a. Draw the structure of salmeterol.
b. Label the one chirality center in salmeterol.
c. Draw both enantiomers of salmeterol in three dimensions using wedges and dashes (see Section 15.3).

**16.93** When cinnamon is ingested, the cinnamaldehyde it contains is oxidized by the coenzyme $NAD^+$ and an enzyme in a similar fashion to the biological oxidation described in Section 14.6. What oxidation product is formed from cinnamaldehyde?

cinnamaldehyde

**16.94** Safrole is a naturally occurring compound isolated from sassafras plants. Once used as a common food additive in root beer and other beverages, it is now banned because it is carcinogenic.

safrole

a. Label the functional groups in safrole.
b. What products are formed when safrole undergoes hydrolysis with water and sulfuric acid?

**16.95** 2-Deoxyribose is a building block of DNA, very large organic molecules that store all genetic information. Label each OH group in 2-deoxyribose as being part of a regular alcohol or a hemiacetal.

2-deoxyribose

**16.96** Paraldehyde, a hypnotic and sedative once commonly used to treat seizures and induce sleep in some hospitalized patients, is formed from three molecules of acetaldehyde ($CH_3CHO$). Label the acetal carbons in paraldehyde.

paraldehyde

**16.97** Describe the main reaction that occurs in the rod cells in the retina, which generates a nerve impulse that allows us to see. What role does the geometry of 11-*cis*-retinal play in this process?

**16.98** What reactions convert all-*trans*-retinal back to 11-*cis*-retinal so that the process of vision can continue?

# CHALLENGE PROBLEMS

**16.99** Monensin, a complex antibiotic produced by the bacterium *Streptomyces cinamonsis,* is added to cattle feed to protect the cattle from infection. Identify each oxygen-containing functional group.

monensin

**16.100** Chloral hydrate is a sedative formed by the addition of water to chloral ($Cl_3CCHO$). Chloral hydrate is sometimes used to calm a patient prior to a surgical procedure. It has also been used for less reputable purposes. Adding it to an alcoholic beverage forms a so-called "knock-out drink," causing an individual to pass out. Although we have not studied the formation of hydrates from aldehydes, this reaction resembles the addition of alcohols to aldehydes to form hemiacetals. What is the structure of chloral hydrate?

# 17

Soaps are salts of carboxylic acids, which clean clothes by dissolving the hydrocarbons of dirt in their long nonpolar carbon chains.

# Carboxylic Acids, Esters, and Amides

## CHAPTER GOALS

*In this chapter you will learn how to:*

1. Identify the characteristics of carboxylic acids, esters, and amides

2. Name carboxylic acids, esters, and amides

3. Give examples of useful carboxylic acids

4. Give examples of useful esters and amides

5. Draw the products of acid–base reactions of carboxylic acids

6. Explain how soap cleans away dirt

7. Discuss the acid–base chemistry of aspirin

8. Convert carboxylic acids to esters and amides

9. Draw the products of the hydrolysis of esters and amides

10. Draw the structures of polyesters and polyamides

11. Explain how penicillin works

hapter 17 is the second of two chapters that concentrates on compounds that contain a **carbonyl group (C=O).** While Chapter 16 focused on aldehydes (RCHO) and ketones ($R_2CO$), Chapter 17 discusses the chemistry and properties of **carboxylic acids (RCOOH), esters (RCOOR'), and amides (RCONR'$_2$).** All three families of organic compounds occur widely in nature, and many useful synthetic compounds have been prepared as well. Simple carboxylic acids like acetic acid ($CH_3COOH$) have a sour taste and a biting odor, and long-chain carboxylic acids form vegetable oils and animal fat. Simple esters have easily recognized fragrances, and the most abundant lipids contain three ester groups. Several useful drugs are amides, and all proteins, such as those that form hair, muscle, and connective tissue, contain many amide units.

## 17.1 Structure and Bonding

**Carboxylic acids, esters,** and **amides** are three families of organic molecules that contain a **carbonyl group (C=O)** bonded to an element more electronegative than carbon.

- *Carboxylic acids* are organic compounds containing a carboxyl group (COOH).

General structure

carboxylic acid    **carboxyl group**    acetic acid    $CH_3CO_2H$

The word **carboxyl** (for a COOH group) is derived from **carb**onyl (C=O) + hyd**roxyl** (OH).

Although the structure of a carboxylic acid is often abbreviated as **RCOOH** or **RCO$_2$H,** keep in mind that the central carbon atom of the functional group has a double bond to one oxygen atom and a single bond to another.

- *Esters* are carbonyl compounds that contain an alkoxy group (OR') bonded to the carbonyl carbon.

General structure

ester    methyl acetate    $CH_3CO_2CH_3$

The structure of an ester is often abbreviated as RCOOR' or RCO$_2$R'.

- *Amides* are carbonyl compounds that contain a nitrogen atom bonded to the carbonyl carbon.

General structure

amide          1° amide          2° amide          3° amide
R' = H or alkyl   1 C—N bond     2 C—N bonds    3 C—N bonds

The N atom of an amide may be bonded to other hydrogen atoms or alkyl groups. Amides are classified as **1°, 2°,** or **3°** depending on the number of carbon atoms bonded directly to the *nitrogen* atom.

- A primary (1°) amide contains one C—N bond. A 1° amide has the structure $RCONH_2$.
- A secondary (2°) amide contains two C—N bonds. A 2° amide has the structure RCONHR'.
- A tertiary (3°) amide contains three C—N bonds. A 3° amide has the structure $RCONR'_2$.

Cyclic esters and amides are known. **A cyclic ester is called a** *lactone*. **A cyclic amide is called a** *lactam*.

The carbonyl carbon is bonded to an OR group that is part of a ring.

cyclic ester
**lactone**

The carbonyl carbon is bonded to a nitrogen atom that is part of a ring.

cyclic amide
**lactam**

Carboxylic acids, esters, and amides are called **acyl compounds,** since they contain an **acyl group (RCO)** bonded to an electronegative atom.

N or O atom bonded here

acyl group

The two most important features of acyl compounds, like other carbonyl compounds, are the following:

120°   120°

trigonal planar

polar bond

- The carbonyl carbon is trigonal planar, so all bond angles are 120°.
- The electronegative oxygen atom makes the carbonyl group polar, so the carbonyl carbon is electron poor (δ⁺) and the carbonyl oxygen is electron rich (δ⁻).

Oxalic acid (a carboxylic acid) in spinach, propyl acetate (an ester) in pears, and capsaicin (an amide) in hot peppers are examples of acyl compounds.

$CH_3$   $OCH_2CH_2CH_3$
propyl acetate

HO   OH
oxalic acid

capsaicin

### PROBLEM 17.1

Draw out each compound to clearly show what groups are bonded to the carbonyl carbon. Label each compound as a carboxylic acid, ester, or amide.

a. $CH_3CH_2CO_2CH_2CH_3$     b. $CH_3CONHCH_3$     c. $(CH_3)_3CCO_2H$     d. $(CH_3)_2CHCON(CH_3)_2$

### PROBLEM 17.2

Invirase is the trade name for saquinavir, a drug used to treat HIV. Classify each amide in Invirase as 1°, 2°, or 3°.

saquinavir
(Trade name: Invirase)

### PROBLEM 17.3

(a) Label each functional group in lisinopril, a drug used to treat high blood pressure. (b) How many trigonal planar carbons does lisinopril contain?

lisinopril

Lisinopril (trade name: Zestril) lowers blood pressure by decreasing the concentration of the polyamide angiotensin in the blood, as we will learn in Section 21.10.

## 17.2   Nomenclature

To name carboxylic acids, esters, and amides, we must learn the suffix that identifies each functional group in the IUPAC system. Since the names of esters and amides are derived from carboxylic acids, we must first learn how to name carboxylic acids. With esters, 2° amides, and 3° amides, the name of the acyl compound has two distinct portions: an acyl group that contains the carbonyl, and one or two alkyl groups bonded to the oxygen or nitrogen atom.

### 17.2A   Naming a Carboxylic Acid—RCOOH

- In the IUPAC system, carboxylic acids are identified by the suffix *-oic acid.*

To name a carboxylic acid using the IUPAC system:

1. Find the longest chain containing the COOH group, and change the **-e** ending of the parent alkane to the suffix **-oic acid.**
2. Number the carbon chain to put the COOH group at C1, but omit this number from the name. Apply all of the other usual rules of nomenclature.

Many simple carboxylic acids are often referred to by their common names. A common name uses the suffix *-ic acid.* Three common names are virtually always used.

formic acid
(methanoic acid)

acetic acid
(ethanoic acid)

benzoic acid
(benzenecarboxylic acid)

[IUPAC names are given in parentheses, and are rarely used.]

Greek letters are sometimes used to designate the carbons near carbonyl groups. These terms can be used for any carbonyl group.

- The carbon adjacent to the COOH is called the α (alpha) carbon.
- The carbon bonded to the α carbon is the β (beta) carbon.

## SAMPLE PROBLEM 17.1

Give the IUPAC name of the following carboxylic acid.

$$CH_3CHCHCH_2CH_2COOH$$

with $CH_3$ substituents

### Analysis and Solution

[1] Find and name the longest chain containing COOH.

$CH_3CHCHCH_2CH_2COOH$

hexane ----→ hexanoic acid
(6 C's)

The COOH contributes one C to the longest chain.

[2] Number and name the substituents, making sure the COOH group is at C1.

$CH_3CHCHCH_2CH_2COOH$

two methyl substituents on C4 and C5

**Answer: 4,5-dimethylhexanoic acid**

## PROBLEM 17.4

Give the IUPAC name for each compound.

a. $CH_3CH_2CH_2CCH_2COOH$ with $CH_3$

b. $CH_3CHCH_2CH_2COOH$ with $Cl$

c. $(CH_3CH_2)_2CHCH_2CHCOOH$ with $CH_2CH_3$

## PROBLEM 17.5

Give the structure corresponding to each IUPAC name.

a. 2-bromobutanoic acid
b. 2,3-dimethylpentanoic acid

c. 2-ethyl-5,5-dimethyloctanoic acid
d. 3,4,5,6-tetraethyldecanoic acid

## 17.2B Naming an Ester—RCOOR'

The names of esters are derived from the names of the parent carboxylic acids. Keep in mind that the common names **formic acid, acetic acid,** and **benzoic acid** are used for the parent acid, so these common parent names are used for their derivatives as well.

An ester has two parts to its structure, each of which must be named separately: an **acyl group** that contains the carbonyl group (**RCO—**) and an **alkyl group** (designated as **R'**) bonded to the oxygen atom.

- In the IUPAC system, esters are identified by the suffix *-ate.*

---

### *How To* Name an Ester (RCO$_2$R') Using the IUPAC System

**Example:** Give a systematic name for the ester CH$_3$CO$_2$CH$_2$CH$_3$.

**Step [1] Name the R' group bonded to the oxygen atom as an alkyl group.**
- The name of the alkyl group, ending in the suffix *-yl,* becomes the *first* part of the ester name. In this case, a two-carbon *ethyl* group is bonded to the ester oxygen atom.

**Step [2] Name the acyl group (RCO–) by changing the *-ic acid* ending of the parent carboxylic acid to the suffix *-ate.***
- The name of the acyl group becomes the *second* part of the name.
- In this case, the name of the parent two-carbon carboxylic acid, acet*ic acid,* becomes acet*ate.*

Esters are often written as RCOOR', where the alkyl group (R') is written *last.* When an ester is named, however, the R' group appears *first* in the name.

**Answer: ethyl acetate**

---

### SAMPLE PROBLEM 17.2

Give the IUPAC name of the following ester, which occurs naturally in apples.

#### Analysis and Solution

[1] Name the alkyl group on the O atom.

The word *methyl* becomes the first part of the name.

[2] To name the acyl group, find and name the longest chain containing the carbonyl group, placing the C=O at C1.

butano*ic acid* ---→ butano*ate*
(4 C's)

**Answer: methyl butanoate**

**PROBLEM 17.6**

Give an acceptable name for each ester.

a.  $CH_3(CH_2)_4CO_2CH_3$       b.        c.  $CH_3CH_2CH_2CH_2COOCH_2CH_2CH_3$

**PROBLEM 17.7**

Give the structure corresponding to each name.

a.  propyl propanoate                    c.  ethyl hexanoate
b.  butyl acetate                        d.  methyl benzoate

## 17.2C   Naming an Amide

> • In the IUPAC system, amides are identified by the suffix -amide.

All 1° amides are named by replacing the **-oic acid** ending (or -ic acid ending of a common name) with the suffix **-amide.**

**Naming 1° amides**

$$CH_3 - \overset{\overset{\displaystyle O}{\|}}{C} - NH_2$$

derived from
acetic acid  ----→  **acetamide**

$$\text{(benzene ring)} - \overset{\overset{\displaystyle O}{\|}}{C} - NH_2$$

derived from
benzoic acid  ----→  **benzamide**

A 2° or 3° amide has two parts to its structure: an **acyl group** that contains the carbonyl group (**RCO–**) and one or two **alkyl groups** bonded to the nitrogen atom.

---

*How To* **Name a 2° or 3° Amide**

**Example:** Give a systematic name for each amide.

a.  $\overset{\overset{\displaystyle O}{\|}}{H - C - NHCH_2CH_3}$

b.  $\text{(benzene ring)} - \overset{\overset{\displaystyle O}{\|}}{C} - \overset{\displaystyle N}{\underset{CH_3}{|}} - CH_3$

**Step [1]  Name the alkyl group (or groups) bonded to the N atom of the amide. Use the prefix "N-" preceding the name of each alkyl group.**

• The name of the alkyl groups forms the first part of each amide name.
• For 3° amides, use the prefix **di-** if the two alkyl groups on N are the same. If the two alkyl groups are different, **alphabetize** their names. One "**N-**" is needed for each alkyl group, even if both R groups are identical.

a.  $\overset{\overset{\displaystyle O}{\|}}{H - C - NHCH_2CH_3}$   ethyl group          • The compound is a 2° amide with one ethyl group → N-ethyl.

b.  $\text{(benzene ring)} - \overset{\overset{\displaystyle O}{\|}}{C} - \overset{\displaystyle N}{\underset{CH_3}{|}} - CH_3$   two methyl groups          • The compound is a 3° amide with two methyl groups.
                                                                      • Use the prefix di- and two "N-" to begin the name → N,N-dimethyl.

—Continued

**Step [2]** **Name the acyl group (RCO–) with the suffix** *-amide.*

a.

derived from
for**mic** acid ----→ form**amide**

- Change the *-ic acid* or *-oic acid* suffix of the parent carboxylic acid to the suffix *-amide.*
- Put the two parts of the name together.
**Answer: *N*-ethylformamide**

b.

derived from
benz**oic** acid ----→ benz**amide**

- Change benz*oic acid* to benz*amide.*
- Put the two parts of the name together.
**Answer: *N,N*-dimethylbenzamide**

---

**PROBLEM 17.8**

Give an acceptable name for each amide.

a. $CH_3CH_2CH_2CH_2$ —C(=O)—$NH_2$

b. benzene-C(=O)-NHCH$_3$

c. H—C(=O)—$N(CH_2CH_2CH_3)_2$

**PROBLEM 17.9**

Draw the structure of each amide.

a. propanamide
b. *N*-ethylhexanamide
c. *N,N*-dimethylacetamide
d. *N*-butyl-*N*-methylbutanamide

## 17.3 Physical Properties

Carboxylic acids, esters, and amides are polar compounds because they possess a polar carbonyl group. All C—O, O—H, C—N, and N—H bonds in these compounds are polar bonds as well, and thus contribute to the net dipole of each compound.

Carboxylic acids also exhibit intermolecular **hydrogen bonding** since they possess a hydrogen atom bonded to an electronegative oxygen atom. Carboxylic acids often exist as **dimers,** held together by *two* intermolecular hydrogen bonds, as shown in Figure 17.1. The carbonyl oxygen atom of one molecule hydrogen bonds to the hydrogen atom of another molecule.

**Figure 17.1** Two Molecules of Acetic Acid (CH$_3$COOH) Held Together by Two Hydrogen Bonds

As a result:

- Carboxylic acids have stronger intermolecular forces than esters, giving them higher boiling points and melting points, when comparing compounds of similar size.

$$CH_3-\overset{\displaystyle O}{\underset{\displaystyle OCH_3}{C}}$$

bp 58 °C

no hydrogen bonding possible

$$CH_3CH_2-\overset{\displaystyle O}{\underset{\displaystyle OH}{C}}$$ hydrogen bonding possible

bp 141 °C

stronger intermolecular forces
**higher boiling point**

Carboxylic acids also have stronger intermolecular forces than alcohols, even though both functional groups exhibit hydrogen bonding; two molecules of a carboxylic acid are held together by *two* intermolecular hydrogen bonds, whereas only *one* hydrogen bond is possible between two molecules of an alcohol (Section 14.2). As a result:

- Carboxylic acids have higher boiling points and melting points than alcohols of comparable size.

$$CH_3CH_2CH_2OH$$

1-propanol
bp 97 °C

$$CH_3-\overset{\displaystyle O}{\underset{\displaystyle OH}{C}}$$

acetic acid
bp 118 °C

more hydrogen-bonding interactions possible
**higher boiling point**

Primary (1°) and 2° amides contain N—H bonds, so hydrogen bonding is possible between two molecules of the amide, as shown in Figure 17.2. This gives 1° and 2° amides stronger intermolecular forces than 3° amides and esters, which can't intermolecularly hydrogen bond. As a result:

- Primary (1°) and 2° amides have higher boiling points and melting points than esters and 3° amides of comparable size.

$$CH_3-\overset{\displaystyle O}{\underset{\displaystyle OCH_3}{C}}$$

ester
bp 58 °C

$$H-\overset{\displaystyle O}{\underset{\displaystyle N(CH_3)_2}{C}}$$

3° amide
bp 153 °C

$$CH_3CH_2-\overset{\displaystyle O}{\underset{\displaystyle NH_2}{C}}$$ hydrogen bonding possible

1° amide
bp 213 °C

strongest intermolecular forces
**highest boiling point**

**Figure 17.2** Intermolecular Hydrogen Bonding Between Two $CH_3CONH_2$ Molecules

hydrogen bond

Like other oxygen-containing compounds, carboxylic acids, esters, and amides having less than six carbons are soluble in water. Higher molecular weight acyl compounds are insoluble in water because the nonpolar portion of the molecule, the C—C and C—H bonds, gets larger than the polar carbonyl group.

### PROBLEM 17.10

Which compound in each pair has the higher boiling point?

a. $CH_3COOH$ or $CH_3CH_2CHO$

b. $CH_3CH_2CH_2CONH_2$ or $CH_3CH_2CO_2CH_3$

c.

### PROBLEM 17.11

Rank the following compounds in order of increasing boiling point. Which compound is the most water soluble? Which compound is the least water soluble?

## 17.4 Interesting Carboxylic Acids in Consumer Products and Medicines

Ginkgo trees have existed for over 280 million years. Extracts of the ginkgo tree have long been used in China, Japan, and India in medicine and cooking.

Simple carboxylic acids have biting or foul odors.

$HCO_2H$            $CH_3CO_2H$            $CH_3CH_2CH_2CH_2CH_2CO_2H$

- **Formic acid** ($HCO_2H$) is responsible for the sting of some types of ants.
- **Acetic acid** ($CH_3CO_2H$) is the sour-tasting component of vinegar. Air oxidation of ethanol ($CH_3CH_2OH$) to acetic acid makes "bad" wine taste sour.
- **Hexanoic acid** [$(CH_3(CH_2)_4COOH$] has the foul odor associated with dirty socks and locker rooms. It also contributes to the unpleasant odor of ginkgo seeds. The common name for hexanoic acid is caproic acid, derived from the Latin word caper, meaning "goat."

### 17.4A FOCUS ON HEALTH & MEDICINE
Skin Care Products

Several skin care products that purportedly smooth fine lines and improve skin texture contain α-hydroxy acids. **α-Hydroxy acids contain a hydroxyl group on the α (alpha) carbon to the carboxyl group.** Two common α-hydroxy acids are glycolic acid and lactic acid. Glycolic acid occurs naturally in sugarcane, and lactic acid gives sour milk its distinctive taste.

General structure

α carbon

α-hydroxy acid            glycolic acid            lactic acid α-Hydroxy acids are used in skin care products that are promoted to remove wrinkles and age spots.

Do products that contain α-hydroxy acids make the skin look younger? α-Hydroxy acids react with the outer layer of skin cells, causing them to loosen and flake off. Underneath is a layer of healthier looking skin that has not been exposed to the sun. In this way, these skin products do not actually reverse the aging process; rather, they remove a layer of old skin that may be less pliant or contain small age spots. They can, however, give the appearance of younger skin for a time.

### PROBLEM 17.12

Which compounds are α-hydroxy acids?

a.

tartaric acid
(isolated from grapes)

b. $CH_3CHCH_2$—C

3-hydroxybutanoic acid
(starting material for
polymer synthesis)

c.

—COOH

salicylic acid
(isolated from meadowsweet)

## 17.4B   FOCUS ON HEALTH & MEDICINE
### Aspirin and Anti-Inflammatory Agents

Three common pain relievers that are also anti-inflammatory agents contain a carboxyl group—aspirin, ibuprofen, and naproxen.

aspirin

ibuprofen

naproxen

How does aspirin relieve pain and reduce inflammation? Although aspirin is the most widely used pain reliever and anti-inflammatory agent and has been sold since the late 1800s, its mechanism of action remained unknown until the 1970s. At that time it was shown that aspirin blocks the synthesis of **prostaglandins,** carboxylic acids containing 20 carbons that are responsible for mediating pain, inflammation, and a wide variety of other biological functions.

Prostaglandins are not stored in cells. Rather, they are synthesized on an as-needed basis from arachidonic acid, an unsaturated fatty acid with four cis double bonds. **Aspirin relieves pain and decreases inflammation because it prevents the synthesis of prostaglandins, the compounds responsible for both of these physiological responses, from arachidonic acid.**

arachidonic acid

**Aspirin blocks this process.**

$PGF_{2\alpha}$ and compounds like it cause pain and inflammation.

$PGF_{2\alpha}$
a prostaglandin

The 1982 Nobel Prize in Physiology or Medicine was awarded to John Vane, Bengt Samuelsson, and Sune Bergstrom for unraveling the details of prostaglandin synthesis, thus showing how aspirin acts.

### PROBLEM 17.13
Which compound, $PGF_{2\alpha}$ (a prostaglandin) or arachidonic acid, is more water soluble? Explain your choice.

## 17.5 Interesting Esters and Amides

Many low molecular weight esters have pleasant and very characteristic odors. These include ethyl butanoate (from mangoes), pentyl butanoate (from apricots), and methyl salicylate (oil of wintergreen).

$CH_3CH_2CH_2COOCH_2CH_3$

ethyl butanoate
(isolated from mangoes)

$CH_3CH_2CH_2COO(CH_2)_4CH_3$

pentyl butanoate
(isolated from apricots)

methyl salicylate
(oil of wintergreen)

Esters are a common functional group in many lipids, as we will learn in Section 17.9 and Chapter 19.

**Melatonin,** an amide synthesized by the brain's pineal gland, is thought to induce sleep. Melatonin levels in the body rise as less light falls upon the eye and drop quickly at dawn. For this reason, melatonin has become a popular supplement for travelers suffering from jet lag and individuals with mild sleep disorders.

melatonin

We will learn about proteins, naturally occurring polyamides, in Chapter 21.

Many useful drugs are esters or amides. **Benzocaine,** an ester, is the active ingredient in many over-the-counter oral topical anesthetics such as Orajel. **Acetaminophen,** an amide, is the active ingredient in Tylenol. Acetaminophen relieves pain and fever. In large doses acetaminophen causes liver damage, so dosage recommendations must be carefully followed.

benzocaine
(local anesthetic)

acetaminophen
(pain reliever in Tylenol)

### PROBLEM 17.14

In addition to ethyl butanoate (Section 17.5), mangoes contain several other esters. Draw the structure of each of the following esters that has been isolated from the mango: (a) butyl formate; (b) ethyl octanoate; (c) ethyl propanoate.

## 17.6    The Acidity of Carboxylic Acids

As their name implies, **carboxylic acids are acids;** that is, **they are *proton donors*.** When a carboxylic acid is dissolved in water, an acid–base equilibrium occurs: the carboxylic acid donates a proton to $H_2O$, forming its conjugate base, a **carboxylate anion,** and water gains a proton, forming its conjugate acid, $H_3O^+$.

**General reaction**

carboxylic acid          This proton is removed.          carboxylate anion

$K_a$ values for a variety of acids are given in Section 9.4.

While carboxylic acids are more acidic than other families of organic compounds, they are weak acids compared to inorganic acids like HCl or $H_2SO_4$. Typical acid dissociation constants ($K_a$) for carboxylic acids fall in the range $10^{-4}$ to $10^{-5}$. Thus, only a small percentage of a carboxylic acid is ionized in aqueous solution.

**Example**

acetic acid          acetate anion

### 17.6A    Reaction with Bases

**Carboxylic acids react with bases such as NaOH to form water-soluble salts.** In this reaction, the acid–base equilibrium is shifted to the right, and essentially all of the carboxylic acid is converted to its carboxylate anion.

acetic acid          base          sodium acetate

This proton is transferred from the acid to the base.

- A proton is removed from acetic acid ($CH_3COOH$) to form its conjugate base, the acetate anion ($CH_3COO^-$), which is present in solution as its sodium salt, sodium acetate.
- Hydroxide ($OH^-$) gains a proton to form neutral $H_2O$.

Similar acid–base reactions occur with other hydroxide bases (KOH), sodium bicarbonate ($NaHCO_3$), and sodium carbonate ($Na_2CO_3$). **In each reaction, a proton is transferred from the acid (RCOOH) to the base.**

### SAMPLE PROBLEM 17.3

What products are formed when propanoic acid ($CH_3CH_2COOH$) reacts with potassium hydroxide (KOH)?

### Analysis

In any acid–base reaction with a carboxylic acid:

- Remove a proton from the carboxyl group (COOH) and form the carboxylate anion ($RCOO^-$).
- Add a proton to the base. If the base has a –1 charge to begin with, it becomes a neutral product when a proton ($H^+$) is added to it.
- Balance the charge of the carboxylate anion by drawing it as a salt with a metal cation.

### Solution

This proton is transferred from the acid to the base.

Thus, $CH_3CH_2COOH$ loses a proton to form $CH_3CH_2COO^-$, which is present in solution as its potassium salt, $CH_3CH_2COO^- K^+$. Hydroxide ($OH^-$) gains a proton to form $H_2O$.

### PROBLEM 17.15

Draw the products of each acid–base reaction.

### PROBLEM 17.16

What products are formed when benzoic acid ($C_6H_5COOH$) is treated with each base: (a) NaOH; (b) $Na_2CO_3$; (c) $NaHCO_3$?

## 17.6B   Carboxylate Anions—Salts of Carboxylic Acids

**The salts of carboxylic acids that are formed by acid–base reactions are water-soluble ionic solids.** Thus, a water-*insoluble* carboxylic acid like octanoic acid can be converted to its water-*soluble* sodium salt by reaction with NaOH. This reaction is important in determining the solubility of drugs that contain a carboxyl group, as we will learn in Section 17.7.

The acid has more than 5 C's, so it is **insoluble** in water.

The ionic salt is **soluble** in water.

To name the metal salts of carboxylate anions, three parts must be put together: the name of the metal cation, the parent name indicating the number of carbons in the parent carboxylic acid, and the suffix indicating that the species is a salt. The suffix is added by changing the **-ic acid** ending of the parent carboxylic acid to the suffix **-ate**.

## SAMPLE PROBLEM 17.4

Give an acceptable name for each salt.

a.

$$CH_3-C(=O)-O^-\ Na^+$$

b.

$$CH_3CH_2-C(=O)-O^-\ K^+$$

### Analysis

Name the carboxylate salt by putting three parts together:

- the name of the metal cation
- the parent name that indicates the number of carbons in the parent chain
- the suffix, *-ate*

### Solution

a.

sodium cation

$$CH_3-C(=O)-O^-\ Na^+$$

parent + suffix
acet-        -ate

- The first part of the name is the metal cation, sodium.
- The parent name is derived from the common name, acetic acid. Change the **-ic acid** ending to **-ate;** acetic acid → acetate.

**Answer: sodium acetate**

b.

potassium cation

$$CH_3CH_2-C(=O)-O^-\ K^+$$

parent + suffix
propano-   -ate

- The first part of the name is the metal cation, potassium.
- The parent name is derived from the IUPAC name, propanoic acid. Change the **-ic acid** ending to **-ate;** propanoic acid → propanoate.

**Answer: potassium propanoate**

## PROBLEM 17.17

Name each salt of a carboxylic acid.

a. $CH_3CH_2CH_2CO_2^-\ Na^+$

b. ⟨benzene ring⟩—COO⁻Li⁺

---

**Salts of carboxylic acids** are commonly used as preservatives. **Sodium benzoate,** which inhibits the growth of fungus, is a preservative used in soft drinks, and potassium sorbate is an additive that prolongs the shelf-life of baked goods and other foods. These salts do not kill bacteria or fungus. They increase the pH of the product, thus preventing further growth of microorganisms.

(structure) sodium benzoate

(structure) $CH_3CH=CHCH=CH-C(=O)-O^-\ K^+$   potassium sorbate

## PROBLEM 17.18

Draw the structure of sodium propanoate, a common preservative.

## 17.6C   How Does Soap Clean Away Dirt?

Soap has been used by humankind for some 2,000 years. Historical records describe its manufacture in the first century and document the presence of a soap factory in Pompeii. Prior to this time, clothes were cleaned by rubbing them on rocks in water, or by forming soapy lathers from the roots, bark, and leaves of certain plants. These plants produced natural materials called *saponins,* which act in much the same way as modern-day soaps.

**Soaps are salts of carboxylic acids that have many carbon atoms in a long hydrocarbon chain.** A soap molecule has two parts.

- The ionic end is called the *polar head.*
- The carbon chain of nonpolar C—C and C—H bonds is called the *nonpolar tail.*

Dissolving soap in water forms **spherical droplets having the ionic heads on the surface and the nonpolar tails packed together in the interior.** These spherical droplets are called *micelles* and are illustrated in Figure 17.3. In this arrangement, the ionic heads can interact with the polar solvent water, and this brings the nonpolar, "greasy" hydrocarbon portion of the soap into solution.

**Figure 17.3**

Dissolving Soap in Water

When soap is dissolved in $H_2O$, the molecules form spherical droplets with the nonpolar tails in the interior and the polar heads on the surface.

Saturday Evening Post, November 29, 1941.

All soaps are metal salts of carboxylate anions. The main difference between brands is the addition of other ingredients that do not alter their cleaning properties: dyes for color, scents for a pleasing odor, and oils for lubrication. Soaps that float have been aerated so that they are less dense than water.

The modern history of aspirin dates back to 1763 when Reverend Edmund Stone reported on the analgesic effects of chewing on the bark of the willow tree. Willow bark is now known to contain salicin, which is structurally similar to aspirin.

The word *aspirin* is derived from the prefix **a-** for *acetyl* + **spir** from the Latin name *spirea* for the meadowsweet plant.

How does soap dissolve grease and oil? The polar solvent water alone cannot dissolve dirt, which is composed largely of nonpolar hydrocarbons. When soap is mixed with water, however, the nonpolar hydrocarbon tails dissolve the dirt in the interior of the micelle. The polar head of the soap remains on the surface to interact with water. The nonpolar tails of the soap molecules are so well sealed off from the water by the polar head groups that the micelles are water soluble, so they can separate from the fibers of our clothes and be washed down the drain with water. In this way, soaps do a seemingly impossible task: they remove nonpolar hydrocarbon material from skin and clothes by dissolving it in the polar solvent water.

Cross-section of a soap micelle with a grease particle dissolved in the interior — Grease

**PROBLEM 17.19**

Draw the structure of a soap molecule that has a potassium cation and a carboxylate anion containing 16 carbons.

## 17.7 FOCUS ON HEALTH & MEDICINE
### Aspirin

**Aspirin** is one of the most widely used over-the-counter drugs. Whether you purchase Anacin, Bufferin, Bayer, or a generic, the active ingredient is the same—**acetylsalicylic acid.** Aspirin is a synthetic compound; that is, it does not occur in nature, but it is similar in structure to salicin found in willow bark and salicylic acid found in meadowsweet blossoms.

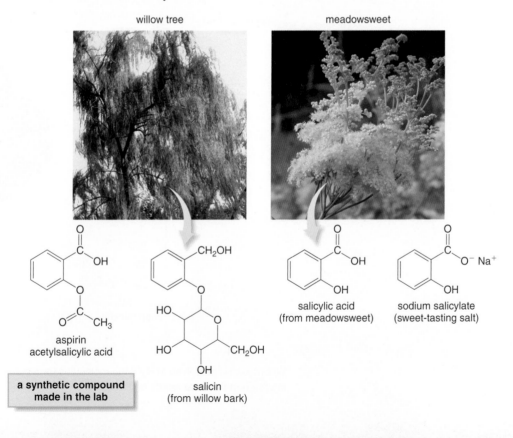

Both salicylic acid and sodium salicylate, its sodium salt, were used to relieve pain in the nineteenth century, but both had undesirable side effects. Salicylic acid irritated the mucous membranes of the mouth and stomach, and sodium salicylate was too sweet for most patients. This prompted a search for a related compound that did not have these same drawbacks. In 1899, Felix Hoffman, a German chemist at Bayer Company, developed an economical commercial synthesis of acetylsalicylic acid, and aspirin was marketed to the general public. Hoffman's work was motivated by personal reasons; his father suffered from rheumatoid arthritis and he was unable to tolerate the sweet taste of sodium salicylate.

Aspirin was first used in medicine for its analgesic (pain-relieving), antipyretic (fever-reducing), and anti-inflammatory properties. Today it is also commonly used as an antiplatelet agent; that is, it is used to prevent blood clots from forming in arteries. In this way, it is used to treat and prevent heart attacks and strokes.

Like other carboxylic acids, **aspirin is a proton donor.** When aspirin is dissolved in water, an acid–base equilibrium occurs, and the carboxyl group (COOH) donates a proton to form its conjugate base, a carboxylate anion. Because it is a weak acid, only a small percentage of the carboxylic acid is ionized in water.

After ingestion, aspirin travels first into the stomach and then the intestines. In the acidic environment of the stomach, aspirin remains in its neutral form. When aspirin travels into the basic environment of the small intestines, however, aspirin is converted to its carboxylate anion, as shown in Figure 17.4. In the intestines, therefore, aspirin is predominantly in its ionic form.

**Figure 17.4**    The Acid–Base Chemistry of Aspirin

Why is this acid–base reaction important? **To be active, aspirin must cross a cell membrane, and to do so, it must be neutral, not ionic.** This means that aspirin crosses a cell membrane and is absorbed by the body in its neutral form in the stomach. Whether aspirin is present as its acid or its conjugate base is thus very important in determining whether it can enter a cell and act as a pain reliever and anti-inflammatory agent.

### PROBLEM 17.20

Draw the acid–base reaction that occurs when aspirin is treated with NaOH.

### PROBLEM 17.21

Ibuprofen is another pain reliever that is a carboxylic acid. (a) Draw the acid–base reaction that occurs when ibuprofen is treated with NaOH. (b) What form of ibuprofen (neutral or ionic) exists in the stomach? (c) What form of ibuprofen exists in the intestines?

$$(CH_3)_2CHCH_2 \text{—} \overset{CH_3}{\underset{}{\text{—CHCOOH}}}$$

ibuprofen

## 17.8   The Conversion of Carboxylic Acids to Esters and Amides

**All acyl compounds undergo a common type of reaction—*substitution.*** When an acyl compound (RCOZ) undergoes substitution, the group Z containing an electronegative atom bonded to the carbonyl carbon is *replaced* by another atom or group of atoms (Y).

**Substitution**

$$\underset{R}{\overset{O}{\underset{Z}{\|}}}C \quad + \quad H\text{—}Y \quad \longrightarrow \quad \underset{R}{\overset{O}{\underset{Y}{\|}}}C \quad + \quad H\text{—}Z$$

Y replaces Z.

$$Z = OH, OR', NR'_2 \qquad\qquad Y = OH, OR', NR'_2$$

For example, carboxylic acids react with alcohols to form esters and with ammonia to form amides.

**Ester formation**

$$\underset{R}{\overset{O}{\underset{OH}{\|}}}C \quad + \quad H\text{—}OR' \quad \underset{}{\overset{H_2SO_4}{\rightleftharpoons}} \quad \underset{R}{\overset{O}{\underset{OR'}{\|}}}C \quad + \quad H\text{—}OH$$

carboxylic acid        alcohol                              ester

OR' replaces OH.

The Greek letter Δ (delta) is used over the arrow to indicate that a reaction requires heat (Section 5.1).

**Amide formation**

$$\underset{R}{\overset{O}{\underset{OH}{\|}}}C \quad + \quad H\text{—}NH_2 \quad \overset{\Delta}{\longrightarrow} \quad \underset{R}{\overset{O}{\underset{NH_2}{\|}}}C \quad + \quad H\text{—}OH$$

carboxylic acid        ammonia                              amide

NH₂ replaces OH.

### 17.8A   Ester Formation

Treatment of a carboxylic acid (RCOOH) with an alcohol (R'OH) in the presence of an acid catalyst forms an ester (RCOOR'). This reaction is called a **Fischer esterification.** Esterification is a substitution because the OR' group of an alcohol replaces the OH group of the starting carboxylic acid.

CONSUMER NOTE

The ester ethyl acetate, a common organic solvent with a very characteristic odor, is used in non-acetone nail polish remover.

**Fischer esterification**

$$CH_3-C(=O)-OH \ + \ H-OCH_2CH_3 \ \underset{}{\overset{H_2SO_4}{\rightleftarrows}} \ CH_3-C(=O)-OCH_2CH_3 \ + \ H-OH$$

acetic acid  +  ethanol ⇌ ethyl acetate  +  H—OH

$$C_6H_5-C(=O)-OH \ + \ H-OCH_3 \ \underset{}{\overset{H_2SO_4}{\rightleftarrows}} \ C_6H_5-C(=O)-OCH_3 \ + \ H-OH$$

benzoic acid  +  methanol ⇌ methyl benzoate  +  H—OH

This reaction is an equilibrium process. According to Le Châtelier's principle (Section 6.6), it is driven to the right by using excess alcohol or by removing the water as it is formed. Note where the elements of $H_2O$ originate: the OH group comes from the carboxylic acid, and one H atom comes from the hydrogen of the alcohol (R'OH).

## SAMPLE PROBLEM 17.5

What ester is formed when propanoic acid ($CH_3CH_2COOH$) is treated with methanol ($CH_3OH$) in the presence of $H_2SO_4$?

### Analysis

To draw the products of any acyl substitution, arrange the carboxyl group of the carboxylic acid next to the functional group with which it reacts—the OH group of the alcohol in this case. Then, replace the OH group of the carboxylic acid by the OR' group of the alcohol, forming a new C—O bond at the carbonyl carbon.

Remove OH and H to form $H_2O$.

new C—O bond

$$R-C(=O)-OH \ + \ H-OR' \ \longrightarrow \ R-C(=O)-OR' \ + \ H-OH$$

carboxylic acid  +  H—OR' → ester  +  H—OH

### Solution

Replace the OH group of propanoic acid by the $OCH_3$ group of methanol to form the ester.

new C—O bond

$$CH_3CH_2-C(=O)-OH \ + \ H-OCH_3 \ \underset{}{\overset{H_2SO_4}{\rightleftarrows}} \ CH_3CH_2-C(=O)-OCH_3 \ + \ H-OH$$

$OCH_3$ replaces OH.

## PROBLEM 17.22

What ester is formed when each carboxylic acid is treated with ethanol ($CH_3CH_2OH$) in the presence of $H_2SO_4$?

a. $(CH_3)_2CH-C(=O)-OH$

b. $HCO_2H$

c. $CH_3(CH_2)_6-C(=O)-OH$

d. cyclohexyl—$CO_2H$

A short laboratory synthesis of the ester blattellaquinone, the sex pheromone of the female German cockroach (Problem 17.23), opens new possibilities for cockroach population control using pheromone-baited traps.

Fischer esterification can be used to synthesize aspirin from salicylic acid.

salicylic acid        acetic acid              aspirin          new C—O bond

## PROBLEM 17.23

Identify **A** in the following reaction. **A** was converted in one step to blattellaquinone, the sex pheromone of the female German cockroach, *Blattella germanica*.

blattellaquinone

## PROBLEM 17.24

What carboxylic acid and alcohol are needed to synthesize the local anesthetic benzocaine (Section 17.5)?

$H_2N$—⟨benzene ring⟩—$CO_2CH_2CH_3$

benzocaine

## 17.8B  Amide Formation

**Heating a carboxylic acid (RCOOH) with ammonia (NH₃) or an amine (R'NH₂ or R'₂NH) forms an amide.** Formation of an amide from a carboxylic acid is a substitution because the OH group of the acid is replaced by a nitrogen-containing group.

Amide formation

carboxylic acid      R' = H or alkyl              amide

The identity of the nitrogen compound determines the type of amide formed.

- Reaction of RCOOH with $NH_3$ forms a 1° amide ($RCONH_2$).
- Reaction of RCOOH with $R'NH_2$ forms a 2° amide (RCONHR').
- Reaction of RCOOH with $R'_2NH$ forms a 3° amide ($RCONR'_2$).

Examples

acetic acid            ammonia                1° amide

acetic acid            methylamine            2° amide

$$CH_3-\overset{\overset{O}{\|}}{C}-OH \;+\; H-\underset{\underset{CH_3}{|}}{N}-CH_3 \;\xrightarrow{\Delta}\; CH_3-\overset{\overset{O}{\|}}{C}-N(CH_3)_2 \;+\; H-OH$$

acetic acid     dimethylamine     3° amide

Useful amides can be made by this reaction. Heating carboxylic acid **X** with diethylamine forms the 3° amide *N,N*-diethyl-*m*-toluamide, popularly known as **DEET.** DEET, the active ingredient in the most widely used insect repellents, is effective against mosquitoes, fleas, and ticks.

$$\text{(benzene ring with }\overset{O}{\overset{\|}{C}}-OH\text{ and }CH_3) \;+\; H-N(CH_2CH_3)_2 \;\xrightarrow{\Delta}\; \text{(benzene ring with }\overset{O}{\overset{\|}{C}}-N\big(CH_2CH_3\big)_2\text{ and }CH_3) \;+\; H_2O$$

    diethylamine

**X**         *N,N*-diethyl-*m*-toluamide
                    (DEET)

### SAMPLE PROBLEM 17.6

What amide is formed when propanoic acid ($CH_3CH_2COOH$) is heated with ethylamine ($CH_3CH_2NH_2$)?

#### Analysis

To draw the products of amide formation, arrange the carboxyl group of the carboxylic acid next to the H—N bond of the amine. Then, replace the OH group of the carboxylic acid by the $NHCH_2CH_3$ group of the amine, forming a new C—N bond at the carbonyl carbon.

#### Solution

Reaction of RCOOH with an amine that has one alkyl group on the N atom ($R'NH_2$) forms a 2° amide (RCONHR').

$$CH_3CH_2-\overset{\overset{O}{\|}}{C}-OH \;+\; H-\underset{\underset{H}{|}}{N}-CH_2CH_3 \;\xrightarrow{\Delta}\; CH_3CH_2-\overset{\overset{O}{\|}}{C}-NHCH_2CH_3 \;+\; H-OH$$

           ethylamine                  2° amide

new C—N bond

$NHCH_2CH_3$ replaces OH.

### PROBLEM 17.25

What amide is formed when $CH_3CH_2CH_2CH_2COOH$ is treated with each compound?

a. $NH_3$      b. $(CH_3)_2NH$      c. ⬡—$NH_2$      d. $CH_3NH_2$

### PROBLEM 17.26

What carboxylic acid and amine are needed to synthesize acetaminophen, the active pain reliever in Tylenol?

$$HO-\text{(benzene ring)}-\underset{}{\overset{H}{\underset{|}{N}}}-\overset{\overset{}{}}{\underset{\underset{O}{\|}}{C}}-CH_3$$

acetaminophen

## 17.9   Hydrolysis of Esters and Amides

Esters and amides undergo substitution at the carbonyl carbon as well. For example, **esters and amides react with water to form carboxylic acids.** This reaction is another example of **hydrolysis,** since bonds are cleaved on reaction with water.

### 17.9A   Ester Hydrolysis

Esters are hydrolyzed with water in the presence of acid or base. **Treatment of an ester (RCOOR') with water in the presence of an acid catalyst forms a carboxylic acid (RCOOH) and a molecule of alcohol (R'OH).** The hydrolysis of esters in aqueous acid is an equilibrium reaction that is driven to the right by using a large excess of water.

Esters are hydrolyzed in aqueous base to form carboxylate anions and a molecule of alcohol. Basic hydrolysis of an ester is called **saponification.**

### SAMPLE PROBLEM 17.7

What products are formed when ethyl propanoate ($CH_3CH_2CO_2CH_2CH_3$) is hydrolyzed with water in the presence of $H_2SO_4$?

#### Analysis

To draw the products of hydrolysis in acid, replace the OR' group of the ester by an OH group from water, forming a new C—O bond at the carbonyl carbon. A molecule of alcohol (R'OH) is also formed from the alkoxy group (OR') of the ester.

## Solution

Replace the $OCH_2CH_3$ group of ethyl propanoate by the $OH$ group of water to form propanoic acid ($CH_3CH_2CO_2H$) and ethanol ($CH_3CH_2OH$).

ethyl propanoate

OH replaces $OCH_2CH_3$.

### PROBLEM 17.27

What products are formed when each ester is treated with $H_2O$ and $H_2SO_4$?

a. $CH_3(CH_2)_8$ ... $OCH_3$

b. $CH_3CHCH_2$ ... $OCH_2CH_3$ with $CH_3$

c. ...$CO_2CH_2CH_2CH_3$

### PROBLEM 17.28

What products are formed when each ester in Problem 17.27 is treated with $H_2O$ and NaOH?

### PROBLEM 17.29

Aspirin cannot be sold as a liquid solution for children because it slowly undergoes hydrolysis in water. What products are formed when aspirin is hydrolyzed?

aspirin

## 17.9B  Amide Hydrolysis

Amides are much less reactive than esters in substitution reactions. Nonetheless, under forcing conditions amides can be hydrolyzed with water in the presence of acid or base. **Treatment of an amide (RCONHR') with water in the presence of an acid catalyst (HCl) forms a carboxylic acid (RCOOH) and an amine salt (R'NH$_3^+$ Cl$^-$).**

amide                    carboxylic acid        amine salt

Amides are also hydrolyzed in aqueous base to form carboxylate anions and a molecule of ammonia ($NH_3$) or amine.

amide                    carboxylate anion        ammonia

The relative lack of reactivity of the amide bond is important in the proteins in the body. Proteins are polymers connected by amide linkages, as we will learn in Chapter 21. Proteins are stable in water in the absence of acid or base, so they can perform their various functions in the cell without breaking down. The hydrolysis of the amide bonds in proteins requires a variety of specific enzymes.

## SAMPLE PROBLEM 17.8

What products are formed when *N*-methylacetamide (CH₃CONHCH₃) is hydrolyzed with water in the presence of NaOH?

### Analysis

To draw the products of amide hydrolysis in base, replace the NHR' group of the amide by an oxygen anion (O⁻), forming a new C—O bond at the carbonyl carbon. A molecule of amine (R'NH₂) is also formed from the nitrogen group (NHR') of the amide.

### Solution

Replace the NHCH₃ group of *N*-methylacetamide by a negatively charged oxygen atom (O⁻) to form sodium acetate (CH₃CO₂⁻ Na⁺) and methylamine (CH₃NH₂).

## PROBLEM 17.30

What products are formed when each amide is treated with H₂O and H₂SO₄?

a. CH₃(CH₂)₈CONH₂   b. CH₃CHCH₂CONHCH₃ with CH₃   c. cyclohexyl–CON(CH₂CH₂CH₃)₂

## PROBLEM 17.31

What products are formed when each amide in Problem 17.30 is treated with H₂O and NaOH?

## 17.9C  FOCUS ON HEALTH & MEDICINE
### Olestra, a Synthetic Fat

The most prevalent naturally occurring esters are the **triacylglycerols.** *Triacylglycerols* **contain three ester groups, each having a long carbon chain (abbreviated as R, R', and R'') bonded to the carbonyl group.** Triacylglycerols are **lipids;** that is, they are water-insoluble organic compounds found in biological systems. Animal fats and vegetable oils are composed of triacylglycerols.

R groups have 11–19 C's.

[Three ester groups are labeled in red.]

triacylglycerol

Animals store energy in the form of triacylglycerols kept in a layer of fat cells below the surface of the skin. This fat serves to insulate the organism, as well as provide energy for its metabolic needs for long periods of time. The first step in the metabolism of a triacylglycerol is hydrolysis of the ester bonds to form glycerol and three fatty acids—long-chain carboxylic acids. **This reaction is simply ester hydrolysis.** In cells, this reaction is carried out with enzymes called **lipases.**

The three bonds drawn in red are broken in hydrolysis.

triacylglycerol

glycerol

Three carboxylic acids containing 12–20 C's are formed as products.

We will learn more about triacylglycerols in Chapter 19.

The fatty acids produced on hydrolysis are then oxidized, yielding $CO_2$ and $H_2O$, as well as a great deal of energy. Diets high in fat content can lead to a large amount of stored fat, ultimately causing an individual to be overweight. One recent attempt to reduce calories in common snack foods has been to substitute "fake fats" such as **olestra** (trade name: **Olean**) for triacylglycerols.

**olestra**
a "fake fat"

R groups have long chains of C's joined together.

The ester groups are so crowded that hydrolysis does not readily take place.

Olestra has many ester groups formed from long-chain carboxylic acids and sucrose, the sweet-tasting carbohydrate in table sugar. Olestra has many properties similar to the triacylglycerols in fats and oils. In one way, however, olestra is different. Olestra has so many ester units clustered together that they are too crowded to be hydrolyzed. As a result, olestra is *not* metabolized nor is it absorbed. Instead, it passes through the body unchanged, *providing no calories to the consumer.*

**PROBLEM 17.32**

What products are formed when the following triacylglycerol is hydrolyzed with water and $H_2SO_4$?

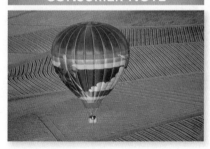
Polymers were first discussed in detail in Section 13.8.

## 17.10   Synthetic Polymers in Modern Society— Polyamides and Polyesters

All natural and synthetic fibers are polymers. Natural fibers are obtained from either plant or animal sources, and this determines the fundamental nature of their chemical structure. Fibers like **wool and silk obtained from animals are proteins,** and so they are joined together by many amide linkages.

wool and silk—polymers with many amide bonds
(labeled in red)

An important practical application of organic chemistry has been the synthesis of synthetic fibers, many of which have properties that are different from and sometimes superior to their naturally occurring counterparts. Two common classes of synthetic polymers are polyamides and polyesters.

### 17.10A   Nylon—A Polyamide

The search for a synthetic fiber with properties similar to silk led to the discovery of **nylon,** a **polyamide.** There are several different kinds of nylon, but the best known is nylon 6,6.

nylon 6,6
[The amide bonds are labeled in red.]

To synthesize nylon 6,6, two monomers are needed. Each monomer has six carbons (hence its name) and two functional groups. One monomer is a dicarboxylic acid, adipic acid [$HO_2C(CH_2)_4CO_2H$], and the second monomer is a diamine, hexamethylenediamine [$H_2N(CH_2)_6NH_2$]. Heating the two monomers together at high temperature forms the amide bonds of the long polymer chain. When each amide is formed, a molecule of $H_2O$ is lost from the starting materials. Nylon is an example of a **condensation polymer.**

Each $NH_2$ and COOH react.

loss of $H_2O$     loss of $H_2O$     loss of $H_2O$

$\Delta$

new amide bonds

nylon 6,6

Armadillo bicycle tires reinforced with Kevlar are hard to pierce with sharp objects, so a cyclist rarely gets a flat tire.

- A *condensation polymer* is a polymer formed when monomers containing two functional groups come together with loss of a small molecule such as water.

**Kevlar** is a polyamide formed from terephthalic acid and 1,4-diaminobenzene. The aromatic rings of the polymer backbone make the chains less flexible than those of nylon 6,6, resulting in a very strong material. Kevlar is light in weight compared to other materials that are similar in strength, so it is used in many products, such as bulletproof vests, army helmets, and the protective clothing used by fire fighters.

terephthalic acid  +  1,4-diaminobenzene  $\xrightarrow[(-H_2O)]{\Delta}$  Kevlar   new amide bond

### PROBLEM 17.33
What two monomers are needed to prepare nylon 6,10?

$$\text{—N—(CH}_2)_6\text{—N—C—(CH}_2)_8\text{—C—N—(CH}_2)_6\text{—N—C—(CH}_2)_8\text{—C—}$$

nylon 6,10

## 17.10B   Polyesters

**Polyesters** constitute a second major class of condensation polymers. The most common polyester is polyethylene terephthalate (**PET**), which is sold under a variety of trade names depending on its use (Dacron, Terylene, and Mylar). Plastic soft drink bottles are made of PET.

polyethylene terephthalate
PET
[Ester bonds are drawn in red.]

One method of synthesizing PET is by the acid-catalyzed reaction of a dicarboxylic acid (terephthalic acid) with ethylene glycol ($HOCH_2CH_2OH$) in a Fischer esterification reaction.

Each OH and COOH react.

loss of $H_2O$

HO—  terephthalic acid  —OH  +  $HOCH_2CH_2OH$  +  HO—  —OH  +  $HOCH_2CH_2OH$

loss of $H_2O$                         loss of $H_2O$

$\downarrow$ acid catalyst

polyethylene terephthalate
PET

Figure 17.5    Medical Uses of PET

a. PET is used to make the knitted material      b. Some replacement blood vessels are made
   present in artificial heart valves.                with PET.

Because these polymers are easily and cheaply prepared and they form strong and chemically stable materials, they have been used in clothing, films, tires, and plastic drink bottles. Polyester fiber is also used in artificial heart valves and replacement blood vessels (Figure 17.5).

### PROBLEM 17.34

Draw the structure of Kodel, a polyester formed from 1,4-dihydroxymethylcyclohexane and terephthalic acid. Suggest a reason why fabrics made from Kodel are stiff and crease resistant.

$$HOCH_2 - \bigcirc - CH_2OH \quad + \quad$$

1,4-dihydroxymethylcyclohexane                terephthalic acid

## 17.10C  FOCUS ON HEALTH & MEDICINE
### Dissolving Sutures

Although PET is a stable material, the ester bonds in some other polyesters are quite readily hydrolyzed to carboxylic acids and alcohols in aqueous medium. Polyesters of this sort are suited for applications in which slow degradation is a useful feature. One example of a degradable polymer is formed from two α-hydroxy acids—glycolic acid ($HOCH_2COOH$) and lactic acid [$CH_3CH(OH)COOH$].

Join the C=O of one acid with the
OH group of the second acid.

glycolic acid            lactic acid                                     new C—O bonds

dissolving suture material

When glycolic acid and lactic acid are combined, the hydroxyl group of one α-hydroxy acid reacts with the carboxyl group of the second α-hydroxy acid. The resulting polymer is used by surgeons in dissolving sutures. Within weeks, the polymer is hydrolyzed to the monomers from which it was prepared, which are metabolized readily by the body. These sutures are used internally to hold tissues together while healing and scar formation occur.

Recycled PET is used to make shopping bags.

### 17.10D FOCUS ON THE ENVIRONMENT
Polymer Recycling

The same desirable characteristics that make polymers popular materials for consumer products—durability, strength, and lack of reactivity—also contribute to environmental problems. Many polymers do not degrade readily, and as a result, billions of pounds of polymers end up in landfills every year. Recycling polymers is one way to help combat the waste problem they create.

The most common polymers are each assigned a recycling code (1–6); **the lower the number, the easier the polymer is to recycle.** PET materials are assigned recycling code "1" because they are the easiest to recycle. Since recycled polymers are often still contaminated with small amounts of adhesives and other materials, these recycled polymers are generally not used for storing food or drink products. Recycled PET is used to make fibers for fleece clothing and carpeting.

PET can also be converted back to the monomers from which it was made. For example, heating PET with water and acid breaks the ester bonds of the polymer chain to give ethylene glycol ($HOCH_2CH_2OH$) and terephthalic acid. These monomers then serve as starting materials for more PET.

polyethylene terephthalate
PET

terephthalic acid

$+$ $HOCH_2CH_2OH$
ethylene glycol

chemical recycling

**PROBLEM 17.35**

A polyester can be converted back to the monomers from which it is made much more easily than a polymer like polyethylene, $[—CH_2CH_2—]_n$. Explain why this is so.

### 17.11 FOCUS ON HEALTH & MEDICINE
Penicillin

Penicillin was used to treat injured soldiers in World War II before its structure had been conclusively determined.

In the twenty-first century it is hard to imagine that an infected cut or scrape could be life-threatening. Before antibiotics were discovered in the early twentieth century, however, that was indeed the case.

The antibiotic properties of **penicillin** were first discovered in 1928 by Sir Alexander Fleming, who noticed that a mold of the genus *Penicillium* inhibited the growth of certain bacteria. After years of experimentation, penicillin was first used to treat a female patient who had developed a streptococcal infection in 1942. By 1944, penicillin production was given high priority by the United States government, because it was needed to treat the many injured soldiers in World War II.

The penicillins are a group of related antibiotics. All penicillins contain two amide units. One amide is part of a four-membered ring called a **β-lactam.** The second amide is bonded to the α carbon of the β-lactam carbonyl group. Particular penicillins differ in the identity of the R group in the amide side chain. The first penicillin to be discovered was penicillin G. Amoxicillin is another example in common use today.

**General structure Penicillin**

α carbon

β-lactam

penicillin G

amoxicillin

Penicillin has no effect on mammalian cells because they are surrounded by a flexible membrane composed of a lipid bilayer (Chapter 19) and not a cell wall.

Unlike mammalian cells, bacterial cells are surrounded by a fairly rigid cell wall, which allows the bacterium to live in many different environments. **Penicillin interferes with the synthesis of the bacterial cell wall.** Penicillin kills bacteria by a substitution reaction that occurs at the amide that is part of the β-lactam. The β-lactam is more reactive than a regular amide because the bond angles in the small ring must be 90°. This feature makes the ring unstable. The β-lactam ring of the penicillin molecule reacts with an enzyme needed to synthesize the cell wall, and this deactivates the enzyme. Cell wall construction is halted, killing the bacterium. This process is discussed further in Section 21.9C.

**PROBLEM 17.36**

How many chirality centers does penicillin G contain?

# CHAPTER HIGHLIGHTS

## KEY TERMS

Acyl group (17.1)
Alpha (α) carbon (17.2)
Amide (17.1)
Beta (β) carbon (17.2)
Carboxyl group (17.1)
Carboxylate anion (17.6)
Carboxylic acid (17.1)
Condensation polymer (17.10)
Ester (17.1)

Fischer esterification (17.8)
Hydrolysis (17.9)
α-Hydroxy acid (17.4)
Lactam (17.1)
Lactone (17.1)
Lipid (17.9)
Micelle (17.6)
Nylon (17.10)
Penicillin (17.11)

Polyamide (17.10)
Polyester (17.10)
Primary (1°) amide (17.1)
Prostaglandin (17.4)
Saponification (17.9)
Secondary (2°) amide (17.1)
Soap (17.6)
Tertiary (3°) amide (17.1)
Triacylglycerol (17.9)

## KEY REACTIONS

[1]   Acid–base reaction of carboxylic acids (17.6)

$$\underset{R}{\overset{O}{\|}}\underset{O-H}{C} + Na^+ \; OH^- \longrightarrow \underset{R}{\overset{O}{\|}}\underset{O^- \, Na^+}{C} + H_2O$$

[2]   Substitution reactions of carboxylic acids (17.8)

a. Formation of esters

$$\underset{R}{\overset{O}{\|}}\underset{OH}{C} + R'OH \underset{}{\overset{H_2SO_4}{\rightleftharpoons}} \underset{R}{\overset{O}{\|}}\underset{OR'}{C} + H_2O$$

b. Formation of amides

$$\underset{R}{\overset{O}{\|}}\underset{OH}{C} + R'_2NH \overset{\Delta}{\longrightarrow} \underset{R}{\overset{O}{\|}}\underset{NR'_2}{C} + H_2O$$

R' = H or alkyl

[3]   Hydrolysis of acyl compounds (17.9)

a. Ester hydrolysis

$$\underset{R}{\overset{O}{\underset{\phantom{}}{\parallel}}}C\!-\!OR' \ + \ H_2O \ \xrightarrow[\text{(H}^+ \text{ or OH}^-)]{} \ \underset{(\text{in acid})}{\overset{O}{\parallel}}R\!-\!C\!-\!OH \ \ \text{or} \ \ \underset{(\text{in base})}{\overset{O}{\parallel}}R\!-\!C\!-\!O^- \ + \ R'OH$$

b. Amide hydrolysis

$$\underset{R}{\overset{O}{\parallel}}C\!-\!NR'_2 \ + \ H_2O \ \xrightarrow[\text{(H}^+ \text{ or OH}^-)]{} \ \underset{(\text{in acid})}{\overset{O}{\parallel}}R\!-\!C\!-\!OH \ \ \text{or} \ \ \underset{(\text{in base})}{\overset{O}{\parallel}}R\!-\!C\!-\!O^- \ + \ R'_2NH$$

R' = H or alkyl

# KEY CONCEPTS

**❶ What are the characteristics of carboxylic acids, esters, and amides?**

- Carboxylic acids have the general structure RCOOH; esters have the general structure RCOOR'; amides have the general structure RCONR'$_2$, where R' = H or alkyl. (17.1)
- The carbonyl carbon is trigonal planar with bond angles of 120°. (17.1)
- All acyl compounds have a polar C=O. RCO$_2$H, RCONH$_2$, and RCONHR' are capable of intermolecular hydrogen bonding. (17.3)

**❷ How are carboxylic acids, esters, and amides named? (17.2)**

- Carboxylic acids are identified by the suffix -oic acid.
- Esters are identified by the suffix -ate.
- Amides are identified by the suffix -amide.

**❸ Give examples of useful carboxylic acids. (17.4)**

- α-Hydroxy carboxylic acids are used in skin care products.
- Aspirin, ibuprofen, and naproxen are pain relievers and anti-inflammatory agents.
- Aspirin is an anti-inflammatory agent because it blocks the synthesis of prostaglandins from arachidonic acid.

**❹ Give examples of useful esters and amides. (17.5)**

- Some esters—ethyl butanoate, pentyl butanoate, and methyl salicylate—have characteristic odors and flavors.
- Benzocaine is the active ingredient in over-the-counter oral topical anesthetics.
- Acetaminophen is the active ingredient in Tylenol.

**❺ What products are formed when carboxylic acids are treated with base? (17.6)**

- Carboxylic acids react with bases to form carboxylate anions (RCOO$^-$).
- Carboxylate anions are water soluble and commonly used as preservatives.

**❻ How does soap clean away dirt? (17.6C)**

- Soaps are salts of carboxylic acids that have many carbon atoms in a long hydrocarbon chain. A soap molecule has an ionic head and a nonpolar hydrocarbon tail.
- Soap forms micelles in water with the polar heads on the surface and the hydrocarbon tails in the interior. Grease and dirt dissolve in the nonpolar tails, so they can be washed away with water.

**❼ Discuss the acid–base chemistry of aspirin. (17.7)**

- Aspirin remains in its neutral form in the stomach, and in this form it can cross a cell membrane and serve as an anti-inflammatory agent.
- A proton is removed from aspirin in the basic environment of the intestines to form an ionic carboxylate anion. This form is not absorbed.

**❽ How are carboxylic acids converted to esters and amides? (17.8)**

- Carboxylic acids are converted to esters by reaction with alcohols (R'OH) and acid (H$_2$SO$_4$).
- Carboxylic acids are converted to amides by heating with ammonia (NH$_3$) or amines (R'NH$_2$ or R'$_2$NH).

**❾ What hydrolysis products are formed from esters and amides? (17.9)**

- Esters are hydrolyzed to carboxylic acids (RCOOH) in the presence of an acid catalyst (H$_2$SO$_4$). Esters are converted to carboxylate anions (RCOO$^-$) with aqueous base (NaOH in H$_2$O).
- Amides are hydrolyzed to carboxylic acids (RCOOH) in the presence of an acid catalyst (HCl). Amides are converted to carboxylate anions (RCOO$^-$) with aqueous base (NaOH in H$_2$O).

**❿ What are polyamides and polyesters and how are they formed? (17.10)**

- Polyamides like nylon are polymers that contain many amide bonds. They are formed when a dicarboxylic acid is heated with a diamine.
- Polyesters like PET are polymers that contain many ester bonds. They are formed when a dicarboxylic acid is treated with a diol in the presence of acid (H$_2$SO$_4$).

**⓫ How does penicillin act as an antibiotic? (17.11)**

- The β-lactam of penicillin is more reactive than a regular amide and it reacts with an enzyme needed to synthesize the cell wall of a bacterium. Without a cell wall, the bacterium dies.

## PROBLEMS

Selected in-chapter and odd-numbered end-of-chapter problems have brief answers in Appendix B. The *Student Study Guide and Solutions Manual* contains detailed solutions to all in-chapter and odd-numbered end-of-chapter problems, as well as additional worked examples and a chapter self-test.

### Structure and Bonding

**17.37** Draw the structure of a compound that fits each description:
  a. a carboxylic acid of molecular formula $C_8H_{16}O_2$ that has six carbons in its longest chain
  b. an ester of molecular formula $C_6H_{12}O_2$ that contains a methoxy group ($OCH_3$) bonded to the carbonyl group
  c. an ester of molecular formula $C_6H_{10}O_2$ that contains a ring
  d. a carboxylic acid of molecular formula $C_6H_{10}O_2$ that has the carboxyl group bonded to a ring

**17.38** Draw the structure of a constitutional isomer of octanoic acid [$CH_3(CH_2)_6CO_2H$] that:
  a. contains a carboxyl group and no chirality center
  b. contains a carboxyl group and a chirality center
  c. contains an ester

**17.39** Draw the structure of a compound of molecular formula $C_5H_{11}NO$ that contains: (a) a 1° amide; (b) a 2° amide; (c) a 3° amide.

**17.40** Draw the structure of a compound of molecular formula $C_9H_{11}NO$ that contains a benzene ring and: (a) a 1° amide; (b) a 2° amide; (c) a 3° amide.

**17.41** Draw the structure of four constitutional isomers of molecular formula $C_4H_8O_2$ that contain an ester.

**17.42** Draw the structure of four constitutional isomers of molecular formula $C_5H_{10}O_2$ that have the general formula $HCO_2R$; that is, compounds that are esters of formic acid, $HCO_2H$.

**17.43** What is the difference between a lactone and a lactam?

**17.44** What is the difference between a lactone and an ester?

### Nomenclature

**17.45** Give an acceptable name for each compound depicted in the ball-and-stick models.

a.

b.

c.

**17.46** Give an acceptable name for each compound depicted in the ball-and-stick models.

a.

b.

c.

**17.47** Give an acceptable name for each carboxylic acid.
  a. $(CH_3)_2CHCH_2CH_2COOH$
  b. $CH_3CH_2CH_2\overset{\displaystyle CH_2CH_3}{\underset{\displaystyle CH_2CH_3}{CHCHCH_2CH_2COOH}}$
  c. $CH_3CH_2CH_2CH_2CH_2\underset{\displaystyle CO_2H}{CHCH_2CH_3}$

**17.48** Give an acceptable name for each carboxylic acid.
  a. $(CH_3)_2CHCH_2CH_2CH_2CH_2CH_2COOH$
  b. $CH_3\overset{\displaystyle CH_3}{CH}CH\overset{\displaystyle CH_3}{\underset{\displaystyle CH_3}{CH}CH_2COOH}$
  c. $CH_3CH_2CH_2CH_2\underset{\displaystyle CO_2H}{CHCH_2CH_3}$

**17.49** Give an acceptable name for each ester.
  a. $CH_3CH_2CH_2CO_2CH_2CH_2CH_3$
  b. benzene ring $-CO_2(CH_2)_3CH_3$

**17.50** Give an acceptable name for each ester.
  a. $CH_3CO_2(CH_2)_4CH_3$
  b. $HCO_2(CH_2)_5CH_3$

**17.51** Give an acceptable name for each amide.
  a. $CH_3(CH_2)_4CONH_2$
  b. benzene ring $-\overset{\displaystyle O}{\overset{\displaystyle \|}{C}}-N\overset{\displaystyle CH_2CH_3}{\underset{\displaystyle CH_3}{}}$

**17.52** Give an acceptable name for each amide.
 a. $CH_3(CH_2)_6CONH_2$

 b.

**17.53** Give an acceptable name for each compound.
 a. $HCONH_2$                  c. $CH_3CH_2CHCOOH$
                                              $|$
                                             $OH$

 b.

 d. $CH_3CH_2CO_2CH_2CH_2CH_3$

**17.54** Give an acceptable name for each compound.
 a. $CH_3(CH_2)_8CO_2CH_3$       c.

 b. $(CH_3)_2CHCH_2CONH_2$       d. $(CH_3)_3C(CH_2)_3COOH$

**17.55** Draw the structure corresponding to each name.
 a. 2-hydroxyheptanoic acid
 b. 4-chlorononanoic acid
 c. 3,4-dibromobenzoic acid
 d. lithium propanoate
 e. 2,2-dibromobutanoic acid
 f. ethyl 2-methylpropanoate

**17.56** Draw the structure corresponding to each name.
 a. 3-methylhexanoic acid
 b. 3-hydroxy-4-methylheptanoic acid
 c. *p*-nitrobenzoic acid
 d. sodium hexanoate
 e. *m*-ethylbenzoic acid
 f. propyl decanoate

**17.57** Draw the structure corresponding to each name.
 a. propyl formate
 b. butyl butanoate
 c. heptyl benzoate
 d. *N*-ethylhexanamide
 e. *N*-ethyl-*N*-methylheptanamide

**17.58** Draw the structure corresponding to each name.
 a. octyl acetate
 b. hexyl pentanoate
 c. propyl hexanoate
 d. *N*-butylbenzamide
 e. *N,N*-dimethyloctanamide

**17.59** Draw the structures for the four carboxylic acids of molecular formula $C_5H_{10}O_2$. Give the IUPAC name for each compound.

**17.60** Draw the structures for the four sodium salts of the carboxylic acids in Problem 17.59, formed by treating each of these carboxylic acids with NaOH. Give the IUPAC name for each sodium salt.

## Physical Properties and Intermolecular Forces

**17.61** Which compound(s) can hydrogen bond to another molecule like itself? Which compounds can hydrogen bond to water? (a) $HCO_2CH_3$; (b) $CH_3CH_2CO_2H$.

**17.62** Which compound(s) can hydrogen bond to another molecule like itself? Which compounds can hydrogen bond to water? (a) $CH_3CONHCH_3$; (b) $HCON(CH_3)_2$.

**17.63** Rank the following compounds in order of increasing boiling point: $CH_3CH_2CH(CH_3)_2$, $CH_3CH_2CO_2H$, and $CH_3CH_2COCH_3$.

**17.64** Rank the following compounds in order of increasing boiling point: $(CH_3)_2CHCO_2H$, $CH_3CH_2CO_2CH_3$, $(CH_3)_2CHCH(CH_3)_2$.

**17.65** Explain why the boiling point of $CH_3CH_2CONH_2$ is higher than the boiling point of $CH_3CO_2CH_3$.

**17.66** Which compound in each pair is more water soluble? Which compound in each pair is more soluble in an organic solvent? (a) $CH_3CH_2CH_2CH_3$ or $CH_3CH_2CH_2CH_2CO_2H$; (b) $CH_3(CH_2)_4COOH$ or $CH_3(CH_2)_4COO^-$ $Na^+$.

## Acidity

**17.67** Draw the products of each acid–base reaction.

 a. $+$ KOH $\longrightarrow$

 b. $(CH_3)_2CHCH_2CH_2COOH$ $+$ $Na_2CO_3$ $\longrightarrow$

**17.68** Draw the products of each acid–base reaction.

 a. $+$ NaOH $\longrightarrow$

 b. $Cl_3CCOOH$ $+$ $NaHCO_3$ $\longrightarrow$

## Formation of Esters and Amides

**17.69** What ester is formed when butanoic acid ($CH_3CH_2CH_2CO_2H$) is treated with each alcohol in the presence of $H_2SO_4$?

 a. $CH_3OH$                    c. —OH

 b. $CH_3CH_2CH_2OH$           d. —$CH_2CH_2OH$

**17.70** What ester is formed when each carboxylic acid is treated with 2-propanol [$(CH_3)_2CHOH$] in the presence of $H_2SO_4$?

 a. $CH_3CH_2COOH$             c. $HCO_2H$

 b.   d. $CH_3O$——COOH

**17.71** Methylparaben is a common preservative used in cosmetics. What carboxylic acid and alcohol are needed to synthesize methylparaben by Fischer esterification?

$$HO-\langle\text{ }\rangle-CO_2CH_3$$

methylparaben

**17.72** Octinoxate is the trade name for 2-ethylhexyl 4-methoxycinnamate, a widely used sunscreen. What carboxylic acid and alcohol are needed to synthesize octinoxate by Fischer esterification?

octinoxate

**17.73** What amide is formed when butanoic acid ($CH_3CH_2CH_2CO_2H$) is heated with each nitrogen-containing compound?
  a. $NH_3$
  b. $CH_3CH_2NH_2$
  c. $(CH_3CH_2)_2NH$
  d. $CH_3NHCH_2CH_3$

**17.74** What amide is formed when propylamine ($CH_3CH_2CH_2NH_2$) is heated with each carboxylic acid?
  a. $CH_3CH_2COOH$
  b. $CH_3(CH_2)_{10}\overset{O}{\underset{}{C}}OH$
  c. $HCO_2H$
  d. $CH_3O-\langle\text{ }\rangle-COOH$

**17.75** What carboxylic acid and alcohol are needed to synthesize each ester by Fischer esterification?
  a. $\langle\text{ }\rangle-CO_2CH_3$
  b. $\langle\text{ }\rangle-O-\overset{O}{\underset{}{C}}-CH_3$

**17.76** What carboxylic acid and alcohol are needed to synthesize each ester by Fischer esterification?
  a. $(CH_3)_3CCO_2CH_3$
  b. $(CH_3)_3C-O-\overset{O}{\underset{}{C}}-CH_3$

**17.77** What carboxylic acid and amine are needed to synthesize the pain reliever phenacetin? Phenacetin was once a component of the over-the-counter pain reliever APC (aspirin, phenacetin, caffeine), but is no longer used because of its kidney toxicity.

phenacetin

**17.78** What carboxylic acid and amine are needed to synthesize each amide?
  a. $\langle\text{ }\rangle-CONHCH(CH_3)_2$
  b. $(CH_3)_2CHCONH-\langle\text{ }\rangle$

## Hydrolysis

**17.79** What products are formed when each ester is hydrolyzed with water and $H_2SO_4$?
  a. $CH_3CH_2CH_2\overset{O}{\underset{}{C}}-OCH(CH_3)_2$
  b. (decalin ring with $O-\overset{O}{\underset{}{C}}-CH_3$)
  c. $\langle\text{ }\rangle-CH_2CH_2-O-\overset{O}{\underset{}{C}}-H$

**17.80** What products are formed when each ester in Problem 17.79 is hydrolyzed with water and NaOH?

**17.81** What products are formed when each amide is hydrolyzed with water and HCl?
  a. (benzene with $CONH_2$ and $OCH_3$)
  b. $(CH_3)_3CCON(CH_3)_2$
  c. (cyclohexyl $-\overset{H}{\underset{}{N}}-\overset{O}{\underset{}{C}}-CH_3$)

**17.82** What products are formed when each amide in Problem 17.81 is hydrolyzed with water and NaOH?

**17.83** Ethyl phenylacetate ($C_6H_5CH_2CO_2CH_2CH_3$) is a naturally occurring ester in honey. What hydrolysis products are formed when this ester is treated with water and $H_2SO_4$?

**17.84** Benzyl acetate ($CH_3CO_2CH_2C_6H_5$) is a naturally occurring ester in peaches. What hydrolysis products are formed when this ester is treated with water and NaOH?

## Polyesters and Polyamides

**17.85** What dicarboxylic acid and diamine are needed to prepare the following polyamide?

**17.86** What dicarboxylic acid and diol are needed to form the following polyester?

(structure: —C(=O)—(CH₂)₂—C(=O)—O—⟨ring⟩—O—C(=O)—(CH₂)₂—C(=O)—O—⟨ring⟩—O—C(=O)—(CH₂)₂—C(=O)—O—⟨ring⟩—O—)

**17.87** PTT (polytrimethylene terephthalate) is a polyester formed from 1,3-propanediol (HOCH₂CH₂CH₂OH) by the given reaction. PTT is sold under the trade name Sorona by DuPont. 1,3-Propanediol can now be made from a plant source like corn, rather than from petroleum starting materials. This makes PTT a more environmentally friendly polyester than PET. What is the structure of PTT?

HOOC—⟨benzene⟩—COOH + HOCH₂CH₂CH₂OH $\xrightarrow{H_2SO_4}$ PTT

terephthalic acid            1,3-propanediol

**17.88** What polyamide is formed when the following dicarboxylic acid and diamine are heated together?

HO—C(=O)—CH=CH—C(=O)—OH + H₂N(CH₂)₄NH₂

## General Questions

**17.89** What is the difference between saponification and esterification?

**17.90** You have now learned three different types of reactions that involve water—hydration (Chapter 13), dehydration (Chapter 14), and hydrolysis (Chapter 17). Give an example of each type of reaction and explain the similarities and differences among them.

**17.91** Draw the products formed in each reaction.

a. CH₃—C(=O)—OH + CH₃OH $\underset{}{\overset{H_2SO_4}{\rightleftharpoons}}$

b. (CH₃)₂CHO—C(=O)—CH₃ + H₂O $\underset{}{\overset{H_2SO_4}{\rightleftharpoons}}$

c. (CH₃)₂CHCH₂O—C(=O)—CH(CH₃)₂ + H₂O $\xrightarrow{NaOH}$

d. CH₃(CH₂)₄—C(=O)—OH + NaOH $\longrightarrow$

**17.92** Draw the products formed in each reaction.

a. (CH₃)₂CH—C(=O)—OH + CH₃NH₂ $\xrightarrow{\Delta}$

b. (CH₃)₂CHCH₂NH—C(=O)—CH₃ + H₂O $\xrightarrow{HCl}$

c. (CH₃)₂CHNH—C(=O)—CH₂CH₃ + H₂O $\xrightarrow{NaOH}$

d. HO—C(=O)—CH₂CH(CH₃)₂ + NaOH $\longrightarrow$

**17.93** Answer the following questions about **A**, depicted in the ball-and-stick model.

**A**

a. What is the IUPAC name for **A**?
b. Draw an isomer of **A** that has the same functional group.
c. Draw an isomer of **A** that has a different functional group.
d. What products are formed when **A** is treated with NaOH?
e. Predict the solubility properties of **A** in H₂O; in an organic solvent.
f. What product is formed when **A** is treated with CH₃CH₂OH and H₂SO₄?
g. What product is formed when **A** is heated with CH₃CH₂NH₂?

**17.94** Answer the following questions about **B**, depicted in the ball-and-stick model.

**B**

a. What is the IUPAC name for **B**?
b. Draw an isomer of **B** that has the same functional group.
c. Draw an isomer of **B** that has a different functional group.
d. What products are formed when **B** is treated with NaOH?
e. Predict the solubility properties of **B** in H₂O; in an organic solvent.
f. What product is formed when **B** is treated with CH₃CH₂OH and H₂SO₄?
g. What product is formed when **B** is heated with CH₃CH₂NH₂?

## Applications

**17.95** Which of the following structures represent soaps? Explain your answers.

a. $CH_3CO_2^- Na^+$

b. $CH_3(CH_2)_{14}CO_2^- Na^+$

c. $CH_3(CH_2)_{12}COOH$

**17.96** Which of the following structures represent soaps? Explain your answers.

a. $CH_3CH_2CO_2^- K^+$

b. $CH_3(CH_2)_{16}COOH$

c. $CH_3(CH_2)_9CO_2^- Na^+$

**17.97** Like aspirin, naproxen contains a carboxyl group, so it undergoes similar acid–base reactions.

naproxen

a. Draw the reaction that occurs when naproxen is treated with NaOH.

b. What form of naproxen exists in the stomach?

c. What form of naproxen exists in the intestines?

**17.98** Sunscreens that contain an ester can undergo hydrolysis. What products are formed when octyl salicylate, a commercial sunscreen, is hydrolyzed with water?

octyl salicylate

**17.99** How does aspirin act as an anti-inflammatory agent?

**17.100** What structural feature is important in making penicillin a biologically active antibiotic? How does the biological activity of penicillin come about?

**17.101** Explain how soap is able to dissolve nonpolar hydrocarbons in a polar solvent like $H_2O$.

**17.102** Today, synthetic detergents like the compound drawn below are used to clean clothes, not soaps. Synthetic detergents are similar to soaps in that they contain an ionic head bonded to a large hydrocarbon group (the nonpolar tail). Explain how this detergent cleans away dirt.

$$CH_3(CH_2)_9 \text{—} \bigcirc \text{—} SO_3^- \, Na^+$$

a detergent

**17.103** Draw the products formed by acidic hydrolysis of **aspartame,** the artificial sweetener used in Equal and many diet beverages. One of the hydrolysis products of this reaction is the naturally occurring amino acid phenylalanine. Infants afflicted with phenylketonuria cannot metabolize this amino acid so it accumulates, causing mental retardation. When identified early, a diet limiting the consumption of phenylalanine (and compounds like aspartame that are converted to it) can allow for a normal life.

aspartame

**17.104** Polyhydroxybutyrate (PHB) is a biodegradable polyester; that is, the polymer is degraded by microorganisms that naturally occur in the environment. Such biodegradable polymers are attractive alternatives to the commonly used polymers that persist in landfills for years. What is the single product formed when PHB is hydrolyzed with acid and water?

PHB

## CHALLENGE PROBLEMS

**17.105** Compounds that contain both a hydroxyl group (OH) and a carboxyl group (COOH) can undergo an intramolecular esterification reaction. What product is formed when each hydroxy acid undergoes an intramolecular reaction?

a. $HOCH_2CH_2CH_2CH_2CO_2H$

b. $HOCH_2CH_2CH_2CO_2H$

**17.106** Lactams can be hydrolyzed with base, just like other amides. When a lactam is hydrolyzed, the ring is opened to form a product with two functional groups and no ring. What product is formed when caprolactam, the starting material for the synthesis of one type of nylon, is hydrolyzed with water and base?

caprolactam

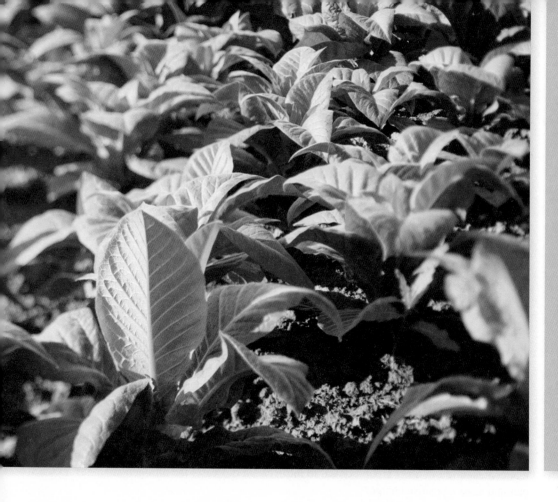

Tobacco products contain the addictive stimulant **nicotine**, an amine that is synthesized by tobacco plants as a defense against insect predators.

# Amines and Neurotransmitters

## CHAPTER GOALS

*In this chapter you will learn how to:*

1. Identify the characteristics of amines
2. Name amines
3. Give examples of common alkaloids
4. Draw the products of acid–base reactions of amines
5. Identify and name ammonium salts
6. Discuss the function of neurotransmitters and explain how neurotransmitters and hormones differ
7. Discuss the role of dopamine and serotonin in the body
8. Give examples of important derivatives of 2-phenylethylamine
9. Discuss the chemistry of histamine, antihistamines, and anti-ulcer drugs

In Chapter 18 we turn our attention to **amines,** organic compounds that contain nitrogen atoms. The amine nitrogen atom can be bonded to one, two, or three alkyl groups, and many amines have a nitrogen atom in a ring. All proteins contain amines, as do many vitamins and hormones. Many common amines, such as the caffeine in coffee and the nicotine in tobacco, are naturally occurring. Synthetic drugs used as sedatives, antihistamines, and bronchodilators also contain the amine functional group. Chapter 18 concludes with a discussion of **neurotransmitters,** important chemical messengers in the body, and many other related physiologically active amines.

## 18.1   Structure and Bonding

*Amines* **are organic nitrogen compounds,** formed by replacing one or more hydrogen atoms of ammonia ($NH_3$) with alkyl groups. Amines are classified as 1°, 2°, or 3° by the number of alkyl groups bonded to the *nitrogen* atom.

$$R{-}\overset{\cdot\cdot}{\underset{|\;H}{N}}{-}H \qquad\qquad R{-}\overset{\cdot\cdot}{\underset{|\;R}{N}}{-}H \qquad\qquad R{-}\overset{\cdot\cdot}{\underset{|\;R}{N}}{-}R$$

1° amine           2° amine           3° amine

- A primary (1°) amine has one C—N bond and the general structure $RNH_2$.
- A secondary (2°) amine has two C—N bonds and the general structure $R_2NH$.
- A tertiary (3°) amine has three C—N bonds and the general structure $R_3N$.

> **Classifying amines as 1°, 2°, or 3° is reminiscent of classifying amides** in Chapter 17, but is *different* from classifying alcohols and alkyl halides as 1°, 2°, and 3°. Compare, for example, a 2° amine and a 2° alcohol. A 2° amine ($R_2NH$) has *two* C—N bonds. A 2° alcohol ($R_2CHOH$) has only *one* C—O bond, but *two* C—C bonds on the carbon bonded to oxygen.

Like ammonia, **the amine nitrogen atom has a lone pair of electrons,** which is generally omitted in condensed structures. In Section 18.7, we will also learn about **quaternary ammonium ions** that contain a fourth alkyl group bonded to nitrogen. In this case, the nitrogen atom has no lone pair and bears a positive charge.

**General structure**             **Example**

quaternary ammonium ion        N has no lone pair.

The amine nitrogen atom can also be part of a ring to form a **heterocycle.** For example, piperidine, one compound isolated from black pepper, and coniine, the poisonous principle of hemlock, both contain a nitrogen atom in a six-membered ring.

> **Recall from Section 14.7 that a** *heterocycle* **is a ring that contains a heteroatom such as N, O, or S.**

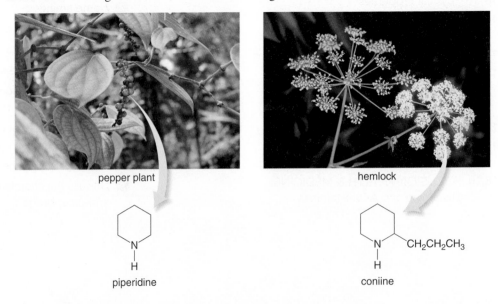

pepper plant                          hemlock

piperidine                          coniine

An amine nitrogen atom is surrounded by three atoms and one nonbonded electron pair, making it trigonal pyramidal in shape, with bond angles of approximately 109.5°.

trigonal pyramidal

trigonal pyramidal

## SAMPLE PROBLEM 18.1

Classify each amine in the following compounds as 1°, 2°, or 3°. Putrescine is partly responsible for the foul odor of decaying fish. MDMA is the illegal stimulant commonly called "Ecstasy."

a. $H_2N(CH_2)_4NH_2$

putrescine

b.

MDMA
"Ecstasy"

### Analysis

To determine whether an amine is 1°, 2°, or 3°, count the number of carbons bonded to the nitrogen atom. A 1° amine has one C—N bond, and so forth.

### Solution

Draw out the structure or add H's to the skeletal structure to clearly see how many C—N bonds the amine contains.

a. H—N—CH₂CH₂CH₂CH₂—N—H

Each N is bonded to only 1 C.
Both amines are **1°**.

b.

This N is bonded to 2 C's,
making it a **2° amine.**

MDMA
"Ecstasy"

## PROBLEM 18.1

Classify each amine in the following compounds as 1°, 2°, or 3°.

a. $H_2N(CH_2)_3NH(CH_2)_4NH(CH_2)_3NH_2$

spermine
(isolated from semen)

b. $CH_3CH_2O$

meperidine
(Trade name: Demerol)

Angel's trumpets are ornamental
plants that contain the toxic amine
scopolamine (Problem 18.2).
Transdermal patches that release
a minute dose of scopolamine are
used to treat the nausea and vomiting
associated with motion sickness.

**PROBLEM 18.2**

Label the amine and hydroxyl group in scopolamine, a drug used to treat motion sickness,
as 1°, 2°, or 3°.

scopolamine

**Methamphetamine** (Figure 18.1) is one of the many biologically active amines discussed in this
chapter. Because it imparts to the user a pleasurable "high," methamphetamine is a widely abused
illegal drug that has profound effects on the body and mind. Methamphetamine, known as speed,
meth, or crystal meth, is highly addictive, easy to synthesize, and has adverse effects on the heart,
lungs, blood vessels, and other organs. Prolonged use can lead to sleeplessness, seizures, hallucinations, paranoia, and serious heart disease.

**PROBLEM 18.3**

(a) What type of amine does methamphetamine contain? (b) Give the molecular shape around each
indicated atom in methamphetamine.

methamphetamine

**Figure 18.1**

Effects of Methamphetamine Use

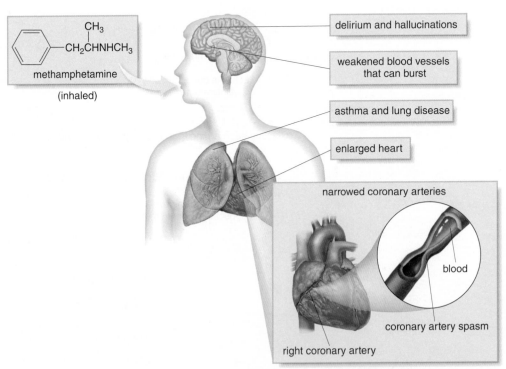

Blood flow is constricted during an artery spasm,
resulting in a heart attack.

## 18.2  Nomenclature

### 18.2A  Primary Amines

Primary (1°) amines are named using either systematic or common names. Systematic names can be used for any amine. To assign the **systematic name,** find the longest carbon chain bonded to the amine nitrogen, and change the **-e** ending of the parent alkane to the suffix **-amine.** Then use the usual rules of nomenclature to number the chain and name the substituents.

Common names are used only for simple amines. To assign a **common name,** name the alkyl group bonded to the nitrogen atom and add the suffix **-amine,** forming a single word.

$$CH_3NH_2$$
Common name:  methylamine
Systematic name:  methanamine

$$CH_3CH_2CH_2CH_2NH_2$$
          4    3    2    1
Common name:  butylamine
Systematic name:  1-butanamine

### 18.2B  Secondary and Tertiary Amines

Secondary (2°) and 3° amines having identical alkyl groups are named by using the prefix **di-** or **tri-** with the name of the primary amine.

$$CH_3CH_2-\underset{\underset{CH_2CH_3}{|}}{N}-CH_2CH_3$$

triethylamine

$$CH_3CH_2CH_2-\underset{\underset{CH_2CH_2CH_3}{|}}{\overset{\overset{H}{|}}{N}}$$

dipropylamine

Secondary and tertiary amines having more than one kind of alkyl group are named as **N-substituted primary amines** using the following *How To* procedure.

---

### How To  Name 2° and 3° Amines with Different Alkyl Groups

**Example:**  Name the following 2° amine: $(CH_3)_2CHNHCH_3$.

**Step [1]**  Name the longest alkyl chain (or largest ring) bonded to the N atom as the parent amine.

• Since the longest carbon chain has 3 C's, the parent name is *propanamine.*
• Since the N atom is bonded to the middle carbon, the name becomes *2-propanamine.*

**Step [2]**  Name the other groups on the N atom as alkyl groups, alphabetize the names when there is more than one substituent, and precede each name with the prefix *N-*.

**Answer: *N*-methyl-2-propanamine**

one methyl substituent

## SAMPLE PROBLEM 18.2

Give a systematic name for each amine.

a.  $CH_3CH_2CH_2CH_2CH_2NH_2$

b.

### Analysis and Solution

a.  [1] For a 1° amine, find and name the longest chain containing the amine group.

| [2] Number the carbon skeleton.

$$CH_3CH_2CH_2CH_2CH_2NH_2$$

pentane  ----→  pentan*amine*
(5 C's)

$$CH_3CH_2CH_2CH_2CH_2NH_2$$
$$\phantom{CH_3}5\phantom{CH_2CH_2}2\phantom{CH_2}1$$

You must use a number to show the location of the $NH_2$ group.
**Answer: 1-pentanamine**

b.  For a 3° amine, one alkyl group on N is the principal R group and the others are substituents.

[1] Name the ring bonded to the N.

5 C's in the ring

↓

cyclopentanamine

| [2] Name the substituents.

a methyl and ethyl group on N

• 2 N's are needed, one for each alkyl group.
• Alphabetize the *e* of **e**thyl before the *m* of **m**ethyl.

**Answer: *N*-ethyl-*N*-methylcyclopentanamine**

## PROBLEM 18.4

Give an acceptable name for each amine.

a.  $CH_3CH_2CHCH_3$
      |
      $NH_2$

b.  $CH_3CH_2CH_2NHCH_3$

c.  —$N(CH_3)_2$

d.  $(CH_3CH_2CH_2CH_2)_2NH$

## 18.2C   Aromatic Amines

Aromatic amines, amines having a nitrogen atom bonded directly to a benzene ring, are named as derivatives of aniline.

aniline

*N*-ethylaniline

*o*-bromoaniline

## PROBLEM 18.5

Draw a structure corresponding to each name: (a) *N*-methylaniline; (b) *m*-ethylaniline; (c) 3,5-diethylaniline; (d) *N,N*-diethylaniline.

## 18.2D  Miscellaneous Nomenclature Facts

An **NH$_2$** group named as a substituent is called an **amino group.**

There are many different **nitrogen heterocycles,** and each ring type is named differently, depending on the number of N atoms in the ring and the ring size. The structures and names of four common nitrogen heterocycles are shown.

|  |  |  |  |
|---|---|---|---|
| piperidine | pyrrolidine | pyridine | pyrrole |

### PROBLEM 18.6

Draw a structure corresponding to each name.

a. 3-hexanamine
b. *N*-methylpentylamine
c. *p*-nitroaniline
d. *N*-methylpiperidine

e. *N,N*-dimethylethylamine
f. 2-aminocyclohexanone
g. 1-propylcyclohexanamine
h. *N*-propylaniline

## 18.3  Physical Properties

Many low molecular weight amines have *very* foul odors. **Trimethylamine** [(CH$_3$)$_3$N], formed when enzymes break down certain fish proteins, has the characteristic odor of rotting fish. **Cadaverine** (NH$_2$CH$_2$CH$_2$CH$_2$CH$_2$CH$_2$NH$_2$) is a poisonous diamine with a putrid odor also present in rotting fish, and partly responsible for the odor of semen, urine, and bad breath.

Because nitrogen is much more electronegative than carbon or hydrogen, amines contain polar C—N and N—H bonds. **Primary (1°) and 2° amines are also capable of intermolecular hydrogen bonding,** because they contain N—H bonds.

Since nitrogen is less electronegative than oxygen, however, intermolecular hydrogen bonds between N and H are *weaker* than those between O and H. As a result:

- In comparing compounds of similar size, 1° and 2° amines have higher boiling points than compounds incapable of hydrogen bonding, but lower boiling points than alcohols that have stronger intermolecular hydrogen bonds.

| CH$_3$CH$_2$OCH$_2$CH$_3$ | CH$_3$CH$_2$CH$_2$CH$_2$NH$_2$ | CH$_3$CH$_2$CH$_2$CH$_2$OH |
|---|---|---|
| diethyl ether | 1-butanamine | 1-butanol |
| bp = 38 °C | bp = 78 °C | bp = 118 °C |

**Increasing intermolecular forces**
**Increasing boiling point**

- Tertiary (3°) amines have lower boiling points than 1° and 2° amines of comparable size, because they have no N—H bonds.

$$3° \text{ amine} \qquad CH_3CH_2N(CH_3)_2 \qquad\qquad CH_3CH_2-\overset{\overset{\displaystyle H}{|}}{N}-CH_2CH_3 \qquad 2° \text{ amine}$$

**no** N—H bond          bp = 38 °C                    bp = 56 °C              N—H bond

**higher boiling point**

Amines are soluble in organic solvents regardless of size. Amines with fewer than six carbons are water soluble since they can hydrogen bond with water. Larger amines are water insoluble since the nonpolar alkyl portion is too large to dissolve in the polar water solvent.

### SAMPLE PROBLEM 18.3

Which compound in each pair has the higher boiling point: (a) $CH_3CH_2NHCH_3$ or $CH_3CH_2OCH_3$; (b) $(CH_3)_3N$ or $CH_3CH_2CH_2NH_2$?

### Analysis

Keep in mind the general rule: For compounds of comparable size, **the stronger the intermolecular forces, the higher the boiling point.** Compounds that can hydrogen bond have higher boiling points than compounds that are polar but cannot hydrogen bond. Polar compounds have higher boiling points than nonpolar compounds.

### Solution

a. The 2° amine ($CH_3CH_2NHCH_3$) has an N—H bond, so intermolecular hydrogen bonding is possible. The ether ($CH_3CH_2OCH_3$) has only C—H bonds, so there is no possibility of intermolecular hydrogen bonding. $CH_3CH_2NHCH_3$ has a higher boiling point because it has stronger intermolecular forces.

$$CH_3CH_2-\overset{\overset{\displaystyle }{|}}{\underset{\underset{\displaystyle H}{|}}{N}}-CH_3 \qquad\qquad\qquad CH_3CH_2-O-CH_3$$

a 2° amine with an N—H bond          an ether with only C—H bonds
intermolecular hydrogen bonding
higher boiling point

b. The 1° amine ($CH_3CH_2CH_2NH_2$) has N—H bonds, so intermolecular hydrogen bonding is possible. The 3° amine [$(CH_3)_3N$] has only C—H bonds, so there is no possibility of intermolecular hydrogen bonding. $CH_3CH_2CH_2NH_2$ has a higher boiling point because it has stronger intermolecular forces.

$$CH_3CH_2CH_2NH_2 \qquad\qquad\qquad CH_3-\overset{\overset{\displaystyle }{|}}{\underset{\underset{\displaystyle CH_3}{|}}{N}}-CH_3$$

a 1° amine with N—H bonds          a 3° amine with only C—H bonds
intermolecular hydrogen bonding
higher boiling point

### PROBLEM 18.7

Which compound in each pair has the higher boiling point?

a.  $CH_3-\overset{\overset{\displaystyle O}{||}}{C}-CH_2CH_3$   or   $(CH_3)_2CHCH_2NH_2$        c.   —$NH_2$   or   —$CH_3$

b.  $(CH_3)_2CHCH_2NH_2$   or   $(CH_3)_2CHCH_2OH$

## 18.4 FOCUS ON HEALTH & MEDICINE
### Caffeine and Nicotine

**Caffeine** and **nicotine** are widely used stimulants of the central nervous system that contain amine heterocycles. Caffeine and nicotine, like other amines discussed in Section 18.5, are ***alkaloids,* naturally occurring amines derived from plant sources.**

caffeine            nicotine

### 18.4A Caffeine

**Caffeine** (Figure 18.2) is a bitter-tasting amine found in coffee and tea. Caffeine is also present in soft drinks and chocolate bars. The pain reliever Anacin contains aspirin and caffeine, and over-the-counter remedies like NoDoz used to ward off sleep contain caffeine. Table 18.1 lists the average caffeine content of several products.

Caffeine is a mild stimulant, usually imparting a feeling of alertness after consumption. It also increases heart rate, dilates airways, and stimulates the secretion of stomach acid. These effects are observed because caffeine increases glucose production, making an individual feel energetic. Caffeine's effects are temporary, so an individual must consume it throughout the day to maintain the same "high."

**Figure 18.2**    Caffeine—An Alkaloid from the Coffee Plant

coffee plant

coffee "cherries"

caffeine
$C_8H_{10}N_4O_2$

Coffee is grown in 50 tropical countries worldwide, and ranks second only to oil in the amount traded internationally. The coffee "cherries" are picked by hand and dried to give two seeds per fruit. Raw beans are shipped to roasting facilities around the world.

Table 18.1  Average Caffeine Content in Common Foods and Drugs

| Product | Serving Size | Caffeine (mg) |
|---|---|---|
| Coffee, brewed | 8 oz | 133 |
| Coffee, instant | 16 oz | 47 |
| Coffee, decaffeinated | 8 oz | 5 |
| Tea, brewed | 8 oz | 53 |
| Coca-Cola Classic | 12 oz | 35 |
| Diet Coke | 12 oz | 47 |
| Hershey's Chocolate Bar | 1.55 oz | 9 |
| Hershey's Special Dark Chocolate | 1.45 oz | 31 |
| Anacin | 2 tablets | 64 |
| NoDoz | 1 tablet | 200 |

[Data taken from the web, Center for Science in the Public Interest.]

In moderation, caffeine consumption poses no health risks, but large quantities can cause insomnia, anxiety, and dehydration. Since caffeine is somewhat addicting, withdrawal symptoms—headache, irritability, and mild depression—can be observed when it is eliminated from the diet. Several studies suggest that pregnant women should limit their intake of caffeine, and that excessive caffeine consumption increases the risk of miscarriage. Nursing mothers are likewise advised to limit caffeine intake, since it passes into breast milk and can adversely affect newborn babies.

### PROBLEM 18.8

Decaffeinated coffee is produced by extracting the caffeine from coffee with a solvent. Initially dichloromethane ($CH_2Cl_2$) was used, but concerns arose over the ill health effects of trace amounts of $CH_2Cl_2$ remaining in the coffee. Why is caffeine soluble in $CH_2Cl_2$?

### 18.4B  Nicotine

**Nicotine** (Figure 18.3) is a highly toxic amine isolated from tobacco. In small doses it acts as a stimulant, but in larger doses causes depression, nausea, and even death. Nicotine is synthesized in tobacco plants as a defense against insect predators, and is used commercially as an insecticide.

Although inhaled tobacco smoke contains over 4,000 compounds, many of which are toxic or cancer causing, nicotine is the compound that makes smoking addictive. Nicotine imparts a sense of pleasure to the smoker, and once a smoker is "hooked," an individual needs to continue smoking to avoid the extreme discomforts of withdrawal—restlessness, anxiety, and craving.

Cigarette smoking causes lung disease, heart disease, and cancer, and it is recognized today as the leading cause of avoidable death in the United States. Despite this well known fact, the nicotine addiction makes it difficult for current smokers to quit. In fact, the sale of nicotine-free cigarettes many years ago was an unsuccessful enterprise because the nicotine in cigarettes is what smokers really crave when they light up.

One method employed by some to quit smoking involves the use of a nicotine patch. The patch is applied to the skin and nicotine diffuses through the skin and into the bloodstream. In this way, a smoker still derives pleasure from the nicotine in the system, but is no longer exposed to the ill effects of the other components of cigarette smoke. Slowly the concentration of nicotine in the patch is reduced, with the hope that eventually the smoker will no longer need nicotine. A similar strategy is used with chewing gum that contains nicotine.

Nicotine patches and nicotine-containing chewing gum have been effectively used by many individuals to quit smoking.

Figure 18.3    Nicotine—An Alkaloid from the Tobacco Plant

tobacco plant

nicotine
$C_{10}H_{14}N_2$

dried tobacco leaves

Tobacco is grown in temperate climates. The leaves are harvested and dried, and then converted to cigarettes and other tobacco products.

### PROBLEM 18.9

What two types of nitrogen heterocycles are present in nicotine?

### PROBLEM 18.10

Locate the single chirality center in nicotine. Draw both enantiomers of nicotine (see Section 15.4).

## 18.5    Alkaloids—Amines from Plant Sources

The word **alkaloid** is derived from the word *alkali,* since aqueous solutions of alkaloids are slightly basic.

**Morphine, quinine,** and **atropine** are three alkaloids with useful medicinal properties. All three compounds contain nitrogen heterocycles and have a complex structure with several functional groups.

### 18.5A    Morphine and Related Alkaloids

The psychological and analgesic effects of the opium poppy *Papaver somniferum* have been known for probably 6,000 years, and it has been widely used as a recreational drug and pain-killing remedy for centuries. The analgesic and narcotic effects of opium are largely due to **morphine. Codeine,** an alkaloid of similar structure with a single methyl ether, is also present, but in much smaller amounts.

opium poppy

morphine

codeine

Poppy seed tea, which contains morphine, was used as a folk remedy in parts of England until World War II. Since poppy seeds contain morphine, eating poppy seed cake or bagels can introduce enough morphine into the system to produce a positive test in a drug screen.

Morphine is especially useful in relieving severe chronic pain, so it is often prescribed for patients with terminal cancer. Morphine is also very addictive, and with time, higher doses are needed to produce the same effects. Approximately 95% of the morphine obtained from legally grown poppies is converted to codeine, a useful drug for the relief of less severe pain.

**Heroin,** a widely used, very addictive illicit drug, is readily prepared by converting the two hydroxyl groups of morphine to acetate esters. Heroin is less polar than morphine, making it more soluble in fat cells in the body. As a result, it is two to three times more potent than morphine in producing euphoria and pain relief.

Both OH groups are converted to esters.

morphine

heroin

## PROBLEM 18.11

Classify the amine in morphine as 1°, 2°, or 3°.

## PROBLEM 18.12

Identify all the functional groups in heroin.

## 18.5B  Quinine

**Quinine** is an alkaloid isolated from the bark of the cinchona tree native to the Andes Mountains. Quinine is a powerful antipyretic—that is, it reduces fever—and for centuries it was the only effective treatment for malaria. Its bitter taste gives tonic water its characteristic flavor.

cinchona tree

quinine

PROBLEM 18.13

(a) How many trigonal planar carbon atoms does quinine contain? (b) How many tetrahedral carbon atoms does quinine contain?

### 18.5C  Atropine

**Atropine** is an alkaloid isolated from *Atropa belladonna*, the deadly nightshade plant.

deadly nightshade plant

During the Renaissance (fourteenth to seventeenth centuries), women used the juice of the berries of the nightshade to enlarge the pupils of their eyes for cosmetic reasons. Sometimes ophthalmologists today use atropine to dilate pupils. Atropine also increases heart rate, so physicians administer atropine for this purpose. Atropine relaxes smooth muscles and interferes with nerve impulses. In higher doses atropine is toxic, leading to convulsions, coma, and death.

## 18.6  Amines as Bases

Like ammonia ($NH_3$), **amines are bases;** that is, **they are *proton acceptors*.** When an amine is dissolved in water, an acid–base equilibrium occurs: the amine accepts a proton from $H_2O$, forming its conjugate acid, an **ammonium ion,** and water loses a proton, forming hydroxide, $OH^-$.

This acid–base reaction occurs with 1°, 2°, and 3° amines. While amines are more basic than other families of organic compounds, they are weak bases compared to inorganic bases like NaOH.

## 18.6A   Reaction of Amines with Acids

**Amines also react with acids such as HCl to form water-soluble salts.** The lone pair of electrons from the amine nitrogen atom is always used to form a new bond to a proton from the acid.

**Example**   $CH_3-\overset{\cdot\cdot}{N}-CH_3$ + H—Cl $\rightleftharpoons$ $\left[ CH_3-\overset{\overset{H}{|}}{N}-CH_3 \right]^{+}$ + Cl⁻
                           $\underset{CH_3}{|}$                                                   $\underset{CH_3}{|}$

3° amine

This proton is transferred
from the acid to the base.

- The amine [$(CH_3)_3N$] gains a proton to form its conjugate acid, an ammonium cation [$(CH_3)_3NH^+$].
- A proton is removed from the acid (HCl) to form its conjugate base, the chloride anion (Cl⁻).

Similar acid–base reactions occur with other inorganic acids ($H_2SO_4$), and with organic acids like $CH_3COOH$, as well. **In each reaction, the amine gains a proton and the acid loses a proton.** This fundamental reaction of amines occurs no matter how complex the amine, as shown in Sample Problem 18.4.

- In an acid–base reaction of an amine, the amine nitrogen always forms a new bond to a proton forming an ammonium ion.

### SAMPLE PROBLEM 18.4

What products are formed when methamphetamine (Section 18.1) reacts with HCl?

$\underset{CH_3}{\overset{CH_3}{|}}$
—$CH_2CHNHCH_3$   +   HCl   $\longrightarrow$

methamphetamine

### Analysis

In any acid–base reaction with an amine:

- Locate the N atom of the amine and add a proton to it. Since the amine nitrogen is neutral to begin with, adding a proton gives it a +1 charge.
- Remove a proton from the acid (HCl) and form its conjugate base (Cl⁻).

### Solution

Transfer a proton from the acid to the base. Use the lone pair on the N atom to form the new bond to the proton of the acid.

$\overset{CH_3}{|}$
—$CH_2CH-\overset{\cdot\cdot}{N}-CH_3$   +   H—Cl   $\longrightarrow$   $\left[ —CH_2CH-\overset{H}{\underset{H}{N}}-CH_3 \right]^{+}$   +   Cl⁻
              $\underset{H}{|}$

methamphetamine

This proton is transferred from
the acid to the amine base.

Thus, HCl loses a proton to form Cl⁻, and the N atom of methamphetamine gains a proton to form an ammonium cation.

### PROBLEM 18.14

What products are formed when each of the following amines is treated with HCl: (a) $CH_3CH_2NH_2$; (b) $(CH_3CH_2)_2NH$; (c) $(CH_3CH_2)_3N$?

### PROBLEM 18.15

Draw the products of each acid–base reaction.

a.  $CH_3CH_2CH_2CH_2$—$NH_2$   +   HCl   $\longrightarrow$

b.  $(CH_3)_2NH$   +   $C_6H_5COOH$   $\longrightarrow$

c.  [piperidine structure] + $H_2O$ $\longrightarrow$

### PROBLEM 18.16

What products are formed when epinephrine is treated with $H_2SO_4$?

[structure of epinephrine]
HO, HO— aromatic ring —CHCH₂NHCH₃ with OH

epinephrine
(adrenaline)

## 18.6B  Ammonium Salts

When an amine reacts with an acid, the product is an **ammonium salt: the amine forms a positively charged ammonium ion and the acid forms an anion.**

positively charged
ammonium ion              chloride anion

$CH_3CH_2CH_2$—$\overset{..}{N}$—H   +   H—Cl   $\longrightarrow$   $\left[ CH_3CH_2CH_2-\overset{H}{\underset{H}{N}}-H \right]^+$   +   $Cl^-$

ammonium salt

To name an ammonium salt, change the suffix *-amine* of the parent amine from which the salt is formed to the suffix *-ammonium*. Then add the name of the anion. Two examples are shown in Sample Problem 18.5.

### SAMPLE PROBLEM 18.5

Name each ammonium salt.

a.  $(CH_3CH_2NH_3)^+$  $Cl^-$

b.  $\left[ (CH_3)_3NH \right]^+$  $CH_3COO^-$

#### Analysis

To name an ammonium salt, draw out the four groups bonded to the N atom. Remove one hydrogen from the N atom to draw the structure of the parent amine. Then put the two parts of the name together.

*   Name the ammonium ion by changing the suffix *-amine* of the parent amine to the suffix *-ammonium.*
*   Add the name of the anion.

Solution

a.
$$\left[ CH_3CH_2-\overset{\overset{\displaystyle H}{|}}{\underset{\underset{\displaystyle H}{|}}{N}}-H \right]^+ \quad Cl^- \quad \text{chloride}$$

derived from $CH_3CH_2-\overset{}{\underset{\underset{\displaystyle H}{|}}{N}}-H$

ethylamine

- Change the name ethyl*amine* to ethyl*ammonium*.
- Add the name of the anion, chloride.

**Answer: ethylammonium chloride**

b.
$$\left[ CH_3-\overset{\overset{\displaystyle H}{|}}{\underset{\underset{\displaystyle CH_3}{|}}{N}}-CH_3 \right]^+ \quad CH_3COO^- \quad \text{acetate}$$

derived from $CH_3-\overset{}{\underset{\underset{\displaystyle CH_3}{|}}{N}}-CH_3$

trimethylamine

- Change the name trimethyl*amine* to trimethyl*ammonium*.
- Add the name of the anion, acetate.

**Answer: trimethylammonium acetate**

---

**PROBLEM 18.17**

Name each ammonium salt.

a. $(CH_3NH_3)^+ \quad Cl^-$      b. $\left[ (CH_3CH_2CH_2)_2NH_2 \right]^+ \quad Br^-$      c. $\left[ (CH_3)_2NHCH_2CH_3 \right]^+ \quad CH_3COO^-$

---

Ammonium salts are ionic compounds, and as a result:

- **Ammonium salts are water-soluble solids.**

In this way, the solubility properties of an amine can be changed by treatment with acid. For example, octylamine has eight carbons, making it water insoluble. Reaction with HCl forms octylammonium chloride. This ionic solid is now soluble in water.

$$CH_3CH_2CH_2CH_2CH_2CH_2CH_2CH_2-\overset{}{\underset{\underset{\displaystyle H}{|}}{N}}-H \quad + \quad H-Cl \quad \longrightarrow \quad \left[ CH_3CH_2CH_2CH_2CH_2CH_2CH_2CH_2-\overset{\overset{\displaystyle H}{|}}{\underset{\underset{\displaystyle H}{|}}{N}}-H \right]^+ \quad Cl^-$$

octylamine                                                                        octylammonium chloride

| **water-insoluble amine** | - - - - - - - - - - - - - - - - - - - - - - -▸ | **water-soluble salt** |

**The solubility properties change.**

- **A water-insoluble amine can be converted to a water-soluble ammonium salt by treatment with acid.**

---

**PROBLEM 18.18**

Label each compound as water soluble or water insoluble.

a. $(CH_3CH_2)_3N$      b. $\left[ (CH_3CH_2)_3NH \right]^+ \quad Br^-$      c. $CH_3CH_2NH_2$      d. $\left[ \text{(cyclohexyl)} \overset{\overset{\displaystyle H}{|}}{\underset{\underset{\displaystyle H}{|}}{N}} \right]^+ \quad Cl^-$

Ammonium salts can be re-converted to amines by treatment with base. Base removes a proton from the nitrogen atom of the amine, regenerating the neutral amine.

octylammonium chloride
**water-soluble salt**

octylamine
**water-insoluble amine**

### PROBLEM 18.19

What product is formed when each ammonium salt is treated with NaOH?

a. $\left[(CH_3CH_2)_3NH\right]^+$ $Br^-$      b. $(CH_3CH_2NH_3)^+$ $HSO_4^-$      c. (piperidinium chloride structure) $Cl^-$

## 18.7 FOCUS ON HEALTH & MEDICINE
### Ammonium Salts as Useful Drugs

Many amines with useful medicinal properties are sold as their ammonium salts. Since the ammonium salts are more water soluble than the parent amine, they are easily transported through the body in the aqueous medium of the blood.

For example, diphenhydramine is a 3° amine that is sold as its ammonium salt under the name of Benadryl. Benadryl, formed by treating diphenhydramine with HCl, is an over-the-counter antihistamine that is used to relieve the itch and irritation of skin rashes and hives.

(reaction scheme)

diphenhydramine   +   HCl   ⟶   ammonium salt
Benadryl

The names of medicines sold as ammonium salts are often derived from the names of the amine and the acid used to form them. Since Benadryl is formed from diphenhydramine and HCl, it is called **diphenhydramine hydrochloride.**

Two other examples of amines sold as their ammonium salts are phenylephrine hydrochloride, the decongestant in Sudafed PE, Theraflu, and DayQuil, and methadone hydrochloride, a long-acting narcotic taken orally to treat chronic painful conditions. Methadone hydrochloride is also used as a substitute narcotic for heroin addicts.

phenylephrine hydrochloride
(decongestant in Sudafed PE,
Theraflu, and DayQuil)

methadone hydrochloride
(narcotic analgesic)

Some **quaternary ammonium salts** ($R_4N^+$ $X^-$, Section 18.1)—that is, ammonium salts with nitrogen atoms bonded to *four* alkyl groups—are also useful agents. Bitrex is a foul-tasting nontoxic salt used on children's fingers to keep them from biting their nails or sucking their thumbs. Benzalkonium chloride is a disinfectant and antiseptic in mouthwash.

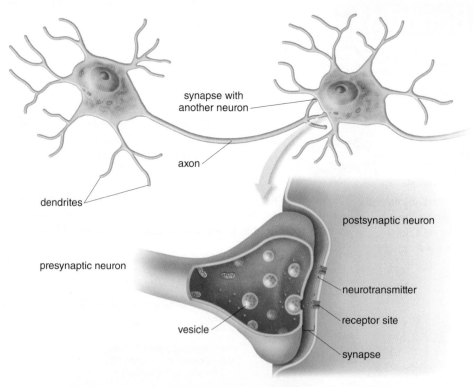

Bitrex

benzalkonium chloride

## PROBLEM 18.20

Draw the structures of the amines from which phenylephrine hydrochloride and methadone hydrochloride are derived.

## PROBLEM 18.21

When Benadryl is treated with a base like NaOH, the free amine, diphenhydramine, is re-formed, as we learned in Section 18.6. Explain why a similar reaction does not occur with a quaternary ammonium salt like Bitrex.

## 18.8 Neurotransmitters

**A *neurotransmitter* is a chemical messenger that transmits nerve impulses from one nerve cell—neuron—to another cell.** As shown in Figure 18.4, a neuron consists of many short filaments called **dendrites** connected to a cell body. A long stem called an **axon** also protrudes from

### Figure 18.4

Neurotransmitters—Transmitting Information Between Neurons

Neurotransmitters are released from vesicles in the presynaptic neuron and diffuse through the synapse to bind to the receptor sites on the postsynaptic neuron.

the cell body. The axon ends in numerous small filaments at its opposite end. These filaments are separated from the dendrites of a nearby neuron by a small gap called the **synapse.**

Neurotransmitters are stored in small packets called **vesicles** in the filaments of the axon near the synapse. When an electrical signal flows from the cell body of the neuron along the axon to the filaments, the neurotransmitter is released, diffuses across the synapse, and binds to a receptor on the dendrites of an adjacent neuron.

- **The presynaptic neuron releases the neurotransmitter.**
- **The postsynaptic neuron contains the receptors that bind the neurotransmitter.**

Once the neurotransmitter is bound to the receptor, the chemical message is delivered. The neurotransmitter is then degraded or it is returned to the presynaptic neuron to begin the process again.

Drugs may be used to affect neurotransmitters in many different ways. Some drugs prevent the release of a neurotransmitter or prevent its binding to a receptor. Other drugs increase the amount of neurotransmitter released. Some drugs affect the degradation of a neurotransmitter or prevent its reuptake by the presynaptic neuron.

All neurotransmitters contain nitrogen atoms. Three important neurotransmitters are amines—**norepinephrine, dopamine,** and **serotonin**—and one is an ammonium ion—**acetylcholine.**

norepinephrine
(noradrenaline)

dopamine

serotonin

acetylcholine

## 18.8A   Norepinephrine and Dopamine

**Norepinephrine,** commonly called **noradrenaline,** and **dopamine** are two structurally related neurotransmitters that are both synthesized from the amino acid tyrosine, as shown in Figure 18.5.

**Figure 18.5**

Synthesis of Norepinephrine and Dopamine

tyrosine

L-dopa

norepinephrine

dopamine

Norepinephrine and dopamine are both synthesized from the amino acid tyrosine by a multistep route. The newly introduced group at each stage is shown in red.

norepinephrine

dopamine

serotonin

Proper levels of both amines are needed for good mental health. For example, when **norepinephrine** levels are above normal, an individual feels unusually elated, and very high levels are associated with manic behavior. Norepinephrine is also converted to adrenaline when an individual experiences fear or stress, as we will learn in Section 18.9.

**Dopamine** affects brain processes that control movement, emotions, and pleasure. When dopamine-producing neurons die and there is too little dopamine in the brain, an individual loses control of fine motor skills and Parkinson's disease results. As we learned in Section 15.5, the level of dopamine in the brain cannot be increased simply by giving an individual dopamine, because dopamine does not cross the blood–brain barrier. L-Dopa, a precursor of dopamine shown in Figure 18.5, can travel from the bloodstream to the brain, so it is an effective treatment for Parkinson's disease. Elevated dopamine levels are also unhealthy and are associated with schizophrenia.

**Dopamine plays an important role in addiction.** Normal dopamine levels give an individual a pleasurable, satisfied feeling. Increased levels result in an intense "high." Drugs such as heroin, cocaine, and alcohol increase dopamine levels. When dopamine receptors are stimulated more than normal, the number and sensitivity of the receptors decreases, and an individual requires more of a drug to feel the same sense of pleasure.

### PROBLEM 18.22

Indicate the chirality center in each of the compounds in Figure 18.5. Which compounds are achiral and contain no chirality centers?

### 18.8B   Serotonin

The neurotransmitter **serotonin** is synthesized from the amino acid tryptophan. Serotonin plays an important role in mood, sleep, perception, and temperature regulation. We get sleepy after eating a turkey dinner on Thanksgiving because the unusually high level of tryptophan in turkey is converted to serotonin.

tryptophan                    serotonin

A deficiency of serotonin causes depression. Understanding the central role of serotonin in determining one's mood has led to the development of a wide variety of drugs for the treatment of depression. The most widely used antidepressants today are **selective serotonin reuptake inhibitors (SSRIs).** These drugs act by inhibiting the reuptake of serotonin by the presynaptic neuron, thus effectively increasing its concentration. Fluoxetine (trade name: Prozac) and sertraline (trade name: Zoloft) are two common antidepressants that act in this way.

fluoxetine
(Trade name: Prozac)

sertraline
(Trade name: Zoloft)

The discovery that migraine headaches result from improper levels of serotonin in the brain has led to the synthesis of several drugs that combat the pain, nausea, and light sensitivity that are associated with this condition. These drugs include sumatriptan (trade name: Imitrex) and rizatriptan (trade name: Maxalt).

sumatriptan
(Trade name: Imitrex)

rizatriptan
(Trade name: Maxalt)

Drugs that interfere with the metabolism of serotonin have a profound effect on mental state. For example, bufotenin, isolated from *Bufo* toads from the Amazon jungle, and psilocin isolated from *Psilocybe* mushrooms, are very similar in structure to serotonin and both cause intense hallucinations.

*Bufo* toad

*Psilocybe* mushrooms

bufotenin

psilocin

### PROBLEM 18.23

The conversion of tryptophan to serotonin is a two-step process. What functional groups must be added or removed during this process?

### PROBLEM 18.24

How are serotonin, bufotenin, and psilocin similar in structure? Classify the amines in these three compounds as 1°, 2°, or 3°.

## 18.8C   Acetylcholine and Nicotine Addiction

Acetylcholine is a quaternary ammonium ion that serves as a neurotransmitter between neurons and muscle cells. In the brain, acetylcholine is involved in memory, mood, and other functions.

acetylcholine

nicotine

The pleasurable high that a smoker feels is due to nicotine interacting with acetylcholine receptors. At low concentrations, nicotine is a stimulant because it binds to these receptors, resulting in a feeling of well-being and alertness. Other nerve cells are also activated and this releases dopamine. The sense of pleasure resulting from the release of dopamine is what causes nicotine to be addictive. Over time receptors are inactivated and some degenerate, so tolerance to nicotine develops and larger quantities are needed to maintain the same sense of pleasure.

## 18.9  FOCUS ON THE HUMAN BODY
### Epinephrine and Related Compounds

While neurotransmitters are the chemical messengers of the nervous system, **hormones** are the chemical messengers of the endocrine system. **A *hormone* is a compound produced by an endocrine gland, which then travels through the bloodstream to a target tissue or organ.**

**Epinephrine,** or **adrenaline** as it is commonly called, is a hormone synthesized in the adrenal glands from norepinephrine (noradrenaline).

norepinephrine
(noradrenaline)

epinephrine
(adrenaline)

When an individual senses danger or is confronted by stress, the hypothalamus region of the brain signals the adrenal glands to synthesize and release epinephrine, which enters the bloodstream and then stimulates a response in many organs (Figure 18.6). Stored carbohydrates are metabolized in the liver to form glucose, which is further metabolized to provide an energy boost. Heart rate and blood pressure increase, and lung passages are dilated. These physiological changes are commonly referred to as a "rush of adrenaline," and they prepare an individual for "fight or flight."

**Figure 18.6**

Epinephrine—
The "Fight or Flight" Hormone

## 18.9A   Derivatives of 2-Phenylethylamine

Like epinephrine and norepinephrine, a large number of physiologically active compounds are derived from **2-phenylethylamine, $C_6H_5CH_2CH_2NH_2$.** Each of these compounds has a common structural unit: a benzene ring bonded to a two-carbon chain that is bonded to a nitrogen atom.

2-phenylethylamine        common structural feature

For example, **amphetamine** and **methamphetamine** are derivatives of 2-phenylethylamine that are powerful stimulants of the central nervous system. Both amines increase heart rate and respiratory rate. Since they increase glucose concentration in the bloodstream, they decrease hunger and fatigue. While amphetamine and methamphetamine may be prescribed for attention deficit hyperactivity disorder (ADHD) and weight reduction under the trade names Adderall and Desoxyn, respectively, they are highly addictive and widely abused drugs that must be used with extreme care. Both amphetamine and methamphetamine increase the level of dopamine in the brain, causing a pleasurable "high."

amphetamine                    methamphetamine

**Pseudoephedrine,** the decongestant in Sudafed, is another derivative of 2-phenylethylamine. Since pseudoephedrine can be readily converted to methamphetamine, it has been replaced in many products by a related amine, **phenylephrine.** For example, Pfizer markets its pseudoephedrine-free decongestant as Sudafed PE. Products that contain pseudoephedrine are still over-the-counter remedies, but they are now stocked behind the pharmacy counter so their sale can be more closely monitored.

pseudoephedrine
(decongestant in Sudafed)            methamphetamine            phenylephrine
(decongestant in Sudafed PE)

### PROBLEM 18.25

Pseudoephedrine can be readily converted to methamphetamine by replacing one OH group by a hydrogen atom. Examine the structure of phenylephrine, and suggest a reason why it cannot be readily converted to methamphetamine.

### PROBLEM 18.26

Label the atoms of 2-phenylethylamine in each compound. Mescaline is the active hallucinogen in peyote, a cactus native to the southwestern United States and Mexico. LSD, commonly called "acid," was first synthesized in 1938 by Swiss chemist Albert Hoffman. Its hallucinogenic properties were first discovered when Hoffman himself ingested small amounts of the drug.

a.                                         b.

mescaline                                LSD

---

**CONSUMER NOTE**

Sudafed contains the decongestant pseudoephedrine, while Sudafed PE contains the decongestant phenylephrine.

## 18.9B   Drugs to Treat Asthma

The search for drugs that were structurally related to epinephrine but exhibited only some components of its wide range of biological activities led to the discovery of some useful medications. Both **albuterol** and **salmeterol** are derivatives of 2-phenylethylamine that dilate lung passages; that is, they are ***bronchodilators.*** They do not, however, stimulate the heart. This makes both compounds useful for the treatment of asthma. Albuterol is a short-acting drug used to relieve the wheezing associated with asthma. Salmeterol is much longer acting, and thus it is often used before bedtime to keep an individual symptom free overnight.

albuterol
(Trade names: Ventolin, Proventil)

salmeterol
(Trade name: Serevent)

### PROBLEM 18.27
Classify the amines and the alcohols (not the phenols) in albuterol and salmeterol as 1°, 2°, or 3°.

## 18.10   FOCUS ON HEALTH & MEDICINE
### Histamine and Antihistamines

Scombroid fish poisoning, associated with facial flushing, hives, and general itching, is caused by the ingestion of inadequately refrigerated fish, typically mahimahi and tuna. Bacteria convert the amino acid histidine to histamine, and when consumed in large amounts, this clinical syndrome results.

**Histamine** is a biologically active amine formed in many tissues from the amino acid histidine.

histidine

histamine

Histamine is a neurotransmitter that binds to two different receptors, the H1 and H2 receptors, and produces a wide range of physiological effects on the body. Histamine is a vasodilator (it dilates capillaries), so it is released at the site of an injury or infection to increase blood flow. It is also responsible for the symptoms of allergies, including a runny nose and watery eyes. In the stomach, histamine stimulates the secretion of acid.

**Antihistamines** bind to the H1 histamine receptor, but they evoke a different response. An antihistamine like chlorpheniramine or diphenhydramine, for example, inhibits vasodilation, so it is used to treat the symptoms of the common cold and environmental allergies. These antihistamines also cause drowsiness by crossing the blood–brain barrier and binding to H1 receptors in the central nervous system. Newer antihistamines like fexofenadine (trade name: Allegra) also bind to H1 receptors, but they do not cause drowsiness because they cannot cross the blood–brain barrier and bind to the H1 receptors in the central nervous system.

chlorpheniramine
(antihistamine)

diphenhydramine
(antihistamine)

fexofenadine
(nonsedating antihistamine)

Drugs that bind to the H2 receptor produce a different effect. For example, cimetidine (trade name: Tagamet) binds to the H2 histamine receptor and, as a result, reduces acid secretion in the stomach. Thus, cimetidine is an effective **anti-ulcer** medication.

cimetidine
(Trade name: Tagamet)
anti-ulcer drug

### PROBLEM 18.28
Draw a complete structure for cimetidine including all lone pairs on heteroatoms.

## CHAPTER HIGHLIGHTS

## KEY TERMS

Alkaloid (18.4)

Amine (18.1)

Ammonium salt (18.6)

Antihistamine (18.10)

Anti-ulcer drug (18.10)

Axon (18.8)

Dendrite (18.8)

Heterocycle (18.1)

Hormone (18.9)

Neuron (18.8)

Neurotransmitter (18.8)

Postsynaptic neuron (18.8)

Presynaptic neuron (18.8)

Primary (1°) amine (18.1)

Quaternary ammonium ion (18.1)

Secondary (2°) amine (18.1)

SSRI (18.8)

Synapse (18.8)

Tertiary (3°) amine (18.1)

Vesicle (18.8)

## KEY REACTIONS

Amines react as bases with inorganic and organic acids (18.6).

## KEY CONCEPTS

**❶ What are the characteristics of amines? (18.1, 18.3)**
- Amines are organic nitrogen compounds, formed by replacing one or more hydrogen atoms of $NH_3$ by alkyl groups.
- Primary (1°) amines have one C—N bond; 2° amines have two C—N bonds; 3° amines have three C—N bonds.
- An amine has a lone pair of electrons on the N atom, and is trigonal pyramidal in shape.

- Amines contain polar C—N and N—H bonds. Primary (1°) and 2° amines can hydrogen bond. Intermolecular hydrogen bonds between N and H are weaker than those between O and H.
- Tertiary (3°) amines have lower boiling points than 1° and 2° amines since they cannot hydrogen bond.

**❷ How are amines named? (18.2)**
- Primary (1°) amines are identified by the suffix -*amine*.

- Secondary (2°) and 3° amines with identical alkyl groups are named by adding the prefix *di-* or *tri-* to the name of the 1° amine.
- Secondary (2°) and 3° amines with different alkyl groups are named as *N*-substituted 1° amines.

**③ What are alkaloids? Give examples of common alkaloids. (18.4, 18.5)**

- Alkaloids are naturally occurring amines isolated from plant sources.
- Examples of alkaloids include caffeine (from coffee and tea), nicotine (from tobacco), morphine and codeine (from the opium poppy), quinine (from the cinchona tree), and atropine (from the deadly nightshade plant).

**④ What products are formed when an amine is treated with acid? (18.6)**

- Amines act as proton acceptors in water and acid. For example, the reaction of $RNH_2$ with HCl forms the water-soluble ammonium salt $RNH_3^+ \ Cl^-$.

**⑤ What are the characteristics of ammonium salts and how are they named? (18.6, 18.7)**

- An ammonium salt consists of a positively charged ammonium ion and an anion.
- An ammonium salt is named by changing the suffix *-amine* of the parent amine to the suffix *-ammonium* followed by the name of the anion.
- Ammonium salts are water-soluble solids.
- Water-insoluble amine drugs are sold as their ammonium salts to increase their solubility in the aqueous environment of the blood.

**⑥ What are neurotransmitters and how do they differ from hormones? (18.8, 18.9)**

- A neurotransmitter is a chemical messenger that transmits a nerve impulse from a neuron to another cell.

- A hormone is a compound produced by an endocrine gland that travels through the bloodstream to a target tissue or organ.

**⑦ What roles do dopamine and serotonin play in the body? (18.8)**

- Dopamine affects movement, emotions, and pleasure. Too little dopamine causes Parkinson's disease. Too much dopamine causes schizophrenia. Dopamine plays a role in addiction.
- Serotonin is important in mood, sleep, perception, and temperature regulation. A deficiency of serotonin causes depression. SSRIs are antidepressants that effectively increase the concentration of serotonin.

**⑧ Give examples of important derivatives of 2-phenylethylamine. (18.9)**

- Derivatives of 2-phenylethylamine contain a benzene ring bonded to a two-carbon chain that is bonded to a nitrogen atom.
- Examples of 2-phenylethylamine derivatives include epinephrine, norepinephrine, amphetamine, and methamphetamine. Albuterol and salmeterol are also derivatives of 2-phenylethylamine that are used to treat asthma.

**⑨ What is histamine, and how do antihistamines and anti-ulcer drugs work? (18.10)**

- Histamine is an amine with a wide range of physiological effects. Histamine dilates capillaries, is responsible for the runny nose and watery eyes of allergies, and stimulates the secretion of stomach acid.
- Antihistamines bind to the H1 histamine receptor and inhibit vasodilation, so they are used to treat the symptoms of colds and allergies.
- Anti-ulcer drugs bind to the H2 histamine receptor and reduce the production of stomach acid.

## PROBLEMS

Selected in-chapter and odd-numbered end-of-chapter problems have brief answers in Appendix B. The *Student Study Guide and Solutions Manual* contains detailed solutions to all in-chapter and odd-numbered end-of-chapter problems, as well as additional worked examples and a chapter self-test.

### Structure and Bonding

**18.29** Label each nitrogen-containing functional group in lidocaine, a local anesthetic (Figure 13.7), as an amine or amide, and classify it as 1°, 2°, or 3°.

lidocaine

**18.30** Label each nitrogen-containing functional group in fentanyl, a narcotic pain reliever, as an amine or amide, and classify it as 1°, 2°, or 3°.

fentanyl

**18.31** Classify each amine as 1°, 2°, or 3°.

a. CH$_3$CHCH$_2$CH$_2$NHCH$_3$
      |
     CH$_3$

b. [piperidine ring]N—CH$_3$

**18.32** Classify each amine as 1°, 2°, or 3°.

        CH$_3$
        |
a. CH$_3$—C—CH$_2$NH$_2$
        |
        CH$_3$

b. [benzene ring]—N(CH$_3$)$_2$

**18.33** Draw the structure of a compound that fits each description:
a. a 1° amine with molecular formula C$_5$H$_{13}$N
b. a 2° amine with molecular formula C$_6$H$_{15}$N
c. a 3° amine with molecular formula C$_6$H$_{13}$N
d. a quaternary ammonium ion with molecular formula C$_8$H$_{20}$N$^+$

**18.34** Draw the structure of a compound of molecular formula C$_4$H$_{11}$NO that fits each description:
a. a compound that contains a 1° amine and a 1° alcohol
b. a compound that contains a 2° amine and a 2° alcohol
c. a compound that contains a 1° amine and a 3° alcohol
d. a compound that contains a 3° amine and a 1° alcohol

## Nomenclature

**18.35** Give an acceptable name for each amine.

a.

b.

**18.36** Give an acceptable name for each amine.

a.

b.

**18.37** Give an acceptable name for each amine.

         H
         |
a. CH$_3$CH$_2$—N—CH$_2$CH$_3$

         NH$_2$
         |
b. CH$_3$CH$_2$CHCH$_2$CH$_2$CH$_2$CH$_3$

         NHCH$_3$
         |
c. CH$_3$CH$_2$CH$_2$CHCH$_2$CH$_3$

d. CH$_3$CHCH$_2$CH$_2$CH$_2$CH$_2$CH$_3$
     |
   NHCH$_2$CH$_3$

**18.38** Give an acceptable name for each amine.
a. CH$_3$(CH$_2$)$_6$NH$_2$

b. [cyclopentane ring]—NHCH$_2$CH$_3$

c. [pyrrolidine ring]N—CH$_2$CH$_3$

      CH$_3$CHCH$_3$
       |
d.    N—CH$_2$CH$_3$
       |
       CH$_3$

**18.39** Draw the structure corresponding to each name.
a. 1-decanamine
b. tricyclohexylamine
c. *p*-bromoaniline
d. 3-aminobutanoic acid
e. *N,N*-dipropyl-2-octanamine
f. *N*-ethylhexylamine

**18.40** Draw the structure corresponding to each name.
a. cyclobutylamine
b. 4-nonanamine
c. *N*-pentylaniline
d. 3-amino-2-butanone
e. 3-methyl-1-butanamine
f. *N*-ethyl-*N*-propylcyclopentylamine

**18.41** What is the difference between *N,N*-dimethylaniline and 2,4-diethylaniline? Draw structures to illustrate the difference.

**18.42** What is the difference between *N*-butylaniline and *o*-butylaniline? Draw structures to illustrate the difference.

**18.43** Draw the structure of each ammonium salt.
a. dipropylammonium chloride
b. butylammonium bromide
c. ethyldimethylammonium hydroxide

**18.44** Draw the structure of each ammonium salt.
a. cyclohexylammonium fluoride
b. triethylammonium iodide
c. ethylmethylammonium chloride

**18.45** Draw the structures for the four amines of molecular formula C$_3$H$_9$N. Give the systematic name for each amine.

**18.46** (a) Draw the structures for the eight constitutional isomers of molecular formula $C_4H_{11}N$. (b) Give the systematic name for each amine. (c) Identify the chirality center present in one of the amines.

## Physical Properties and Intermolecular Forces

**18.47** Explain why pyridine is more water soluble than benzene. How would you expect the boiling point of pyridine and benzene to compare?

**18.48** Explain why $CH_3CH_2CH_2NH_2$ is water soluble but $CH_3CH_2CH_2CH_3$ is not water soluble.

**18.49** Which compound in each pair has the higher boiling point?
a. $CH_3CH_2CH_2NH_2$    or    $CH_3(CH_2)_7NH_2$
b. $CH_3(CH_2)_6OH$    or    $CH_3(CH_2)_6NH_2$
c. ⬡–$CH_2N(CH_3)_2$    or    ⬡–$CH_2CH_2CH_2NH_2$

**18.50** Which compound in each pair has the higher boiling point?
a. $(CH_3CH_2)_2C{=}O$    or    $(CH_3CH_2)_2CHNH_2$
b. ⬡    or    ⬡NH
c. $CH_3CHCH_2CHCH_3$ (Cl, $NH_2$)    or    $[CH_3CH_2CH_2CHCH_3 (NH_3)]^+$ $Cl^-$

**18.51** Draw the hydrogen-bonding interactions that occur between two molecules of diethylamine $[(CH_3CH_2)_2NH]$.

**18.52** Draw the hydrogen-bonding interactions that occur between diethylamine $[(CH_3CH_2)_2NH]$ and water.

**18.53** Explain why a 1° amine and a 3° amine having the same number of carbons are soluble in water to a similar extent, but the 1° amine has a higher boiling point.

**18.54** Which compound has the higher water solubility: $CH_3(CH_2)_5NH_2$ or $CH_3(CH_2)_5NH_3^+$ $Cl^-$? Explain your choice.

## Acid–Base Reactions of Amines

**18.55** Draw the acid–base reaction that occurs when each amine dissolves in water: (a) $CH_3CH_2NH_2$; (b) $(CH_3CH_2)_2NH$; (c) $(CH_3CH_2)_3N$.

**18.56** What ammonium salt is formed when each amine is treated with HCl?
a. ⬡–$NH_2$
b. ⬡–$CH_2NHCH_3$
c. ⬡–$N(CH_2CH_3)_2$

**18.57** Draw the products of each acid–base reaction.
a. $CH_3CH_2CH_2N(CH_3)_2$   +   HCl  ⟶
b. $CH_3CH_2CHCH_2CH_3$ ($NH_2$)   +   $H_2SO_4$  ⟶
c. pyridine   +   HBr  ⟶
d. $[CH_3CH_2{-}\overset{H}{\underset{CH_2CH_3}{N}}{-}CH_2CH_3]^+$   +   NaOH  ⟶

**18.58** Draw the products of each acid–base reaction.
a. quinoline   +   HCl  ⟶
b. $CH_3CH_2CHCH_2CH_3$ ($NHCH_3$)   +   $H_2SO_4$  ⟶
c. $CH_3NH_2$   +   $CH_3COOH$  ⟶
d. $[CH_3(CH_2)_5NH_3]^+$   +   NaOH  ⟶

**18.59** What ammonium salt is formed when each alkaloid is treated with HCl?

a.
coniine

b.
morphine

**18.60** What ammonium salt is formed when each biologically active amine is treated with $H_2SO_4$?

a. ⬡–$CH_2CHNH_2$ ($CH_3$)
amphetamine

b. HO⬡(HO)–$CH_2CH_2NH_2$
dopamine

## Neurotransmitters, Alkaloids, and Other Biologically Active Amines

**18.61** What type of nitrogen heterocycle occurs in both coniine and morphine (Problem 18.59)?

**18.62** Only one of the N atoms in nicotine has a trigonal pyramidal shape. Identify which N is trigonal pyramidal and explain why the other N atom has a different molecular shape.

**18.63** What physiological effects does caffeine produce on the body?

**18.64** Why should caffeine intake be limited in pregnant and nursing mothers?

**18.65** Why are aqueous solutions of an alkaloid slightly basic?

**18.66** For each alkaloid, list its natural source and give one of its uses in medicine: (a) morphine; (b) quinine; (c) atropine.

**18.67** What are the physiological effects of dopamine? What conditions result when dopamine levels are too high or too low?

**18.68** Explain why patients with Parkinson's disease cannot be treated by giving them dopamine, even though the disease results from low dopamine levels.

**18.69** What are the physiological effects of serotonin? What condition results when there is too little serotonin?

**18.70** Give two examples of SSRIs and explain how they combat depression.

**18.71** In the body, what amino acid is used to synthesize each compound: (a) dopamine; (b) norepinephrine; (c) serotonin; (d) histamine?

**18.72** What is the difference between a neurotransmitter and a hormone?

**18.73** Which of the following amines are derivatives of 2-phenylethylamine? Label the atoms of 2-phenylethylamine in those amines that contain this unit.

a.

$$\text{C}_6\text{H}_5\text{—C(CH}_3)_2\text{—CH}_2\text{N(CH}_3)_2$$

b.

$$\text{C}_6\text{H}_5\text{—CH}_2\text{CH}_2\text{CH}_2\text{NH}_2$$

c.

**18.74** Which of the following amines are derivatives of 2-phenylethylamine? Label the atoms of 2-phenylethylamine in those amines that contain this unit.

a.

b. $\text{C}_6\text{H}_5\text{—CH}_2\text{NH—}$

c. $\text{C}_6\text{H}_5\text{—CH}_2\text{CH}_2\text{—N}$

**18.75** Locate the atoms of 2-phenylethylamine in the banned diet drug phentermine. (See also Problem 18.80.)

phentermine

**18.76** Locate the atoms of 2-phenylethylamine in the broncodilator albuterol.

albuterol

**18.77** Give an example of an antihistamine. Explain how an antihistamine relieves the runny nose and watery eyes of a cold or allergies.

**18.78** Give an example of an anti-ulcer drug, and explain how it is used to treat a stomach ulcer.

## General Questions

**18.79** Benzphetamine (trade name: Didrex) is a habit-forming diet pill with many of the same properties as amphetamine.

$$\text{C}_6\text{H}_5\text{—CH}_2\text{CHNCH}_2\text{—C}_6\text{H}_5$$

benzphetamine

a. Label the amine as 1°, 2°, or 3°.
b. Label the chirality center in benzphetamine.
c. Draw the two enantiomers of benzphetamine.
d. Draw a constitutional isomer that contains a 1° amine.
e. Draw a constitutional isomer that contains a 3° amine.
f. Draw the structure of benzphetamine hydrochloride.
g. What products are formed when benzphetamine is treated with acetic acid, $CH_3COOH$?

**18.80** Phentermine is one component of the banned diet drug fen–phen.

$$\text{C}_6\text{H}_5\text{—CH}_2\text{CNH}_2$$

phentermine

a. Label the amine as 1°, 2°, or 3°.
b. Indicate the molecular shape around each atom.
c. Draw a constitutional isomer that contains a 1° amine.
d. Draw a constitutional isomer that contains a 2° amine.
e. Draw the structure of phentermine hydrobromide.
f. What products are formed when phentermine is treated with benzoic acid, $C_6H_5COOH$?

**18.81** Ritalin is the trade name for methylphenidate, a drug used to treat attention deficit hyperactivity disorder (ADHD).

methylphenidate
(Trade name: Ritalin)

a. Identify the functional groups.
b. Label the amine as 1°, 2°, or 3°.
c. Locate the chirality centers.
d. Locate the atoms of 2-phenylethylamine.
e. Draw the structure of methylphenidate hydrochloride.

**18.82** Seldane is the trade name for terfenadine, an antihistamine once used in the United States but withdrawn from the market because of cardiac side effects observed in some patients.

terfenadine
(Trade name: Seldane)

a. Identify the functional groups.
b. Label the amine as 1°, 2°, or 3°.
c. Label any alcohol as 1°, 2°, or 3°.
d. Label any 4° carbon.
e. Locate any chirality centers.
f. Draw the structure of terfenadine hydrochloride.

## Applications

**18.83** The antihistamine in the over-the-counter product Chlortrimeton is chlorpheniramine maleate. Draw the structure of the amine and carboxylic acid that are used to form this ammonium salt.

chlorpheniramine maleate

**18.84** Dextromethorphan hydrobromide is a cough suppressant used in many over-the-counter cough and cold medications. Given the structure of the parent amine dextromethorphan, what is the structure of its hydrobromide salt?

dextromethorphan

**18.85** What is the difference between a vasodilator and a bronchodilator? Give an example of a drug that fits each category.

**18.86** Why do some antihistamines cause drowsiness while others do not?

**18.87** In Section 17.7 we learned that aspirin exists in different forms (neutral or ionic) in the stomach and the intestines. Similar behavior occurs with amines that are ingested, since they undergo acid–base reactions. In what form does the drug albuterol (Section 18.9B) exist in the stomach? In the intestines?

**18.88** Explain why eating a poppy seed bagel can produce a positive test in a drug screening.

# CHALLENGE PROBLEMS

**18.89** Compare the structures of morphine and heroin. Suggest a method to convert morphine to heroin.

**18.90** Heroin and the morphine from which it is made are both odorless solids. Drug-sniffing dogs can sometimes locate heroin because of a biting odor that is present in a small enough concentration that humans cannot detect, but the keen nose of a canine can. Suggest what compound might cause the odor that allows for heroin detection. (Hint: What products would be formed by the hydrolysis of heroin in moist air?)

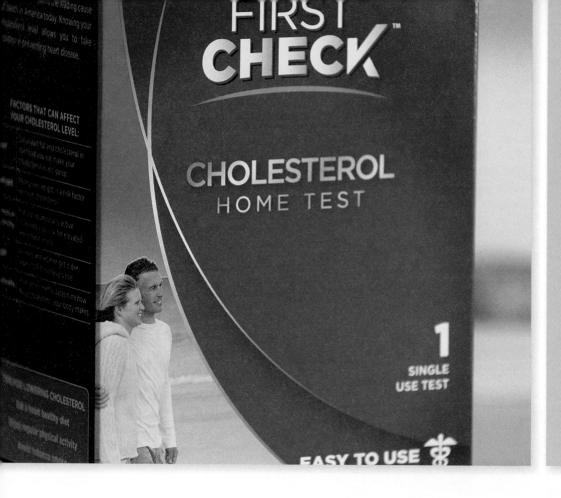

Elevated levels of **cholesterol**, a prominent steroid that belongs to the lipid family of biological molecules, are associated with coronary artery disease.

# 19

# Lipids

## CHAPTER OUTLINE

## CHAPTER GOALS

*In this chapter you will learn how to:*

1. Describe the general characteristics of lipids

2. Classify fatty acids and describe the relationship between melting point and the number of double bonds

3. Draw the structure of a wax and identify the carboxylic acid and alcohol components

4. Draw the structure of triacylglycerols and describe the difference between a fat and an oil

5. Draw the hydrolysis products of triacylglycerols

6. Identify the two major classes of phospholipids

7. Describe the structure of a cell membrane, as well as different mechanisms of transport across the membrane

8. Recognize the main structural features of steroids like cholesterol, and describe the relationship between blood cholesterol level and cardiovascular disease

9. Define what a hormone is and list several examples of steroid hormones

10. Identify fat-soluble vitamins

11. Discuss the general structural features and biological activity of prostaglandins and leukotrienes

Chapter 19 is the first of four chapters that deal with the chemistry of *biomolecules,* **organic molecules found in biological systems.** Chapter 19 focuses on lipids, biomolecules that contain many carbon–carbon and carbon–hydrogen bonds, making them soluble in organic solvents and insoluble in water. Chapter 20 discusses carbohydrates, the largest group of biomolecules in nature, while Chapter 21 focuses on proteins and the amino acids that compose them. Finally, the properties of DNA, the polymer responsible for the storage of genetic information in the chromosomes of cells, is presented in Chapter 22. These compounds are all organic molecules, so many of the principles and chemical reactions that you have already learned will be examined once again. But, as you will see, each class of compound has its own unique features that we will discuss as well.

## 19.1   Introduction to Lipids

- *Lipids* are biomolecules that are soluble in organic solvents and insoluble in water.

Lipids are unique among organic molecules because their identity is defined on the basis of a *physical property* and not by the presence of a particular functional group. Because of this, lipids come in a wide variety of structures and they have many different functions. Common lipids include triacylglycerols in vegetable oils, cholesterol in egg yolk, and vitamin E in leafy greens.

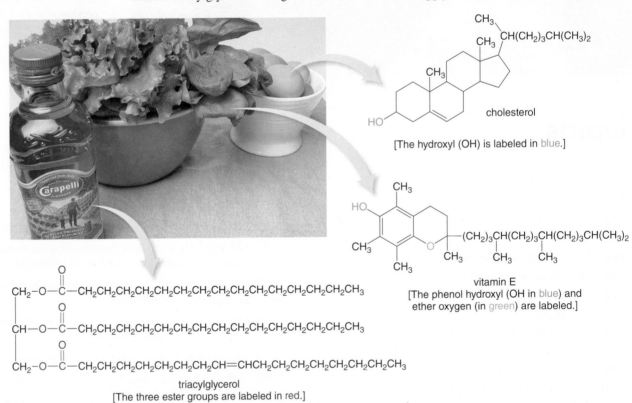

cholesterol

[The hydroxyl (OH) is labeled in blue.]

vitamin E
[The phenol hydroxyl (OH in blue) and ether oxygen (in green) are labeled.]

triacylglycerol
[The three ester groups are labeled in red.]

The word *lipid* comes from the Greek word *lipos* for *fat.*

Lipids contain a large number of nonpolar carbon–carbon and carbon–hydrogen bonds. In addition, most lipids have a few polar bonds that may be found in a variety of functional groups. For example, a triacylglycerol contains three esters, cholesterol possesses a hydroxyl group, and vitamin E has both a phenol (an OH group on a benzene ring) and an ether. The size of these functional groups is small compared to the overall size of the molecules. As a result, lipids are nonpolar or weakly polar molecules that are very soluble in organic solvents like hexane ($C_6H_{14}$) and carbon tetrachloride ($CCl_4$), and insoluble in a polar medium like water.

### SAMPLE PROBLEM 19.1

Which compounds are likely to be lipids? Sorbitol is a sweetener used in sugar-free mints and gum. β-Carotene is the orange pigment in carrots, and the precursor of vitamin A.

a. sorbitol

b. β-carotene

### Analysis

Lipids contain many nonpolar C—C and C—H bonds and few polar bonds.

### Solution

a. Sorbitol is not likely to be a lipid since it contains six polar OH groups bonded to only six carbon atoms.

b. β-Carotene is likely to be a lipid since it contains only nonpolar C—C and C—H bonds.

### PROBLEM 19.1

Which compounds are likely to be lipids?

a. $HO_2CCH_2$—$\overset{\overset{\displaystyle CH_3}{|}}{\underset{\underset{\displaystyle OH}{|}}{C}}$—$CH_2CH_2OH$

mevalonic acid

b. menthol

c. estradiol

| Table 19.1 | Summary of Lipid Chemistry Prior to Chapter 19 |
|---|---|

| Topic | Section |
|---|---|
| Vitamin A | 11.7A |
| Fatty acids | 13.3B |
| Oral contraceptives | 13.5 |
| Margarine and butter | 13.7 |
| Aspirin and prostaglandins | 17.4B |
| Soap | 17.6C |
| Olestra, a synthetic fat | 17.9C |

Because lipids share many properties with hydrocarbons, several features of lipid structure and properties have been discussed in previous chapters, as summarized in Table 19.1.

Lipids can be categorized as hydrolyzable or nonhydrolyzable.

1. *Hydrolyzable lipids* can be converted into smaller molecules by hydrolysis with water. We will examine three subgroups: waxes, triacylglycerols, and phospholipids.

Hydrolyzable lipids

Waxes    Triacylglycerols    Phospholipids

Most hydrolyzable lipids contain an ester. In the presence of acid, base, or an enzyme, the C—O bond of the ester is cleaved, and a carboxylic acid and an alcohol are formed.

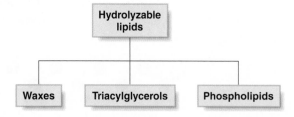

2. *Nonhydrolyzable lipids* cannot be cleaved into smaller units by aqueous hydrolysis. Non-hydrolyzable lipids tend to be more varied in structure. We will examine three different types: steroids, fat-soluble vitamins, and eicosanoids.

Lipids have many important roles in biological systems. Since lipids release over twice the amount of energy per gram than carbohydrates or proteins (9 kcal/g for lipids compared to 4 kcal/g for carbohydrates and proteins, Section 6.1), lipids are an excellent source of energy. Moreover, lipids are key components of the cell membrane, and they serve as chemical messengers in the body. A lipid coating protects a leaf's surface and keeps it from drying out. Ducks are insulated by a protective layer of lipids on their feathers.

### PROBLEM 19.2

In which solvents or solutions will a lipid be soluble: (a) $CH_2Cl_2$; (b) 5% aqueous NaCl solution; (c) $CH_3CH_2CH_2CH_2CH_3$?

## 19.2 Fatty Acids

Hydrolyzable lipids are derived from **fatty acids,** carboxylic acids that were first discussed in Section 13.3B.

• *Fatty acids* are carboxylic acids (RCOOH) with long carbon chains of 12–20 carbon atoms.

Because they have many nonpolar C—C and C—H bonds and few polar bonds, fatty acids are lipids, making them soluble in organic solvents and insoluble in water. Palmitic acid is a common 16-carbon fatty acid whose structure is given in condensed, skeletal, and three-dimensional representations.

$$CH_3CH_2CH_2CH_2CH_2CH_2CH_2CH_2CH_2CH_2CH_2CH_2CH_2CH_2CH_2COOH$$
palmitic acid
$C_{16}H_{32}O_2$

skeletal structure

polar C—O and O—H bonds
hydrophilic portion

nonpolar C—C and C—H bonds

hydrophobic portion

The nonpolar part of the molecule (comprised of C—C and C—H bonds) is not attracted to water, so it is said to be *hydrophobic* (water fearing). The polar part of the molecule is attracted to water, so it is said to be *hydrophilic* (water loving). In a lipid, the hydrophobic portion is always much larger than the hydrophilic portion.

Recall from Section 13.3 that a **cis** alkene has two alkyl groups on the *same* side of the double bond, while a **trans** alkene has two alkyl groups on *opposite* sides of the double bond.

Naturally occurring fatty acids have an even number of carbon atoms. There are two types of fatty acids.

- *Saturated* fatty acids have no double bonds in their long hydrocarbon chains.
- *Unsaturated* fatty acids have one or more double bonds in their long hydrocarbon chains. Generally, double bonds in naturally occurring fatty acids are cis.

Three-dimensional models for stearic acid, a saturated fatty acid, and oleic acid, an unsaturated fatty acid with one cis double bond, are shown. Table 19.2 lists the structures of the most common saturated and unsaturated fatty acids.

stearic acid

**a saturated fatty acid**
no double bonds in the long chain

cis double bond

oleic acid

**an unsaturated fatty acid**
one cis double bond in the long chain

### Table 19.2 Common Fatty Acids

| Number of C's | Number of C=C's | Structure | Name | Mp (°C) |
|---|---|---|---|---|
| | | **Saturated Fatty Acids** | | |
| 12 | 0 | $CH_3(CH_2)_{10}COOH$ | Lauric acid | 44 |
| 14 | 0 | $CH_3(CH_2)_{12}COOH$ | Myristic acid | 58 |
| 16 | 0 | $CH_3(CH_2)_{14}COOH$ | Palmitic acid | 63 |
| 18 | 0 | $CH_3(CH_2)_{16}COOH$ | Stearic acid | 71 |
| 20 | 0 | $CH_3(CH_2)_{18}COOH$ | Arachidic acid | 77 |
| | | **Unsaturated Fatty Acids** | | |
| 16 | 1 | $CH_3(CH_2)_5CH=CH(CH_2)_7COOH$ | Palmitoleic acid | 1 |
| 18 | 1 | $CH_3(CH_2)_7CH=CH(CH_2)_7COOH$ | Oleic acid | 16 |
| 18 | 2 | $CH_3(CH_2)_4CH=CHCH_2CH=CH(CH_2)_7COOH$ | Linoleic acid | −5 |
| 18 | 3 | $CH_3CH_2CH=CHCH_2CH=CHCH_2CH=CH(CH_2)_7COOH$ | Linolenic acid | −11 |
| 20 | 4 | $CH_3(CH_2)_4(CH=CHCH_2)_4(CH_2)_2COOH$ | Arachidonic acid | −49 |

The most common saturated fatty acids are palmitic and stearic acid. The most common unsaturated fatty acid is oleic acid. Linoleic and linolenic acids are called **essential fatty acids** because humans cannot synthesize them and must acquire them in our diets.

Oils formed from omega-3 fatty acids may provide health benefits to individuals with cardiovascular disease, as discussed in Section 19.4.

Unsaturated fatty acids are sometimes classified as **omega-*n* acids,** where *n* is the carbon at which the first double bond occurs in the carbon chain, beginning at the end of the chain that contains the $CH_3$ group. Thus, linoleic acid is an omega-6 acid and linolenic acid is an omega-3 acid.

first C=C at C6 ⟶ an **omega-6 acid**

$CH_3CH_2CH_2CH_2CH_2CH=CHCH_2CH=CHCH_2CH_2CH_2CH_2CH_2CH_2CH_2COOH$

linoleic acid

1  2  3  4  5  6

first C=C at C3 ⟶ an **omega-3 acid**

$CH_3CH_2CH=CHCH_2CH=CHCH_2CH=CHCH_2CH_2CH_2CH_2CH_2CH_2CH_2COOH$

linolenic acid

1  2  3

As we learned in Section 13.3B, the presence of cis double bonds affects the melting point of these fatty acids greatly.

> • As the number of double bonds in the fatty acid *increases,* the melting point *decreases.*

The cis double bonds introduce kinks in the long hydrocarbon chain, which makes it difficult for the molecules to pack closely together in a solid. **The larger the number of cis double bonds, the more kinks in the hydrocarbon chain, and the lower the melting point.**

### SAMPLE PROBLEM 19.2

(a) Draw a skeletal structure of gadoleic acid, $CH_3(CH_2)_9CH=CH(CH_2)_7COOH$, a 20-carbon fatty acid obtained from fish oils. (b) Label the hydrophobic and hydrophilic portions. (c) Predict how its melting point compares to the melting points of arachidic acid and arachidonic acid (Table 19.2).

### Analysis

- Skeletal structures have a carbon at the intersection of two lines and at the end of every line. The double bond must have the cis arrangement in an unsaturated fatty acid.
- The nonpolar C—C and C—H bonds comprise the hydrophobic portion of a molecule and the polar bonds comprise the hydrophilic portion.
- For the same number of carbons, increasing the number of double bonds decreases the melting point of a fatty acid.

### Solution

a. and b.  The skeletal structure for gadoleic acid is drawn below. The hydrophilic portion is the COOH group and the hydrophobic portion is the rest of the molecule.

c.  Gadoleic acid has one cis double bond, giving it a lower melting point than arachidic acid (no double bonds), but a higher melting point than arachidonic acid (four double bonds).

Gadoleic acid (Sample Problem 19.2) and DHA (Problem 19.4) are two fatty acids derived from tuna fish oil.

### PROBLEM 19.3

(a) Draw a skeletal structure for each fatty acid. (b) Label the hydrophobic and hydrophilic portions of each molecule. (c) Without referring to Table 19.2, which fatty acid has the higher melting point, **A** or **B?** Explain your choice.

$CH_3(CH_2)_{16}COOH$         $CH_3(CH_2)_4CH=CHCH_2CH=CH(CH_2)_7COOH$

**A**              **B**

### PROBLEM 19.4

DHA (4,7,10,13,16,19-docosahexaenoic acid) is a common fatty acid present in tuna fish oil. (a) Draw a skeletal structure for DHA. (b) Give the omega-*n* designation for DHA.

$CH_3CH_2CH=CHCH_2CH=CHCH_2CH=CHCH_2CH=CHCH_2CH=CHCH_2CH=CHCH_2CH_2COOH$

DHA

### PROBLEM 19.5

Give the omega-*n* designation for (a) oleic acid; (b) arachidonic acid (Table 19.2).

When commercial whaling was commonplace, spermaceti wax obtained from sperm whales was used extensively in cosmetics and candles.

# 19.3 Waxes

Waxes are the simplest hydrolyzable lipids.

- *Waxes* are esters (RCOOR') formed from a fatty acid (RCOOH) and a high molecular weight alcohol (R'OH).

For example, spermaceti wax, isolated from the heads of sperm whales, is largely cetyl palmitate, an ester with the structure $CH_3(CH_2)_{14}COO(CH_2)_{15}CH_3$. Cetyl palmitate is formed from a 16-carbon fatty acid [$CH_3(CH_2)_{14}COOH$] and a 16-carbon alcohol [$CH_3(CH_2)_{15}OH$].

Water beads up on the surface of a leaf because of its waxy coating.

Because of their long nonpolar carbon chains, **waxes are very hydrophobic.** They form a protective coating on the feathers of birds to make them water repellent, and on leaves to prevent water evaporation. Lanolin is a wax that coats the wool fibers of sheep. Beeswax, a complex mixture of over 200 different compounds, contains the wax myricyl palmitate as its major component. The three-dimensional structure of this compound shows how small the polar ester group is compared to the long hydrocarbon chains.

## SAMPLE PROBLEM 19.3

Draw the structure of cetyl myristate, a minor component of spermaceti wax, formed from a 14-carbon fatty acid and a 16-carbon straight chain alcohol.

### Analysis

To draw the wax, arrange the carboxyl group of the fatty acid (RCOOH) next to the OH group of the alcohol (R'OH) with which it reacts. Then, replace the OH group of the fatty acid with the OR' group of the alcohol, forming an ester RCOOR' with a new C—O bond at the carbonyl carbon.

**Solution**

Draw the structures of the fatty acid and the alcohol, and replace the OH group of the 14-carbon acid with the $O(CH_2)_{15}CH_3$ group of the alcohol.

$$CH_3(CH_2)_{12}\text{—}\underset{\underset{O}{\parallel}}{C}\text{—}OH \quad + \quad H\text{—}O(CH_2)_{15}CH_3 \quad \longrightarrow \quad CH_3(CH_2)_{12}\text{—}\underset{\underset{O}{\parallel}}{C}\text{—}O(CH_2)_{15}CH_3 \quad + \quad H_2O$$

new C—O bond

14-carbon fatty acid          16-carbon alcohol                          cetyl myristate

### PROBLEM 19.6

Draw the structure of a wax formed from stearic acid [$CH_3(CH_2)_{16}COOH$] and each alcohol.

  a.  $CH_3(CH_2)_9OH$         b.  $CH_3(CH_2)_{11}OH$         c.  $CH_3(CH_2)_{29}OH$

### PROBLEM 19.7

One component of jojoba oil is a wax formed from eicosenoic acid [$CH_3(CH_2)_7CH{=}CH(CH_2)_9CO_2H$] and $CH_3(CH_2)_7CH{=}CH(CH_2)_8OH$. Draw the structure of the wax, indicating the cis geometry that both carbon–carbon double bonds possess.

### PROBLEM 19.8

Explain why beeswax is insoluble in water, slightly soluble in ethanol ($CH_3CH_2OH$), and very soluble in chloroform ($CHCl_3$).

---

Like other esters, **waxes (RCOOR') are hydrolyzed with water in the presence of acid or base to re-form the carboxylic acid (RCOOH) and alcohol (R'OH)** from which they are prepared (Section 17.9). Thus, hydrolysis of cetyl palmitate in the presence of $H_2SO_4$ forms a fatty acid and a long chain alcohol by cleaving the carbon–oxygen single bond of the ester.

$$CH_3(CH_2)_{14}\text{—}\underset{\underset{O}{\parallel}}{C}\text{—}O(CH_2)_{15}CH_3 \quad + \quad H_2O \quad \xrightarrow{\;H_2SO_4\;} \quad CH_3(CH_2)_{14}\text{—}\underset{\underset{O}{\parallel}}{C}\text{—}OH \quad + \quad H\text{—}O(CH_2)_{15}CH_3$$

The C—O bond is broken.

      cetyl palmitate                                           fatty acid       alcohol

### PROBLEM 19.9

What hydrolysis products are formed when cetyl myristate (Sample Problem 19.3) is treated with aqueous acid?

## 19.4  Triacylglycerols—Fats and Oils

Animal fats and vegetable oils, the most abundant lipids, are composed of **triacylglycerols.**

- *Triacylglycerols,* or triglycerides, are triesters formed from glycerol and three molecules of fatty acids.

$$\begin{matrix} CH_2\text{—}OH \\ | \\ CH\text{—}OH \\ | \\ CH_2\text{—}OH \end{matrix} \quad + \quad \begin{matrix} HO\text{—}\underset{\underset{O}{\parallel}}{C}\text{—}R \\ HO\text{—}\underset{\underset{O}{\parallel}}{C}\text{—}R' \\ HO\text{—}\underset{\underset{O}{\parallel}}{C}\text{—}R'' \end{matrix} \quad \longrightarrow \quad \begin{matrix} CH_2\text{—}O\text{—}\underset{\underset{O}{\parallel}}{C}\text{—}R \\ | \\ CH\text{—}O\text{—}\underset{\underset{O}{\parallel}}{C}\text{—}R' \\ | \\ CH_2\text{—}O\text{—}\underset{\underset{O}{\parallel}}{C}\text{—}R'' \end{matrix}$$

glycerol        fatty acids        triacylglycerol        block diagram

                R groups have      [Three ester groups are
                11–19 C's.          labeled in red.]

glycerol — fatty acid / fatty acid / fatty acid

## 19.4A   General Features

**Simple triacylglycerols** are composed of three identical fatty acid side chains, whereas **mixed triacylglycerols** have two or three different fatty acids. The fatty acids may be saturated or unsaturated. **Monounsaturated triacylglycerols** have a single carbon–carbon double bond, while **polyunsaturated triacylglycerols** have more than one carbon–carbon double bond.

**Fats** and **oils** are triacylglycerols with different physical properties.

- Fats have higher melting points—they are *solids* at room temperature.
- Oils have lower melting points—they are *liquids* at room temperature.

The identity of the three fatty acids in the triacylglycerol determines whether it is a fat or an oil. *Increasing* **the number of double bonds in the fatty acid side chains** *decreases* **the melting point of the triacylglycerol.**

- Fats are derived from fatty acids having few double bonds.
- Oils are derived from fatty acids having a larger number of double bonds.

Table 19.3 lists the fatty acid composition of some common fats and oils. Solid fats have a relatively high percentage of saturated fatty acids and are generally animal in origin. Thus, lard (hog fat), butter, and whale blubber contain a high percentage of saturated fats. With no double bonds, the three side chains of the saturated lipid lie parallel with each other, making it possible for the triacylglycerol molecules to pack relatively efficiently in a crystalline lattice, thus leading to a high melting point.

animal products
source of saturated fats

no double bonds in the long carbon chains

a saturated triacylglycerol

Liquid oils have a higher percentage of unsaturated fatty acids and are generally vegetable in origin. Thus, oils derived from corn, soybeans, and olives contain more unsaturated lipids. In the unsaturated lipid, a cis double bond places a kink in the side chain, making it more difficult to pack efficiently in the solid state, thus leading to a lower melting point.

Table 19.3 Fatty Acid Composition of Some Fats and Oils

| Substance | % Saturated | % Monounsaturated | % Polyunsaturated | % Trans[a] |
|---|---|---|---|---|
| **Cooking Fat** | | | | |
| Lard | 39 | 44 | 11 | 1 |
| Butter | 60 | 26 | 5 | 5 |
| Shortening | 22 | 29 | 29 | 18 |
| **Oils** | | | | |
| Canola | 7 | 58 | 29 | 0 |
| Safflower | 9 | 12 | 24 | 0 |
| Sunflower | 10 | 20 | 66 | 0 |
| Corn | 13 | 24 | 60 | 0 |
| Olive | 13 | 72 | 8 | 0 |
| Soybean | 16 | 44 | 37 | 0 |
| Peanut | 17 | 49 | 32 | 0 |
| Palm | 50 | 37 | 10 | 0 |
| Coconut | 87 | 6 | 2 | 0 |
| **Margarine/Spreads** | | | | |
| 70% Soybean oil, stick | 18 | 2 | 29 | 23 |
| 60% Vegetable oil spread | 18 | 22 | 54 | 5 |

[a]Trans double bonds are formed when triacylglycerols are partially hydrogenated, as described in Section 13.7.
[Source: Harvard School of Public Health website at www.hsph.harvard.edu/nutritionsource/fats.html, but similar data is available from many other sources.]

one (or more) cis double bonds in the long carbon chains

vegetable oil
source of unsaturated oils

an unsaturated triacylglycerol

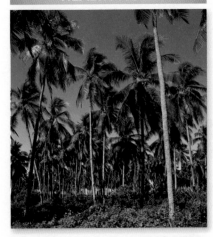

HEALTH NOTE

Oil in the coconuts from plantations like this one is high in saturated fats, which are believed to contribute to a greater risk of heart disease.

Unlike other vegetable oils, oils from palm and coconut trees are very high in saturated fats. Considerable evidence currently suggests that diets high in saturated fats lead to a greater risk of heart disease (Sections 19.4B and 19.8). For this reason, the demand for coconut and palm oil has decreased considerably in recent years, and many coconut plantations previously farmed in the South Pacific are no longer in commercial operation.

Fish oils are high in unsaturated triacylglycerols derived from omega-3 fatty acids.

Oils derived from fish such as salmon, herring, mackerel, and sardines are very rich in polyunsaturated triacylglycerols. These triacylglycerols pack so poorly that they have very low melting points, and they remain liquids even in very cold water. Fish oils derived from omega-3 fatty acids are thought to be especially beneficial for individuals at risk for developing coronary artery disease.

### SAMPLE PROBLEM 19.4

Draw the structure of a triacylglycerol formed from glycerol, one molecule of stearic acid, and two molecules of oleic acid. Bond the stearic acid to the 2° OH group (OH on the middle carbon atom) of glycerol.

#### Analysis

To draw the triacylglycerol, arrange each OH group of glycerol next to the carboxyl group of a fatty acid. Then join each O atom of glycerol to a carbonyl carbon of a fatty acid, to form three new C—O bonds.

#### Solution

Form three new ester bonds (RCOOR') from OH groups of glycerol and the three fatty acids (RCOOH).

$$
\begin{array}{l}
\text{CH}_2\text{—OH} \\
\text{CH—OH} \\
\text{CH}_2\text{—OH}
\end{array}
\;+\;
\begin{array}{l}
\text{HO—C(=O)—(CH}_2)_7\text{CH}=\text{CH(CH}_2)_7\text{CH}_3 \\
\text{HO—C(=O)—(CH}_2)_{16}\text{CH}_3 \\
\text{HO—C(=O)—(CH}_2)_7\text{CH}=\text{CH(CH}_2)_7\text{CH}_3
\end{array}
\;\longrightarrow\;
\begin{array}{l}
\text{CH}_2\text{—O—C(=O)—(CH}_2)_7\text{CH}=\text{CH(CH}_2)_7\text{CH}_3 \\
\text{CH—O—C(=O)—(CH}_2)_{16}\text{CH}_3 \\
\text{CH}_2\text{—O—C(=O)—(CH}_2)_7\text{CH}=\text{CH(CH}_2)_7\text{CH}_3
\end{array}
\;+\; 3\,\text{H}_2\text{O}
$$

glycerol
2° OH

oleic acid (R group in blue)
stearic acid (R group in red)

triacylglycerol

### PROBLEM 19.10

Draw the structure of a triacylglycerol that contains (a) three molecules of stearic acid; (b) three molecules of oleic acid.

### PROBLEM 19.11

Draw the structure of two different triacylglycerols that contain two molecules of stearic acid and one molecule of palmitic acid.

**Nutrition Facts**
Serving Size 11 Crackers (31g)
Servings Per Container About 7

**Amount Per Serving**
**Calories** 150   Calories from Fat 50

| | % Daily Value* |
|---|---|
| **Total Fat** 6g | **9%** |
| Saturated Fat 1g | **5%** |
| Trans Fat 0g | |
| Polyunsaturated Fat 3g | |
| Monounsaturated Fat 1g | |
| **Cholesterol** 0mg | **0%** |
| **Sodium** 270mg | **11%** |
| **Total Carbohydrate** 21g | **7%** |
| Dietary Fiber 1g | **4%** |
| Sugars 4g | |

## 19.4B   FOCUS ON HEALTH & MEDICINE
### Fats and Oils in the Diet

Fats and oils in our diet come from a variety of sources—meat, dairy products, seeds and nuts, salad dressing, fried foods, and any baked good or packaged food made with oil. Some fat is required in the diet. Fats are the building blocks of cell membranes, and stored body fat insulates an organism and serves as an energy source that can be used at a later time.

Currently, the United States Food and Drug Administration recommends that no more than 20–35% of an individual's calorie intake come from lipids. Moreover, a high intake of *saturated* triacylglycerols is linked to an increased incidence of heart disease. Saturated fats stimulate cholesterol synthesis in the liver and transport to the tissues, resulting in an increase in cholesterol concentration in the blood. An elevated cholesterol level in the blood can lead to cholesterol deposits or plaques on arteries, causing a narrowing of blood vessels, heart attack, and stroke (Section 19.8).

In contrast, *unsaturated* triacylglycerols lower the risk of heart disease by decreasing the amount of cholesterol in the blood. Unsaturated triacylglycerols from omega-3 fatty acids appear to reduce the risk of heart attack, especially in individuals who already have heart disease.

**Figure 19.1**    Saturated, Unsaturated, and Trans Triacylglycerols in the Diet

**Food source**

**Triacylglycerol**

**Foods rich in saturated triacylglycerols:**
fatty red meat, cheese, butter, fried foods,
ice cream

• no double bonds in the carbon chains
• solid at room temperature
• increases blood cholesterol level

**Foods rich in unsaturated triacylglycerols:**
plant oils, nuts, soybeans, fish (salmon,
herring, mackerel)

• one (or more) double bonds in the carbon chains
• liquid at room temperature
• decreases blood cholesterol level

**Foods rich in trans triacylglycerols:**
margarine, processed foods, fried foods,
some baked goods

• one (or more) trans double bonds in the carbon chains
• semi-solid at room temperature
• increases blood cholesterol level

Dietary recommendations on fat intake must also take into account trans triacylglycerols, so-called *trans fats*. As we learned in Section 13.7, trans fats are formed when liquid oils are partially hydrogenated to form semi-solid triacylglycerols. The three-dimensional structure of a trans triacylglycerol shows its similarity to saturated triacylglycerols. Like saturated fats, trans fats also *increase* the amount of cholesterol in the bloodstream, thus increasing an individual's risk of developing coronary artery disease.

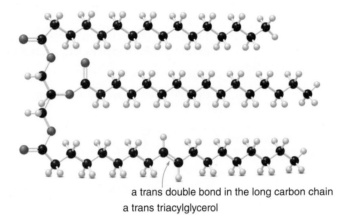

a trans double bond in the long carbon chain
a trans triacylglycerol

Thus, while lipids are a necessary part of anyone's diet, the amount of saturated fat and trans fat should be limited. Calories from lipids should instead be obtained from unsaturated oils. Figure 19.1 illustrates some foods high in saturated, unsaturated, and trans triacylglycerols.

### PROBLEM 19.12

Draw the structure of a triacylglycerol that fits each description:

a. a saturated triacylglycerol formed from three 12-carbon fatty acids
b. an unsaturated triacylglycerol that contains three cis double bonds
c. a trans triacylglycerol that contains a trans double bond in each hydrocarbon chain

## 19.5   Hydrolysis of Triacylglycerols

Like other esters, **triacylglycerols are hydrolyzed with water in the presence of acid, base, or enzymes (in biological systems) to form glycerol and three molecules of fatty acids.** Thus, hydrolysis of tristearin with aqueous sulfuric acid forms glycerol and three molecules of stearic acid.

The three bonds drawn in red are broken in hydrolysis.

$$CH_2-O-\overset{\overset{O}{\|}}{C}-(CH_2)_{16}CH_3$$
$$CH-O-\overset{\overset{O}{\|}}{C}-(CH_2)_{16}CH_3 \ + \ 3\,H_2O \ \xrightarrow{H_2SO_4}$$
$$CH_2-O-\overset{\overset{O}{\|}}{C}-(CH_2)_{16}CH_3$$
tristearin

$$CH_2-OH$$
$$CH-OH \ + \ 3\,HO-\overset{\overset{O}{\|}}{C}-(CH_2)_{16}CH_3$$
$$CH_2-OH$$
glycerol                    stearic acid

Hydrolysis cleaves the three single bonds between the carbonyl carbons and the oxygen atoms of the esters (Section 17.9). Since tristearin contains three identical R groups on the carbonyl carbons, three molecules of a single fatty acid, stearic acid, are formed. Triacylglycerols that contain different R groups bonded to the carbonyl carbons form mixtures of fatty acids, as shown in Sample Problem 19.5.

### SAMPLE PROBLEM 19.5

Draw the products formed when the given triacylglycerol is hydrolyzed with water in the presence of sulfuric acid.

$$CH_2-O-\overset{\overset{O}{\|}}{C}-(CH_2)_{16}CH_3$$
$$CH-O-\overset{\overset{O}{\|}}{C}-(CH_2)_{14}CH_3$$
$$CH_2-O-\overset{\overset{O}{\|}}{C}-(CH_2)_7CH=CH(CH_2)_5CH_3$$

### Analysis

To draw the products of ester hydrolysis, cleave the three C—O single bonds at the carbonyl carbons to form glycerol and three fatty acids (RCOOH).

### Solution

Hydrolysis forms glycerol and stearic, palmitic, and palmitoleic acids.

$$
\begin{array}{c}
\text{Bonds broken during hydrolysis} \\
\end{array}
$$

Bonds broken during hydrolysis

$$
\begin{aligned}
&CH_2-O-\overset{\displaystyle O}{\overset{\|}{C}}-(CH_2)_{16}CH_3 \\
&CH-O-\overset{\displaystyle O}{\overset{\|}{C}}-(CH_2)_{14}CH_3 \\
&CH_2-O-\overset{\displaystyle O}{\overset{\|}{C}}-(CH_2)_7CH=CH(CH_2)_5CH_3
\end{aligned}
$$

$\xrightarrow[\text{H}_2\text{SO}_4]{3\ \text{H—OH}}$

$$
\begin{aligned}
&CH_2-OH \\
&CH-OH \\
&CH_2-OH
\end{aligned}
$$

glycerol

+

$HO-\overset{\displaystyle O}{\overset{\|}{C}}-(CH_2)_{16}CH_3$
stearic acid

$HO-\overset{\displaystyle O}{\overset{\|}{C}}-(CH_2)_{14}CH_3$
palmitic acid

$HO-\overset{\displaystyle O}{\overset{\|}{C}}-(CH_2)_7CH=CH(CH_2)_5CH_3$
palmitoleic acid

### PROBLEM 19.13

Draw the products formed from hydrolysis of each triacylglycerol.

a. $\begin{aligned} &CH_2-O-\overset{\displaystyle O}{\overset{\|}{C}}-(CH_2)_{12}CH_3 \\ &CH-O-\overset{\displaystyle O}{\overset{\|}{C}}-(CH_2)_{12}CH_3 \\ &CH_2-O-\overset{\displaystyle O}{\overset{\|}{C}}-(CH_2)_{12}CH_3 \end{aligned}$

b. $\begin{aligned} &CH_2-O-\overset{\displaystyle O}{\overset{\|}{C}}-(CH_2)_{12}CH_3 \\ &CH-O-\overset{\displaystyle O}{\overset{\|}{C}}-(CH_2)_7CH=CH(CH_2)_5CH_3 \\ &CH_2-O-\overset{\displaystyle O}{\overset{\|}{C}}-(CH_2)_7CH=CH(CH_2)_7CH_3 \end{aligned}$

## 19.5A   FOCUS ON THE HUMAN BODY
### Metabolism of Triacylglycerols

Humans store energy in the form of triacylglycerols, kept in a layer of fat cells, called **adipose cells,** below the surface of the skin, in bone marrow, in the breast area (of women), around the kidneys, and in the pelvis (Figure 19.2). Adipose tissue contains large groups of adipose cells, some of which may be so laden with lipid molecules that the remainder of the cell—the cytoplasm and the nucleus—occupies only a small volume on one side. In adulthood, the number of adipose cells is constant. When weight is lost or gained the amount of stored lipid in each cell changes, but the number of adipose cells does not change.

Adipose tissue serves to insulate the organism, as well as provide energy for its metabolic needs for long periods of time. The first step in the metabolism of a triacylglycerol is hydrolysis of the ester bonds to form glycerol and three fatty acids. **This reaction is simply ester hydrolysis.** In cells, this reaction is carried out with enzymes called **lipases.**

A grizzly bear uses its stored body fat as its sole energy source during its many months of hibernation.

$$
\begin{aligned}
&CH_2-O-\overset{\displaystyle O}{\overset{\|}{C}}-R \\
&CH-O-\overset{\displaystyle O}{\overset{\|}{C}}-R' \\
&CH_2-O-\overset{\displaystyle O}{\overset{\|}{C}}-R''
\end{aligned}
$$
triacylglycerol

$\xrightarrow[\text{lipase}]{3\ \text{H}_2\text{O}}$

$$
\begin{aligned}
&CH_2-OH \\
&CH-OH \\
&CH_2-OH
\end{aligned}
$$
glycerol

+ $HO-\overset{\displaystyle O}{\overset{\|}{C}}-R$ + $HO-\overset{\displaystyle O}{\overset{\|}{C}}-R'$ + $HO-\overset{\displaystyle O}{\overset{\|}{C}}-R''$

three fatty acids

Figure 19.2    The Storage and Metabolism of Triacylglycerols

triacylglycerol

metabolism

$CO_2$ + $H_2O$ + **Energy** 9 kcal/g

adipose cells

Triacylglycerols are stored in adipose cells below the skin and concentrated in some regions of the body. The average fat content of men and women is ~20% and ~25%, respectively. This stored fat provides two to three months of the body's energy needs.

ENVIRONMENTAL NOTE

*veggie* • POWERED

When the price of crude oil is high, the use of **biofuels** such as biodiesel becomes economically attractive. Although biofuels are prepared from renewable resources such as vegetable oils and animal fats, they still burn to form $CO_2$, a gas that contributes to global warming.

**Complete metabolism of a triacylglycerol yields $CO_2$ and $H_2O$, and a great deal of energy** (Section 24.7). This overall reaction is reminiscent of the combustion of alkanes in fossil fuels, a process that also yields $CO_2$ and $H_2O$ and provides energy to heat homes and power automobiles (Section 12.8). Fundamentally, both processes convert C—C and C—H bonds to C—O and O—H bonds, a highly exothermic reaction. Carbohydrates provide an energy boost, but only for the short term, such as during strenuous exercise. Our long-term energy needs are provided by triacylglycerols, because they store 9 kcal/g, whereas carbohydrates and proteins store only 4 kcal/g.

Because triacylglycerols release heat on combustion, they can in principle be used as fuels for vehicles. In fact, coconut oil was used as a fuel during both World Wars I and II, when gasoline and diesel supplies ran short. Since coconut oil is more viscous than petroleum products and freezes at 24 °C, engines must be modified to use it and it can't be used in cold climates. Nonetheless, a limited number of trucks and boats can now use vegetable oils, sometimes blended with diesel—*biodiesel*—as a fuel source.

## PROBLEM 19.14

Review Section 5.2 on balancing chemical equations. Then, write a balanced equation for the complete combustion (or metabolism) of tristearin to $CO_2$ and $H_2O$.

$$CH_2-O-\overset{\overset{O}{\|}}{C}-(CH_2)_{16}CH_3$$
$$CH-O-\overset{\overset{O}{\|}}{C}-(CH_2)_{16}CH_3 \quad + \quad O_2 \xrightarrow{\text{enzymes}} CO_2 \quad + \quad H_2O$$
$$CH_2-O-\overset{\overset{O}{\|}}{C}-(CH_2)_{16}CH_3$$

tristearin

## 19.5B    Soap Synthesis

As we learned in Section 17.6, soaps are metal salts of carboxylic acids that contain many carbon atoms in a long hydrocarbon chain; that is, **soaps are metal salts of fatty acids.** For example, sodium stearate is the sodium salt of stearic acid, an 18-carbon saturated fatty acid.

**Soap is prepared by the basic hydrolysis (saponification) of a triacylglycerol.** Heating an animal fat or vegetable oil with aqueous base hydrolyzes the three esters to form glycerol and sodium salts of three fatty acids.

These carboxylate salts are **soaps,** which clean away dirt as shown in Figure 17.3. The nonpolar tail dissolves grease and oil and the polar head makes it soluble in water. Most triacylglycerols have two or three different R groups in their hydrocarbon chains, so soaps are usually mixtures of two or three different carboxylate salts.

Soaps are typically made from lard (from hogs), tallow (from cattle or sheep), coconut oil, or palm oil. All soaps work in the same way, but have somewhat different properties depending on the lipid source. The length of the carbon chain in the fatty acids and the number of sites of unsaturation affect the properties of the soap to a limited extent.

### PROBLEM 19.15

What is the composition of the soap formed by basic hydrolysis of each triacylglycerol?

a. $CH_2-O-\overset{\overset{\displaystyle O}{\|}}{C}-(CH_2)_{12}CH_3$
$CH-O-\overset{\overset{\displaystyle O}{\|}}{C}-(CH_2)_{12}CH_3$
$CH_2-O-\overset{\overset{\displaystyle O}{\|}}{C}-(CH_2)_{12}CH_3$

b. $CH_2-O-\overset{\overset{\displaystyle O}{\|}}{C}-(CH_2)_{12}CH_3$
$CH-O-\overset{\overset{\displaystyle O}{\|}}{C}-(CH_2)_7CH=CH(CH_2)_5CH_3$
$CH_2-O-\overset{\overset{\displaystyle O}{\|}}{C}-(CH_2)_7CH=CH(CH_2)_7CH_3$

## 19.6   Phospholipids

**Phospholipids are lipids that contain a phosphorus atom.** Two common types of phospholipids are **phosphoacylglycerols** and **sphingomyelins.** Both classes are found almost exclusively in the cell membranes of plants and animals as discussed in Section 19.7. Block diagrams that compare the general structural features of triacylglycerols, phosphoacylglycerols, and sphingomyelins are drawn.

     **triacylglycerol**             **phosphoacylglycerol**           **sphingomyelin**

Phospholipids can be considered organic derivatives of phosphoric acid ($H_3PO_4$), formed by replacing two of the H atoms by R groups. This type of functional group is called a **phosphodiester.** In cells, the remaining OH group on phosphorus loses its proton, giving the phosphodiester a net negative charge.

O             O             O
‖             ‖             ‖

H—O—P—O—H     R—O—P—O—R'     R—O—P—O—R'

|             |             |
OH            OH            $O^-$

**phosphoric acid**    **phosphodiester**    **phosphodiester in**
$H_3PO_4$                       **cells**

### 19.6A   Phosphoacylglycerols

**Phosphoacylglycerols** (or **phosphoglycerides**) are the most common type of phospholipid. They form the principal lipid component of most cell membranes. Their structure resembles the triacylglycerols of the preceding section with one important difference. Only *two* of the hydroxyl groups of glycerol are esterified with fatty acids. The third OH group is part of a phosphodiester, which is also bonded to an alkyl group (R") derived from a low molecular weight alcohol.

**General structure of a phosphoacylglycerol**

There are two prominent types of phosphoacylglycerols. They differ in the identity of the R" group in the phosphodiester.

- When R" = $CH_2CH_2NH_3^+$, the compound is called a *cephalin* or phosphatidylethanolamine.
- When R" = $CH_2CH_2N(CH_3)_3^+$, the compound is called a *lecithin* or phosphatidylcholine.

**cephalin**
(phosphatidylethanolamine)

Derived from the alcohol: H—OCH$_2$CH$_2$NH$_3^+$

ethanolamine

**lecithin**
(phosphatidylcholine)

Derived from the alcohol: H—OCH$_2$CH$_2$N(CH$_3$)$_3^+$

choline

The phosphorus side chain of a phosphoacylglycerol makes it different from a triacylglycerol. **The two fatty acid side chains form two nonpolar "tails" that lie parallel to each other, while the phosphodiester end of the molecule is a charged or polar "head."** A three-dimensional structure of a phosphoacylglycerol is shown in Figure 19.3.

**Figure 19.3**　　Three-Dimensional Structure of a Phosphoacylglycerol

C$_{18}$ fatty acid chains

**a lecithin molecule**

charged atoms

two nonpolar tails

polar head

Often drawn as:

polar head　　nonpolar tails

A phosphoacylglycerol has two distinct regions: two nonpolar tails due to the long-chain fatty acids, and a very polar head from the charged phosphodiester.

### SAMPLE PROBLEM 19.6

Draw the structure of a cephalin formed from two molecules of stearic acid.

#### Analysis

Substitute the 18-carbon saturated fatty acid stearic acid for the R and R' groups in the general structure of a cephalin molecule. In a cephalin, $-CH_2CH_2NH_3^+$ forms part of the phosphodiester.

#### Solution

general structure      **Answer**

### PROBLEM 19.16

Draw the structure of two different cephalins containing oleic acid and palmitic acid as fatty acid side chains.

## 19.6B Sphingomyelins

**Sphingomyelins,** the second major class of phospholipids, differ in two important ways from the triacylglycerols and the phosphoacylglycerols.

- Sphingomyelins do *not* contain a glycerol backbone. Instead, sphingomyelins are derived from sphingosine.
- Sphingomyelins do *not* contain an ester. Instead, their single fatty acid is bonded to the carbon backbone by an amide bond.

**General structure of a sphingomyelin**

sphingosine

$R' = CH_2CH_2\overset{+}{N}H_3$

$R' = CH_2CH_2\overset{+}{N}(CH_3)_3$

Like the phosphoacylglycerols in Section 19.6A, sphingomyelins contain a phosphodiester derived from ethanolamine or choline. As a result, sphingomyelins also contain a polar (ionic) head and two nonpolar tails. An example of a sphingomyelin is drawn.

$$HO-CH-CH=CH(CH_2)_{12}CH_3$$

amide formed with oleic acid

$$CH-NH-\overset{O}{\overset{\|}{C}}-(CH_2)_7CH=CH(CH_2)_7CH_3$$

$$CH_2-O-\overset{O}{\underset{O^-}{\overset{\|}{P}}}-O-CH_2CH_2\overset{+}{N}(CH_3)_3$$

derived from choline

a sphingomyelin

The coating that surrounds and insulates nerve cells, the **myelin sheath,** is particularly rich in sphingomyelins, and is vital for proper nerve function (Figure 19.4). Deterioration of the myelin sheath, as seen in multiple sclerosis, leads to disabling neurological disorders.

Figure 19.5 compares the structural features of the most common hydrolyzable lipids: a triacylglycerol, a phosphoacylglycerol, and a sphingomyelin.

**Figure 19.4**    Focus on Health & Medicine: Nerve Cells and Multiple Sclerosis

layers of healthy myelin sheath surrounding a nerve fiber

neuron

myelinated axons

$$HO-CH-CH=CH(CH_2)_{12}CH_3$$

nonpolar tails

$$CH-NH-\overset{O}{\overset{\|}{C}}-(CH_2)_{16}CH_3$$

$$CH_2-O-\overset{O}{\underset{O^-}{\overset{\|}{P}}}-O-CH_2CH_2\overset{+}{N}(CH_3)_3$$

The charged portion makes up the polar head.

sphingomyelin molecule present in the myelin sheath

exposed nerve fiber

damaged myelin sheath present in individuals with multiple sclerosis

Multiple sclerosis (MS) is a degenerative disease characterized by scarring of the myelin sheath, the insulating layer that surrounds a nerve fiber. Without the protective myelin sheath, normal nerve transmission is disrupted and a variety of effects—numbness, blindness, speech disorders, and tremors—can result.

Figure 19.5    A Comparison of a Triacylglycerol, a Phosphoacylglycerol, and a Sphingomyelin

$$CH_2-O-\overset{\overset{\displaystyle O}{\|}}{C}-R$$

$$CH-O-\overset{\overset{\displaystyle O}{\|}}{C}-R'$$

$$CH_2-O-\overset{\overset{\displaystyle O}{\|}}{C}-R''$$

$$CH_2-O-\overset{\overset{\displaystyle O}{\|}}{C}-R$$

$$CH-O-\overset{\overset{\displaystyle O}{\|}}{C}-R'$$

$$CH_2-O-\overset{\overset{\displaystyle O}{\|}}{\underset{\underset{\displaystyle O^-}{|}}{P}}-O-CH_2CH_2\overset{+}{N}R''_3$$

R'' = H, CH$_3$

$$HO-CH-CH=CH(CH_2)_{12}CH_3$$

$$CH-NH-\overset{\overset{\displaystyle O}{\|}}{C}-R$$

$$CH_2-O-\overset{\overset{\displaystyle O}{\|}}{\underset{\underset{\displaystyle O^-}{|}}{P}}-O-CH_2CH_2\overset{+}{N}R''_3$$

R'' = H, CH$_3$

- A **triacylglycerol** has three nonpolar side chains.
- Glycerol is the backbone.
- There are three esters formed from three fatty acids.

- A **phosphoacylglycerol** has two non-polar side chain tails and one ionic head.
- Glycerol is the backbone.
- There are two esters formed with the two fatty acids.
- A phosphodiester is located on a terminal carbon of glycerol.

- A **sphingomyelin** has two nonpolar side chain tails and one ionic head.
- Sphingosine is the backbone.
- A sphingomyelin contains an amide, not an ester.
- A phosphodiester is located on a terminal carbon of sphingosine.

PROBLEM 19.17

Identify the components of each lipid and classify it as a triacylglycerol, a phosphoacylglycerol, or a sphingomyelin. Classify any phosphoacylglycerol as a cephalin or lecithin.

a.
$$CH_2-O-\overset{\overset{\displaystyle O}{\|}}{C}-(CH_2)_{12}CH_3$$
$$CH-O-\overset{\overset{\displaystyle O}{\|}}{C}-(CH_2)_{12}CH_3$$
$$CH_2-O-\overset{\overset{\displaystyle O}{\|}}{\underset{\underset{\displaystyle O^-}{|}}{P}}-O-CH_2CH_2\overset{+}{N}H_3$$

c.
$$HO-CH-CH=CH(CH_2)_{12}CH_3$$
$$CH-NH-\overset{\overset{\displaystyle O}{\|}}{C}-(CH_2)_{12}CH_3$$
$$CH_2-O-\overset{\overset{\displaystyle O}{\|}}{\underset{\underset{\displaystyle O^-}{|}}{P}}-O-CH_2CH_2\overset{+}{N}(CH_3)_3$$

b.
$$CH_2-O-\overset{\overset{\displaystyle O}{\|}}{C}-(CH_2)_{12}CH_3$$
$$CH-O-\overset{\overset{\displaystyle O}{\|}}{C}-(CH_2)_7CH=CH(CH_2)_5CH_3$$
$$CH_2-O-\overset{\overset{\displaystyle O}{\|}}{C}-(CH_2)_{12}CH_3$$

## 19.7    Cell Membranes

The cell membrane is a beautifully complex example of how chemistry comes into play in a biological system.

### 19.7A    Structure of the Cell Membrane

The basic unit of living organisms is the **cell.** The cytoplasm is the aqueous medium inside the cell, separated from water outside the cell by the **cell membrane.** The cell membrane serves two apparently contradictory functions. It acts as a barrier to the passage of ions and molecules into and out of the cell, but it is also selectively permeable, allowing nutrients in and waste out.

To review London dispersion forces, re-read Section 7.7A.

Phospholipids, especially phosphoacylglycerols, are the major component of the cell membrane. **Phospholipids contain a hydrophilic polar head and two nonpolar tails composed of C—C and C—H bonds.** When phospholipids are mixed with water, they assemble in an arrangement called a **lipid bilayer,** with the ionic heads oriented on the outside and the nonpolar tails on the inside. The polar heads electrostatically interact with the polar solvent $H_2O$, while the nonpolar tails are held in close proximity by numerous London dispersion forces.

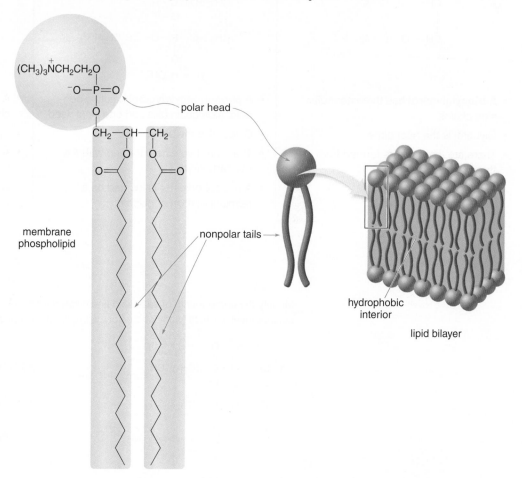

**Cell membranes** are composed of these lipid bilayers (Figure 19.6). The charged heads of the phospholipids are oriented towards the aqueous interior and exterior of the cell. The nonpolar tails form the hydrophobic interior of the membrane, thus serving as an insoluble barrier that protects the cell from the outside. The identity of the fatty acids in the phospholipid determines the rigidity of this bilayer. When the fatty acids are saturated, they pack well in the interior of the lipid bilayer, and the membrane is less fluid. When there are many unsaturated fatty acids, the nonpolar tails cannot pack as well and the bilayer is more fluid.

While the phospholipid bilayer forms the main fabric of the cell membrane, proteins and cholesterol (Section 19.8) are embedded in the membrane as well. **Peripheral proteins** are embedded within the membrane and extend outward on one side only. **Integral proteins** extend through the entire bilayer. Some lipids and proteins on the membrane surface are bonded to carbohydrates, forming **glycolipids** and **glycoproteins.** The polar carbohydrate chains extend into the surrounding aqueous environment.

## PROBLEM 19.18

Why are phospholipids rather than triacylglycerols present in cell membranes?

**Figure 19.6** Composition of the Cell Membrane

Cell membranes are composed of a lipid bilayer having the hydrophilic polar heads of phospholipids arranged on the exterior of the bilayer, where they can interact with the polar aqueous environment inside and outside the cell. The hydrophobic tails of the phospholipid are arranged in the interior of the bilayer, forming a "greasy" layer that is only selectively permeable to the passage of species from one side to the other.

**PROBLEM 19.19**

A cell membrane from one source (**A**) contains phospholipids formed from linoleic and oleic acid. A cell membrane from a second source (**B**) contains phospholipids formed from stearic and palmitic acids. How will these two cell membranes differ?

## 19.7B   Transport Across a Cell Membrane

How does a molecule or ion in the water on one side of a cell membrane pass through the non-polar interior of the cell membrane to the other side? A variety of transport mechanisms occur (Figure 19.7).

**Figure 19.7**

How Substances Cross a Cell Membrane

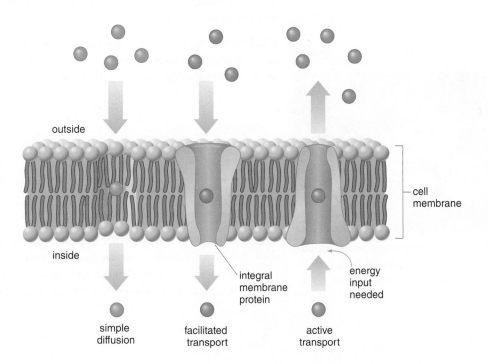

Small molecules like $O_2$ and $CO_2$ can simply diffuse through the cell membrane, traveling from the side of higher concentration to the side of lower concentration. With larger polar molecules and some ions, simple diffusion is too slow or not possible, so a process of **facilitated transport** occurs. Ions such as $Cl^-$ or $HCO_3^-$ and glucose molecules travel through the channels created by integral proteins.

Some ions, notably $Na^+$, $K^+$, and $Ca^{2+}$, must move across the cell membrane against the concentration gradient—that is, from a region of lower concentration to a region of higher concentration. To move an ion across the membrane in this fashion requires energy input, and the process is called **active transport.** Active transport occurs whenever a nerve impulse causes a muscle to contract. In this process, energy is supplied to move $K^+$ ions from outside to inside a cell, against a concentration gradient.

### PROBLEM 19.20

Why don't ions readily diffuse through the interior of the cell membrane?

## 19.8  FOCUS ON HEALTH & MEDICINE
### Cholesterol, the Most Prominent Steroid

The steroids are a group of lipids whose carbon skeletons contain three six-membered rings and one five-membered ring. This tetracyclic carbon skeleton is drawn below.

steroid skeleton                                                numbering the steroid skeleton

Many steroids also contain two methyl groups that are bonded to the rings. The steroid rings are lettered **A, B, C,** and **D,** and the 17 ring carbons are numbered as shown. The two methyl groups are numbered C18 and C19. Steroids differ in the identity and location of the substituents attached to the skeleton.

**Cholesterol,** the most prominent member of the steroid family, is synthesized in the liver and found in almost all body tissues. It is a vital component for healthy cell membranes, and it serves as the starting material for the synthesis of all other steroids and vitamin D.

cholesterol

Cholesterol is obtained in the diet from a variety of sources, including meat, cheese, butter, and eggs. Table 19.4 lists the cholesterol content in some foods. While the American Heart Association currently recommends that the daily intake of cholesterol should be less than 300 mg, the average American diet includes 400–500 mg of cholesterol each day.

**HEALTH NOTE**

Plants do not synthesize cholesterol, so fresh fruits and vegetables, nuts, and whole grains are cholesterol free.

| Table 19.4 Cholesterol Content in Some Foods | | |
| --- | --- | --- |
| Food | Serving Size | Cholesterol (mg) |
| Boiled egg | 1 | 225 |
| Cream cheese | 1 oz | 27 |
| Cheddar cheese | 1 oz | 19 |
| Butter | 3.5 oz | 250 |
| Beefsteak | 3.5 oz | 70 |
| Chicken | 3.5 oz | 60 |
| Ice cream | 3.5 oz | 45 |
| Sponge cake | 3.5 oz | 260 |

**PROBLEM 19.21**

Why is cholesterol classified as a lipid?

**PROBLEM 19.22**

(a) Label the rings of the steroid nucleus in cholesterol. (b) Give the number of the carbon to which the OH group is bonded. (c) Between which two carbons is the double bond located? (d) Label the polar bonds in cholesterol and explain why it is insoluble in water.

While health experts agree that the amount of cholesterol in the diet should be limited, it is also now clear that elevated *blood* cholesterol (serum cholesterol) can lead to coronary artery disease. It is estimated that only 25% of the cholesterol in the blood comes from dietary sources, with the remainder synthesized in the liver. High blood cholesterol levels are associated with an increased risk of developing coronary artery disease, heart attack, and stroke. To understand the relationship between cholesterol and heart disease, we must learn about how cholesterol is transported through the bloodstream.

Like other lipids, cholesterol is insoluble in the aqueous medium of the blood, since it has only one polar OH group and many nonpolar C—C and C—H bonds. In order for it to be transported from the liver where it is synthesized, to the tissues, cholesterol combines with phospholipids and proteins to form small water-soluble spherical particles called **lipoproteins.**

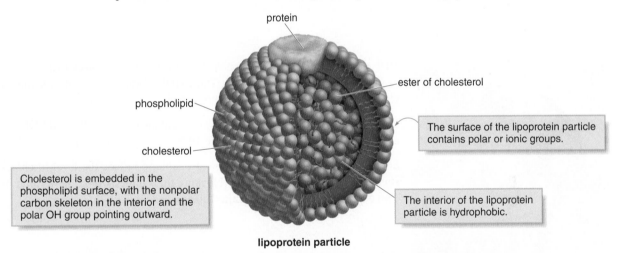

protein

ester of cholesterol

phospholipid

The surface of the lipoprotein particle contains polar or ionic groups.

cholesterol

Cholesterol is embedded in the phospholipid surface, with the nonpolar carbon skeleton in the interior and the polar OH group pointing outward.

The interior of the lipoprotein particle is hydrophobic.

**lipoprotein particle**

In a lipoprotein, the polar heads of phospholipids and the polar portions of protein molecules are arranged on the surface. The nonpolar molecules are buried in the interior of the particle. In this way, the nonpolar material is "dissolved" in an aqueous environment.

Lipoproteins are classified on the basis of their density, with two types being especially important in determining serum cholesterol levels.

- **Low-density lipoproteins (LDLs) transport cholesterol from the liver to the tissues.**
- **High-density lipoproteins (HDLs) transport cholesterol from the tissues back to the liver.**

LDL particles transport cholesterol to tissues where it is incorporated in cell membranes. When LDLs supply more cholesterol than is needed, LDLs deposit cholesterol on the wall of arteries, forming plaque (Figure 19.8). Atherosclerosis is a disease that results from the buildup of these fatty deposits, restricting the flow of blood, increasing blood pressure, and increasing the likelihood of a heart attack or stroke. As a result, LDL cholesterol is often called "bad" cholesterol.

Figure 19.8    Plaque Formation in an Artery

a. Open artery

b. Blocked artery

a. Cross-section of a clear artery with no buildup of plaque

b. Artery almost completely blocked by the buildup of plaque

A physical examination by a physician includes blood work that measures three quantities: total serum cholesterol, HDL cholesterol, and LDL cholesterol.

HDL particles transport excess cholesterol from the tissues back to the liver, where it is converted to other substances or eliminated. Thus, HDLs reduce the level of serum cholesterol, so HDL cholesterol is often called "good" cholesterol.

Current recommendations for these values and the role of HDLs and LDLs in determining serum cholesterol levels are shown in Figure 19.9.

Several drugs called **statins** are now available to reduce the level of cholesterol in the bloodstream. These compounds act by blocking the synthesis of cholesterol at its very early stages. Two examples include atorvastatin (Lipitor) and simvastatin (Zocor).

Figure 19.9    HDLs, LDLs, and Cholesterol Level

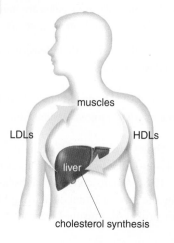

muscles

LDLs                    HDLs

liver

cholesterol synthesis

Current recommendations by the National Cholesterol Education Program:

- Total serum cholesterol: < 200 mg/dL

- HDL cholesterol: > 40 mg/dL

- LDL cholesterol: < 100 mg/dL

Cholesterol is synthesized in the liver. High HDL levels are considered desirable since HDL transports cholesterol back to the liver. Low LDLs are considered desirable to avoid the buildup of plaque in the arteries.

Generic name: atorvastatin
Trade name: Lipitor

Generic name: simvastatin
Trade bame: Zocor

### PROBLEM 19.23

Would you expect triacylglycerols to be contained in the interior of a lipoprotein particle or on the surface with the phospholipids? Explain your choice.

### PROBLEM 19.24

Identify the functional groups in (a) atorvastatin; (b) simvastatin.

## 19.9  Steroid Hormones

Many biologically active steroids are hormones secreted by the endocrine glands. **A *hormone* is a molecule that is synthesized in one part of an organism, which then elicits a response at a different site.** Two important classes of steroid hormones are the **sex hormones** and the **adrenal cortical steroids.**

There are two types of female sex hormones, **estrogens** and **progestins.**

estradiol            estrone            progesterone

Estradiol, progesterone, and oral contraceptives were discussed in Section 13.5.

- Estradiol and estrone are estrogens synthesized in the ovaries. They control the development of secondary sex characteristics in females and regulate the menstrual cycle.
- Progesterone is a progestin often called the "pregnancy hormone." It is responsible for the preparation of the uterus for implantation of a fertilized egg.

The male sex hormones are called **androgens.**

testosterone            androsterone

- Testosterone and androsterone are androgens synthesized in the testes. They control the development of secondary sex characteristics in males—growth of facial hair, increase in muscle mass, and deepening of the voice.

Some body builders use anabolic steroids to increase muscle mass. Long-term or excessive use can cause many health problems, including high blood pressure, liver damage, and cardiovascular disease.

Synthetic androgen analogues, called **anabolic steroids,** promote muscle growth. They were first developed to help individuals whose muscles had atrophied from lack of use following surgery. They have since come to be used by athletes and body builders, although their use is not permitted in competitive sports. Many physical and psychological problems result from their prolonged use.

Anabolic steroids, such as stanozolol, nandrolone, and tetrahydrogestrinone have the same effect on the body as testosterone, but they are more stable, so they are not metabolized as quickly. Tetrahydrogestrinone (also called THG or The Clear), the performance-enhancing drug used by track star Marion Jones during the 2000 Sydney Olympics, was considered a "designer steroid" because it was initially undetected in urine tests for doping. After its chemical structure and properties were determined, it was added to the list of banned anabolic steroids in 2004.

|  |  |  |
|---|---|---|
| stanozolol | nandrolone | tetrahydrogestrinone |

A second group of steroid hormones includes the **adrenal cortical steroids.** Three examples of these hormones are aldosterone, cortisone, and cortisol. All of these compounds are synthesized in the outer layer of the adrenal gland. Aldosterone regulates blood pressure and volume by controlling the concentration of $Na^+$ and $K^+$ in body fluids. Cortisone and cortisol serve as anti-inflammatory agents and they regulate carbohydrate metabolism.

right adrenal gland — cortex — medulla

kidney

|  |  |  |
|---|---|---|
| aldosterone | cortisone | cortisol |

Cortisone and related compounds are used to suppress organ rejection after transplant surgery and to treat many allergic and autoimmune disorders. Prolonged use of these steroids can have undesired side effects, including bone loss and high blood pressure. Prednisone, a widely used synthetic alternative, has similar anti-inflammatory properties but can be taken orally.

prednisone
(synthetic steroid)

### PROBLEM 19.25

Compare the structures of estrone and progesterone. (a) Identify the differences in the A ring of these hormones. (b) How do these hormones differ in functionality at C17?

### PROBLEM 19.26

Identify the functional groups in aldosterone. Classify each alcohol as 1°, 2°, or 3°.

### PROBLEM 19.27

The male sex hormone testosterone and the anabolic steroid nandrolone have very similar structures and, as you might expect, similar biological activity. Point out the single structural difference in these two compounds.

## 19.10 FOCUS ON HEALTH & MEDICINE
### Fat-Soluble Vitamins

**Vitamins are organic compounds required in small quantities for normal metabolism** (Section 11.7). Since our cells cannot synthesize these compounds, they must be obtained in the diet. Vitamins can be categorized as fat soluble or water soluble. **The fat-soluble vitamins are lipids.**

The four fat-soluble vitamins—**A, D, E,** and **K**—are found in fruits and vegetables, fish, liver, and dairy products. Although fat-soluble vitamins must be obtained from the diet, they do not have to be ingested every day. Excess vitamins are stored in adipose cells, and then used when needed. Table 19.5 summarizes the dietary sources and recommended daily intake of the fat-soluble vitamins.

### Table 19.5 Fat-Soluble Vitamins

| Vitamin | Food Source | Recommended Daily Intake |
|---------|-------------|--------------------------|
| A | Liver, kidney, oily fish, dairy products, eggs, fortified breakfast cereals | 900 µg (men) 700 µg (women) |
| D | Fortified milk and breakfast cereals | 5 µg |
| E | Sunflower and safflower oils, nuts, beans, whole grains, leafy greens | 15 mg |
| K | Cauliflower, soybeans, broccoli, leafy greens, green tea | 120 µg (men) 90 µg (women) |

Source: Data from Harvard School of Public Health.

**Vitamin A** (Section 11.7) is obtained from liver, oily fish, and dairy products, and is synthesized from β-carotene, the orange pigment in carrots. In the body, vitamin A is converted to 11-*cis*-retinal, the light-sensitive compound responsible for vision in all vertebrates (Section 16.7). It is also needed for healthy mucous membranes. A deficiency of vitamin A causes night blindness, as well as dry eyes and skin.

vitamin A

**Vitamin D,** strictly speaking, is not a vitamin because it can be synthesized in the body from cholesterol. Nevertheless, it is classified as such, and many foods (particularly milk) are fortified with vitamin D so that we get enough of this vital nutrient. Vitamin D helps regulate both calcium and phosphorus metabolism. A deficiency of vitamin D causes rickets, a bone disease characterized by knock-knees, spinal curvature, and other skeletal deformities.

vitamin D

**Vitamin E** is an antioxidant, and in this way it protects unsaturated side chains in fatty acids from unwanted oxidation (Section 13.12). A deficiency of vitamin E causes numerous neurological problems, although it is rare for vitamin E deficiency to occur.

vitamin E

**Vitamin K** regulates the synthesis of prothrombin and other proteins needed for blood to clot. A severe deficiency of vitamin K leads to excessive and sometimes fatal bleeding because of inadequate blood clotting.

vitamin K

### PROBLEM 19.28

Why is it much easier to overdose on a fat-soluble vitamin than a water-soluble vitamin?

## 19.11 FOCUS ON HEALTH & MEDICINE
### Prostaglandins and Leukotrienes

**Prostaglandins** (Section 17.4) and **leukotrienes** are two types of **eicosanoids,** a group of biologically active compounds containing 20 carbon atoms derived from the fatty acid, arachidonic acid.

$CH_3(CH_2)_4(CH=CHCH_2)_4(CH_2)_2COOH$

arachidonic acid
(four cis double bonds)

a fatty acid

$PGF_{2\alpha}$
a prostaglandin

$LTC_4$
a leukotriene

The word *eicosanoid* is derived from the Greek word *eikosi,* meaning 20.

All eicosanoids are very potent compounds present in low concentration in cells. Eicosanoids are not stored in cells; rather, they are synthesized from arachidonic acid in response to an external stimulus. They are **local mediators,** meaning that they perform their function in the environment in which they are synthesized. This distinguishes them from hormones, which are first synthesized and then transported to their site of action.

### 19.11A Prostaglandins

**Prostaglandins** are a group of carboxylic acids that contain a five-membered ring and have a wide range of biological activities. $PGF_{2\alpha}$ and $PGE_1$ are two examples.

$PGF_{2\alpha}$

$PGE_1$

As we learned in Section 17.4, prostaglandins are responsible for inflammation. Aspirin and ibuprofen relieve pain and decrease inflammation because they block the synthesis of prostaglandins by inhibiting the cyclooxygenase enzyme needed for their synthesis.

Prostaglandins also decrease gastric secretions, inhibit blood platelet aggregation, stimulate uterine contractions, and relax the smooth muscles of the uterus. Because of these many biological functions, prostaglandins and their analogues have found several clinical uses. For example, dinoprostone, the generic name for PGE$_2$, is administered to relax the smooth muscles of the uterus when labor is induced, and to terminate early pregnancies. Misoprostol, a synthetic prostaglandin, prevents gastric ulcers in patients who are at high risk of developing them.

PGE$_2$
(dinoprostone)

misoprostol

More recently, it has been discovered that two *different* cyclooxygenase enzymes, called COX-1 and COX-2, are responsible for prostaglandin synthesis. COX-1 is involved with the usual production of prostaglandins, but COX-2 is responsible for the synthesis of additional prostaglandins in inflammatory diseases like arthritis. **NSAIDs—nonsteroidal anti-inflammatory drugs**—like aspirin and ibuprofen, inactivate both the COX-1 and COX-2 enzymes. This activity also results in an increase in gastric secretions, making an individual more susceptible to ulcer formation.

A group of anti-inflammatory drugs that block only the COX-2 enzyme was developed in the 1990s. These drugs—rofecoxib, valdecoxib, and celecoxib—do not cause an increase in gastric secretions, and thus were touted as an especially effective treatment for patients with arthritis, who need daily doses of these medications. Unfortunately, both rofecoxib and valdecoxib have been removed from the market, since their use has been associated with an increased risk of heart attack and stroke. Celecoxib, on the other hand, has fewer side effects, so it is still available and widely used.

Generic name: rofecoxib
Trade name: Vioxx

Generic name: valdecoxib
Trade name: Bextra

Generic name: celecoxib
Trade name: Celebrex

**PROBLEM 19.29**

(a) What functional groups are present in PGE$_2$? (b) Draw a skeletal structure for PGE$_2$. The double bond closest to the COOH group is cis and the remaining double bond is trans.

## 19.11B   Asthma and Leukotrienes

**Asthma** is an obstructive lung disease that affects millions of Americans. Because it involves episodic constriction of small airways, bronchodilators such as albuterol (Section 15.3) are used to treat symptoms by widening airways. Since asthma is also characterized by chronic inflammation, inhaled steroids that reduce inflammation are also commonly used.

The **leukotrienes** are molecules that contribute to the asthmatic response by constricting smooth muscles, especially in the lungs. Leukotrienes, such as leukotriene $C_4$ ($LTC_4$), are synthesized in several steps from arachidonic acid. The first step involves an oxidation reaction catalyzed by an enzyme called a lipoxygenase.

New asthma drugs act by blocking the synthesis of leukotriene $C_4$ from arachidonic acid. For example, zileuton (trade name: Zyflo CR) inhibits the lipoxygenase enzyme needed in the first step. By blocking the synthesis of leukotriene $C_4$, a compound responsible for the disease, zileuton treats the cause of asthma, not just its symptoms.

Generic name: zileuton
Trade name: Zyflo CR

## PROBLEM 19.30

(a) A sulfur atom between two alkyl groups (RSR) is called a sulfide. Identify all other functional groups in $LTC_4$. (b) Label the double bonds in $LTC_4$ as cis or trans.

# CHAPTER HIGHLIGHTS

## KEY TERMS

Active transport (19.7)
Adrenal cortical steroid (19.9)
Anabolic steroid (19.9)
Androgen (19.9)
Cell membrane (19.7)
Cephalin (19.6)
Eicosanoid (19.11)
Estrogen (19.9)
Facilitated transport (19.7)
Fat (19.4)
Fat-soluble vitamin (19.10)
Fatty acid (19.2)
High-density lipoprotein (19.8)
Hormone (19.9)

Hydrolyzable lipid (19.1)
Hydrophilic (19.2)
Hydrophobic (19.2)
Lecithin (19.6)
Leukotriene (19.11)
Lipid (19.1)
Lipid bilayer (19.7)
Lipoprotein (19.8)
Low-density lipoprotein (19.8)
Nonhydrolyzable lipid (19.1)
Oil (19.4)
Omega-*n* acid (19.2)
Phosphatidylcholine (19.6)
Phosphatidylethanolamine (19.6)

Phosphoacylglycerol (19.6)
Phosphodiester (19.6)
Phospholipid (19.6)
Progestin (19.9)
Prostaglandin (19.11)
Saponification (19.5)
Saturated fatty acid (19.2)
Soap (19.5)
Sphingomyelin (19.6)
Steroid (19.8)
Triacylglycerol (19.4)
Unsaturated fatty acid (19.2)
Wax (19.3)

## KEY REACTIONS

[1]    Hydrolysis of waxes (19.3)

[2]    Hydrolysis of triacylglycerols in the presence of acid or enzymes (19.5)

[3]    Hydrolysis of triacylglycerols in the presence of base—Saponification (19.5)

## KEY CONCEPTS

**❶  What are the general characteristics of lipids? (19.1)**
- Lipids are biomolecules that contain many nonpolar C—C and C—H bonds, making them soluble in organic solvents and insoluble in water.
- Hydrolyzable lipids, including waxes, triacylglycerols, and phospholipids, can be converted to smaller molecules on reaction with water.
- Nonhydrolyzable lipids, including steroids, fat-soluble vitamins, and eicosanoids, cannot be cleaved into smaller units by hydrolysis.

**❷  How are fatty acids classified and what is the relationship between their melting points and the number of double bonds they contain? (19.2)**
- Fatty acids are saturated if they contain no carbon–carbon double bonds and unsaturated if they contain one or more double bonds. Unsaturated fatty acids generally contain cis double bonds.
- As the number of double bonds in the fatty acid increases, its melting point decreases.

**❸  What are waxes? (19.3)**
- A wax is an ester (RCOOR') formed from a fatty acid (RCOOH) and a high molecular weight alcohol (R'OH). Since waxes contain many nonpolar C—C and C—H bonds, they are hydrophobic.
- Waxes (RCOOR') are hydrolyzed to fatty acids (RCOOH) and alcohols (R'OH).

**❹  What are triacylglycerols, and how do the triacylglycerols in a fat and oil differ? (19.4)**
- Triacylglycerols, or triglycerides, are triesters formed from glycerol and three molecules of fatty acids. A monounsaturated triacylglycerol contains one carbon–carbon double bond, whereas polyunsaturated triacylglycerols have more than one carbon–carbon double bond.
- Fats are triacylglycerols derived from fatty acids having few double bonds, making them solids at room temperature. Fats are generally obtained from animal sources.
- Oils are triacylglycerols derived from fatty acids having a larger number of double bonds, making them liquid at room temperature. Oils are generally obtained from plant sources.

**5** **What hydrolysis products are formed from a triacylglycerol? (19.5)**

- Triacylglycerols are hydrolyzed in acid or with enzymes (in biological systems) to form glycerol and three molecules of fatty acids. Base hydrolysis of a triacylglycerol forms glycerol and sodium salts of fatty acids—soaps.

**6** **What are the major types of phospholipids? (19.6)**

- All phospholipids contain a phosphorus atom, and have a polar (ionic) head and two nonpolar tails. Phosphoacylglycerols are derived from glycerol, two molecules of fatty acids, phosphate, and an alcohol (either ethanolamine or choline). Sphingomyelins are derived from sphingosine, a fatty acid (that forms an amide), a phosphate, and an alcohol (either ethanolamine or choline).

**7** **Describe the structure of the cell membrane. How do molecules and ions cross the cell membrane? (19.7)**

- The main component of the cell membrane is phospholipids, arranged in a lipid bilayer with the ionic heads oriented towards the outside of the bilayer, and the nonpolar tails on the interior.
- Small molecules like $O_2$ and $CO_2$ diffuse through the membrane from the side of higher concentration to the side of lower concentration. Larger polar molecules and some ions travel through channels created by integral membrane proteins (facilitated diffusion). Some cations ($Na^+$, $K^+$, and $Ca^{2+}$) must travel against the concentration gradient, a process called active transport, which requires energy input.

**8** **What are the main structural features of steroids? What is the relationship between the steroid cholesterol and cardiovascular disease? (19.8)**

- Steroids are tetracyclic lipids that contain three six-membered rings and one five-membered ring. Because cholesterol is insoluble in the aqueous medium of the blood, it is transported through the bloodstream in water-soluble particles called lipoproteins.

- Low-density lipoprotein particles (LDLs) transport cholesterol from the liver to the tissues. If the blood cholesterol level is high, it forms plaque on the walls of arteries, increasing the risk of heart attack and stroke. High-density lipoprotein particles (HDLs) transport cholesterol from the tissues to the liver, where it is metabolized or eliminated.

**9** **What is a hormone? Give examples of steroid hormones. (19.9)**

- A hormone is a molecule that is synthesized in one part of an organism, and elicits a response at a different site. Steroid hormones include estrogens and progestins (female sex hormones), androgens (male sex hormones), and adrenal cortical steroids such as cortisone, which are synthesized in the adrenal gland.

**10** **Which vitamins are fat soluble? (19.10)**

- Fat-soluble vitamins are lipids required in small quantities for normal cell function, and which cannot be synthesized in the body. Vitamins A, D, E, and K are fat soluble.

**11** **What are the general characteristics of prostaglandins and leukotrienes? (19.11)**

- Prostaglandins are a group of carboxylic acids that contain a five-membered ring and are derived from arachidonic acid. Prostaglandins cause inflammation, decrease gastric secretions, inhibit blood platelet aggregation, stimulate uterine contractions, and relax the smooth muscle of the uterus.
- Leukotrienes, acyclic molecules derived from arachidonic acid, contribute to the asthmatic response by constricting smooth muscles in the lungs.

## PROBLEMS

Selected in-chapter and odd-numbered end-of-chapter problems have brief answers in Appendix B. The *Student Study Guide and Solutions Manual* contains detailed solutions to all in-chapter and odd-numbered end-of-chapter problems, as well as additional worked examples and a chapter self-test.

### General Characteristics of Lipids

**19.31** Label each compound as a hydrolyzable or nonhydrolyzable lipid.
    a. prostaglandin
    b. triacylglycerol
    c. leukotriene
    d. vitamin A
    e. phosphoacylglycerol
    f. lecithin
    g. cholesterol

**19.32** Label each compound as a hydrolyzable or nonhydrolyzable lipid.
    a. eicosanoid
    b. oleic acid
    c. phospholipid
    d. cephalin
    e. wax
    f. estrogen
    g. $PGE_1$

**19.33** In which solvents might a wax be soluble: (a) $H_2O$; (b) $CH_2Cl_2$; (c) $CH_3CH_2OCH_2CH_3$?

**19.34** In which solvents or solutions might a steroid be soluble: (a) blood plasma; (b) $CCl_4$; (c) 5% NaCl solution?

## Fatty Acids, Waxes, and Triacylglycerols

**19.35** Rank the fatty acids in each group in order of increasing melting point.

    a. $CH_3(CH_2)_{14}COOH$, $CH_3(CH_2)_3CH=CH(CH_2)_7COOH$, $CH_3(CH_2)_{12}COOH$

    b. $CH_3(CH_2)_{16}COOH$, $CH_3(CH_2)_7CH=CH(CH_2)_7COOH$, $CH_3(CH_2)_5CH=CH(CH_2)_7COOH$

**19.36** (a) What is the difference between a saturated, monounsaturated, and polyunsaturated fatty acid? (b) Give an example of each having the same number of carbons. (c) Rank these compounds in order of increasing melting point.

**19.37** How does each of the following affect the melting point of a fatty acid: (a) increasing the number of carbon atoms; (b) increasing the number of double bonds?

**19.38** How would you expect the melting points of the following fatty acids to compare? Explain your choice.

**19.39** Some fish oils contain triacylglycerols formed from the polyunsaturated fatty acid, 7,10,13,16,19-docosapentaenoic acid.

$$CH_3CH_2CH=CHCH_2CH=CHCH_2CH=CHCH_2CH=CHCH_2CH=CH(CH_2)_5COOH$$

7,10,13,16,19-docosapentaenoic acid

    a. Draw a skeletal structure showing the cis arrangement at each double bond.

    b. Label the hydrophobic and hydrophilic portions of the fatty acid.

    c. How does the melting point of this fatty acid compare to its all trans isomer?

    d. Would you expect this fatty acid to be a solid or a liquid at room temperature?

    e. What type of omega-*n* acid is this fatty acid?

**19.40** Some marine plankton contain triacylglycerols formed from the polyunsaturated fatty acid, 3,6,9,12,15-octadecapentaenoic acid.

$$CH_3CH_2CH=CHCH_2CH=CHCH_2CH=CHCH_2CH=CHCH_2COOH$$

3,6,9,12,15-octadecapentaenoic acid

    a. Draw a skeletal structure showing the cis arrangement at each double bond.

    b. Label the hydrophobic and hydrophilic portions of the fatty acid.

    c. How does the melting point of this fatty acid compare to the melting point of oleic acid?

    d. Would you expect this fatty acid to be a solid or a liquid at room temperature?

    e. What type of omega-*n* acid is this fatty acid?

**19.41** Consider fatty acid **A** depicted in the ball-and-stick model.

**A**

    a. Draw a skeletal structure for **A** and clearly show the cis double bond.

    b. What type of omega-*n* acid is this fatty acid?

    c. Draw a stereoisomer of **A.**

    d. Draw the structure of the wax formed from **A** and $CH_3(CH_2)_{10}OH$.

**19.42** Consider fatty acid **B** depicted in the ball-and-stick model.

**B**

    a. Draw a skeletal structure for **B** and clearly show the cis double bond.

    b. What type of omega-*n* acid is this fatty acid?

    c. Draw a stereoisomer of **B.**

    d. Draw the structure of the wax formed from **B** and $CH_3(CH_2)_8OH$.

**19.43** Draw the structure of a wax formed from palmitic acid $[CH_3(CH_2)_{14}COOH]$ and each alcohol.

    a. $CH_3(CH_2)_{21}OH$

    b. $CH_3(CH_2)_{11}OH$

    c. $CH_3(CH_2)_9OH$

**19.44** Draw the structure of a wax formed from a 30-carbon straight chain alcohol and each carboxylic acid.

    a. lauric acid

    b. myristic acid

    c. $CH_3(CH_2)_{22}COOH$

**19.45** What hydrolysis products are formed when each wax is treated with aqueous sulfuric acid?

    a. $CH_3(CH_2)_{16}COO(CH_2)_{17}CH_3$

    b. $CH_3(CH_2)_{12}COO(CH_2)_{25}CH_3$

    c. $CH_3(CH_2)_{14}COO(CH_2)_{27}CH_3$

    d. $CH_3(CH_2)_{22}COO(CH_2)_{13}CH_3$

**19.46** What hydrolysis products are formed when each wax is treated with aqueous sulfuric acid?

    a. $CH_3(CH_2)_{18}COO(CH_2)_{29}CH_3$

    b. $CH_3(CH_2)_{24}COO(CH_2)_{23}CH_3$

    c. $CH_3(CH_2)_{14}COO(CH_2)_{17}CH_3$

    d. $CH_3(CH_2)_{12}COO(CH_2)_{15}CH_3$

**19.47** Draw a triacylglycerol that fits each description:

    a. a triacylglycerol formed from lauric, myristic, and linoleic acids

    b. an unsaturated triacylglycerol that contains two cis double bonds in one fatty acid side chain

c. a saturated triacylglycerol formed from three 14-carbon fatty acids

d. a monounsaturated triacylglycerol

**19.48** Draw a triacylglycerol that fits each description:

a. a triacylglycerol formed from two molecules of lauric acid and one molecule of palmitic acid

b. a polyunsaturated triacylglycerol formed from three molecules of linoleic acid

c. a trans triacylglycerol that contains two trans double bonds

d. an unsaturated triacylglycerol formed from linolenic acid

**19.49** Draw the structure of a triacylglycerol that yields only the sodium carboxylate depicted in the ball-and-stick model when it is hydrolyzed in base.

Na$^+$

**19.50** Draw the structure of a triacylglycerol that yields only the sodium carboxylate depicted in the ball-and-stick model when it is hydrolyzed in base.

Na$^+$

**19.51** Consider the following four types of compounds: [1] fatty acids; [2] soaps; [3] waxes; [4] triacylglycerols. For each type of compound: (a) give the general structure; (b) draw the structure of a specific example; (c) label the compound as water soluble or water insoluble; (d) label the compound as soluble or insoluble in the organic solvent hexane [CH$_3$(CH$_2$)$_4$CH$_3$].

**19.52** How do fats and oils compare with respect to each of the following features?

a. identity and number of functional groups present

b. number of carbon–carbon double bonds present

c. melting point

d. natural source

**19.53** Answer the following questions about the given triacylglycerol.

$$CH_2-O-\overset{\overset{O}{\|}}{C}-(CH_2)_{18}CH_3$$
$$CH-O-\overset{\overset{O}{\|}}{C}-(CH_2)_{16}CH_3$$
$$CH_2-O-\overset{\overset{O}{\|}}{C}-(CH_2)_{10}CH_3$$

a. What fatty acids are used to form this triacylglycerol?

b. Would you expect this triacylglycerol to be a solid or a liquid at room temperature?

c. What regions are hydrophobic?

d. What regions are hydrophilic?

e. What hydrolysis products are formed when the triacylglycerol is treated with aqueous sulfuric acid?

**19.54** Answer the following questions about the given triacylglycerol.

$$CH_2-O-\overset{\overset{O}{\|}}{C}-(CH_2)_{14}CH_3$$
$$CH-O-\overset{\overset{O}{\|}}{C}-(CH_2)_7(CH=CHCH_2)_2(CH_2)_3CH_3$$
$$CH_2-O-\overset{\overset{O}{\|}}{C}-(CH_2)_7CH=CH(CH_2)_5CH_3$$

a. What fatty acids are used to form this triacylglycerol?

b. Would you expect this triacylglycerol to be a solid or a liquid at room temperature?

c. What regions are hydrophobic?

d. What regions are hydrophilic?

e. What hydrolysis products are formed when the triacylglycerol is treated with aqueous sulfuric acid?

**19.55** Draw the products formed when each triacylglycerol is hydrolyzed under each of the following conditions: [1] water and H$_2$SO$_4$; [2] water and NaOH.

a. $$CH_2-O-\overset{\overset{O}{\|}}{C}-(CH_2)_{14}CH_3$$
$$CH-O-\overset{\overset{O}{\|}}{C}-(CH_2)_{14}CH_3$$
$$CH_2-O-\overset{\overset{O}{\|}}{C}-(CH_2)_{16}CH_3$$

b. $$CH_2-O-\overset{\overset{O}{\|}}{C}-(CH_2)_{14}CH_3$$
$$CH-O-\overset{\overset{O}{\|}}{C}-(CH_2)_7CH=CH(CH_2)_7CH_3$$
$$CH_2-O-\overset{\overset{O}{\|}}{C}-(CH_2)_7CH=CH(CH_2)_5CH_3$$

**19.56** Draw the products formed when each triacylglycerol is hydrolyzed under each of the following conditions: [1] water and H$_2$SO$_4$; [2] water and NaOH.

a. $$CH_2-O-\overset{\overset{O}{\|}}{C}-(CH_2)_{10}CH_3$$
$$CH-O-\overset{\overset{O}{\|}}{C}-(CH_2)_{14}CH_3$$
$$CH_2-O-\overset{\overset{O}{\|}}{C}-(CH_2)_{16}CH_3$$

b. $$CH_2-O-\overset{\overset{O}{\|}}{C}-(CH_2)_7CH=CH(CH_2)_7CH_3$$
$$CH-O-\overset{\overset{O}{\|}}{C}-(CH_2)_{16}CH_3$$
$$CH_2-O-\overset{\overset{O}{\|}}{C}-(CH_2)_7CH=CH(CH_2)_5CH_3$$

## Phospholipids and Cell Membranes

**19.57** Which of the following are phospholipids: (a) triacylglycerols; (b) leukotrienes; (c) sphingomyelins; (d) fatty acids?

**19.58** Which of the following are phospholipids: (a) prostaglandins; (b) cephalins; (c) lecithins; (d) steroids?

**19.59** Draw a phospholipid that fits each description.
   a. a cephalin formed from two molecules of palmitoleic acid
   b. a phosphatidylcholine formed from two molecules of lauric acid
   c. a sphingomyelin formed from stearic acid and ethanolamine

**19.60** Draw a phospholipid that fits each description.
   a. a lecithin formed from two molecules of oleic acid
   b. a phosphatidylethanolamine formed from two molecules of myristic acid
   c. a sphingomyelin formed from palmitic acid and choline

**19.61** Why don't triacylglycerols form lipid bilayers?

**19.62** How would a cell membrane having phospholipids that contain a high percentage of oleic acid differ from a cell membrane having phospholipids that contain a high percentage of stearic acid?

**19.63** In transporting molecules or ions across a cell membrane, what is the difference between diffusion and facilitated transport? Give an example of a molecule or ion that crosses the membrane by each method.

**19.64** In transporting molecules or ions across a cell membrane, what is the difference between facilitated transport and active transport? Give an example of a molecule or ion that crosses the membrane by each method.

## Steroids

**19.65** Draw the structure of the anabolic steroid 4-androstene-3,17-dione, also called "andro," from the following description. Andro contains the tetracyclic steroid skeleton with carbonyl groups at C3 and C17, a double bond between C4 and C5, and methyl groups bonded to C10 and C13.

**19.66** Draw the structure of the anabolic steroid methenolone from the following description. Methenolone contains the tetracyclic steroid skeleton with a carbonyl group at C3, a hydroxyl at C17, a double bond between C1 and C2, and methyl groups bonded to C1, C10, and C13.

**19.67** Why must cholesterol be transported through the bloodstream in lipoprotein particles?

**19.68** Why are LDLs soluble in the blood?

**19.69** Describe the role of HDLs and LDLs in cholesterol transport in the blood. What is the relationship of HDL and LDL levels to cardiovascular disease?

**19.70** What are anabolic steroids? Give an example. What adverse effects arise from using anabolic steroids?

**19.71** (a) Draw the structure of an estrogen and an androgen. (b) What structural features are similar in the two steroids? (c) What structural features are different? (d) Describe the biological activity of each steroid.

**19.72** (a) Draw the structure of an androgen and a progestin. (b) What structural features are similar in the two steroids? (c) What structural features are different? (d) Describe the biological activity of each steroid.

## Prostaglandins and Leukotrienes

**19.73** What are the similarities and differences between prostaglandins and leukotrienes?

**19.74** Why aren't prostaglandins classified as hormones?

**19.75** What two structural features characterize all prostaglandins?

**19.76** List three biological functions of prostaglandins in the body.

**19.77** Explain why aspirin and celecoxib differ in how they act as anti-inflammatory agents.

**19.78** How does zileuton treat the cause of asthma, not just relieve its symptoms?

## Vitamins

**19.79** What are vitamins and why must they be present in the diet?

**19.80** Why is vitamin D technically not a vitamin?

**19.81** Answer each question with regards to vitamins A and D.
   a. How many tetrahedral carbons does the vitamin contain?
   b. How many trigonal planar carbons does the vitamin contain?
   c. Identify the functional groups.
   d. Label all polar bonds.
   e. What function does the vitamin serve in the body?
   f. What problems result when there is a deficiency of the vitamin?
   g. Give a dietary source.

**19.82** Answer each question in Problem 19.81 for vitamins E and K.

## General Questions

**19.83** Give an example of each type of lipid.
   a. a monounsaturated fatty acid
   b. a wax that contains a total of 30 carbons
   c. a saturated triacylglycerol
   d. a sphingomyelin derived from ethanolamine

**19.84** Give an example of each type of lipid.
   a. a polyunsaturated fatty acid
   b. a wax derived from a 12-carbon fatty acid
   c. a polyunsaturated triacylglycerol
   d. a cephalin

**19.85** Block diagrams representing the general structures of three types of lipids are drawn. Which terms describe each diagram: (a) phospholipid; (b) triacylglycerol; (c) hydrolyzable lipid; (d) sphingomyelin; (e) phosphoacylglycerol? More than one term may apply to a diagram.

**19.86** Which "cartoon" represents a soap and which represents a phosphoacylglycerol? What structural features are present in the polar head and nonpolar tails of each compound?

**19.87** Why are phosphoacylglycerols more water soluble than triacylglycerols?

**19.88** How are soaps and phosphoacylglycerols similar in structure? How do they differ?

## Applications

**19.89** The main fatty acid component of the triacylglycerols in coconut oil is lauric acid, $CH_3(CH_2)_{10}COOH$. Explain why coconut oil is a liquid at room temperature despite the fact that it contains a large fraction of this saturated fatty acid.

**19.90** Unlike many fats and oils, the cocoa butter used to make chocolate is remarkably uniform in composition. All triacylglycerols contain oleic acid bonded to the 2° OH group of glycerol, and either palmitic acid or stearic acid esterified to the 1° OH groups. Draw the structures of two possible triacylglycerols that compose cocoa butter.

**19.91** What is the difference between vegetable oil from plants and motor oil, obtained from crude oil (Section 12.6)?

**19.92** Why do laboratory blood results now report the levels of cholesterol, HDLs, and LDLs? What are the current recommendations for these values?

**19.93** Can an individual survive on a completely fat-free diet?

**19.94** Can an individual survive on a cholesterol-free diet?

**19.95** Why should saturated fats in the diet be avoided?

**19.96** Why is it recommended that polyunsaturated oils be substituted for saturated fats in the diet?

**19.97** Why do animals that live in cold climates have triacylglycerols that contain a higher percentage of unsaturated fatty acid side chains?

**19.98** If the serum cholesterol level in an adult is 167 mg/dL, how much cholesterol is contained in 5.0 L of blood? (Recall from Chapter 1 that 1 L = 10 dL.)

## CHALLENGE PROBLEMS

**19.99** Sometimes it is possible to convert one lipid molecule to another by a simple organic reaction that you learned in previous chapters. What type of reaction converts each starting material to the given product?
   a. cortisone → cortisol (Section 19.9)
   b. estradiol → estrone (Section 19.9)
   c. PGE$_2$ → PGE$_1$ (Section 19.11)

**19.100** How many triacylglycerols can be prepared from three different fatty acids? Draw all possible structures, excluding stereoisomers.

# 20

Milk contains **lactose,** a carbohydrate formed from two simple sugars, glucose and galactose.

# Carbohydrates

## CHAPTER GOALS

*In this chapter you will learn how to:*

1. Identify the three major types of carbohydrates

2. Recognize the major structural features of monosaccharides

3. Draw the cyclic forms of monosaccharides and classify them as α or β anomers

4. Draw reduction and oxidation products of monosaccharides

5. Recognize the major structural features of disaccharides

6. Describe the characteristics of cellulose, starch, and glycogen

7. Give examples of some carbohydrate derivatives that contain amino groups, amides, or carboxylate anions

8. Describe the role that carbohydrates play in determining blood type

In Chapter 20, we turn our attention to **carbohydrates,** the largest group of organic molecules in nature, comprising approximately 50% of the earth's biomass. Carbohydrates can be simple or complex, having as few as three or as many as thousands of carbon atoms. The glucose metabolized for energy in cells, the sucrose of table sugar, and the cellulose of plant stems and tree trunks are all examples of carbohydrates. Carbohydrates on cell surfaces determine blood type, and carbohydrates form the backbone of DNA, the carrier of all genetic information in the cell. Unlike the lipids of Chapter 19, which are composed of mainly carbon–carbon and carbon–hydrogen bonds and few functional groups, carbohydrates have many polar functional groups, whose structure and properties can be understood by applying the basic principles of organic chemistry.

## 20.1 Introduction

**Carbohydrates, commonly referred to as sugars and starches, are polyhydroxy aldehydes and ketones, or compounds that can be hydrolyzed to them.** Historically, the word *carbohydrate* was given to this group of compounds because the molecular formula of simple carbohydrates could be written as $C_n(H_2O)_n$, making them *hydrates of carbon.*

Carbohydrates are classified into three groups:

- Monosaccharides (Sections 20.2–20.4)
- Disaccharides (Section 20.5)
- Polysaccharides (Sections 20.6–20.7)

**Monosaccharides or simple sugars are the simplest carbohydrates.** Glucose and fructose, the two major constituents of honey, are monosaccharides. Glucose contains an aldehyde at one end of a six-carbon chain, and fructose contains a ketone. Every other carbon atom has a hydroxyl group bonded to it. Monosaccharides cannot be converted to simpler compounds by hydrolysis.

honey

common monosaccharides

glucose          fructose

**Disaccharides are composed of two monosaccharides joined together.** Lactose, the principal carbohydrate in milk, is a disaccharide. Disaccharides contain at least one acetal carbon—a carbon atom singly bonded to two OR (alkoxy) groups. Although disaccharides contain no carbonyl groups, they are hydrolyzed to simple monosaccharides that contain an aldehyde or ketone, as we will learn in Section 20.5.

lactose
**a common disaccharide**

**Polysaccharides have three or more monosaccharides joined together.** Starch, the main carbohydrate found in the seeds and roots of plants, is a polysaccharide composed of hundreds of glucose molecules joined together. Like disaccharides, polysaccharides contain acetals but no carbonyl groups, and they are hydrolyzed to simple monosaccharides that contain carbonyl groups. Pasta, bread, rice, and potatoes are foods that contain a great deal of starch.

one form of starch
**a polysaccharide**
[Acetal carbons are labeled with *.]

Carbohydrates are storehouses of chemical energy. Carbohydrates are synthesized in green plants and algae through **photosynthesis,** a process that uses the energy from the sun to convert carbon dioxide and water into glucose and oxygen. Almost all of the oxygen in the atmosphere results from photosynthesis. Plants store glucose in the form of polysaccharides like starch and cellulose (Section 20.6).

Energy is stored in **photosynthesis.**

$$6\ CO_2\ +\ 6\ H_2O\ \xrightarrow[\text{chlorophyll}]{\text{sunlight}}\ \underset{\text{glucose}}{C_6H_{12}O_6}\ +\ 6\ O_2$$

Energy is released in **metabolism.**

The energy stored in glucose bonds is released when glucose is metabolized. The oxidation of glucose is a multistep process that forms carbon dioxide, water, and a great deal of energy. Although the metabolism of lipids provides more energy per gram than the metabolism of carbohydrates, glucose is the preferred source when a burst of energy is needed during exercise. Glucose is water soluble, so it can be quickly and easily transported through the bloodstream to tissues.

Chlorophyll in green leaves converts $CO_2$ and $H_2O$ to glucose and $O_2$ during photosynthesis.

### PROBLEM 20.1

Draw a Lewis structure for glucose that clearly shows the aldehyde carbonyl group and all lone pairs on the oxygen atoms.

### PROBLEM 20.2

Label the hemiacetal carbon—the carbon bonded to one OH and one OR group—in lactose (Section 16.8). Label all other hydroxyls as 1°, 2°, or 3°.

## 20.2 Monosaccharides

**Monosaccharides, the simplest carbohydrates, generally have three to six carbon atoms** in a chain, with a **carbonyl group** at either the terminal carbon, numbered C1, or the carbon adjacent to it, numbered C2. In most carbohydrates, each of the remaining carbon atoms has a **hydroxyl group.** Monosaccharides are drawn vertically, with the carbonyl group at (or near) the top.

Dihydroxyacetone (DHA) is the active ingredient in many artificial tanning agents.

carbonyl at C1 ----→ aldehyde ----→ **aldose**

carbonyl at C2 ----→ ketone ----→ **ketose**

3–6 C's

OH on all (or most) other C's

monosaccharide

- Monosaccharides with a carbonyl group at C1 are aldehydes called *aldoses.*
- Monosaccharides with a carbonyl group at C2 are ketones called *ketoses.*

Glyceraldehyde is the simplest aldose and dihydroxyacetone is the simplest ketose. Glyceraldehyde and dihydroxyacetone both have molecular formula $C_3H_6O_3$, so they are **constitutional isomers;** that is, they have the same molecular formula but a different arrangement of atoms. Glucose is the most prevalent aldose.

aldehyde ----→ **aldose**  ketone ----→ **ketose**  aldehyde ----→ **aldose**

glyceraldehyde

dihydroxyacetone

glucose

All carbohydrates have common names. The simplest aldehyde, glyceraldehyde, and the simplest ketone, dihydroxyacetone, are the only monosaccharides whose names do not end in the suffix *-ose.*

A monosaccharide is characterized by the number of carbons in its chain.

- A triose has three carbons.
- A tetrose has four carbons.
- A pentose has five carbons.
- A hexose has six carbons.

These terms are then combined with the words *aldose* and *ketose* to indicate both the number of carbon atoms in the monosaccharide and whether it contains an aldehyde or ketone. Thus, glyceraldehyde is an aldotriose (three carbons and an aldehyde), dihydroxyacetone is a ketotriose (three carbons and a ketone), and glucose is an aldohexose (six carbons and an aldehyde).

### SAMPLE PROBLEM 20.1

Classify each monosaccharide by the type of carbonyl group and the number of carbons in the chain.

a.

ribose

b.

fructose

### Analysis

Identify the type of carbonyl group to label the monosaccharide as an aldose or ketose. An aldose has the C=O at C1 so that a hydrogen atom is bonded to the carbonyl carbon. A ketose has two carbons bonded to the carbonyl carbon. Count the number of carbons in the chain to determine the suffix—namely, *-triose, -tetrose,* and so forth.

### Solution

a.
$$CHO$$
$$H—C—OH$$
$$H—C—OH$$
$$H—C—OH$$
$$CH_2OH$$

aldehyde

ribose
5 C's in the chain
**Answer:** aldopentose

b.
$$CH_2OH$$
$$C=O$$
$$HO—C—H$$
$$H—C—OH$$
$$H—C—OH$$
$$CH_2OH$$

ketone

fructose
6 C's in the chain
**Answer:** ketohexose

### PROBLEM 20.3

Classify each monosaccharide by the type of carbonyl group and the number of carbons in the chain.

a.
$$CHO$$
$$HO—C—H$$
$$H—C—OH$$
$$H—C—OH$$
$$CH_2OH$$

arabinose

b.
$$CHO$$
$$HO—C—H$$
$$H—C—OH$$
$$CH_2OH$$

threose

c.
$$CH_2OH$$
$$C=O$$
$$H—C—OH$$
$$CH_2OH$$

erythrulose

### PROBLEM 20.4

Draw the structure of (a) an aldotetrose; (b) a ketopentose; (c) an aldohexose.

---

Monosaccharides are all sweet tasting, but their relative sweetness varies a great deal. Monosaccharides are polar compounds with high melting points. The presence of so many polar functional groups capable of hydrogen bonding makes them very water soluble.

### PROBLEM 20.5

Rank the following compounds in order of increasing water solubility: glucose, hexane $[CH_3(CH_2)_4CH_3]$, and 1-decanol $[CH_3(CH_2)_9OH]$. Explain your choice.

---

## 20.2A   Fischer Projection Formulas

A striking feature of carbohydrate structure is the presence of chirality centers. **All carbohydrates except for dihydroxyacetone contain one or more chirality centers.** The simplest aldose, glyceraldehyde, has one chirality center—one carbon atom bonded to four different groups. Thus, there are two possible enantiomers—mirror images that are not superimposable.

Chirality centers and enantiomers were first encountered in Section 15.2.

**Two enantiomers of glyceraldehyde**

chirality center
$$CHO$$
$$H►C◄OH$$
$$CH_2OH$$

naturally occurring isomer
D-glyceraldehyde

chirality center
$$CHO$$
$$HO►C◄H$$
$$CH_2OH$$

unnatural isomer
L-glyceraldehyde

Only one enantiomer of glyceraldehyde occurs in nature. When the carbon chain is drawn vertically with the aldehyde at the top, the naturally occurring enantiomer has the OH group drawn on the right side of the carbon chain. **To distinguish the two enantiomers, the prefixes D and L precede the name.** Thus, the naturally occurring enantiomer is labeled D-glyceraldehyde, while the unnatural isomer is L-glyceraldehyde.

Fischer projection formulas are commonly used to depict the chirality centers in monosaccharides. Recall from Section 15.6 that a Fischer projection formula uses a cross to represent a tetrahedral carbon in which the horizontal bonds come forward (on wedges) and vertical bonds go behind (on dashes). In a Fischer projection formula:

- A carbon atom is located at the intersection of the two lines of the cross.
- The horizontal bonds come forward, on wedges.
- The vertical bonds go back, on dashed lines.

Using a Fischer projection formula, D-glyceraldehyde becomes:

CHO                         CHO

H—C—OH    - - - →      H——OH

CH$_2$OH                      CH$_2$OH

D-glyceraldehyde         Fischer projection formula

### PROBLEM 20.6

Draw L-glyceraldehyde using a Fischer projection formula.

## 20.2B   Monosaccharides with More Than One Chirality Center

A 5% intravenous glucose (dextrose) solution provides a patient with calories and hydration.

Fischer projection formulas are also used for compounds like aldohexoses that contain several chirality centers. Glucose, for example, contains four chirality centers labeled in the structure below. To convert the molecule to a Fischer projection, the molecule is drawn with a vertical carbon skeleton with the aldehyde at the top, and the horizontal bonds are assumed to come forward (on wedges). In the Fischer projection, each chirality center is replaced by a cross.

glucose                   Fischer projection formula

The letters **D** and **L** are used to label all monosaccharides, even those with many chirality centers. **The configuration of the chirality center *farthest* from the carbonyl group determines whether a monosaccharide is D or L.**

- A D monosaccharide has the OH group on the chirality center farthest from the carbonyl on the right (like D-glyceraldehyde).
- An L monosaccharide has the OH group on the chirality center farthest from the carbonyl on the left (like L-glyceraldehyde).

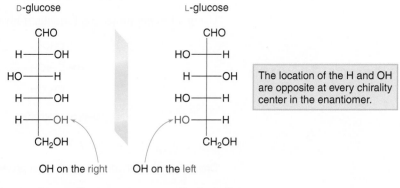

D-glucose          L-glucose

OH on the right    OH on the left
D sugar            L sugar

**Glucose and all other naturally occurring sugars are D sugars.** L-Glucose, a compound that does not occur in nature, is the enantiomer of D-glucose. L-Glucose has the opposite configuration at *every* chirality center.

> The location of the H and OH are opposite at every chirality center in the enantiomer.

naturally occurring enantiomer          unnatural enantiomer

## SAMPLE PROBLEM 20.2

Consider the aldopentose ribose. (a) Label all chirality centers. (b) Classify ribose as a D or L monosaccharide. (c) Draw the enantiomer.

```
        CHO
    H───────OH
    H───────OH
    H───────OH
        CH2OH
```
ribose

### Analysis

- A chirality center has four different groups around a carbon atom.
- The labels D and L are determined by the position of the OH group on the chirality center farthest from the carbonyl group: a D sugar has the OH group on the right and an L sugar has the OH group on the left.
- To draw an enantiomer, draw the mirror image so that each group is a reflection of the group in the original compound.

## Solution

a. The three carbons that contain both H and OH groups in ribose are chirality centers.

b. Ribose is a D sugar since the OH group on the chirality center farthest from the carbonyl is on the right.

c. The enantiomer of D-ribose, L-ribose, has all three OH groups on the left side of the carbon chain.

```
      CHO                      CHO                      CHO
   H──*──OH                 H──┼──OH                 HO──┼──H
   H──*──OH                 H──┼──OH                 HO──┼──H
   H──*──OH                 H──┼──OH,                HO──┼──H
      CH₂OH                    CH₂OH                    CH₂OH
 * = chirality center         D sugar                 enantiomer
```

### PROBLEM 20.7

For each monosaccharide: [1] label all chirality centers; [2] classify the monosaccharide as D or L; [3] draw the enantiomer.

```
a.      CHO           b.      CHO           c.      CHO
     H──┼──OH              HO──┼──H              HO──┼──H
     H──┼──OH              H───┼──OH             HO──┼──H
        CH₂OH             HO──┼──H              H───┼──OH
                             CH₂OH                 CH₂OH
```

### PROBLEM 20.8

For each type of monosaccharide, [1] give an example of a D sugar; [2] label each chirality center: (a) an aldopentose; (b) a ketohexose; (c) a ketotetrose.

## 20.2C Common Monosaccharides

The most common monosaccharides in nature are the aldohexoses D-glucose and D-galactose, and the ketohexose D-fructose.

Insulin injections taken by diabetic patients help to maintain a proper blood glucose level.

```
       CHO                      CHO                     CH₂OH
   H──C──OH                 H──C──OH                  C══O
  HO──C──H                 HO──C──H                 HO──C──H
   H──C──OH                HO──C──H                  H──C──OH
   H──C──OH                 H──C──OH                  H──C──OH
      CH₂OH                    CH₂OH                     CH₂OH

   D-glucose                D-galactose              D-fructose
```

**Glucose,** also called dextrose, is the sugar referred to when blood sugar is measured. It is the most abundant monosaccharide. Glucose is the building block for the polysaccharides starch and cellulose. Glucose, the carbohydrate that is transported in the bloodstream, provides energy for cells when it is metabolized. Normal blood glucose levels are in the range of 70–110 mg/dL. Excess glucose is converted to the polysaccharide glycogen (Section 20.6) or fat.

Insulin, a protein produced in the pancreas, regulates blood glucose levels. When glucose concentration increases after eating, insulin stimulates the uptake of glucose in tissues and its conversion to glycogen. Patients with diabetes produce insufficient insulin to adequately regulate blood glucose levels, and the concentration of glucose rises. With close attention to diet and

An individual with galactosemia must avoid cow's milk and all products derived from cow's milk.

daily insulin injections or other medications, a normal level of glucose can be maintained in most diabetic patients. Individuals with poorly controlled diabetes can develop many other significant complications, including cardiovascular disease, chronic renal failure, and blindness.

**Galactose** is one of the two monosaccharides that form the disaccharide lactose (Section 20.5). Galactose is a stereoisomer of glucose, since the position of a hydrogen atom and hydroxyl group at a single chirality center are different in the two monosaccharides.

Individuals with galactosemia, a rare inherited disease, lack an enzyme needed to metabolize galactose. Galactose accumulates, causing a variety of physical problems, including cataracts, cirrhosis, and mental retardation. Galactosemia can be detected in newborn screening, and affected infants must be given soy-based formula to avoid all milk products with lactose.

**Fructose** is one of two monosaccharides that form the disaccharide sucrose (Section 20.5). Fructose is a ketohexose found in honey and is almost twice as sweet as normal table sugar with about the same number of calories per gram.

### PROBLEM 20.9

D-Glucose and D-galactose are stereoisomers because they have the same molecular formula but a different three-dimensional geometry. How are D-glucose and D-fructose related? How are D-galactose and D-fructose related?

### PROBLEM 20.10

(a) Draw a Fischer projection formula for D-galactose. (b) Draw a Fischer projection formula for the enantiomer of D-galactose.

## 20.3 The Cyclic Forms of Monosaccharides

In Section 16.8 we learned that an aldehyde or ketone reacts with one equivalent of an alcohol to form a **hemiacetal,** a compound that contains a hydroxyl group (OH) and an alkoxy group (OR) on the same carbon.

Generally, hemiacetals from acyclic reactants are unstable. When a compound contains *both* a hydroxyl group and an aldehyde or ketone, however, an intramolecular cyclization reaction forms a stable cyclic hemiacetal.

Some "lite" food products have fewer calories because they use only half as much fructose as sucrose for the same level of sweetness.

$$HOCH_2CH_2CH_2CH_2 \overset{H}{\underset{\underset{O}{\parallel}}{C}} \quad \xrightarrow{\text{re-draw}} \quad \overset{5}{\underset{3}{4}} \overset{OH}{\underset{2}{\underset{1}{H}}} \quad \longrightarrow \quad \overset{5}{\underset{3}{4}} \overset{O}{\underset{2}{\underset{1}{}}} \text{—OH} \quad \text{hemiacetal}$$

5-hydroxypentanal                        The C=O and OH groups react.

**The carbon atom that is part of the hemiacetal is a new chirality center, called the *anomeric carbon*.** Thus, two different products called **anomers** are formed.

- The α anomer has the OH group drawn down, below the ring (shown in red).
- The β anomer has the OH group drawn up, above the ring (shown in blue).

### PROBLEM 20.11

Locate the hemiacetal carbon in each compound and label the compound as an α or β anomer.

a.          b.          c.

## 20.3A The Cyclic Forms of D-Glucose

Although the monosaccharides in Section 20.2 were drawn as acyclic carbonyl compounds, the hydroxyl and carbonyl groups of monosaccharides undergo intramolecular cyclization to form **hemiacetals.** Let's illustrate the process with D-glucose, and then learn a general method for drawing the cyclic forms of any aldohexose.

Which of the five OH groups in glucose is at the right distance from the carbonyl group to form a six-membered ring? The **O atom on the chirality center farthest from the carbonyl** (C5) is six atoms from the carbonyl carbon, placing it at the proper distance for cyclization to form a six-membered ring with a hemiacetal.

This OH group is the right distance away from the carbonyl for cyclization to a six-membered ring.

D-glucose

To convert this acyclic form (labeled **A**) into a cyclic hemiacetal, first rotate the carbon skeleton clockwise 90° to form **B.** Note that groups that were drawn on the right side of the carbon skeleton in **A** end up *below* the carbon chain in **B.** Then twist the chain to put the OH group on C5 close to the aldehyde carbonyl, forming **C.** In this process, the CH$_2$OH group at the end of the chain ends up *above* the carbon skeleton. Realize that **A, B,** and **C** are all different representations of D-glucose. The molecule has been rotated and twisted but the carbon skeleton and relative arrangement of the substituents have not changed.

We are now set to draw the cyclic hemiacetals formed by reaction of the OH group on C5 with the aldehyde carbonyl. Since cyclization creates a new chirality center, there are *two* **cyclic forms of D-glucose,** an **α anomer** and a **β anomer.**

- The α anomer, called α-D-glucose, has the OH group on the anomeric carbon drawn down (shown in red).
- The β anomer, called β-D-glucose, has the OH group on the anomeric carbon drawn up (shown in blue).

These flat, six-membered rings used to represent the cyclic hemiacetals of glucose and other sugars are called **Haworth projections.**

Thus, D-glucose really exists in three different forms—an acyclic aldehyde and two cyclic hemiacetals—all of which are in equilibrium. Each cyclic hemiacetal can be isolated and crystallized separately, but when any one compound is placed in solution, an equilibrium mixture of all three forms results. This process is called **mutarotation.** At equilibrium, the mixture has 37% of the α anomer, 63% of the β anomer, and only a trace amount of the acyclic aldehyde. Three-dimensional models for the three forms of D-glucose are shown in Figure 20.1.

## 20.3B Haworth Projections

All aldohexoses exist primarily as cyclic hemiacetals typically drawn in Haworth projections. To convert an acyclic monosaccharide to a Haworth projection, follow the stepwise *How To* procedure.

**Figure 20.1**

The Three Forms of D-Glucose

α-D-glucose

acyclic D-glucose

β-D-glucose

α anomer
37%

aldehyde C=O
trace

β anomer
63%

Although Haworth projections represent the six-membered ring of glucose as a flat hexagon, in reality, the ring is puckered as shown in the three-dimensional models (c.f. the ball-and-stick model of cyclohexane in Section 12.5).

## How To Draw a Haworth Projection from an Acyclic Aldohexose

**Example:** Draw both anomers of D-mannose in a Haworth projection.

D-mannose

**Step [1]** Place the O atom in the upper right corner of a hexagon, and add the CH₂OH group on the first carbon to the left of the O atom.

- For naturally occurring D sugars, the CH₂OH group is drawn *up,* above the plane of the six-membered ring.

D-mannose

CH₂OH ← CH₂OH is above the plane of the six-membered ring.

**Step [2]** Place the anomeric carbon on the first carbon clockwise from the O atom.

- For an **α anomer,** the **OH** is drawn *down* in a D sugar.
- For a **β anomer,** the **OH** is drawn *up* in a D sugar.

anomeric carbon

α anomer

anomeric carbon

β anomer

—Continued

Step [3] **Add the substituents (OH and H) to the three remaining carbons (C2–C4), clockwise around the ring.**
  • The substituents on the *right* side of the carbon skeleton (shown in red) are drawn *down* in the Haworth projection.
  • The substituents on the *left* side of the carbon skeleton (shown in blue) are drawn *up* in the Haworth projection.

SAMPLE PROBLEM 20.3

Draw the α anomer of D-galactose.

D-galactose

Analysis and Solution

[1] **Draw a hexagon with an O atom in the upper right corner. Add the CH₂OH above the ring on the first carbon to the left of the O atom.**

D-galactose

[2] **Draw the anomeric carbon on the first carbon clockwise from the O atom.**
  • The α anomer has the OH group drawn down.

[3] **Add the OH groups and H atoms to the three remaining carbons (C2–C4).**
  • Groups on the *right* side in the acyclic form are drawn *down,* below the six-membered ring, and groups on the *left* side in the acyclic form are drawn *up,* above the six-membered ring.

α anomer of cyclic D-galactose

**PROBLEM 20.12**

Convert each aldohexose to the indicated anomer using a Haworth projection.

a.    CHO
H——OH
H——OH
H——OH
H——OH
      CH₂OH

α anomer

b.    CHO
HO——H
HO——H
HO——H
H——OH
      CH₂OH

β anomer

c.    CHO
HO——H
H——OH
H——OH
H——OH
      CH₂OH

α anomer

## 20.3C The Cyclic Forms of Fructose, a Ketohexose

**Certain monosaccharides—notably aldopentoses and ketohexoses—form five-membered rings, *not* six-membered rings, in solution.** The same principles apply to drawing these structures as for drawing six-membered rings, except the ring size is one atom smaller.

> • Cyclization forms two anomers at the hemiacetal carbon. For a D sugar, the OH group is drawn down in the α anomer and up in the β anomer.

For example, D-fructose forms a five-membered ring when it cyclizes to a hemiacetal because the carbonyl group is a ketone at C2, instead of an aldehyde at C1. Note that the cyclic structures of fructose contain two $CH_2OH$ groups bonded to the five-membered ring, one of which is located at the anomeric carbon.

$$
\begin{array}{c}
\overset{1}{CH_2OH} \\
\overset{2}{C}=O \\
HO-C-H \\
H-C-OH \\
H-C-OH \\
CH_2OH
\end{array}
$$

This OH group is the right distance away from the carbonyl group for cyclization to a five-membered ring.

acyclic D-fructose

│ re-draw
↓

α anomer
α-D-fructose

anomeric carbon

β anomer
β-D-fructose

> The two cyclic forms of D-fructose contain a five-membered ring.

Locate the anomeric carbon in each compound and label the compound as an α or β anomer.

a.

b.

c.

## 20.4   Reduction and Oxidation of Monosaccharides

The aldehyde carbonyl group of the acyclic form of a monosaccharide undergoes two common reactions—**reduction to an alcohol** and **oxidation to a carboxylic acid.** Even though the acyclic form may be present in only trace amounts, the equilibrium can be tipped in its favor by Le Châtelier's principle (Section 6.6). When the carbonyl group of the acyclic form reacts with a reagent, thus depleting its equilibrium concentration, the equilibrium will shift to compensate for the loss. More of the acyclic form will be produced, which can react further.

### 20.4A   Reduction of the Aldehyde Carbonyl Group

Like other aldehydes, the **carbonyl group of an aldose is reduced to a 1° alcohol** using hydrogen ($H_2$) in the presence of palladium (Pd) metal (Section 16.6). This alcohol is called an **alditol,** sometimes referred to as a "sugar alcohol." For example, reduction of D-glucose with $H_2$ and Pd yields glucitol, commonly called sorbitol.

β-D-glucose
+ α anomer

D-glucose
(D-sorbose)

This form reacts.

glucitol
(sorbitol)

The alditol contains an OH group on every C.

Sorbitol is 60% as sweet as table sugar (sucrose) and contains two-thirds the calories per gram. Sorbitol is used as a sweetening agent in a variety of sugar-free candies and gum.

### SAMPLE PROBLEM 20.4

Draw the structure of the compound formed when D-xylose is treated with $H_2$ in the presence of a Pd catalyst. The product, xylitol, is a sweetener used in sugarless chewing gum and other products.

D-xylose

### Analysis

- Locate the C=O and mentally break one bond in the double bond.
- Mentally break the H—H bond of the reagent and add one H atom to each atom of the C=O, forming new C—H and O—H bonds.

### Solution

xylose

xylitol

## PROBLEM 20.14

What compound is formed when each aldose is treated with $H_2$ in the presence of a Pd catalyst?

a.
```
    CHO
     |
H—C—OH
     |
H—C—OH
     |
H—C—OH
     |
   CH₂OH
```

b.
```
    CHO
     |
H—C—OH
     |
HO—C—H
     |
HO—C—H
     |
H—C—OH
     |
   CH₂OH
```

c.
```
    CHO
     |
H—C—OH
     |
H—C—OH
     |
   CH₂OH
```

## 20.4B  Oxidation of the Aldehyde Carbonyl Group

**The aldehyde carbonyl of an aldose is easily oxidized with a variety of reagents to form a carboxyl group,** yielding an **aldonic acid.** For example, D-glucose is oxidized with a $Cu^{2+}$ reagent called **Benedict's reagent** to form gluconic acid. In the process, a characteristic color change occurs as the blue $Cu^{2+}$ is reduced to $Cu^+$, forming brick-red $Cu_2O$.

D-glucose

gluconic acid

This reaction is an oxidation since the product carboxylic acid has one more C—O bond than the starting aldehyde. Carbohydrates that are oxidized with Benedict's reagent are called **reducing sugars,** because the $Cu^{2+}$ in Benedict's reagent is reduced to $Cu^+$ during the reaction. Those that do not react with Benedict's reagent are called **nonreducing sugars. All aldoses are reducing sugars.**

Perhaps surprisingly, **ketoses are also reducing sugars.** Although ketoses do not contain an easily oxidized aldehyde, they do contain a ketone carbonyl adjacent to a $CH_2OH$ group that undergoes rearrangement under basic reaction conditions to form an aldose, which is then oxidized with Benedict's reagent. For example, fructose rearranges to an aldose, which is then oxidized to an aldonic acid. Thus, fructose is a reducing sugar.

C=O at C1
an **aldehyde**

C=O at C2
a **ketone**    CH₂OH

```
        CH₂OH                          CHO                              COOH
        |                              |                                |
        C=O                        H—C—OH                           H—C—OH
        |                              |                                |
    HO—C—H     rearrangement     HO—C—H        2 Cu²⁺            HO—C—H              +   Cu₂O
        |      ⇌                      |          ─────→              |
    H—C—OH                        H—C—OH         OH⁻             H—C—OH
        |                              |                                |
    H—C—OH                        H—C—OH                           H—C—OH
        |                              |                                |
        CH₂OH                          CH₂OH                            CH₂OH
      fructose                        aldose                        aldonic acid
```

## SAMPLE PROBLEM 20.5

Draw the product formed when each monosaccharide is oxidized with Benedict's reagent.

a.
```
        CHO
        |
    H—C—OH
        |
   HO—C—H
        |
        CH₂OH
```
ʟ-threose

b.
```
        CH₂OH
        |
        C=O
        |
    H—C—OH
        |
        CH₂OH
```
ᴅ-erythrulose

### Analysis

To draw the oxidation product of an aldose, convert the CHO group to COOH. To oxidize a ketose, first rearrange the ketose to an aldose by moving the carbonyl group to C1 to give an aldehyde. Then convert the CHO group to COOH.

### Solution

ʟ-Threose in part (a) is an aldose, so its oxidation product can be drawn directly. ᴅ-Erythrulose in part (b) is a ketose, so it undergoes rearrangement prior to oxidation.

a.
aldehyde
```
        CHO                              COOH
        |                                |
    H—C—OH        oxidation          H—C—OH
        |         ─────→                 |
   HO—C—H                           HO—C—H
        |                                |
        CH₂OH                            CH₂OH
```
ʟ-threose

b.
```
             CH₂OH                    CHO                        COOH
             |                        |                          |
   ketone    C=O    rearrangement  H—C—OH     oxidation      H—C—OH
             |      ─────────→         |       ─────→            |
         H—C—OH                    H—C—OH                    H—C—OH
             |                        |                          |
             CH₂OH                    CH₂OH                      CH₂OH
```
ᴅ-erythrulose

## PROBLEM 20.15

What aldonic acid is formed by oxidation of each monosaccharide?

a.
```
        CHO
        |
    H—C—OH
        |
    H—C—OH
        |
    H—C—OH
        |
        CH₂OH
```

b.
```
        CHO
        |
    H—C—OH
        |
    H—C—OH
        |
        CH₂OH
```

c.
```
        CH₂OH
        |
        C=O
        |
   HO—C—H
        |
   HO—C—H
        |
    H—C—OH
        |
        CH₂OH
```

**PROBLEM 20.16**

What product is formed when D-arabinose is treated with each reagent: (a) $H_2$, Pd; (b) Benedict's reagent?

$$
\begin{array}{c}
\text{CHO} \\
| \\
\text{HO}-\text{C}-\text{H} \\
| \\
\text{H}-\text{C}-\text{OH} \\
| \\
\text{H}-\text{C}-\text{OH} \\
| \\
\text{CH}_2\text{OH}
\end{array}
$$

D-arabinose

## 20.4C　FOCUS ON HEALTH & MEDICINE
### Monitoring Glucose Levels

In order to make sure that their blood glucose levels are in the proper range, individuals with diabetes frequently measure the concentration of glucose in their blood. A common method for carrying out this procedure today involves the oxidation of glucose to gluconic acid using the enzyme glucose oxidase.

$$
\begin{array}{c}
\text{CHO} \\
| \\
\text{H}-\text{C}-\text{OH} \\
| \\
\text{HO}-\text{C}-\text{H} \\
| \\
\text{H}-\text{C}-\text{OH} \\
| \\
\text{H}-\text{C}-\text{OH} \\
| \\
\text{CH}_2\text{OH}
\end{array}
\quad + \quad O_2 \quad
\xrightarrow[\text{oxidase}]{\text{glucose}}
\quad
\begin{array}{c}
\text{COOH} \\
| \\
\text{H}-\text{C}-\text{OH} \\
| \\
\text{HO}-\text{C}-\text{H} \\
| \\
\text{H}-\text{C}-\text{OH} \\
| \\
\text{H}-\text{C}-\text{OH} \\
| \\
\text{CH}_2\text{OH}
\end{array}
\quad + \quad H_2O_2
$$

D-glucose　　　　　　　　　　　　　　gluconic acid

In the presence of glucose oxidase, oxygen ($O_2$) in the air oxidizes the aldehyde of glucose to a carboxyl group. The $O_2$, in turn, is reduced to hydrogen peroxide, $H_2O_2$. In the first generation of meters for glucose monitoring, the $H_2O_2$ produced in this reaction was allowed to react with another organic compound to produce a colored product. The intensity of the colored product was then correlated to the amount of glucose in the blood. Test strips used for measuring glucose concentration in the urine are still based on this technology.

Modern glucose meters are electronic devices that measure the amount of oxidizing agent that reacts with a known amount of blood (Figure 20.2). This value is correlated with blood glucose concentration and the result is displayed digitally. A high blood glucose level may mean that an individual needs more insulin, while a low level may mean that it is time to ingest some calories.

**Figure 20.2**

Monitoring Blood Glucose Levels

glucose meter

test strip

small pin prick for a blood sample

A small drop of blood is placed on a disposable test strip that is inserted in an electronic blood glucose meter, and the glucose concentration is read on a digital display.

## 20.5  Disaccharides

**Disaccharides are carbohydrates composed of two monosaccharides.** Disaccharides are acetals, compounds that contain two alkoxy groups (OR groups) bonded to the same carbon. Recall from Section 16.8 that reaction of a hemiacetal with an alcohol forms an **acetal.**

In a similar fashion, a disaccharide results when a hemiacetal of one monosaccharide reacts with a hydroxyl group of a second monosaccharide to form an acetal. The new C—O bond that joins the two rings together is called a **glycosidic linkage.**

general structure
of a disaccharide

[The acetal O's are labeled in red.]

The two monosaccharide rings may be five-membered or six-membered. All disaccharides contain at least one acetal that joins the rings together. Each ring is numbered beginning at the anomeric carbon, the carbon in each ring bonded to two oxygen atoms.

The glycosidic linkage that joins the two monosaccharides in a disaccharide can be oriented in two different ways, shown with Haworth projections in structures **A** and **B.**

Maltose gets its name from malt, the liquid obtained from barley used in the brewing of beer.

α glycoside

The glycoside bond is **down.**

1→4-α-glycosidic linkage

**A**

β glycoside

The glycoside bond is **up.**

1→4-β-glycosidic linkage

**B**

- An α glycoside has the glycosidic linkage oriented down, below the plane of the ring that contains the acetal joining the monosaccharides.
- A β glycoside has the glycosidic linkage oriented up, above the plane of the ring that contains the acetal joining the monosaccharides.

Numbers are used to designate which ring atoms are joined in the disaccharide. Disaccharide **A** has a **1→4-α-glycosidic linkage** since the glycoside bond is oriented down and joins C1 of one ring to C4 of the other. Disaccharide **B** has a **1→4-β-glycosidic linkage** since the glycoside bond is oriented up and joins C1 of one ring to C4 of the other.

Sample Problem 20.6 illustrates these structural features in the disaccharide **maltose.** Maltose, which is formed by the hydrolysis of starch, is found in grains such as barley. Maltose is formed from two molecules of glucose.

glycosidic linkage

maltose

## SAMPLE PROBLEM 20.6

(a) Locate the glycosidic linkage in maltose. (b) Number the carbon atoms in both rings. (c) Classify the glycosidic linkage as α or β, and use numbers to designate its location.

maltose

### Analysis and Solution

a. and b. The glycosidic linkage is the acetal C—O bond that joins the two monosaccharides, labeled in red. Each ring is numbered beginning at the anomeric carbon, the carbon bonded to two oxygen atoms.

c. Maltose has an α glycosidic linkage since the C—O bond is drawn down. The glycosidic linkage joins C1 of one ring to C4 of the other ring, so maltose contains a 1→4-α-glycosidic linkage.

## PROBLEM 20.17

(a) Locate the glycosidic linkage in cellobiose. (b) Number the carbon atoms in both rings. (c) Classify the glycosidic linkage as α or β, and use numbers to designate its location.

cellobiose

**The hydrolysis of a disaccharide cleaves the C—O glycosidic linkage and forms two monosaccharides.** For example, hydrolysis of maltose yields two molecules of glucose.

Water is added in hydrolysis.

## SAMPLE PROBLEM 20.7

Draw the products formed when the following disaccharide is hydrolyzed with water.

### Analysis

Locate the glycosidic linkage, the acetal C—O bond that joins the two monosaccharides. Cleave the C—O bond by adding the elements of $H_2O$ across the bond.

### Solution

Two monosaccharides are formed by cleaving the glycosidic linkage.

## PROBLEM 20.18

What monosaccharides are formed when cellobiose (Problem 20.17) is hydrolyzed with water?

## 20.5A FOCUS ON HEALTH & MEDICINE
### Lactose Intolerance

**Lactose** is the principal disaccharide found in milk from both humans and cows. Unlike many mono- and disaccharides, lactose is not appreciably sweet. Lactose consists of one galactose ring and one glucose ring, joined by a 1→4-β-glycoside bond from the anomeric carbon of galactose to C4 of glucose.

Individuals who are lactose intolerant can drink lactose-free milk. Tablets that contain the lactase enzyme can also be taken when ice cream or other milk products are ingested.

Lactose is digested in the body by first cleaving the 1→4-β-glycoside bond using the enzyme *lactase*. **Individuals who are lactose intolerant no longer produce this enzyme,** and so lactose cannot be properly digested, causing abdominal cramps and diarrhea. Lactose intolerance is especially prevalent in Asian and African populations whose diets have not traditionally included milk beyond infancy.

### PROBLEM 20.19

Lactose contains both an acetal and a hemiacetal. Label both functional groups. What products are formed when lactose is hydrolyzed with water?

## 20.5B FOCUS ON HEALTH & MEDICINE
### Sucrose and Artificial Sweeteners

**Sucrose,** the disaccharide found in sugarcane and the compound generally referred to as "sugar," is the most common disaccharide in nature. It contains one glucose ring and one fructose ring. Unlike maltose and lactose, which contain only six-membered rings, sucrose contains one six-membered and one five-membered ring.

sugarcane

two varieties of refined sugar

sucrose

Sucrose's pleasant sweetness has made it a widely used ingredient in baked goods, cereals, bread, and many other products. It is estimated that the average American ingests 100 lb of sucrose annually. Like other carbohydrates, however, sucrose contains many calories. To reduce caloric intake while maintaining sweetness, a variety of artificial sweeteners have been developed. These include aspartame, saccharin, and sucralose (Figure 20.3). These compounds are much sweeter than sucrose, so only a small amount of each compound is needed to achieve the same level of perceived sweetness.

A relative sweetness scale ranks the sweetness of carbohydrates and synthetic sweeteners, as shown in Table 20.1.

Aspartame (trade name: Nutrasweet) is used in the artificial sweetener Equal and many diet beverages. While harmless to most individuals, aspartame is hydrolyzed in the body to the amino acid phenylalanine (and other products). Infants afflicted with phenylketonuria cannot metabolize this amino acid, so it accumulates, causing mental retardation. When this condition is identified early, a diet limiting the consumption of phenylalanine (and compounds like aspartame that are converted to it) can make a normal life possible.

**Table 20.1** Relative Sweetness of Some Carbohydrates and Artificial Sweeteners

| Compound | Relative Sweetness |
|---|---|
| Sorbitol | 0.60 |
| Glucose | 0.75 |
| Sucrose | 1.00 |
| Fructose | 1.75 |
| Aspartame | 150 |
| Saccharin | 350 |
| Sucralose | 600 |

## Figure 20.3

Artificial Sweeteners

sucralose
(Trade name: Splenda)

aspartame
(Trade name: Equal)

saccharin
(Trade name: Sweet'n Low)

The sweetness of these artificial sweeteners was discovered accidentally. The sweetness of sucralose was discovered in 1976 when a chemist misunderstood his superior, and so he *tasted* rather than *tested* his compound. Aspartame was discovered in 1965 when a chemist licked his dirty fingers in the lab and tasted its sweetness. Saccharin, the oldest known artificial sweetener, was discovered in 1879 by a chemist who failed to wash his hands after working in the lab. Saccharin was not used extensively until sugar shortages occurred during World War I. Although there were concerns in the 1970s that saccharin causes cancer, there is no proven link between cancer occurrence and saccharin intake at normal levels.

### CONSUMER NOTE

Rebaudioside A, a naturally occurring glycoside about 400 times sweeter than table sugar, is obtained from the leaves of the stevia plant, a shrub native to Central and South America. Rebaudioside A is sold as a natural, low-calorie sweetener under the trade name Truvia.

### PROBLEM 20.20

Rebaudioside A is a sweet glycoside obtained from the stevia plant. Locate the three acetals in rebaudioside A.

rebaudioside A
Trade name: Truvia
$R = C_{26}H_{39}O_6$

PROBLEM 20.21
Sucralose is prepared from sucrose. Locate the acetals in sucralose. Label each alkyl halide as 1°, 2°, or 3°.

## 20.6 Polysaccharides

**Polysaccharides contain three or more monosaccharides joined together.** Three prevalent polysaccharides in nature are **cellulose, starch,** and **glycogen,** each of which consists of repeating glucose units joined by glycosidic bonds.

β glycosidic linkage

**cellulose—repeating structure**

α glycosidic linkage

**starch and glycogen—repeating structure**

- Cellulose contains glucose rings joined in 1→4-β-glycosidic linkages.
- Starch and glycogen contain glucose rings joined in 1→4-α-glycosidic linkages.

### 20.6A Cellulose

**Cellulose** is found in the cell walls of nearly all plants, where it gives support and rigidity to wood, plant stems, and grass (Figure 20.4). Wood, cotton, and flax are composed largely of cellulose.

**Figure 20.4**

Cellulose

layers of microfibrils in the plant cell wall

cell wall

cellulose fiber

plant cell

cellulose molecules

glucose

long chains of cellulose molecules hydrogen bonded together

**Cellulose is an unbranched polymer composed of repeating glucose units joined in a 1→4-β-glycosidic linkage.** The β glycosidic linkages create long linear chains of cellulose molecules that stack in sheets, making an extensive three-dimensional array.

β glycosidic linkage
(shown in blue)

cellulose

In some cells, cellulose is hydrolyzed by an enzyme called a **β-glycosidase,** which cleaves all of the β glycoside bonds, forming glucose. **Humans do not possess this enzyme, and therefore *cannot* digest cellulose.** Ruminant animals, on the other hand, such as cattle, deer, and camels, have bacteria containing this enzyme in their digestive systems, so they can derive nutritional benefit from eating grass and leaves.

Much of the insoluble fiber in our diet is cellulose, which passes through the digestive system without being metabolized. Foods rich in cellulose include whole wheat bread, brown rice, and bran cereals. Fiber is an important component of the diet even though it gives us no nutrition; fiber adds bulk to solid waste, so that it is eliminated more readily.

## 20.6B　Starch

**Starch** is the main carbohydrate found in the seeds and roots of plants. Corn, rice, wheat, and potatoes are common foods that contain a great deal of starch. **Starch is a polymer composed of repeating glucose units joined in α glycosidic linkages.** The two common forms of starch are **amylose** and **amylopectin.**

α glycosidic linkage
(shown in red)

**amylose**
(the linear form of starch)

Two polysaccharide chains are connected at a branch point along one chain.

α glycosidic linkage
(shown in red)

**amylopectin**
(the branched form of starch)

Figure 20.5    Starch—Amylose and Amylopectin

wheat kernels

wheat stalks

amylopectin

amylose

**Amylose,** which comprises about 20% of starch molecules, has an unbranched skeleton of glucose molecules with **1→4-α-glycoside bonds.** Because of this linkage, an amylose chain adopts a helical arrangement, giving it a very different three-dimensional shape from the linear chains of cellulose (Figure 20.5).

**Amylopectin,** which comprises about 80% of starch molecules, consists of a backbone of glucose units joined in **α glycosidic bonds,** but it also contains considerable branching along the chain. The linear linkages of amylopectin are formed by **1→4-α-glycoside bonds,** similar to amylose.

Both forms of starch are water soluble. Since the OH groups in these starch molecules are not buried in a three-dimensional network, they are available for hydrogen bonding with water molecules, leading to greater water solubility than cellulose.

Both amylose and amylopectin are hydrolyzed to glucose with cleavage of the glycosidic bonds. The human digestive system has the necessary amylase enzymes needed to catalyze this process. Bread and pasta made from wheat flour, rice, and corn tortillas are all sources of starch that are readily digested.

### PROBLEM 20.22

Label all acetal carbons in the structure of amylopectin drawn at the beginning of Section 20.6B.

## 20.6C    Glycogen

**Glycogen is the major form in which polysaccharides are stored in animals.** Glycogen, a polymer of glucose containing **α glycosidic bonds,** has a branched structure similar to amylopectin, but the branching is much more extensive (Figure 20.6).

Figure 20.6   Glycogen

branching

glycogen in liver cells

glycogen

Glycogen is stored principally in the liver and muscle. When glucose is needed for energy in the cell, glucose units are hydrolyzed from the ends of the glycogen polymer, and then further metabolized with the release of energy. Because glycogen has a highly branched structure, there are many glucose units at the ends of the branches that can be cleaved whenever the body needs them.

**PROBLEM 20.23**

Cellulose is water *in*soluble, despite its many OH groups. Based on its three-dimensional structure, why do you think this is so?

## 20.7   FOCUS ON THE HUMAN BODY
### Useful Carbohydrate Derivatives

Many other simple and complex carbohydrates with useful properties exist in the biological world. Several are derived from monosaccharides that contain an amino ($NH_2$) or amide ($NHCOCH_3$) group in place of an OH group. Examples include D-glucosamine, the most abundant amino sugar in nature, and *N*-acetyl-D-glucosamine (NAG). Other carbohydrates are derived from D-glucuronate, which contains a carboxylate anion, $COO^-$, in place of the $CH_2OH$ group of the typical monosaccharide skeleton.

D-glucosamine        *N*-acetyl-D-glucosamine        D-glucuronate

### 20.7A   Glycosaminoglycans

**Glycosaminoglycans (GAGs)** are a group of unbranched carbohydrates derived from alternating amino sugar and glucuronate units. Glycosaminoglycans form a gel-like matrix that acts as a lubricant, making them key components in connective tissue and joints.

Injections of heparin in an intravenous line keep the line from clogging with blood.

Both chondroitin and glucosamine are sold as dietary supplements for individuals suffering from osteoarthritis. On-going research is examining the role of these supplements in replacing and rebuilding lost joint cartilage in the hope of halting or reversing the progression of arthritis.

Figure 20.7   Glycosaminoglycans

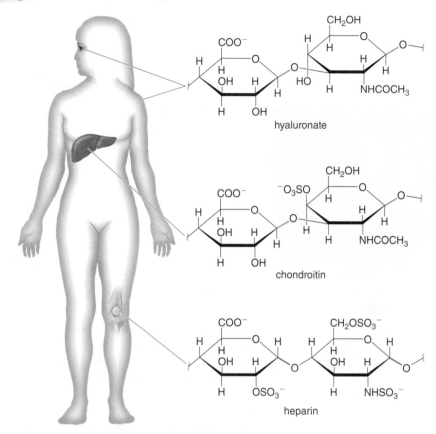

Hyaluronates form viscous solutions that act as lubricants in the fluid around joints. They also give the vitreous humor of the eye its gelatin-like consistency. Chondroitin strengthens cartilage, tendons, and the walls of blood vessels. Heparin is an anticoagulant.

Examples include **hyaluronate,** which is found in the extracellular fluid that lubricates joints and the vitreous humor of the eye; **chondroitin,** a component of cartilage and tendons; and **heparin,** which is stored in the mast cells of the liver and other organs and prevents blood clotting (Figure 20.7). While the monosaccharide rings of hyaluronate and chondroitin are joined by β glycosidic linkages (shown in blue), those of heparin are joined by α glycosidic linkages (shown in red).

### PROBLEM 20.24

Classify the glycosidic linkages in chondroitin and heparin (Figure 20.7) as α or β, and use numbers to designate their location.

## 20.7B   Chitin

**Chitin,** the second most abundant carbohydrate polymer, is a polysaccharide formed from $N$-acetyl-D-glucosamine units joined together in **1→4-β-glycosidic linkages.** Chitin is identical in structure to cellulose, except that each OH group at C2 is now replaced by $NHCOCH_3$. The exoskeletons of lobsters, crabs, and shrimp are composed of chitin. Like cellulose, chitin chains are held together by an extensive network of hydrogen bonds, forming water-insoluble sheets.

The rigidity of a crab shell is due to chitin, a high molecular weight carbohydrate molecule. Much of the D-glucosamine sold in over-the-counter dietary supplements comes from shellfish.

β glycosidic linkage (shown in blue)

chitin

hydrolysis

D-glucosamine

Chitin-based coatings have found several commercial applications, such as extending the shelf life of fruits. Processing plants now convert the shells of crabs, lobsters, and shrimp to chitin and various derivatives for use in many consumer products. Complete hydrolysis of the glycoside and amide bonds in chitin forms the dietary supplement D-glucosamine.

### PROBLEM 20.25

Suppose that chitin contained α glycosidic linkages. Draw a portion of the resulting polysaccharide that contains four N-acetyl-D-glucosamine units joined together.

## 20.8  FOCUS ON THE HUMAN BODY
### Blood Type

Human blood is classified into one of four types using the ABO system proposed in the early 1900s by Karl Landsteiner. There are four blood types—A, B, AB, and O. An individual's blood type is determined by three or four monosaccharides attached to a membrane protein of red blood cells. These monosaccharides include:

D-galactose                L-fucose                N-acetyl-D-glucosamine                N-acetyl-D-galactosamine

Each blood type is associated with a different carbohydrate structure, as shown in Figure 20.8. Three monosaccharides occur in all blood types—N-acetyl-D-glucosamine, D-galactose, and L-fucose. Type A blood contains a fourth monosaccharide, N-acetyl-D-galactosamine, and type B blood contains an additional D-galactose unit. Type AB blood has both type A and type B carbohydrates.

The short polysaccharide chains distinguish one type of red blood cell from another, and signal the cells about foreign viruses, bacteria, and other agents. When a foreign substance enters the blood, the body's immune system uses antibodies to attack and destroy the invading substance so that it does the host organism no harm.

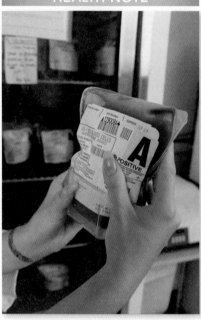

The blood type of a blood donor and recipient must be compatible, so donated blood is clearly labeled with the donor's blood type.

Figure 20.8    Carbohydrates and Blood Types

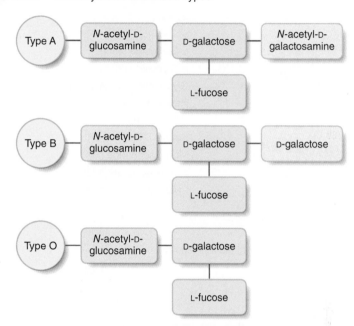

Each blood type is characterized by a different polysaccharide that is covalently bonded to a membrane protein of the red blood cell. There are three different carbohydrate sequences, one each for A, B, and O blood types. Blood type AB contains the sequences for both blood type A and blood type B.

Knowing an individual's blood type is necessary before receiving a blood transfusion. Because the blood of an individual may contain antibodies to another blood type, the types of blood that can be given to a patient are often limited. An individual with blood type A produces antibodies to type B blood, and an individual with blood type B produces antibodies to type A blood. Type AB blood contains no antibodies to other blood types, while type O blood contains antibodies to both types A and B. As a result:

- Individuals with type O blood are called *universal donors* because no antibodies to type O are produced by those with types A, B, and AB blood. Type O blood can be given to individuals of any blood type.
- Individuals with type AB blood are called *universal recipients* because their blood contains no antibodies to blood types A, B, or O. Individuals with type AB blood can receive blood of any type.

Table 20.2 lists what blood types can be safely given to an individual. Blood must be carefully screened to make sure that the blood types of the donor and recipient are compatible. Should the wrong blood type be administered, antibodies of the immune system will attack the foreign red blood cells, causing them to clump together, which can block blood vessels and even result in death.

Table 20.2 Compatibility Chart of Blood Types

| Blood Type | Can Receive Blood Type: | Can Donate to Blood Type: |
|---|---|---|
| A | A, O | A, AB |
| B | B, O | B, AB |
| AB | A, B, AB, O | AB |
| O | O | A, B, AB, O |

PROBLEM 20.26

How do *N*-acetyl-D-glucosamine and *N*-acetyl-D-galactosamine differ in structure? Are these two compounds constitutional isomers or stereoisomers? Explain your choice.

# CHAPTER HIGHLIGHTS

## KEY TERMS

Alditol (20.4)

Aldonic acid (20.4)

Aldose (20.2)

α Anomer (20.3)

β Anomer (20.3)

Anomeric carbon (20.3)

Benedict's reagent (20.4)

Carbohydrate (20.1)

Disaccharide (20.1)

α Glycoside (20.5)

β Glycoside (20.5)

Glycosidic linkage (20.5)

Haworth projection (20.3)

Hexose (20.2)

Ketose (20.2)

Monosaccharide (20.1)

D Monosaccharide (20.2)

L Monosaccharide (20.2)

Mutarotation (20.3)

Nonreducing sugar (20.4)

Pentose (20.2)

Polysaccharide (20.1)

Reducing sugar (20.4)

Tetrose (20.2)

Triose (20.2)

## KEY REACTIONS

[1]   Reduction of monosaccharides to alditols (20.4A)

[2]   Oxidation of monosaccharides to aldonic acids (20.4B)

[3]   Hydrolysis of disaccharides (20.5)

## KEY CONCEPTS

❶ **What are the three major types of carbohydrates? (20.1)**

- Monosaccharides, which cannot be hydrolyzed to simpler compounds, generally have three to six carbons with a carbonyl group at either the terminal carbon or the carbon adjacent to it. Generally, all other carbons have OH groups bonded to them.
- Disaccharides are composed of two monosaccharides.
- Polysaccharides are composed of three or more monosaccharides.

❷ **What are the major structural features of monosaccharides? (20.2)**

- Monosaccharides with a carbonyl group at C1 are called aldoses and those with a carbonyl at C2 are called ketoses. Generally, OH groups are bonded to every other carbon. The terms triose, tetrose, and so forth are used to indicate the number of carbons in the chain.

- The acyclic form of monosaccharides is drawn with Fischer projection formulas. A D sugar has the OH group of the chirality center farthest from the carbonyl on the right side. An L sugar has the OH group of the chirality center farthest from the carbonyl on the left side.

**③ How are the cyclic forms of monosaccharides drawn? (20.3)**
- In aldohexoses the OH group on C5 reacts with the aldehyde carbonyl to give two cyclic hemiacetals called anomers. The acetal carbon is called the anomeric carbon. The $\alpha$ anomer has the OH group drawn down for a D sugar and the $\beta$ anomer has the OH group drawn up.

$\alpha$ anomer     $\beta$ anomer

**④ What reduction and oxidation products are formed from monosaccharides? (20.4)**
- Monosaccharides are reduced to alditols with $H_2$ and Pd.
- Monosaccharides are oxidized to aldonic acids with Benedict's reagent. Sugars that are oxidized with Benedict's reagent are called reducing sugars.

**⑤ What are the major structural features of disaccharides? (20.5)**
- Disaccharides contain two monosaccharides joined by an acetal C—O bond called a glycosidic linkage. An $\alpha$ glycoside has the glycosidic linkage oriented down and a $\beta$ glycoside has the glycosidic linkage oriented up.
- Disaccharides are hydrolyzed to two monosaccharides by the cleavage of the glycosidic C—O bond.
- Lactose (the principal disaccharide in milk) and sucrose (table sugar) are common disaccharides.

**⑥ What are the differences in the polysaccharides cellulose, starch, and glycogen? (20.6)**
- Cellulose, starch, and glycogen are all polymers of the monosaccharide glucose.
- Cellulose is an unbranched polymer composed of repeating glucose units joined in 1→4-$\beta$-glycosidic linkages. Cellulose forms long chains that stack in three-dimensional sheets. The human digestive system does not contain the needed enzyme to metabolize cellulose.
- There are two forms of starch—amylose, which is an unbranched polymer, and amylopectin, which is a branched polysaccharide polymer. Both forms contain 1→4-$\alpha$-glycosidic linkages, and the polymer winds in a helical arrangement. Starch is digestible since the human digestive system has the needed amylase enzyme to catalyze hydrolysis.
- Glycogen resembles amylopectin but is more extensively branched. Glycogen is the major form in which polysaccharides are stored in animals.

**⑦ Give examples of some carbohydrate derivatives that contain amino groups, amides, or carboxylate anions. (20.7)**
- Glycosaminoglycans are a group of unbranched carbohydrates derived from amino sugar and glucuronate units. Examples include hyaluronate, which forms a gel-like matrix in joints and the vitreous humor of the eye; chondroitin, which is a component of cartilage and tendons; and heparin, an anticoagulant.
- Chitin, a polymer of *N*-acetyl-D-glucosamine, forms the hard exoskeletons of crabs, lobsters, and shrimp.

**⑧ What role do carbohydrates play in determining blood type? (20.8)**
- Human blood type—A, B, AB, or O—is determined by three or four monosaccharides attached to a membrane protein on the surface of red blood cells. There are three different carbohydrate sequences, one for each of the A, B, and O blood types. Blood type AB contains the sequences for both blood type A and blood type B. Since the blood of an individual may contain antibodies to another blood type, blood type must be known before receiving a transfusion.

## PROBLEMS

Selected in-chapter and odd-numbered end-of-chapter problems have brief answers in Appendix B. The *Student Study Guide and Solutions Manual* contains detailed solutions to all in-chapter and odd-numbered end-of-chapter problems, as well as additional worked examples and a chapter self-test.

### Monosaccharides

**20.27** What is the difference between an aldose and a ketose? Give an example of each type of carbohydrate.

**20.28** What is the difference between a tetrose and a pentose? Give an example of each type of carbohydrate.

**20.29** Draw the structure of each type of carbohydrate.
 a. an L-aldopentose     c. a five-carbon alditol
 b. a D-aldotetrose

**20.30** Draw the structure of each type of carbohydrate.
 a. a D-aldotriose     c. a four-carbon aldonic acid
 b. an L-ketohexose

**20.31** Are $\alpha$-D-glucose and $\beta$-D-glucose enantiomers? Explain your choice.

**20.32** Are D-fructose and L-fructose enantiomers? Explain your choice.

**20.33** Classify each monosaccharide by the type of carbonyl group and the number of carbons in the chain.

a.
```
      CHO
      |
HO—C—H
      |
HO—C—H
      |
    CH2OH
```

b.
```
      CHO
      |
HO—C—H
      |
HO—C—H
      |
HO—C—H
      |
  H—C—OH
      |
    CH2OH
```

c.
```
    CH2OH
      |
      C=O
      |
  H—C—OH
      |
HO—C—H
      |
    CH2OH
```

**20.34** Classify each monosaccharide by the type of carbonyl group and the number of carbons in the chain.

a.
```
      CHO
       |
HO —  C — H
       |
      CH₂OH
```

b.
```
      CHO
       |
 H —  C — OH
       |
HO —  C — H
       |
HO —  C — H
       |
      CH₂OH
```

c.
```
      CHO
       |
 H —  C — OH
       |
 H —  C — OH
       |
HO —  C — H
       |
HO —  C — H
       |
      CH₂OH
```

**20.35** (a) Draw a Fischer projection of the monosaccharide depicted in the ball-and-stick model and label it as a D or L sugar.
(b) Classify the monosaccharide by the type of carbonyl group and number of carbons it contains.

**20.36** (a) Draw a Fischer projection of the monosaccharide depicted in the ball-and-stick model and label it as a D or L sugar.
(b) Classify the monosaccharide by the type of carbonyl group and number of carbons it contains.

**20.37** For each compound in Problem 20.33: [1] label all the chirality centers; [2] classify the compound as a D or L monosaccharide; [3] draw the enantiomer; [4] draw a Fischer projection.

**20.38** For each compound in Problem 20.34: [1] label all the chirality centers; [2] classify the compound as a D or L monosaccharide; [3] draw the enantiomer; [4] draw a Fischer projection.

**20.39** Consider monosaccharides **A, B,** and **C.**

```
      CHO                CHO              CH₂OH
       |                  |                |
 H —  C — OH        H —  C — OH        C = O
       |                  |                |
 H —  C — OH       HO —  C — H        H — C — OH
       |                  |                |
      CH₂OH              CH₂OH            CH₂OH

       A                  B                C
```

a. Which two monosaccharides are stereoisomers?
b. Identify two compounds that are constitutional isomers.
c. Draw the enantiomer of **B.**
d. Draw a Fischer projection for **A.**

**20.40** Consider monosaccharides **D, E,** and **F.**

```
      CHO               CH₂OH             CHO
       |                  |                |
 H —  C — OH        C = O            HO — C — H
       |                  |                |
 H —  C — OH       HO —  C — H       HO — C — H
       |                  |                |
 H —  C — OH       HO —  C — H        H — C — OH
       |                  |                |
      CH₂OH              CH₂OH            CH₂OH

       D                  E                F
```

a. Which two monosaccharides are stereoisomers?
b. Identify two compounds that are constitutional isomers.
c. Draw the enantiomer of **F.**
d. Draw a Fischer projection for **D.**

**20.41** Using Haworth projections, draw the α and β anomers of the following D monosaccharide.

```
      CHO
       |
HO —  C — H
       |
 H —  C — OH
       |
HO —  C — H
       |
 H —  C — OH
       |
      CH₂OH
```

**20.42** Using Haworth projections, draw the α and β anomers of the following D monosaccharide.

```
      CHO
       |
 H —  C — OH
       |
 H —  C — OH
       |
HO —  C — H
       |
 H —  C — OH
       |
      CH₂OH
```

**20.43** (a) Label the hemiacetal carbon in the given monosaccharide, and identify the hydroxyl group on the anomeric carbon.
(b) Label all other OH groups as 1°, 2°, or 3°.

**20.44** (a) Label the hemiacetal carbon in the given monosaccharide, and identify the hydroxyl group on the anomeric carbon.
(b) Label all other OH groups as 1°, 2°, or 3°.

**20.45** Consider the following cyclic monosaccharide.

a. Label the hemiacetal carbon.
b. Label the monosaccharide as an α or β anomer.
c. Draw the other anomer.
d. Draw a stereoisomer that differs in the arrangement of substituents at C2.

**20.46** Consider the following cyclic monosaccharide.

a. Label the hemiacetal carbon.
b. Label the monosaccharide as an α or β anomer.
c. Draw the other anomer.
d. Draw a stereoisomer that differs in the arrangement of substituents at C3.

**20.47** For each monosaccharide: [1] label all acetal and hemiacetal carbons; [2] label the anomeric carbon; [3] designate the compound as an α or β anomer.

**20.48** For each monosaccharide: [1] label all acetal and hemiacetal carbons; [2] label the anomeric carbon; [3] designate the compound as an α or β anomer.

**20.49** Why are no D, L labels used for a ketotriose?

**20.50** Explain how the labels D and L are assigned in a monosaccharide with three chirality centers.

**20.51** Aldopentoses exist as five-membered rings in their cyclic forms. For each aldopentose: [1] label the hemiacetal carbon; [2] designate the monosaccharide as an α or β anomer.

**20.52** Aldopentoses exist as five-membered rings in their cyclic forms. For each aldopentose: [1] label the hemiacetal carbon; [2] designate the monosaccharide as an α or β anomer.

## Reactions of Carbohydrates

**20.53** Draw the structures of an alditol and an aldonic acid that contain four carbons.

**20.54** Draw the structures of an alditol and an aldonic acid that contain six carbons.

**20.55** Draw the organic products formed when each monosaccharide is treated with each of the following reagents: [1] $H_2$, Pd; [2] $Cu^{2+}$, $OH^-$.

a.
```
   CHO
HO—C—H
 H—C—OH
   CH₂OH
```

b.
```
    CHO
 H—C—OH
HO—C—H
HO—C—H
   CH₂OH
```

c.
```
    CHO
 H—C—OH
 H—C—OH
HO—C—H
HO—C—H
   CH₂OH
```

**20.56** Draw the organic products formed when each monosaccharide is treated with each of the following reagents: [1] $H_2$, Pd; [2] $Cu^{2+}$, $OH^-$.

a.
```
    CHO
HO—C—H
HO—C—H
   CH₂OH
```

b.
```
    CHO
HO—C—H
 H—C—OH
 H—C—OH
   CH₂OH
```

c.
```
    CHO
 H—C—OH
 H—C—OH
 H—C—OH
 H—C—OH
   CH₂OH
```

**20.57** What product is formed when each compound is treated with Benedict's reagent?

a.
```
    CHO
 H—C—OH
 H—C—OH
HO—C—H
   CH₂OH
```

b.
```
   CH₂OH
   C=O
 H—C—OH
 H—C—OH
   CH₂OH
```

**20.58** What product is formed when each compound is treated with Benedict's reagent?

a.
```
    CHO
HO—C—H
HO—C—H
 H—C—OH
   CH₂OH
```

b.
```
   CH₂OH
   C=O
 H—C—OH
HO—C—H
   CH₂OH
```

**20.59** What does the term *reducing sugar* mean? Give an example.

**20.60** What does the term *mutarotation* mean?

**20.61** What monosaccharides are formed when each disaccharide is hydrolyzed?

a.

b.

**20.62** What monosaccharides are formed when each disaccharide is hydrolyzed?

a.

b.

## Disaccharides and Polysaccharides

**20.63** What is the difference between an α anomer and an α glycoside?

**20.64** What is the difference between a β anomer and a β glycoside?

**20.65** Draw the structure of a disaccharide that contains two six-membered rings and an α glycosidic linkage.

**20.66** Draw the structure of a disaccharide that contains one six-membered ring and one five-membered ring as well as a β glycosidic linkage.

**20.67** Consider the disaccharide isomaltose.

isomaltose

a. Label any acetal and hemiacetal in isomaltose.
b. Number each monosaccharide ring.
c. Classify the glycosidic linkage as α or β, and use numbers to designate its location.
d. Is the hemiacetal drawn as an α or β anomer?
e. What monosaccharides are formed when isomaltose is hydrolyzed?

**20.68** Consider the disaccharide sophorose.

sophorose

a. Label any acetal and hemiacetal in sophorose.
b. Number each monosaccharide ring.
c. Classify the glycosidic linkage as α or β, and use numbers to designate its location.
d. Is the hemiacetal drawn as an α or β anomer?
e. What monosaccharides are formed when sophorose is hydrolyzed?

**20.69** Draw the structure of a disaccharide formed from two galactose units joined by a 1→4-β-glycosidic linkage. (The cyclic structure of galactose appears in Sample Problem 20.3.)

**20.70** Draw the structure of a disaccharide formed from two mannose units joined by a 1→4-α-glycosidic linkage. (The cyclic structure of mannose appears in Section 20.3B.)

**20.71** In what ways are cellulose and amylose similar? How do the structures of cellulose and amylose differ?

**20.72** In what ways are amylopectin and glycogen similar? How do the structures of amylopectin and glycogen differ?

**20.73** Draw a short segment of a polysaccharide that contains three galactose units joined together in 1→4-α-glycosidic linkages. (The cyclic structure of galactose appears in Sample Problem 20.3.)

**20.74** Draw a short segment of a polysaccharide that contains three mannose units joined together in 1→4-β-glycosidic linkages. (The cyclic structure of mannose appears in Section 20.3B.)

## General Questions

**20.75** Consider the following monosaccharide.

$$
\begin{array}{c}
\text{CHO} \\
\text{HO–C–H} \\
\text{HO–C–H} \\
\text{HO–C–H} \\
\text{H–C–OH} \\
\text{CH}_2\text{OH}
\end{array}
$$

a. Is the monosaccharide a D or L sugar?
b. Classify the monosaccharide by the type of carbonyl and the number of atoms in the chain.
c. Draw the enantiomer.
d. Label the chirality centers.
e. Draw the α anomer of the cyclic form.
f. What product is formed when the monosaccharide is treated with Benedict's reagent?
g. What product is formed when the monosaccharide is treated with $H_2$ and Pd?
h. Label the monosaccharide as a reducing or nonreducing sugar.

**20.76** Consider the following monosaccharide.

$$
\begin{array}{c}
\text{CHO} \\
\text{HO–C–H} \\
\text{HO–C–H} \\
\text{H–C–OH} \\
\text{H–C–OH} \\
\text{CH}_2\text{OH}
\end{array}
$$

a. Is the monosaccharide a D or L sugar?
b. Classify the monosaccharide by the type of carbonyl and the number of atoms in the chain.
c. Draw the enantiomer.
d. Label the chirality centers.
e. Draw the β anomer of the cyclic form.
f. What product is formed when the monosaccharide is treated with Benedict's reagent?
g. What product is formed when the monosaccharide is treated with $H_2$ and Pd?
h. Label the monosaccharide as a reducing or nonreducing sugar.

## Applications

**20.77** Describe the difference between lactose intolerance and galactosemia.

**20.78** Explain why cellulose is a necessary component of our diet even though we don't digest it.

**20.79** Explain why fructose is called a reduced calorie sweetener while sucralose is called an artificial sweetener.

**20.80** How do oxidation reactions help an individual with diabetes monitor blood glucose levels?

**20.81** Why can an individual with type A blood receive only blood types A and O, but he or she can donate to individuals with either type A or AB blood?

**20.82** Why can an individual with type B blood receive only blood types B and O, but he or she can donate to individuals with either type B or AB blood?

**20.83** Would you predict chitin to be digestible by humans? Explain why or why not.

**20.84** Why can horses derive nutritional value from eating grass but humans cannot?

**20.85** Name three glycosaminoglycans and their roles in the body.

**20.86** Why is chitin water insoluble but the N-acetyl-D-glucosamine from which it is made water soluble?

# CHALLENGE PROBLEMS

**20.87** In much the same way that aldoses are reduced with $H_2$ and Pd, 2-ketohexoses are also reduced. One difference occurs, however, in that two products are formed on reduction of 2-ketohexoses. Draw the two products formed when fructose (Section 20.2C) is reduced, and label the products as stereoisomers, constitutional isomers, or anomers. Explain your choice.

**20.88** Convert each cyclic form to an acyclic monosaccharide.

a.

b.

# 21

# Amino Acids, Proteins, and Enzymes

Whales have a high concentration of the protein myoglobin in their muscles. Myoglobin binds oxygen, so it serves as an oxygen reservoir while the whale is submerged for long periods of time.

## CHAPTER GOALS

*In this chapter you will learn how to:*

1 Identify the general structural features of amino acids

2 Describe the acid–base properties of amino acids

3 Draw simple peptides from individual amino acids, and label the N- and C-terminal amino acids

4 Give examples of simple biologically active peptides

5 Describe the characteristics of the primary, secondary, tertiary, and quaternary structure of proteins

6 Describe the features of fibrous proteins like α-keratin and collagen

7 Describe the features of globular proteins like hemoglobin and myoglobin

8 Draw the products of protein hydrolysis

9 Describe protein denaturation

10 Describe the main features of enzymes

11 Describe the use of enzymes to diagnose and treat disease

Meat, fish, beans, and nuts are all high-protein foods.

Of the four major groups of biomolecules—lipids, carbohydrates, proteins, and nucleic acids—proteins have the widest array of functions. **Keratin** and **collagen,** for example, form long insoluble fibers, giving strength and support to tissues. Hair, horns, hooves, and fingernails are all made up of keratin. **Collagen** is found in bone, connective tissue, tendons, and cartilage. **Membrane proteins** transport small organic molecules and ions across cell membranes. **Insulin,** the hormone that regulates blood glucose levels, and **hemoglobin,** which transports oxygen from the lungs to tissues, are proteins. **Enzymes** are proteins that catalyze and regulate all aspects of cellular function. In Chapter 21 we discuss proteins and their primary components, the amino acids.

## 21.1  Introduction

*Proteins* **are biomolecules that contain many amide bonds, formed by joining amino acids together.**

$$H_2N-\underset{R}{\overset{H}{C}}-COOH \longrightarrow \overset{O}{\underset{H}{N}}-\underset{R_1}{CH}-\overset{O}{C}-\underset{H}{N}-\underset{R_2}{CH}-\overset{O}{C}-\underset{H}{N}-\underset{R_3}{CH}-\overset{O}{C}-\underset{H}{N}-\underset{R_4}{CH}-\overset{O}{C}$$

amino acid                                          protein
                                    [Amide bonds are shown in red.]

The word *protein* comes from the Greek *proteios* meaning "of first importance." Proteins occur widely in the human body, accounting for approximately 50% of its dry weight (Figure 21.1). Fibrous proteins, like keratin in hair, skin, and nails and collagen in connective tissue, give support and structure to tissues and cells. Protein hormones and enzymes regulate the body's metabolism. Transport proteins carry substances through the blood, and storage proteins store elements and ions in organs. Contractile proteins control muscle movements, and immunoglobulins are proteins that defend the body against foreign substances.

**Figure 21.1**   Proteins in the Human Body

**keratin**
• fibrous protein in hair, skin, and nails

**myoglobin**
• protein that stores $O_2$ in tissues

**insulin**
• protein hormone synthesized in the pancreas
• controls blood glucose levels

**hemoglobin**
• transport protein that carries $O_2$ in the blood

**collagen**
• fibrous protein in connective tissue
• found in tendons, bone, cartilage, and blood vessels

**ferritin**
• protein that stores iron in the liver

**actin and myosin**
• proteins that control muscle contractions

Source: Data from U.S. Food and Drug Administration.

| Table 21.1 | Recommended Daily Protein Intake | |
| --- | --- | --- |
| Group | Daily Protein Intake (g protein/kg body weight) | |
| Children (1–3 years) | 1.1 | |
| Children (4–13 years) | 0.95 | |
| Children (14–18 years) | 0.85 | |
| Adult | 0.8 | |

Unlike lipids and carbohydrates, which the body stores for use when needed, protein is not stored so it must be consumed on a daily basis. The current recommended daily intake for adults is 0.8 g of protein per kg of body weight. Since children need protein for both growth and maintenance, the recommended daily intake is higher, as shown in Table 21.1. The average protein intake in the United States is often twice what is necessary.

## 21.2  Amino Acids

To understand protein properties and structure, we must first learn about the amino acids that compose them.

### 21.2A  General Features of Amino Acids

**Amino acids contain two functional groups—an amino group ($NH_2$) and a carboxyl group ($COOH$).** In most naturally occurring amino acids, the amino group is bonded to the α carbon, the carbon adjacent to the carbonyl group (Section 17.2), making them **α-amino acids.**

α-amino acid

glycine
the simplest amino acid

The 20 amino acids that occur naturally in proteins differ in the identity of the R group bonded to the α carbon. The R group is called the **side chain** of the amino acid. The simplest amino acid, called **glycine,** has R = H. Other side chains may be simple alkyl groups, or have additional functional groups such as OH, SH, COOH, or $NH_2$. Table 21.2 lists the structures of the 20 common amino acids that occur in proteins.

- Amino acids with an additional COOH group in the side chain are called acidic amino acids.
- Those with an additional basic N atom in the side chain are called basic amino acids.
- All others are neutral amino acids.

All amino acids have common names, which are abbreviated by a three-letter or one-letter designation. For example, glycine is often written as the three-letter abbreviation **Gly,** or the one-letter abbreviation **G.** These abbreviations are also given in Table 21.2.

Amino acids never exist in nature as neutral molecules with all uncharged atoms. Since amino acids contain a base ($NH_2$ group) and an acid (COOH), proton transfer from the acid to the base forms a salt called a **zwitterion,** which contains both a positive and a negative charge. These salts have high melting points and are water soluble.

The acid–base chemistry of amino acids is discussed in greater detail in Section 21.3. The structures in Table 21.2 show the charged form of the amino acids at the physiological pH of the blood.

a base

an acid

This neutral form of an amino acid does *not* exist.

**proton transfer**

(+) and (−) charges in the same compound

zwitterion

a **salt**

This salt is the neutral form of an amino acid.

Humans can synthesize only 10 of the 20 amino acids needed for proteins. The remaining 10, called **essential amino acids,** must be obtained from the diet and consumed on a regular, almost

A diet of rice and tofu provides all essential amino acids. A peanut butter sandwich on wheat bread does the same.

daily basis. Diets that include animal products readily supply all of the needed amino acids. Since no one plant source has sufficient amounts of all of the essential amino acids, vegetarian diets must be carefully balanced. Grains—wheat, rice, and corn—are low in lysine, and legumes—beans, peas, and peanuts—are low in methionine, but a combination of these foods provides all the needed amino acids.

### PROBLEM 21.1

In addition to the amino and carboxyl groups, what other functional groups are present in each amino acid: (a) asparagine; (b) serine; (c) cysteine?

### PROBLEM 21.2

How do the OH groups in Ser, Thr, and Tyr differ?

## 21.2B  Stereochemistry of Amino Acids

Except for the simplest amino acid, glycine, **all other amino acids have a chirality center—a carbon bonded to four different groups—on the α carbon.** Thus, an amino acid like alanine (R = $CH_3$) has two possible enantiomers, drawn below in both three-dimensional representations with wedges and dashed bonds, and Fischer projections.

The essential amino acid leucine is sold as a dietary supplement that is used by body builders to help prevent muscle loss and heal muscle tissue after injury.

$$
\begin{array}{ccc}
\underset{\text{L isomer}}{\underset{\text{naturally occurring}}{\underset{\text{enantiomer}}{\text{H}_3\overset{+}{\text{N}}\text{—}|\text{—H} \atop \text{CH}_3}}}
\;=\;
\underset{\text{L-alanine}}{\text{H}_3\overset{+}{\text{N}}\text{—C—H} \atop \text{CH}_3}
\;\Bigg|\;
\underset{\text{D-alanine}}{\text{H—C—}\overset{+}{\text{N}}\text{H}_3 \atop \text{CH}_3}
\;=\;
\underset{\text{D isomer}}{\text{H—}|\text{—}\overset{+}{\text{N}}\text{H}_3 \atop \text{CH}_3}
\end{array}
$$

Like monosaccharides, the prefixes **D** and **L** are used to designate the arrangement of groups on the chirality center of amino acids. When drawn with a vertical carbon chain having the $-COO^-$ group at the top and the R group at the bottom,

- **L** Amino acids have the $-NH_3^+$ group on the *left* side in the Fischer projection. Common naturally occurring amino acids are **L** isomers.
- **D** Amino acids have the $-NH_3^+$ group on the *right* side in the Fischer projection. **D** Amino acids occur infrequently in nature.

### SAMPLE PROBLEM 21.1

Draw the Fischer projection for each amino acid: (a) L-leucine; (b) D-cysteine.

#### Analysis

To draw an amino acid in a Fischer projection, place the $-COO^-$ group at the top and the R group at the bottom. The L isomer has the $-NH_3^+$ on the left side and the D isomer has the $-NH_3^+$ on the right side.

#### Solution

a. For leucine, R = $CH_2CH(CH_3)_2$

$$
\underset{\text{L isomer}}{\underset{\overset{+}{\text{N}}\text{H}_3 \text{ on left}}{\text{H}_3\overset{+}{\text{N}}\text{—}|\text{—H} \atop \text{CH}_2\text{CH(CH}_3)_2}}
$$

b. For cysteine, R = $CH_2SH$

$$
\underset{\text{D isomer}}{\underset{\overset{+}{\text{N}}\text{H}_3 \text{ on right}}{\text{H—}|\text{—}\overset{+}{\text{N}}\text{H}_3 \atop \text{CH}_2\text{SH}}}
$$

## Table 21.2 The 20 Common Naturally Occurring Amino Acids

| Neutral Amino Acids | | | | | |
| --- | --- | --- | --- | --- | --- |
| Name | Structure | Abbreviations | Name | Structure | Abbreviations |
| Alanine | $H_3\overset{+}{N}-\overset{\underset{\displaystyle CH_3}{\overset{\displaystyle H}{|}}}{C}-COO^-$ | Ala   A | Phenylalanine* | $H_3\overset{+}{N}-\overset{\underset{\displaystyle CH_2-C_6H_5}{\overset{\displaystyle H}{|}}}{C}-COO^-$ | Phe   F |
| Asparagine | $H_3\overset{+}{N}-\overset{\underset{\displaystyle CH_2CONH_2}{\overset{\displaystyle H}{|}}}{C}-COO^-$ | Asn   N | Proline | (ring structure) $\overset{}{C}OO^-$ | Pro   P |
| Cysteine | $H_3\overset{+}{N}-\overset{\underset{\displaystyle CH_2SH}{\overset{\displaystyle H}{|}}}{C}-COO^-$ | Cys   C | Serine | $H_3\overset{+}{N}-\overset{\underset{\displaystyle CH_2OH}{\overset{\displaystyle H}{|}}}{C}-COO^-$ | Ser   S |
| Glutamine | $H_3\overset{+}{N}-\overset{\underset{\displaystyle CH_2CH_2CONH_2}{\overset{\displaystyle H}{|}}}{C}-COO^-$ | Gln   Q | Threonine* | $H_3\overset{+}{N}-\overset{\underset{\displaystyle CH(OH)CH_3}{\overset{\displaystyle H}{|}}}{C}-COO^-$ | Thr   T |
| Glycine | $H_3\overset{+}{N}-\overset{\underset{\displaystyle H}{\overset{\displaystyle H}{|}}}{C}-COO^-$ | Gly   G | Tryptophan* | $H_3\overset{+}{N}-\overset{\underset{\displaystyle CH_2}{\overset{\displaystyle H}{|}}}{C}-COO^-$ (indole ring) | Trp   W |
| Isoleucine* | $H_3\overset{+}{N}-\overset{\underset{\displaystyle CH(CH_3)CH_2CH_3}{\overset{\displaystyle H}{|}}}{C}-COO^-$ | Ile   I | Tyrosine | $H_3\overset{+}{N}-\overset{\underset{\displaystyle CH_2-C_6H_4-OH}{\overset{\displaystyle H}{|}}}{C}-COO^-$ | Tyr   Y |
| Leucine* | $H_3\overset{+}{N}-\overset{\underset{\displaystyle CH_2CH(CH_3)_2}{\overset{\displaystyle H}{|}}}{C}-COO^-$ | Leu   L | Valine* | $H_3\overset{+}{N}-\overset{\underset{\displaystyle CH(CH_3)_2}{\overset{\displaystyle H}{|}}}{C}-COO^-$ | Val   V |
| Methionine* | $H_3\overset{+}{N}-\overset{\underset{\displaystyle CH_2CH_2SCH_3}{\overset{\displaystyle H}{|}}}{C}-COO^-$ | Met   M | | | |

Essential amino acids are labeled with an asterisk (*).

(continued on next page)

## Table 21.2 (continued)

| Acidic Amino Acids | | | Basic Amino Acids | | |
|---|---|---|---|---|---|
| Name | Structure | Abbreviations | Name | Structure | Abbreviations |
| Aspartic acid |  | Asp  D | Arginine* | | Arg  R |
| Glutamic acid | | Glu  E | Histidine* | | His  H |
| | | | Lysine* | | Lys  K |

Essential amino acids are labeled with an asterisk (*).

### PROBLEM 21.3

Draw both enantiomers of each amino acid in Fischer projections and label them as D or L:
(a) phenylalanine; (b) methionine.

### PROBLEM 21.4

Which of the following amino acids is naturally occurring? By referring to the structures in Table 21.2, name each amino acid and include its D or L designation in the name.

a. $H_3\overset{+}{N}$—H, COO⁻, $CH_2OH$
b. H—$\overset{+}{N}H_3$, COO⁻, $CH_2CH_2COO^-$
c. $H_3\overset{+}{N}$—H, COO⁻, $CH_2COO^-$

## 21.3  Acid–Base Behavior of Amino Acids

As mentioned in Section 21.2, an amino acid contains both a basic amino group ($NH_2$) and an acidic carboxyl group (COOH). As a result, proton transfer from the acid to the base forms a **zwitterion,** a salt that contains both a positive and a negative charge. The zwitterion is *neutral;* that is, the net charge on the salt is zero.

The lone pair can bond to a proton.

$H_2\overset{..}{N}$—C—COOH → **proton transfer** → $H_3\overset{+}{N}$—C—COO⁻  **zwitterion**

The carboxyl group can donate a proton.

In actuality, **an amino acid can exist in different forms, depending on the pH of the aqueous solution in which it is dissolved.** When the pH of a solution is around 6, alanine (R = $CH_3$) and other neutral amino acids exist in their zwitterionic form (**A**), having no net charge. In this form, the carboxyl group bears a net negative charge—it is a **carboxylate anion**—and the amino group bears a net positive charge (an **ammonium cation**).

ammonium cation

H₃N⁺—C—COO⁻    carboxylate anion

H (top)

CH₃

alanine
no net charge
**A**
pH ≈ 6

When strong acid is added to lower the pH to 2 or less, the carboxylate anion gains a proton and the **amino acid has a net positive charge** (form **B**).

| Adding acid: | The carboxylate anion picks up a proton. |

H₃N⁺—C—COO⁻    —H⁺→    H₃N⁺—C—COOH    pH ≤ 2

CH₃              CH₃

**A**            overall +1 charge
                 **B**

When strong base is added to **A** to raise the pH to 10 or higher, the ammonium cation loses a proton and the **amino acid has a net negative charge** (form **C**).

| Adding base: | The ammonium cation loses a proton. |

H₃N⁺—C—COO⁻    —OH⁻→    H₂N—C—COO⁻  +  H₂O    pH ≥ 10

CH₃              CH₃

**A**            overall −1 charge
                 **C**

Thus, **alanine exists in one of three different forms depending on the pH of the solution in which it is dissolved.** At the physiological pH of 7.4, neutral amino acids are primarily in their zwitterionic forms.

- The pH at which the amino acid exists primarily in its neutral form is called its *isoelectric point,* abbreviated as p*I.*

The isoelectric points of neutral amino acids are generally around 6. Acidic amino acids (Table 21.2), which have an additional carboxyl group that can lose a proton, have lower p*I* values (around 3). The three basic amino acids, which have an additional basic nitrogen atom that can accept a proton, have higher p*I* values (7.6–10.8).

### SAMPLE PROBLEM 21.2

Draw the structure of the amino acid glycine at each pH: (a) 6; (b) 2; (c) 11.

### Analysis

A neutral amino acid exists in its zwitterionic form (no net charge) at its isoelectric point, which is pH ≈ 6. The zwitterionic forms of neutral amino acids appear in Table 21.2. At low pH (≤ 2), the carboxylate anion is protonated and the amino acid has a net positive (+1) charge. At high pH (≥ 10), the ammonium cation loses a proton and the amino acid has a net negative (−1) charge.

### Solution

a. At pH = 6, the neutral, zwitterionic form of glycine predominates.

H₃N⁺—C—COO⁻

H

neutral
pH = 6

b. At pH = 2, glycine has a net +1 charge.

H₃N⁺—C—COOH

H

+1 charge
pH = 2

c. At pH = 11, glycine has a net −1 charge.

H₂N—C—COO⁻

H

−1 charge
pH = 11

Draw the structure of the amino acid valine at each pH: (a) 6; (b) 2; (c) 11. Which form predominates at valine's isoelectric point?

Draw the positively charged, neutral, and negatively charged forms for the amino acid phenylalanine. Which species predominates at pH 11? Which species predominates at pH 1?

## 21.4 Peptides

When amino acids are joined together by amide bonds, they form larger molecules called **peptides** and **proteins.**

- A *dipeptide* has two amino acids joined together by *one* amide bond.
- A *tripeptide* has three amino acids joined together by *two* amide bonds.

dipeptide                     tripeptide

[Amide bonds are shown in red.]

**Polypeptides** and **proteins** both have many amino acids joined together in long linear chains, but the term **protein** is usually reserved for polymers of more than 40 amino acids.

- The amide bonds in peptides and proteins are called *peptide bonds.*
- The individual amino acids are called *amino acid residues.*

To form a dipeptide, **the $-NH_3^+$ group of one amino acid forms an amide bond with the carboxylate ($-COO^-$) of another amino acid, and the elements of $H_2O$ are removed.** Because each amino acid has both functional groups, two different dipeptides can be formed. This is illustrated with alanine (Ala) and serine (Ser) to form dipeptides **A** and **B.**

**1.** The $-COO^-$ group of alanine can combine with the $-NH_3^+$ group of serine.

**2.** The $-COO^-$ group of serine can combine with the $-NH_3^+$ group of alanine.

Dipeptides **A** and **B** are **constitutional isomers** of each other. Both have an ammonium cation ($-NH_3^+$) at one end of their chains and a carboxylate anion ($-COO^-$) at the other.

- The amino acid with the free $-NH_3^+$ group on the α carbon is called the N-terminal amino acid.
- The amino acid with the free $-COO^-$ group on the α carbon is called the C-terminal amino acid.

By convention, **the N-terminal amino acid is always written at the *left* end of the chain and the C-terminal amino acid at the *right*.**

alanylserine
Ala–Ser

serylalanine
Ser–Ala

Peptides are named as derivatives of the C-terminal amino acid. To name a peptide:

- Name the C-terminal amino acid using the names in Table 21.2.
- Name all other amino acids from left to right as substituents of the C-terminal amino acid. Change the *-ine* or *-ic acid* ending of the amino acid name to the suffix *-yl.*

Thus, peptide **A,** which has serine as its C-terminal amino acid, is named as *alanylserine.* Peptide **B,** which has alanine as its C-terminal amino acid, is named as *serylalanine.*

The peptide can be abbreviated by writing the one- or three-letter symbols for the amino acids in the chain from the N-terminal to the C-terminal end. Thus, Ala–Ser has alanine at the N-terminal end and serine at the C-terminal end, whereas Ser–Ala has serine at the N-terminal end and alanine at the C-terminal end.

### PROBLEM 21.7

Identify the N-terminal and C-terminal amino acid in each peptide.

b. Arg–His–Asn–Tyr

d. Val–Thr–Pro–Phe

### PROBLEM 21.8

(a) Identify the N-terminal amino acid in the tetrapeptide alanylglycylleucylmethionine. (b) What is the C-terminal amino acid? (c) Write the peptide using three-letter symbols for the amino acids.

Drawing a dipeptide from component amino acids is illustrated in the stepwise *How To* procedure. Sample Problem 21.3 illustrates how to identify and name the component amino acids from a given tripeptide.

## *How To*  Draw a Dipeptide from Two Amino Acids

**Example:** Draw the structure of the dipeptide Val–Gly, and label the N-terminal and C-terminal amino acids.

**Step [1]   Draw the structures of the individual amino acids from left to right.**
  - Use the three-letter symbols to identify the amino acids in the peptide. In this example, Val is valine and Gly is glycine.
  - Draw the structures of the amino acids by placing the $-COO^-$ of one amino acid next to the $-NH_3^+$ group of the adjacent amino acid.
  - Always draw the $-NH_3^+$ group on the left and the $-COO^-$ group on the right.

**Step [2]   Join the adjacent $-COO^-$ and $-NH_3^+$ groups together.**
  - Form a new amide bond by joining the carbonyl carbon of one amino acid to the N atom of the second amino acid.

  - Valine is the N-terminal amino acid since it contains a free $-NH_3^+$ group on the α carbon.
  - Glycine is the C-terminal amino acid since it contains a free $-COO^-$ group on the α carbon.

---

### PROBLEM 21.9

Draw the structure of each dipeptide: (a) Gly–Phe; (b) Gln–Ile; (c) Leu–Cys.

### PROBLEM 21.10

(a) Draw the structures of the two possible dipeptides that can be formed by combining leucine and asparagine. (b) In each dipeptide label the N- and C-terminal amino acids. (c) Name each peptide using three-letter abbreviations.

### SAMPLE PROBLEM 21.3

Identify the individual amino acids used to form the following tripeptide. What is the name of the tripeptide?

### Analysis

- Locate the amide bonds in the peptide. To draw the structures of the individual amino acids, break the amide bonds by adding water. Add $O^-$ to the carbonyl carbon to form a carboxylate anion $-COO^-$ and 2 H's to the N atom to form $-NH_3^+$.
- Identify the amino acids by comparing with Table 21.2.
- To name the peptide: [1] Name the C-terminal amino acid. [2] Name the other amino acids as substituents by changing the -ine (or -ic acid) ending to the suffix -yl. Place the names of the substituent amino acids in order from left to right.

### Solution

To determine the amino acids that form the peptide, work backwards. Break the amide bonds in red that join the amino acids together. This forms leucine, alanine, and tyrosine.

leucine                     alanine                     tyrosine

The tripeptide is named as a derivative of the C-terminal amino acid, tyrosine, with leucine and alanine as substituents; thus, the tripeptide is named: **leucylalanyltyrosine.**

### PROBLEM 21.11

Identify the individual amino acids in each dipeptide, and then name the dipeptide using three-letter abbreviations.

a. $H_3\overset{+}{N}-CH-\overset{O}{\overset{||}{C}}-N-CH-\overset{O}{\overset{||}{C}}-O^-$
   with $CH_3$ and $H$ $CH(CH_3)CH_2CH_3$

b. $H_3\overset{+}{N}-CH-\overset{O}{\overset{||}{C}}-N-CH-\overset{O}{\overset{||}{C}}-O^-$
   with $CH_2$ (benzene ring with OH) and $H$ $CH(CH_3)_2$

### SAMPLE PROBLEM 21.4

Locate the peptide bond in the dipeptide shown in the ball-and-stick model, and identify the amino acids that form the dipeptide. Name the dipeptide using the three-letter abbreviations for the amino acids.

### Analysis

- Convert the ball-and-stick model to a structural formula. The peptide bond is the amide bond that joins the two amino acids together.
- Identify the side chains of the amino acids and use Table 21.2 to determine the names.
- Name the dipeptide by writing the three-letter abbreviations for the amino acids with the N-terminal amino acid first, followed by the C-terminal amino acid.

### Solution

The peptide bond is the amide bond that contains a carbon atom doubly bonded to oxygen and singly bonded to nitrogen.

The side chains of the two amino acids, the R groups that extend from the peptide backbone, identify them as alanine and cysteine (Table 21.2). The dipeptide is named with the N-terminal amino acid (alanine) first, followed by the C-terminal amino acid (cysteine), using the three-letter abbreviations: **Ala–Cys**.

### PROBLEM 21.12

Locate the peptide bond in the dipeptide shown in the ball-and-stick model, and identify the amino acids that form the dipeptide. Name the dipeptide using the three-letter abbreviations for the amino acids.

## 21.5 FOCUS ON THE HUMAN BODY
### Biologically Active Peptides

Many relatively simple peptides have important biological functions.

### 21.5A Neuropeptides—Enkephalins and Pain Relief

**Enkephalins,** pentapeptides synthesized in the brain, act as pain killers and sedatives by binding to pain receptors. Two enkephalins that differ in the identity of only one amino acid are known. Met-enkephalin contains a C-terminal methionine residue, while leu-enkephalin contains a C-terminal leucine.

Tyr–Gly–Gly–Phe–Met
met-enkephalin

Tyr–Gly–Gly–Phe–Leu
leu-enkephalin

The addictive narcotic analgesics morphine and heroin (Section 18.5) bind to the same receptors as the enkephalins, and thus produce a similar physiological response. Enkephalins, however, produce only short-term pain-relieving effects because their peptide bonds are readily hydrolyzed by enzymes in the brain. Morphine and heroin, on the other hand, are not readily hydrolyzed, so they are biologically active for a much longer time period.

Enkephalins are related to a group of larger polypeptides called **endorphins** that contain 16–31 amino acids. Endorphins also block pain and are thought to produce the feeling of well-being experienced by an athlete after excessive or strenuous exercise.

### PROBLEM 21.13

(a) Label the four amide bonds in met-enkephalin. (b) What N-terminal amino acid is present in both enkephalins? (c) How many chirality centers are present in met-enkephalin?

## 21.5B   Peptide Hormones—Oxytocin and Vasopressin

**Oxytocin** and **vasopressin** are cyclic nonapeptide hormones secreted by the pituitary gland. Their sequences are identical except for two amino acids, yet this is enough to give them very different biological activities.

oxytocin                   vasopressin

**Figure 21.2**

Physiological Effects of Oxytocin

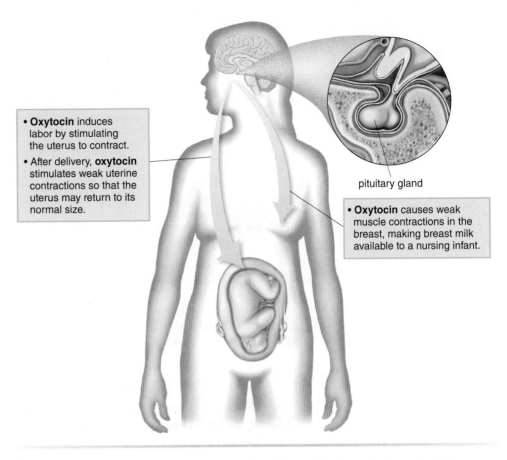

**Figure 21.2**

Physiological Effects of Oxytocin

- **Oxytocin** induces labor by stimulating the uterus to contract.
- After delivery, **oxytocin** stimulates weak uterine contractions so that the uterus may return to its normal size.

pituitary gland

- **Oxytocin** causes weak muscle contractions in the breast, making breast milk available to a nursing infant.

**Oxytocin** stimulates the contraction of uterine muscles, and it initiates the flow of milk in nursing mothers (Figure 21.2). Oxytocin, sold under the trade names Pitocin and Syntocinon, is used to induce labor.

**Vasopressin,** also called antidiuretic hormone (ADH), targets the kidneys and helps to keep the electrolytes in body fluids in the normal range. Vasopressin is secreted when the body is dehydrated and causes the kidneys to retain fluid, thus decreasing the volume of the urine (Figure 21.3).

**Figure 21.3**

Vasopressin—An Antidiuretic Hormone

pituitary gland

- Secretion of **vasopressin** by the pituitary gland causes the kidneys to retain fluid, resulting in decreased urine output.

decreased urine output

The N-terminal amino acid in both hormones is a cysteine residue, and the C-terminal residue is glycine. Instead of a free carboxylate (–COO⁻), both peptides have an amide (–CONH₂) at the C-terminal end, so this is indicated with the additional NH₂ group drawn at the end of the chain.

The structure of both peptides includes a **disulfide bond,** a form of covalent bonding in which the –SH groups from two cysteine residues are oxidized to form a sulfur–sulfur bond (Section 14.10). In oxytocin and vasopressin, the disulfide bonds make the peptides cyclic.

$$2 \ \ R{-}S{-}H \ \ \xrightarrow{[O]} \ \ R{-}S{-}S{-}R$$

thiol                       disulfide bond

## PROBLEM 21.14

Draw the structure of the disulfide formed when cysteine is oxidized.

# 21.6   Proteins

To understand proteins, the large polymers of amino acids that are responsible for so much of the structure and function of all living cells, we must learn about four levels of structure, called the **primary, secondary, tertiary, and quaternary structure** of proteins.

## 21.6A   Primary Structure

**The *primary structure* of a protein is the particular sequence of amino acids that is joined together by peptide bonds.** The most important element of this primary structure is the amide bond that joins the amino acids.

The carbonyl carbon of the amide has **trigonal planar** geometry. All six atoms involved in the peptide bond lie in the same plane. All bond angles are 120° and the C=O and N—H bonds are oriented 180° from each other. As a result, the backbone of the protein adopts a zigzag arrangement as shown in the three-dimensional structure of a portion of a protein molecule.

These six atoms lie in a plane.

[Amide bonds are shown in red.]

The primary structure of a protein—the exact sequence of amino acids—determines all properties and function of a protein. As we will see in Section 21.7, substitution of a single amino acid by a different amino acid can result in very different properties.

## PROBLEM 21.15

Can two *different* proteins be composed of the same number and type of amino acids?

## 21.6B  Secondary Structure

**The three-dimensional arrangement of localized regions of a protein is called its secondary structure.** These regions arise due to hydrogen bonding between the N—H proton of one amide and the C=O oxygen of another. Two arrangements that are particularly stable are called the **α-helix** and the **β-pleated sheet.**

### α-Helix

The **α-helix** forms when a peptide chain twists into a right-handed or clockwise spiral, as shown in Figure 21.4. Several important features characterize an α-helix.

- Each turn of the helix has 3.6 amino acids.
- The N—H and C=O bonds point along the axis of the helix in opposite directions.
- The C=O group of one amino acid is hydrogen bonded to an N—H group four amino acid residues farther along the chain.
- The R groups of the amino acids extend outward from the core of the helix.

Both the myosin in muscle and the α-keratin in hair are proteins composed almost entirely of α-helices.

**Figure 21.4**  Two Different Illustrations of the α-Helix

a. The right-handed α-helix

b. The backbone of the α-helix

hydrogen bond

3.6 residues

All atoms of the α-helix are drawn in this representation. All C=O bonds are pointing up and all N—H bonds are pointing down.

Only the peptide backbone is drawn in this representation. The hydrogen bonds between the C=O and N—H of amino acids four residues away from each other are shown.

## β-Pleated Sheet

The **β-pleated sheet** forms when two or more peptide chains, called **strands,** line up side-by-side, as shown in Figure 21.5. All β-pleated sheets have the following characteristics:

- The C=O and N—H bonds lie in the plane of the sheet.
- Hydrogen bonding often occurs between the N—H and C=O groups of nearby amino acid residues.
- The R groups are oriented above and below the plane of the sheet, and alternate from one side to the other along a given strand.

**Figure 21.5**    Three-Dimensional Structure of the β-Pleated Sheet

hydrogen bond

The β-pleated sheet consists of extended strands of the peptide chains held together by hydrogen bonding. The C=O and N—H bonds lie in the plane of the sheet, while the R groups (shown as yellow balls) alternate above and below the plane.

The β-pleated sheet arrangement is favored by amino acids with small R groups, like alanine and glycine. With larger R groups, steric interactions prevent the chains from getting close together, so the sheet cannot be stabilized by hydrogen bonding.

Most proteins have regions of α-helix and β-pleated sheet, in addition to other regions that cannot be characterized by either of these arrangements. Shorthand symbols are often used to indicate these regions of secondary structure, as well as disulfide bonds that are sometimes present (Figure 21.6). In particular, a flat helical ribbon is used for the α-helix, while a flat wide arrow is used for the β-pleated sheet. These representations are often used in **ribbon diagrams** to illustrate protein structure.

**Figure 21.6**    Shorthand Symbols Representing Protein Structure

α-helix                                β-sheet                     random region

**Figure 21.7** Lysozyme

a. Ball-and-stick model

b. Space-filling model

c. Ribbon diagram

(a) The ball-and-stick model of lysozyme shows the protein backbone with color-coded C, N, O, and S atoms. Individual amino acids are most clearly located using this representation. (b) The space-filling model uses color-coded balls for each atom in the backbone of the enzyme and illustrates how the atoms fill the space they occupy. (c) The ribbon diagram shows regions of $\alpha$-helix and $\beta$-sheet that are not clearly in evidence in the other two representations.

Proteins are drawn in a variety of ways to show different aspects of their structure. Figure 21.7 illustrates three different representations of the protein lysozyme, an enzyme found in both plants and animals. Lysozyme catalyzes the hydrolysis of bonds in bacterial cell walls, weakening them, often causing the bacteria to burst.

Spider dragline silk is a strong yet elastic protein because it has regions of $\beta$-pleated sheet and regions of $\alpha$-helix (Figure 21.8). $\alpha$-Helical regions impart elasticity to the silk because the peptide chain is twisted (not fully extended), so it can stretch. $\beta$-Pleated sheet regions are almost fully extended, so they can't be stretched further, but their highly ordered three-dimensional structure imparts strength to the silk. Thus, spider silk suits the spider by having both types of secondary structure with beneficial properties.

**Figure 21.8**

Spider Dragline Silk

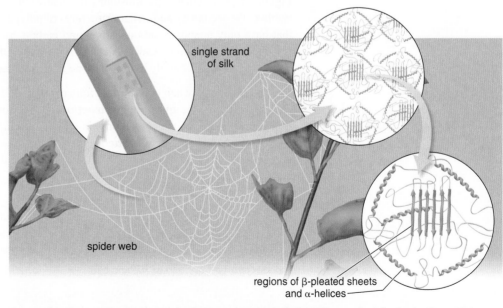

single strand
of silk

spider web

regions of $\beta$-pleated sheets
and $\alpha$-helices

Spider dragline silk has regions of $\alpha$-helix and $\beta$-pleated sheet that make it both elastic and strong. The green coils represent the $\alpha$-helical regions, while the purple arrows represent the $\beta$-pleated sheet regions. The thin gray lines represents other areas of the protein that are neither $\alpha$-helix nor $\beta$-pleated sheet.

## 21.6C    Tertiary and Quaternary Structure

**The three-dimensional shape adopted by the entire peptide chain is called its tertiary structure.** A peptide generally folds into a shape that maximizes its stability. In the aqueous environment of the cell, proteins often fold in such a way as to place a large number of polar and charged groups on their outer surface, to maximize the dipole–dipole and hydrogen bonding interactions with water. This generally places most of the nonpolar side chains in the interior of the protein, where **London dispersion forces** between these hydrophobic groups help stabilize the molecule, too.

In addition, polar functional groups **hydrogen bond** with each other (not just water), and amino acids with charged side chains like $-COO^-$ and $-NH_3^+$ can stabilize tertiary structure by **electrostatic interactions.**

Finally, **disulfide bonds are the only covalent bonds that stabilize tertiary structure.** As mentioned in Section 21.5, these strong bonds form by the oxidation of two cysteine residues on either the same polypeptide chain or another polypeptide chain of the same protein.

| Disulfide bonds can form in two different ways. |
|---|

**Between two SH groups on the same chain:** | **Between two SH groups on different chains:**

$$-CH_2SH \quad\quad -CH_2-S$$
$$\xrightarrow{[O]}$$
$$-CH_2SH \quad\quad -CH_2-S$$

intramolecular disulfide bond

$$-CH_2SH \quad\quad -CH_2S$$
$$\xrightarrow{[O]}$$
$$HSCH_2- \quad\quad SCH_2-$$

intermolecular disulfide bond

**Insulin,** for example, consists of two separate polypeptide chains (labeled the **A** and **B** chains) that are covalently linked by two intermolecular disulfide bonds, as shown in Figure 21.9. The **A** chain, which also has an intramolecular disulfide bond, has 21 amino acid residues, whereas the **B** chain has 30.

Figure 21.10 schematically illustrates the many different kinds of intramolecular forces that stabilize the secondary and tertiary structures of polypeptide chains. Nearby amino acid residues that have only nonpolar carbon–carbon and carbon–hydrogen bonds are stabilized by London dispersion forces. Amino acids that contain hydroxyl (OH) and amino groups ($NH_2$) in their side chains can intermolecularly hydrogen bond to each other.

The shape adopted when two or more folded polypeptide chains come together into one protein complex is called the **quaternary structure** of the protein. Each individual polypeptide chain is called a **subunit** of the overall protein. **Hemoglobin,** for example, consists of two α and two β subunits held together by intermolecular forces in a compact three-dimensional shape. The unique function of hemoglobin is possible only when all four subunits are together.

The four levels of protein structure are summarized in Figure 21.11.

### PROBLEM 21.16

Draw the structures of each pair of amino acids and indicate what types of intermolecular forces are present between the side chains. Use Figure 21.10 as a guide.

a. Ser and Tyr        b. Val and Leu        c. 2 Phe residues

### PROBLEM 21.17

The fibroin proteins found in silk fibers consist of large regions of β-pleated sheets stacked one on top of another. The polypeptide sequence in these regions has the amino acid glycine at every other residue. Explain how this allows the β-pleated sheets to stack on top of each other.

Figure 21.9    Insulin

**Insulin** is a small protein consisting of two polypeptide chains (designated as the **A** and **B** chains), held together by two disulfide bonds. An additional disulfide bond joins two cysteine residues within the **A** chain.

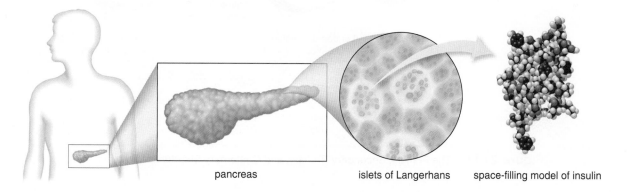

Synthesized by groups of cells in the pancreas called the islets of Langerhans, insulin is the protein that regulates blood glucose levels.

pancreas          islets of Langerhans          space-filling model of insulin

A relative or complete lack of insulin results in diabetes. Many of the abnormalities associated with this disease can be controlled by the injection of insulin. Until the recent availability of human insulin through genetic engineering techniques (Section 22.10), all insulin used by diabetics was obtained from pigs and cattle. The amino acid sequences of these insulin proteins are slightly different from that of human insulin. Pig insulin differs in one amino acid only, while bovine insulin has three different amino acids. This is shown in the accompanying table.

| | Chain A | | | Chain B |
|---|---|---|---|---|
| **Position of Residue →** | 8 | 9 | 10 | 30 |
| Human insulin | Thr | Ser | Ile | Thr |
| Pig insulin | Thr | Ser | Ile | Ala |
| Bovine insulin | Ala | Ser | Val | Ala |

**Figure 21.10**   The Stabilizing Interactions in Secondary and Tertiary Protein Structure

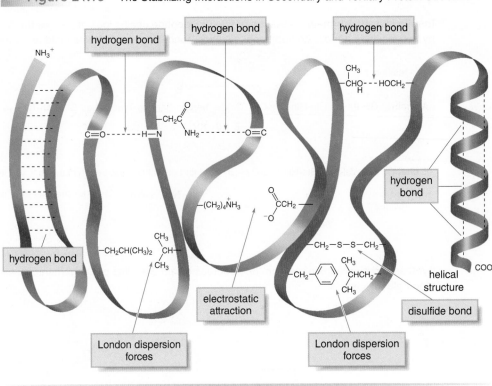

**Figure 21.11**   The Primary, Secondary, Tertiary, and Quaternary Structure of Proteins

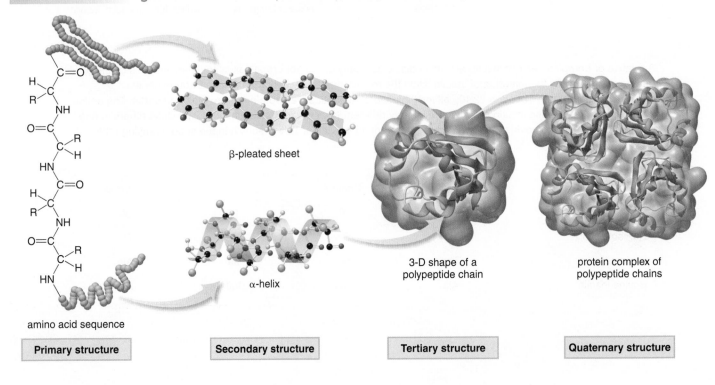

amino acid sequence

**Primary structure**          **Secondary structure**          **Tertiary structure**          **Quaternary structure**

β-pleated sheet

α-helix

3-D shape of a
polypeptide chain

protein complex of
polypeptide chains

## 21.7 FOCUS ON THE HUMAN BODY
### Common Proteins

Proteins are generally classified according to their three-dimensional shapes.

- *Fibrous proteins* are composed of long linear polypeptide chains that are bundled together to form rods or sheets. These proteins are insoluble in water and serve structural roles, giving strength and protection to tissues and cells.
- *Globular proteins* are coiled into compact shapes with hydrophilic outer surfaces that make them water soluble. Enzymes and transport proteins are globular to make them soluble in blood and other aqueous environments.

### 21.7A   α-Keratins

**α-Keratins** are the proteins found in hair, hooves, nails, skin, and wool. They are composed almost exclusively of long sections of α-helix units, having large numbers of alanine and leucine residues. Since these nonpolar amino acids extend outward from the α-helix, these proteins are very insoluble in water. Two α-keratin helices coil around each other, forming a structure called a **supercoil** or **superhelix.** These, in turn, form larger and larger bundles of fibers, ultimately forming a strand of hair, as shown schematically in Figure 21.12.

α-Keratins also have a number of cysteine residues, and because of this, disulfide bonds are formed between adjacent helices. The number of disulfide bridges determines the strength of the material. Claws, horns, and fingernails have extensive networks of disulfide bonds, making them extremely hard.

**Figure 21.12**   Anatomy of a Hair

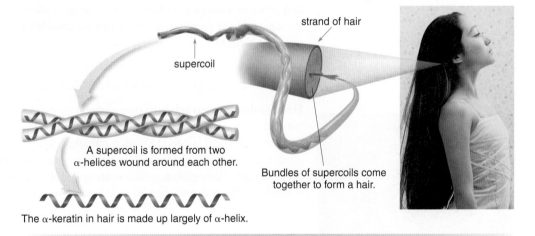

strand of hair

supercoil

A supercoil is formed from two α-helices wound around each other.

Bundles of supercoils come together to form a hair.

The α-keratin in hair is made up largely of α-helix.

### 21.7B   Collagen

**Collagen,** the most abundant protein in vertebrates, is found in connective tissues such as bone, cartilage, tendons, teeth, and blood vessels. Glycine and proline account for a large fraction of its amino acid residues. Collagen forms an elongated left-handed helix, and then three of these helices wind around each other to form a right-handed **superhelix** or **triple helix.** The side chain of glycine is only a hydrogen atom, so the high glycine content allows the collagen superhelices to lie compactly next to each other, thus stabilizing the superhelices via hydrogen bonding. Two views of the collagen superhelix are shown in Figure 21.13.

**Figure 21.13**   Two Different Representations for the Triple Helix of Collagen

In collagen, three polypeptide chains having an unusual left-handed helix wind around each other in a right-handed triple helix. The high content of small glycine residues allows the chains to lie close to each other, permitting hydrogen bonding between the chains.

Vitamin C is required for a reaction that modifies the original amino acids incorporated into the collagen chain so that strong hydrogen bonds form between the helices. When there is a deficiency of vitamin C in the diet, the collagen fibers do not form properly and scurvy results. Weakened blood vessels and poorly formed cartilage lead to spongy and bloody gums and dark purple skin lesions.

## 21.7C   Hemoglobin and Myoglobin

**Hemoglobin** and **myoglobin,** two globular proteins, are called **conjugated proteins** because they are composed of a protein unit and a nonprotein molecule. In hemoglobin and myoglobin, the nonprotein unit is called **heme,** a complex organic compound containing the $Fe^{2+}$ ion complexed with a large nitrogen-containing ring system. The $Fe^{2+}$ ion of hemoglobin and myoglobin binds oxygen. Hemoglobin, which is present in red blood cells, transports oxygen to wherever it is needed in the body, whereas myoglobin stores oxygen in tissues.

The high concentration of myoglobin in a whale's muscles allow it to remain underwater for long periods of time.

heme

Figure 21.14  Protein Ribbon Diagrams for Myoglobin and Hemoglobin

a. Myoglobin

heme

b. Hemoglobin

heme

Myoglobin consists of a single polypeptide chain with a heme unit shown in a ball-and-stick model.

Hemoglobin consists of two α and two β chains shown in red and blue, respectively, and four heme units shown in ball-and-stick models.

**Myoglobin** has 153 amino acid residues in a single polypeptide chain (Figure 21.14a). It has eight separate α-helical sections and a heme group held in a cavity inside the polypeptide. Myoglobin gives cardiac muscle its characteristic red color.

**Hemoglobin** consists of four polypeptide chains (two α subunits and two β subunits), each of which carries a heme unit (Figure 21.14b). Hemoglobin has more nonpolar amino acid residues than myoglobin. When each subunit is folded, some of these remain on the surface. The London dispersion forces between these hydrophobic groups are what stabilize the quaternary structure of the four subunits.

Carbon monoxide is poisonous because it binds to the $Fe^{2+}$ of hemoglobin 200 times more strongly than does oxygen. Hemoglobin complexed with CO cannot carry $O_2$ from the lungs to the tissues. Without $O_2$ available to the tissues for metabolism, cells cannot function, and they die.

The properties of all proteins depend on their three-dimensional shape, and their shape depends on their primary structure—that is, their amino acid sequence. This is particularly well exemplified by comparing normal hemoglobin with **sickle cell hemoglobin,** a mutant variation in which a single amino acid of both β subunits is changed from glutamic acid to valine. The replacement of one acidic amino acid (Glu) with one nonpolar amino acid (Val) changes the shape of hemoglobin, which has profound effects on its function. Red blood cells with sickle cell hemoglobin become elongated and crescent shaped, and they are unusually fragile. As a result, they rupture and occlude capillaries, causing pain and inflammation, leading to severe anemia and organ damage. The end result is often a painful and premature death.

This disease, called **sickle cell anemia,** is found almost exclusively among people originating from central and western Africa, where malaria is an enormous health problem. Sickle cell hemoglobin results from a genetic mutation in the DNA sequence that is responsible for the synthesis of hemoglobin. Individuals who inherit this mutation from both parents develop sickle cell anemia, whereas those who inherit it from only one parent are said to have the sickle cell trait. They do not develop sickle cell anemia and they are more resistant to malaria than individuals without the mutation. The relative benefit of this mutation apparently accounts for this detrimental gene being passed on from generation to generation.

### HEALTH NOTE

When red blood cells take on a "sickled" shape in persons with sickle cell disease, they block capillaries causing organ injury and they break easily leading to profound anemia. This devastating illness results from the change of a single amino acid in hemoglobin. Note the single sickled cell surrounded by three red cells with normal shape.

PROBLEM 21.18

Why is hemoglobin more water soluble than α-keratin?

## 21.8   Protein Hydrolysis and Denaturation

The properties of a protein are greatly altered and often entirely destroyed when any level of protein structure is disturbed.

### 21.8A   Protein Hydrolysis

Like other amide bonds, the peptide bonds in proteins are hydrolyzed by treatment with aqueous acid, base, or certain enzymes.

> • The hydrolysis of the amide bonds in a protein forms the individual amino acids that comprise the primary structure.

For example, hydrolysis of the amide bonds in the tripeptide Ile–Gly–Phe forms the amino acids isoleucine, glycine, and phenylalanine. When each amide bond is broken, the elements of $H_2O$ are added, forming a carboxylate anion ($-COO^-$) in one amino acid and an ammonium cation ($-NH_3^+$) in the other.

The first step in the digestion of dietary protein is hydrolysis of the amide bonds of the protein backbone. The enzyme pepsin in the acidic gastric juices of the stomach cleaves some of the amide bonds to form smaller peptides, which pass into the small intestines and are further broken down into individual amino acids by the enzymes trypsin and chymotrypsin.

Proteins in the diet serve a variety of nutritional needs. Like carbohydrates and lipids, proteins can be metabolized for energy. Moreover, the individual amino acids formed by hydrolysis are used as starting materials to make new proteins that the body needs. Likewise the N atoms in the amino acids are incorporated into other biomolecules that contain nitrogen.

### SAMPLE PROBLEM 21.5

Draw the structures of the amino acids formed by hydrolysis of the neuropeptide leu-enkephalin (Section 21.5).

### Analysis

Locate each amide bond in the protein or peptide backbone. To draw the hydrolysis products, break each amide bond by adding the elements of $H_2O$ to form a carboxylate anion ($-COO^-$) in one amino acid and an ammonium cation ($-NH_3^+$) in the other.

Solution

[1] Locate the amide bonds in the peptide backbone.
[2] Break each bond by adding $H_2O$.

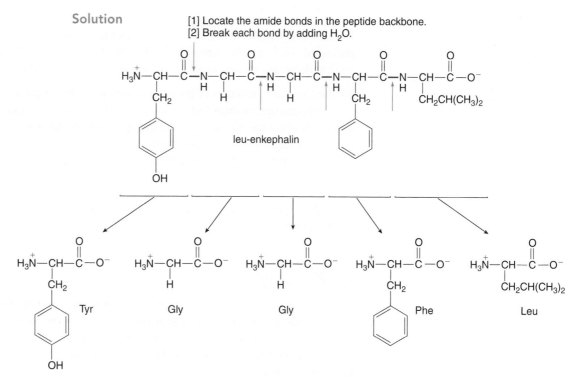

leu-enkephalin

Tyr · Gly · Gly · Phe · Leu

## PROBLEM 21.19

Draw the structure of the products formed by hydrolysis of each tripeptide: (a) Ala–Leu–Gly; (b) Ser–Thr–Phe; (c) Leu–Tyr–Asn.

## 21.8B Protein Denaturation

When the secondary, tertiary, or quaternary structure of a protein is disturbed, the properties of a protein are also altered and the biological activity is often lost.

- *Denaturation* is the process of altering the shape of a protein without breaking the amide bonds that form the primary structure.

Cooking or whipping egg whites denatures the globular proteins they contain, forming insoluble protein.

High temperature, acid, base, and even agitation can disrupt the noncovalent interactions that hold a protein in a specific shape. Heat breaks up weak London forces between nonpolar amino acids. Heat, acid, and base disrupt hydrogen-bonding interactions between polar amino acids, which account for much of the secondary and tertiary structure. As a result, denaturation causes a globular protein to uncoil into an undefined randomly looped structure.

coiled globular protein — heat → loose coils and loops

Denaturation often makes globular proteins less water soluble. Globular proteins are typically folded with hydrophobic regions in the interior to maximize the interaction of polar residues on the outside surface with water. This makes them water soluble. When the protein is denatured, more hydrophobic regions are exposed and the protein often loses water solubility.

We witness many examples of protein denaturation in the kitchen. As milk ages it becomes sour from enzymes that produce lactic acid. The acid also denatures milk proteins, which precipitate as an insoluble curd. Ovalbumin, the major protein in egg white, is denatured when an egg is boiled or fried, forming a solid. Even vigorously whipping egg whites denatures its protein, forming the stiff meringue used to top a lemon meringue pie.

### PROBLEM 21.20

Heating collagen, a water-insoluble fibrous protein, forms the jelly-like substance called gelatin. Explain how this process may occur.

## 21.9  Enzymes

We conclude the discussion of proteins with **enzymes, proteins that serve as biological catalysts for reactions in all living organisms.** Like all catalysts (Section 6.4), enzymes increase the rate of reactions, but they themselves are not permanently changed in the process. Moreover, the position of equilibrium is not altered by an enzyme, nor are the relative energies of the starting material and product.

Enzymes are crucial to the biological reactions that occur in the body, which would otherwise often proceed too slowly to be of any use. In humans, enzymes must catalyze reactions under very specific physiological conditions, usually a pH around 7.4 and a temperature of 37 °C.

### 21.9A  Characteristics of Enzymes

Enzymes are generally water-soluble, globular proteins that exhibit two characteristic features.

- **Enzymes greatly enhance reaction rates. An enzyme-catalyzed reaction can be $10^6$ to $10^{12}$ times faster than a similar uncatalyzed reaction.**
- **Enzymes are very specific.**

The specificity of an enzyme varies. Some enzymes, such as catalase, catalyze a single reaction. Catalase catalyzes the conversion of hydrogen peroxide ($H_2O_2$) to $O_2$ and $H_2O$ (Section 5.1).

$$2\ H_2O_2(l) \xrightarrow{\text{catalase}} 2\ H_2O(l)\ +\ O_2(g)$$

Other enzymes, such as carboxypeptidase A, catalyze a particular type of reaction with a variety of substrates. Carboxypeptidase A, a digestive enzyme that breaks down proteins, catalyzes the hydrolysis of a specific type of peptide bond—the amide bond closest to the C-terminal end of the protein.

When a bloody wound is cleaned with hydrogen peroxide, the enzyme catalase in the blood converts the $H_2O_2$ to $H_2O$ and $O_2$, forming a white foam of oxygen bubbles.

Only this amide bond is broken.

As is the case with catal*ase* and carboxypeptid*ase* A, **the names of most enzymes end in the suffix -*ase*.** Enzymes are classified into groups depending on the type of reaction they catalyze. For example, **an enzyme that catalyzes a hydrolysis reaction is called a *hydrolase*.** Hydrolases can be further subdivided into **lipases,** which catalyze the hydrolysis of the ester bonds in lipids (Section 19.5), or **proteases,** which catalyze the hydrolysis of proteins. Carboxypeptidase A is a protease.

The conversion of lactate to pyruvate illustrates other important features of enzyme-catalyzed reactions.

> Additional classes of enzymes are listed in Table 24.1.

The enzyme for this process is *lactate dehydrogenase,* a name derived from the substrate (lactate) and the type of reaction, a **dehydrogenation**—that is, the removal of two hydrogen atoms. To carry out this reaction a **cofactor** is needed.

> A **dehydrogenase** catalyzes the removal of two hydrogen atoms from a substrate to form a double bond.

• A *cofactor* is a metal ion or a nonprotein organic molecule needed for an enzyme-catalyzed reaction to occur.

$NAD^+$ (nicotinamide adenine dinucleotide, Section 16.6) is the cofactor that oxidizes lactate to pyruvate. **An organic compound that serves as an enzyme cofactor is called a *coenzyme*.** While lactate dehydrogenase greatly speeds up this oxidation reaction, $NAD^+$ is the coenzyme that actually oxidizes the substrate, lactate. $NAD^+$ is a common biological oxidizing agent used as a coenzyme (Section 23.4).

The need for metal ions as enzyme cofactors explains why trace amounts of certain metals must be present in our diet. For example, certain **oxidases,** enzymes that catalyze oxidation reactions, require either $Fe^{2+}$ or $Cu^{2+}$ as a cofactor needed for transferring electrons.

### PROBLEM 21.21

From the name alone, decide which of the following might be enzymes: (a) sucrose; (b) sucrase; (c) lactose; (d) lactase; (e) phosphofructokinase.

### PROBLEM 21.22

Lyase is the general name for an enzyme that catalyses either the addition of elements to a double bond or the elimination of elements from a double bond. Fumarase is a lyase that catalyzes the conversion of fumarate to malate.

a. What elements are added to fumarate to form malate?
b. Would you expect this enzyme to be subclassified as a dehydrase or hydratase? Explain your choice.

## 21.9B  How Enzymes Work

An enzyme contains a region called the **active site** that binds the substrate, forming an **enzyme–substrate complex.** The active site is often a small cavity that contains amino acids that are attracted to the substrate with various types of intermolecular forces. Sometimes polar amino acids of the enzyme hydrogen bond to the substrate or nonpolar amino acids have stabilizing hydrophobic interactions.

Two models have been proposed to explain the specificity of a substrate for an enzyme's active site: the **lock-and-key model** and the **induced-fit model.**

**In the lock-and-key model, the shape of the active site is rigid.** The three-dimensional geometry of the substrate must exactly match the shape of the active site for catalysis to occur. The lock-and-key model explains the high specificity observed in many enzyme reactions.

**In the induced-fit model, the shape of the active site is more flexible.** It is thought that when the substrate and the enzyme interact, the shape of the active site can adjust to fit the shape of the substrate.

This model is often used to explain why some enzymes catalyze reactions with a wider variety of substrates. The shape of the active site and the substrate must still be reasonably similar, but once bound, the shape of the active site is different from the active site in the unbound enzyme. A well-characterized example of the induced-fit model is seen in the binding of glucose to the enzyme hexokinase, shown in Figure 21.15.

**Figure 21.15** Hexokinase—An Example of the Induced-Fit Model

a. Shape of the active site before binding

b. Shape of the active site after binding

active site   glucose

glucose in the active site

The open cavity of the active site of the enzyme closes around the substrate for a tighter fit.

(a) The free enzyme has a small open cavity that fits a glucose molecule. (b) Once bound, the cavity encloses the glucose molecule more tightly in the enzyme–substrate complex.

## 21.9C Enzyme Inhibitors

Some substances bind to enzymes and in the process, greatly alter or destroy the enzyme's activity.

- An *inhibitor* is a molecule that causes an enzyme to lose activity.

An inhibitor can bind to an enzyme reversibly or irreversibly.

- A *reversible* inhibitor binds to an enzyme but then enzyme activity is restored when the inhibitor is released.
- An *irreversible* inhibitor covalently binds to an enzyme, permanently destroying its activity.

**Penicillin** is an antibiotic that kills bacteria because it irreversibly binds to glycopeptide transpeptidase, an enzyme required for the synthesis of a bacterial cell wall (Section 17.11). Penicillin binds to a hydroxyl group (OH) of the enzyme, thus inactivating it, halting cell wall construction, and killing the bacterium. Penicillin has no effect on human cells because they are surrounded by a flexible cell membrane and not a cell wall.

penicillin G

enzyme

Penicillin is covalently bound to the enzyme, inactivating it.

inactive enzyme

Reversible inhibition can be **competitive** or **noncompetitive.**

A *noncompetitive* **inhibitor binds to the enzyme but does not bind at the active site.** The inhibitor causes the enzyme to change shape so that the active site can no longer bind the substrate. When the noncompetitive inhibitor is no longer bound to the enzyme, normal enzyme activity resumes.

Without the inhibitor, the substrate fits into the active site.

When the inhibitor is bound, the active site changes shape and the substrate no longer fits.

A *competitive* **inhibitor has a shape and structure similar to the substrate, so it competes with the substrate for binding to the active site.** The antibiotic **sulfanilamide** (Section 13.13B) is a competitive inhibitor of the enzyme needed to synthesize the vitamin folic acid from *p*-aminobenzoic acid in bacteria. When sulfanilamide binds to the active site, *p*-aminobenzoic acid cannot be converted to folic acid, so a bacterium cannot grow and reproduce. Sulfanilamide does not affect human cells because humans do not synthesize folic acid, and must obtain it in the diet.

sulfanilamide
a competitive inhibitor

*p*-aminobenzoic acid
PABA

folic acid

Both compounds can bind to the active site.

## PROBLEM 21.23

Use the given representations for an enzyme, substrate, and inhibitor to illustrate the process of competitive inhibition.

enzyme    substrate    inhibitor

## PROBLEM 21.24

The nerve gas sarin acts as a poison by covalently bonding to a hydroxyl group in the active site of the enzyme acetylcholinesterase. This binding results in a higher-than-normal amount of acetylcholine at a nerve synapse, resulting in muscle spasms. From this description, would you expect sarin to be a competitive, noncompetitive, or irreversible inhibitor?

### 21.9D  Zymogens

Sometimes an enzyme is synthesized in an inactive form, and then it is converted to its active form when it is needed. The inactive precursor of an enzyme is called a **zymogen** or **proenzyme.** Often the zymogen contains additional amino acids in its peptide chain, which are then cleaved when activation is desired.

cleavage here

inactive zymogen                          active enzyme

For example, the digestive enzymes trypsin and chymotrypsin are synthesized in the pancreas as the zymogens trypsinogen and chymotrypsinogen, respectively. As zymogens, these proteins are inactive and thus they do not digest the proteins that make up the pancreas. When they pass into the small intestines, however, some of the amino acids are removed from the peptide chain to form the active enzymes, which then catalyze the hydrolysis of peptide bonds during protein digestion.

#### PROBLEM 21.25

Explain why the proteins involved in blood clotting, fibrin and thrombin, are first synthesized as the zymogens fibrinogen and prothrombin, respectively.

## 21.10  FOCUS ON HEALTH & MEDICINE
### Using Enzymes to Diagnose and Treat Diseases

Measuring enzyme levels in the blood and understanding the key role of enzymes in biological reactions have aided greatly in both diagnosing and treating diseases.

### 21.10A  Enzyme Levels as Diagnostic Tools

Certain enzymes are present in a higher concentration in particular cells. When the cells are damaged by disease or injury, the cells rupture and die, releasing the enzymes into the bloodstream. Measuring the activity of the enzymes in the blood then becomes a powerful tool to diagnose the presence of disease or injury in some organs.

Measuring enzyme levels is now routine for many different conditions. For example, when a patient comes into an emergency room with chest pain, measuring the level of creatine phosphokinase (CPK) and other enzymes indicates whether a heart attack, which results in damage to some portion of the heart, has occurred. Common enzymes used for diagnosis are listed in Table 21.3.

#### Table 21.3  Common Enzymes Used for Diagnosis

| Enzyme | Condition |
|---|---|
| Creatine phosphokinase | Heart attack |
| Alkaline phosphatase | Liver or bone disease |
| Acid phosphatase | Prostate cancer |
| Amylase, lipase | Diseases of the pancreas |

## 21.10B   Treating Disease with Drugs That Interact with Enzymes

Molecules that inhibit an enzyme can be useful drugs. The antibiotics penicillin and sulfanilamide are two examples discussed in Section 21.9. Drugs used to treat high blood pressure and acquired immune deficiency syndrome (AIDS) are also enzyme inhibitors.

**ACE inhibitors** are a group of drugs used to treat individuals with high blood pressure. Angiotensin is an octapeptide that narrows blood vessels, thus increasing blood pressure. Angiotensin is formed from the zymogen angiotensinogen by action of **ACE, the angiotensin-converting enzyme,** which cleaves two amino acids from the inactive decapeptide.

ACE cleaves here.

Arg–Arg–Val–Tyr–Ile–His–Pro–Phe–His–Leu  ⟶  Arg–Arg–Val–Tyr–Ile–His–Pro–Phe  +  His–Leu

angiotensinogen                                      angiotensin

increases blood pressure

By blocking the conversion of angiotensinogen to angiotensin, blood pressure is decreased. Several effective ACE inhibitors are currently available, including captopril and enalapril.

Generic name: captopril
Trade name: Capoten

Generic name: enalapril
Trade name: Vasotec

Several enzyme inhibitors are also available to treat human immunodeficiency virus (HIV), the virus that causes AIDS. The most effective treatments are **HIV protease inhibitors.** These drugs inhibit the action of the HIV protease enzyme, an essential enzyme needed by HIV to make copies of itself that go on to infect other cells. Deactivating the HIV protease enzyme decreases the virus population, bringing the disease under control. Several protease inhibitors are currently available, and often an individual takes a "cocktail" of several drugs to keep the disease in check. Amprenavir (trade name: Agenerase) is a protease inhibitor taken twice daily by individuals who are HIV positive. The three-dimensional structure of the HIV-1 protease enzyme is shown in Figure 21.16.

Generic name: amprenavir
Trade name: Agenerase

PROBLEM 21.26

How are the structures of the ACE inhibitors captopril and enalapril similar? How are they different?

Figure 21.16 The HIV Protease Enzyme

a. Ball-and-stick model of the HIV protease enzyme

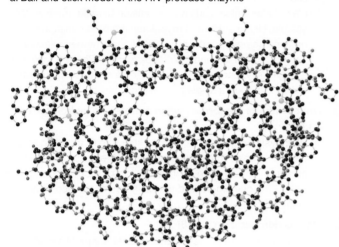

b. Ribbon diagram with the protease inhibitor amprenavir in the active site

# CHAPTER HIGHLIGHTS

## KEY TERMS

Active site (21.9)

Amino acid (21.2)

Coenzyme (21.9)

Cofactor (21.9)

Competitive inhibitor (21.9)

Conjugated protein (21.7)

C-Terminal amino acid (21.4)

Denaturation (21.8)

Dipeptide (21.4)

Enzyme (21.9)

Enzyme–substrate complex (21.9)

Fibrous protein (21.7)

Globular protein (21.7)

α-Helix (21.6)

Heme (21.7)

Induced-fit model (21.9)

Inhibitor (21.9)

Irreversible inhibitor (21.9)

Isoelectric point (21.3)

Lock-and-key model (21.9)

Noncompetitive inhibitor (21.9)

N-Terminal amino acid (21.4)

Peptide (21.4)

Peptide bond (21.4)

β-Pleated sheet (21.6)

Primary structure (21.6)

Protein (21.1)

Quaternary structure (21.6)

Reversible inhibitor (21.9)

Secondary structure (21.6)

Tertiary structure (21.6)

Tripeptide (21.4)

Zwitterion (21.2)

Zymogen (21.9)

## KEY CONCEPTS

❶ **What are the main structural features of an amino acid? (21.2)**

- Amino acids contain an amino group ($NH_2$) on the α carbon to the carboxyl group (COOH). Because they contain both an acid and a base, amino acids exist in their neutral form as zwitterions having the general structure $^+H_3NCH(R)COO^-$. Because they are salts, amino acids are water soluble and have high melting points.

- All amino acids except glycine (R = H) have a chirality center on the α carbon. L Amino acids are naturally occurring.

- Amino acids are subclassified as neutral, acidic, or basic by the functional groups present in the R group, as shown in Table 21.2.

❷ **Describe the acid–base properties of amino acids. (21.3)**

- Neutral, uncharged amino acids exist as zwitterions containing an ammonium cation ($-NH_3^+$) and a carboxylate anion ($-COO^-$).

- When strong acid is added, the carboxylate anion gains a proton and the amino acid has a net +1 charge. When strong base is added, the ammonium cation loses a proton and the amino acid has a net −1 charge.

$$H_3\overset{+}{N}-\underset{\underset{CH_3}{|}}{\overset{\overset{H}{|}}{C}}-COOH \quad \xleftarrow{H^+} \quad H_3\overset{+}{N}-\underset{\underset{CH_3}{|}}{\overset{\overset{H}{|}}{C}}-COO^- \quad \xrightarrow{OH^-} \quad H_2N-\underset{\underset{CH_3}{|}}{\overset{\overset{H}{|}}{C}}-COO^-$$

overall +1 charge            overall −1 charge

pH ≤ 2             pH ≈ 6             pH ≥ 10

**❸ What are the main structural features of peptides? (21.4)**

- Peptides contain amino acids, called amino acid residues, joined together by amide (peptide) bonds. The amino acid that contains the free $-NH_3^+$ group on the $\alpha$ carbon is called the N-terminal amino acid, and the amino acid that contains the free $-COO^-$ group on the $\alpha$ carbon is the C-terminal amino acid.
- Peptides are written from left to right, from the N-terminal to the C-terminal end, using the one- or three-letter abbreviations for the amino acids listed in Table 21.2.

**❹ Give examples of simple biologically active peptides. (21.5)**

- Enkephalins are pentapeptides that act as sedatives and pain killers by binding to pain receptors.
- Oxytocin is a nonapeptide hormone that stimulates the contraction of uterine muscles and initiates the flow of milk in nursing mothers.
- Vasopressin is a nonapeptide hormone that serves as an antidiuretic; that is, vasopressin causes the kidneys to retain water.

**❺ What are the general characteristics of the primary, secondary, tertiary, and quaternary structure of proteins? (21.6)**

- The primary structure of a protein is the particular sequence of amino acids joined together by amide bonds.
- The two most common types of secondary structure are the $\alpha$-helix and the $\beta$-pleated sheet. Both structures are stabilized by hydrogen bonds between the N—H and C=O groups.
- The tertiary structure is the three-dimensional shape adopted by the entire peptide chain. London dispersion forces stabilize hydrophobic interactions between nonpolar amino acids. Hydrogen bonding and ionic interactions occur between polar or charged amino acid residues. Disulfide bonds are covalent sulfur–sulfur bonds that occur between cysteine residues in different parts of the peptide chain.
- When a protein contains more than one polypeptide chain, the quaternary structure describes the shape of the protein complex formed by two or more chains.

**❻ What are the basic features of fibrous proteins like $\alpha$-keratin and collagen? (21.7)**

- Fibrous proteins are composed of long linear polypeptide chains that serve structural roles and are water insoluble.
- $\alpha$-Keratin in hair is a fibrous protein composed almost exclusively of $\alpha$-helix units that wind together to form a superhelix. Disulfide bonds between chains make the resulting bundles of protein chains strong.
- Collagen, found in connective tissue, is composed of a superhelix formed from three elongated left-handed helices.

**❼ What are the basic features of globular proteins like hemoglobin and myoglobin? (21.7)**

- Globular proteins have compact shapes and are folded to place polar amino acids on the outside to make them water soluble. Hemoglobin and myoglobin are both conjugated proteins composed of a protein unit and a heme molecule. The $Fe^{2+}$ ion of the heme binds oxygen. While myoglobin has a single polypeptide chain, hemoglobin contains four peptide chains that form a single protein molecule.

**❽ What products are formed when a protein is hydrolyzed? (21.8)**

- Hydrolysis breaks up the primary structure of a protein to form the amino acids that compose it. All of the amide bonds are broken by the addition of water, forming a carboxylate anion ($-COO^-$) in one amino acid and an ammonium cation ($-NH_3^+$) in the other.

**❾ What is denaturation? (21.8)**

- Denaturation is a process that alters the shape of a protein by disrupting the secondary, tertiary, or quaternary structure. High temperature, acid, base, and agitation can denature a protein. Compact water-soluble proteins uncoil and become less water soluble.

**❿ What are the main structural features of enzymes? (21.9)**

- Enzymes are biological catalysts that greatly increase the rate of biological reactions and are highly specific for a substrate or a type of substrate. An enzyme binds a substrate at its active site, forming an enzyme–substrate complex by either the lock-and-key model or the induced-fit model.
- Enzyme inhibitors cause an enzyme to lose activity. Irreversible inhibition occurs when an inhibitor covalently binds the enzyme and permanently destroys its activity. Competitive reversible inhibition occurs when the inhibitor is structurally similar to the substrate and competes with it for occupation of the active site. Noncompetitive reversible inhibition occurs when an inhibitor binds to a location other than the active site, altering the shape of the active site.

**⓫ How are enzymes used in medicine? (21.10)**

- Measuring blood enzyme levels is used to diagnose heart attacks and diseases that cause higher-than-normal concentrations of certain enzymes to enter the blood.
- Drugs that inhibit the action of an enzyme can be used to kill bacteria. ACE inhibitors are used to treat high blood pressure. HIV protease inhibitors are used to treat HIV by binding to an enzyme needed by the virus to replicate itself.

# PROBLEMS

Selected in-chapter and odd-numbered end-of-chapter problems have brief answers in Appendix B. The *Student Study Guide and Solutions Manual* contains detailed solutions to all in-chapter and odd-numbered end-of-chapter problems, as well as additional worked examples and a chapter self-test.

## Amino Acids

**21.27** Naturally occurring amino acids are L-α-amino acids. What do the L and α designations represent?

**21.28** Why do neutral amino acids exist as zwitterions with no net charge?

**21.29** The amino acid alanine is a solid at room temperature and has a melting point of 315 °C, while pyruvic acid ($CH_3COCO_2H$) has a similar molecular weight but is a liquid at room temperature with a boiling point of 165 °C. Account for the difference.

**21.30** Why is phenylalanine water soluble but 4-phenylbutanoic acid ($C_6H_5CH_2CH_2CH_2COOH$), a compound of similar molecular weight, water insoluble?

**21.31** Draw the structure of a naturally occurring amino acid that:
  a. contains a 1° alcohol
  b. contains an amide
  c. is an essential amino acid with an aromatic ring
  d. is a neutral amino acid with a 3° carbon atom in its side chain

**21.32** Draw the structure of a naturally occurring amino acid that:
  a. contains a 2° alcohol
  b. contains a thiol
  c. is an acidic amino acid
  d. is a neutral amino acid with a phenol in the side chain

**21.33** What two amino acids contain two chirality centers?

**21.34** What makes proline different from all of the other amino acids in Table 21.2?

**21.35** For each amino acid: [1] draw the L enantiomer in a Fischer projection; [2] classify the amino acid as neutral, acidic, or basic; [3] give the three-letter symbol; [4] give the one-letter symbol.
  a. leucine         c. lysine
  b. tryptophan      d. aspartic acid

**21.36** For each amino acid: [1] draw the L enantiomer in a Fischer projection; [2] classify the amino acid as neutral, acidic, or basic; [3] give the three-letter symbol; [4] give the one-letter symbol.
  a. arginine        c. glutamic acid
  b. tyrosine        d. valine

**21.37** Draw both enantiomers of each amino acid and label them as D or L: (a) methionine; (b) asparagine.

**21.38** Which of the following Fischer projections represent naturally occurring amino acids? Name each amino acid and designate it as a D or L isomer.

a.
$$COO^-$$
$$H_3\overset{+}{N}{-}{-}H$$
$$CH_2CH(CH_3)_2$$

b.
$$COO^-$$
$$H{-}{-}\overset{+}{N}H_3$$
$$CH_2COO^-$$

**21.39** For each amino acid: [1] give the name; [2] give the three-letter abbreviation; [3] give the one-letter abbreviation; [4] classify the amino acid as neutral, acidic, or basic.

a.
$$COO^-$$
$$H_3\overset{+}{N}{-}{-}H$$
$$CH_2CH_2CONH_2$$

b.
$$COO^-$$
$$H_3\overset{+}{N}{-}{-}H$$
$$CH_2{-}\!\!\!\bigcirc\!\!\!{-}OH$$

**21.40** For each amino acid: [1] give the name; [2] give the three-letter abbreviation; [3] give the one-letter abbreviation; [4] classify the amino acid as neutral, acidic, or basic.

a.
$$COO^-$$
$$H_3\overset{+}{N}{-}{-}H$$
$$CH_2CH_2SCH_3$$

b.
$$COO^-$$
$$H_3\overset{+}{N}{-}{-}H$$
$$CH_2{-}\text{(imidazole)}$$

## Acid–Base Properties of Amino Acids

**21.41** Draw the amino acid leucine at each pH: (a) 6; (b) 10; (c) 2. Which form predominates at leucine's isoelectric point?

**21.42** Draw the amino acid isoleucine at each pH: (a) 6; (b) 10; (c) 2. Which form predominates at isoleucine's isoelectric point?

**21.43** Draw the structure of the neutral, positively charged, and negatively charged forms of the amino acid tyrosine. Which form predominates at pH 1? Which form predominates at pH 11? Which form predominates at the isoelectric point?

**21.44** Draw the structure of the neutral, positively charged, and negatively charged forms of the amino acid valine. Which form predominates at pH 1? Which form predominates at pH 11? Which form predominates at the isoelectric point?

## Peptides

**21.45** Locate the peptide bond in the dipeptide shown in the ball-and-stick model, and identify the amino acids that form the dipeptide. Name the dipeptide using the three-letter abbreviations for the amino acids.

**21.46** Label the N-terminal and C-terminal amino acids in the dipeptide shown in the ball-and-stick model. Name the dipeptide using the one-letter abbreviations for the amino acids.

**21.47** (a) Draw the structure of the two possible dipeptides that can be formed by combining valine and phenylalanine. (b) In each dipeptide, label the N- and C-terminal amino acids. (c) Name each peptide using three-letter symbols.

**21.48** (a) Draw the structure of the two possible dipeptides that can be formed by combining glycine and asparagine. (b) In each dipeptide, label the N- and C-terminal amino acids. (c) Name each peptide using three-letter symbols.

**21.49** For each tripeptide: [1] draw the structure of the tripeptide; [2] label the amide bonds; [3] identify the N-terminal and C-terminal amino acids; [4] name the peptide using three-letter symbols for the amino acids.
  a. leucylvalyltryptophan
  b. phenylalanylserylthreonine

**21.50** For each tripeptide: [1] draw the structure of the tripeptide; [2] label the amide bonds; [3] identify the N-terminal and C-terminal amino acids; [4] name the peptide using three-letter symbols for the amino acids.
  a. tyrosylleucylisoleucine
  b. methionylisoleucylcysteine

**21.51** For each tripeptide: [1] identify the amino acids that form the peptide; [2] label the N- and C-terminal amino acids; [3] name the tripeptide using three-letter symbols.

a. $H_3\overset{+}{N}-CH-\overset{\overset{\displaystyle O}{\|}}{C}-N-CH-\overset{\overset{\displaystyle O}{\|}}{C}-N-CH-\overset{\overset{\displaystyle O}{\|}}{C}-O^-$
$\quad\quad\quad\ \ CH(CH_3)_2\ \ H\ \ H\quad\quad\quad H\ \ CH_2$ — (phenyl ring)

b. $H_3\overset{+}{N}-CH-\overset{\overset{\displaystyle O}{\|}}{C}-N-CH-\overset{\overset{\displaystyle O}{\|}}{C}-N-CH-\overset{\overset{\displaystyle O}{\|}}{C}-O^-$
$\quad\quad\quad\ \ CH_2\ \ \ H\ \ CH_2\quad\ H\ \ CH_2CH_2SCH_3$
$\quad\quad\quad\ \ CH(CH_3)_2$ — (phenol ring with OH)

**21.52** For each tripeptide: [1] identify the amino acids that form the peptide; [2] label the N- and C-terminal amino acids; [3] name the tripeptide using three-letter symbols.

a. $H_3\overset{+}{N}-CH-\overset{\overset{\displaystyle O}{\|}}{C}-N-CH-\overset{\overset{\displaystyle O}{\|}}{C}-N-CH-\overset{\overset{\displaystyle O}{\|}}{C}-O^-$
$\quad\quad\quad\ \ CH_2\ \ \ H\ \ CH_3\quad\ H\ \ CH(CH_3)CH_2CH_3$
$\quad\quad\quad\ \ COO^-$

b. $H_3\overset{+}{N}-CH-\overset{\overset{\displaystyle O}{\|}}{C}-N-CH-\overset{\overset{\displaystyle O}{\|}}{C}-N-CH-\overset{\overset{\displaystyle O}{\|}}{C}-O^-$
$\quad\quad\quad\ \ CH_2OH\ \ H\ \ CH_2\quad\ H\ \ CH_2CH_2CONH_2$ — (phenyl ring)

**21.53** Draw the structure of the three different tripeptides formed from two moles of serine and one mole of alanine.

**21.54** How many different tripeptides can be formed from three different amino acids, methionine, histidine, and arginine? Using three-letter abbreviations, give the names for all of the possible tripeptides.

**21.55** What amino acids are formed by hydrolysis of the tripeptide depicted in the ball-and-stick model?

**21.56** Give the three-letter abbreviations for the amino acids formed by hydrolysis of the tripeptide depicted in the ball-and-stick model.

**21.57** Draw the structures of the amino acids formed when the tripeptides in Problem 21.51 are hydrolyzed.

**21.58** Draw the structures of the amino acids formed when the tripeptides in Problem 21.52 are hydrolyzed.

**21.59** Bradykinin is a nonapeptide that stimulates smooth muscle contraction, dilates blood vessels, causes pain, and is a component of bee venom. Draw the structure of the amino acids formed on hydrolysis of one mole of bradykinin, and tell how many moles of each amino acid are formed.

Arg–Pro–Pro–Gly–Phe–Ser–Pro–Phe–Arg
bradykinin

**21.60** Aspartame, the methyl ester of a dipeptide, is the common artificial sweetener NutraSweet (Section 20.5B). Draw the structure of the products formed when the amide and ester bonds are hydrolyzed. Which amino acid contains the carbonyl group of the peptide bond? Which amino acid contains the nitrogen atom of the amide bond?

$$H_3\overset{+}{N}-CH-\overset{\overset{\displaystyle O}{\|}}{C}-N-CH-\overset{\overset{\displaystyle O}{\|}}{C}-OCH_3$$

aspartame

**21.61** Chymotrypsin is a digestive enzyme that hydrolyzes only certain peptide bonds: the carbonyl group in the amide bond must come from phenylalanine, tyrosine, or tryptophan. Draw the structure of the amino acids and peptides formed by hydrolysis of the following peptide with chymotrypsin: Gly–Tyr–Gly–Ala–Phe–Val.

**21.62** Trypsin is a digestive enzyme that hydrolyzes peptide bonds only when the carbonyl group in the amide bond comes from lysine or arginine. Draw the structure of the amino acids and peptides formed by hydrolysis of the following peptide with trypsin: Gly–Lys–Arg–Ala–Ala–Arg.

## Proteins

**21.63** What is the difference between the primary and secondary structure of a protein?

**21.64** What is the difference between the tertiary and quaternary structure of a protein?

**21.65** What type of intermolecular forces exist between the side chains of each of the following pairs of amino acids?
  a. isoleucine and valine　　　c. Lys and Glu
  b. threonine and phenylalanine　　d. Arg and Asp

**21.66** Which of the following pairs of amino acids can have intermolecular hydrogen bonding between the functional groups in their side chains?
  a. two tyrosine residues　　　c. phenylalanine and tyrosine
  b. serine and threonine　　　d. alanine and threonine

**21.67** Draw the structures of the amino acids asparagine and serine and show how hydrogen bonding is possible between the two side chains.

**21.68** Draw the structures of the amino acids tyrosine and threonine and show how hydrogen bonding is possible between the two side chains.

**21.69** Label the regions of secondary structure in the following protein ribbon diagram.

**21.70** Label the regions of secondary structure in the following protein ribbon diagram.

**21.71** Compare α-keratin and hemoglobin with regards to each of the following: (a) secondary structure; (b) water solubility; (c) function; (d) location in the body.

**21.72** Compare collagen and myoglobin with regards to each of the following: (a) secondary structure; (b) water solubility; (c) function; (d) location in the body.

**21.73** When a protein is denatured, how is its primary, secondary, tertiary, and quaternary structure affected?

**21.74** Hydrogen bonding stabilizes both the secondary and tertiary structures of a protein. (a) What functional groups hydrogen bond to stabilize secondary structure? (b) What functional groups hydrogen bond to stabilize tertiary structure?

**21.75** Describe the function or biological activity of each protein or peptide: (a) insulin; (b) myoglobin; (c) α-keratin; (d) chymotrypsin; (e) oxytocin.

**21.76** Describe the function or biological activity of each protein or peptide: (a) collagen; (b) hemoglobin; (c) vasopressin; (d) pepsin; (e) met-enkephalin.

## Enzymes

**21.77** What is the difference between reversible and irreversible inhibition?

**21.78** Explain the role of zymogens in (a) controlling blood pressure; (b) the action of digestive enzymes.

**21.79** How are enzyme inhibitors used to treat high blood pressure? Give a specific example of a drug used and an enzyme inhibited.

**21.80** How are enzyme inhibitors used to treat HIV? Give a specific example of a drug used and an enzyme inhibited.

**21.81** Use the given representations for an enzyme, substrate, and inhibitor to illustrate the process of noncompetitive inhibition.

active site

enzyme          substrate          inhibitor

**21.82** Use the given representations for an enzyme and substrate to illustrate the difference between the lock-and-key model and the induced-fit model of enzyme specificity.

active site

enzyme                  substrate

## Applications

**21.83** What structural feature in α-keratin makes fingernails harder than skin?

**21.84** Why does the α-keratin in hair contain many cysteine residues?

**21.85** Why must vegetarian diets be carefully balanced?

**21.86** Why does cooking meat make it easier to digest?

**21.87** Sometimes an incision is cauterized (burned) to close the wound and prevent bleeding. What does cauterization do to protein structure?

**21.88** Why is insulin administered by injection instead of taken in tablet form?

**21.89** How is sickle cell disease related to hemoglobin structure?

**21.90** The silk produced by a silkworm is a protein with a high glycine and alanine content. With reference to the structure, how does this make the silk fiber strong?

**21.91** Explain the difference in the mechanism of action of penicillin and sulfanilamide. How is enzyme inhibition involved in both mechanisms? Why don't penicillin and sulfanilamide kill both human and bacterial cells?

**21.92** How are blood enzyme levels used to diagnose certain diseases? Give an example of a specific condition and enzyme used for diagnosis.

## CHALLENGE PROBLEMS

**21.93** Explain why two amino acids—aspartic acid and glutamic acid—have a +1 net charge at low pH, but a –2 net charge at high pH.

**21.94** Suggest a reason for the following observation. Proteins like collagen that are high in proline content do not contain an α-helix in their secondary structure.

Techniques to analyze DNA samples are commonly utilized in criminal investigations and to screen for genetic diseases.

# Nucleic Acids and Protein Synthesis

## CHAPTER OUTLINE

## CHAPTER GOALS

*In this chapter you will learn how to:*

1. Draw the structure of nucleosides and nucleotides
2. Draw short segments of the nucleic acids DNA and RNA
3. Describe the basic features of the DNA double helix
4. Outline the main steps of replication
5. List the three types and functions of RNA molecules
6. Explain the process of transcription
7. Describe the basic elements of the genetic code
8. Explain the process of translation
9. Define the terms "mutation" and "genetic disease"
10. Describe the basic features of recombinant DNA, the polymerase chain reaction, and DNA fingerprinting
11. Describe the main characteristics of viruses

Whether you are tall or short, fair-skinned or dark-complexioned, blue-eyed or brown-eyed, your unique characteristics are determined by the nucleic acid polymers that reside in the chromosomes of your cells. The nucleic acid **DNA** stores the genetic information of a particular organism, while the nucleic acid **RNA** translates this genetic information into the synthesis of proteins needed by cells for proper function and development. Even minor alterations in the nucleic acid sequence can have significant effects on an organism, sometimes resulting in devastating diseases like sickle cell anemia and cystic fibrosis. In Chapter 22, we study nucleic acids and learn how the genetic information stored in DNA is translated into protein synthesis.

## 22.1  Nucleosides and Nucleotides

**Nucleic acids are unbranched polymers composed of repeating monomers called** *nucleotides.* There are two types of nucleic acids.

- DNA, deoxyribonucleic acid, stores the genetic information of an organism and transmits that information from one generation to another.
- RNA, ribonucleic acid, translates the genetic information contained in DNA into proteins needed for all cellular functions.

The nucleotide monomers that compose DNA and RNA consist of three components—a **monosaccharide, a nitrogen-containing base, and a phosphate group.**

DNA molecules contain several million nucleotides while RNA molecules are much smaller, containing perhaps a few thousand nucleotides. DNA is contained in the chromosomes of the nucleus, each chromosome having a different type of DNA. The number of chromosomes differs from species to species. Humans have 46 chromosomes (23 pairs). An individual chromosome is composed of many genes. **A** *gene* **is a portion of the DNA molecule responsible for the synthesis of a single protein.**

We begin our study of nucleic acids with a look at the structure and formation of the nucleotide monomers.

### 22.1A   Nucleosides—Joining a Monosaccharide and a Base

The nucleotides of both DNA and RNA contain a five-membered ring monosaccharide, often called simply the *sugar* component.

- In RNA, the monosaccharide is the aldopentose D-ribose.
- In DNA the monosaccharide is D-2-deoxyribose, an aldopentose that lacks a hydroxyl group at C2.

D-ribose
(present in RNA)

D-2-deoxyribose
(present in DNA)

Only five common nitrogen-containing bases are present in nucleic acids. Three bases with one ring (**cytosine, uracil,** and **thymine**) are derived from the parent compound **pyrimidine.** Two bases with two rings (**adenine** and **guanine**) are derived from the parent compound **purine.** Each base is designated by a one-letter abbreviation as shown.

pyrimidine
(parent compound)

cytosine
**C**

uracil
**U**

thymine
**T**

purine
(parent compound)

adenine
**A**

guanine
**G**

Uracil (U) occurs only in RNA, while thymine (T) occurs only in DNA. As a result:

- **DNA contains the bases A, G, C, and T.**
- **RNA contains the bases A, G, C, and U.**

A *nucleoside* **is formed by joining the anomeric carbon of the monosaccharide with a nitrogen atom of the base.** A nucleoside is an *N*-glycoside, because it is a nitrogen derivative of the glycosides discussed in Chapter 20. Primes (') are used to number the carbons of the monosaccharide in a nucleoside, to distinguish them from the atoms in the rings of the base.

D-ribose

cytosine
**C**

cytidine
a ribonucleoside

D-2-deoxyribose

adenine
**A**

deoxyadenosine
a deoxyribonucleoside

With pyrimidine bases, the nitrogen atom at the 1 position bonds with the 1' carbon of the sugar. With purine bases, the nitrogen atom at the 9 position bonds with the 1' carbon of the sugar. For example, joining cytosine with ribose forms the ribonucleoside **cytidine.** Joining adenine with 2-deoxyribose forms the deoxyribonucleoside **deoxyadenosine.**

Nucleosides are named as derivatives of the bases from which they are formed.

- To name a nucleoside derived from a pyrimidine base, use the suffix *-idine* (cytosine → cy*tidine*).
- To name a nucleoside derived from a purine base, use the suffix *-osine* (adenine → aden*osine*).
- For deoxyribonucleosides, add the prefix *deoxy-,* as in *deoxy*adenosine.

### SAMPLE PROBLEM 22.1

Identify the base and monosaccharide used to form the following nucleoside, and then name it.

### Analysis

- The sugar portion of a nucleoside contains the five-membered ring. If there is an OH group at C2', the sugar is ribose, and if there is no OH group at C2', the sugar is deoxyribose.
- The base is joined to the five-membered ring as an *N*-glycoside. A pyrimidine base has one ring, and is derived from either cytosine, uracil, or thymine. A purine base has two rings, and is derived from either adenine or guanine.
- Nucleosides derived from pyrimidines end in the suffix *-idine.* Nucleosides derived from purines end in the suffix *-osine.*

### Solution

The sugar contains no OH at C2', so it is derived from deoxyribose. The base is thymine. To name the deoxyribonucleoside, change the suffix of the base to *-idine* and add the prefix *deoxy*; thus, thymine → deoxythymidine.

### PROBLEM 22.1

Identify the base and monosaccharide used to form the following nucleosides, and then assign names.

### PROBLEM 22.2

Draw the structure of guanosine. Number the carbon atoms in the monosaccharide. Classify the compound as a ribonucleoside or a deoxyribonucleoside.

## 22.1B Nucleotides—Joining a Nucleoside with a Phosphate

**Nucleotides are formed by adding a phosphate group to the 5'-OH of a nucleoside.** Nucleotides are named by adding the term *5'-monophosphate* to the name of the nucleoside from which they are derived. **Ribonucleotides** are derived from ribose, while **deoxyribonucleotides** are derived from 2-deoxyribose.

cytidine
a ribonucleoside

cytidine 5'-monophosphate
a ribonucleotide

**CMP**

deoxyadenosine
a deoxyribonucleoside

deoxyadenosine 5'-monophosphate
a deoxyribonucleotide

**dAMP**

Because of the lengthy names of nucleotides, three- or four-letter abbreviations are commonly used instead. Thus, **c**ytidine 5'-**m**ono**p**hosphate is **CMP** and **d**eoxy**a**denosine 5'-**m**ono**p**hosphate is **dAMP.**

Figure 22.1 summarizes the information about nucleic acids and their components learned thus far. Table 22.1 summarizes the names and abbreviations used for the bases, nucleosides, and nucleotides needed in nucleic acid chemistry.

| Figure 22.1 | Type of Compound | Components |
|---|---|---|
| Summary of the Components of Nucleosides, Nucleotides, and Nucleic Acids | Nucleoside | • A monosaccharide + a base<br>• A ribonucleoside contains the monosaccharide ribose.<br>• A deoxyribonucleoside contains the monosaccharide 2-deoxyribose. |
| | Nucleotide | • A nucleoside + phosphate = a monosaccharide + a base + phosphate<br>• A ribonucleotide contains the monosaccharide ribose.<br>• A deoxyribonucleotide contains the monosaccharide 2-deoxyribose. |
| | DNA | • A polymer of deoxyribonucleotides<br>• The monosaccharide is 2-deoxyribose.<br>• The bases are A, G, C, and T. |
| | RNA | • A polymer of ribonucleotides<br>• The monosaccharide is ribose.<br>• The bases are A, G, C, and U. |

**Table 22.1** Names of Bases, Nucleosides, and Nucleotides in Nucleic Acids

| Base | Abbreviation | Nucleoside | Nucleotide | Abbreviation |
|------|------------|-----------|-----------|------------|
| **DNA** | | | | |
| Adenine | A | Deoxyadenosine | Deoxyadenosine 5'-monophosphate | dAMP |
| Guanine | G | Deoxyguanosine | Deoxyguanosine 5'-monophosphate | dGMP |
| Cytosine | C | Deoxycytidine | Deoxycytidine 5'-monophosphate | dCMP |
| Thymine | T | Deoxythymidine | Deoxythymidine 5'-monophosphate | dTMP |
| **RNA** | | | | |
| Adenine | A | Adenosine | Adenosine 5'-monophosphate | AMP |
| Guanine | G | Guanosine | Guanosine 5'-monophosphate | GMP |
| Cytosine | C | Cytidine | Cytidine 5'-monophosphate | CMP |
| Uracil | U | Uridine | Uridine 5'-monophosphate | UMP |

## PROBLEM 22.3

Identify the base and monosaccharide in each nucleotide. Name the nucleotide and give its three- or four-letter abbreviation.

## PROBLEM 22.4

Which nucleic acid (DNA or RNA) contains each of the following components?

a. the sugar ribose
b. the sugar deoxyribose

c. the base T
d. the base U

e. the nucleotide GMP
f. the nucleotide dCMP

Di- and triphosphates can also be prepared from nucleosides by adding two and three phosphate groups, respectively, to the 5'-OH. For example, adenosine can be converted to adenosine 5'-diphosphate and adenosine 5'-triphosphate, abbreviated as ADP and ATP, respectively. We will learn about the central role of these phosphates, especially ATP, in energy production in Chapter 23.

adenosine 5'-diphosphate
**ADP**

adenosine 5'-triphosphate
**ATP**

## SAMPLE PROBLEM 22.2

Draw the structure of the nucleotide GMP.

### Analysis

Translate the abbreviation to a name; GMP is guanosine 5'-monophosphate. First, draw the sugar. Since there is no *deoxy* prefix in the name, GMP is a ribonucleotide and the sugar is ribose. Then draw the base, in this case guanine, bonded to C1' of the sugar ring. Finally, add the phosphate. GMP has one phosphate group bonded to the 5'-OH of the nucleoside.

### Solution

ribose

guanosine 5'-monophosphate
GMP

## PROBLEM 22.5

Draw the structure of each nucleotide: (a) UMP; (b) dTMP; (c) AMP.

## PROBLEM 22.6

Give the name that corresponds to each abbreviation: (a) GTP; (b) dCDP; (c) dTTP; (d) UDP.

## 22.2  Nucleic Acids

phosphodiester

**Nucleic acids—both DNA and RNA—are polymers of nucleotides,** formed by joining the 3'-OH group of one nucleotide with the 5'-phosphate of a second nucleotide in a **phosphodiester** linkage (Section 19.6).

For example, joining the 3'-OH group of dCMP (deoxycytidine 5'-monophosphate) and the 5'-phosphate of dAMP (deoxyadenosine 5'-monophosphate) forms a dinucleotide that contains a 5'-phosphate on one end (called the **5' end**) and a 3'-OH group on the other end (called the **3' end**).

**Figure 22.2**    Primary Structure of a Polynucleotide

In a polynucleotide, phosphodiester bonds join the 3'-carbon of one nucleotide to the 5'-carbon of another. The name of a polynucleotide is read from the 5' end to the 3' end, using the one-letter abbreviations for the bases it contains. Drawn is the structure of the polynucleotide CATG.

As additional nucleotides are added, the nucleic acid grows, each time forming a new phosphodiester linkage that holds the nucleotides together. Figure 22.2 illustrates the structure of a polynucleotide formed from four different nucleotides. Several features are noteworthy.

- A polynucleotide contains a backbone consisting of alternating sugar and phosphate groups. All polynucleotides contain the same sugar–phosphate backbone.
- The identity and order of the bases distinguish one polynucleotide from another.
- A polynucleotide has one free phosphate group at the 5' end.
- A polynucleotide has a free OH group at the 3' end.

The **primary structure** of a polynucleotide is the sequence of nucleotides that it contains. This sequence, which is determined by the identity of the bases, is unique to a nucleic acid. **In DNA, the sequence of bases carries the genetic information of the organism.**

Polynucleotides are named by the sequence of the bases they contain, beginning at the 5' end and using the one-letter abbreviation for the bases. Thus, the polynucleotide in Figure 22.2 contains the bases cytosine, adenine, thymine, and guanine, in order from the 5' end; thus, it is named CATG.

### SAMPLE PROBLEM 22.3

(a) Draw the structure of a dinucleotide formed by joining the 3'-OH group of AMP to the 5'-phosphate in GMP. (b) Label the 5' and 3' ends. (c) Name the dinucleotide.

### Analysis

Draw the structure of each nucleotide, including the sugar, the phosphate bonded to C5', and the base at C1'. In this case the sugar is ribose since the names of the mononucleotides do not contain the prefix *deoxy*. Bond the 3'-OH group to the 5'-phosphate to form the phosphodiester bond. The name of the dinucleotide begins with the nucleotide that contains the free phosphate at the 5' end.

### Solution

a. and b.

c.  Since polynucleotides are named beginning at the 5' end, this dinucleotide is named AG.

### PROBLEM 22.7

Draw the structure of a dinucleotide formed by joining the 3'-OH group of dTMP to the 5'-phosphate in dGMP.

### PROBLEM 22.8

Draw the structure of each polynucleotide: (a) CU; (b) TAG.

## 22.3  The DNA Double Helix

Our current understanding of the structure of DNA is based on the model proposed initially by James Watson and Francis Crick in 1953 (Figure 22.3).

- **DNA consists of two polynucleotide strands that wind into a right-handed double helix.**

The sugar–phosphate backbone lies on the outside of the helix and the bases lie on the inside, perpendicular to the axis of the helix. The two strands of DNA run in *opposite* directions; that is, one strand runs from the 5' end to the 3' end, while the other runs from the 3' end to the 5' end.

The double helix is stabilized by hydrogen bonding between the bases of the two DNA strands as shown in Figure 22.4. A purine base on one strand always hydrogen bonds with a pyrimidine base on the other strand. Two bases hydrogen bond together in a predictable manner, forming **complementary base pairs.**

- **Adenine pairs with thymine using two hydrogen bonds, forming an A–T base pair.**
- **Cytosine pairs with guanine using three hydrogen bonds, forming a C–G base pair.**

**Figure 22.3**    The Three-Dimensional Structure of DNA—A Double Helix

DNA consists of a double helix of polynucleotide chains. In view (a), the three-dimensional molecular model shows the sugar–phosphate backbone with the red (O), black (C), and white (H) atoms visible on the outside of the helix. In view (b), the bases on the interior of the helix are labeled.

**Figure 22.4**    Hydrogen Bonding in the DNA Double Helix

Hydrogen bonding of base pairs (A–T and C–G) holds the two strands of DNA together.

Because of this consistent pairing of bases, knowing the sequence of one strand of DNA allows us to write the sequence of the other strand, as shown in Sample Problem 22.4.

### SAMPLE PROBLEM 22.4

Write the sequence of the complementary strand of the following portion of a DNA molecule: 5'–TAGGCTA–3'.

### Analysis

The complementary strand runs in the opposite direction, from the 3' to the 5' end. Use base pairing to determine the corresponding sequence on the complementary strand: A pairs with T and C pairs with G.

### Solution

Original strand:  5'–T A G G C T A–3'

Complementary strand:  3'–A T C C G A T–5'

### PROBLEM 22.9

Write the complementary strand for each of the following strands of DNA.

a. 5'–AAACGTCC–3'

b. 5'–TATACGCC–3'

c. 5'–ATTGCACCCGC–3'

d. 5'–CACTTGATCGG–3'

Identical twins have the same genetic makeup, so that characteristics determined by DNA—such as hair color, eye color, or complexion—are also identical.

The enormously large DNA molecules that compose the **human genome**—the total DNA content of an individual—pack tightly into the nucleus of the cell. The double-stranded DNA helices wind around a core of protein molecules called **histones** to form a chain of **nucleosomes,** as shown in Figure 22.5. The chain of nucleosomes winds into a supercoiled fiber called **chromatin,** which composes each of the 23 pairs of chromosomes in humans.

In Section 22.2 we learned that the **genetic information of an organism is stored in the sequence of bases of its DNA molecules.** How is this information transferred from one generation to another? How, too, is the information stored in DNA molecules used to direct the synthesis of proteins?

To answer these questions we must understand three key processes.

- *Replication* is the process by which DNA makes a copy of itself when a cell divides.
- *Transcription* is the ordered synthesis of RNA from DNA. In this process, the genetic information stored in DNA is passed onto RNA.
- *Translation* is the synthesis of proteins from RNA. In this process, the genetic message contained in RNA determines the specific amino acid sequence of a protein.

Each chromosome contains many **genes,** those portions of the DNA molecules that result in the synthesis of specific proteins. We say that the genetic message of the DNA molecule is *expressed* in the protein. Only a small fraction (1–2%) of the DNA in a chromosome contains genetic messages or genes that result in protein synthesis.

Figure 22.5    The Structure of a Chromosome

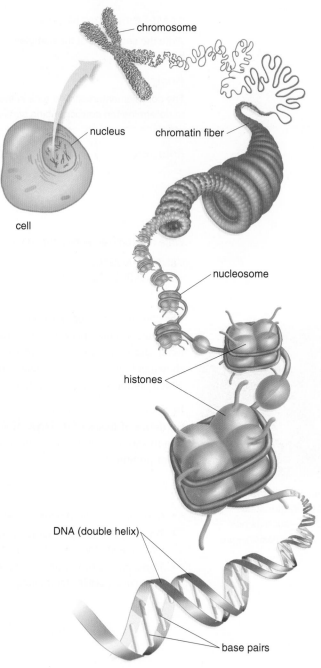

## 22.4    Replication

How is the genetic information in the DNA of a parent cell passed onto new daughter cells during replication? The structure of the double helix and the presence of complementary base pairs are central to the replication process.

During replication, the strands of DNA separate and each serves as a template for a new strand. Thus, **the original DNA molecule forms two DNA molecules, each of which contains one strand from the parent DNA and one new strand.** This process is called **semiconservative replication.** The sequence of both strands of the daughter DNA molecules exactly matches the sequence in the parent DNA.

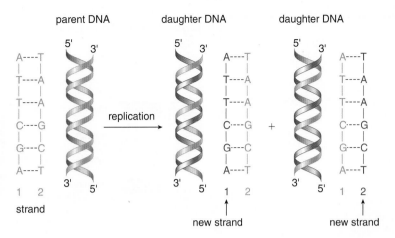

parent DNA     daughter DNA     daughter DNA

Although the semiconservative nature of replication has been known since the elegant experiments of Matthew Meselson and Franklin Stahl were reported in 1958, the details of replication have only slowly been determined over the last 50 years. The first step in replication is the unwinding of the DNA helix to expose the bases on each strand. Unwinding occurs at many places simultaneously along the helix, creating "bubbles" where replication can occur. The point at which unwinding occurs is called the **replication fork.** Unwinding breaks the hydrogen bonds that hold the two strands of the double helix together.

Once bases have been exposed on the unwound strands of DNA, the enzyme DNA polymerase catalyzes the replication process using the four nucleoside triphosphates (derived from the bases A, T, G, and C) that are available in the nucleus. Three features are key and each is illustrated in Figure 22.6.

- The identity of the bases on the template strand determines the order of the bases on the new strand: A must pair with T, and G must pair with C.
- A new phosphodiester bond is formed between the 5'-phosphate of the nucleoside triphosphate and the 3'-OH group of the new DNA strand.
- Replication occurs in only one direction on the template strand, from the 3' end to the 5' end.

Since replication proceeds in only one direction—that is, from the 3' end to the 5' end of the template—the two new strands of DNA must be synthesized by somewhat different techniques. One strand, called the **leading strand,** grows continuously. Since its sequence is complementary to the template, its nucleotide sequence grows in the 5' to 3' direction. The other strand, called the **lagging strand,** is synthesized in small fragments, which are then joined together by a DNA ligase enzyme. The end result is two new strands of DNA, one in each of the daughter DNA molecules, both with complementary base pairs joining the two DNA strands together.

### SAMPLE PROBLEM 22.5

What is the sequence of a newly synthesized DNA segment if the template strand has the sequence 3'–TGCACC–5'?

### Analysis

The newly synthesized strand runs in the opposite direction, from the 5' end to the 3' end in this example. Use base pairing to determine the corresponding sequence on the new strand: A pairs with T and C pairs with G.

### Solution

Template strand:    3'–T G C A C C–5'

New strand:    5'–A C G T G G–3'

**Figure 22.6** DNA Replication

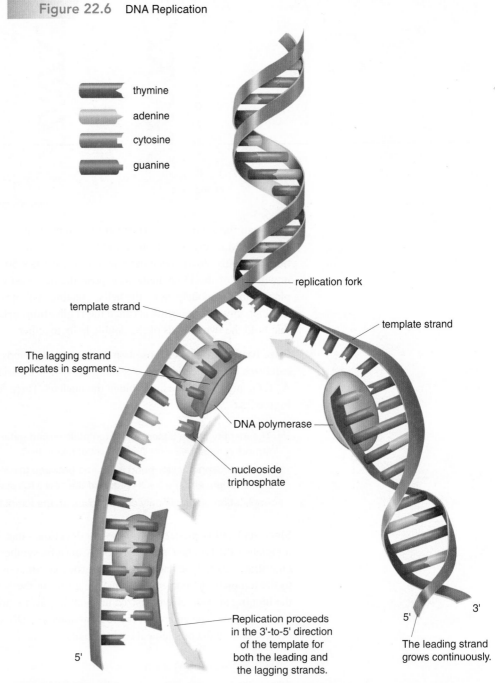

Replication proceeds along both strands of unwound DNA. Replication always occurs in the same direction, from the 3' to the 5' end of the template strand. The leading strand grows continuously, while the lagging strand must be synthesized in fragments that are joined together by a DNA ligase enzyme.

## PROBLEM 22.10

What is the sequence of a newly synthesized DNA segment if the template strand has each of the following sequences?

a. 3'–AGAGTCTC–5'

b. 5'–ATTGCTC–3'

c. 3'–ATCCTGTAC–5'

d. 5'–GGCCATACTC–3'

## 22.5 RNA

While RNA is also composed of nucleotides, there are important differences between DNA and RNA. In RNA,

- The sugar is ribose.
- U (uracil) replaces T (thymine) as one of the bases.
- RNA is single stranded.

RNA molecules are much smaller than DNA molecules. Although RNA contains a single strand, the chain can fold back on itself, forming loops, and intermolecular hydrogen bonding between paired bases on a single strand can form helical regions. When base pairing occurs within an RNA molecule (or between RNA and DNA), **C and G form base pairs,** and **A and U form base pairs.**

There are three different types of RNA molecules.

- Ribosomal RNA (rRNA)
- Messenger RNA (mRNA)
- Transfer RNA (tRNA)

**Ribosomal RNA,** the most abundant type of RNA, is found in the ribosomes in the cytoplasm of the cell. Each ribosome is composed of one large subunit and one small subunit that contain both RNA and protein. rRNA provides the site where polypeptides are assembled during protein synthesis.

**Messenger RNA** is the carrier of information from DNA (in the cell nucleus) to the ribosomes (in the cytoplasm). Each gene of a DNA molecule corresponds to a specific mRNA molecule. The sequence of nucleotides in the mRNA molecule determines the amino acid sequence in a particular protein. mRNA is synthesized from DNA on an as-needed basis, and then rapidly degraded after a particular protein is synthesized.

**Transfer RNA,** the smallest type of RNA, interprets the genetic information in mRNA and brings specific amino acids to the site of protein synthesis in the ribosome. Each amino acid is recognized by one or more tRNA molecules, which contain 70–90 nucleotides. tRNAs have two important sites. The 3' end, called the **acceptor stem,** always contains the nucleotides ACC and has a free OH group that binds a specific amino acid. Each tRNA also contains a sequence of three nucleotides called an **anticodon,** which is complementary to three bases in an mRNA molecule, and identifies what amino acid must be added to a growing polypeptide chain.

tRNA molecules are often drawn in the cloverleaf fashion shown in Figure 22.7a. The acceptor stem and anticodon region are labeled. Folding creates regions of the tRNA in which nearby complementary bases hydrogen bond to each other. A model that more accurately depicts the three-dimensional structure of a tRNA molecule is shown in Figure 22.7b.

Table 22.2 summarizes the characteristics of the three types of RNAs.

**Table 22.2 Three Types of RNA Molecules**

| Type of RNA | Abbreviation | Function |
| --- | --- | --- |
| Ribosomal RNA | rRNA | The site of protein synthesis, found in the ribosomes |
| Messenger RNA | mRNA | Carries the information from DNA to the ribosomes |
| Transfer RNA | tRNA | Brings specific amino acids to the ribosomes for protein synthesis |

**Figure 22.7**

Transfer RNA

a. tRNA–Cloverleaf representation

Folding of the tRNA molecule creates regions in which complementary base pairs hydrogen bond to each other. Each tRNA binds a specific amino acid to its 3' end and contains an anticodon that identifies that amino acid for protein synthesis.

b. tRNA–Three-dimensional representation

In the three-dimensional model of a tRNA, the binding site for the amino acid is shown in yellow and the anticodon is shown in red.

## 22.6  Transcription

The conversion of the information in DNA to the synthesis of proteins begins with *transcription—that is, the synthesis of messenger RNA from DNA.*

RNA synthesis begins in the same manner as DNA replication: the double helix of DNA unwinds (Figure 22.8). Since RNA is single stranded, however, only one strand of DNA is needed for RNA synthesis.

**Figure 22.8**

Transcription

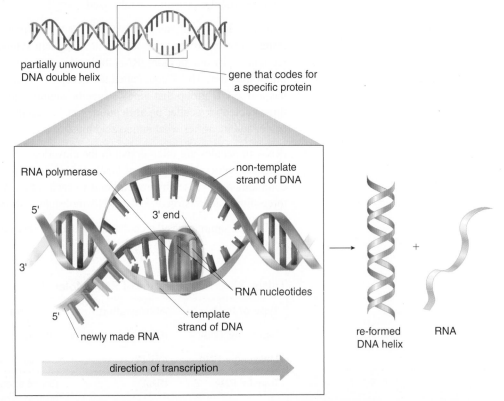

In transcription, the DNA helix unwinds and RNA polymerase catalyzes the formation of mRNA along the DNA template strand. Transcription proceeds from the 3' end to the 5' end of the template, forming an mRNA molecule with base pairs complementary to the DNA template strand.

- The *template* strand is the strand of DNA used for RNA synthesis.
- The *informational* strand (the non-template strand) is the strand of DNA not used for RNA synthesis.

Each mRNA molecule corresponds to a small segment of a DNA molecule. Transcription begins at a particular sequence of bases on the DNA template using an RNA polymerase enzyme, and proceeds from the 3' end to the 5' end of the template strand. Complementary base pairing determines what RNA nucleotides are added to the growing RNA chain: C pairs with G, T pairs with A, and A pairs with U. Thus, the RNA chain grows from the 5' to 3' direction. Transcription is completed when a particular sequence of bases on the DNA template is reached. The new mRNA molecule is released and the double helix of the DNA molecule re-forms.

In bacteria, the new mRNA molecule is ready for protein synthesis immediately after it is prepared. In humans, the mRNA molecule first formed is modified before it is ready for protein synthesis. Portions of the mRNA molecule are removed and pieces of mRNA are spliced together by mechanisms that will not be discussed here.

- Transcription forms a messenger RNA molecule with a sequence that is *complementary* to the DNA template from which it is prepared.
- Since the informational strand of DNA is complementary to the template strand, the mRNA molecule is an *exact copy of the informational strand,* except that the base U replaces T on the RNA strand.

How the base sequence of an RNA molecule compares with the informational and template strands of a DNA molecule is shown in Sample Problem 22.6.

## SAMPLE PROBLEM 22.6

If a portion of the template strand of a DNA molecule has the sequence 3'–CTAGGATAC–5', what is the sequence of the mRNA molecule produced from this template? What is the sequence of the informational strand of this segment of the DNA molecule?

### Analysis

mRNA has a base sequence that is complementary to the template from which it is prepared. mRNA has a base sequence that is identical to the informational strand of DNA, except that it contains the base U instead of T.

### Solution

```
                                                              complementary
Template strand of DNA:   3'–C T A G G A T A C–5'
                                                          complementary
       mRNA sequence:   5'–G A U C C U A U G–3'
Informational strand of DNA:   5'–G A T C C T A T G–3'
```

## PROBLEM 22.11

For each DNA segment: [1] What is the sequence of the mRNA molecule synthesized from each DNA template? [2] What is the sequence of the informational strand of the DNA molecule?

a. 3'–TGCCTAACG–5'          c. 3'–TTAACGCGA–5'
b. 3'–GACTCC–5'             d. 3'–CAGTGACCGTAC–5'

## PROBLEM 22.12

What is the sequence of the DNA template strand from which each of the following mRNA strands were synthesized?

a. 5'–UGGGGCAUU–3'          c. 5'–CCGACGAUG–3'
b. 5'–GUACCU–3'             d. 5'–GUAGUCACG–3'

## 22.7  The Genetic Code

Once the genetic information of DNA has been transcribed in a messenger RNA molecule, RNA can direct the synthesis of an individual protein. How can RNA, which is composed of only four different nucleotides, direct the synthesis of polypeptides that are formed from 20 different amino acids? The answer lies in the **genetic code.**

- A sequence of three nucleotides (a triplet) codes for a specific amino acid. Each triplet is called a *codon.*

For example, the codon UAC in an mRNA molecule codes for the amino acid serine, and the codon UGC codes for the amino acid cysteine. The same genetic code occurs in almost all organisms, from bacteria to whales to humans.

Given four different nucleotides (A, C, G, and U), there are 64 different ways to combine them into groups of three, so there are 64 different codons. Sixty-one codons code for specific amino acids, so many amino acids correspond to more than one codon, as shown in Table 22.3. For example, the codons GGU, GGC, GGA, and GGG all code for the amino acid glycine. Three codons—UAA, UAG, and UGA—do not correspond to any amino acids; they are called **stop codons** because they signal the termination of protein synthesis.

**Table 22.3** The Genetic Code—Triplets in Messenger RNA

| First Base (5' end) | Second Base | | | | | | | Third Base (3' end) |
|---|---|---|---|---|---|---|---|---|
| | U | | C | | A | | G | |
| U | UUU | Phe | UCU | Ser | UAU | Tyr | UGU | Cys | U |
| | UUC | Phe | UCC | Ser | UAC | Tyr | UGC | Cys | C |
| | UUA | Leu | UCA | Ser | UAA | Stop | UGA | Stop | A |
| | UUG | Leu | UCG | Ser | UAG | Stop | UGG | Trp | G |
| C | CUU | Leu | CCU | Pro | CAU | His | CGU | Arg | U |
| | CUC | Leu | CCC | Pro | CAC | His | CGC | Arg | C |
| | CUA | Leu | CCA | Pro | CAA | Gln | CGA | Arg | A |
| | CUG | Leu | CCG | Pro | CAG | Gln | CGG | Arg | G |
| A | AUU | Ile | ACU | Thr | AAU | Asn | AGU | Ser | U |
| | AUC | Ile | ACC | Thr | AAC | Asn | AGC | Ser | C |
| | AUA | Ile | ACA | Thr | AAA | Lys | AGA | Arg | A |
| | AUG | Met | ACG | Thr | AAG | Lys | AGG | Arg | G |
| G | GUU | Val | GCU | Ala | GAU | Asp | GGU | Gly | U |
| | GUC | Val | GCC | Ala | GAC | Asp | GGC | Gly | C |
| | GUA | Val | GCA | Ala | GAA | Glu | GGA | Gly | A |
| | GUG | Val | GCG | Ala | GAG | Glu | GGG | Gly | G |

### PROBLEM 22.13

What amino acid is coded for by each codon?

   a. GCC        b. AAU        c. CUA        d. AGC        e. CAA        f. AAA

### PROBLEM 22.14

What codons code for each amino acid?

   a. glycine        b. isoleucine        c. lysine        d. glutamic acid

Codons are written from the 5' to 3' end of mRNA. The 5' end of the mRNA molecule codes for the N-terminal amino acid in a protein, and the 3' end of the mRNA molecule codes for the C-terminal amino acid. Sample Problem 22.7 illustrates the conversion of a sequence of bases in mRNA to a sequence of amino acids in a peptide.

### SAMPLE PROBLEM 22.7

Derive the amino acid sequence that is coded for by the following mRNA sequence.

5' CAU AAA ACG GUG UUA AUA 3'

#### Analysis

Use Table 22.3 to identify the codons that correspond to each amino acid. Codons are written from the 5' to 3' end of an mRNA molecule and correspond to a peptide written from the N-terminal to C-terminal end.

#### Solution

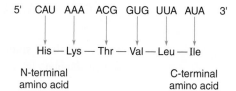

### PROBLEM 22.15

Derive the amino acid sequence that is coded for by each mRNA sequence.

   a. 5' CAA GAG GUA UCC UAC AGA 3'
   b. 5' GUC AUC UGG AGG GGC AUU 3'
   c. 5' CUA UGC AGU AGG ACA CCC 3'

### PROBLEM 22.16

Write a possible mRNA sequence that codes for each of the following peptides.

   a. Met–Arg–His–Phe             c. Gln–Asn–Gly–Ile–Val
   b. Gly–Ala–Glu–Gln             d. Thr–His–Asp–Cys–Trp

### PROBLEM 22.17

Considering the given sequence of nucleotides in an mRNA molecule, (a) what is the sequence of the DNA template strand from which the RNA was synthesized? (b) What peptide is synthesized by this mRNA sequence?

5' GAG CCC GUA UAC GCC ACG 3'

## 22.8 Translation and Protein Synthesis

The translation of the information in messenger RNA to protein synthesis occurs in the ribosomes. Each type of RNA plays a role in protein synthesis.

- mRNA contains the sequence of codons that determines the order of amino acids in the protein.
- Individual tRNAs bring specific amino acids to add to the peptide chain.
- rRNA contains binding sites that provide the platform on which protein synthesis occurs.

Each individual tRNA contains an **anticodon** of three nucleotides that is complementary to the codon in mRNA and identifies individual amino acids (Section 22.5). For example, a codon of UCA in mRNA corresponds to an anticodon of AGU in a tRNA molecule, which identifies serine as the amino acid. Other examples are shown in Table 22.4.

mRNA          tRNA          amino acid

UCA  ⟶  AGU  ⟶  serine

codon          anticodon

### Table 22.4  Relating Codons, Anticodons, and Amino Acids

| mRNA Codon | | tRNA Anticodon | | Amino Acid |
|:---:|:---:|:---:|:---:|:---:|
| ACA | ⟶ | UGU | ⟶ | threonine |
| GCG | ⟶ | CGC | ⟶ | alanine |
| AGA | ⟶ | UCU | ⟶ | arginine |
| UCC | ⟶ | AGG | ⟶ | serine |

### PROBLEM 22.18

For each codon: [1] Write the anticodon. [2] What amino acid does each codon represent?

  a. CGG       b. GGG       c. UCC       d. AUA       e. CCU       f. GCC

**There are three stages in translation: initiation, elongation, and termination.** Figure 22.9 depicts the main features of translation.

## [1] Initiation

Translation begins when an mRNA molecule binds to the smaller subunit of the ribosome and a tRNA molecule carries the first amino acid of the peptide chain to the binding site. Translation always begins at the codon AUG, which codes for the amino acid methionine. The arriving tRNA contains an anticodon with the complementary base sequence UAC. The large and small subunits of the ribosome combine to form a tight complex where protein synthesis takes place.

## [2] Elongation

The next tRNA molecule containing an anticodon for the second codon binds to mRNA, delivering its amino acid, and a peptide bond forms between the two amino acids. The first tRNA molecule, which has delivered its amino acid and is no longer needed, dissociates from the complex. The ribosome shifts to the next codon along the mRNA strand and the process continues when a new tRNA molecule binds to the mRNA. Protein synthesis always occurs on two adjacent sites of the ribosome.

## [3] Termination

Translation continues until a stop codon is reached. There is no tRNA that contains an anticodon complementary to any of the three stop codons (UAA, UAG, and UGA), so protein synthesis ends and the protein is released from the ribosome. Often the first amino acid in the chain, methionine, is not needed in the final protein and so it is removed after protein synthesis is complete.

Figure 22.10 shows a representative segment of DNA, and the mRNA, tRNA, and amino acid sequences that correspond to it.

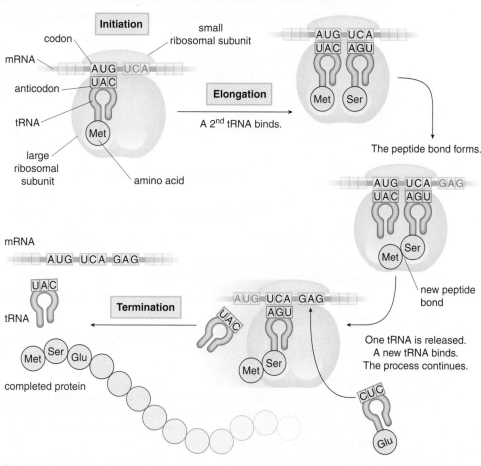

Figure 22.9    Translation—The Synthesis of Proteins from RNA

- **Initiation** consists of the binding of the ribosomal subunits to mRNA and the arrival of the first tRNA carrying its amino acid. Hydrogen bonding occurs between the complementary bases of the codon of mRNA and the anticodon of the tRNA.

- The protein is synthesized during **elongation.** One by one a tRNA with its designated amino acid binds to a site on the ribosome adjacent to the first tRNA. A peptide bond forms and a tRNA is released. The ribosome shifts to the next codon and the process continues.

- **Termination** occurs when a stop codon is reached. The synthesis is complete and the protein is released from the complex.

Figure 22.10    Comparing the Sequence of DNA, mRNA, tRNA, and a Polypeptide

| | | | | | | | |
|---|---|---|---|---|---|---|---|
| DNA informational strand → 5' end | ATG | TTG | GGA | GCC | GGA | TCA | 3' end |
| DNA template strand → 3' end | TAC | AAC | CCT | CGG | CCT | AGT | 5' end |
| mRNA → 5' end | AUG | UUG | GGA | GCC | GGA | UCA | 3' end |
| tRNA anticodons → | UAC | AAC | CCU | CGG | CCU | AGU | |
| Polypeptide → | Met | Leu | Gly | Ala | Gly | Ser | |

### SAMPLE PROBLEM 22.8

What sequence of amino acids would be formed from the following mRNA sequence:
5' CAA AAG ACG UAC CGA 3'? List the anticodons contained in each of the needed
tRNA molecules.

### Analysis

Use Table 22.3 to determine the amino acid that is coded for by each codon. The anticodons contain
complementary bases to the codons: A pairs with U, and C pairs with G.

### Solution

### PROBLEM 22.19

What sequence of amino acids would be formed from each mRNA sequence? List the anticodons
contained in each of the needed tRNA molecules.

  a. 5' CCA CCG GCA AAC GAA GCA 3'          b. 5' GCA CCA CUA AGA GAC 3'

### SAMPLE PROBLEM 22.9

What polypeptide would be synthesized from the following template strand of DNA:
3' CGG TGT CTT TTA 5'?

### Analysis

To determine what polypeptide is synthesized from a DNA template, two steps are needed. First use
the DNA sequence to determine the transcribed mRNA sequence: C pairs with G, T pairs with A,
and A (on DNA) pairs with U (on mRNA). Then use the codons in Table 22.3 to determine what amino
acids are coded for by a given codon in mRNA.

### Solution

|  | | |
|---|---|---|
| DNA template strand: ⟶ | 3' CGG  TGT  CTT  TTA 5' |
| mRNA: ⟶ | 5' GCC  ACA  GAA  AAU 3' |
| Polypeptide: ⟶ | Ala — Thr — Glu — Asn |

### PROBLEM 22.20

What polypeptide would be synthesized from each of the following template strands of DNA?

  a. 3' TCT CAT CGT AAT GAT TCG 5'          b. 3' GCT CCT AAA TAA CAC TTA 5'

## 22.9  Mutations and Genetic Diseases

Although replication provides a highly reliable mechanism for making an exact copy of DNA,
occasionally an error occurs, thus producing a DNA molecule with a slightly different nucleotide
sequence.

> • A *mutation* is a change in the nucleotide sequence in a molecule of DNA.

If the mutation occurs in a nonreproductive cell, the mutation is passed on to daughter cells within
the organism, but is not transmitted to the next generation. If the mutation occurs in an egg or
sperm cell, it is passed on to the next generation of an organism. Some mutations are random
events, while others are caused by **mutagens,** chemical substances that alter the structure of DNA.
Exposure to high-energy radiation such as X-rays or ultraviolet light can also produce mutations.

Mutations can be classified according to the change that results in a DNA molecule.

- A *point* mutation is the *substitution* of one nucleotide for another.

- A *deletion* mutation occurs when one or more nucleotides is *lost* from a DNA molecule.

- An *insertion* mutation occurs when one or more nucleotides is *added* to a DNA molecule.

A mutation can have a negligible, minimal, or catastrophic effect on an organism. To understand the effect of a mutation, we must determine the mRNA sequence that is transcribed from the DNA sequence as well as the resulting amino acid for which it codes. A point mutation in the three-base sequence CTT in a gene that codes for a particular protein illustrates some possible outcomes of a mutation.

The sequence CTT in DNA is transcribed to the codon GAA in mRNA, and using Table 22.3, this triplet codes for the amino acid glutamic acid. If a point mutation replaces CTT by CTC in DNA, CTC is transcribed to the codon GAG in mRNA. Since GAG codes for the *same* amino acid—glutamic acid—this mutation does not affect the protein synthesized by this segment of DNA. Such a mutation is said to be **silent.**

Alternatively, suppose a point mutation replaces CTT by CAT in DNA. CAT is transcribed to the codon GUA in mRNA, and GUA codes for the amino acid valine. Now, the mutation produces a protein with one *different* amino acid—namely, valine instead of glutamic acid. In some proteins this alteration of the primary sequence may have little effect on the protein's secondary and tertiary structure. In other proteins, such as hemoglobin, the substitution of valine for glutamic acid produces a protein with vastly different properties, resulting in the fatal disease sickle cell anemia (Section 21.7).

Finally, suppose a point mutation replaces CTT by ATT in DNA. ATT is transcribed to the codon UAA in mRNA, and UAA is a stop codon. This terminates protein synthesis and no more amino acids are added to the protein chain. In this case, a needed protein is not synthesized and depending on the protein's role, the organism may die.

Original: CTT ⟶ GAA ⟶ Glu
DNA      mRNA

Point mutation: ATT ⟶ UAA ⟶ Stop

Protein synthesis stops and the effects may be catastrophic.

## SAMPLE PROBLEM 22.10

(a) What dipeptide is produced from the following segment of DNA: AGAGAT? (b) What happens to the dipeptide when a point mutation occurs and the DNA segment contains the sequence ATAGAT instead?

### Analysis

Transcribe the DNA sequence to an mRNA sequence with complementary base pairs. Then use Table 22.3 to determine what amino acids are coded for by each codon.

### Solution

a. Since UCU codes for serine and CUA codes for leucine, the dipeptide Ser–Leu results.

b. Since UAU codes for tyrosine, the point mutation results in the synthesis of the dipeptide Tyr–Leu.

## PROBLEM 22.21

Consider the following sequence of DNA: AACTGA. (a) What dipeptide is formed from this DNA after transcription and translation? (b) How is the amino acid sequence affected when point mutations produce each of the following DNA sequences: [1] AACGGA; [2] ATCTGA; [3] AATTGA?

## PROBLEM 22.22

Suppose a deletion mutation occurs and the DNA segment TATGCACTT is converted to TAACTT. How do the peptides synthesized from each of these DNA segments compare?

**HEALTH NOTE**

A patient with cystic fibrosis must regularly receive chest physiotherapy, a procedure that involves pounding on the chest to dislodge thick mucus clogging the lungs.

When a mutation causes a protein deficiency or results in a defective protein and the condition is inherited from one generation to another, a **genetic disease** results. For example, cystic fibrosis, the most common genetic disease in Caucasians, is caused by a mutation resulting in the synthesis of a defective protein—cystic fibrosis transmembrane conductance regulator (CFTR)—needed for proper passage of ions across cell membranes. Individuals with cystic fibrosis have decreased secretions of pancreatic enzymes, resulting in a failure to thrive (poor growth), and they produce thick sticky mucus in the lungs that leads to devastating lung infections and a shortened life span. Other genetic diseases and their molecular bases are listed in Table 22.5.

## Table 22.5  Genetic Diseases

| Disease | Characteristics |
|---|---|
| Tay–Sachs disease | Mental retardation; caused by a defective hexosaminidase A enzyme |
| Sickle cell anemia | Anemia; occlusion and inflammation of blood capillaries, caused by defective hemoglobin |
| Phenylketonuria | Mental retardation; caused by a deficiency of the enzyme phenylalanine hydroxylase needed to convert the amino acid phenylalanine to tyrosine |
| Galactosemia | Mental retardation; caused by a deficiency of an enzyme needed for galactose metabolism |
| Huntington's disease | Progressive physical disability; caused by a defect in the gene that codes for the Htt protein, resulting in degeneration in the neurons in certain areas of the brain. |

## 22.10 Recombinant DNA

Laboratory techniques devised over the last 30 years allow scientists to manipulate DNA molecules and produce new forms of DNA that do not occur in nature.

- • *Recombinant DNA* is synthetic DNA that contains segments from more than one source.

The term **genetic engineering** is often used to describe the process of manipulating DNA in the laboratory that allows a gene (a segment of DNA) in one organism to be spliced (inserted) into the DNA of another organism, thus forming recombinant DNA.

### 22.10A General Principles

Three key elements are needed to form recombinant DNA:

- • A **DNA molecule** into which a new DNA segment will be inserted
- • An **enzyme** that cleaves DNA at specific locations
- • A **gene from a second organism** that will be inserted in the original DNA molecule

Forming recombinant DNA often begins with circular, double-stranded DNA molecules called **plasmids** in the bacteria *Escherichia coli* (*E. coli*) (Figure 22.11). Plasmid DNA is isolated from the bacteria and then cleaved (cut) at a specific site with an enzyme called a **restriction endonuclease.** Many different restriction endonucleases are known. Each enzyme recognizes a specific sequence of bases in a DNA molecule and cuts the double-stranded DNA at a particular position.

**Figure 22.11**

Preparing Recombinant DNA

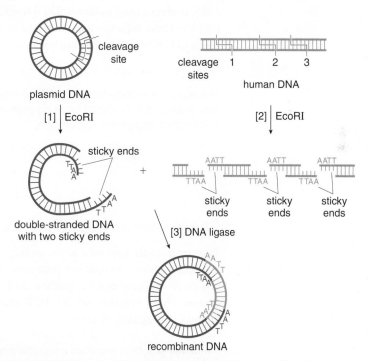

[1] Bacterial plasmid DNA is cut by the restriction endonuclease EcoRI to form double-stranded linear DNA with two sticky ends.

[2] A second sample of human DNA is cut with the same restriction endonuclease to form DNA segments having sticky ends that are complementary to those of the plasmid DNA.

[3] Combining the two pieces of DNA in the presence of a DNA ligase enzyme forms DNA containing the new segment. The recombinant DNA is larger than the original plasmid because of the inserted segment of DNA.

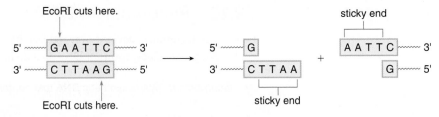

For example, the enzyme EcoRI recognizes the sequence GAATTC, and cuts the DNA molecule between G and A on *both* strands. Since the plasmid DNA is circular to begin with, this forms linear double-stranded DNA with two ends of known sequence. These ends are called **sticky ends** because one strand contains unpaired bases that are ready to hydrogen bond with another DNA segment having the complementary base sequence.

If the same restriction endonuclease is now used to cut DNA from another source, say human DNA, a second segment of DNA is now available having the needed complementary base sequence. When the two segments of DNA are combined together in the presence of a DNA ligase enzyme, the DNA segment is joined to the open plasmid DNA and a recombinant DNA molecule is formed.

The newly engineered recombinant DNA molecule can then be re-inserted into a bacterial cell. Transcription converts the recombinant DNA into RNA and RNA directs the synthesis of the protein that corresponds to the inserted DNA sequence. Since bacteria rapidly grow and divide, large amounts of protein can be synthesized by this method in a short period of time.

Insulin, a hormone used by millions of individuals with diabetes, was the first genetically engineered protein available in significant quantities by these methods. Prior to its availability in 1983, diabetics used insulin isolated from cows or pigs. This insulin has a similar but not identical amino acid sequence to human insulin, as we learned in Section 21.6. These small differences can lead to allergic reactions in some individuals.

### PROBLEM 22.23

The restriction endonuclease HindIII recognizes the DNA sequence AAGCTT and cuts the DNA between A and A. Given the following segment of double-stranded DNA, draw the sticky ends that result from cleavage with this enzyme.

5' ∼∼∼ C C A A G C T T G G A T T ∼∼∼ 3'

3' ∼∼∼ G G T T C G A A C C T A A ∼∼∼ 5'

## 22.10B   Polymerase Chain Reaction

In order to study a specific gene, such as the gene that causes the fatal inherited disorder cystic fibrosis, millions of copies of pure gene are needed. In fact, virtually an unlimited number of copies of any gene can be synthesized in just a few hours using a technique called the **polymerase chain reaction (PCR)**. PCR *clones* a segment of DNA; that is, PCR produces exact copies of a fragment of DNA.

- In this way, PCR *amplifies* a specific portion of a DNA molecule, producing millions of copies of a single molecule.

Four elements are needed to amplify DNA by PCR:

- The **segment of DNA** that must be copied
- **Two primers**—short polynucleotides that are complementary to the two ends of the segment to be amplified
- A **DNA polymerase enzyme** that will catalyze the synthesis of a complementary strand of DNA from a template strand
- **Nucleoside triphosphates** that serve as the source of the nucleotides A, T, C, and G needed in the synthesis of the new strands of DNA

Each cycle of the polymerase chain reaction involves three steps, illustrated in the stepwise *How To* procedure.

## How To Use the Polymerase Chain Reaction to Amplify a Sample of DNA

**Step [1]** Heat the DNA segment to unwind the double helix to form single strands.

double-stranded DNA segment

two single strands of DNA

**Step [2]** Add primers that are complementary to the DNA sequence at either end of the DNA segment to be amplified.

primers

short segment of double-stranded DNA

two single strands of DNA

short segment of double-stranded DNA

- The primers must hydrogen bond to a single strand of DNA and thus they must have the complementary sequence to the template strand.
- The primers form a short segment of double-stranded DNA on each strand, to which the DNA polymerase can add new nucleotides to the 3' end.

**Step [3]** Use a DNA polymerase and added nucleotides to lengthen the DNA segment.

nucleotides

DNA polymerase

two double-stranded DNA segments

- DNA polymerase catalyzes the synthesis of a new strand of DNA complementary to the existing strand using nucleoside triphosphates (dATP, dCTP, dGTP, and dTTP) available in the reaction mixture.
- After one three-step cycle, *one* molecule of double-stranded DNA has formed *two* molecules of double-stranded DNA. Each double-stranded DNA molecule contains one original strand and one newly synthesized strand.
- **After each cycle, the amount of DNA *doubles*.** After 20 cycles, about 1,000,000 copies have been made.

Each step of a PCR cycle is carried out at a different temperature. PCR is now a completely auto-mated process using a **thermal cycler,** an apparatus that controls the heating and cooling needed for each step. A heat-tolerant DNA polymerase called **Taq polymerase** is also typically used, so that new enzyme need not be added as each new cycle begins.

## 22.10C FOCUS ON THE HUMAN BODY
### DNA Fingerprinting

Because the DNA of each individual is unique, **DNA fingerprinting** is now routinely used as a method of identification.

Almost any type of cell—skin, saliva, semen, blood, and so forth—can be used to obtain a DNA fingerprint. After the DNA in a sample is amplified using PCR techniques, the DNA is cut into fragments with various restriction enzymes and the fragments are separated by size using a technique called gel electrophoresis. DNA fragments can be visualized on X-ray film after they react with a radioactive probe. The result is an image consisting of a set of horizontal bands, each band corresponding to a segment of DNA, sorted from low to high molecular weight.

To compare the DNA of different individuals, samples are placed next to each other on the same gel and the position of the horizontal bands compared. DNA fingerprinting is now routinely used in criminal cases to establish the guilt or innocence of a suspect (Figure 22.12). Only identical twins have identical DNA, but related individuals have several similar DNA fragments. Thus, DNA fingerprinting can be used to establish paternity by comparing the DNA of a child with that of each parent. DNA is also used to identify a body when no other means of identification is possible. DNA analysis was instrumental in identifying human remains found in the rubble of the World Trade Center after the towers collapsed on September 11, 2001.

Each band corresponds to a fragment of DNA.

Decreasing size of DNA fragments

### Figure 22.12

DNA Fingerprinting in Forensic Analysis

Each vertical lane (numbered 1–13) corresponds to a DNA sample.

- Lanes 1, 3, 9, and 13 are called DNA ladders. They correspond to DNA fragments of known size and are used to show the approximate size of the DNA fragments of the fingerprints.

- Lane 4 is the DNA obtained from a female assault victim and lane 7 is the female DNA from the crime scene. The two lanes match, indicating that they are from the same individual.

- Two individuals (**A** and **B**), whose DNA appears in lanes 5 and 6, were considered suspects.

- The male DNA obtained at the crime scene is shown in lane 8. The horizontal bands correspond to those of suspect **A**, incriminating him and eliminating individual **B** as a suspect.

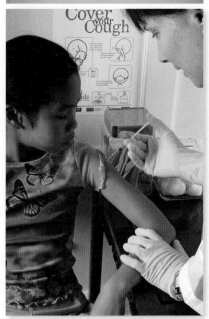

Childhood vaccinations have significantly decreased the incidence of once common diseases such as chickenpox, measles, and mumps.

## 22.11   FOCUS ON HEALTH & MEDICINE
### Viruses

**A *virus* is an infectious agent consisting of a DNA or RNA molecule that is contained within a protein coating.** Since a virus contains no enzymes or free nucleotides of its own, it is incapable of replicating. When it invades a host organism, however, it takes over the biochemical machinery of the host.

A virus that contains DNA uses the materials in the host organism to replicate its DNA, transcribe DNA to RNA, and synthesize a protein coating, thus forming new virus particles. These new virus particles leave the host cell and infect new cells and the process continues. Many prevalent diseases, including the common cold, influenza, and herpes are viral in origin.

A vaccine is an inactive form of a virus that causes an individual's immune system to produce antibodies to the virus to ward off infection. Many childhood diseases that were once very common, including mumps, measles, and chickenpox, are now prevented by vaccination. Polio has been almost completely eradicated, even in remote areas worldwide, by vaccination.

A virus that contains a core of RNA is called a **retrovirus.** Once a retrovirus invades a host organism, it must first make DNA by a process called **reverse transcription** (Figure 22.13). Once viral DNA has been synthesized, the DNA can transcribe RNA, which can direct protein synthesis. New retrovirus particles are thus synthesized and released to infect other cells.

AIDS (acquired immune deficiency syndrome) is caused by HIV (human immunodeficiency virus), a retrovirus that attacks lymphocytes central to the body's immune response against invading organisms. As a result, an individual infected with HIV becomes susceptible to life-threatening bacterial infections. HIV is spread by direct contact with the blood or other body fluids of an infected individual.

Major progress in battling the AIDS epidemic has occurred in recent years. HIV is currently best treated with a "cocktail" of drugs designed to destroy the virus at different stages of its reproductive cycle. One group of drugs, the protease inhibitors such as amprenavir (Section 21.10), act as enzyme inhibitors that prevent viral RNA from synthesizing needed proteins.

AZT, also called zidovudine and originally sold under the trade name Retrovir, has been available since the 1990s for the treatment of HIV.

Other drugs are designed to interfere with reverse transcription, an essential biochemical process unique to the virus. Two drugs in this category are **AZT** (azidodeoxythymidine) and **ddI** (dideoxyinosine). These drugs are synthetic analogues of nucleosides. The structure of each drug closely resembles the nucleotides that must be incorporated in viral DNA, and thus they are inserted into a growing DNA strand after a phosphate is introduced at the 5'-OH. Each drug lacks a hydroxyl group at the 3' position, however, so no additional nucleotide can be added to the DNA chain, thus halting DNA synthesis.

no OH group → 3' N$_3$

**azidodeoxythymidine
AZT**

no OH group → 3'

**dideoxyinosine
ddI**

**Figure 22.13**

How a Retrovirus Infects an Organism

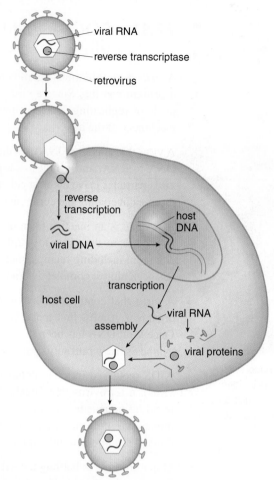

A retrovirus (containing viral RNA and a reverse transcriptase) binds and infects a host cell. Reverse transcription forms viral DNA from RNA. One strand of viral DNA becomes a template to transcribe viral RNA, which is then translated into viral proteins. A new virus is assembled and the virus leaves the host cell to infect other cells.

Thus, HIV protease inhibitors and nucleoside analogues both disrupt the life cycle of HIV but they do so by very different mechanisms.

## PROBLEM 22.24

Explain why antibiotics such as sulfanilamide and penicillin (Sections 21.9) are effective in treating bacterial infections but are completely ineffective in treating viral infections.

# CHAPTER HIGHLIGHTS

## KEY TERMS

Anticodon (22.8)

Codon (22.7)

Complementary base pairs (22.3)

Deletion mutation (22.9)

Deoxyribonucleic acid (DNA, 22.1, 22.3)

Deoxyribonucleoside (22.1)

Deoxyribonucleotide (22.1)

DNA fingerprinting (22.10)

Gene (22.1)

Genetic code (22.7)

Genetic disease (22.9)

Genetic engineering (22.10)

Insertion mutation (22.9)

Lagging strand (22.4)

Leading strand (22.4)

Messenger RNA (mRNA, 22.5)

Mutation (22.9)

Nucleic acid (22.1, 22.2)

Nucleoside (22.1)

Nucleotide (22.1)

Plasmid (22.10)

Point mutation (22.9)

Polymerase chain reaction (PCR, 22.10)

Polynucleotide (22.2)

Recombinant DNA (22.10)

Replication (22.4)

Restriction endonuclease (22.10)

Retrovirus (22.11)

Reverse transcription (22.11)

Ribonucleic acid (RNA, 22.1, 22.5)

Ribonucleoside (22.1)

Ribonucleotide (22.1)

Ribosomal RNA (rRNA, 22.5)

Transcription (22.6)

Transfer RNA (tRNA, 22.5)

Translation (22.8)

Virus (22.11)

## KEY CONCEPTS

**❶ What are the main structural features of nucleosides and nucleotides? (22.1)**

- A nucleoside contains a monosaccharide joined to a base at the anomeric carbon.
- A nucleotide contains a monosaccharide joined to a base, and a phosphate bonded to the 5'-OH group of the monosaccharide.
- The monosaccharide is either ribose or 2-deoxyribose, and the bases are abbreviated as A, G, C, T, and U.

**❷ How do the nucleic acids DNA and RNA differ in structure? (22.2)**

- DNA is a polymer of deoxyribonucleotides, where the sugar is 2-deoxyribose and the bases are A, G, C, and T. DNA is double stranded.
- RNA is a polymer of ribonucleotides, where the sugar is ribose and the bases are A, G, C, and U. RNA is single stranded.

**❸ Describe the basic features of the DNA double helix. (22.3)**

- DNA consists of two polynucleotide strands that wind into a right-handed double helix. The sugar–phosphate backbone lies on the outside of the helix and the bases lie on the inside. The two strands run in opposite directions; that is, one strand runs from the 5' end to the 3' end and the other runs from the 3' end to the 5' end. The double helix is stabilized by hydrogen bonding between complementary base pairs; A pairs with T and C pairs with G.

**❹ Outline the main steps in the replication of DNA. (22.4)**

- Replication of DNA is semiconservative; an original DNA molecule forms two DNA molecules, each of which has one strand from the parent DNA and one new strand.
- In replication, DNA unwinds and the enzyme DNA polymerase catalyzes replication on both strands. The identity of the bases on the template strand determines the order of the bases on the new strand, with A pairing with T and C pairing with G. Replication occurs from the 3' end to the 5' end of each strand. One strand, the leading strand, grows continuously, while the other strand, the lagging strand, is synthesized in fragments and then joined together with a DNA ligase enzyme.

**❺ List the three types of RNA molecules and describe their functions. (22.5)**

- Ribosomal RNA (rRNA), which consists of one large subunit and one small subunit, provides the site where proteins are assembled.
- Messenger RNA (mRNA) contains the sequence of nucleotides that determines the amino acid sequence in a protein. mRNA is transcribed from DNA such that each DNA gene corresponds to a different mRNA molecule.
- Transfer RNA (tRNA) contains an anticodon that identifies the amino acid that it carries on its acceptor stem and delivers that amino acid to a growing polypeptide.

**6** **What is transcription? (22.6)**

- Transcription is the synthesis of mRNA from DNA. The DNA helix unwinds and RNA polymerase catalyzes RNA synthesis from the 3' to 5' end of the template strand, forming mRNA with complementary bases.

**7** **What are the main features of the genetic code? (22.7)**

- mRNAs contain sequences of three bases called codons that code for individual amino acids. There are 61 codons that correspond to the 20 amino acids, as well as three stop codons that signal the end of protein synthesis.

**8** **How are proteins synthesized by the process of translation? (22.8)**

- Translation begins with initiation, the binding of the ribosomal subunits to mRNA and the arrival of the first tRNA with an amino acid. During elongation, tRNAs bring individual amino acids to the ribosome one after another, and new peptide bonds are formed. Termination occurs when a stop codon is reached.

**9** **What is a mutation and how are mutations related to genetic diseases? (22.9)**

- Mutations are changes in the nucleotide sequence in a DNA molecule. A point mutation results in the substitution of one nucleotide for another. Deletion and insertion mutations result in the loss or addition of nucleotides, respectively. A mutation that causes an inherited condition may result in a genetic disease.

**10** **What are the principal features of three techniques using DNA in the laboratory—recombinant DNA, the polymerase chain reaction (PCR), and DNA fingerprinting? (22.10)**

- Recombinant DNA is synthetic DNA formed when a segment of DNA from one source is inserted into the DNA of another source. When inserted into a bacterium, recombinant DNA can be used to prepare large quantities of useful proteins.
- The polymerase chain reaction (PCR) is used to amplify a portion of a DNA molecule to produce millions of copies of a single gene.
- DNA fingerprinting is used to identify an individual by cutting DNA with restriction endonucleases to give a unique set of fragments.

**11** **What are the main characteristics of viruses? (22.11)**

- A virus is an infectious agent that contains either DNA or RNA within a protein coat. When the virus invades a host cell, it uses the biochemical machinery of the host to replicate. A retrovirus contains RNA and a reverse transcriptase that allow the RNA to synthesize viral DNA, which then transcribes RNA that directs protein synthesis.

# PROBLEMS

Selected in-chapter and odd-numbered end-of-chapter problems have brief answers in Appendix B. The *Student Study Guide and Solutions Manual* contains detailed solutions to all in-chapter and odd-numbered end-of-chapter problems, as well as additional worked examples and a chapter self-test.

## Nucleosides, Nucleotides, and Nucleic Acids

**22.25** What is the difference between a ribonucleoside and a ribonucleotide? Give an example of each.

**22.26** What is the difference between a ribonucleotide and a deoxyribonucleotide? Give an example of each.

**22.27** What is the difference between a gene and a chromosome?

**22.28** What is the difference between uracil and uridine?

**22.29** Label each statement as pertaining to DNA, RNA, or both.
   a. The polynucleotide is double stranded.
   b. The polynucleotide may contain adenine.
   c. The polynucleotide may contain dGMP.
   d. The polynucleotide is a polymer of ribonucleotides.

**22.30** Label each statement as pertaining to DNA, RNA, or both.
   a. The polynucleotide is single stranded.
   b. The polynucleotide may contain guanine.
   c. The polynucleotide may contain UMP.
   d. The polynucleotide is a polymer of deoxyribonucleotides.

**22.31** Identify the base and monosaccharide in each compound and then name it.

**22.32** Identify the base and monosaccharide in each compound and then name it.

a.

b.

**22.33** Draw the structure of each of the following:
a. a purine base
b. a nucleoside that contains 2-deoxyribose and a pyrimidine base
c. a nucleotide that contains ribose and a purine base
d. a triphosphate of guanosine

**22.34** Draw the structure of each of the following:
a. a pyrimidine base
b. a nucleoside that contains 2-deoxyribose and a purine base
c. a nucleotide that contains ribose and a pyrimidine base
d. a diphosphate of uridine

**22.35** Draw the structure of each nucleoside or nucleotide.
a. adenosine
b. deoxyguanosine
c. GDP
d. dTDP

**22.36** Draw the structure of each nucleoside or nucleotide.
a. uridine
b. deoxycytidine
c. dGMP
d. UTP

**22.37** Consider the given dinucleotide.

a. Identify the bases present in the dinucleotide.
b. Label the 5' and 3' ends.
c. Give the three- or four-letter abbreviations for the two nucleotides.

d. Is this dinucleotide a ribonucleotide or a deoxyribonucleotide? Explain your choice.
e. Name the dinucleotide.

**22.38** Answer Problem 22.37 for the following dinucleotide.

**22.39** Draw the structures of the two possible dinucleotides formed from uridine 5'-monophosphate and adenosine 5'-monophosphate.

**22.40** Draw the structures of the two possible dinucleotides formed from deoxythymidine 5'-monophosphate and deoxycytidine 5'-monophosphate.

**22.41** Draw the structure of each dinucleotide and identify the 5' and 3' ends.
a. the deoxyribonucleotide formed by joining the 3'-OH group of dTMP with the 5'-phosphate of dAMP
b. the ribonucleotide formed by joining the 5'-phosphate of GMP with the 3'-OH of CMP

**22.42** Draw the structure of each dinucleotide and identify the 5' and 3' ends.
a. the deoxyribonucleotide formed by joining two deoxyguanosine 5'-phosphates together
b. the ribonucleotide formed by joining the 5'-phosphate of UMP with the 3'-OH of AMP

**22.43** Draw the deoxyribonucleotide TGA. Label the 5' and 3' ends.

**22.44** Draw the ribonucleotide CGU. Label the 5' and 3' ends.

**22.45** Describe in detail the DNA double helix with reference to each of the following features: (a) the sugar–phosphate backbone; (b) the functional groups at the end of each strand; (c) the hydrogen bonding between strands.

**22.46** Describe in detail the DNA double helix with reference to each of the following features: (a) the location of the bases; (b) the complementary base pairing; (c) the phosphodiester linkages.

**22.47** Write the sequence of the complementary strand of each segment of a DNA molecule.
a. 5'–AAATAAC–3'
b. 5'–ACTGGACT–3'
c. 5'–CGATATCCCG–3'
d. 5'–TTCCCGGGATA–3'

**22.48** Write the sequence of the complementary strand of each segment of a DNA molecule.
a. 5'–TTGCGA–3'
b. 5'–CGCGTAAT–3'
c. 5'–ACTTCAGGT–3'
d. 5'–CCGGTTAATACGGC–3'

**22.49** If 27% of the nucleotides in a sample of DNA contain the base adenine (A), what are the percentages of bases T, G, and C?

**22.50** If 19% of the nucleotides in a sample of DNA contain the base cytosine (C), what are the percentages of bases G, A, and T?

**22.51** Complementary base pairing occurs between two strands of DNA, between two different sites on an RNA molecule, and between one strand of DNA and one strand of RNA. Which base pairs are the same in all three settings?

**22.52** Complementary base pairing occurs between two strands of DNA, and between one strand of DNA and one strand of RNA. Give an example of a base pair that is unique to each setting.

## Replication, Transcription, Translation, and Protein Synthesis

**22.53** What is the sequence of a newly synthesized DNA segment if the template strand has the sequence 3'–ATGGCCTATGCGAT–5'?

**22.54** What is the sequence of a newly synthesized DNA segment if the template strand has the sequence 3'–CGCGATTAGATATTGCCGC–5'?

**22.55** During replication, why is there a leading strand and a lagging strand?

**22.56** Why is replication said to be semiconservative?

**22.57** Explain the roles of messenger RNA and transfer RNA in converting the genetic information coded in DNA into protein synthesis.

**22.58** In what ways are replication and transcription similar? In what ways are they different?

**22.59** What mRNA is transcribed from each DNA sequence in Problem 22.47?

**22.60** What mRNA is transcribed from each DNA sequence in Problem 22.48?

**22.61** For each DNA segment: [1] What is the sequence of the mRNA molecule synthesized from each DNA template? [2] What is the sequence of the informational strand of the DNA molecule?
  a. 3'–ATGGCTTA–5'          c. 3'–GGTATACCG–5'
  b. 3'–CGGCGCTTA–5'        d. 3'–TAGGCCGTA–5'

**22.62** For each DNA segment: [1] What is the sequence of the mRNA molecule synthesized from each DNA template? [2] What is the sequence of the informational strand of the DNA molecule?
  a. 3'–GGCCTATA–5'         c. 3'–CTACTG–5'
  b. 3'–GCCGAT–5'            d. 3'–ATTAGAGC–5'

**22.63** For each codon, give its anticodon and the amino acid for which it codes.
  a. CUG          b. UUU          c. AAG          d. GCA

**22.64** For each codon, give its anticodon and the amino acid for which it codes.
  a. GUU          b. AUA          c. CCC          d. GCG

**22.65** Fill in the missing information in the schematic of a tRNA during the elongation phase of translation.

**22.66** Fill in the missing information in the schematic of a tRNA during the elongation phase of translation.

**22.67** Derive the amino acid sequence that is coded for by each mRNA sequence.
  a. 5' CCA ACC UGG GUA GAA 3'
  b. 5' AUG UUU UUA UGG UGG 3'
  c. 5' GUC GAC GAA CCG CAA 3'

**22.68** Derive the amino acid sequence that is coded for by each mRNA sequence.
  a. 5' AAA CCC UUU UGU 3'
  b. 5' CCU UUG GAA GUA CUU 3'
  c. 5' GGG UGU AUG CAC CGA UUG 3'

**22.69** Write a possible mRNA sequence that codes for each peptide.
  a. Ile–Met–Lys–Ser–Tyr
  b. Pro–Gln–Glu–Asp–Phe
  c. Thr–Ser–Asn–Arg

**22.70** Write a possible mRNA sequence that codes for each peptide.
  a. Phe–Phe–Leu–Lys
  b. Val–Gly–Gln–Asp–Asn
  c. Arg–His–Ile–Ser

**22.71** Considering each nucleotide sequence in an mRNA molecule: [1] write the sequence of the DNA template strand from which the mRNA was synthesized; [2] give the peptide synthesized by the mRNA.
  a. 5' UAU UCA AUA AAA AAC 3'
  b. 5' GAU GUA AAC AAG CCG 3'

**22.72** Considering each nucleotide sequence in an mRNA molecule: [1] write the sequence of the DNA template strand from which the mRNA was synthesized; [2] give the peptide synthesized by the mRNA.
  a. 5' UUG CUC AAC CAA 3'
  b. 5' AUU GUA CCA CAA CCC 3'

## Mutations

**22.73** What is the difference between a point mutation and a silent mutation?

**22.74** Explain why some mutations cause no effect on a cell whereas others have a major effect.

**22.75** Consider the following mRNA sequence:
5'–CUU CAG CAC–3'.

  a. What amino acid sequence is coded for by this mRNA?

  b. What is the amino acid sequence if a mutation converts CAC to AAC?

  c. What is the amino acid sequence if a mutation converts CUU to CUC?

  d. What occurs when a mutation converts CAG to UAG?

  e. What occurs if CU is deleted from the beginning of the chain?

**22.76** Consider the following mRNA sequence:
5'–ACC UUA CGA–3'.

  a. What amino acid sequence is coded for by this mRNA?

  b. What is the amino acid sequence if a mutation converts ACC to ACU?

  c. What is the amino acid sequence if a mutation converts UUA to UCA?

  d. What is the amino acid sequence if a mutation converts CGA to AGA?

  e. What occurs if C is added to the beginning of the chain?

**22.77** Consider the following sequence of DNA: 3'–TTA CGG–5'.

  a. What dipeptide is formed from this DNA after transcription and translation?

  b. If a mutation converts CGG to CGT in DNA, what dipeptide is formed?

  c. If a mutation converts CGG to CCG in DNA, what dipeptide is formed?

  d. If a mutation converts CGG to AGG in DNA, what dipeptide is formed?

**22.78** Consider the following sequence of DNA: 3'–ATA GGG–5'.

  a. What dipeptide is formed from this DNA after transcription and translation?

  b. If a mutation converts ATA to ATG in DNA, what dipeptide is formed?

  c. If a mutation converts ATA to AGA in DNA, what dipeptide is formed?

  d. What occurs when a mutation converts ATA to ATT in DNA?

### Recombinant DNA and Related Techniques

**22.79** What is a restriction endonuclease?

**22.80** What is meant by the term "sticky end"?

**22.81** The restriction enzyme BamHI recognizes the sequence GGATCC and cuts the DNA between the two G's. Given the following segment of double-stranded DNA, draw the sticky ends that result from cleavage with this enzyme.

    5' 〜〜〜 C C G G T T G G A T C C T T 〜〜〜 3'

    3' 〜〜〜 G G C C A A C C T A G G A A 〜〜〜 5'

**22.82** The restriction enzyme PstI recognizes the sequence GACGTC and cuts the DNA between the G and A. Given the following segment of double-stranded DNA, draw the sticky ends that result from cleavage with this enzyme.

    5' 〜〜〜 G G A T G A C G T C A A T T 〜〜〜 3'

    3' 〜〜〜 C C T A C T G C A G T T A A 〜〜〜 5'

**22.83** Describe the main steps in preparing recombinant DNA from plasmid DNA.

**22.84** Describe the main steps in using the polymerase chain reaction to amplify a small amount of DNA.

**22.85** The given gel contains the DNA fingerprint of a mother (lane 1), father (lane 2), and four children (lanes 3–6). One child is adopted, two children are the offspring of both parents, and one child is the offspring of one parent only.

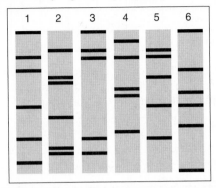

  a. Which lanes, if any, represent a biological child of both parents? Explain your choice.

  b. Which lanes, if any, represent an adopted child? Explain your choice.

**22.86** With reference to the gel in Problem 22.85: (a) which lanes (if any) represent a biological child of the mother only; (b) which lanes (if any) represent a biological child of the father only; (c) which lanes (if any) represent twins? Explain each choice.

### Viruses

**22.87** Lamivudine, also called 3TC, is a nucleoside analogue used in the treatment of HIV and the virus that causes hepatitis B. (a) What nucleoside does lamivudine resemble? (b) How does lamivudine inhibit reverse transcription?

lamivudine
3TC

**22.88** What is reverse transcription?

### General Questions

**22.89** Consider a template strand of DNA with the following sequence: 3'–CAA TGT ATT TTT GCT–5'. (a) What is the informational strand of DNA that corresponds to this template? (b) What mRNA is prepared from this template? (c) What polypeptide is prepared from the mRNA?

**22.90** Consider a template strand of DNA with the following sequence: 3'–ATT AAA GCC TTC TGT–5'. (a) What is the informational strand of DNA that corresponds to this template? (b) What mRNA is prepared from this template? (c) What polypeptide is prepared from the mRNA?

**22.91** Fill in the base, codon, anticodon, or amino acid needed to complete the following table that relates the sequences of DNA, mRNA, tRNA, and the resulting polypeptide.

| DNA informational strand: | 5' end | | | | | | | 3' end |
|---|---|---|---|---|---|---|---|---|
| DNA template strand: | 3' end | TTG | ATA | GGT | TGC | TTC | TAC | 5' end |
| mRNA codons: | 5' end | | | | | | | 3' end |
| tRNA anticodons: | | | | | | | | |
| Polypeptide: | | | | | | | | |

**22.92** Fill in the base, codon, anticodon, or amino acid needed to complete the following table that relates the sequences of DNA, mRNA, tRNA, and the resulting polypeptide.

| DNA informational strand: | 5' end | | | | | | | 3' end |
|---|---|---|---|---|---|---|---|---|
| DNA template strand: | 3' end | TCC | GAC | TTG | TGC | CAT | CAC | 5' end |
| mRNA codons: | 5' end | | | | | | | 3' end |
| tRNA anticodons: | | | | | | | | |
| Polypeptide: | | | | | | | | |

**22.93** Fill in the base, codon, anticodon, or amino acid needed to complete the following table that relates the sequences of DNA, mRNA, tRNA, and the resulting polypeptide.

| DNA informational strand: | 5' end | AAC | | | | | 3' end |
|---|---|---|---|---|---|---|---|
| DNA template strand: | 3' end | | CAT | | | | 5' end |
| mRNA codons: | 5' end | | | UCA | | AUG | 3' end |
| tRNA anticodons: | | | | | GUG | | |
| Polypeptide: | | | | Thr | | | |

**22.94** Fill in the base, codon, anticodon, or amino acid needed to complete the following table that relates the sequences of DNA, mRNA, tRNA, and the resulting polypeptide.

| DNA informational strand: | 5' end | ACA | | | | 3' end |
|---|---|---|---|---|---|---|
| DNA template strand: | 3' end | CAA | | | GTC | 5' end |
| mRNA codons: | 5' end | | UAC | | | 3' end |
| tRNA anticodons: | | | | ACA | | |
| Polypeptide: | | | | Lys | | |

**22.95** If there are 325 amino acids in a polypeptide, how many bases are present in a single strand of the gene that codes for it, assuming that every base is transcribed and then translated to polypeptide?

**22.96** If a single strand of a gene contains 678 bases, how many amino acids result in the polypeptide prepared from it, assuming every base of the gene is transcribed and then translated?

**22.97** Met-enkephalin (Tyr–Gly–Gly–Phe–Met) is a pain killer and sedative (Section 21.5). What is a possible nucleotide sequence in the template strand of the gene that codes for met-enkephalin, assuming that every base of the gene is transcribed and then translated?

**22.98** Leu-enkephalin (Tyr–Gly–Gly–Phe–Leu) is a pain killer and sedative (Section 21.5). What is a possible nucleotide sequence in the template strand of the gene that codes for leu-enkephalin, assuming that every base of the gene is transcribed and then translated?

## CHALLENGE PROBLEMS

**22.99** Give a possible nucleotide sequence in the template strand of the gene that codes for the following tripeptide.

**22.100** Give a possible nucleotide sequence in the template strand of the gene that codes for the following tripeptide.

The immediate energy needs of a sprinter are supplied by ATP and creatine phosphate, two reactive molecules that release energy by cleaving a bond during hydrolysis.

# 23

# Metabolism and Energy Production

## CHAPTER OUTLINE

## CHAPTER GOALS

*In this chapter you will learn how to:*

1. Define metabolism and explain where energy production occurs in cells

2. Describe the main characteristics of the four stages of catabolism

3. Explain the role of ATP in energy production and how coupled reactions drive energetically unfavorable reactions

4. Describe the roles of the main coenzymes used in metabolism

5. List the main features of the citric acid cycle

6. Describe the main components of the electron transport chain and oxidative phosphorylation

7. Explain why compounds such as cyanide that disrupt the electron transport chain are poisons

**D**espite the wide diversity among life forms, virtually all organisms contain the same types of biomolecules—lipids, carbohydrates, proteins, and nucleic acids—and use the same biochemical reactions. Chapter 23 is the first of two chapters that deal with the complex biochemical pathways that convert one molecule into another in cells. In Chapter 23 we concentrate on the fundamental reactions that produce energy, while in Chapter 24 we examine specific pathways for the metabolism of lipids, carbohydrates, and proteins. Although the pathways often involve many steps, individual reactions can be understood by applying the same chemical principles you have already learned.

## 23.1  Introduction

Each moment thousands of reactions occur in a living cell: large molecules are broken down into smaller components, small molecules are converted into larger molecules, and energy changes occur.

- *Metabolism* is the sum of all of the chemical reactions that take place in an organism.

There are two types of metabolic processes called **catabolism** and **anabolism.**

- *Catabolism* is the breakdown of large molecules into smaller ones. Energy is generally released during catabolism.
- *Anabolism* is the synthesis of large molecules from smaller ones. Energy is generally absorbed during anabolism.

The oxidation of glucose ($C_6H_{12}O_6$) to carbon dioxide ($CO_2$) and water ($H_2O$) is an example of catabolism, while the synthesis of a protein from component amino acids is an example of anabolism. Often the conversion of a starting material to a final product occurs by an organized series of consecutive reactions called a **metabolic pathway.** A metabolic pathway may be **linear** or **cyclic.**

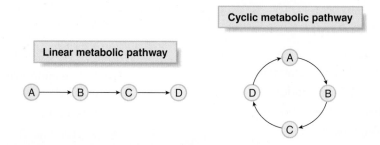

- A *linear* pathway is a series of reactions that generates a final product different from any of the reactants.
- A *cyclic* pathway is a series of reactions that regenerates the first reactant.

In this chapter we concentrate on energy changes that occur during metabolism. The human body needs energy to move, think, talk, laugh, and breathe. It also requires energy to maintain a constant temperature and to synthesize new cells and tissues.

While the reactions in living organisms follow the same principles as reactions in the laboratory, the energy needs of the body come with some special requirements. The body usually can't use the calories of a big meal all at once, so the energy must be stored and then gradually released. Moreover, energy must be stored in molecules that are readily accessible for use anywhere in the body at any time the energy is needed.

**Figure 23.1**     The Mitochondrion in a Typical Animal Cell

A mitochondrion is a small organelle located in the cytoplasm of the cell. Cellular energy production occurs in the mitochondria.

Mitochondr*ion* is the singular form of the plural mitochondr*ia.*

Where does energy production occur in cells? A typical animal cell, such as the one shown in Figure 23.1, is surrounded by a cell membrane (Section 19.7) and has a nucleus that contains DNA in chromosomes (Section 22.3). The **cytoplasm,** the region of the cell between the cell membrane and the nucleus, contains various specialized structures called **organelles,** each of which has a specific function. **Mitochondria** are small sausage-shaped organelles in which energy production takes place. Mitochondria contain an outer membrane and an inner membrane with many folds. The area between these two membranes is called the **intermembrane space.** Energy production occurs within the **matrix,** the area surrounded by the inner membrane of the mitochondrion. The number of mitochondria in a cell varies depending on its energy needs. Cells in the heart, brain, and muscles of the human body typically contain many mitochondria.

## 23.2   An Overview of Metabolism

Just as gasoline is the fuel that powers automobiles, so, too, food is the fuel that is metabolized by the body to provide energy. Catabolism breaks down the carbohydrates, proteins, and lipids in food into smaller molecules, releasing energy to supply the body's needs. This process involves numerous catabolic pathways that can be organized into four stages, as shown in Figure 23.2.

### 23.2A   Stage [1]—Digestion

The catabolism of food begins with **digestion,** which is catalyzed by enzymes in the saliva, stomach, and small intestines (Figure 23.3). Digestion converts large molecules into smaller components. The hydrolysis of carbohydrates to monosaccharides begins with amylase enzymes in the saliva, and continues in the small intestines. Protein digestion begins in the stomach, where acid denatures the protein, and the protease pepsin begins to cleave the protein backbone into smaller polypeptides and amino acids. Digestion continues in the small intestines, where trypsin and chymotrypsin further cleave the protein backbone to form amino acids. Triacylglycerols, the most common lipids, are first emulsified by bile secreted by the liver, and then hydrolyzed to glycerol and fatty acids by lipases in the small intestines.

Figure 23.2    The Four Stages in Biochemical Catabolism and Energy Production

Once these small molecules are formed during digestion, they are each absorbed through the intestinal wall into the bloodstream and transported to other cells in the body. Some substances such as cellulose are not metabolized as they travel through the digestive tract. When these materials can't be absorbed, they pass into the large intestines and are excreted.

## 23.2B   Stages [2]–[4] of Catabolism

Once small molecules are formed, catabolism continues to break down each type of molecule to smaller units releasing energy in the process.

**Figure 23.3** Digestion of Carbohydrates, Proteins, and Triacylglycerols

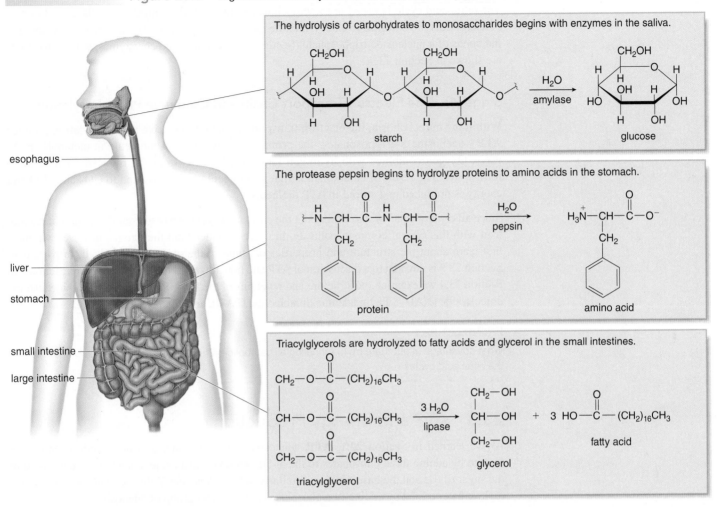

The hydrolysis of carbohydrates to monosaccharides begins with enzymes in the saliva.

starch → (H₂O, amylase) → glucose

The protease pepsin begins to hydrolyze proteins to amino acids in the stomach.

protein → (H₂O, pepsin) → amino acid

Triacylglycerols are hydrolyzed to fatty acids and glycerol in the small intestines.

triacylglycerol → (3 H₂O, lipase) → glycerol + 3 fatty acid

The first stage of catabolism, **digestion,** is the hydrolysis of large molecules to small molecules: polysaccharides such as starch are hydrolyzed to monosaccharides (Section 20.6), proteins are hydrolyzed to their component amino acids (Section 21.8), and triacylglycerols are hydrolyzed to glycerol and fatty acids (Section 19.5). Each of these molecules enters its own metabolic pathway to be further broken down into smaller components, releasing energy.

## Stage [2]—Formation of Acetyl CoA

Monosaccharides, amino acids, and fatty acids are degraded into **acetyl groups (CH₃CO–),** two-carbon units that are bonded to coenzyme A (a coenzyme), forming **acetyl CoA.** Details of the structure of acetyl CoA are given in Section 23.4.

acetyl group

acetyl CoA

from coenzyme A

The product of the catabolic pathways is the *same* for all three types of molecules. As a result, a common catabolic pathway, the **citric acid cycle,** continues the processing of all types of biomolecules to generate energy.

### Stage [3]—The Citric Acid Cycle

The citric acid cycle is based in the mitochondria. In this biochemical cycle, the acetyl groups of acetyl CoA are oxidized to carbon dioxide. Some energy produced by this process is stored in the bonds of a nucleoside triphosphate (Section 22.1) and reduced coenzymes, whose structures are shown in Section 23.4.

### Stage [4]—The Electron Transport Chain and Oxidative Phosphorylation

Within the mitochondria, the electron transport chain and oxidative phosphorylation produce **ATP**—adenosine 5'-triphosphate—the primary energy-carrying molecule in metabolic pathways. Oxygen combines with hydrogen ions and electrons from the reduced coenzymes to form water. The result of catabolism is that biomolecules are converted to $CO_2$ and $H_2O$ and energy is produced and stored in ATP molecules.

Since all catabolic pathways converge in the citric acid cycle, we begin our discussion of catabolism with this central common pathway. In order to understand the details, however, we must first learn about the structure and properties of some of the molecules involved. In particular, Section 23.3 is devoted to a discussion of ATP and how it is used to supply energy in reactions. In Section 23.4 we examine the structure and reactions of the key coenzymes nicotinamide adenine dinucleotide ($NAD^+$), flavin adenine dinucleotide (FAD), and coenzyme A.

#### PROBLEM 23.1

What advantage might there be to funneling all catabolic pathways into a single common pathway, the citric acid cycle?

## 23.3 ATP and Energy Production

As we learned in Section 22.1, **ATP,** adenosine 5'-triphosphate, is a nucleoside triphosphate formed by adding three phosphates to the 5'-OH group of adenosine, a nucleoside composed of the sugar ribose and the base adenine. Similarly, **ADP,** adenosine 5'-diphosphate, is a nucleoside diphosphate formed by adding two phosphates to the 5'-OH group of adenosine.

### 23.3A General Features of ATP Hydrolysis and Formation

In metabolic pathways, the interconversion of ATP and ADP is the most important process for the storage and release of energy.

- Hydrolysis of ATP cleaves one phosphate group, forming ADP and hydrogen phosphate, $HPO_4^{2-}$, often abbreviated as $P_i$ (inorganic phosphate). This reaction *releases* 7.3 kcal/mol of energy.

Any process, such as walking, running, swallowing, or breathing, is fueled by the release of energy from the hydrolysis of ATP to ADP. ATP is the most prominent member of a group of "high-energy" molecules, reactive molecules that release energy by cleaving a bond during hydrolysis. Because ATP contains four negatively charged oxygen atoms in close proximity, the electronic repulsion of the like charges drives the hydrolysis to ADP, which has fewer negatively charged oxygens and therefore less electronic repulsion.

- **The reverse reaction, phosphorylation, adds a phosphate group to ADP, forming ATP. Phosphorylation *requires* 7.3 kcal/mol of energy.**

By way of these reactions, ATP is a transporter of energy.

- **Energy is absorbed and stored in ATP when it is synthesized from ADP.**
- **Energy is released when ATP is hydrolyzed to ADP.**

Figure 23.4 summarizes the reactions and energy changes that occur when ATP is synthesized and hydrolyzed. As we learned in Section 6.2, when energy is *released* in a reaction, the energy change is reported as a *negative* (–) value, so the energy change for ATP hydrolysis is –7.3 kcal/mol. When energy is *absorbed* in a reaction, the energy change is reported as a *positive* (+) value, so the energy change for the phosphorylation of ADP is +7.3 kcal/mol. The synthesis of ATP with $HPO_4^{2-}$ is the reverse of ATP hydrolysis, and the energy changes for such reactions are *equal* in value but *opposite* in sign.

**Figure 23.4** ATP Hydrolysis and Synthesis

ATP is constantly synthesized and hydrolyzed. It is estimated that each ATP molecule exists for about a minute before it is hydrolyzed and its energy released. Even though the body contains only about one gram of ATP at a given time, the energy needs of the body are such that an average individual synthesizes 40 kg of ATP daily!

**PROBLEM 23.2**

GTP, guanosine 5'-triphosphate, is another high-energy molecule that releases 7.3 kcal of energy when it is hydrolyzed to GDP. Write the equation for the hydrolysis of GTP to GDP.

GTP

## 23.3B   Coupled Reactions in Metabolic Pathways

As we learned in Section 6.5, a reaction that releases energy is a favorable process because it forms products that are lower in energy than the reactants. On the other hand, a reaction that absorbs energy is an unfavorable process because it forms products that are higher in energy than the reactants.

The hydrolysis of ATP to ADP is a favorable reaction: energy is released and some of the electronic repulsion due to many closely situated negative charges is relieved. The energy released in ATP hydrolysis can be used to drive a reaction that has an unfavorable energy change by **coupling** the two reactions together.

- Coupled reactions are pairs of reactions that occur together. The energy released by one reaction provides the energy to drive the other reaction.

Let's consider the catabolism of glucose to $CO_2$ and $H_2O$, a process that requires a large number of steps in various biochemical pathways. Although the overall conversion releases a great deal of energy, the energy change associated with each individual step is much smaller. In some reactions energy is released, while in others energy is absorbed. The hydrolysis of ATP provides the energy to drive the reactions that require energy.

In the first step in the metabolism of glucose, for example, glucose reacts with hydrogen phosphate ($HPO_4^{2-}$) to form glucose 6-phosphate, a process that requires 3.3 kcal/mol of energy. This process is energetically unfavorable because energy is absorbed (+3.3 kcal/mol). However, by coupling this reaction with ATP hydrolysis, an energetically favorable reaction (−7.3 kcal/mol of energy released), the coupled reaction becomes an energetically favorable process (−4.0 kcal/mol of energy released).

| | | | Energy change | |
|---|---|---|---|---|
| **Phosphorylation** | glucose + $HPO_4^{2-}$ ⟶ glucose 6-phosphate + $H_2O$ | +3.3 kcal/mol ⟵ energy required |
| **Hydrolysis** | ATP + $H_2O$ ⟶ ADP + $HPO_4^{2-}$ | −7.3 kcal/mol ⟵ energy released |
| **Coupled reaction** | glucose + ATP ⟶ glucose 6-phosphate + ADP | −4.0 kcal/mol |

Energy is released.

- The coupled reaction is the net reaction, written by summing the substances in both equations and eliminating those compounds that appear on both sides of the reaction arrows.
- The overall energy change is found by summing the energies for the individual steps.

Thus, in this example:

- The hydrolysis of ATP provides the energy for the phosphorylation of glucose.

Although the coupled reactions are written as two separate equations for emphasis in the preceding example, in reality, a single reaction takes place. ATP transfers a phosphate to glucose, forming glucose 6-phosphate and ADP, while both molecules are held in close proximity at the active site of hexokinase, as shown in Figure 23.5.

- Coupling an energetically unfavorable reaction with an energetically favorable reaction that releases *more* energy than the amount required is a common phenomenon in biochemical reactions.

Coupled reactions explain how ATP can be synthesized by the energetically unfavorable process of phosphorylation. Phosphorylation must be coupled with a reaction that releases *more* than 7.3 kcal/mol of energy. Such a reaction is the hydrolysis of phosphoenolpyruvate to form pyruvate.

| | | Energy change | |
|---|---|---|---|
| **Phosphorylation** | $ADP + HPO_4^{2-} \longrightarrow ATP + H_2O$ | +7.3 kcal/mol | ← energy required |
| **Hydrolysis** | $\underset{\text{phosphoenolpyruvate}}{CH_2{=}\overset{\displaystyle OPO_3^{2-}}{\underset{\displaystyle |}{C}}{-}COO^-} + H_2O \longrightarrow \underset{\text{pyruvate}}{CH_3{-}\overset{\displaystyle O}{\overset{\displaystyle ||}{C}}{-}COO^-} + HPO_4^{2-}$ | −14.8 kcal/mol | ← energy released |
| **Coupled reaction** | $CH_2{=}\overset{\displaystyle OPO_3^{2-}}{\underset{\displaystyle |}{C}}{-}COO^- + ADP \longrightarrow CH_3{-}\overset{\displaystyle O}{\overset{\displaystyle ||}{C}}{-}COO^- + ATP$ | −7.5 kcal/mol | |

**Energy is released.**

---

**Figure 23.5**   A Coupled Reaction—Phosphorylation of Glucose by ATP

The enzyme hexokinase binds glucose at its active site and ATP is also bound in close proximity. ATP transfers a phosphate directly to the glucose molecule to form ADP and glucose 6-phosphate. This coupled reaction is energetically favorable.

Since the hydrolysis of phosphoenolpyruvate releases more energy than the phosphorylation of ADP (–14.8 kcal versus +7.3 kcal), the coupled reaction becomes energetically favorable (–7.5 kcal/mol of energy released).

## SAMPLE PROBLEM 23.1

The phosphorylation of fructose to fructose 6-phosphate requires 3.8 kcal/mol of energy. This unfavorable reaction can be driven by the hydrolysis of ATP to ADP. (a) Write the equation for the coupled reaction. (b) How much energy is released in the coupled reaction?

|  |  |  |  |  |  | Energy change |
|---|---|---|---|---|---|---|
| fructose | + | $HPO_4^{2-}$ | ⟶ | fructose 6-phosphate | + $H_2O$ | +3.8 kcal/mol |

### Analysis

Write the equation for the hydrolysis of ATP to ADP (Section 23.3A). Add together the substances in this equation and the given equation to give the net equation—that is, the equation for the coupled reaction. To determine the overall energy change, add together the energy changes for each step.

### Solution

a. The coupled equation shows the overall reaction that combines the phosphorylation of fructose and the hydrolysis of ATP.

Cross out compounds that appear on both sides of the reaction arrows.

[1]    fructose  +  $HPO_4^{2-}$  ⟶  fructose 6-phosphate  +  $H_2O$

[2]    ATP  +  $H_2O$  ⟶  ADP  +  $HPO_4^{2-}$

**Coupled reaction:**  fructose  +  ATP  ⟶  fructose 6-phosphate  +  ADP

b. The overall energy change is the sum of the energy changes for each step:
+3.8 kcal/mol + (–7.3) kcal/mol = –3.5 kcal/mol.

## PROBLEM 23.3

The phosphorylation of glucose to glucose 1-phosphate requires 5.0 kcal/mol of energy. This unfavorable reaction can be driven by the hydrolysis of ATP to ADP. (a) Write the equation for the coupled reaction. (b) How much energy is released in the coupled reaction?

glucose + $HPO_4^{2-}$ ⟶ glucose 1-phosphate + $H_2O$

Coupled reactions that use ATP or coenzymes are often drawn using a combination of horizontal and curved arrows. The principal organic reactants and products are drawn from left to right with a reaction arrow as usual, but additional compounds like ATP and ADP are drawn on a curved arrow. This technique is meant to emphasize the organic substrates of the reaction, while making it clear that other materials are needed for the reaction to occur.

$$OPO_3^{2-}$$
$$CH_2=\overset{|}{C}-COO^-$$      $\overset{ADP \quad ATP}{\curvearrowright}$      $CH_3-\overset{O}{\overset{||}{C}}-COO^-$

phosphoenolpyruvate                                      pyruvate

## PROBLEM 23.4

Write each of the following reactions using curved arrow symbolism.

a. reaction of fructose with ATP to form fructose 6-phosphate and ADP (Sample Problem 23.1)
b. reaction of glucose with ATP to form glucose 6-phosphate and ADP

### 23.3C  FOCUS ON THE HUMAN BODY
Creatine and Athletic Performance

Many athletes take creatine supplements to boost their performance. Creatine is synthesized in the body from the amino acid arginine, and is present in the diet in meat and fish. Creatine is stored in muscles as creatine phosphate, a high-energy molecule that releases energy by cleavage of its P—N bond on hydrolysis.

creatine phosphate $+ H_2O \longrightarrow$ creatine $+ HPO_4^{2-}$

Energy change $-10.3$ kcal/mol

Energy is released.

Since more energy is released from the hydrolysis of creatine phosphate than is needed for the phosphorylation of ADP, the coupling of these two reactions results in the formation of ATP from ADP.

creatine phosphate $\longrightarrow$ creatine
(ADP → ATP)

Creatine phosphate is stored in muscles. When existing ATP supplies are depleted during strenuous exercise, creatine phosphate reacts with ADP to form a new supply of ATP as a source of more energy. Once existing supplies of both ATP and creatine phosphate have been depleted—which occurs in as little as 10 seconds—other catabolic processes must supply more ATP to continue an activity. Energy-generating pathways that need oxygen input—**aerobic reactions**—are discussed in Sections 23.5–23.6. Energy-generating pathways that do not need oxygen input—**anaerobic reactions**—are discussed in Sections 24.3–24.4.

Do creatine supplements increase athletic performance? Some evidence suggests that in athletic events that require short bursts of intense energy, increased creatine intake increases the amount of creatine phosphate in the muscle. This, in turn, allows an athlete to maintain a high rate of activity for a longer period of time. It is questionable whether creatine alone adds body mass. It is thought, however, that since an athlete has a greater energy reserve, an individual can train harder and longer, resulting in greater muscle mass.

### PROBLEM 23.5
Use the values for the hydrolysis of creatine phosphate to creatine (–10.3 kcal/mol) and the phosphorylation of ADP to ATP (+7.3 kcal/mol) to calculate the energy change in the following reaction. Is energy released or required in this reaction?

creatine phosphate + ADP $\longrightarrow$ creatine + ATP

## 23.4  Coenzymes in Metabolism

Many reactions in metabolic pathways involve coenzymes. As we learned in Section 21.9, a *coenzyme* is an organic compound needed for an enzyme-catalyzed reaction to occur. Some coenzymes serve as important oxidizing and reducing agents (Sections 23.4A and 23.4B), while coenzyme A activates acetyl groups ($CH_3CO-$), resulting in the transfer of a two-carbon unit to other substrates (Section 23.4C).

## 23.4A   Coenzymes NAD⁺ and NADH

Many coenzymes are involved in oxidation and reduction reactions. As we learned in Section 5.9, oxidation and reduction can be defined in terms of changes in electrons, hydrogen atoms, or oxygen atoms.

- Oxidation results in . . .   a loss of electrons, *or*
  a loss of hydrogen, *or*
  a gain of oxygen.
- Reduction results in . . .   a gain of electrons, *or*
  a gain of hydrogen, *or*
  a loss of oxygen.

A coenzyme may serve as an oxidizing agent or a reducing agent in a biochemical pathway.

- An oxidizing agent causes an oxidation reaction to occur, so the oxidizing agent is reduced.
- A reducing agent causes a reduction reaction to occur, so the reducing agent is oxidized.

In examining what happens to a coenzyme during oxidation and reduction, it is convenient to think in terms of hydrogen atoms being composed of protons ($H^+$) and electrons ($e^-$).

- When a coenzyme gains hydrogen atoms—that is, $H^+$ and $e^-$—the coenzyme is reduced; thus, the coenzyme is an *oxidizing* agent.
- When a coenzyme loses hydrogen atoms—that is, $H^+$ and $e^-$—the coenzyme is oxidized; thus, the coenzyme is a *reducing* agent.

The coenzyme **nicotinamide adenine dinucleotide, NAD⁺,** is a common biological oxidizing agent. Although its structure is complex, it is the six-membered ring containing the positively charged nitrogen atom (shown in red) that participates in oxidation reactions. When NAD⁺ reacts with two hydrogen atoms, this ring gains one proton and two electrons and one proton is left over. Thus, the ring is reduced and a new C—H bond is formed in the product, written as **NADH,** and referred to as the *reduced form* of nicotinamide adenine dinucleotide.

**NAD⁺**
nicotinamide adenine dinucleotide

**NADH**
(reduced form of NAD⁺)

Curved arrow symbolism is often used to depict reactions with coenzymes.

isocitrate

oxalosuccinate

The conversion of isocitrate to oxalosuccinate is an **oxidation** since the number of C—O bonds in the substrate *increases*. **NAD⁺ serves as the oxidizing agent, and in the process, is reduced to NADH.** The reduced form of the coenzyme, NADH, is a biological reducing agent, as we learned in Section 16.6. When NADH reacts, it forms NAD⁺ as a product. Thus, **NAD⁺ and NADH are interconverted by oxidation and reduction reactions.**

## SAMPLE PROBLEM 23.2

Label each reaction as an oxidation or reduction, and give the reagent, NAD⁺ or NADH, that would be used to carry out the reaction.

a.

$$CH_3-\underset{\underset{H}{|}}{\overset{\overset{H}{|}}{C}}-OH \longrightarrow CH_3-\overset{\overset{H}{|}}{C}=O$$

    ethanol                 acetaldehyde

b.

$$CH_3-\overset{\overset{O}{||}}{C}-COO^- \longrightarrow CH_3-\underset{\underset{H}{|}}{\overset{\overset{OH}{|}}{C}}-COO^-$$

    pyruvate                lactate

### Analysis

Count the number of C—O bonds in the starting material and product. Oxidation increases the number of C—O bonds and reduction decreases the number of C—O bonds. NAD⁺ is the coenzyme needed for an oxidation, and NADH is the coenzyme needed for a reduction.

### Solution

a. The conversion of ethanol to acetaldehyde is an oxidation, since the product has two C—O bonds and the reactant has only one. To carry out the oxidation, the oxidizing agent NAD⁺ could be used.

$$CH_3-\underset{\underset{H}{|}}{\overset{\overset{H}{|}}{C}}-OH \xrightarrow{\quad NAD^+ \quad NADH + H^+ \quad} CH_3-\overset{\overset{H}{|}}{C}=O$$

    ethanol                   acetaldehyde

b. The conversion of pyruvate to lactate is a reduction, since the product has one fewer C—O bond than the reactant. To carry out the reduction, the reducing agent NADH could be used.

$$CH_3-\overset{\overset{O}{||}}{C}-COO^- \xrightarrow{\quad NADH + H^+ \quad NAD^+ \quad} CH_3-\underset{\underset{H}{|}}{\overset{\overset{OH}{|}}{C}}-COO^-$$

    pyruvate                 lactate

## PROBLEM 23.6

Label each reaction as an oxidation or reduction, and give the reagent, NAD⁺ or NADH, that would be used to carry out the reaction.

a. $H_2C=O \longrightarrow CH_3OH$      b. $CH_3-\underset{\underset{H}{|}}{\overset{\overset{OH}{|}}{C}}-COO^- \longrightarrow CH_3-\overset{\overset{O}{||}}{C}-COO^-$

## 23.4B Coenzymes FAD and FADH$_2$

**Flavin adenine dinucleotide, FAD,** is another common biological oxidizing agent. Although its structure is complex, just four atoms of the tricyclic ring system (2 N's and 2 C's shown in red) participate in redox reactions. When it acts as an oxidizing agent, FAD is reduced by adding two hydrogen atoms, forming **FADH$_2$**, the *reduced form* of flavin adenine dinucleotide.

Add 2 H$^+$ and 2 e$^-$.

FAD
flavin adenine dinucleotide

FADH$_2$
(reduced form of FAD)

Table 23.1 summarizes the common coenzymes used in oxidation and reduction reactions.

### Table 23.1 Coenzymes Used for Oxidation and Reduction

| Coenzyme Name | Abbreviation | Role |
| --- | --- | --- |
| Nicotinamide adenine dinucleotide | NAD$^+$ | Oxidizing agent |
| Nicotinamide adenine dinucleotide (reduced form) | NADH | Reducing agent |
| Flavin adenine dinucleotide | FAD | Oxidizing agent |
| Flavin adenine dinucleotide (reduced form) | FADH$_2$ | Reducing agent |

**HEALTH NOTE**

Leafy green vegetables, soybeans, and almonds are good sources of riboflavin, vitamin B$_2$. Since this vitamin is light sensitive, riboflavin-fortified milk contained in glass or clear plastic bottles should be stored in the dark.

FAD is synthesized in cells from vitamin B$_2$, **riboflavin.** Riboflavin is a yellow, water-soluble vitamin obtained in the diet from leafy green vegetables, soybeans, almonds, and liver. When large quantities of riboflavin are ingested, excess amounts are excreted in the urine, giving it a bright yellow appearance.

riboflavin
vitamin B$_2$

### PROBLEM 23.7

What makes riboflavin a water-soluble vitamin?

### 23.4C   Coenzyme A

Coenzyme A differs from other coenzymes in this section because it is not an oxidizing or a reducing agent. In addition to many other functional groups, coenzyme A contains a **sulfhydryl group (SH group),** making it a **thiol (RSH).** To emphasize this functional group, we sometimes abbreviate the structure as **HS–CoA.**

coenzyme A

$= \boxed{\text{HS—CoA}}$

The sulfhydryl group of coenzyme A reacts with acetyl groups ($CH_3CO–$) or other acyl groups ($RCO—$) to form thioesters, RCOSR'. When an acetyl group is bonded to coenzyme A, the product is called **acetyl coenzyme A,** or simply **acetyl CoA.**

**General structure of a thioester**

$$CH_3—\overset{\overset{\displaystyle O}{\|}}{C}—\overset{\cdot}{\text{ }} \quad + \quad HS—CoA \quad \longrightarrow \quad CH_3—\overset{\overset{\displaystyle O}{\|}}{C}—S—CoA \qquad R—\overset{\overset{\displaystyle O}{\|}}{C}—S—R'$$

**acetyl CoA**

**HEALTH NOTE**

Avocados are an excellent dietary source of pantothenic acid, vitamin $B_5$.

Thioesters such as acetyl CoA are another group of high-energy compounds that release energy on reaction with water. In addition, acetyl CoA reacts with other substrates in metabolic pathways to deliver its two-carbon acetyl group, as in the citric acid cycle in Section 23.5.

This bond is broken.

$$CH_3—\overset{\overset{\displaystyle O}{\|}}{C}—S—CoA \quad + \quad H_2O \quad \longrightarrow \quad CH_3—\overset{\overset{\displaystyle O}{\|}}{C}—O^- \quad + \quad HS—CoA$$

| | | Energy change |
|---|---|---|
| acetyl CoA | coenzyme A | −7.5 kcal/mol |

Coenzyme A is synthesized in cells from **pantothenic acid, vitamin $B_5$,** which is obtained in the diet from a variety of sources, especially whole grains and eggs.

pantothenic acid
vitamin $B_5$

### PROBLEM 23.8

Predict the water solubility of vitamin $B_5$.

### PROBLEM 23.9

What products are formed when the thioester $CH_3CH_2CH_2COSCoA$ is hydrolyzed with water?

## 23.5   The Citric Acid Cycle

The **citric acid cycle,** a series of enzyme-catalyzed reactions that occur in mitochondria, comprises the third stage of the catabolism of biomolecules—carbohydrates, lipids, and amino acids—to carbon dioxide, water, and energy.

- The citric acid cycle is a cyclic metabolic pathway that begins with the addition of acetyl CoA to a four-carbon substrate and ends when the same four-carbon compound is formed as a product eight steps later.
- The citric acid cycle produces high-energy compounds for ATP synthesis in stage [4] of catabolism.

### 23.5A   Overview of the Citric Acid Cycle

The citric acid cycle is also called the tricarboxylic acid cycle (TCA cycle) or the **Krebs cycle,** named for Hans Krebs, a German chemist and Nobel Laureate who worked out the details of these reactions in 1937. A general scheme of the citric acid cycle, shown in Figure 23.6, illustrates the key features. All intermediates in the citric acid cycle are carboxylate anions derived from di- and tricarboxylic acids.

- The citric acid cycle begins when two carbons of acetyl CoA ($CH_3COSCoA$) react with a four-carbon organic substrate to form a six-carbon product (step [1]).
- Two carbon atoms are removed to form two molecules of $CO_2$ (steps [3] and [4]).
- Four molecules of reduced coenzymes (NADH and $FADH_2$) are formed in steps [3], [4], [6], and [8]. These molecules serve as carriers of electrons to the electron transport chain in stage [4] of catabolism, which ultimately results in the synthesis of a great deal of ATP.
- One mole of GTP is synthesized in step [5]. GTP is a high-energy nucleoside triphosphate similar to ATP.

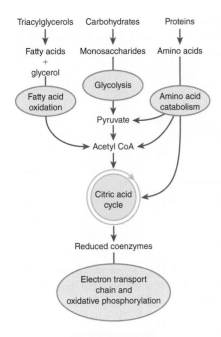

Glycolysis, fatty acid oxidation, and amino acid catabolism—three processes that generate acetyl CoA—are discussed in detail in Chapter 24.

**Figure 23.6**   General Features of the Citric Acid Cycle

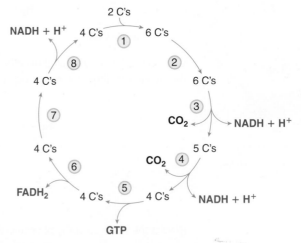

The citric acid cycle begins with the addition of two carbons from acetyl CoA in step [1] to a four-carbon organic substrate, drawn at the top of the cyclic pathway. Each turn of the citric acid cycle forms two molecules of $CO_2$, four molecules of reduced coenzymes (3 NADH and 1 $FADH_2$), and one high-energy GTP molecule.

## 23.5B  Specific Steps of the Citric Acid Cycle

The eight reactions of the citric acid cycle, which can be conceptually divided into two parts, are shown in Figure 23.7. The first part of the cycle includes the addition of acetyl CoA to oxaloacetate to form the six-carbon product citrate, which undergoes two separate **decarboxylations**—reactions that give off $CO_2$. In part [2], functional groups are added and oxidized to re-form oxaloacetate, the substrate needed to begin the cycle again.

### Part [1] of the Citric Acid Cycle

As shown in Figure 23.7, acetyl CoA enters the cycle by reaction with oxaloacetate at step [1] of the pathway. This reaction, catalyzed by citrate synthase, adds two carbons to oxaloacetate, forming citrate. In step [2], the 3° alcohol of citrate is isomerized to the 2° alcohol isocitrate using aconitase. These first two steps add carbon atoms and rearrange functional groups.

**Figure 23.7**  Steps in the Citric Acid Cycle

Each step of the citric acid cycle is enzyme catalyzed. The net result of the eight-step cycle is the conversion of the two carbons added to oxaloacetate to two molecules of $CO_2$. Reduced coenzymes (NADH and $FADH_2$) are also formed, which carry electrons to the electron transport chain to synthesize ATP. One molecule of high-energy GTP is synthesized in step [5].

Loss of two carbon atoms begins in step [3], by decarboxylation of isocitrate using isocitrate dehydrogenase. The oxidizing agent $NAD^+$ also converts the 2° alcohol to a ketone to form α-ketoglutarate, which now contains one fewer carbon atom. This reaction forms NADH and $H^+$, which will carry electrons and protons gained in this reaction to the electron transport chain. In step [4], decarboxylation releases a second molecule of $CO_2$. Also, oxidation with $NAD^+$ in the presence of coenzyme A forms the thioester succinyl CoA using the enzyme α-ketoglutarate dehydrogenase. **By the end of step [4], two carbons are lost as $CO_2$ and two molecules of NADH are formed.**

Although it might be convenient to think of the two molecules of $CO_2$ as originating in the acetyl CoA added in step [1], the carbon atoms in $CO_2$ were *not* added during this cycle of the pathway.

## Part [2] of the Citric Acid Cycle

Part [2] consists of four reactions that manipulate the functional groups of succinyl CoA to re-form oxaloacetate. In step [5], the thioester bond of succinyl CoA is hydrolyzed to form succinate, releasing energy to convert GDP to GTP. GTP, guanosine 5'-triphosphate, is similar to ATP: GTP is a high-energy molecule that releases energy when a P—O bond is hydrolyzed. This is the only step of the citric acid cycle that directly generates a triphosphate.

In step [6], succinate is converted to fumarate with FAD and succinate dehydrogenase. This reaction forms the reduced coenzyme $FADH_2$, which will carry electrons and protons to the electron transport chain. Addition of water in step [7] forms malate and oxidation of the 2° alcohol in malate with $NAD^+$ forms oxaloacetate in step [8]. Another molecule of NADH is also formed in step [8]. By the end of step [8], two more molecules of reduced coenzymes ($FADH_2$ and NADH) are formed. **Since the product of step [8] is the starting material of step [1], the cycle can continue as long as additional acetyl CoA is available for step [1].**

Overall, the citric acid cycle results in formation of

- two molecules of $CO_2$
- four molecules of reduced coenzymes (3 NADH and 1 $FADH_2$)
- one molecule of GTP

The net equation for the citric acid cycle can be written as shown. The ultimate fate of each product is also indicated.

$$CH_3-\overset{\overset{O}{\|}}{C}-SCoA \;+\; 2\,H_2O \;+\; 3\,NAD^+ \;+\; FAD \;+\; GDP \;+\; HPO_4^{2-}$$

**overall reaction**

$$2\,CO_2 \;+\; HSCoA \;+\; 3\,NADH \;+\; 3\,H^+ \;+\; FADH_2 \;+\; GTP$$

| exhaled gas | The coenzyme re-enters the cycle. | The reduced coenzymes enter the electron transport chain. | energy source |

- **The main function of the citric acid cycle is to produce reduced coenzymes that enter the electron transport chain and ultimately produce ATP.**

The rate of the citric acid cycle depends on the body's need for energy. When energy demands are high and the amount of available ATP is low, the cycle is activated. When energy demands are low and NADH concentration is high, the cycle is inhibited.

Although the citric acid cycle is complex, many individual reactions can be understood by applying the basic principles of organic chemistry learned in previous chapters.

### SAMPLE PROBLEM 23.3

(a) Write out the reaction that converts succinate to fumarate with FAD using curved arrow symbolism. (b) Classify the reaction as an oxidation, reduction, or decarboxylation.

#### Analysis

Use Figure 23.7 to draw the structures for succinate and fumarate. Draw the organic reactant and product on the horizontal arrow and the oxidizing reagent FAD, which is converted to $FADH_2$, on the curved arrow. Oxidation reactions result in a loss of electrons, a loss of hydrogen, or a gain of oxygen. Reduction reactions result in a gain of electrons, a gain of hydrogen, or a loss of oxygen. A decarboxylation results in the loss of $CO_2$.

#### Solution

a. Equation:

succinate                    fumarate

b. Since succinate contains four C—H bonds and fumarate contains only two C—H bonds, hydrogen atoms have been lost, making this reaction an oxidation. In the process FAD is reduced to $FADH_2$.

### PROBLEM 23.10

(a) Write out the reaction that converts malate to oxaloacetate with $NAD^+$ using curved arrow symbolism. (b) Classify the reaction as an oxidation, reduction, or decarboxylation.

### PROBLEM 23.11

From what you learned about classifying enzymes in Section 21.9, explain why the enzyme used to convert succinate to fumarate is called succinate dehydrogenase.

## 23.6 The Electron Transport Chain and Oxidative Phosphorylation

Most of the energy generated during the breakdown of biomolecules is formed during stage [4] of catabolism. Because oxygen is required, this process is called **aerobic respiration.** There are two facets to this stage:

- the electron transport chain, or the respiratory chain
- oxidative phosphorylation

The reduced coenzymes formed in the citric acid cycle enter the **electron transport chain** and the electrons they carry are transferred from one molecule to another by a series of oxidation–reduction reactions. Each reaction releases energy until electrons and protons react with oxygen to form water. Electron transfer also causes $H^+$ ions to be pumped across the inner mitochondrial cell membrane, creating an energy reservoir that is used to synthesize ATP by the **phosphorylation** of ADP.

In contrast to the combustion of gasoline, which releases energy all at once in a single reaction, the energy generated during metabolism is released in small portions as the result of many reactions.

## 23.6A    The Electron Transport Chain

The electron transport chain is a multistep process that relies on four enzyme systems, called **complexes I, II, III, and IV,** as well as mobile electron carriers. Each complex is composed of enzymes, additional protein molecules, and metal ions that can gain and lose electrons in oxidation and reduction reactions. The complexes are situated in the inner membrane of the mitochondria, arranged so that electrons can be passed to progressively stronger oxidizing agents (Figure 23.8).

The electron transport chain begins with the reduced coenzymes—3 NADH and 1 FADH$_2$— formed during the citric acid cycle. These reduced coenzymes are electron rich and as such, they are capable of donating electrons to other species. Thus, **NADH and FADH$_2$ are *reducing agents* and when they donate electrons, they are oxidized.** When NADH donates two electrons, it is oxidized to NAD$^+$, which can re-enter the citric acid cycle. Likewise, when FADH$_2$ donates two electrons, it is oxidized to FAD, which can be used as an oxidant in step [6] of the citric acid cycle once again.

Once in the electron transport chain, the electrons are passed down from complex to complex in a series of redox reactions, and small packets of energy are released along the way. At the end of the chain, **the electrons and protons (obtained from the reduced coenzymes or the matrix of the mitochondrion) react with inhaled oxygen to form water** and this facet of the process is complete.

$$4\ e^- \ + \ 4\ H^+ \ + \ O_2 \longrightarrow 2\ H_2O$$

Because oxygen is needed for the final stage of electron transport, this process is **aerobic.**

---

**Figure 23.8**    The Electron Transport Chain and ATP Synthesis in a Mitochondrion

The four enzyme complexes (I–IV) of the electron transport chain are located within the inner membrane of a mitochondrion, between the matrix and the intermembrane space. Electrons enter the chain when NADH and FADH$_2$ are oxidized and then transported through a series of complexes along the pathway shown in red. The electrons ultimately combine with O$_2$ to form H$_2$O. Protons (H$^+$) are pumped across the inner membrane into the intermembrane space at three locations shown by blue arrows. The energy released when protons return to the matrix by traveling through a channel (in green) in the ATP synthase enzyme is used to convert ADP to ATP.

PROBLEM 23.12

If NADH and $FADH_2$ were not oxidized in the electron transport chain, what would happen to the citric acid cycle?

PROBLEM 23.13

At several points in the electron transport chain, iron cations gain or lose electrons by reactions that interconvert $Fe^{2+}$ and $Fe^{3+}$ cations. (a) When $Fe^{3+}$ is converted to $Fe^{2+}$, is the reaction an oxidation or a reduction? (b) Is $Fe^{3+}$ an oxidizing agent or a reducing agent?

## 23.6B ATP Synthesis by Oxidative Phosphorylation

Although the electron transport chain illustrates how electrons carried by reduced coenzymes ultimately react with oxygen to form water, we have still not learned how ATP, the high-energy triphosphate needed for energy transport, is synthesized. The answer lies in what happens to the $H^+$ ions in the mitochondrion.

$H^+$ ions generated by reactions in the electron transport chain, as well as $H^+$ ions present in the matrix of the mitochondria, are pumped across the inner mitochondrial membrane into the intermembrane space at three different sites (Figure 23.8). This process requires energy, since it moves protons against the concentration gradient. The energy comes from redox reactions in the electron transport chain. Since the concentration of $H^+$ ions is then higher on one side of the membrane, this creates a potential energy gradient, much like the potential energy of water that is stored behind a dam.

To return to the matrix, the $H^+$ ions travel through a channel in the ATP synthase enzyme. ATP synthase is the enzyme that catalyzes the phosphorylation of ADP to form ATP. The energy released as the protons return to the matrix converts ADP to ATP. This process is called **oxidative phosphorylation,** since the energy that results from the oxidation of the reduced coenzymes is used to transfer a phosphate group.

> **Energy released from $H^+$ movement fuels phosphorylation.**

$$ADP \ + \ HPO_4^{2-} \ \longrightarrow \ ATP \ + \ H_2O$$

PROBLEM 23.14

In which region of the mitochondrion—the matrix or the intermembrane space—would the pH be lower? Explain your choice.

## 23.6C ATP Yield from Oxidative Phosphorylation

How much ATP is generated during stage [4] of catabolism?

- Each NADH enters the electron transport chain at complex I in the inner mitochondrial membrane and the resulting cascade of reactions produces enough energy to synthesize 2.5 ATPs.
- $FADH_2$ enters the electron transport chain at complex II, producing energy for the synthesis of 1.5 ATPs.

How much ATP is generated for each acetyl CoA fragment that enters the entire common catabolic pathway—that is, stages [3] and [4] of catabolism?

For each turn of the citric acid cycle, three NADH molecules and one FADH$_2$ molecule are formed. In addition, one GTP molecule is produced directly during the citric acid cycle (step [5]); one GTP molecule is equivalent in energy to one ATP molecule. These facts allow us to calculate the total number of ATP molecules formed for each acetyl CoA.

$$
\begin{array}{rcl}
3\ \text{NADH} \times 2.5\ \text{ATP/NADH} &=& 7.5\ \text{ATP} \\
1\ \text{FADH}_2 \times 1.5\ \text{ATP/FADH}_2 &=& 1.5\ \text{ATP} \\
1\ \text{GTP} &=& \underline{1\ \ \ \text{ATP}} \\
&& 10\ \ \ \text{ATP}
\end{array}
$$

- Complete catabolism of each acetyl CoA molecule that enters the citric acid cycle forms 10 ATP molecules.

Each ATP molecule can now provide the energy to drive energetically unfavorable reactions.

## 23.7  FOCUS ON HEALTH & MEDICINE
### Hydrogen Cyanide

The reactions detailed in the electron transport chain and oxidative phosphorylation are so crucial for the health of an organism that disruption of even a single step can have disastrous consequences. When any one step is inhibited, energy production ceases, and an organism cannot survive.

**Hydrogen cyanide** (HCN, Section 4.6) is a lethal gas used as a chemical weapon during World War I and in the gas chambers of Nazi Germany during World War II. HCN is a poison because it produces cyanide (CN$^-$), which irreversibly binds to the Fe$^{3+}$ ion of cytochrome oxidase. Cytochrome oxidase is the key enzyme in complex IV of the electron transport chain. When bonded to cyanide, Fe$^{3+}$ cannot be reduced to Fe$^{2+}$ and the transfer of electrons to oxygen to form water cannot occur. ATP synthesis is halted and cell death ensues.

A few naturally occurring compounds that contain CN groups form HCN when they are hydrolyzed in the presence of certain enzymes. As an example, **amygdalin** is present in the seeds and pits of apricots, peaches, and wild cherries. Commonly known as laetrile, amygdalin was once touted as an anticancer drug, and is still available in some countries for this purpose. Amygdalin's effectiveness in targeting cancer cells is unproven, and the HCN produced by hydrolysis kills all types of cells in the body.

**ENVIRONMENTAL NOTE**

The golden bamboo lemur of Madagascar subsists primarily on giant bamboo, despite the high levels of toxic cyanide it contains.

amygdalin

The side effects that result from taking amygdalin resemble those of chronic exposure to cyanide and include headache, vomiting, coma, and in some cases, death.

Interestingly, the diet of the golden bamboo lemur, a critically endangered species that inhabits Madagascar, contains shoots of giant bamboo as its main component. Giant bamboo contains such high levels of cyanide that most mammals would die after ingesting it. Evidently, the golden bamboo lemur has developed a mechanism for detoxifying cyanide, although that mechanism is currently unknown.

# CHAPTER HIGHLIGHTS

## KEY TERMS

Acetyl CoA (23.4)
Adenosine 5'-diphosphate (ADP, 23.3)
Adenosine 5'-triphosphate (ATP, 23.3)
Anabolism (23.1)
Catabolism (23.1)
Citric acid cycle (23.5)

Coenzyme A (23.4)
Coupled reactions (23.3)
Electron transport chain (23.6)
$FADH_2$ (23.4)
Flavin adenine dinucleotide (FAD, 23.4)
Metabolism (23.1)

Mitochondrion (23.1)
NADH (23.4)
Nicotinamide adenine dinucleotide
    ($NAD^+$, 23.4)
Oxidative phosphorylation (23.6)
Phosphorylation (23.3)

## KEY CONCEPTS

**❶ What is metabolism and where is energy produced in cells? (23.1)**

- Metabolism is the sum of all of the chemical reactions that take place in an organism. Catabolic reactions break down large molecules and release energy, while anabolic reactions synthesize larger molecules and require energy.
- Energy is produced in the mitochondria, sausage-shaped organelles that contain an outer and inner cell membrane. Energy is produced in the matrix, the area surrounded by the inner membrane.

**❷ What are the four stages of metabolism? (23.2)**

- Metabolism begins with digestion in stage [1], in which large molecules—polysaccharides, proteins, and triacylglycerols—are hydrolyzed to smaller molecules—monosaccharides, amino acids, fatty acids, and glycerol.
- In stage [2], biomolecules are degraded into two-carbon acetyl units.
- The citric acid cycle comprises stage [3]. The citric acid cycle converts two carbon atoms to two molecules of $CO_2$, and forms reduced coenzymes, NADH and $FADH_2$, which carry electrons and energy to the electron transport chain.
- In stage [4], the electron transport chain and oxidative phosphorylation produce ATP, and oxygen is converted to water.

**❸** **What is ATP and how do coupled reactions with ATP drive energetically unfavorable reactions? (23.3)**

- ATP is the primary energy-carrying molecule in metabolic pathways. The hydrolysis of ATP cleaves one phosphate group and releases 7.3 kcal/mol of energy.
- The hydrolysis of ATP provides the energy to drive a reaction that requires energy. A pair of reactions of this sort is said to be coupled.

**❹** **List the main coenzymes in metabolism and describe their roles. (23.4)**

- Nicotinamide adenine dinucleotide ($NAD^+$) is a biological oxidizing agent that accepts electrons and protons, thus generating its reduced form NADH. NADH is a reducing agent that donates electrons and protons, re-forming $NAD^+$.
- Flavin adenine dinucleotide (FAD) is a biological oxidizing agent that accepts electrons and protons, thus yielding its reduced form, $FADH_2$. $FADH_2$ is a reducing agent that donates electrons and protons, re-forming FAD.
- Coenzyme A reacts with acetyl groups ($CH_3CO-$) to form high-energy thioesters that deliver two-carbon acetyl groups to other substrates.

**❺** **What are the main features of the citric acid cycle? (23.5)**

- The citric acid cycle is an eight-step cyclic pathway that begins with the addition of acetyl CoA to a four-carbon substrate. In the citric acid cycle, two carbons are converted to $CO_2$ and four molecules of reduced coenzymes are formed. One molecule of a high-energy nucleoside triphosphate is also formed.

**❻** **What are the main components of the electron transport chain and oxidative phosphorylation? (23.6)**

- The electron transport chain is a multistep process that takes place in the inner membrane of mitochondria. Electrons from reduced coenzymes enter the chain and are passed from one molecule to another in a series of redox reactions, releasing energy along the way. At the end of the chain, electrons and protons react with inhaled oxygen to form water.
- $H^+$ ions are pumped across the inner membrane of the mitochondrion, forming a high concentration of $H^+$ ions in the intermembrane space, thus creating a potential energy gradient. When the $H^+$ ions travel through the channel in the ATP synthase enzyme, this energy is used to convert ADP to ATP—a process called oxidative phosphorylation.

**❼** **Why do compounds such as cyanide act as poisons when they disrupt the electron transport chain? (23.7)**

- Since all catabolic pathways converge at the electron transport chain, these steps are needed to produce energy for normal cellular processes. Compounds that disrupt a single step can halt ATP synthesis so that an organism cannot survive.
- Cyanide from HCN irreversibly binds to the $Fe^{3+}$ ion of the enzyme cytochrome oxidase and, as a result, $Fe^{3+}$ cannot be reduced to $Fe^{2+}$ and water cannot be formed from oxygen. Since the electron transport chain is disrupted, energy is not generated for oxidative phosphorylation, ATP is not synthesized, and cell death often follows.

## PROBLEMS

Selected in-chapter and odd-numbered end-of-chapter problems have brief answers in Appendix B. The *Student Study Guide and Solutions Manual* contains detailed solutions to all in-chapter and odd-numbered end-of-chapter problems, as well as additional worked examples and a chapter self-test.

### Metabolism

**23.15** Describe the main features of a mitochondrion. Where does energy production occur in a mitochondrion?

**23.16** Explain why mitochondria are called the powerhouses of the cell.

**23.17** Place the following steps in the catabolism of carbohydrates in order: the electron transport chain, the conversion of glucose to acetyl CoA, the hydrolysis of starch, oxidative phosphorylation, and the citric acid cycle.

**23.18** Describe the main features of the four stages of catabolism.

**23.19** In what stage of catabolism does each of the following processes occur?

   a. cleavage of a protein with chymotrypsin

   b. oxidation of a fatty acid to acetyl CoA

   c. oxidation of malate to oxaloacetate with $NAD^+$

   d. conversion of ADP to ATP with ATP synthase

   e. hydrolysis of starch to glucose with amylase

**23.20** In what stage of catabolism does each of the following processes occur?

   a. conversion of a monosaccharide to acetyl CoA

   b. hydrolysis of a triacylglycerol with lipase

   c. reaction of oxygen with protons and electrons to form water

   d. conversion of succinate to fumarate with FAD

   e. degradation of a fatty acid to acetyl CoA

### ATP and Coupled Reactions

**23.21** What are coupled reactions and why does coupling occur?

**23.22** Explain why ATP and GTP are called "high-energy" compounds.

**23.23** Acetyl phosphate is another example of a high-energy phosphate. What products would be formed when acetyl phosphate is hydrolyzed with water?

acetyl phosphate

**23.24** ADP undergoes hydrolysis in a similar manner to ATP; that is, a P—O bond is cleaved. Draw the structure of the product of ADP hydrolysis.

**23.25** The reaction of succinate with coenzyme A to form succinyl CoA requires energy, and the hydrolysis of ATP releases energy as shown in the given equations.

|  | Energy change |
|---|---|
| succinate + HSCoA $\longrightarrow$ succinyl CoA + $H_2O$ | +9.4 kcal/mol |
| ATP + $H_2O$ $\longrightarrow$ ADP + $HPO_4^{2-}$ | −7.3 kcal/mol |

a. Combine the equations and write the coupled reaction.
b. Is the coupled reaction energetically favorable? Explain.

**23.26** The hydrolysis of succinyl CoA to succinate and coenzyme A releases energy, and the phosphorylation of ADP requires energy as shown in the given equations.

|  | Energy change |
|---|---|
| succinyl CoA + $H_2O$ $\longrightarrow$ succinate + HSCoA | −9.4 kcal/mol |
| ADP + $HPO_4^{2-}$ $\longrightarrow$ ATP + $H_2O$ | +7.3 kcal/mol |

a. Combine the equations and write the coupled reaction.
b. Is the coupled reaction energetically favorable? Explain.

**23.27** The phosphorylation of glucose with $HPO_4^{2-}$ forms glucose 1-phosphate and water and requires 5.0 kcal/mol of energy.
a. Write the equation for this reaction.
b. This unfavorable reaction can be driven by the hydrolysis of ATP to ADP. Write an equation for the coupled reaction.
c. Calculate the energy change for the coupled reaction.

**23.28** Write an equation for the reverse reaction described in Problem 23.27—that is, the hydrolysis of glucose 1-phosphate to form glucose and $HPO_4^{2-}$. What is the energy change in this reaction?

**23.29** The phosphorylation of fructose 6-phosphate to form fructose 1,6-bisphosphate and water requires 3.9 kcal/mol of energy.

fructose 6-phosphate + $HPO_4^{2-}$ $\longrightarrow$ fructose 1,6-bisphosphate + $H_2O$

a. What is the energy change for the reverse reaction—that is, the hydrolysis of fructose 1,6-bisphosphate to form fructose 6-phosphate?
b. Write a coupled reaction that shows how the energy from ATP hydrolysis (–7.3 kcal/mol) can be used to drive the given reaction.
c. What is the energy change for the coupled reaction?

**23.30** a. Use the values in Problem 23.29 to calculate the energy change in the following reaction.

fructose 1,6-bisphosphate + ADP $\longrightarrow$ fructose 6-phosphate + ATP

b. Is this reaction energetically favorable or unfavorable?
c. Write this reaction using curved arrow symbolism.
d. Can this reaction be used to synthesize ATP from ADP? Explain.

**23.31** Refer to the following equations to answer the questions.

|  | Energy change |
|---|---|
| 1,3-bisphosphoglycerate + $H_2O$ $\longrightarrow$ | |
| 3-phosphoglycerate + $HPO_4^{2-}$ | −11.8 kcal/mol |
| ATP + $H_2O$ $\longrightarrow$ ADP + $HPO_4^{2-}$ | −7.3 kcal/mol |

a. Write the equation for the coupled reaction of 1,3-bisphosphoglycerate with ADP to form 3-phosphoglycerate and ATP.
b. Calculate the energy change for this coupled reaction.
c. Can this reaction be used to synthesize ATP from ADP? Explain.

**23.32** Refer to the equations in Problem 23.31 to answer the following questions.
a. Write the equation for the coupled reaction of 3-phosphoglycerate with ATP to form 1,3-bisphosphoglycerate and ADP.
b. Calculate the energy change for this coupled reaction.
c. Is this reaction energetically favorable? Explain.

**23.33** (a) Draw the structure of the high-energy nucleoside triphosphate GTP. (b) Draw the structure of the hydrolysis product formed when one phosphate is removed.

**23.34** If the phosphorylation of GDP to form GTP requires 7.3 kcal/mol of energy, how much energy is released when GTP is hydrolyzed to GDP?

## Coenzymes

**23.35** Classify each substance as an oxidizing agent, a reducing agent, or neither: (a) $FADH_2$; (b) ATP; (c) $NAD^+$.

**23.36** Classify each substance as an oxidizing agent, a reducing agent, or neither: (a) NADH; (b) ADP; (c) FAD.

**23.37** When a substrate is oxidized, is $NAD^+$ oxidized or reduced? Is $NAD^+$ an oxidizing agent or a reducing agent?

**23.38** When a substrate is reduced, is $FADH_2$ oxidized or reduced? Is $FADH_2$ an oxidizing agent or a reducing agent?

**23.39** Label each reaction as an oxidation or a reduction and give the coenzyme, $NAD^+$ or NADH, which might be used to carry out the reaction. Write each reaction using curved arrow symbolism.

**23.40** Label each reaction as an oxidation or a reduction and give the coenzyme, $NAD^+$ or NADH, which might be used to carry out the reaction. Write each reaction using curved arrow symbolism.

a. $CH_3CH_2CHO \longrightarrow CH_3CH_2CH_2OH$

## Citric Acid Cycle

**23.41** What reactions in the citric acid cycle have each of the following characteristics?

    a. The reaction generates NADH.

    b. $CO_2$ is removed.

    c. The reaction utilizes FAD.

    d. The reaction forms a new carbon–carbon single bond.

**23.42** What reactions in the citric acid cycle have each of the following characteristics?

    a. The reaction generates $FADH_2$.

    b. The organic substrate is oxidized.

    c. The reaction utilizes $NAD^+$.

    d. The reaction breaks a carbon–carbon bond.

**23.43** (a) Convert the ball-and-stick model of **A**, one of the eight synthetic intermediates in the citric acid cycle, to a structural formula, and name the compound. (b) What is the immediate precursor of **A** in the citric acid cycle; that is, what compound forms **A** as a reaction product? (c) What compound is formed from **A** in the citric acid cycle?

**A**

**23.44** (a) Convert the ball-and-stick model of **B**, one of the eight synthetic intermediates in the citric acid cycle, to a structural formula, and name the compound. (b) What is the immediate precursor of **B** in the citric acid cycle; that is, what compound forms **B** as a reaction product? (c) What compound is formed from **B** in the citric acid cycle?

**B**

**23.45** (a) Which intermediate(s) in the citric acid cycle contain two chirality centers? (b) Which intermediate(s) contain a 2° alcohol?

**23.46** (a) Which intermediate(s) in the citric acid cycle contain one chirality center? (b) Which intermediate(s) contain a 3° alcohol?

**23.47** The conversion of isocitrate to α-ketoglutarate in step [3] of the citric acid cycle actually occurs by a two-step process: isocitrate is converted first to oxalosuccinate, which then goes on to form α-ketoglutarate.

$$
\underset{\text{isocitrate}}{
\begin{array}{c}
CO_2^- \\
| \\
CH_2 \\
| \\
H-C-CO_2^- \\
| \\
HO-C-H \\
| \\
CO_2^-
\end{array}}
\xrightarrow{[3a]}
\underset{\text{oxalosuccinate}}{
\begin{array}{c}
CO_2^- \\
| \\
CH_2 \\
| \\
H-C-CO_2^- \\
| \\
C=O \\
| \\
CO_2^-
\end{array}}
\xrightarrow{[3b]}
\underset{\text{α-ketoglutarate}}{
\begin{array}{c}
CO_2^- \\
| \\
CH_2 \\
| \\
CH_2 \\
| \\
C=O \\
| \\
CO_2^-
\end{array}}
$$

    a. Classify reaction [3a] as an oxidation, reduction, or decarboxylation.

    b. Classify reaction [3b] as an oxidation, reduction, or decarboxylation.

    c. For which step is $NAD^+$ necessary?

    d. Why is the enzyme that catalyzes this reaction called isocitrate dehydrogenase?

**23.48** The conversion of citrate to isocitrate in step [2] of the citric acid cycle actually occurs by a two-step process (steps [2a] and [2b]) with aconitate formed as an intermediate.

$$
\underset{\text{citrate}}{
\begin{array}{c}
CO_2^- \\
| \\
CH_2 \\
| \\
HO-C-CO_2^- \\
| \\
CH_2 \\
| \\
CO_2^-
\end{array}}
\xrightarrow{[2a]}
\underset{\text{aconitate}}{
\begin{array}{c}
CO_2^- \\
| \\
CH_2 \\
| \\
C-CO_2^- \\
|| \\
CH \\
| \\
CO_2^-
\end{array}}
\xrightarrow{[2b]}
\underset{\text{isocitrate}}{
\begin{array}{c}
CO_2^- \\
| \\
CH_2 \\
| \\
H-C-CO_2^- \\
| \\
HO-C-H \\
| \\
CO_2^-
\end{array}}
$$

    a. What atoms are added or removed in each step?

    b. Steps [2a] and [2b] are not considered oxidation or reduction reactions despite the fact that the number of C—H and C—O bonds changes in these reactions. Explain why this is so.

    c. From your knowledge of organic chemistry learned in previous chapters, what type of reaction occurs in step [2a]? In step [2b]?

**23.49** In what step does a hydration reaction occur in the citric acid cycle?

**23.50** What products of the citric acid cycle are funneled into the electron transport chain?

## Electron Transport Chain and Oxidative Phosphorylation

**23.51** Why are the reactions that occur in stage [4] of catabolism sometimes called aerobic respiration?

**23.52** What is the role of each of the following in the electron transport chain: (a) NADH; (b) $O_2$; (c) complexes I–IV; (d) $H^+$ ion channel?

**23.53** What is the role of each of the following in the electron transport chain: (a) $FADH_2$; (b) ADP; (c) ATP synthase; (d) the inner mitochondrial membrane?

**23.54** Explain the importance of the movement of $H^+$ ions across the inner mitochondrial membrane and then their return passage through the $H^+$ ion channel in ATP synthase.

**23.55** What are the final products of the electron transport chain?

**23.56** What product is formed from each of the following compounds during the electron transport chain: (a) NADH; (b) $FADH_2$; (c) ADP; (d) $O_2$?

**23.57** Why does one NADH that enters the electron transport chain ultimately produce 2.5 ATPs, while one $FADH_2$ produces 1.5 ATPs?

**23.58** How does the energy from the proton gradient result in ATP synthesis?

## General Questions and Applications

**23.59** What reaction or process in metabolism is catalyzed by each of the following enzymes: (a) pepsin; (b) succinate dehydrogenase; (c) ATP synthase?

**23.60** What reaction or process in metabolism is catalyzed by each of the following enzymes: (a) lipase; (b) $\alpha$-ketoglutarate dehydrogenase; (c) amylase?

**23.61** How does the metabolism of the two carbons of acetyl CoA form 10 molecules of ATP?

**23.62** What is the difference between phosphorylation and oxidative phosphorylation?

**23.63** What is the structural difference between ATP and ADP?

**23.64** What is the structural difference between coenzyme A and acetyl CoA?

**23.65** From what you learned about monosaccharides in Chapter 20 and phosphates in Chapter 23: (a) Draw the structure of glucose 1-phosphate. (b) Using structures, write the equation for the hydrolysis of glucose 1-phosphate to glucose and $HPO_4^{2-}$.

**23.66** From what you learned about monosaccharides in Chapter 20 and phosphates in Chapter 23: (a) Draw the structure of glucose 6-phosphate. (b) Using structures, write the equation for the hydrolysis of glucose 6-phosphate to glucose and $HPO_4^{2-}$.

**23.67** How are the citric acid cycle and the electron transport chain interrelated?

**23.68** Why is the citric acid cycle considered to be part of the aerobic catabolic pathways, even though oxygen is not directly involved in any step in the cycle?

**23.69** In which tissue would a cell likely have more mitochondria, the heart or the bone? Explain your choice.

**23.70** What is the fate of an acetyl CoA molecule after several turns of the citric acid cycle?

**23.71** What is the role of stored creatine phosphate in muscles?

**23.72** Explain how HCN acts as a poison by interfering with the synthesis of ATP.

# CHALLENGE PROBLEMS

**23.73** How many moles of ATP can be synthesized from ADP using the 500. Calories ingested during a fast-food lunch? How many molecules of ATP does this correspond to?

**23.74** With reference to the structure of amygdalin (Section 23.7): (a) Locate each acetal. (b) How many chirality centers are present? (c) What monosaccharide is used to form amygdalin?

# 24

A complex set of biochemical pathways converts ingested carbohydrates, lipids, and proteins to usable materials and energy to meet the body's needs.

# Carbohydrate, Lipid, and Protein Metabolism

## CHAPTER GOALS

*In this chapter you will learn how to:*

1. Understand the basic features of biochemical reactions
2. Describe the main aspects of glycolysis
3. List the pathways for pyruvate metabolism
4. Calculate the energy yield from glucose metabolism
5. Describe the main features of gluconeogenesis
6. Summarize the process of the β-oxidation of fatty acids
7. Calculate the energy yield from fatty acid oxidation
8. Identify the structures of ketone bodies and describe their role in metabolism
9. Describe the main components of amino acid catabolism

The metabolism of ingested food begins with the hydrolysis of large biomolecules into small compounds that can be absorbed through the intestinal wall. In Chapter 23 we learned that the last stages of catabolism, which produce energy from acetyl coenzyme A (acetyl CoA) by means of the citric acid cycle, electron transport chain, and oxidative phosphorylation, are the same for all types of biomolecules. The catabolic pathways that form acetyl CoA are different, however, depending on the particular type of biomolecule. In Chapter 24 we examine the specific metabolic pathways for carbohydrates, lipids, and proteins.

## 24.1  Introduction

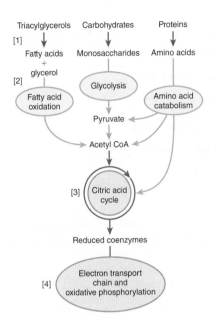

Recall from Section 23.2 that we can conceptually consider catabolism as the sum of four stages. Catabolism begins with digestion in stage [1] in which polysaccharides, triacylglycerols, and proteins are hydrolyzed to smaller compounds that can be absorbed by the bloodstream and delivered to individual cells. Each type of biomolecule is then converted to acetyl CoA by different pathways in stage [2]. Acetyl CoA enters the citric acid cycle and produces reduced coenzymes, whose energy is stored in ATP (stages [3] and [4]). Since we already learned many important facts about stages [1], [3], and [4] of catabolism, we now consider the metabolic pathways that convert monosaccharides, fatty acids and glycerol, and amino acids to acetyl CoA in stage [2].

- **Carbohydrates: Glycolysis** converts glucose, the most common monosaccharide, to pyruvate, which is then metabolized to acetyl CoA (Sections 24.3–24.4).

- **Lipids:** Fatty acids are converted to thioesters, which are oxidized by a stepwise procedure that sequentially cleaves two-carbon units from the carbonyl end to form acetyl CoA (Section 24.7).

$$CH_3(CH_2)_{16}-\overset{\overset{\displaystyle O}{\|}}{C}-OH \longrightarrow CH_3(CH_2)_{16}-\overset{\overset{\displaystyle O}{\|}}{C}-SCoA \longrightarrow 9\ CH_3-\overset{\overset{\displaystyle O}{\|}}{C}-SCoA$$

fatty acid                    thioester                    acetyl CoA

- **Amino acids:** The amino acids formed from protein hydrolysis are often assembled into new proteins without any other modification. Since excess amino acids are not stored in the body, they are catabolized for energy as discussed in Section 24.9. The amino groups ($NH_2$) of amino acids are converted to urea $[(NH_2)_2C=O]$, which is excreted in urine.

## 24.2  Understanding Biochemical Reactions

Before examining the specific reactions of glycolysis, let's pause to consider some principles that will help us better understand these processes.

The biochemical reactions we learned in Chapter 23 and those we will examine in Chapter 24 are often challenging for a student to tackle. On the one hand, cells use the basic principles of organic chemistry in oxidation, reduction, acid–base, and other reactions. On the other hand, the use of enzymes and coenzymes allows cells to carry out transformations that are not easily replicated or even possible in the lab, so many reactions take on a new and different appearance. Moreover, many substrates have several functional groups and these reactions often proceed with complete selectivity at just one of them.

While it is often difficult to predict the exact product of some reactions, it should be possible to *understand* and *analyze* a reaction by examining the reactants and products, the reagents (coenzymes and other materials), and the enzymes. The name of an enzyme is often a clue as to the type of reaction. Common types of enzymes encountered in metabolism, such as kinases and isomerases, are listed in Table 24.1.

- A *kinase* catalyzes the transfer of a phosphate group from one substrate to another.
- An *isomerase* catalyzes the conversion of one isomer to another.

**Table 24.1** Common Enzymes in Metabolism

| Type of Enzyme | Type of Reaction |
| --- | --- |
| Carboxylase | Addition of a carboxylate ($-COO^-$) |
| Decarboxylase | Removal of carbon dioxide ($CO_2$) |
| Dehydrogenase | Removal of two hydrogen atoms |
| Isomerase | Isomerization of one isomer to another |
| Kinase | Transfer of a phosphate |

As an example, consider the conversion of fructose 6-phosphate to fructose 1,6-bisphosphate, step [3] in glycolysis (Section 24.3). In this reaction, a phosphate group is transferred from ATP to fructose 6-phosphate.

fructose 6-phosphate

ATP as a reactant means "transfer a phosphate."

phosphofructo**kinase**

A kinase enzyme means "transfer a phosphate."

fructose 1,6-bisphosphate

It would probably be hard for you to predict that this reaction converts only the OH group at C1 to a phosphate, given that the substrate has four OH groups. Nonetheless, it is possible to *understand* the reaction by looking at all of its components.

- A phosphate is added to fructose 6-phosphate to form fructose 1,6-bisphosphate, a product with two phosphate groups.
- The new phosphate in the product comes from ATP, a high-energy nucleoside triphosphate that transfers a phosphate to other compounds—in this case, fructose 6-phosphate.
- Loss of a phosphate from ATP forms ADP.
- The reaction is catalyzed by a kinase enzyme, also indicating that a phosphate is transferred.

Sample Problems 24.1 and 24.2 illustrate the process in other examples.

## SAMPLE PROBLEM 24.1

Analyze the following reaction by considering the functional groups that change and the name of the enzyme.

$$CH_3-\underset{\underset{pyruvate}{}}{\overset{O}{\overset{\|}{C}}}-\overset{O}{\overset{\|}{C}}-O^- \xrightarrow[\text{decarboxylase}]{\text{pyruvate}} CH_3-\overset{O}{\overset{\|}{C}}-H \;+\; CO_2$$

### Analysis

- Consider the functional groups that are added or removed as a clue to the type of reaction.
- Classify the reagent (when one is given) as to the type of reaction it undergoes.
- Use the name of the enzyme as a clue to the reaction type.

### Solution

The $-COO^-$ of pyruvate is lost as $CO_2$, meaning that a **decarboxylation** has occurred. This is supported by the type of enzyme, a *decarboxylase,* which typically catalyzes decarboxylations. A carbon–carbon bond is broken in the process, giving $CO_2$ as one of the products. No coenzyme is used here; the reaction does not involve oxidation, reduction, or thioester synthesis.

## SAMPLE PROBLEM 24.2

Analyze the following reaction by considering the functional groups that change, the coenzyme utilized, and the name of the enzyme.

$$^-O-\overset{O}{\overset{\|}{\underset{\underset{O^-}{|}}{P}}}-O-CH_2-\overset{OH}{\overset{|}{CH}}-\overset{O}{\overset{\|}{C}}-O-\overset{O}{\overset{\|}{\underset{\underset{O^-}{|}}{P}}}-O^- \xrightarrow[\text{kinase}]{\overset{\text{ADP} \quad \text{ATP}}{\curvearrowright}}\, ^-O-\overset{O}{\overset{\|}{\underset{\underset{O^-}{|}}{P}}}-O-CH_2-\overset{OH}{\overset{|}{CH}}-\overset{O}{\overset{\|}{C}}-O^-$$

1,3-bisphosphoglycerate      phosphoglycerate kinase      3-phosphoglycerate

### Analysis

- Consider the functional groups that are added or removed as a clue to the type of reaction.
- Classify the reagent—that is, any coenzyme or other reactant—as to the type of reaction it undergoes. For example, $NAD^+$ is an oxidizing agent, while NADH is a reducing agent. ATP transfers phosphate groups to substrates, while ADP accepts phosphate groups from substrates.
- Use the name of the enzyme as a clue to the reaction type.

### Solution

A phosphate group is removed from the reactant to give 3-phosphoglycerate. This phosphate is transferred to the nucleoside diphosphate ADP to form the nucleoside triphosphate ATP. Since kinase enzymes catalyze the addition or removal of phosphates, the enzyme used for the reaction is phosphoglycerate *kinase.* No coenzyme is used here; the reaction does not involve oxidation, reduction, or thioester synthesis.

## PROBLEM 24.1

Analyze the following reaction by considering the functional groups that change and the name of the enzyme.

$$^-O-\overset{O}{\overset{\|}{\underset{\underset{O^-}{|}}{P}}}-O-CH_2-\overset{O}{\overset{\|}{C}}-CH_2OH \xrightarrow[\text{isomerase}]{\text{triose phosphate}}\, ^-O-\overset{O}{\overset{\|}{\underset{\underset{O^-}{|}}{P}}}-O-CH_2-\overset{OH}{\overset{|}{CH}}-\overset{O}{\overset{\|}{C}}-H$$

dihydroxyacetone phosphate            glyceraldehyde 3-phosphate

## PROBLEM 24.2

Analyze the following reaction by considering the functional groups that change, the coenzyme utilized, and the name of the enzyme.

glyceraldehyde 3-phosphate　　　　　　　　　　　　　　3-phosphoglycerate

# 24.3 Glycolysis

The metabolism of monosaccharides centers around glucose. Whether it is obtained by the hydrolysis of ingested polysaccharides or stored glycogen (Section 20.6), glucose is the principal monosaccharide used for energy in the human body.

- *Glycolysis* is a linear, 10-step pathway that converts glucose, a six-carbon monosaccharide, to two molecules of pyruvate ($CH_3COCO_2^-$).

**Glycolysis is an anaerobic pathway** that takes place in the cytoplasm and can be conceptually divided into two parts (Figure 24.1).

**Figure 24.1**

An Overview of Glycolysis

In the energy-investment phase of glycolysis, ATP supplies energy needed for steps [1] and [3]. In the energy-generating phase, each three-carbon product from step [5] forms one NADH and two ATP molecules. Since two glyceraldehyde 3-phosphate molecules are formed from each glucose molecule, a total of two NADH and four ATP molecules are formed in the energy-generating phase.

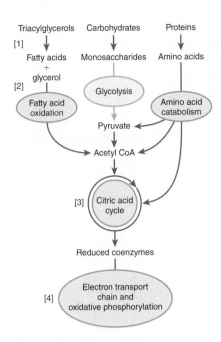

Triacylglycerols   Carbohydrates   Proteins

[1]

Fatty acids      Monosaccharides   Amino acids
+
glycerol

[2]

Fatty acid        Glycolysis      Amino acid
oxidation                        catabolism

Pyruvate

Acetyl CoA

[3]   Citric acid
cycle

Reduced coenzymes

[4]   Electron transport
chain and
oxidative phosphorylation

- Steps [1]–[5] comprise the *energy-investment phase.* The addition of two phosphate groups requires the energy stored in two ATP molecules. Cleavage of a carbon–carbon bond forms two three-carbon products.
- Steps [6]–[10] comprise the *energy-generating phase.* Each of the three-carbon products is ultimately oxidized, forming NADH, and two high-energy phosphate bonds are broken to form two ATP molecules.

The specific reactions of glycolysis are discussed in Section 24.3A. To better understand these reactions, recall a few facts from Chapter 23.

- Coenzyme $NAD^+$ is a biological *oxidizing* agent that converts C—H bonds to C—O bonds. In the process, $NAD^+$ is reduced to NADH + $H^+$.
- The phosphorylation of ADP *requires* energy and forms ATP, a high-energy nucleoside triphosphate.
- The hydrolysis of ATP *releases* energy and forms ADP.

### 24.3A   The Steps in Glycolysis

The specific steps and all needed enzymes in glycolysis are shown in Figures 24.2–24.4.

### Glycolysis: Steps [1]–[3]

Glycolysis begins with the phosphorylation of glucose to form glucose 6-phosphate (Figure 24.2). This energetically unfavorable reaction is coupled with the hydrolysis of ATP to ADP to make the reaction energetically favorable. Isomerization of glucose 6-phosphate to fructose 6-phosphate takes place with an isomerase enzyme in step [2]. Phosphorylation in step [3], an energy-absorbing reaction, can be driven by the hydrolysis of ATP, yielding fructose 1,6-bisphosphate.

- Overall, the first three steps of glycolysis add two phosphate groups and isomerize a six-membered glucose ring to a five-membered fructose ring.
- The energy stored in two ATP molecules is utilized to modify the structure of glucose for the later steps that generate energy.

### PROBLEM 24.3

What type of isomers—constitutional isomers or stereoisomers—do glucose 6-phosphate and fructose 6-phosphate represent? Explain your choice.

### Glycolysis: Steps [4]–[5]

Cleavage of the six-carbon chain of fructose 1,6-bisphosphate forms two three-carbon products—dihydroxyacetone phosphate and glyceraldehyde 3-phosphate—as shown in Figure 24.3. These two products have the same molecular formula but a different arrangement of atoms; that is, they are *constitutional isomers* of each other. Since only glyceraldehyde 3-phosphate continues on in glycolysis, dihydroxyacetone phosphate is isomerized to glyceraldehyde 3-phosphate in step [5], completing the energy-investment phase of glycolysis.

In summary:

- The first phase of glycolysis converts glucose to *two* molecules of glyceraldehyde 3-phosphate.
- The energy from two ATP molecules is utilized.

**Figure 24.2**

Glycolysis: Steps [1]–[3]

- All $-PO_3^{2-}$ groups in glycolysis are abbreviated as $-\text{P}$.
- The energy from two ATP molecules is used for phosphorylation in steps [1] and [3].

**Figure 24.3**

Glycolysis: Steps [4] and [5]

Cleavage of a carbon–carbon bond and isomerization form two molecules of glyceraldehyde 3-phosphate from glucose, completing the energy-investment phase of glycolysis.

## PROBLEM 24.4

As we learned in Section 23.3, the hydrolysis of ATP to ADP releases 7.3 kcal/mol of energy. If the coupled reaction, fructose 6-phosphate + ATP → fructose 1,6-bisphosphate + ADP, releases 3.4 kcal/mol of energy, how much energy is required for the phosphorylation of fructose 6-phosphate?

fructose 6-phosphate + $HPO_4^{2-}$ ⟶ fructose 1,6-bisphosphate + $H_2O$

## Glycolysis: Steps [6]–[10]

Each three-carbon aldehyde (glyceraldehyde 3-phosphate) produced in step [5] of glycolysis is carried through a series of five reactions that ultimately form pyruvate (Figure 24.4).

**Figure 24.4**

Glycolysis: Steps [6]–[10]

In the energy-generating phase of glycolysis, NADH is formed in step [6] and ATP is formed in steps [7] and [10]. Since one glucose molecule yields two molecules of glyceraldehyde that begin the sequence, 2 $CH_3COCO_2^-$, 2 NADH, and 4 ATP are ultimately formed in steps [6]–[10].

In step [6], oxidation of the –CHO group of glyceraldehyde 3-phosphate and phosphorylation with $HPO_4{}^{2-}$ form 1,3-bisphosphoglycerate. In this process, the oxidizing agent $NAD^+$ is reduced to NADH. Transfer of a phosphate group from 1,3-bisphosphoglycerate to ADP forms 3-phosphoglycerate and generates ATP in step [7]. Isomerization of the phosphate group in step [8] and loss of water in step [9] form phosphoenolpyruvate. Finally, transfer of a phosphate to ADP forms ATP and pyruvate in step [10]. Thus, **one NADH molecule is produced in step [6] and two ATPs are formed in steps [7] and [10] for each glyceraldehyde 3-phosphate.**

- Since each glucose molecule yielded *two* glyceraldehyde 3-phosphate molecules in step [5], overall *two* NADH molecules and *four* ATP molecules are formed in the energy-generating phase of glycolysis.

### PROBLEM 24.5

A kinase is an enzyme that catalyzes the transfer of a phosphate group from one substrate to another. Identify all of the reactions of glycolysis that utilize kinases. What species is phosphorylated in each reaction?

### PROBLEM 24.6

Identify the three reactions in glycolysis that involve the conversion of one constitutional isomer to another. Name the enzymes involved in each reaction.

## 24.3B    The Net Result of Glycolysis

Three major products are formed in glycolysis—**ATP, NADH,** and **pyruvate.**

- Two ATP molecules are used in the energy-investment phase (steps [1] and [3]), and four molecules of ATP are formed in the energy-generating phase (steps [7] and [10]). The net result is the *synthesis of two molecules of ATP from glycolysis.*

- Two molecules of NADH are formed from two glyceraldehyde 3-phosphate molecules in step [6]. The NADH formed in glycolysis must be transported from the cytoplasm to the mitochondria for use in the electron transport chain to generate more ATP.

- Two three-carbon molecules of pyruvate ($CH_3COCO_2{}^-$) are formed from the six carbon atoms of glucose. The fate of pyruvate depends on oxygen availability, as discussed in Section 24.4.

Thus, the ATP production of glycolysis is small compared to that produced from the electron transport chain and oxidative phosphorylation. The overall process of glycolysis can be summarized in the following equation.

$$C_6H_{12}O_6 \; + \; 2\,NAD^+ \quad \xrightarrow[\text{2 ADP} \quad \text{2 ATP}]{} \quad 2\,CH_3\!-\!\overset{\displaystyle O}{\overset{\|}{C}}\!-\!\overset{\displaystyle O}{\overset{\|}{C}}\!-\!O^- \; + \; 2\,NADH \; + \; 2\,H^+$$

glucose                                                     pyruvate

Although glycolysis is an ongoing pathway in cells, the rate of glycolysis depends on the body's need for the products it forms—that is, pyruvate, ATP, and NADH. When ATP levels are high, glycolysis is inhibited at various stages. When ATP levels are depleted, such as during strenuous exercise, glycolysis is activated so that more ATP is synthesized.

### PROBLEM 24.7

The level of citrate, one intermediate in the citric acid cycle, also regulates the rate of glycolysis. How might a high level of citrate affect the rate of glycolysis?

## 24.3C  Glycolysis and Other Hexoses

Although glucose is the major monosaccharide obtained by the hydrolysis of ingested carbohydrates, three other six-carbon monosaccharides are also obtained in lesser amounts in the diet.

sugar beets          milk          cranberries

fructose          galactose          mannose

- **Fructose** is obtained by the hydrolysis of the disaccharide sucrose, found in sugar beets and sugarcane.
- **Galactose** is obtained by the hydrolysis of the disaccharide lactose in milk.
- **Mannose** is obtained from polysaccharides in fruits such as cranberries and currants.

These hexoses enter glycolysis at various points along the metabolic pathway. Fructose enters glycolysis in two different ways. In the muscle and kidneys, it is phosphorylated with ATP to form fructose 6-phosphate, the substrate for step [3]. In the liver, fructose is converted by a multistep route to glyceraldehyde 3-phosphate, which enters the pathway at step [6].

Galactose is phosphorylated with ATP to form galactose 1-phosphate, which is converted to glucose 6-phosphate in several steps. Individuals with **galactosemia** lack one of the necessary enzymes required for this process, resulting in an abnormally high galactose concentration, with disabling and sometimes fatal results (Section 20.2). Galactosemia can be detected in newborn screening, and is treated by eliminating galactose from the diet.

Mannose is converted to mannose 6-phosphate and is then isomerized to fructose 6-phosphate, the substrate in step [3] of glycolysis. In this way, all of the other common hexoses are converted to intermediates in the glycolytic pathway, and as a result, they are metabolized to pyruvate.

### PROBLEM 24.8

(a) Are galactose and mannose constitutional isomers or stereoisomers? (b) Draw the structure of galactose 1-phosphate and mannose 6-phosphate. (c) Are these two phosphates constitutional isomers or stereoisomers?

## 24.3D  FOCUS ON HEALTH & MEDICINE
### Glycolysis and Cancer Cells

It has been known for a long time that many cancerous tumors depend largely on glycolysis to supply their energy needs, even though the yield of ATP from glycolysis is small—only two molecules of ATP for each glucose molecule. This occurs in part because glycolysis is an anaerobic pathway and often tumor cells are not located in proximity to oxygen-carrying blood vessels. As a result, glycolysis often proceeds ten times faster in cancer cells compared to healthy cells.

Although many cancer chemotherapies target derailing DNA synthesis as a method of killing fast-growing cancer cells, some recent research has aimed at attacking specific points on the glycolytic pathway. This strategy was pinned on the theory that without the ATP generated from glycolysis, cancer cells would be energy starved and unable to survive. In fact, promising results have been obtained by shutting down glycolysis in breast cancer cells by targeting a specific enzyme, thus opening the way for new therapies with perhaps fewer side effects than traditional chemotherapy.

## 24.4　The Fate of Pyruvate

While pyruvate is the end product of glycolysis, it is not the final product of glucose metabolism. What happens to pyruvate depends on the existing conditions and the organism. In particular, there are three possible products:

$$CH_3-\overset{O}{\underset{}{C}}-\overset{O}{\underset{}{C}}-O^- \longrightarrow CH_3-\overset{O}{\underset{}{C}}-SCoA \quad or \quad CH_3-\overset{OH}{\underset{H}{C}}-\overset{O}{\underset{}{C}}-O^- \quad or \quad CH_3CH_2OH$$

　　　　pyruvate　　　　　　　　　　　acetyl CoA　　　　　　　lactate　　　　　　　ethanol

- **Acetyl CoA,** $CH_3COSCoA$, is formed under aerobic conditions.
- **Lactate,** $CH_3CH(OH)CO_2^-$, is formed under anaerobic conditions.
- **Ethanol,** $CH_3CH_2OH$, is formed in fermentation.

### 24.4A　Conversion to Acetyl CoA

When oxygen is plentiful, oxidation of pyruvate by $NAD^+$ in the presence of coenzyme A and a dehydrogenase enzyme forms acetyl CoA and carbon dioxide. For this process to occur, pyruvate must diffuse across the outer membrane of a mitochondrion, and then be transported across the inner mitochondrial membrane into the matrix.

$$CH_3-\overset{O}{\underset{}{C}}-\overset{O}{\underset{}{C}}-O^- + HS-CoA \xrightarrow{\quad NAD^+ \quad NADH + H^+ \quad} CH_3-\overset{O}{\underset{}{C}}-SCoA + CO_2$$

　　　　　　pyruvate　　　　　　　　　　　　　　　　　　　　　　acetyl CoA

Although oxygen is not needed for this specific reaction, oxygen is needed to oxidize NADH back to $NAD^+$. Without an adequate supply of $NAD^+$, this pathway cannot occur. The acetyl CoA formed in this process then enters the common metabolic pathways—the citric acid cycle, the electron transport chain, and oxidative phosphorylation—to generate a great deal of ATP.

### 24.4B　FOCUS ON HEALTH & MEDICINE
Conversion to Lactate

When oxygen levels are low, the metabolism of pyruvate must follow a different course. Oxygen is needed to oxidize the NADH formed in step [6] of glycolysis back to $NAD^+$. If there is not enough $O_2$ to re-oxidize NADH, cells must get $NAD^+$ in a different way. The conversion of pyruvate to lactate provides the solution.

Reduction of pyruvate with NADH forms lactate and $NAD^+$, which can now re-enter glycolysis and oxidize glyceraldehyde 3-phosphate at step [6].

$NAD^+$ can re-enter glycolysis at step [6].

$$CH_3-\overset{O}{\underset{}{C}}-\overset{O}{\underset{}{C}}-O^- \xrightarrow{\quad NADH + H^+ \quad NAD^+ \quad} CH_3-\overset{OH}{\underset{H}{C}}-\overset{O}{\underset{}{C}}-O^-$$

　　　　　　pyruvate　　　　　　　　　　　　　　　　　　　　　　lactate

HEALTH NOTE

Muscle fatigue is caused by lactate buildup due to the anaerobic metabolism of glucose. Deep breaths after exercise replenish $O_2$ in oxygen-depleted tissues and allow the re-oxidation of lactate to pyruvate.

At rest, the $O_2$ level in cells is sufficient for the aerobic oxidation of pyruvate to acetyl CoA in humans, so lactate production occurs regularly only in red blood cells, which have no mitochondria and therefore no machinery of aerobic catabolism. During periods of strenuous exercise, when ATP needs are high, however, there is an inadequate level of oxygen to re-oxidize NADH in the electron transport chain. At these times, pyruvate is reduced to lactate for the sole purpose of re-oxidizing NADH to $NAD^+$ to maintain glycolysis. Under anaerobic conditions, therefore, lactate becomes the main product of glucose metabolism and only two ATP molecules are formed per glucose.

$$\text{Anaerobic conditions} \quad C_6H_{12}O_6 \xrightarrow[\quad]{2\ ADP \quad 2\ ATP} 2\ CH_3-\underset{\underset{H}{|}}{\overset{\overset{OH}{|}}{C}}-CO_2^-$$

glucose ⟶ lactate

Anaerobic metabolism leads to an increase in lactate levels in muscles, which in turn is associated with soreness and cramping. During these periods an "oxygen debt" is created. When vigorous activity ceases, an individual inhales deep breaths of air to repay the oxygen debt caused by heavy exercise. Lactate is then gradually re-oxidized to pyruvate, which can once again be converted to acetyl CoA, and muscle soreness, fatigue, and shortness of breath resolve.

In any tissue deprived of oxygen, pyruvate is converted to lactate rather than acetyl CoA. The pain produced during a heart attack, for example, is caused by an increase in lactate concentration that results when the blood supply to part of the heart muscle is blocked (Figure 24.5). The lack of oxygen delivery to heart tissue results in the anaerobic metabolism of glucose to lactate rather than acetyl CoA.

Measuring lactate levels in the blood is a common diagnostic tool used by physicians to assess how severely ill an individual is. A higher-than-normal lactate concentration generally indicates inadequate oxygen delivery to some tissues. Lactate levels increase transiently during exercise, but can remain elevated because of lung disease, congestive heart failure, or the presence of a serious infection.

**Figure 24.5**

Lactate Production During a Heart Attack

artery

coronary arteries

blood clot

cholesterol plaque

healthy muscle

The $O_2$ supply is cut off.

Under anaerobic conditions in the dying muscle, pyruvate is converted to lactate.

dying muscle

## 24.4C  FOCUS ON HEALTH & MEDICINE
### Conversion to Ethanol

In yeast and other microorganisms, pyruvate is converted to ethanol ($CH_3CH_2OH$) and carbon dioxide ($CO_2$) by a two-step process: decarboxylation (loss of $CO_2$) to acetaldehyde followed by reduction to ethanol.

The $NAD^+$ generated during reduction can enter glycolysis as an oxidizing agent in step [6]. As a result, glucose can be metabolized by yeast under anaerobic conditions: glycolysis forms pyruvate, which is further metabolized to ethanol and carbon dioxide. Two molecules of ATP are generated during glycolysis.

- *Fermentation* is the anaerobic conversion of glucose to ethanol and $CO_2$.

Fermentation plays a key role in the production of bread, beer, and cheese.

The ethanol in beer, wine, and other alcoholic beverages is obtained by the fermentation of sugar, quite possibly the oldest example of chemical synthesis. The carbohydrate source determines the type of alcoholic beverage formed. The sugars in grapes are fermented to form wine, barley malt is used for beer, and the carbohydrates in corn or rye form whiskey. When the fermented ethanol reaches a concentration of about 12%, the yeast cells that provide the enzymes for the process die and fermentation stops. Any alcoholic beverage with an ethanol concentration of greater than 12% must be distilled to increase the ethanol content. While ethanol consumption is considered socially acceptable in most societies, the irresponsible consumption of alcoholic beverages is a major health and social problem in many parts of the world (Section 14.6).

Fermentation plays a role in forming other food products. Cheese is produced by fermenting curdled milk, while yogurt is prepared by fermenting fresh milk. When yeast is mixed with flour, water, and sugar, the enzymes in yeast carry out fermentation to produce the $CO_2$ that causes bread to rise. Some of the characteristic and "intoxicating" odor associated with freshly baked bread is due to the ethanol that has evaporated during the baking process.

### PROBLEM 24.9

What role does NADH play in the conversion of pyruvate to lactate? What role does NADH play in the conversion of pyruvate to ethanol?

### PROBLEM 24.10

(a) In what way(s) is the conversion of pyruvate to acetyl CoA similar to the conversion of pyruvate to ethanol? (b) In what way(s) are the two processes different?

### PROBLEM 24.11

(a) In what way(s) is the conversion of pyruvate to lactate similar to the conversion of pyruvate to ethanol? (b) In what way(s) are the two processes different?

## 24.5 The ATP Yield from Glucose

How much ATP is generated from the complete catabolism of glucose ($C_6H_{12}O_6$) to carbon dioxide ($CO_2$)? To answer this question we must take into account the number of ATP molecules formed in the following sequential pathways:

- the glycolysis of glucose to two pyruvate molecules
- the oxidation of two pyruvate molecules to two molecules of acetyl CoA
- the citric acid cycle
- the electron transport chain and oxidative phosphorylation

To calculate how much ATP is generated, we must consider both the ATP formed directly in reactions, as well as the ATP produced from reduced coenzymes after oxidative phosphorylation.

As we learned in Section 23.6, each NADH formed in the mitochondrial matrix provides the energy to yield 2.5 ATPs, while each $FADH_2$ yields 1.5 ATPs. In contrast, the NADH formed during glycolysis is generated in the cytoplasm *outside* the mitochondria. Although it cannot pass through the mitochondrial membrane, its electrons and energy can be transferred to other molecules—NADH or $FADH_2$—ultimately yielding 1.5 or 2.5 ATPs for each NADH. To simplify calculations, we will use the value 2.5 ATP/NADH consistently in calculations.

Finally, any calculation must also take into account that glucose is split into *two* three-carbon molecules at step [4] of glycolysis, so the **ATP yield in each reaction must be *doubled* after this step.** With this information and Figure 24.6 in hand, we can now determine the total yield of ATP from the complete catabolism of glucose.

**Figure 24.6**    The ATP Yield from the Aerobic Metabolism of Glucose to $CO_2$

The complete catabolism of glucose forms six $CO_2$ molecules and 32 ATP molecules.

- Glycolysis yields a net of two ATP molecules. The two molecules of NADH formed during step [6] of glycolysis yield five additional ATPs.

$$C_6H_{12}O_6 \longrightarrow 2\ CH_3COCO_2^- + 2\ ATP + 2\ NADH$$

glucose     pyruvate

$\hookrightarrow 2 \times (2.5\ \text{ATP/NADH}) = 5\ \text{ATP}$

- Oxidation of two molecules of pyruvate to acetyl CoA in the mitochondria forms two NADH molecules that yield five ATP molecules.

$$2\ CH_3COCO_2^- \longrightarrow 2\ CH_3COSCoA + 2\ CO_2 + 2\ NADH$$

pyruvate     acetyl CoA

$\hookrightarrow 2 \times (2.5\ \text{ATP/NADH}) = 5\ \text{ATP}$

- Beginning with two acetyl CoA molecules, the citric acid cycle (Figure 23.7) forms two GTP molecules, the energy equivalent of two ATPs, in step [5]. The six NADH molecules and two FADH$_2$ molecules also formed yield an additional 18 ATPs from the electron transport chain and oxidative phosphorylation. Thus, 20 ATPs are formed from two acetyl CoA molecules.

$\hookrightarrow 2 \times (1.5\ \text{ATP/FADH}_2) = 3\ \text{ATP}$

$$2\ CH_3COSCoA \longrightarrow 4\ CO_2 + 2\ GTP + 6\ NADH + 2\ FADH_2$$

acetyl CoA

$\downarrow$

2 ATP

$\hookrightarrow 6 \times (2.5\ \text{ATP/NADH}) = 15\ \text{ATP}$

Adding up the ATP formed in each pathway gives a **total of 32 molecules of ATP for the complete catabolism of each glucose molecule.** Most of the ATP generated from glucose metabolism results from the citric acid cycle, electron transport chain, and oxidative phosphorylation.

Glucose is the main source of energy for cells and the only source of energy used by the brain. When energy demands are low, glucose is stored as the polymer glycogen in the liver and muscles. When blood levels of glucose are low, glycogen is hydrolyzed to keep adequate blood glucose levels to satisfy the body's energy needs.

Blood glucose levels are carefully regulated by two hormones. When blood glucose concentration rises after a meal, **insulin** stimulates the passage of glucose into cells for metabolism. When blood glucose levels are low, the hormone **glucagon** stimulates the conversion of stored glycogen to glucose.

### PROBLEM 24.12

How much ATP results from each transformation?

a. glucose → 2 pyruvate       c. glucose → 2 acetyl CoA
b. pyruvate → acetyl CoA      d. 2 acetyl CoA → 4 $CO_2$

### PROBLEM 24.13

What three reactions form $CO_2$ when glucose is completely catabolized?

### PROBLEM 24.14

What is the difference in ATP generation between the aerobic oxidation of glucose to $CO_2$ and the anaerobic conversion of glucose to lactate?

## 24.6 Gluconeogenesis

Now that we have learned how glucose is converted to $CO_2$ and energy, we can also consider one other metabolic pathway that involves glucose.

- *Gluconeogenesis* is the synthesis of glucose from noncarbohydrate sources—lactate, amino acids, or glycerol.

As such, **gluconeogenesis is an *anabolic* pathway rather than a catabolic pathway since it results in the synthesis of glucose from smaller molecules.** Gluconeogenesis occurs in the liver when the body has depleted both available glucose and stored glycogen reserves. Such a condition results during sustained vigorous exercise or fasting.

For example, the lactate that builds up in muscles as a result of vigorous exercise can be transported to the liver where it is oxidized to pyruvate, which is then converted to glucose by means of gluconeogenesis. The newly synthesized glucose is then utilized for energy or stored in the muscle as glycogen.

$$2\ CH_3-\underset{\underset{H}{|}}{\overset{\overset{OH}{|}}{C}}-CO_2^- \xrightarrow{\text{oxidation}} 2\ CH_3-\overset{\overset{O}{\|}}{C}-CO_2^-\ \xrightarrow{\text{gluconeogenesis}}\ C_6H_{12}O_6$$

lactate                      pyruvate               glucose

Conceptually, gluconeogenesis is the reverse of glycolysis; that is, **two molecules of pyruvate are converted to glucose by a stepwise pathway that passes through all of the same intermediates encountered in glycolysis.** In fact, seven of the 10 steps of gluconeogenesis use the same enzymes as glycolysis. Three steps in glycolysis (steps [1], [3], and [10]), however, must use different enzymes to be energetically feasible for gluconeogenesis to occur. As a result, **gluconeogenesis provides a mechanism for synthesizing new glucose molecules from other substrates.**

- Glycolysis is a catabolic process that converts glucose to pyruvate.
- Gluconeogenesis is an anabolic process that synthesizes glucose from pyruvate.

Cycling compounds from the muscle to the liver and back to the muscle is called the **Cori cycle.** The Cori cycle involves the four operations shown in Figure 24.7.

**Figure 24.7**

The Cori Cycle—
Glycolysis and Gluconeogenesis

[1] Glycolysis in muscle

$C_6H_{12}O_6 \longrightarrow 2\ CH_3COCO_2^- \longrightarrow 2\ CH_3CH(OH)CO_2^-$
glucose        pyruvate        lactate

[4] Transport to the muscle        [2] Transport to the liver

$C_6H_{12}O_6 \longleftarrow 2\ CH_3COCO_2^- \longleftarrow 2\ CH_3CH(OH)CO_2^-$
glucose        pyruvate        lactate

[3] Gluconeogenesis in the liver

Steps in the Cori cycle:

[1]  The catabolism of glucose in muscle forms pyruvate, which is reduced to lactate when the oxygen supply is limited.
[2]  Lactate is transported to the liver.
[3]  Oxidation of lactate forms pyruvate, which is then converted to glucose by the 10-step process of gluconeogenesis.
[4]  Glucose is transported back to the muscle.

Because the brain relies solely on glucose as an energy source, gluconeogenesis is a mechanism that ensures that the brain has a supply of glucose even when a diet is low in carbohydrates and glycogen reserves are low. Gluconeogenesis is not a commonly used metabolic pathway when carbohydrate intake is high. On the other hand, a low carbohydrate diet makes gluconeogenesis an important pathway that converts noncarbohydrate substrates—fats and amino acids—to needed glucose.

**PROBLEM 24.15**

From what you learned about glycolysis in Section 24.3, what is the starting material and product of each of the following steps in gluconeogenesis: (a) step [1]; (b) step [3]; (c) step [10]?

## 24.7 The Catabolism of Triacylglycerols

The first step in the catabolism of triacylglycerols, the most common lipids, is the hydrolysis of the three ester bonds to form glycerol and fatty acids, which are then metabolized in separate pathways.

### 24.7A Glycerol Catabolism

The glycerol formed from triacylglycerol hydrolysis is converted in two steps to dihydroxyacetone phosphate. Phosphorylation of glycerol with ATP forms glycerol 3-phosphate, which is then oxidized with NAD$^+$.

Since dihydroxyacetone phosphate is an intermediate in both glycolysis and gluconeogenesis, two pathways are available, depending on the energy needs of the organism.

**PROBLEM 24.16**

Analyze the phosphorylation of glycerol in step [1] of glycerol metabolism by looking at the functional groups, the reagent, and the name of the enzyme, as discussed in Section 24.2.

### 24.7B Fatty Acid Catabolism by β-Oxidation

Fatty acids are catabolized by **β-oxidation,** a process in which two-carbon acetyl CoA units are sequentially cleaved from the fatty acid. Key to this process is the oxidation of the β carbon to the carbonyl group of a thioester (RCOSR′), which then undergoes cleavage between the α and β carbons.

This carbon is oxidized. — These C's come off as acetyl CoA.

$$-CH_2-CH_2-CH_2-CH_2-CH_2-\overset{\overset{\displaystyle O}{\|}}{C}-$$

β   α

This C—C bond is cleaved.

Fatty acid oxidation begins with conversion of the fatty acid to a thioester with coenzyme A. This process requires energy, which comes from the hydrolysis of two P—O bonds in ATP to form AMP, adenosine *mono*phosphate. Much like the beginning of glycolysis requires an energy investment, so, too, the initial step of fatty acid oxidation requires energy input.

ATP     AMP + 2 HPO$_4^{2-}$

$$CH_3(CH_2)_{14}-CH_2-CH_2-\overset{\overset{\displaystyle O}{\|}}{C}-OH \ + \ HS-CoA \xrightarrow{\text{acyl CoA synthetase}} CH_3(CH_2)_{14}-CH_2-CH_2-\overset{\overset{\displaystyle O}{\|}}{C}-SCoA$$

stearic acid                                                                         an acyl CoA

Once the product, an **acyl CoA,** is inside the mitochondrion, the process of β-oxidation is set to begin. β-Oxidation requires four steps to cleave a two-carbon acetyl CoA unit from the acyl CoA, as shown with the 18-carbon fatty acid stearic acid in Figure 24.8.

In step [1], FAD removes two hydrogen atoms to form FADH$_2$ and a double bond between the α and β carbons of the thioester. Water is added to the double bond in step [2] to place an OH group on the β carbon to the carbonyl group, which is then oxidized in step [3] to form a carbonyl group. The NAD$^+$ oxidizing agent is reduced to NADH in step [3] as well. Finally, cleavage of the bond between the α and β carbons forms acetyl CoA and a 16-carbon acyl CoA in step [4].

- As a result, a new acyl CoA having two carbons fewer than the original acyl CoA is formed.

**Figure 24.8**

β-Oxidation of a Fatty Acid

This bond is cleaved in β-oxidation.

$$18 \ C's \longrightarrow CH_3(CH_2)_{14}-\underset{\beta}{CH_2}-\underset{\alpha}{CH_2}-\overset{\overset{\displaystyle O}{\|}}{C}-SCoA$$

C$_{18}$ acyl CoA

acyl CoA                FAD            ① **Oxidation**
dehydrogenase          FADH$_2$

$$CH_3(CH_2)_{14}-\underset{\beta}{CH}=\underset{\alpha}{CH}-\overset{\overset{\displaystyle O}{\|}}{C}-SCoA$$

enoyl CoA hydratase        H$_2$O         ② **Hydration**

$$CH_3(CH_2)_{14}-\underset{\beta}{\overset{\overset{\displaystyle OH}{|}}{CH}}-\overset{\overset{\displaystyle H}{|}}{CH}-\overset{\overset{\displaystyle O}{\|}}{C}-SCoA$$

β-hydroxyacyl CoA          NAD$^+$        ③ **Oxidation**
dehydrogenase           NADH + H$^+$

$$CH_3(CH_2)_{14}-\overset{\overset{\displaystyle O}{\|}}{C}-CH_2-\overset{\overset{\displaystyle O}{\|}}{C}-SCoA$$

This bond is cleaved.      acyl CoA        HSCoA        ④ **Cleavage**
                          acyltransferase

$$16 \ C's \longrightarrow CH_3(CH_2)_{14}-\overset{\overset{\displaystyle O}{\|}}{C}-SCoA \ + \ CH_3-\overset{\overset{\displaystyle O}{\|}}{C}-SCoA$$

C$_{16}$ acyl CoA                               2 C's

The following equation summarizes the important components of β-oxidation for a general acyl CoA, $RCH_2CH_2COSCoA$. **Each four-step sequence forms one molecule each of acetyl CoA, NADH, and FADH$_2$.**

Once the 16-carbon acyl CoA is formed in step [4], it becomes the substrate for a new four-step β-oxidation sequence. This type of metabolic pathway is called a **spiral pathway,** because the same set of reactions is repeated on increasingly smaller substrates. The process continues until a four-carbon acyl CoA is cleaved to form *two* acetyl CoA molecules. As a result:

- An 18-carbon acyl CoA is cleaved to *nine* two-carbon acetyl CoA molecules.
- A total of *eight* cycles of β-oxidation are needed to cleave the eight carbon–carbon bonds.

Thus, complete β-oxidation of the acyl CoA derived from stearic acid forms:

- **9 CH$_3$COSCoA molecules** (from the 18-carbon fatty acid)
- **8 NADH** (from eight cycles of β-oxidation)
- **8 FADH$_2$** (from eight cycles of β-oxidation)

β-Oxidation of unsaturated fatty acids proceeds in a similar fashion, although an additional step is required. **Ultimately every carbon in the original fatty acid ends up as a carbon atom of acetyl CoA.**

## SAMPLE PROBLEM 24.3

Consider lauric acid, $CH_3(CH_2)_{10}CO_2H$. (a) How many molecules of acetyl CoA are formed from complete β-oxidation? (b) How many cycles of β-oxidation are needed for complete catabolism?

### Analysis

The number of carbons in the fatty acid determines the number of molecules of acetyl CoA formed and the number of times β-oxidation occurs.

- The number of molecules of acetyl CoA equals one-half the number of carbons in the original fatty acid.
- Because the final turn of the cycle forms *two* molecules of acetyl CoA, the number of cycles is one fewer than the number of acetyl CoA molecules formed.

### Solution

Since lauric acid has 12 carbons, it forms six molecules of acetyl CoA from five cycles of β-oxidation.

### PROBLEM 24.17

For each fatty acid: [1] How many molecules of acetyl CoA are formed from complete catabolism? [2] How many cycles of β-oxidation are needed for complete oxidation?

a.  arachidic acid ($C_{20}H_{40}O_2$)          b.  palmitoleic acid ($C_{16}H_{30}O_2$)

## 24.7C   The Energy Yield from Fatty Acid Oxidation

How much energy—in terms of the number of molecules of ATP formed—results from the complete catabolism of a fatty acid? To determine this quantity, we must take into account the ATP cost for the conversion of the fatty acid to the acyl CoA, as well as the ATP production from the coenzymes (NADH and $FADH_2$) and acetyl CoA formed during β-oxidation. The steps are shown in the accompanying *How To* procedure.

---

*How To* **Determine the Number of Molecules of ATP Formed from a Fatty Acid**

**Example:**  How much ATP is formed by the complete catabolism of stearic acid, $C_{18}H_{36}O_2$?

**Step [1]**  **Determine the amount of ATP required to synthesize the acyl CoA from the fatty acid.**
- Since the conversion of stearic acid ($C_{17}H_{35}COOH$) to an acyl CoA ($C_{17}H_{35}COSCoA$) requires the hydrolysis of two P—O bonds, this is equivalent to the energy released when 2 ATPs are converted to 2 ADPs.
- Thus, the **first step in catabolism costs the equivalent of 2 ATPs—that is, –2 ATPs.**

**Step [2]**  **Add up the ATP generated from the coenzymes produced during β-oxidation.**
- As we learned in Section 24.7B, each cycle of β-oxidation produces one molecule each of NADH and $FADH_2$. To cleave eight carbon–carbon bonds in stearic acid requires eight cycles of β-oxidation, so 8 NADH and 8 $FADH_2$ are produced.

$$8 \text{ NADH} \times 2.5 \text{ ATP/NADH} = 20 \text{ ATP}$$
$$8 \text{ FADH}_2 \times 1.5 \text{ ATP/FADH}_2 = 12 \text{ ATP}$$
$$\text{From reduced coenzymes:} \quad 32 \text{ ATP}$$

- Thus, 32 ATPs would be produced from oxidative phosphorylation after the reduced coenzymes enter the electron transport chain.

**Step [3]**  **Determine the amount of ATP that results from each acetyl CoA, and add the results for steps [1]–[3].**
- From Section 24.7B, stearic acid generates nine molecules of acetyl CoA, which then enter the citric acid cycle and go on to produce ATP by the electron transport chain and oxidative phosphorylation. As we learned in Section 23.6, each acetyl CoA results in 10 ATPs.

$$9 \text{ acetyl CoA} \times 10 \text{ ATP/acetyl CoA} = 90 \text{ ATP}$$

- Totaling the values obtained in steps [1]–[3]:

$$(-2) + 32 + 90 = 120 \text{ ATP molecules from stearic acid}$$
**Answer**

---

### PROBLEM 24.18

Calculate the number of molecules of ATP formed by the complete catabolism of palmitic acid, $C_{16}H_{32}O_2$.

### PROBLEM 24.19

Calculate the number of molecules of ATP formed by the complete catabolism of arachidic acid, $C_{20}H_{40}O_2$.

A grizzly bear uses stored body fat as its sole energy source during its many months of hibernation. β-Oxidation of fatty acids releases sufficient energy to maintain a constant body temperature between 32 and 35 °C and operate all necessary cellular processes.

How does the energy generated in fatty acid catabolism compare to the energy generated from glucose catabolism? In Section 24.5, we determined that one molecule (or one mole) of glucose generates 32 molecules (or moles) of ATP, while the *How To* calculation demonstrates that one molecule (or one mole) of stearic acid generates 120 molecules (or moles) of ATP.

To compare these values, we need to compare the amount of ATP generated *per gram* of each material. To carry out a calculation of this sort we need to use the molar masses of glucose (180 g/mol) and stearic acid (284 g/mol).

$$\boxed{\text{molar mass conversion factor}}$$

For glucose: $\dfrac{32 \text{ ATP}}{\text{mol glucose}} \times \dfrac{1 \text{ mol}}{180 \text{ g}} = \dfrac{0.18 \text{ mol ATP}}{\text{g glucose}}$

For stearic acid: $\dfrac{120 \text{ ATP}}{\text{mol stearic acid}} \times \dfrac{1 \text{ mol}}{284 \text{ g}} = \dfrac{0.42 \text{ mol ATP}}{\text{g stearic acid}}$ — over twice as much energy per gram

This calculation demonstrates that **a fatty acid produces over *twice as much energy per gram* (in terms of moles of ATP generated) than glucose.** This is why lipids are so much more effective as energy-storing molecules than carbohydrates.

### PROBLEM 24.20

Use the number of molecules of ATP formed from the complete catabolism of palmitic acid, $C_{16}H_{32}O_2$, in Problem 24.18 to calculate the molecules (or moles) of ATP formed per gram of palmitic acid (molar mass 256 g/mol).

### PROBLEM 24.21

Another way to compare the energy content of molecules is to compare the number of ATPs they generate *per carbon* atom they contain. (a) How many ATPs are formed per carbon when glucose is completely catabolized? (b) How many ATPs are formed per carbon when stearic acid is completely catabolized? (c) Do these data support or refute the fact that lipids are more effective energy-storing molecules than carbohydrates?

## 24.8   Ketone Bodies

When carbohydrates do not meet energy needs, the body turns to catabolizing stored triacylglycerols, which generate acetyl CoA by β-oxidation of fatty acids. Normally the acetyl CoA is metabolized in the citric acid cycle. When acetyl CoA levels exceed the capacity of the citric acid cycle, however, acetyl CoA is converted to three compounds that are collectively called **ketone bodies**—acetoacetate, β-hydroxybutyrate, and acetone.

$$2\ CH_3-\overset{O}{\underset{}{C}}-SCoA \xrightarrow{\text{several steps}} CH_3-\overset{O}{\underset{}{C}}-CH_2-\overset{O}{\underset{}{C}}-O^-$$

acetoacetate

$$\xrightarrow{\text{NADH + H}^+ \quad \text{NAD}^+} CH_3-\overset{OH}{\underset{H}{C}}-CH_2-\overset{O}{\underset{}{C}}-O^-$$

β-hydroxybutyrate

$$\downarrow CO_2$$

$$CH_3-\overset{O}{\underset{}{C}}-CH_3$$

acetone

Ketostix are a brand of test strips that detect ketone bodies in urine.

Low carbohydrate diets such as the Atkins plan induce the use of stored fat for energy production to assist weight loss.

• *Ketogenesis* is the synthesis of ketone bodies from acetyl CoA.

Acetoacetate is first formed from two molecules of acetyl CoA by a multistep process. Acetoacetate is either reduced to β-hydroxybutyrate with NADH or undergoes decarboxylation to form acetone. Ketone bodies are produced in the liver, and since they are small molecules that can hydrogen bond with water, they are readily soluble in blood and urine. Once they reach tissues, β-hydroxybutyrate and acetoacetate can be re-converted to acetyl CoA and metabolized for energy.

### PROBLEM 24.22

Are any structural features common to the three ketone bodies?

### PROBLEM 24.23

Why is the term "ketone body" a misleading name for β-hydroxybutyrate?

Under some circumstances—notably starvation, vigorous dieting, and uncontrolled diabetes—when glucose is unavailable or cannot pass into a cell for use as fuel, ketone bodies accumulate, a condition called **ketosis.** As a result, ketone bodies are eliminated in urine and the sweet odor of acetone can be detected in exhaled breath. Sometimes the first indication of diabetes in a patient is the detection of excess ketone bodies in a urine test.

An abnormally high concentration of ketone bodies can lead to **ketoacidosis**—that is, a lowering of the blood pH caused by the increased level of β-hydroxybutyrate and acetoacetate. Although the carbonic acid/bicarbonate buffer in the blood prevents drastic pH changes (Section 9.11), even a small drop in pH can alter many critical biochemical processes.

Low carbohydrate diets, popularized by Dr. Robert Atkins in a series of diet books published in the 1990s, restrict carbohydrate intake to induce the utilization of the body's stored fat as its main energy source. This increased level of fatty acid metabolism leads to an increased concentration of ketone bodies in the blood. Increased levels of ketone bodies in the urine—which can be detected using ketone test strips—can be used as an indicator that the body has switched to metabolic machinery that relies on fat rather than carbohydrates as its principal energy source. Some physicians recommend that the level of ketone bodies be monitored to avoid the risk of ketoacidosis.

### PROBLEM 24.24

What type of enzymes catalyzes the conversion of acetoacetate to acetone?

### PROBLEM 24.25

How is the concentration of acetyl CoA related to the production of ketone bodies?

## 24.9 Amino Acid Metabolism

After proteins are hydrolyzed in the stomach and intestines, the individual amino acids are reassembled to new proteins or converted to intermediates in other metabolic pathways. The catabolism of amino acids provides energy when the supply of carbohydrates and lipids is exhausted.

**The catabolism of amino acids can be conceptually divided into two parts: the fate of the amino group and the fate of the carbon atoms.** As shown in Figure 24.9, amino acid carbon skeletons are converted to pyruvate, acetyl CoA, or various carbon compounds that are part of the citric acid cycle.

**Figure 24.9**    An Overview of the Catabolism of Amino Acids

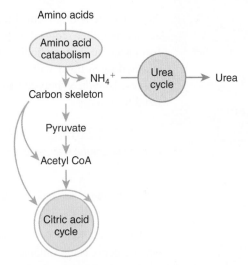

The breakdown of amino acids forms $NH_4^+$, which enters the urea cycle to form urea, and a carbon skeleton that is metabolized to either pyruvate, acetyl CoA, or an intermediate in the citric acid cycle.

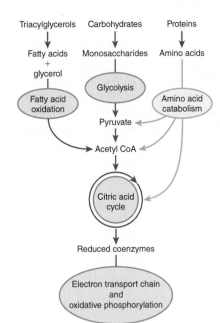

## 24.9A    Degradation of Amino Acids—The Fate of the Amino Group

The catabolism of carbohydrates and triacylglycerols deals with the oxidation of carbon atoms only. With amino acids, an **amino group (–NH₂)** must be metabolized, as well. The catabolism of amino acids begins with the removal of the amino group from the carbon skeleton and the formation of ammonium ($NH_4^+$) by a two-step pathway: **transamination followed by oxidative deamination.**

- *Transamination* is the transfer of an amino group from an amino acid to an α-keto acid, usually α-ketoglutarate.

**In transamination, the amino group of the amino acid and the ketone carbonyl oxygen of the α-keto acid are interchanged to form a new amino acid and a new α-keto acid.** As an example, transfer of an amino group from alanine to α-ketoglutarate forms pyruvate and glutamate, the completely ionized form of the amino acid glutamic acid.

**Transamination removes the amino group to form a carbon skeleton that contains only carbon, hydrogen, and oxygen atoms.** These products are then degraded along other catabolic pathways as described in Section 24.9B.

### SAMPLE PROBLEM 24.4

What products are formed in the following transamination reaction?

### Analysis

To draw the products of transamination, convert the C—H and C—NH$_3^+$ groups of the amino acid to a C=O, forming an $\alpha$-keto acid.

### Solution

### PROBLEM 24.26

Draw the products formed when each amino acid undergoes transamination with $\alpha$-ketoglutarate.

The glutamate formed by transamination is then degraded by oxidative deamination using NAD$^+$.

- **In oxidative deamination, the C—H and C—NH$_3^+$ bonds on the $\alpha$ carbon of glutamate are converted to C=O and an ammonium ion, NH$_4^+$.**

In oxidative deamination, glutamate is re-converted to $\alpha$-ketoglutarate, which can undergo transamination with another molecule of an amino acid and the cycle repeats. In this way, $\alpha$-ketoglutarate removes an amino group from an amino acid and then loses that amino group as NH$_4^+$ in a second step.

The ammonium ion then enters the **urea cycle,** where it is converted by a multistep pathway to **urea, (NH$_2$)$_2$C=O,** in the liver. Urea is then transported to the kidneys and excreted in urine.

- The overall result of transamination and oxidative deamination is to remove an amino group from an amino acid and form an ammonium ion, $NH_4^+$.

$$
\underset{\text{amino acid}}{R-\overset{\overset{+}{N}H_3}{\underset{H}{C}}-CO_2^-} \xrightarrow[\text{[2] oxidative deamination}]{\text{[1] transamination}} \underset{\alpha\text{-keto acid}}{R-\overset{O}{C}-CO_2^-} \ + \ NH_4^+
$$

### SAMPLE PROBLEM 24.5

What final products are formed when leucine is subjected to transamination followed by oxidative deamination?

$$
\underset{\text{leucine}}{(CH_3)_2CHCH_2-\overset{\overset{+}{N}H_3}{\underset{H}{C}}-CO_2^-}
$$

### Analysis

To draw the organic product, replace the C—H and C—$NH_3^+$ on the $\alpha$ carbon of the amino acid by C=O. $NH_4^+$ is formed from the amino group.

### Solution

$$
\underset{\phantom{a}}{(CH_3)_2CHCH_2-\overset{\overset{+}{N}H_3}{\underset{\underset{\alpha\ carbon}{H}}{C}}-CO_2^-} \xrightarrow[\text{[2] oxidative deamination}]{\text{[1] transamination}} (CH_3)_2CHCH_2-\overset{O}{C}-CO_2^- \ + \ NH_4^+
$$

### PROBLEM 24.27

What products are formed when each amino acid is subjected to transamination followed by oxidative deamination: (a) threonine; (b) glycine; (c) isoleucine? Use the structures in Table 21.2.

## 24.9B  Degradation of Amino Acids—The Fate of the Carbon Skeleton

Once the nitrogen has been removed from an amino acid, the carbon skeletons of individual amino acids are catabolized in a variety of ways. There are three common fates of the carbon skeletons of amino acids, shown in Figure 24.10:

- conversion to pyruvate, $CH_3COCO_2^-$
- conversion to acetyl CoA, $CH_3COSCoA$
- conversion to an intermediate in the citric acid cycle

Some amino acids such as alanine (Section 24.9A) are catabolized to pyruvate. Since pyruvate is an intermediate in both glycolysis and gluconeogenesis, pyruvate can be broken down for energy or used to synthesize glucose. In considering catabolism, amino acids are often divided into two groups.

- *Glucogenic* amino acids are catabolized to pyruvate or an intermediate in the citric acid cycle. Since these catabolic products can be used for gluconeogenesis, glucogenic amino acids can be used to synthesize glucose.

- *Ketogenic* amino acids are converted to acetyl CoA, or the related thioester acetoacetyl CoA, $CH_3COCH_2COSCoA$. These catabolic products cannot be used to synthesize glucose, but they can be converted to ketone bodies and yield energy by this path.

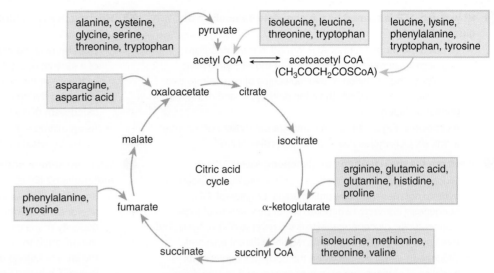

Figure 24.10

Amino Acid Catabolism

Glucogenic amino acids are highlighted in blue, while ketogenic amino acids are highlighted in tan. Amino acids that appear more than once in the scheme can be degraded by multiple routes.

We will not examine the specific pathways that convert the carbon skeletons of individual amino acids into other products. Figure 24.10 illustrates where each amino acid feeds into the metabolic pathways we have already discussed.

### PROBLEM 24.28

What metabolic intermediate is produced from the carbon atoms of each amino acid?

a. cysteine          b. aspartic acid          c. valine          d. threonine

# CHAPTER HIGHLIGHTS

## KEY TERMS

Acyl CoA (24.7)
Cori cycle (24.6)
Decarboxylation (24.2)
Fermentation (24.4)
Glucogenic amino acid (24.9)
Gluconeogenesis (24.6)

Glycolysis (24.3)
Isomerase (24.2)
Ketogenesis (24.8)
Ketogenic amino acid (24.9)
Ketone bodies (24.8)
Ketosis (24.8)

Kinase (24.2)
β-Oxidation (24.7)
Oxidative deamination (24.9)
Transamination (24.9)
Urea cycle (24.9)

## KEY CONCEPTS

❶ **What are the main elements that provide clues to the outcome of a biochemical reaction? (24.2)**
- To understand the course of a biochemical reaction, examine the functional groups that are added or removed, the reagents (coenzymes or other materials), and the enzyme. The name of an enzyme is often a clue as to the type of reaction.

❷ **What are the main aspects of glycolysis? (24.3)**
- Glycolysis is a linear, 10-step pathway that converts glucose to two three-carbon pyruvate molecules. In the energy-investment phase, steps [1]–[5], the energy from two ATP molecules is used for phosphorylation and two three-carbon products are formed. In the energy-generating phase, steps

[6]–[10], the following species are generated: two pyruvate molecules ($CH_3COCO_2^-$), 2 NADHs, and 4 ATPs.
- The net result of glycolysis, considering both phases, is 2 $CH_3COCO_2^-$, 2 NADHs, and 2 ATPs.

❸ **What are the major pathways for pyruvate metabolism? (24.4)**
- When oxygen is plentiful, pyruvate is converted to acetyl CoA, which can enter the citric acid cycle.
- When the oxygen level is low, the anaerobic metabolism of pyruvate forms lactate and $NAD^+$.
- In yeast and other microorganisms, pyruvate is converted to ethanol and $CO_2$ by fermentation.

**④ How much ATP is formed by the complete catabolism of glucose? (24.5)**

- To calculate the amount of ATP formed in the catabolism of glucose, we must take into account the ATP yield from glycolysis, the oxidation of two molecules of pyruvate to two molecules of acetyl CoA, the citric acid cycle, and oxidative phosphorylation.
- As shown in Figure 24.6, the complete catabolism of glucose forms six $CO_2$ molecules and 32 molecules of ATP.

**⑤ What are the main features of gluconeogenesis? (24.6)**

- Gluconeogenesis is the synthesis of glucose from noncarbohydrate sources—lactate, amino acids, or glycerol. Gluconeogenesis converts two molecules of pyruvate to glucose. Conceptually, gluconeogenesis is the reverse of glycolysis, but three steps in gluconeogenesis require different enzymes.
- Gluconeogenesis occurs when the body has depleted its supplies of glucose and stored glycogen, and occurs during sustained physical exercise and fasting.

**⑥ Describe the main features of the β-oxidation of fatty acids. (24.7)**

- β-Oxidation is a spiral metabolic pathway that sequentially cleaves two-carbon acetyl CoA units from an acyl CoA derived from a fatty acid. Each cycle of β-oxidation consists of a four-step sequence that forms one molecule each of acetyl CoA, NADH, and $FADH_2$.

**⑦ How much ATP is formed from complete fatty acid oxidation? (24.7)**

- To determine the ATP yield from the complete catabolism of a fatty acid, we must consider the ATP used up in the synthesis of the acyl CoA, the ATP generated from coenzymes produced during β-oxidation, and the ATP that results from the catabolism of each acetyl CoA.
- As an example, the complete catabolism of stearic acid, $C_{18}H_{36}O_2$, yields 120 ATPs.

**⑧ What are ketone bodies and how do they play a role in metabolism? (24.8)**

- Ketone bodies—acetoacetate, β-hydroxybutyrate, and acetone—are formed when acetyl CoA levels exceed the capacity of the citric acid cycle. Ketone bodies can be re-converted to acetyl CoA and metabolized for energy. When the level of ketone bodies is high, the pH of the blood can be lowered, causing ketoacidosis.

**⑨ What are the main features of amino acid catabolism? (24.9)**

- The catabolism of amino acids involves two parts. First, the amino group is removed by transamination followed by oxidative deamination. The $NH_4^+$ ion formed enters the urea cycle where it is converted to urea and eliminated in urine. The carbon skeletons of the amino acids are catabolized by a variety of pathways to yield pyruvate, acetyl CoA, or an intermediate in the citric acid cycle.

## PROBLEMS

Selected in-chapter and odd-numbered end-of-chapter problems have brief answers in Appendix B. The *Student Study Guide and Solutions Manual* contains detailed solutions to all in-chapter and odd-numbered end-of-chapter problems, as well as additional worked examples and a chapter self-test.

### Analyzing Biochemical Reactions

**24.29** Analyze each reaction by considering the functional groups that change, the coenzyme or other reactant, and the name of the enzyme.

a.
$$CH_3-\underset{\underset{OH}{|}}{CH}-CH_2-\underset{\underset{O}{\|}}{C}-SCoA \xrightarrow[\text{β-hydroxyacyl CoA dehydrogenase}]{NAD^+ \quad NADH + H^+} CH_3-\underset{\underset{O}{\|}}{C}-CH_2-\underset{\underset{O}{\|}}{C}-SCoA$$

b.
$$^-O_2CCH_2-\underset{\underset{O}{\|}}{C}-CO_2^- \xrightarrow[\text{phosphoenolpyruvate carboxykinase}]{GTP \quad GDP} CH_2=\underset{\underset{PO_3^{2-}}{|}}{C}-\underset{\underset{O}{\|}}{C}-O^- \;+\; CO_2$$

**24.30** Analyze each reaction by considering the functional groups that change, the coenzyme or other reactant, and the name of the enzyme.

a.
$$\underset{\text{3-phosphoglycerate}}{\underset{\underset{PO_3^{2-}}{|}}{O}-CH_2-\underset{\underset{OH}{|}}{CH}-\underset{\underset{O}{\|}}{C}-O^-} \xrightarrow[\text{phosphoglycerate kinase}]{ATP \quad ADP} \underset{\text{1,3-bisphosphoglycerate}}{\underset{\underset{PO_3^{2-}}{|}}{O}-CH_2-\underset{\underset{OH}{|}}{CH}-\underset{\underset{O}{\|}}{C}-O-PO_3^{2-}}$$

b.
$$CH_3-\underset{\underset{O}{\|}}{C}-CO_2^- \;+\; CO_2 \xrightarrow[\text{pyruvate carboxylase}]{ATP \quad ADP + HPO_4^{2-}} \;^-O_2CCH_2-\underset{\underset{O}{\|}}{C}-CO_2^-$$

**24.31** In the conversion of glucose to stored glycogen, glucose 6-phosphate is converted to glucose 1-phosphate by the enzyme phosphoglucomutase. Suggest a reason for the name of this enzyme.

**24.32** When mannose is metabolized to an intermediate in glycolysis, mannose 6-phosphate is converted to fructose 6-phosphate by phosphomannose isomerase. (a) Why is an isomerase enzyme used for this reaction? (b) What type of isomers do mannose 6-phosphate and fructose 6-phosphate represent?

mannose 6-phosphate          fructose 6-phosphate

## Glucose Metabolism

**24.33** (a) Convert the ball-and-stick model of **A,** one of the intermediates in glycolysis, to a structural formula, and name the compound. (b) What is the immediate precursor of **A** in glycolysis; that is, what compound forms **A** as a reaction product? (c) What compound is formed from **A** in glycolysis?

**A**

**24.34** (a) Convert the ball-and-stick model of **B,** one of the intermediates in glycolysis, to a structural formula, and name the compound. (b) What is the immediate precursor of **B** in glycolysis; that is, what compound forms **B** as a reaction product? (c) What compound is formed from **B** in glycolysis?

**B**

**24.35** Compare the energy-investment phase and the energy-generating phase of glycolysis with regards to each of the following: (a) the reactant that begins the phase and the final product formed; (b) the amount of ATP used or formed; (c) the number of reduced coenzymes used or formed.

**24.36** Compare glycolysis and gluconeogenesis with regards to the reactant that begins the pathway and the product formed at the end of the pathway.

**24.37** Considering the individual steps in glycolysis:
   a. Which steps form ATP?
   b. Which steps use ATP?
   c. Which steps form a reduced coenzyme?
   d. Which step breaks a C—C bond?

**24.38** Explain the role of the coenzymes NAD$^+$ and NADH in each reaction.
   a. pyruvate → acetyl CoA
   b. pyruvate → lactate
   c. pyruvate → ethanol

**24.39** Glucose is completely metabolized to six molecules of $CO_2$. What specific reactions generate each molecule of $CO_2$?

**24.40** Why is glycolysis described as an anaerobic process?

**24.41** Write the overall equation with key coenzymes for each process.
   a. glucose → pyruvate
   b. glucose → ethanol
   c. pyruvate → lactate

**24.42** Write the overall equation with key coenzymes for each process.
   a. glucose → lactate
   b. pyruvate → ethanol
   c. pyruvate → acetyl CoA

**24.43** Consider the aerobic and anaerobic avenues of pyruvate metabolism in the human body.
   a. Where do the carbon atoms of pyruvate end up in each pathway?
   b. What coenzymes are used and formed?

**24.44** What is the main purpose for the conversion of pyruvate to lactate under anaerobic conditions?

**24.45** What is the difference between glycolysis and gluconeogenesis?

**24.46** Why is it incorrect to say that gluconeogenesis is simply the reverse of glycolysis?

**24.47** What effect is observed on the rate of glycolysis under each of the following conditions?
   a. low ATP concentration          c. high carbohydrate diet
   b. low ADP concentration          d. low carbohydrate diet

**24.48** What effect is observed on the rate of gluconeogenesis under each of the following conditions?
   a. low ATP concentration          c. high carbohydrate diet
   b. low ADP concentration          d. low carbohydrate diet

**24.49** Describe the steps in the Cori cycle. In what organs do key reactions of the cycle occur?

**24.50** How does a defect in monosaccharide metabolism result in galactosemia?

**24.51** What metabolic products are formed from pyruvate in each case: (a) anaerobic conditions in the body; (b) anaerobic conditions in yeast; (c) aerobic conditions?

**24.52** Why must the NADH produced in glycolysis be re-oxidized to $NAD^+$? How is this accomplished aerobically? How is this accomplished anaerobically?

**24.53** Explain in detail how 32 ATP molecules are generated during the complete catabolism of glucose to $CO_2$.

**24.54** What are the starting material and product of each step of gluconeogenesis: (a) step [2]; (b) step [5]; (c) step [8]?

**24.55** In fermentation, where do the six carbon atoms of glucose end up?

**24.56** In what ways is alcohol fermentation similar to lactate production in muscle?

## Triacylglycerol Metabolism

**24.57** How much ATP is used or formed when a fatty acid is converted to an acyl CoA? Explain your reasoning.

**24.58** How much ATP is ultimately generated from each cycle of β-oxidation of a fatty acid?

**24.59** For myristic acid, $C_{13}H_{27}CO_2H$: (a) How many molecules of acetyl CoA are formed from complete β-oxidation? (b) How many cycles of β-oxidation are needed for complete oxidation?

**24.60** For oleic acid, $C_{17}H_{33}CO_2H$: (a) How many molecules of acetyl CoA are formed from complete β-oxidation? (b) How many cycles of β-oxidation are needed for complete oxidation?

**24.61** (a) How many molecules of acetyl CoA are formed from complete β-oxidation of the fatty acid depicted in the ball-and-stick model? (b) How many cycles of β-oxidation are needed for complete oxidation?

**24.62** (a) How many molecules of acetyl CoA are formed from complete β-oxidation of the fatty acid depicted in the ball-and-stick model? (b) How many cycles of β-oxidation are needed for complete oxidation?

**24.63** How much ATP is generated by the complete catabolism of myristic acid in Problem 24.59?

**24.64** How much ATP is generated by the complete catabolism of oleic acid in Problem 24.60?

**24.65** Draw the structure of the acyl CoA formed from palmitic acid, $C_{15}H_{31}CO_2H$. Use this acyl CoA to write out the four steps of β-oxidation.

**24.66** Draw the structure of the acyl CoA formed from hexanoic acid, $C_5H_{11}CO_2H$. Use this acyl CoA to write out the four steps of β-oxidation.

**24.67** Consider decanoic acid, $C_9H_{19}CO_2H$.
   a. Label the α and β carbons.
   b. Draw the acyl CoA derived from this fatty acid.
   c. How many acetyl CoA molecules are formed by complete β-oxidation?
   d. How many cycles of β-oxidation are needed for complete oxidation?
   e. How many molecules of ATP are formed from the complete catabolism of this fatty acid?

**24.68** Consider docosanoic acid, $C_{21}H_{43}CO_2H$.
   a. Label the α and β carbons.
   b. Draw the acyl CoA derived from this fatty acid.
   c. How many acetyl CoA molecules are formed by complete β-oxidation?
   d. How many cycles of β-oxidation are needed for complete oxidation?
   e. How many molecules of ATP are formed from the complete catabolism of this fatty acid?

**24.69** How many moles of ATP per gram of fatty acid are formed from the complete catabolism of decanoic acid (molar mass 172 g/mol) in Problem 24.67?

**24.70** How many moles of ATP per gram of fatty acid are formed from the complete catabolism of docosanoic acid (molar mass 341 g/mol) in Problem 24.68?

## Ketone Bodies

**24.71** What is the difference between ketosis and ketogenesis?

**24.72** How is the production of ketone bodies related to ketoacidosis?

**24.73** Why are more ketone bodies produced in an individual whose diabetes is poorly managed?

**24.74** Why do some individuals use test strips to measure the presence of ketone bodies in their urine?

## Amino Acid Metabolism

**24.75** What is the difference between ketogenic and glucogenic amino acids?

**24.76** What is the difference between transamination and oxidative deamination?

**24.77** Draw the structure of the α-keto acid formed by the transamination of each amino acid: (a) glycine; (b) phenylalanine.

**24.78** Draw the structure of the α-keto acid formed by the transamination of each amino acid: (a) tyrosine; (b) asparagine.

**24.79** Draw the products formed in each transamination reaction.

a. $CH_3-\overset{\overset{+}{N}H_3}{\underset{H}{C}}-CO_2^-$ + $^-O_2CCH_2-\overset{O}{\overset{\|}{C}}-CO_2^-$

b. $(CH_3)_2CHCH_2-\overset{\overset{+}{N}H_3}{\underset{H}{C}}-CO_2^-$ + $^-O_2CCH_2-\overset{O}{\overset{\|}{C}}-CO_2^-$

**24.80** Draw the products formed in each transamination reaction.

a. $(CH_3)_2CH-\overset{\overset{+}{N}H_3}{\underset{H}{C}}-CO_2^-$ + $^-O_2CCH_2-\overset{O}{\overset{\|}{C}}-CO_2^-$

b. $CH_3CH_2CH(CH_3)-\overset{\overset{+}{N}H_3}{\underset{H}{C}}-CO_2^-$ + $^-O_2CCH_2CH_2-\overset{O}{\overset{\|}{C}}-CO_2^-$

**24.81** What products are formed when each amino acid undergoes oxidative deamination with $NAD^+$ and a dehydrogenase enzyme: (a) leucine; (b) phenylalanine?

**24.82** What products are formed when each amino acid undergoes oxidative deamination with $NAD^+$ and a dehydrogenase enzyme: (a) tyrosine; (b) tryptophan?

**24.83** What metabolic intermediate is formed from the carbon skeleton of each amino acid?
a. phenylalanine
b. glutamic acid
c. asparagine
d. glycine

**24.84** What metabolic intermediate is formed from the carbon skeleton of each amino acid?
a. lysine
b. tryptophan
c. methionine
d. serine

**24.85** Can an amino acid be considered both glucogenic and ketogenic? Explain your choice.

**24.86** Which amino acids are classified as only glucogenic?

## General Questions and Applications

**24.87** What is the difference between a spiral and a cyclic metabolic pathway? Give an example of each.

**24.88** What is the cause of the pain and cramping in a runner's muscles?

**24.89** Explain the reaction that occurs during the baking of bread that causes the bread to rise.

**24.90** Why is the concentration of ethanol in wine typically 12% or less?

**24.91** How might pyruvate be metabolized in the cornea, tissue that has little blood supply?

**24.92** How is pyruvate metabolized in red blood cells, which contain no mitochondria?

**24.93** Why is the Atkins low carbohydrate diet called a ketogenic diet?

**24.94** What metabolic conditions induce ketogenesis?

**24.95** What type of enzyme would catalyze the conversion of hydroxyacetone ($CH_3COCH_2OH$) to each compound?

a. $CH_3-\overset{O}{\overset{\|}{C}}-CH_2OPO_3^{2-}$

b. $CH_3-\overset{O}{\overset{\|}{C}}-CHO$

c. $HO_2CCH_2-\overset{O}{\overset{\|}{C}}-CH_2OH$

**24.96** What coenzyme would convert 6-hydroxy-2-hexanone ($CH_3COCH_2CH_2CH_2CH_2OH$) to each compound?

a. $CH_3-\overset{OH}{\underset{}{C}H}(CH_2)_4OH$

b. $CH_3-\overset{O}{\overset{\|}{C}}-(CH_2)_3CHO$

c. $CH_3-\overset{O}{\overset{\|}{C}}-CH=CHCH_2CH_2OH$

## CHALLENGE PROBLEMS

**24.97** How much ATP is produced from the complete catabolism of one molecule of glycerol, $HOCH_2CH(OH)CH_2OH$?

**24.98** How much ATP is produced from the complete catabolism of one molecule of the given triacylglycerol?

$$\begin{array}{l} CH_2-O-\overset{O}{\overset{\|}{C}}-(CH_2)_4CH_3 \\ CH-O-\overset{O}{\overset{\|}{C}}-(CH_2)_4CH_3 \\ CH_2-O-\overset{O}{\overset{\|}{C}}-(CH_2)_4CH_3 \end{array}$$

**24.99** Determine the amount of ATP generated per gram of glucose (molar mass 180.2 g/mol) compared to the amount of ATP generated per gram of arachidic acid (312.5 g/mol) during catabolism. Does your result support or refute the fact that lipids are more effective energy-storing molecules than carbohydrates?

**24.100** Examine the nutrition label of a favorite breakfast cereal. Determine the number of grams of digestible carbohydrates in a serving by subtracting the number of grams of dietary fiber (due to indigestible cellulose) from the total carbohydrate content. Assume this value gives the number of grams of glucose per serving. How many moles of ATP are formed from the glucose (molar mass = 180.2 g/mol) in one serving of cereal?

# Useful Mathematical Concepts

Three common mathematical concepts are needed to solve many problems in chemistry:

- Using scientific notation
- Determining the number of significant figures
- Using a scientific calculator

## Scientific Notation

To write numbers that contain many leading zeros (at the beginning) or trailing zeros (at the end), scientists use **scientific notation.**

> - In scientific notation, a number is written as $y \times 10^x$, where $y$ (the coefficient) is a number between 1 and 10, and $x$ is an exponent, which can be any positive or negative whole number.

To convert a standard number to scientific notation:

1. Move the decimal point to give a number between 1 and 10.
2. Multiply the result by $10^x$, where $x$ is the number of places the decimal point was moved.
   - If the decimal point is moved to the **left,** $x$ is **positive.**
   - If the decimal point is moved to the **right,** $x$ is **negative.**

$$2822. \quad = \quad 2.822 \times 10^3 \qquad \text{the number of places the decimal point was moved to the left}$$

Move the decimal point three places to the left.

$$0.000\ 004\ 5 \quad = \quad 4.5 \times 10^{-6} \qquad \text{the number of places the decimal point was moved to the right}$$

Move the decimal point six places to the right.

To convert a number in scientific notation to a standard number, use the value of $x$ in $10^x$ to indicate the number of places to move the decimal point in the coefficient.

> - Move the decimal point to the **right** when $x$ is **positive.**
> - Move the decimal point to the **left** when $x$ is **negative.**

$2.521 \times 10^2 \qquad 2.521 \quad \text{-----} \rightarrow \quad 252.1$

Move the decimal point to the right two places.

$2.68 \times 10^{-2} \qquad 002.68 \quad \text{-----} \rightarrow \quad 0.0268$

Move the decimal point to the left two places.

Table A.1 shows how several numbers are written in scientific notation.

Table A.1  Numbers in Standard Form and Scientific Notation

| Number | Scientific Notation |
|---|---|
| 26,200 | $2.62 \times 10^4$ |
| 0.006 40 | $6.40 \times 10^{-3}$ |
| 3,000,000 | $3 \times 10^6$ |
| 0.000 000 139 | $1.39 \times 10^{-7}$ |
| 2,000.20 | $2.00020 \times 10^3$ |

Often, numbers written in scientific notation must be multiplied or divided.

- **To multiply two numbers in scientific notation, *multiply* the coefficients together and *add* the exponents in the powers of 10.**

$$(3.0 \times 10^8) \times (2.0 \times 10^3) = 6.0 \times 10^{11}$$

Add exponents. $(8 + 3)$
Multiply coefficients. $(3.0 \times 2.0)$

- **To divide two numbers in scientific notation, *divide* the coefficients and *subtract* the exponents in the powers of 10.**

Divide coefficients. $(6.0 \div 2.0)$ $\dfrac{6.0 \times 10^6}{2.0 \times 10^{10}}$ Subtract exponents. $(6 - 10)$ $= 3.0 \times 10^{-4}$

Table A.2 shows the result of multiplying or dividing several numbers written in scientific notation.

Table A.2  Calculations Using Numbers Written in Scientific Notation

| Calculation | Answer |
|---|---|
| $(3.5 \times 10^3) \times (2.2 \times 10^{22}) =$ | $7.7 \times 10^{25}$ |
| $(3.5 \times 10^3) \div (2.2 \times 10^{22}) =$ | $1.6 \times 10^{-19}$ |
| $(3.5 \times 10^3) \times (2.2 \times 10^{-10}) =$ | $7.7 \times 10^{-7}$ |
| $(3.5 \times 10^3) \div (2.2 \times 10^{-10}) =$ | $1.6 \times 10^{13}$ |

## Significant Figures

Whenever we measure a number, there is a degree of uncertainty associated with the result. The last number (furthest to the right) is an estimate. **Significant figures** are all of the digits in a measured number including one estimated digit. How many significant figures are contained in a number?

- All nonzero digits are always significant.
- A zero *counts* as a significant figure when it occurs between two nonzero digits, or at the end of a number with a decimal point.
- A zero does *not* count as a significant figure when it occurs at the beginning of a number, or at the end of a number that does not have a decimal point.

Table A.3 lists the number of significant figures in several quantities.

### Table A.3 Examples Illustrating Significant Figures

| Quantity | Number of Significant Figures | Quantity | Number of Significant Figures |
|---|---|---|---|
| 1,267 g | Four | 203 L | Three |
| 24,345 km | Five | 6.10 atm | Three |
| 1.200 mg | Four | 0.3040 g | Four |
| 0.000 001 mL | One | 1,200 m | Two |

The number of significant figures must also be taken into account in calculations. To avoid reporting a value with too many digits, we must often **round off the number** to give the correct number of significant figures. Two rules are used in rounding off numbers.

- If the first number that must be dropped is 4 or less, drop it and all remaining numbers.
- If the first number that must be dropped is 5 or greater, *round the number up* by adding one to the last digit that will be retained.

To round 63.854 to two significant figures:

These digits must be retained.

$$\overline{63}.\underline{854}$$   first digit to be dropped

These digits must be dropped.

- Since the first digit to be dropped is 8 (5 or greater), add 1 to the first digit to its left.
- The number 63.854 rounded to two digits is **64**.

Table A.4 gives other examples of rounding off numbers.

### Table A.4 Rounding Off Numbers

| Original Number | Rounded to | Rounded Number |
|---|---|---|
| 15.2538 | Two places | 15 |
| 15.2538 | Three places | 15.3 |
| 15.2538 | Four places | 15.25 |
| 15.2538 | Five places | 15.254 |

The first number to be dropped is indicated in red in each original number.

The number of significant figures in the answer of a problem depends on the type of mathematical calculation—multiplication (and division) or addition (and subtraction).

> • In multiplication and division, the answer has the same number of significant figures as the original number with the *fewest* significant figures.

five significant figures             first digit to be dropped

$$5.5067 \quad \times \quad 2.6 \quad = \quad 14.\overset{\frown}{3}1742 \text{ rounded to } \mathbf{14}$$

two significant figures

The answer must contain only **two** significant figures.

> • In addition and subtraction, the answer has the same number of decimal places as the original number with the *fewest* decimal places.

two digits after the decimal point

$$10.17 \quad + \quad 3.5 \quad = \quad 13.67 \text{ rounded to } \mathbf{13.7}$$

one digit after the decimal point

last significant digit     The answer can have only **one** digit after the decimal point.

Table A.5 lists other examples of calculations that take into account the number of significant figures.

### Table A.5 Calculations Using Significant Figures

| Calculation | Answer |
|---|---|
| $3.2 \times 699 =$ | 2,236.8 rounded to **2,200** |
| $4.66892 \div 2.13 =$ | 2.191981221 rounded to **2.19** |
| $25.3 + 3.668 + 29.1004 =$ | 58.0684 rounded to **58.1** |
| $95.1 - 26.335 =$ | 68.765 rounded to **68.8** |

## Using a Scientific Calculator

A scientific calculator is capable of carrying out more complicated mathematical functions than simple addition, subtraction, multiplication, and division. For example, these calculators allow the user to convert a standard number to scientific notation, as well as readily determine the logarithm (log) or antilogarithm (antilog) of a value. Carrying out these operations is especially important in determining pH or hydronium ion concentration in Chapter 9.

Described in this section are the steps that can be followed in calculations with some types of calculators. Consult your manual if these steps do not produce the stated result.

### Converting a Number to Scientific Notation

To convert a number, such as 1,200, from its standard form to scientific notation:

- Enter 1200.
- Press $2^{nd}$ and then SCI.
- The number will appear as $1.2^{03}$, indicating that $1,200 = 1.2 \times 10^3$.

## Entering a Number Written in Scientific Notation

To enter a number written in scientific notation with a positive exponent, such as $1.5 \times 10^8$:

- Enter 1.5.
- Press EE.
- Enter 8.
- The number will appear as $1.5^{08}$, indicating that it is equal to $1.5 \times 10^8$.

To enter a number written in scientific notation with a negative exponent, such as $3.5 \times 10^{-4}$:

- Enter 3.5.
- Press EE.
- Enter 4.
- Press CHANGE SIGN (+ → –).
- The number will appear as $3.5^{-04}$, indicating that it is equal to $3.5 \times 10^{-4}$.

## Taking the Logarithm of a Number: Calculating pH from a Known [H₃O⁺]

Since $pH = -\log [H_3O^+]$, we must learn how to calculate logarithms on a calculator in order to determine pH values. To determine the pH from a known hydronium ion concentration, say $[H_3O^+] = 1.8 \times 10^{-5}$, carry out the following steps:

- Enter $1.8 \times 10^{-5}$ (Enter 1.8; press EE; enter 5; press CHANGE SIGN). The number $1.8^{-05}$ will appear.
- Press LOG.
- Press CHANGE SIGN (+ → –).
- The number 4.744 727 495 will appear. Since the coefficient, 1.8, contains two significant figures, round the logarithm to 4.74, which has two digits to the right of the decimal point. Thus, the pH of the solution is 4.74.

## Taking the Antilogarithm of a Number: Calculating [H₃O⁺] from a Known pH

Since $[H_3O^+] = \text{antilog}(-pH)$, we must learn how to calculate an antilogarithm—that is, the number that has a given logarithm value—using a calculator. To determine the hydronium ion concentration from a given pH, say 3.91, carry out the following steps:

- Enter 3.91.
- Press CHANGE SIGN (+ → –).
- Press 2$^{nd}$ and then LOG.
- The number 0.000 123 027 will appear. To convert this number to scientific notation, press 2$^{nd}$ and SCI.
- The number $1.230\ 268\ 771^{-04}$ will appear, indicating that $[H_3O^+] = 1.230\ 268\ 771 \times 10^{-4}$. Since the original pH (a logarithm) had two digits to the right of the decimal point, the answer must have two significant figures in the coefficient in scientific notation. As a result, $[H_3O^+] = 1.2 \times 10^{-4}$.

Table A.6 lists pH values that correspond to given $[H_3O^+]$ values. You can practice using a calculator to determine pH or $[H_3O^+]$ by entering a value in one column, following the listed steps, and then checking to see if you obtain the corresponding value in the other column.

Table A.6  The pH of a Solution from a Given Hydronium Ion Concentration $[H_3O^+]$

| $[H_3O^+]$ | pH | $[H_3O^+]$ | pH |
|---|---|---|---|
| $1.8 \times 10^{-10}$ | 9.74 | $4.0 \times 10^{-13}$ | 12.40 |
| $3.8 \times 10^{-2}$ | 1.42 | $6.6 \times 10^{-4}$ | 3.18 |
| $5.0 \times 10^{-12}$ | 11.30 | $2.6 \times 10^{-9}$ | 8.59 |
| $4.2 \times 10^{-7}$ | 6.38 | $7.3 \times 10^{-8}$ | 7.14 |

# Selected Answers to In-Chapter and End-of-Chapter Problems

## CHAPTER 1

1.1 water, rock, tree: natural
tennis ball, CD, plastic bag: synthetic

1.3 b, c, e: chemical   a, d: physical

1.5 a. pure substance   b. mixture

1.7 a. element   b, c, d: compound

1.9 1,000,000,000

1.11 a. 3 cL   b. 1 μg   c. 5 km   d. 2 mL

1.12 a. 4   b. 5   c. 2   d. 4   e. 3   f. 3   g. 7   h. 2

1.13 a. 4   b. 5   c. 6   d. 4   e. 5   f. 4   g. 4   h. 6

1.15 a. 1.3   b. 0.0025   c. 3,800

1.16 a. 37   b. 0.000 007 93   c. 32   d. 3,100

1.17 a. 28.0 cm   b. 127.5 mL   c. 30. mg   d. 2.08 s

1.18 $9.8 \times 10^{-5}$ g/dL

1.19 a. $9.32 \times 10^{4}$   c. $6.78 \times 10^{6}$   e. $4.52 \times 10^{12}$
b. $7.25 \times 10^{-4}$   d. $3.0 \times 10^{-5}$   f. $2.8 \times 10^{-11}$

1.20 6,020,000,000,000,000,000,000 molecules

1.21 a. 6,500   c. 0.037 80   e. 2,221,000
b. 0.000 032 6   d. 104,000,000   f. 0.000 000 000 45

1.22 a. $\dfrac{0.621\ \text{mi}}{1\ \text{km}}$   $\dfrac{1\ \text{km}}{0.621\ \text{mi}}$   c. $\dfrac{454\ \text{g}}{1\ \text{lb}}$   $\dfrac{1\ \text{lb}}{454\ \text{g}}$

b. $\dfrac{1000\ \text{mm}}{1\ \text{m}}$   $\dfrac{1\ \text{m}}{1000\ \text{mm}}$   d. $\dfrac{1000\ \mu\text{g}}{1\ \text{mg}}$   $\dfrac{1\ \text{mg}}{1000\ \mu\text{g}}$

1.23 2,560 mi

1.25 a. 1.91 km   b. 0.7 L   c. 140 cm

1.26 1.5 tsp

1.27 4 tablets

1.29 83.3 °F or 302 K

1.31 7.13 g

1.33 a. **A**   b. **B**

1.35 a. element   b. compound   c, d: mixture

1.37 An element is a pure substance that cannot be broken down into simpler substances by a chemical reaction. A compound is a pure substance formed by combining two or more elements.

1.39

| Phase | a. Volume | b. Shape | c. Organization | d. Particle Proximity |
|---|---|---|---|---|
| Solid | Definite | Definite | Very organized | Very close |
| Liquid | Definite | Assumes shape of container | Less organized | Close |
| Gas | Not fixed | None | Disorganized | Far apart |

1.41 a. physical   b. chemical   c. physical

1.43 This is a physical change since the compound $CO_2$ is unchanged in this transition. The same "particles" exist at the beginning and end of the process.

1.45 a. 76.5 °F   b. three   c. 24.7 °C

1.47 An exact number results from counting objects or is part of a definition, such as having 20 people in a class. An inexact number results from a measurement or observation and contains some uncertainty, such as the distance from the earth to the sun, $9.3 \times 10^{7}$ miles.

1.49 a. 5 dL   b. 10 mg   c. 5 cm   d. 10 Ms

1.51 a. 4   b. 2   c. 3   d. 2   e. 3   f. 4   g. 4   h. 2

1.53 a. 25,400   c. 0.001 27   e. 195
b. 1,250,000   d. 0.123   f. 197

1.55 a. 22   b. 21.97   c. 5.4   d. 50.1   e. 100   f. 1,044

1.57 a. $1.234 \times 10^{3}$ g   c. $5.244 \times 10^{6}$ L   e. $4.4 \times 10^{4}$ km
b. $1.62 \times 10^{-5}$ m   d. $5.62 \times 10^{-3}$ g

1.59 a. 340,000,000   c. 300
b. 0.000 058 22   d. 0.000 000 068 6

1.61 a. $4.44 \times 10^{3}$   c. $1.3 \times 10^{8}$
b. $5.6 \times 10^{-5}$   d. $9.8 \times 10^{-4}$

1.63 a. $4.00 \times 10^{-4}$ g   c. $8.0 \times 10^{-5}$ g
b. $2 \times 10^{-3}$ g   d. $3.4 \times 10^{3}$ mg

1.65 a. 1,500 g   b. 3.3 lb   c. 53 oz

1.67 a. 300,000 mg   d. 10 oz
b. 2,000,000 μL   e. 0.6 m
c. 0.050 m   f. 3.2 m

1.69 a. 106 kg   b. 130 cm   c. 1.4 L   d. 99.9 °F

1.71 a. 946 mL   b. 33.9 fl oz

1.73 a. 127 °F or 326 K   b. 177 °C or 450. K

1.75 a. −10 °C   b. −50 °F

1.77 Density is the mass per unit volume, usually reported in g/mL or g/cc. Specific gravity is the ratio of the density of a substance to the density of water and has no units.

1.79 1.01 g/mL

1.81 0.974 kg

1.83 a. heptane   b. olive oil   c. water   d. water

1.85 a. 13.6   b. 0.789 g/mL

1.87 a. 0.186 g/dL   b. 1,860 mg/L

1.89 three

1.91 7.8 (or 8)

1.93 a. $0.67   b. $1.00

1.95 784.6 doses, so 784 full doses

1.97 16 tablets

1.99 $1.0 \times 10^{2}$ mg

1.101 2 tablets (2.4)

1.103 0.15 g

# CHAPTER 2

**2.1**    a. Ca     b. Rn     c. N     d. Au

**2.3**    a. neon      c. iodine     e. boron
        b. sulfur     d. silicon     f. mercury

**2.5**    As, B, Si: metalloids
       Cr, Co, Cu, Fe, Mn, Mo, Ni, Zn: metals
       F, I, Se: nonmetals

**2.6**    a. 4 hydrogens, 1 carbon
       b. 3 hydrogens, 1 nitrogen
       c. 6 hydrogens, 2 carbons, 1 oxygen

**2.7**    a. 1 sodium, 1 carbon, 1 nitrogen
       b. 2 hydrogens, 1 sulfur
       c. 2 carbons, 6 hydrogens
       d. 1 tin, 2 fluorines
       e. 1 carbon, 1 oxygen
       f. 3 carbons, 8 hydrogens, 3 oxygens

**2.9**    a. 9     b. 9     c. fluorine

**2.10**

| Atomic Number | Element | Protons | Electrons |
|---|---|---|---|
| a.    2 | Helium | 2 | 2 |
| b.    11 | Sodium | 11 | 11 |
| c.    20 | Calcium | 20 | 20 |
| d.    47 | Silver | 47 | 47 |
| e.    78 | Platinum | 78 | 78 |

**2.11**    a. 4 protons and 5 neutrons
       b. atomic number 4, mass number 9
       c. beryllium

**2.12**

| | Protons | Neutrons | Electrons |
|---|---|---|---|
| a. | 17 | 18 | 17 |
| b. | 14 | 14 | 14 |
| c. | 92 | 146 | 92 |

**2.13**    a. 95     b. 52

**2.14**

| | Atomic Number | Mass Number | Protons | Neutrons | Electrons |
|---|---|---|---|---|---|
| a. | 6 | 13 | 6 | 7 | 6 |
| b. | 51 | 121 | 51 | 70 | 51 |

**2.15**

| | Protons | Electrons | Atomic Number | Mass Number |
|---|---|---|---|---|
| $^{24}_{12}Mg$ | 12 | 12 | 12 | 24 |
| $^{25}_{12}Mg$ | 12 | 12 | 12 | 25 |
| $^{26}_{12}Mg$ | 12 | 12 | 12 | 26 |

**2.16**    a. 24.31 amu     b. 50.94 amu

**2.17**

| Element | Period | Group |
|---|---|---|
| a. Oxygen | 2 | 6A (or 16) |
| b. Calcium | 4 | 2A (or 2) |
| c. Phosphorus | 3 | 5A (or 15) |
| d. Platinum | 6 | 8B (or 10) |
| e. Iodine | 5 | 7A (or 17) |

**2.19**    a. titanium, Ti, group 4B (or 4), period 4, transition metal
       b. phosphorus, P, group 5A (or 15), period 3, main group element
       c. dysprosium, Dy, no group number, period 6, inner transition element

**2.21**    a. silicon     b. sulfur     c. scandium     d. zinc

**2.23**

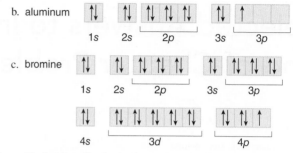

**2.25**    a. 12 electrons, 2 valence electrons, magnesium
       b. 15 electrons, 5 valence electrons, phosphorus
       c. 40 electrons, 2 valence electrons, zirconium
       d. 26 electrons, 2 valence electrons, iron

**2.26**    a. 7 valence electrons: $2s^2 2p^5$
       b. 8 valence electrons: $4s^2 4p^6$
       c. 2 valence electrons: $3s^2$
       d. 4 valence electrons: $4s^2 4p^2$

**2.27**    Se, selenium: $4s^2 4p^4$
       Te, tellurium: $5s^2 5p^4$
       Po, polonium: $6s^2 6p^4$

**2.28**    a. :B̈r:    b. Li·    c. Äl·    d. ·S̈:    e. :N̈e:

**2.29**    a. neon, carbon, boron
       b. beryllium, magnesium, calcium
       c. sulfur, silicon, magnesium
       d. neon, krypton, xenon
       e. oxygen, sulfur, silicon
       f. fluorine, sulfur, aluminum

**2.31**    a. carbon (black), oxygen (red)
       b. carbon (black), hydrogen (gray), chlorine (green)

**2.33**    a. gold, astatine, silver
       b. nitrogen, sodium, nickel
       c. sulfur, silicon, tin
       d. calcium, chromium, chlorine
       e. phosphorus, lead, platinum
       f. titanium, tantalum, thallium

**2.35**    a, c, e: element     b, d: compound

**2.37**    a. cesium         d. beryllium
       b. ruthenium     e. fluorine
       c. chlorine       f. cerium

**2.39**    a. sodium: metal, alkali metal, main group element
       b. silver: metal, transition metal
       c. xenon: nonmetal, noble gas, main group element
       d. platinum: metal, transition metal
       e. uranium: metal, inner transition metal
       f. tellurium: metalloid, main group element

**2.41**    a. 5 protons and 6 neutrons     b. 5     c. 11     d. 5     e. B

**2.43**

|  | Element Symbol | Atomic Number | Mass Number | Number of Protons | Number of Neutrons | Number of Electrons |
|---|---|---|---|---|---|---|
| a. | C | 6 | 12 | 6 | 6 | 6 |
| b. | P | 15 | 31 | 15 | 16 | 15 |
| c. | Zn | 30 | 65 | 30 | 35 | 30 |
| d. | Mg | 12 | 24 | 12 | 12 | 12 |
| e. | I | 53 | 127 | 53 | 74 | 53 |
| f. | Be | 4 | 9 | 4 | 5 | 4 |
| g. | Zr | 40 | 91 | 40 | 51 | 40 |
| h. | S | 16 | 32 | 16 | 16 | 16 |

**2.45**

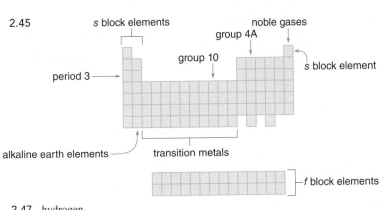

**2.47**  hydrogen

**2.49**  K, Ca, Sc, Ti, V, Cr, Mn, Fe, Co, Ni, Cu, Zn, Ga: metals
Ge, As: metalloids
Se, Br, Kr: nonmetals

**2.51**  8A

**2.53**

| Mass | Protons | Neutrons | Electrons | Group | Symbol |
|---|---|---|---|---|---|
| 16 | 8 | 8 | 8 | 6A | $^{16}_{8}O$ |
| 17 | 8 | 9 | 8 | 6A | $^{17}_{8}O$ |
| 18 | 8 | 10 | 8 | 6A | $^{18}_{8}O$ |

**2.55**

|  | Protons | Neutrons | Electrons |
|---|---|---|---|
| a. | 13 | 14 | 13 |
| b. | 17 | 18 | 17 |
| c. | 16 | 18 | 16 |

**2.57**  a. $^{127}_{53}I$   b. $^{79}_{35}Br$   c. $^{107}_{47}Ag$

**2.59**  107.9 amu

**2.61**  No, two different elements must have a different number of protons and so, in the neutral atom, they must have a different number of electrons.

**2.63**  a. 1   b. 4   c. 9   d. 16

**2.65**  a. B

b. K

**2.67**  a. B: $1s^22s^22p^1$ [He]$2s^22p^1$
b. K: $1s^22s^22p^63s^23p^64s^1$ [Ar]$4s^1$
c. Se: $1s^22s^22p^63s^23p^64s^23d^{10}4p^4$ [Ar]$4s^23d^{10}4p^4$
d. Ar: $1s^22s^22p^63s^23p^6$ [Ar]
e. Zn: $1s^22s^22p^63s^23p^64s^23d^{10}$ [Ar]$4s^23d^{10}$

**2.69**  a. 1   b. 3   c. 1

**2.71**  a. 38 electrons, 2 valence electrons, strontium
b. 16 electrons, 6 valence electrons, sulfur
c. 11 electrons, 1 valence electron, sodium
d. 17 electrons, 7 valence electrons, chlorine

**2.73**  An alkali metal has one valence electron and an alkaline earth element has two valence electrons.

**2.75**

|  | Electrons | Group Number | Valence Electrons | Period | Valence Shell |
|---|---|---|---|---|---|
| a. Carbon | 6 | 4A | 4 | 2 | 2 |
| b. Calcium | 20 | 2A | 2 | 4 | 4 |
| c. Krypton | 36 | 8A | 8 | 4 | 4 |

**2.77**  a. carbon: $1s^22s^22p^2$; $2s^22p^2$
b. calcium: $1s^22s^22p^63s^23p^64s^2$; $4s^2$
c. krypton: $1s^22s^22p^63s^23p^64s^23d^{10}4p^6$; $4s^24p^6$

**2.79**  a. 2   b. 4   c. 7

**2.81**  a. sulfur: 6, $3s^23p^4$
b. chlorine: 7, $3s^23p^5$
c. barium: 2, $6s^2$
d. titanium: 2, $4s^2$
e. tin: 4, $5s^25p^2$

2.83  a. Be·     b. ·Si·     c. ·I:     d. ·Mg·     e. :Ar:

2.85  a. iodine    b. carbon    c. potassium    d. selenium

2.87  a. bromine    b. nitrogen    c. silicon    d. chlorine

2.89  fluorine, oxygen, sulfur, silicon, magnesium

2.91  sodium, magnesium, phosphorus, nitrogen, fluorine

2.93

|  | a. Type | b. Block | c, d: Radius | e, f: Ionization E | g. Valence Electrons |
|---|---|---|---|---|---|
| Sodium | Metal | s |  |  | 1 |
| Potassium | Metal | s | Largest | Lowest | 1 |
| Chlorine | Nonmetal | p | Smallest | Highest | 7 |

2.95  Carbon-11 has the same number of protons and electrons as carbon-12—that is, six. Carbon-11 has only five neutrons, whereas carbon-12 has six neutrons. The symbol for carbon-11 is $^{11}_{6}C$.

2.97  There is only one $4s$ electron.

# CHAPTER 3

3.1  a, d, e, f: covalent     b, c: ionic

3.3  covalent

3.4  a. $K^+$    b. $N^{3-}$    c. $Br^-$    d. $V^{2+}$

3.5  a. 28 protons, 26 electrons      c. 30 protons, 28 electrons
     b. 34 protons, 36 electrons      d. 26 protons, 23 electrons

3.6  a. +2    b. −1    c. −2    d. +1

3.7  a. Ne    b. Xe    c. Kr    d. Kr

3.9  a. 25 protons, 25 electrons
     b. 25 protons, 23 electrons
     c. $1s^2 2s^2 2p^6 3s^2 3p^6 4s^2 3d^5$    The two $4s^2$ valence electrons would be lost to form $Mn^{2+}$.

3.11  a. NaBr    b. BaO    c. $MgI_2$    d. $Li_2O$

3.12  a.

     $S^{2-}$     $Na^+$

     b.

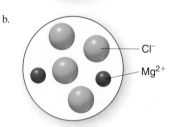

     $Cl^-$     $Mg^{2+}$

3.13  ZnO

3.15  a. $Sn^{4+}$    b. $I^-$    c. $Mn^{2+}$    d. $Pb^{2+}$    e. $Se^{2-}$

3.16  a. sodium fluoride      d. lithium oxide
     b. magnesium oxide      e. titanium oxide
     c. strontium bromide      f. aluminum chloride

3.17  a. chromium(III) chloride, chromic chloride
     b. lead(II) sulfide
     c. tin(IV) fluoride, stannic fluoride
     d. lead(IV) oxide
     e. iron(II) bromide, ferrous bromide
     f. gold(III) chloride

3.19  iron(III) oxide, ferric oxide

3.20  a. $CaBr_2$    c. $FeBr_3$    e. $CrCl_2$
     b. CuI    d. MgS    f. $Na_2O$

3.21  Ionic compounds have high melting points and high boiling points. They usually dissolve in water. Their solutions conduct electricity and they form crystalline solids.

3.22  a. $MgSO_4$    c. $NiSO_4$    e. $Li_2SO_4$
     b. $Na_2SO_4$    d. $Al_2(SO_4)_3$

3.23  a. $NaHCO_3$    c. $(NH_4)_2SO_4$    e. $Ca(HSO_4)_2$
     b. $KNO_3$    d. $Mg_3(PO_4)_2$    f. $Ba(OH)_2$

3.25  a. sodium carbonate      d. manganese acetate
     b. calcium hydroxide      e. iron(III) hydrogen sulfite, ferric bisulfite
     c. magnesium nitrate      f. magnesium phosphate

3.27  a, b, d: covalent    c. ionic

3.29  a. ionic    b, c, d: covalent

3.31  There is a transfer of electrons from the metal to the nonmetal. A metal gains a noble gas configuration of electrons by giving up electrons. A nonmetal can gain a noble gas configuration by gaining electrons.

3.33  a. $Be^{2+}$    c. $S^{2-}$    e. $Cl^-$
     b. $Ti^{2+}$    d. $Al^{3+}$    f. $Ca^{2+}$

3.35  a. Be    b. $Cl^-$    c. $Rb^+$

3.37  By gaining two electrons they have a filled valence shell.

3.39  a. $Na^+$    b. $Se^{2-}$    c. $Mn^{2+}$    d. $Au^{3+}$    e. $Sn^{4+}$    f. $Hg_2^{2+}$

3.41  a, b, c, e: Ne    d. Ar    f. He

3.43  a. lose one electron      c. gain two electrons
     b. gain one electron      d. lose two electrons

3.45  b, d: likely to form
     a, e: only seven electrons in outer shell
     c: one electron in outer shell
     f: two electrons in outer shell

3.47

|  | Number of Valence Electrons | Group Number | Number of Electrons Gained or Lost | Charge | Example |
|---|---|---|---|---|---|
| a. | 1 | 1A | Lose 1 | 1+ | Li |
| b. | 2 | 2A | Lose 2 | 2+ | Mg |
| c. | 6 | 6A | Gain 2 | 2− | S |
| d. | 7 | 7A | Gain 1 | 1− | Cl |

3.49  a. sulfate, $SO_4^{2-}$    b. nitrite, $NO_2^-$    c. sulfide, $S^{2-}$

3.51  a. $SO_4^{2-}$    b. $NH_4^+$    c. $HCO_3^-$    d. $CN^-$

3.53  a. 9 protons, 10 electrons
     b. 11 protons, 10 electrons
     c. 47 protons, 50 electrons

3.55  Transition metals have one or more $d$ electrons. All of these electrons would have to be lost to follow the octet rule, and most transition metals do not lose that many electrons.

3.57  Na donates an electron to F; then each atom has eight electrons in its outer shell.

3.59  a. CaS    b. $AlBr_3$    c. LiI    d. $NiCl_2$    e. $Na_2Se$

3.61  a. $LiNO_2$    c. $NaHSO_3$    e. $Mg(HSO_3)_2$
     b. $Ca(CH_3COO)_2$    d. $Mn_3(PO_4)_2$

3.63

|       | $Y^-$    | $Y^{2-}$  | $Y^{3-}$   |
|-------|----------|-----------|------------|
| $X^+$    | XY    | $X_2Y$    | $X_3Y$     |
| $X^{2+}$ | $XY_2$ | XY       | $X_3Y_2$   |
| $X^{3+}$ | $XY_3$ | $X_2Y_3$ | XY        |

3.65

|          | $Br^-$  | $OH^-$     | $HCO_3^-$      | $SO_3^{2-}$   | $PO_4^{3-}$     |
|----------|---------|------------|----------------|---------------|-----------------|
| $Na^+$    | NaBr   | NaOH      | $NaHCO_3$       | $Na_2SO_3$    | $Na_3PO_4$      |
| $Co^{2+}$ | $CoBr_2$ | $Co(OH)_2$ | $Co(HCO_3)_2$   | $CoSO_3$      | $Co_3(PO_4)_2$  |
| $Al^{3+}$ | $AlBr_3$ | $Al(OH)_3$ | $Al(HCO_3)_3$   | $Al_2(SO_3)_3$ | $AlPO_4$       |

3.67    a. $KHSO_4$      c. $Al(HSO_4)_3$
       b. $Ba(HSO_4)_2$    d. $Zn(HSO_4)_2$

3.69    a. $Ba(CN)_2$      c. $BaHPO_4$
       b. $Ba_3(PO_4)_2$    d. $Ba(H_2PO_4)_2$

3.71    a. sodium oxide       e. cobalt(II) bromide
       b. barium sulfide       f. rubidium bromide
       c. lead(IV) sulfide      g. lead(II) bromide
       d. silver chloride

3.73    a. iron(II) chloride, ferrous chloride
       b. iron(III) bromide, ferric bromide
       c. iron(II) sulfide, ferrous sulfide
       d. iron(III) sulfide, ferric sulfide

3.75    Copper cations can be 1+ or 2+, so the Roman numeral designation is required. Ca only exists as 2+.
       $CuBr_2$: copper(II) bromide or cupric bromide
       $CaBr_2$: calcium bromide

3.77    a. $Na_2S$       $Na_2SO_4$
       b. $MgO$       $Mg(OH)_2$
       c. $MgSO_4$      $Mg(HSO_4)_2$

3.79    a. ammonium chloride
       b. lead(II) sulfate
       c. copper(II) nitrate, cupric nitrate
       d. calcium bicarbonate, calcium hydrogen carbonate
       e. iron(II) nitrate, ferrous nitrate

3.81    a. $MgCO_3$      e. $Au(NO_3)_3$
       b. $NiSO_4$       f. $Li_3PO_4$
       c. $Cu(OH)_2$     g. $Al(HCO_3)_3$
       d. $K_2HPO_4$     h. $Cr(CN)_2$

3.83    a. $Pb(OH)_4$          lead(IV) hydroxide
       b. $Pb(SO_4)_2$        lead(IV) sulfate
       c. $Pb(HCO_3)_4$      lead(IV) bicarbonate
       d. $Pb(NO_3)_4$       lead(IV) nitrate
       e. $Pb_3(PO_4)_4$      lead(IV) phosphate
       f. $Pb(CH_3CO_2)_4$   lead(IV) acetate

3.85    a. True.
       b. False—ionic compounds are solids at room temperature.
       c. False—most ionic compounds are soluble in water.
       d. False—ionic solids exist as crystalline lattices with the ions arranged to maximize the electrostatic interactions of anions and cations.

3.87    NaCl

3.89    a. 30 protons, 30 electrons
       b. 30 protons, 28 electrons
       c. $1s^2 2s^2 2p^6 3s^2 3p^6 4s^2 3d^{10}$      The $4s^2$ electrons are lost to form $Zn^{2+}$.

3.91

| Cation | a. Number of Protons | b. Number of Electrons | c. Noble Gas | d. Role |
|--------|------|------|------|---------|
| $Na^+$  | 11 | 10 | Ne | Major cation in extracellular fluids and blood; maintains blood volume and blood pressure |
| $K^+$   | 19 | 18 | Ar | Major intracellular cation |
| $Ca^{2+}$ | 20 | 18 | Ar | Major cation in solid tissues like bone and teeth; required for normal muscle contraction and nerve function |
| $Mg^{2+}$ | 12 | 10 | Ne | Required for normal muscle contraction and nerve function |

3.93    $AgNO_3$

3.95    calcium sulfite

3.97    $NH_4NO_3$

3.99    a. $MgO$, $KI$
       b. calcium hydrogen phosphate
       c. iron(III) phosphate, ferric phosphate
       d. $Na_2SeO_3$
       e. The name chromium chloride is ambiguous. Without a designation as chromium(II) or chromium(III), one does not know the ratio of chromium cations to chloride anions.

# CHAPTER 4

4.1    H· + ·C̈l: ⟶ H:C̈l:
       H is surrounded by two electrons, giving it the noble gas configuration of He. Cl is surrounded by eight valence electrons, giving it the noble gas configuration of Ar.

4.3    a. 1    b. 4    c. 1    d. 2    e. 3    f. 2

4.5    Ionic bonding is observed in CaO since Ca is a metal and readily transfers electrons to a nonmetal. Covalent bonding is observed in $CO_2$ since carbon is a nonmetal and does not readily transfer electrons.

4.6    a. H—B̈r:     c. H—Ö—Ö—H     e. H—C(H)(H)—C(H)(H)—H

       b. H—C(H)(H)—F̈:     d. H—N̈(H)—N̈(H)—H     f. H—C(H)(:C̈l:)—C̈l:

4.7    H—C(H)(H)—Ö—C(H)(H)—H

4.8    a. H—C≡N̈       b. H—C(H)=Ö      c. H—C(H)=C(H)—C̈l:

4.9    H—C(=O)—Ö—H

4.11    :B̈r—B(:B̈r:)—B̈r:
       Boron has only six electrons around it, so it does not follow the octet rule.

**4.13** a. [Lewis structure: H–C(H)(H)–C=O with O⁻]    b. [Lewis structure: H–C=N–H]⁻

**4.15** :Ö–S=Ö: ⟷ Ö=S–Ö:

**4.17** a. carbon disulfide    c. phosphorus pentachloride
       b. sulfur dioxide    d. boron trifluoride

**4.18** a. $SiO_2$    b. $PCl_3$    c. $SO_3$    d. $N_2O_3$

**4.19** trigonal planar

**4.21** [H–N̈–H]⁻    The ion has a bent geometry (b), because the N is surrounded by four groups.

**4.23** a. polar    c. nonpolar    e. polar
       b. ionic    d. polar    f. polar

**4.25** a. H–Cl (δ⁺ δ⁻) → polar
       b. [ethane structure] nonpolar
       c. [CHF₂ structure] polar
       d. H–C≡N polar
       e. [C₂Cl₄ structure] nonpolar

**4.26** a. [ethanol structure] polar C–O, O–H   All C's are tetrahedral.
       b. [acetaldehyde structure] trigonal planar, tetrahedral

**4.27** a. LiCl: ionic; the metal Li donates electrons to chlorine.
       HCl: covalent; H and Cl share electrons since both are nonmetals and the electronegativity difference is not large enough for electron transfer to occur.
       b. KBr: ionic; the metal K donates electrons to bromine.
       HBr: covalent; H and Br share electrons since the electronegativity difference is not large enough for electron transfer to occur.

**4.29** a. 4 bonds, 0 lone pairs    c. 1 bond, 3 lone pairs
       b. 2 bonds, 2 lone pairs    d. 3 bonds, 1 lone pair

**4.31** a. H–C=C–C≡N̈ [with H's]    b. [larger structure with S, O, N]

**4.33** H–Ö–C–C–Ö–H [with two O: above]

**4.35** a. H–Ï:    c. H–S̈e–H    e. :C̈l–C–C–C̈l: [with Cl's]
       b. [CH₂F₂ structure with :F:]    d. C̈=Ö

**4.37** a. H–C(H)(H)–N̈–H [with H]    b. H–Ö–N̈=Ö    c. H–C(H)–C≡C–H

**4.39** [tetrafluoroethylene structure: C=C with four :F:]

**4.41** a. [H–Ö:]⁻    b. [H–Ö–H with H]⁺
       Ö=S=Ö

**4.43** a. :C̈l–B–C̈l: [with :Cl: above]    b. :Ö: structure

**4.45** A resonance structure is one representation of an electron arrangement with a given placement of atoms. A resonance hybrid is a composite of two or more resonance structures.

**4.47** [resonance structure H–C(H)(H)–C=C–H with O⁻]⁻

**4.49** a. resonance structures      b. not resonance structures

**4.51** [Ö=C–Ö:]²⁻ ⟷ [:Ö–C–Ö:]²⁻ ⟷ [:Ö–C=Ö]²⁻ (with :O: below each)

**4.53** a. phosphorus tribromide    c. nitrogen trichloride
       b. sulfur trioxide    d. diphosphorus pentasulfide

**4.55** a. $SeO_2$    b. $CCl_4$    c. $N_2O_5$

**4.57** water

**4.59** a. [methanol structure] tetrahedral, bent
       b. N̈F₃ trigonal pyramid
       c. [structure] trigonal planar, tetrahedral

**4.61** a. H–N̈–Ö–H trigonal pyramid, bent
       b. [structure with :O:] tetrahedral, trigonal planar
       c. [H–C–N–H structure]⁺ tetrahedral

**4.63** a. [1] A linear geometry means two groups, so no lone pairs. [2] $BeCl_2$
       b. [1] A bent geometry generally means four groups, so two lone pairs. [2] $H_2O$

**4.65** $BCl_3$ is trigonal planar because it has three chlorines bonded to B but no lone pairs. $NCl_3$ is trigonal pyramidal because it has three Cl's around N as well as a lone pair.

**4.67** a. [CH₂F structure] both 109.5°
       b. H–C≡C–C–Ö–H 180° 109.5°
       c. H–C=C=Ö 120° 180° 120°

4.69

CCl₄ is tetrahedral since carbon has four substituents. Each C in C₂Cl₄ has trigonal planar geometry since each carbon has three substituents.

4.71 a. Se, S, O    b. Na, P, Cl    c. S, Cl, F    d. P, N, O

4.73 a, b, c: covalent    d. ionic

4.75 a. nonpolar    b. polar    c. polar    d. polar    e. nonpolar

4.77 a. C—O    b. C—F    c. Si—C

4.79 
$$\overset{\delta^+ \ \ \delta^-}{C-O} \quad \overset{\delta^+ \ \ \delta^-}{C-N} \quad \overset{\delta^+ \ \ \delta^-}{C-F} \quad \overset{\delta^+ \ \ \delta^-}{C-Cl} \quad \overset{\delta^+ \ \ \delta^-}{Si-C} \quad P—H$$
⟼    ⟼    ⟼    ⟼    ⟼    no dipole

4.81 In CH₃NH₂ carbon bears a partial positive charge since nitrogen is more electronegative than carbon. In CH₃MgBr carbon bears a partial negative charge since carbon is more electronegative than magnesium.

4.83 No, a compound with only one polar bond must be polar. The single bond dipole is not cancelled by another bond dipole.

4.85 a.

polar bond, polar compound

b.

polar bonds, nonpolar compound

c.

polar bonds, polar compound

4.87 CHCl₃ has a net dipole, making it polar. CCl₄ has four polar bonds but no net dipole because the four bonds have dipoles that cancel one another.

4.89 a. 20 valence electrons

b, c:

d. bent

e. The compound is polar since the two bond dipoles do not cancel.

4.91 a.–c.

bent
trigonal pyramid
tetrahedral
trigonal planar

d. Glycine is a polar molecule since the many bond dipoles do not cancel.

4.93 One possibility:

4.95 a. The predicted shape around each carbon is tetrahedral.
b. 60°
c. The 60° bond angle deviates greatly from the theoretical tetrahedral bond angle, making the molecule unstable.

# CHAPTER 5

5.1 The process is a chemical reaction because the reactants contain two gray spheres joined (indicating H₂) and two red spheres joined (indicating O₂), while the product (H₂O) contains a red sphere joined to two gray spheres (indicating O–H bonds).

5.3 
reactants             products
a. 2 H₂O₂(aq) ⟶ 2 H₂O(l) + O₂(g)    (4 H, 4 O)
b. 2 C₈H₁₈ + 25 O₂ ⟶ 16 CO₂ + 18 H₂O
(16 C, 50 O, 36 H)
c. 2 Na₃PO₄(aq) + 3 MgCl₂(aq) ⟶ Mg₃(PO₄)₂(s)
+ 6 NaCl(aq)    (3 Mg, 2 P, 8 O, 6 Na, 6 Cl)

5.5 CH₄(g) + 4 Cl₂(g) $\overset{\Delta}{\longrightarrow}$ CCl₄(l) + 4 HCl(g)

5.6 a. 2 H₂ + O₂ ⟶ 2 H₂O
b. 2 NO + O₂ ⟶ 2 NO₂
c. CH₄ + 2 Cl₂ ⟶ CH₂Cl₂ + 2 HCl

5.7 2 CO + O₂ ⟶ 2 CO₂

5.8 2 C₂H₆ + 7 O₂ ⟶ 4 CO₂ + 6 H₂O

5.9 N₂ + 3 H₂ ⟶ 2 NH₃

5.10 a. 2 Al + 3 H₂SO₄ ⟶ Al₂(SO₄)₃ + 3 H₂
b. 3 Na₂SO₃ + 2 H₃PO₄ ⟶ 3 H₂SO₃ + 2 Na₃PO₄

5.11 a, b, c, d: 6.02 × 10²³

5.12 a. 1.20 × 10²⁴ C atoms    c. 3.01 × 10²³ C atoms
b. 3.61 × 10²⁴ C atoms    d. 1.51 × 10²⁵ C atoms

5.13 a. 1.5 × 10²⁴ molecules    c. 2.4 × 10²³ molecules
b. 1.5 × 10²³ molecules    d. 3.33 × 10²⁵ molecules

5.14 a. 100. mol    b. 0.0500 mol    c. 15 mol

5.15 a. 100.09 amu    b. 166.0 amu

5.17 424.4 g/mol

5.18 a. 29.2 g    b. 332 g    c. 101 g    d. 26.3 g

5.19 a. 1.71 mol    c. 1.39 × 10⁻³ mol
b. 1.59 mol    d. 1.39 mol

5.20 1.80 × 10²¹ molecules

5.21 a. 6.6 mol    b. 1.0 mol    c. 1.2 mol

5.23 a. 51 g    b. 22 g    c. 90. g

5.25 a. 72.4 g    b. 24.1 g    c. 7.24 g

5.27 a. 154 g    b. 34.7%

5.29 a. 111 g    b. 59.0%

5.31 a. 35%    b. 11%    c. 19%    d. 1.0%

5.32 H₂ is the limiting reactant.

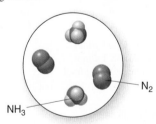

NH₃

N₂

5.33 a, b, d: H₂    c. O₂

5.34 a. 1.0 mol    b. 0.67 mol    c. 1.3 mol    d. 4.0 mol

5.35 a. N₂    b. O₂

5.36 a. 26.8 g    b. 24.4 g

5.37 11.3 g

**5.38** (oxidized)  (reduced)

a. $Zn(s) + 2 H^+(aq) \longrightarrow Zn^{2+}(aq) + H_2(g)$

$Zn \longrightarrow Zn^{2+} + 2 e^-$

$2 H^+ + 2 e^- \longrightarrow H_2$

(reduced)  (oxidized)

b. $Fe^{3+}(aq) + Al(s) \longrightarrow Al^{3+}(aq) + Fe(s)$

$Al \longrightarrow Al^{3+} + 3 e^-$

$Fe^{3+} + 3 e^- \longrightarrow Fe$

(oxidized)  (reduced)

c. $2 I^- + Br_2 \longrightarrow I_2 + 2 Br^-$

$2 I^- \longrightarrow I_2 + 2 e^-$

$Br_2 + 2 e^- \longrightarrow 2 Br^-$

d. $2 AgBr \longrightarrow 2 Ag + Br_2$

$2 Br^-$ (oxidized)  $2 Ag^+$ (reduced)

$2 Br^- \longrightarrow Br_2 + 2 e^-$

$2 Ag^+ + 2 e^- \longrightarrow 2 Ag$

**5.39** a. Zn reducing agent, $H^+$ oxidizing agent

b. $Fe^{3+}$ oxidizing agent, Al reducing agent

c. $I^-$ reducing agent, $Br_2$ oxidizing agent

d. $Br^-$ reducing agent, $Ag^+$ oxidizing agent

**5.41** $H_2$ is oxidized since it gains an O atom and $C_2H_4O_2$ is reduced since it gains hydrogen.

**5.43** $2 CO + 2 O_3 \longrightarrow 2 CO_2 + 2 O_2$ (not balanced)

**5.45** The coefficient indicates the number of molecules or moles undergoing reaction, whereas the subscript indicates the number of atoms of each element in a chemical formula.

**5.47** a. 2 H, 2 Cl, 1 Ca on both sides; therefore balanced

b. 1 Ti, 4 Cl, 4 H, 2 O on left side, and 1 Ti, 1 Cl, 1 H, 2 O on right side; therefore NOT balanced

c. 1 Al, 1 P, 7 O, 6 H on both sides; therefore balanced

**5.49** $H_2 + Cl_2 \longrightarrow 2 HCl$

**5.51** a. $Ni(s) + 2 HCl(aq) \longrightarrow NiCl_2(aq) + H_2(g)$

b. $CH_4(g) + 4 Cl_2(g) \longrightarrow CCl_4(g) + 4 HCl(g)$

c. $2 KClO_3 \longrightarrow 2 KCl + 3 O_2$

d. $Al_2O_3 + 6 HCl \longrightarrow 2 AlCl_3 + 3 H_2O$

e. $2 Al(OH)_3 + 3 H_2SO_4 \longrightarrow Al_2(SO_4)_3 + 6 H_2O$

**5.53** a. $2 C_6H_6 + 15 O_2 \longrightarrow 12 CO_2 + 6 H_2O$

b. $C_7H_8 + 9 O_2 \longrightarrow 7 CO_2 + 4 H_2O$

c. $2 C_8H_{18} + 25 O_2 \longrightarrow 16 CO_2 + 18 H_2O$

**5.55** $2 S(s) + 3 O_2(g) + 2 H_2O(l) \longrightarrow 2 H_2SO_4(l)$

**5.57**

**5.59** a. 69.00 amu, 69.00 g/mol

b. 342.2 amu, 342.2 g/mol

c. 176.12 amu, 176.12 g/mol

**5.61** a. $C_9H_{11}NO_4$        b. 197.2 amu        c. 197.2 g/mol

**5.63** a. 1 mol Sn

b. $6.02 \times 10^{23}$ N atoms

c. 1 mol $N_2$ molecules

d. 1 mol $CO_2$

**5.65** a. 182 g        b. 710. g        c. 130. g        d. 390. g

**5.67** a. $1.46 \times 10^{-3}$ mol        c. 0.0730 mol

b. 0.0146 mol        d. $7.30 \times 10^{-5}$ mol

**5.69** a. $1.20 \times 10^{24}$        c. $1.60 \times 10^{25}$        e. $3.01 \times 10^{29}$

b. $1.51 \times 10^{23}$        d. $1.34 \times 10^{26}$

**5.71** a. 324 g        b. 52.2 g        c. $1.1 \times 10^3$ g        d. 9.82 g

**5.73** a. 12.5 mol        b. 12 mol        c. 0.50 mol        d. 0.40 mol

**5.75** a. 220 g        b. 44 g        c. 4.5 g        d. 240 g

**5.77** 75%

**5.79** a. 23.9 g        b. 62.8%

**5.81** a. **B** limiting reactant        **A** in excess

b. **A** limiting reactant        **B** in excess

c. **B** limiting reactant        **A** in excess

**5.83** a. NO        b. $O_2$        c. NO        d. NO

**5.85** a. 1.0 mol, 46 g        c. 0.333 mol, 15.3 g

b. 1.0 mol, 46 g        d. 0.933 mol, 42.9 g

**5.87** a. 0.285 mol ethylene and 0.329 mol HCl

b. ethylene

c. 0.285 mol

d. 18.4 g

e. 57.6%

**5.89** A substance that is oxidized loses electrons. A substance that gains electrons acts as an oxidizing agent.

**5.91** a. Fe (oxidized)        $Cu^{2+}$ (reduced)

$Fe \longrightarrow Fe^{2+} + 2 e^-$

$Cu^{2+} + 2 e^- \longrightarrow Cu$

b. $Cl_2$ (reduced)        $2 I^-$ (oxidized)

$2 I^- \longrightarrow I_2 + 2 e^-$

$Cl_2 + 2 e^- \longrightarrow 2 Cl^-$

c. 2 Na (oxidized)        $Cl_2$ (reduced)

$2 Na \longrightarrow 2 Na^+ + 2 e^-$

$Cl_2 + 2 e^- \longrightarrow 2 Cl^-$

**5.93**     Zn                    $Ag^+$

oxidized              reduced

reducing agent        oxidizing agent

**5.95** Acetylene is reduced because it gains hydrogen atoms.

**5.97** $2 Mg + O_2 \longrightarrow 2 MgO$

$2 Mg \longrightarrow 2 Mg^{2+} + 4 e^-$    $O_2 + 4 e^- \longrightarrow 2 O^{2-}$

**5.99** a. 342.3 g/mol

b. $C_{12}H_{22}O_{11}(s) + H_2O(l) \longrightarrow 4 C_2H_6O(l) + 4 CO_2(g)$

c. 8 mol        e. 101 g        g. 9.21 g

d. 10 mol        f. 18.4 g        h. 13.6%

**5.101** a. 0.485 mol        b. $2.92 \times 10^{23}$

**5.103** a. $2.38 \times 10^{-4}$ mol        b. $1.43 \times 10^{20}$ molecules

**5.105** $6.3 \times 10^{22}$ ions

**5.107** a. 354.5 g/mol        b. 18 g        c. 17.8 g        d. 84.3%

**5.109** a. $2.1 \times 10^{-3}$ g        b. $3.9 \times 10^{18}$ molecules

# CHAPTER 6

**6.1** a. 10. cal        b. 55,600 cal        c. 1,360 kJ        d. 107,000 J

**6.3** 126 Cal, rounded to 100 Cal

**6.5** a. +88 kcal/mol; endothermic

b. −136 kcal/mol; exothermic

c. +119 kcal/mol; endothermic

**6.6** The indicated bond has the higher bond dissociation energy, making it the stronger bond.

a. $H-C-\overset{..}{\underset{..}{Br}}:$        b. $H-OH$

**6.7** a. absorbed        c. reactants

b. reactants        d. endothermic

**6.8** 106 kcal

**6.9** a. 96 kcal        b. 8.0 kcal        c. 1.8 kcal

**6.10**

6.11

6.13 Yes, $H_2SO_4$ is a catalyst because it speeds up the rate of the reaction. It does not affect the relative energies of reactants and products.

6.15 a. $\dfrac{[PCl_5]}{[PCl_3][Cl_2]}$    c. $\dfrac{[HBr]^2}{[Br_2][H_2]}$

b. $\dfrac{[SO_3]^2}{[SO_2]^2[O_2]}$    d. $\dfrac{[HCl]^3[CHCl_3]}{[CH_4][Cl_2]^3}$

6.16

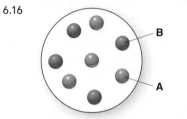

6.17 a. reactants favored    c. products favored
b. products favored    d. reactants and products present

6.19 a. $\dfrac{[H_2S]^2}{[H_2]^2[S_2]}$

b. products favored
c. $\Delta H$ negative
d. products lower in energy
e. One cannot predict the rate of reaction without knowing the energy of activation.

6.20 a. 4.75    b. 218
6.21 a, d: right    b, c: left
6.22 a. right    b. left
6.23 a. left    b. right
6.24 a. right    b. left
6.25 Potential energy is stored energy, while kinetic energy is the energy of motion. A stationary object on a hill has potential energy, but as it moves down the hill this potential energy is converted to kinetic energy.
6.27 a. 563,000 cal/h    c. $2.36 \times 10^6$ J/h
b. 563 kcal/h    d. 2,360 kJ/h
6.29 a. 0.05 kcal    b. 0.23 kJ    c. 230 cal    d. $1.01 \times 10^6$ cal
6.31 236 Calories, rounded to 200 Calories
6.33 30 g
6.35 salmon, 113 Calories vs. chicken, 107 Calories
6.37 When energy is absorbed, the reaction is endothermic and $\Delta H$ is positive (+). When energy is released, the reaction is exothermic and $\Delta H$ is negative (−).
6.39 a. $Cl_2$    b. $Cl_2$    c. HF
6.41 a, d: exothermic    b, c: endothermic
6.43 a. 240 kcal    b. 280 kcal    c. $2.0 \times 10^2$ kcal
6.45 a. stronger bonds in products    c. 339 kcal
b. 2,710 kcal    d. 37.6 kcal

6.47 The transition state is the unstable intermediate located at the top of the energy hill that separates reactants from products. The difference in energy between the reactants and the transition state is the energy of activation, symbolized by $E_a$.
6.49 a. X    b. Z    c. Y    d. X,Y    e. X,Z    f. Y    g. Z
6.51 a.

b.

c.

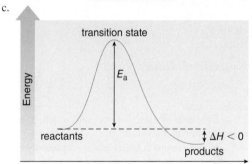

6.53 The reaction is exothermic.

6.55 Reacting molecules must have the proper orientation for new bonds to form.
6.57 Increasing temperature increases the number of collisions. Since the average kinetic energy of the colliding molecules is larger, more collisions are effective at causing reaction.
6.59 a. The reaction with $E_a = 1$ kcal will proceed faster because the energy of activation is lower.
b. $K$ doesn't affect the reaction rate, so we cannot predict which reaction is faster.
c. One cannot predict which reaction will proceed faster from the $\Delta H$.

6.61 b. and c.

6.63 A catalyst increases the reaction rate (a) and lowers the $E_a$ (c). It has no effect on $\Delta H$ (b), $K$ (d), or the relative energies of the reactants and products (e).

6.65 The forward reaction proceeds from left to right as drawn and the reverse reaction proceeds from right to left as drawn.

6.67 a, b: products favored      c, d: reactants favored

6.69 $K > 1$ is associated with a negative value of $\Delta H$. A $K < 1$ means $\Delta H$ has a positive value.

6.71 a. [1]     b. [3]     c. [2]

6.73 a. $\dfrac{[NO_2]^2}{[NO]^2[O_2]}$     b. $\dfrac{[HBr]^2[CH_2Br_2]}{[CH_4][Br_2]^2}$

6.75 a. $2\,A \rightleftharpoons A_2$     b. $A_2 + 3\,B_2 \rightleftharpoons 2\,AB_3$

6.77 a. $\dfrac{[Br_2][H_2]}{[HBr]^2}$

     b. reactants favored
     c. $\Delta H$ positive
     d. reactants lower in energy
     e. You can't predict the reaction rate from the value of $K$.

6.79 a. $\dfrac{[CO_2][H_2]}{[CO][H_2O]}$     b. $K = 4.2$

6.81 a. increases NO and $O_2$, decreases $N_2$
     b. increases $N_2$, NO, and $O_2$

6.83 a, f: favor shift to right
     b, c, d: favor shift to left
     e. no change

6.85 a, c, f: favor shift to right
     b, d, e: favor shift to left

6.87 a. $\dfrac{[C_2H_6]}{[H_2][C_2H_4]}$

     b. reactants higher in energy
     c. $K > 1$
     d. 20. kcal
     e. increase in rate
     f. 1, 2, 4: favor shift to right; 3: favors shift to left; 5: no change, but reduces rate of reaction

6.89 Lactase is an enzyme that converts lactose, a naturally occurring sugar in dairy products, into the two simple sugars, glucose and galactose.

6.91 400 Calories

6.93 1.9 h, rounded to 2 h

6.95 propane 12.0 kcal/g      butane 11.8 kcal/g

6.97 30,200 kcal

## CHAPTER 7

7.1

| | a. Density | b. Intermolecular Spacing | c. Intermolecular Attraction |
|---|---|---|---|
| Gas | Lowest | Greatest | Lowest |
| Liquid | Higher | Smaller | Higher |
| Solid | Highest | Smallest | Highest |

7.2 a. 0.83 atm     b. 12 psi

7.3 a. 2,300 mm Hg     b. 14 psi     c. 0.558 atm

7.5 a. 1.6 L     b. 3.2 L     c. 0.80 L     d. 16 L

7.7 0.44 L

7.9 392 K or 119 °C

7.11 As a sealed container is heated, the gases inside expand and increase the container's internal pressure, eventually popping the lid off.

7.12 290 mm Hg

7.13 a. 1.8 L     b. 2.6 L     c. 15 L

7.14 a. $1.0 \times 10^2$ L     b. 7.8 L     c. 12.6 L

7.15 a. 0.067 mol     b. 0.38 mol     c. $1.1 \times 10^{-3}$ mol

7.16 36 mol

7.17 a. 1.1 atm     b. 1.7 atm

7.18 $O_2$: 2.5 atm     $CO_2$: 1.5 atm

7.19 methane: 640 mm Hg     ethane: 75 mm Hg
     propane: 38 mm Hg

7.21 all: a–d

7.23

| | London Dispersion | Dipole–Dipole | Hydrogen Bonding |
|---|---|---|---|
| a. $Cl_2$ | + | | |
| b. HCN | + | + | |
| c. HF | + | + | + |
| d. $CH_3Cl$ | + | + | |
| e. $H_2$ | + | | |

7.25 For both boiling point and melting point:
     a. $C_2H_6$     b. $CH_3OH$     c. HBr     d. $CH_3Br$

7.27 a. $CH_4$     b. $CH_4$     c. $C_2H_6$

7.29 Benzene cannot hydrogen bond, whereas water can, so benzene has much weaker intermolecular forces than water and is thus less viscous. Ethylene glycol, on the other hand, has two OH groups capable of hydrogen bonding, so it has stronger intermolecular forces than water and is thus more viscous.

7.31 a. ionic     b. metallic     c. molecular     d. molecular

7.32 a. 3,990 cal     b. 2,790 cal     c. 2.79 kcal     d. 1,430 cal

7.33 a. 23,000 cal     b. 23,000 cal     c. 9.7 kcal     d. 34 kcal

7.34 exothermic

7.35 a. heating curve     c. 77 °C     e. liquid
     b. 40 °C     d. solid and liquid

7.37 1.071 atm

7.39 a. 41 psi     b. 0.68 atm     c. 15,200 torr     d. 13,300 Pa

7.41 a. increases     b. decreases     c. increases

7.43 a, b, c: Volume increases.

7.45 a. Volume increases as outside atmospheric pressure decreases.
     b. Volume decreases at the lower temperature.
     c. Volume decreases as external pressure increases.
     d. Volume increases as temperature increases.

7.47 a. 0.75 L     b. 1.1 L     c. 99.7 mm Hg

7.49 35 mL

7.51 a. 4.0 L     b. 1.1 L     c. 820 K

7.53 1.4 L

7.55 a. 4.34 atm     b. 350 mm Hg     c. 1,300 K

7.57 1.1 atm

7.59 a. 1.4 atm     b. 110 L     c. 740 K

7.61 1,200 L

7.63 STP is "standard temperature and pressure," or 0 °C at 760 mm Hg. The standard molar volume is the volume that one mole of a gas occupies at STP, or 22.4 liters.

7.65 a. 0.22 mol     b. 0.500 mol     c. 0.002 23 mol

7.67 a. 94 L     b. 1.8 L     c. 1.7 L

7.69 0.017 mol

7.71 0.19 mol or $1.1 \times 10^{23}$ molecules

7.73 $O_2$ has more moles and more mass.

7.75 **A:** 210 mm Hg     **B:** 420 mm Hg

7.77 97 mm Hg for $O_2$     360 mm Hg for $N_2$

7.79 1,780 mm Hg

7.81 Water is capable of hydrogen bonding and these strong intermolecular attractive forces give it a higher boiling point than $H_2S$.

7.83  a. London forces, dipole–dipole    b. London forces only

7.85  d.

7.87  No, $H_2C{=}O$ has no H on the O atom.

7.89  a. Ethylene has London forces only, whereas methanol has London forces, dipole–dipole forces, and hydrogen bonding.
    b. Methanol has a higher boiling point.
    c. Ethylene has a higher vapor pressure at any given temperature.

7.91  butane, acetaldehyde, Freon-113

7.93  Glycerol is more viscous than water since it has three OH groups and has many opportunities for hydrogen bonding. Acetone cannot hydrogen bond so its intermolecular forces are weaker and thus it has low viscosity.

7.95  a. ionic        c. metallic       e. amorphous
    b. molecular       d. network

7.97  Evaporation is an endothermic process by which a liquid enters the gas phase. Condensation is an exothermic process that occurs when a gas enters the liquid phase.

7.99  vaporization; energy absorbed

7.101  a, d: absorbed        b, c: released

7.103  Vaporizing 50.0 g of water takes more energy; 27,000 cal vs. 20,000 cal.

7.105  a. [1] $W \longrightarrow X$; [2] $Y \longrightarrow Z$    b. 10 °C    c. 85 °C

7.107

7.109  290 mL
    The gases inside the bag had a volume of 250 mL at 760 mm Hg and take up a greater volume at the reduced pressure of 650 mm Hg.

7.111  Water is one of the few substances that expands as it enters the solid phase. This causes the bottle to crack as the water occupies a larger volume as it freezes.

7.113  a. As a person breathes faster, he eliminates more $CO_2$ from the lungs; therefore, the measured value of $CO_2$ is lower than the normal value of 40 mm Hg.
    b. Many people with advanced lung disease have lost lung tissue over time and therefore cannot exchange adequate amounts of oxygen through the lungs and into the blood, leading to a lower-than-normal partial pressure of oxygen. In addition, they often breathe more slowly and with lower volumes than normal, so they cannot eliminate enough $CO_2$ and therefore the partial pressure of $CO_2$ climbs.

7.115  The molar mass is 4 g/mol and the gas is helium.

## CHAPTER 8

8.1  a. heterogeneous mixture    b. colloid    c, d, e: solution

8.3  a, c, d, e: water soluble

8.5  a, c, e, f: water soluble    b, d: water insoluble

8.7  A soft drink becomes "flat" when $CO_2$ escapes from the solution. $CO_2$ comes out of solution faster at room temperature than at the cooler temperature of the refrigerator because the solubility of gases in liquids decreases as the temperature increases.

8.9  3.5%

8.11  8.4% (v/v)

8.12  2.4 mL

8.13  $2.0 \times 10^2$ mL

8.15  a. 0.030 ppm    b. 0.5 ppm    c. 2.0 ppm    d. 0.23 ppm

8.16  a. 2.0 M    c. 10. M    e. 1.2 M
    b. 8.0 M    d. 0.10 M    f. 1.4 M

8.17  10.0 g NaOH in 150 mL gives a concentration of 1.7 M vs. only 1.5 M for 15.0 g in 250 mL.

8.18  a. $1.0 \times 10^2$ mL    c. 2.0 mL
    b. 13 mL    d. $2.0 \times 10^3$ mL

8.19  a. 4.0 moles    c. 0.050 moles
    b. 0.63 moles    d. 0.063 moles

8.20  a. 7.3 g    b. 150 g    c. 40. g    d. 3.7 g

8.21  a. 5.8 mL    b. 23 mL    c. 15 mL    d. 0.58 mL

8.22  0.35 M

8.23  a. 220 mL    b. $5.0 \times 10^2$ mL    c. 7.5 mL    d. 15 mL

8.25  a. 101.0 °C    b. 102.0 °C    c. 103.1 °C    d. 100.4 °C

8.26  a. –3.7 °C    b. –7.4 °C    c. –11 °C    d. –1.27 °C

8.27  –7.4 °C

8.28  a. 5.0% sugar solution    b. 4.0 M NaCl    c. 0.75 M NaCl

8.29  a. Water flows across the membrane.
    b. More water initially flows from the 1.0 M side to the more concentrated 1.5 M side. When equilibrium is reached there is equal flow of water in both directions.
    c. The height of the 1.5 M side will be higher and the height of the 1.0 M NaCl will be lower.

8.31  **A.** The $K^+$ and $I^-$ ions are separated when KI is dissolved in water. The solution contains ions so it conducts an electric current.

8.33  a, b, d, e: solution    c. heterogeneous mixture    f. colloid

8.35  a. unsaturated    b, c: saturated    d. supersaturated

8.37  a, c, d

8.39

hydrogen bond

8.41  Water-soluble compounds are ionic or are small polar molecules that can hydrogen bond with the water solvent, but nonpolar compounds, such as oil, are soluble in nonpolar solvents.

8.43  Iodine would not be soluble in water but is soluble in $CCl_4$ since $I_2$ is nonpolar and $CCl_4$ is a nonpolar solvent.

8.45  Cholesterol is not water soluble because it is a large nonpolar molecule with a single OH group.

8.47  a.

b.

8.49  a. increased    b. decreased    c, d: no change

8.51  A decrease in temperature (a) increases the solubility of a gas and (b) decreases the solubility of a solid.

8.53  The ion–dipole interactions between ions and water provide the energy needed to break apart the ions from the crystal lattice. The water molecules form a loose shell of solvent around each ion.

8.55  a, b, d, e, g: water soluble

8.57   5% (w/v)   $\dfrac{5\text{ g}}{100\text{ mL}}$   $\dfrac{100\text{ mL}}{5\text{ g}}$

      6.0 M   $\dfrac{6.0\text{ mol}}{1.0\text{ L}}$   $\dfrac{1.0\text{ L}}{6.0\text{ mol}}$

      10 ppm   $\dfrac{10\text{ g}}{10^6\text{ g}}$   $\dfrac{10^6\text{ g}}{10\text{ g}}$

8.59   a. 1.3% (w/v)    b. 17% (w/v)    c. 8.00% (w/v)

8.61   17% (v/v)

8.63   a. 2.3 M    b. 0.51 M    c. 0.66 M    d. 0.036 M

8.65   a. Add 12 g of acetic acid to the flask and then water to bring the volume to 250 mL.
      b. Add 55 mL of ethyl acetate to the flask and then water to bring the volume to 250 mL.
      c. Add 37 g of NaCl to the flask and then water to bring the volume to 250 mL.

8.67   a. 0.038 mol    b. 0.090 mol    c. 3.8 mol

8.69   a. 3.2 g    b. 5.7 g    c. 140 g

8.71   83 mL

8.73   a. 95 g    b. 1.6 mol    c. 0.85 M

8.75   a. 0.08 ppm    b. 0.7 ppm

8.77   **B**

8.79   a. 0.05 M    b. 50.0 mL

8.81   Concentration is the amount of solute per unit volume in a solution. Dilution is the addition of solvent to decrease the concentration of solute.

8.83   a. 15.0% (w/v)    c. 5.0% (w/v)
      b. 6.00% (w/v)    d. 14% (w/v)

8.85   1.8 M

8.87   a. 10. mL    b. 450 mL    c. 1.5 mL    d. 2.5 mL

8.89   Ocean water contains nonvolatile dissolved salts, increasing the boiling point.

8.91   a. 101.5 °C    b. 101.2 °C    c. 103.1 °C

8.93   −4.5 °C

8.95   a. NaCl    b. glucose    c. NaCl    d. glucose

8.97   a. 0.10 M glucose    c. 0.10 M $Na_2SO_4$
      b. 0.20 M NaCl    d. 0.10 M glucose

8.99   a. **A > B**    c. no change    e. no change
      b. **B > A**    d. **A > B**

8.101   At warmer temperatures, $CO_2$ is less soluble in water and more is in the gas phase and escapes as the can is opened and pressure is reduced.

8.103   0.09% (w/v)    0.005 M

8.105   a. 280 mL would have to be given.
      b. The hypertonic mannitol draws water out of swollen brain cells and thus reduces the pressure on the brain.

8.107   Water moves out of the cells of the cucumber to the hypertonic salt solution, so the cucumber shrinks and loses its crispness.

8.109   NaCl, KCl, and glucose are found in the bloodstream. If they weren't in the dialyzer fluid, they would move out of the bloodstream into the dialyzer, and their concentrations in the bloodstream would fall.

8.111   6.3% (w/v)

8.113   7.3 g

8.115   4,000 mg

8.119   a. yes    b. 0.000 50 mol

## CHAPTER 9

9.1   a, c

9.2   a, b, d

9.3   a. $\underset{\text{acid}}{HCl(g)} + \underset{\text{base}}{NH_3(g)}$    c. $\underset{\text{base}}{OH^-(aq)} + \underset{\text{acid}}{HSO_4^-(aq)}$
      b. $\underset{\text{acid}}{CH_3COOH(l)} + \underset{\text{base}}{H_2O(l)}$

9.4   a. $H_3O^+$    b. HI    c. $H_2CO_3$

9.5   a. $HS^-$    b. $CN^-$    c. $SO_4^{2-}$

9.6   a. $\underset{\text{base}}{H_2O(l)} + \underset{\text{acid}}{HI(g)} \rightleftharpoons \underset{\substack{\text{conjugate}\\\text{base}}}{I^-(aq)} + \underset{\substack{\text{conjugate}\\\text{acid}}}{H_3O^+(aq)}$

      b. $\underset{\text{acid}}{CH_3COOH(l)} + \underset{\text{base}}{NH_3(g)} \rightleftharpoons \underset{\substack{\text{conjugate}\\\text{base}}}{CH_3COO^-(aq)} + \underset{\substack{\text{conjugate}\\\text{acid}}}{NH_4^+(aq)}$

      c. $\underset{\text{base}}{Br^-(aq)} + \underset{\text{acid}}{HNO_3(aq)} \rightleftharpoons \underset{\substack{\text{conjugate}\\\text{acid}}}{HBr(aq)} + \underset{\substack{\text{conjugate}\\\text{base}}}{NO_3^-(aq)}$

9.7   a. $NH_4^+$    b. $NH_2^-$

9.8   **D < F < E**

9.9   a. $H_2SO_4$ is the stronger acid; $H_3PO_4$ has the stronger conjugate base.
      b. HCl is the stronger acid; HF has the stronger conjugate base.
      c. $H_2CO_3$ is the stronger acid; $NH_4^+$ has the stronger conjugate base.
      d. HF is the stronger acid; HCN has the stronger conjugate base.

9.11   a, c: products    b. reactants

9.13   a. $HPO_4^{2-}$, $H_2PO_4^-$, $H_3PO_4$    b. HCN, $CH_3COOH$, HF

9.15   reactants favored

9.17   a. $10^{-11}$ M acidic    c. $3.6 \times 10^{-5}$ M basic
      b. $10^{-3}$ M basic    d. $1.8 \times 10^{-11}$ M acidic

9.19

|   | $[H_3O^+]$ | $[OH^-]$ |
|---|---|---|
| a. | $10^{-11}$ M | $10^{-3}$ M |
| b. | $10^{-3}$ M | $10^{-11}$ M |
| c. | 1.5 M | $6.7 \times 10^{-15}$ M |
| d. | $3.3 \times 10^{-14}$ M | $3.0 \times 10^{-1}$ M |

9.20   a. 6    b. 12    c. 5    d. 11

9.21   a. $1 \times 10^{-13}$ M   basic
      b. $1 \times 10^{-7}$ M   neutral
      c. $1 \times 10^{-3}$ M   acidic

9.22   a. $6 \times 10^{-11}$ M    b. $2 \times 10^{-8}$ M    c. $5 \times 10^{-5}$ M

9.23   a. 5.74    b. 11.036    c. 4.06    d. 10.118

9.25   a. $HNO_3(aq) + NaOH(aq) \longrightarrow H_2O(l) + NaNO_3(aq)$
      b. $H_2SO_4(aq) + 2\,KOH(aq) \longrightarrow 2\,H_2O(l) + K_2SO_4(aq)$

9.27   $H_2SO_4(aq) + CaCO_3(s) \longrightarrow CaSO_4(aq) + \underset{\text{from } H_2CO_3}{\underline{H_2O(l) + CO_2(g)}}$

9.29   a, c, e: neutral    b, f: basic    d. acidic

9.31   0.41 M

9.33   a. Not a buffer since it contains a strong acid, HBr.
      b. A buffer since HF is a weak acid and $F^-$ is its conjugate base.
      c. Not a buffer since it contains a weak acid only.

9.35   a, b, c: pH 7.21
      The pH remains the same if equal amounts of the weak acid and conjugate base are present.

9.37   a, d, f

9.39   a, d, e, f

9.41   a. $H_2S$    b. $HCO_3^-$    c. $HNO_2$    d. $\left[ \begin{array}{c} \text{H} \quad \text{H} \\ \text{H}-\text{C}-\text{N}-\text{H} \\ \text{H} \quad \text{H} \end{array} \right]^+$

9.43   a. $NO_2^-$    b. $NH_3$    c. $HO_2^-$

9.45   a.   ● + ● ⟶ ● + ●
        acid   base     conjugate base   conjugate acid

      b.   ● + ● ⟶ ● + ●
        base   acid     conjugate acid   conjugate base

9.47  a. HI(g) acid                    $I^-(aq)$ conjugate base
       $NH_3(g)$ base                  $NH_4^+(aq)$ conjugate acid
      b. HCOOH(l) acid                 $HCOO^-(aq)$ conjugate base
       $H_2O(l)$ base                  $H_3O^+(aq)$ conjugate acid
      c. $HSO_4^-(aq)$ base            $H_2SO_4(aq)$ conjugate acid
       $H_2O(l)$ acid                  $OH^-(aq)$ conjugate base

9.49  a. $H_2CO_3$        b. $CO_3^{2-}$

9.51  $HNO_3(aq) + H_2O(l) \longrightarrow H_3O^+(aq) + NO_3^-(aq)$

9.53  **A** represents HCl because it shows a fully dissociated acid.
      **B** represents HF because it is only partially dissociated.

9.55  a. **B**        b. **A**

9.57  a. $CH_3COOH$        b. $H_3PO_4$        c. $H_2SO_4$

9.59  a. $H_2O$        b. $HCO_3^-$        c. $HSO_4^-$

9.61  a. **A**        b. **B**        c. **B**

9.63  a. $HSO_4^-$        stronger acid
         $SO_4^{2-}$        conjugate base
         $H_2PO_4^-$
         $HPO_4^{2-}$        conjugate base, stronger base
      b. $CH_3COOH$        stronger acid
         $CH_3COO^-$        conjugate base
         $CH_3CH_2COOH$
         $CH_3CH_2COO^-$        conjugate base, stronger base

9.65  a. **B**        b. **B**

9.67            acid                              conjugate acid
      a. $H_3PO_4(aq) + CN^-(aq) \rightleftharpoons H_2PO_4^-(aq) + HCN(aq)$
                            products favored
               acid                       conjugate acid
      b. $Br^-(aq) + HSO_4^-(aq) \rightleftharpoons SO_4^{2-}(aq) + HBr(g)$
               reactants favored
                          acid
      c. $CH_3COO^-(aq) + H_2CO_3(aq)$
               reactants favored           conjugate acid
                          $\rightleftharpoons CH_3COOH(aq) + HCO_3^-(aq)$

9.69  a. $10^{-6}$ M basic        c. $3.3 \times 10^{-11}$ M acidic
      b. $10^{-4}$ M basic        d. $4.0 \times 10^{-4}$ M basic

9.71  a. $10^{-12}$ M basic            c. $1.6 \times 10^{-8}$ M basic
      b. $2.5 \times 10^{-7}$ M acidic  d. $1.2 \times 10^{-2}$ M acidic

9.73  a. 12        b. 6.60        c. 7.80        d. 1.92

9.75

| $[H_3O^+]$ | $[OH^-]$ | pH | Classification |
|---|---|---|---|
| $5.3 \times 10^{-3}$ | $1.9 \times 10^{-12}$ | 2.28 | acidic |
| $5.0 \times 10^{-7}$ | $2.0 \times 10^{-8}$ | 6.30 | acidic |
| $4 \times 10^{-5}$ | $2.5 \times 10^{-10}$ | 4.4 | acidic |
| $1.5 \times 10^{-5}$ | $6.8 \times 10^{-10}$ | 4.82 | acidic |

9.77  a. $1 \times 10^{-12}$ M        c. $1.6 \times 10^{-2}$ M
      b. $1 \times 10^{-1}$ M        d. $1.3 \times 10^{-9}$ M

9.79  $[H_3O^+] = 1.3 \times 10^{-6}$ M        $[OH^-] = 7.7 \times 10^{-9}$ M

9.81  $[H_3O^+] = 7.9 \times 10^{-5}$ M        $[OH^-] = 1.3 \times 10^{-10}$ M

9.83  a. 2.60        b. 12.17

9.85  HCl is fully dissociated to $H_3O^+$ and $Cl^-$ and $CH_3COOH$ is not fully dissociated.

9.87  a. $HBr(aq) + KOH(aq) \longrightarrow KBr(aq) + H_2O(l)$
      b. $2 HNO_3(aq) + Ca(OH)_2(aq) \longrightarrow 2 H_2O(l) + Ca(NO_3)_2(aq)$
      c. $HCl(aq) + NaHCO_3(aq) \longrightarrow NaCl(aq) + H_2O(l) + CO_2(g)$
      d. $H_2SO_4(aq) + Mg(OH)_2(aq) \longrightarrow 2 H_2O(l) + MgSO_4(aq)$

9.89  $2 HNO_3(aq) + CaCO_3(s)$
           $\longrightarrow Ca(NO_3)_2(aq) + CO_2(g) + H_2O(l)$

9.91  a, e: neutral        b, d, f: basic        c. acidic

9.93  0.14 M

9.95  0.12 M

9.97  25 mL

9.99  **B** is a buffer because it contains equal amounts of the acid and its conjugate base.

9.101  If the concentrations of the weak acid and its conjugate base are equal, then a proton donor and a proton acceptor are available and the $H_3O^+$ concentration will change very little when acid or base is added to a buffer.

9.103  Yes. HCN is a weak acid and $CN^-$ is its conjugate base, so in equal amounts they form a buffer.

9.105  a. $HNO_2$ is a proton donor that will react with added base and $NO_2^-$ is a proton acceptor that will react with added acid.
       b. The concentration of $HNO_2$ increases and that of $NO_2^-$ decreases when a small amount of acid is added to the buffer.
       c. The concentration of $HNO_2$ decreases and that of $NO_2^-$ increases when a small amount of base is added to the buffer.

9.107  a. 12.66        b. 10.25

9.109  a. 4.74        b. 5.05        c. 4.44

9.111  $CO_2$ combines with rainwater to form $H_2CO_3$, which is acidic, lowering the pH.

9.113  $[H_3O^+] = 3.2 \times 10^{-8}$ M        $[OH^-] = 3.1 \times 10^{-7}$ M

9.115  By breathing into a bag, the individual breathes in air with a higher $CO_2$ concentration. Thus, the $CO_2$ concentration in the lungs and the blood increases, thereby lowering the pH.

9.117  A rise in $CO_2$ concentration leads to an increase in $H^+(aq)$ concentration by the following equilibria:
       $CO_2(g) + H_2O(l) \rightleftharpoons H_2CO_3(aq) \rightleftharpoons HCO_3^-(aq) + H^+(aq)$

9.119  $OCl^-(aq) + H_2O(l) \longrightarrow HOCl(aq) + OH^-(aq)$
       $OH^-$ is formed by this reaction, so the water is basic.

## CHAPTER 10

10.1

|  | Atomic Number | Mass Number | Number of Protons | Number of Neutrons | Isotope Symbol |
|---|---|---|---|---|---|
| Cobalt-59 | 27 | 59 | 27 | 32 | $^{59}_{27}Co$ |
| Cobalt-60 | 27 | 60 | 27 | 33 | $^{60}_{27}Co$ |

10.3  An $\alpha$ particle has no electrons around the nucleus.

10.5  $^{222}_{86}Rn \longrightarrow {}^4_2He + {}^{218}_{84}Po$

10.7  a. $^{218}_{84}Po \longrightarrow {}^4_2He + {}^{214}_{82}Pb$
      b. $^{230}_{90}Th \longrightarrow {}^4_2He + {}^{226}_{88}Ra$
      c. $^{252}_{99}Es \longrightarrow {}^4_2He + {}^{248}_{97}Bk$

10.8  $^{131}_{53}I \longrightarrow {}^0_{-1}e + {}^{131}_{54}Xe$

10.9  a. $^{20}_9F \longrightarrow {}^0_{-1}e + {}^{20}_{10}Ne$
      b. $^{92}_{38}Sr \longrightarrow {}^0_{-1}e + {}^{92}_{39}Y$
      c. $^{55}_{24}Cr \longrightarrow {}^0_{-1}e + {}^{55}_{25}Mn$

10.10  a. $^{74}_{33}As \longrightarrow {}^0_{+1}e + {}^{74}_{32}Ge$
       b. $^{15}_8O \longrightarrow {}^0_{+1}e + {}^{15}_7N$

10.11  $^{192}_{77}Ir \longrightarrow {}^{192}_{78}Pt + {}^0_{-1}e + \gamma$

10.13  a. 0.250 g        b. 0.0625 g        c. 0.003 91 g        d. $9.54 \times 10^{-7}$ g

10.15  17,200 years

10.16  4.4 mL

10.17  a. 0.2 rem        b. 14 mrem        c. "a" is the higher dose.

10.19  a. 62 protons, 91 neutrons, 62 electrons        c. 9.4 mCi
       b. $^{153}_{62}Sm \longrightarrow {}^{153}_{63}Eu + {}^0_{-1}e$

10.21  $^{235}_{92}U + {}^1_0n \longrightarrow {}^{133}_{51}Sb + {}^{100}_{41}Nb + 3 {}^1_0n$

10.23

|  | a. Atomic Number | b. Number of Protons | c. Number of Neutrons | d. Mass Number | Isotope Symbol |
|---|---|---|---|---|---|
| Fluorine-18 | 9 | 9 | 9 | 18 | $^{18}_9F$ |
| Fluorine-19 | 9 | 9 | 10 | 19 | $^{19}_9F$ |

**10.25**

|  | Atomic Number | Mass Number | Number of Protons | Number of Neutrons | Isotope Symbol |
|---|---|---|---|---|---|
| a. Chromium-51 | 24 | 51 | 24 | 27 | $^{51}_{24}$Cr |
| b. Palladium-103 | 46 | 103 | 46 | 57 | $^{103}_{46}$Pd |
| c. Potassium-42 | 19 | 42 | 19 | 23 | $^{42}_{19}$K |
| d. Xenon-133 | 54 | 133 | 54 | 79 | $^{133}_{54}$Xe |

**10.27**

|  | Change in Mass | Change in Charge |
|---|---|---|
| a. α particle | −4 | −2 |
| b. β particle | 0 | +1 |
| c. γ ray | 0 | 0 |
| d. Positron | 0 | −1 |

**10.29**

|  | Mass | Charge |
|---|---|---|
| a. α | 4 | +2 |
| b. n | 1 | 0 |
| c. γ | 0 | 0 |
| d. β | 0 | −1 |

**10.31**

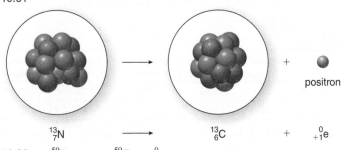

$^{13}_{7}$N $\longrightarrow$ $^{13}_{6}$C + $^{0}_{+1}$e

**10.33**  a. $^{59}_{26}$Fe $\longrightarrow$ $^{59}_{27}$Co + $^{0}_{-1}$e

b. $^{190}_{78}$Pt $\longrightarrow$ $^{186}_{76}$Os + $^{4}_{2}$He

c. $^{178}_{80}$Hg $\longrightarrow$ $^{178}_{79}$Au + $^{0}_{+1}$e

**10.35**  a. $^{90}_{39}$Y $\longrightarrow$ $^{90}_{40}$Zr + $^{0}_{-1}$e

b. $^{135}_{60}$Nd $\longrightarrow$ $^{135}_{59}$Pr + $^{0}_{+1}$e

c. $^{210}_{83}$Bi $\longrightarrow$ $^{206}_{81}$Tl + $^{4}_{2}$He

**10.37**  $^{214}_{83}$Bi $\longrightarrow$ $^{214}_{84}$Po + $^{0}_{-1}$e

$^{214}_{83}$Bi $\longrightarrow$ $^{210}_{81}$Tl + $^{4}_{2}$He

**10.39**  a. $^{232}_{90}$Th $\longrightarrow$ $^{4}_{2}$He + $^{228}_{88}$Ra

b. $^{25}_{11}$Na $\longrightarrow$ $^{25}_{12}$Mg + $^{0}_{-1}$e

c. $^{118}_{54}$Xe $\longrightarrow$ $^{118}_{53}$I + $^{0}_{+1}$e

d. $^{243}_{96}$Cm $\longrightarrow$ $^{4}_{2}$He + $^{239}_{94}$Pu

**10.41**  two

**10.43**  4.0 days

**10.45**

|  | Iodine-131 | Xenon-131 |
|---|---|---|
| a. | 32 mg | 32 mg |
| b. | 16 mg | 48 mg |
| c. | 8.0 mg | 56 mg |
| d. | 4.0 mg | 60. mg |

**10.47**  No, 25% remains.

**10.49**  In artifacts over 50,000 years old, the percentage of carbon-14 is too small to accurately measure.

**10.51**  a. 10 mCi      b. 5 mCi      c. 1 mCi

**10.53**  $1.9 \times 10^8$ disintegrations/s

**10.55**  2.3 mL

**10.57**  2.6 mL

**10.59**  Curie refers to the number of disintegrations per second and the number of rads indicates the radiation absorbed by one gram of a substance.

**10.61**  20 Sv = 2,000 rem

This represents a fatal dose because 600 rem is uniformly fatal.

**10.63**  Nuclear fission refers to the splitting of nuclei and fusion refers to the joining of small nuclei to form larger ones.

**10.65**  a. fusion      b. fission      c. both      d. fusion

**10.67**  a. $^{235}_{92}$U + $^{1}_{0}$n $\longrightarrow$ $^{137}_{50}$Sn + $^{97}_{42}$Mo + 2 $^{1}_{0}$n

b. $^{235}_{92}$U + $^{1}_{0}$n $\longrightarrow$ $^{93}_{36}$Kr + $^{140}_{56}$Ba + 3 $^{1}_{0}$n

**10.69**

**10.71**  tritium; $^{3}_{1}$H

**10.73**  The containment of radiation leaks and disposal of radioactive waste are two problems that are associated with nuclear power production.

**10.75**  $^{209}_{83}$Bi + $^{58}_{26}$Fe $\longrightarrow$ $^{266}_{109}$Mt + $^{1}_{0}$n

meitnerium-266

**10.77**  a. $^{74}_{33}$As $\longrightarrow$ $^{0}_{+1}$e + $^{74}_{32}$Ge      b. 4 mg      c. 1.5 mL

**10.79**  a. 38 protons, 51 neutrons, 38 electrons      c. 0.625 μg

b. $^{89}_{38}$Sr $\longrightarrow$ $^{89}_{39}$Y + $^{0}_{-1}$e

**10.81**  a. used for the treatment and diagnosis of thyroid diseases

b. used for the treatment of breast cancer

c. used for the diagnosis of heart disease

**10.83**  a. Iodine-125, with its longer half-life, is used for the treatment of prostate cancers using implanted radioactive seeds.

b. Iodine-131, with its shorter half-life, is used for the diagnostic and therapeutic treatment of thyroid diseases and tumors. A patient is administered radioactive iodine-131, which is then incorporated into the thyroid hormone, thyroxine. Since its half-life is short, the radioactive iodine isotope decays so that little remains after a month or so.

**10.85**  Radiology technicians must be shielded to avoid exposure to excessive and dangerous doses of radiation.

**10.87**  High doses of stable iodine will prevent the absorption and uptake of the radioactive iodine-131.

**10.89**  370 kcal

# CHAPTER 11

**11.1**  organic (a), (e)

inorganic (b), (c), (d), (f)

**11.2**  a., b., c., d., e.

11.3  a. (1), (2) both trigonal planar
  b. (1) linear; (2) tetrahedral; (3) bent
  c. (1) trigonal planar; (2) bent
  d. (1) trigonal planar; (2) linear

11.5  a. [structure: $CH_3Cl$ — C bonded to three H and Cl]  b. [structure: $CH_3CH_2Br$ — two carbons with H's and Br]

11.6  (1) bent; (2) linear; (3),(4) trigonal planar; (5) bent; (6) tetrahedral

11.7  a. $CH_3(CH_2)_3CH_3$
  b. $Br(CH_2)_2Br$
  c. $CH_3CH_2O(CH_2)_2OH$
  d. $CH_3CH_2C(CH_3)_3$

11.9  a. [ring structure of cyclic hydrocarbon]  c. [branched hydrocarbon with OH]

  b. [ring structure with Cl substituents]

11.10  C1: no H; C2: 1 H; C3: 2 H; C4: 1 H; C5: 1 H

11.11  a. hydroxyl  b. alkene; aromatic ring  c. two amine groups

11.12  a. [aromatic ring with C=O] aldehyde

  b. [chain structure H—C—C—C—C—O—H with :O:] carboxylic acid

  c. [ring with C=O] ketone

  d. [H—C—C—C—O—C—C—H with :O:] ester

  e. [ring with C=O and N amide group] amide

11.13  amide, aromatic ring, ether, hydroxyl, amine

11.14  a. $CH_3CH_2OCH_2CH_3$, ether
  b. $CH_3CH_2CH{=}CHCH_2CHO$, alkene, aldehyde

11.15  three ethers, aromatic ring, alkene

[structure: aromatic ring with three $CH_3O$ groups and allyl chain]

11.17  a. nonpolar; all nonpolar bonds
  b. polar; one polar C=O bond
  c. nonpolar; the four bond dipoles cancel
  d. polar; the polar C—N and N—H bond dipoles don't cancel

11.19  a. insoluble  b. soluble  c. insoluble

11.21  Niacin is soluble in water.

11.23  inorganic: (a), (b)  organic: (c)

11.25  a. [H—C—C=C—C≡C—H structure]  c. [H—C≡C—C—C—H with :Cl:]

  b. [H—C=C—C—O—H structure]  d. [H—C=C—C—C—N—H with :O:]

11.27  a. (1) trigonal planar; (2) linear
  b. (1) tetrahedral; (2) bent; (3) tetrahedral

11.29  a. (1) and (2) 180°
  b. (1) and (2) 120°
  c. (1) and (2) 109.5°

11.31  (1) bent; (2) trigonal planar; (3) tetrahedral; (4) trigonal pyramidal

11.33  Each C is surrounded by three groups, so each carbon is trigonal planar giving 120° bond angles.

11.35  a. $CH_3(CH_2)_2C(CH_3)_3$  c. $(CH_3)_2CHCH_2O(CH_2)_2CH_3$
  b. $BrCH_2CH_2CHCH_2CH_3$  d. $CH_3(CH_2)_2CHO$
  [Cl below b]

11.37  a. [cyclohexane ring with $OCH_3$ and $H_2N$ substituents]  b. [cyclopentane ring with Cl, Cl, and $CH_3$ substituents]

11.39  a. [long branched carbon chain]

  b. [branched structure with O—H]

  c. [H—C—C—O—C—C—C—C—H with :O:]

  d. [ring structure with Cl, Cl, O—H, and chain]

11.41  a. $(CH_3)_3CHCH_2CH_3$  — Five bonds to C

b. $CH_3(CH_2)_4CH_3OH$  — Five bonds to C

c. $(CH_3)_2C{=}CH_3$  — Five bonds to C

d.  CH₃ CH₃  Five bonds to C

e.  CH₃ CH₃ CH₃  Five bonds to C

11.43

11.45  a. two alkenes
b. ketone
c. ester

11.47  a. ester
b. two alkenes, two alkynes, one hydroxyl
c. hydroxyl, ether, aldehyde, aromatic ring

11.49  two hydroxyl groups, aromatic ring, amine

11.51  $(CH_3)_2C{=}CHCH_2CH_2C(CH_3){=}CHCHO$, two alkenes, aldehyde

11.53  In a carboxylic acid, the C=O is bonded to a hydroxyl group. In an ester, the C=O is bonded to an OR group.
Examples: $CH_3CH_2COOH$ (carboxylic acid) and $CH_3CO_2CH_3$ (ester)

11.55  a. $HC{\equiv}C{-}CH_3$        c. $CH_3CH_2CHO$

b. $CH_3CH_2CH_2OH$        d. $CH_3CH_2\overset{\displaystyle O}{\overset{\|}{C}}CH_3$

11.57  alkane   $CH_3CH_2CH_2CH_2CH_3$   $C_5H_{12}$

alkene   $CH_3{-}\underset{H}{\overset{H}{C}}{-}\overset{H}{C}{=}C{-}CH_3$   $C_5H_{10}$

alkyne   $CH_3{-}\underset{H}{\overset{H}{C}}{-}C{\equiv}C{-}CH_3$   $C_5H_8$

11.59  NaCl dissolves in water but not in dichloromethane and cholesterol dissolves in dichloromethane but not in water.

11.61  Net dipoles and molecular geometry will determine whether a molecule is polar or nonpolar. When a molecule has polar bonds, we must determine whether the bond dipoles cancel or reinforce.

11.63

a.

b.

11.65  a. nonpolar
b. polar
c. polar

11.67  Ethylene glycol is more water soluble because it contains two polar hydroxyl groups capable of hydrogen bonding.

11.69  Sucrose has multiple OH groups and this makes it water soluble. 1-Dodecanol has a long hydrocarbon chain and a single OH group so it is not water soluble.

11.71  a. Spermaceti wax is an ester.
b. The very long hydrocarbon chains would make it insoluble in water and soluble in organic solvents.

11.73  Fat-soluble vitamins will persist in tissues and accumulate, whereas any excess of water-soluble vitamins will be excreted in the urine.

11.75  Vitamin E is a fat-soluble vitamin, making it soluble in organic solvents and insoluble in water.

11.77  a. Yes, there are just enough H's to give each C four bonds.
b. No, there are too many H's.
c. Yes, if you put the three C's in a ring, each C gets two H's.

11.79  a. $CH_3CH_2CH_2NHCH_3$

b. $CH_3CH_2CH_2{-}\overset{\overset{\displaystyle \delta^+}{\overset{\displaystyle H}{|}}}{\underset{\delta^-}{N}}{-}\overset{\delta^+}{C}H_3$

c. trigonal pyramid around N
d. This is a polar molecule. The bond dipoles don't cancel.

11.81  a. $C_9H_{11}NO_2$      c. seven      d. water soluble
b, e:  Polar bonds are in **bold.**

11.83

a. functional groups:
(a) ketone
(b) alkene
(c) hydroxyl
(d) aldehyde
(e) ketone
(f) hydroxyl

b. Each O needs two lone pairs.
c. 21 C's
d. number of H's at carbon:
1'- 0 H's
2'- 0 H's
3'- 1 H
4'- 2 H's
5'- 1 H
6'- 1 H

e. shape at each carbon:
1- tetrahedral
2- tetrahedral
3- bent
4- trigonal planar
5- tetrahedral

f.

**11.85** The waxy coating will prevent loss of water from leaves and will keep leaves crisp.

**11.87** THC is not water soluble. THC is fat soluble and will therefore persist in tissues for an extended period of time. Ethanol is water soluble and will be quickly excreted in the urine.

## CHAPTER 12

**12.1**  a. 8      b. 8      c. 18      d. 16

**12.3**  a. not isomers      b. isomers      c. isomers

**12.4**

**12.5**  d.

**12.6**  a.     c.

b.     d.

**12.7**  a. $CH_3CH_2CH_3$      b.      c.

**12.9**  a.

b.

c.

**12.10** a. 3-methylpentane
b. 4-methyl-5-propylnonane
c. 2,4-dimethylhexane

**12.11** a. 2,3-dimethylbutane
b. 4-ethyldecane
c. 4-ethyl-3,4-dimethyloctane

**12.12** a.

b.

c.

d.

**12.13** a.

b.

c.

d.

**12.15** Vitamin $D_3$ has many nonpolar C—C and C—H bonds, which make it water insoluble but fat soluble.

**12.16** a. methylcyclobutane
b. 1,1-dimethylcyclohexane
c. 1-ethyl-3-propylcyclopentane
d. 1-ethyl-4-methylcyclohexane

**12.17** a.

b.

c.

d.

12.19 Vaseline is nonpolar, so it is insoluble in a polar solvent like water and soluble in a weakly polar solvent like dichloromethane.

12.21 a. $CH_3CH_2CH_3 + 5\ O_2 \longrightarrow 3\ CO_2 + 4\ H_2O$
b. $2\ CH_3CH_2CH_2CH_3 + 13\ O_2 \longrightarrow 8\ CO_2 + 10\ H_2O$

12.23 64

12.25 26 C has 54 H's
27 C has 56 H's
28 C has 58 H's
29 C has 60 H's
30 C has 62 H's

12.27 To form a cycloalkane, you need to form a C—C bond between 2 C's in a chain. To do this, 1 H from each C must be removed. This means a cycloalkane always has two fewer H's than an acyclic alkane of the same number of C's.

12.29 a. $CH_3(CH_2)_3CH_3$     c. $(CH_3)_3CC(CH_3)_3$

b. $CH_3CH_2CHCHCH_3$ d. (structure with CH₃ groups)

12.31 a. $CH_3CH_2CH_2C(CH_3)_2-CH_3$    b. $CH_3CH_2CH_2CH_2CH_2CH_2CH_3$

12.33 a, c, d: constitutional isomers
b. identical

12.35 a, d: constitutional isomers
b, c, e: identical

12.37 a. (cyclohexane with CH₃) (cyclopentane with CH₂CH₃)

b. $CH_3CH_2CH_2CH_2CH_2OH$     $CH_3OCH_2CH_2CH_2CH_3$

c. $CH_3CH_2CH_2Cl$     $CH_3CHCH_3$ with $Cl$

12.39 $CH_3CHCH_2CH_2CH_2CH_2CH_3$ with $CH_3$

$CH_3CH_2CHCH_2CH_2CH_2CH_3$ with $CH_3$

$CH_3CH_2CH_2CHCH_2CH_2CH_3$ with $CH_3$

12.41 (cyclopropane)—OH

$CH_3CCH_3$ with =O

(epoxide)—CH₃ with O

12.43 hexane; 2-methylpentane; 3-methylpentane; 2,2-dimethylbutane; 2,3-dimethylbutane

12.45 a. 4-methylheptane     b. ethylcyclopentane

12.47 a. 3-methylheptane
b. 3,5-dimethyloctane
c. 3,3-diethylhexane

d. 4-ethyl-2,6-dimethyloctane
e. 6-ethyl-2-methyloctane
f. 2,2,8,8-tetramethyldecane

12.49 a. cyclooctane
b. methylcyclopropane
c. 1,1,2,2-tetramethylcyclobutane
d. 1,3-diethylcyclohexane

12.51 a. $CH_3CH_2CHCH_2CH_2CH_3$ with $CH_2CH_3$

b. $CH_3CH_2CCH_2CH_2CH_2CH_3$ with $CH_3$ and $CH_2CH_3$

c. $CH_3CHCHCHCHCH_2CH_2CH_2CH_2CH_3$ with $CH_3$, $CH_3$ and $CH_3$, $CH_3$

d. (cyclooctane)

e. (cyclohexane with $H_3C$, $CH_3$ and $CH_3$)

f. (cyclopentane with $CH_2CH_3$, $CH_3$, $CH_3$)

12.53 a. 2-methylbutane: Number to give $CH_3$ the lower number, 2 not 3.
b. methylcyclopentane: no number assigned if only one substituent
c. 2-methylpentane: five-carbon chain
d. 2,5-dimethylheptane: longest chain not chosen
e. 1,3-dimethylcyclohexane: Number to give the second substituent the lower number.
f. 1-ethyl-2-propylcyclopentane: lower number assigned alphabetically

12.55 (cyclopentane with two $CH_3$)
1,2-dimethylcyclopentane

(cyclopentane with two $CH_3$)
1,3-dimethylcyclopentane

(cyclopentane with two $CH_3$)
1,1-dimethylcyclopentane

12.57 a. (zigzag chain)

b. (cyclopentane with two $CH_3$)

c. (branched chain)

**12.59** a.

b.

c.

**12.61** a.

b.

**12.63** a. $(CH_3)_4C$, $(CH_3)_2CHCH_2CH_3$, $CH_3CH_2CH_2CH_2CH_3$
b. $(CH_3)_2CHCH(CH_3)_2$, $CH_3CH_2CH_2CH(CH_3)_2$, $CH_3(CH_2)_4CH_3$

**12.65** Hexane is a nonpolar hydrocarbon and is soluble in organic solvents but not in water.

**12.67** a. $2\ CH_3CH_3 + 7\ O_2 \longrightarrow 4\ CO_2 + 6\ H_2O$
b. $(CH_3)_2CHCH_2CH_3 + 8\ O_2 \longrightarrow 5\ CO_2 + 6\ H_2O$

**12.69** a. $2\ CH_3CH_2CH_3 + 7\ O_2 \longrightarrow 6\ CO + 8\ H_2O$
b. $2\ CH_3CH_2CH_2CH_3 + 9\ O_2 \longrightarrow 8\ CO + 10\ H_2O$

**12.71** $C_6H_{12}O_6 + 6\ O_2 \longrightarrow 6\ CO_2 + 6\ H_2O$

**12.73** Higher molecular weight alkanes in warmer weather means less evaporation. Lower molecular weight alkanes in colder weather means the gasoline won't freeze.

**12.75** The mineral oil can prevent the body's absorption of important fat-soluble vitamins, which are expelled with the mineral oil.

**12.77** c. The nonpolar asphalt will be most soluble in the paint thinner because "like dissolves like."

**12.79** a. 3-ethyl-4,4-dimethylheptane
b. 
c. not water soluble
d. soluble in organic solvents
e. $C_{11}H_{24} + 17\ O_2 \longrightarrow 11\ CO_2 + 12\ H_2O$
f.

**12.81** a. propylcyclopentane
b.
c. not water soluble
d. soluble in organic solvents
e. $C_8H_{16} + 12\ O_2 \longrightarrow 8\ CO_2 + 8\ H_2O$
f.

**12.83** $C_{10}H_{18}$

**12.85** Cyclopentane has a more rigid structure. The rings can get closer together since they are not floppy, resulting in an increased force of attraction.

## CHAPTER 13

**13.1** a.

b.

c.

**13.3** a. $C_4H_8$  b. $C_6H_{14}$  c. $C_7H_{12}$  d. $C_5H_{10}$

**13.4** a. 3-methyl-1-pentene
b. 3-ethyl-3-heptene
c. 2,4-heptadiene
d. 3-ethylcyclopentene

**13.5** a. 2-methyl-3-nonyne  b. 6,6-dimethyl-3-octyne

**13.6** a. $CH_2=CHCH_2CHCH_2CH_3$ with $CH_3$
b. $CH_3C=CHCH_2CHCH_2CH_3$ with $CH_2CH_3$
c. $CH_3CHC\equiv CCHCH_3$ with $CH_3$
d.
e.
f. $CH_3CH_2CH_2CH_2CH_2CH_2CHCH_2C\equiv CH$ with $CH_2CH_3$

**13.7**　a. [structure: $C=C$ with $H$, $H$ on left carbon and $CH_3$, $CH_2CH_2CH_2CH_2CH_3$]

b. [structure: $C=C$ with $H$, $CH_2CH_2CH_3$ on one side and $CH_3CH_2$, $H$]

c. [structure: $C=C$ with $H$, $CHCH_3$ (bearing $CH_3$) and $CH_3$, $H$]

**13.9** [structure: conjugated diene labeled cis and trans; $HOCH_2(CH_2)_7CH_2$ ... $CH_2CH_2CH_3$]

**13.11** [structure: polyene chain $CH_3CH_2CH_2CH_2CH_2$—(four C=C units)—$CH_2CH_2CH_2COH$ with terminal $C=O$ (carboxylic acid)]

**13.13**　three aromatic rings, alkene, ether, amine

**13.15**　a. $CH_3CH_2CH_2CH_2CH_2CH_3$　　c. [cyclohexane with $CH_3$]

b. $CH_3CHCH_2CH_2CH(CH_3)_2$
　　　　　$CH_3$

**13.17**　a. $CH_3C$—$CCH_3$ (with Br, H)　　c. $CH_3$—$C$—$CCH_3$ (with $CH_3$, H and Cl, H)
　　　　　　　　Br H

b. [cyclohexane with Br, $CH_3$, H]　　d. [cyclopentane with $CH_3$, H, Cl, H]

**13.19**　a. $CH_3CH_2CH_2C$—$C$—$H$ (with H H, H H)　　d. $CH_3CH_2CH_2C$—$C$—$H$ (with H H, Br H)

b. $CH_3CH_2CH_2C$—$C$—$H$ (with H H, Cl Cl)　　e. $CH_3CH_2CH_2C$—$C$—$H$ (with H H, Cl H)

c. $CH_3CH_2CH_2C$—$C$—$H$ (with H H, Br Br)　　f. $CH_3CH_2CH_2C$—$C$—$H$ (with H H, HO H)

**13.21**　a. [polymer backbone with $CH_3$ and $CH_2$/$CH_2CH_3$ substituents]

b. [polymer backbone with $CH_3$ and CN substituents]

c. [polymer backbone with chlorophenyl (Cl) substituents]

**13.23**　a. propylbenzene
　　b. *p*-ethyliodobenzene
　　c. *m*-butylphenol
　　d. 2-bromo-5-chlorotoluene

**13.25**　Compound (a) might be found in a sunscreen since it contains two aromatic rings.

**13.27**　a. [benzene ring with Cl, Cl, Cl]　　c. [benzene ring with Cl, $SO_3H$, Cl]

b. [benzene ring with Cl, $NO_2$, Cl]

**13.29**　a. $C_{10}H_{12}O$
　　b. aromatic ring, alkene, ether
　　c. trans
　　d. [structure with tetrahedral labels, $CH_3$—$C$, $C$, $OCH_3$, tetrahedral]

　　　　All other C's are trigonal planar.

**13.31**　a. $C_{10}H_{22}$
　　b. $C_{10}H_{20}$
　　c. $C_{10}H_{18}$

**13.33**　$HC\equiv CCH_2CH_2CH_3$

　　$CH_3C\equiv CCH_2CH_3$

　　$HC\equiv C$—$C$—$H$ (with $CH_3$, $CH_3$)

13.35  a.

trigonal planar — tetrahedral

trigonal planar

linear

b.

—C≡CH

all trigonal planar

c.  tetrahedral — trigonal planar

13.37  a.  2-ethyl-1-butene       b.  2-hexyne
13.39  a.  5,5-dimethyl-1-hexene
       b.  3-ethyl-5,7-dimethyl-3-octene
       c.  2-ethyl-1-heptene
       d.  5,5-dimethyl-2-hexyne
       e.  6-ethyl-5,6-dimethyl-2-octyne
       f.  3,3-dimethyl-1,5-hexadiene
13.41  a.  4-methylcyclohexene
       b.  3,3-diethylcyclobutene

13.43  a.  CH₂=CHCHCH₂CH₂CH₂CH₃
                    |
                    CH₃

       b.  (cyclobutene with CH₂CH₃)

       c.  CH₃CH₂C≡CCCH₃
                       |
                       CH₃
                       |
                       H

       d.  CH₃CH₂CHC=C—CHCH₃
                 |    |     |
              CH₂CH₃ CH₃   CH₂CH₃
                 |
                 H

       e.  CH₂=CH—CH=CHCH₂CH₂CH₃

       f.  CH₃          CH₂CH₂CH₂CHCH₃
              \        /              |
               C=C                    CH₃
              /    \
             H      H

13.45  a.  Assign lower number to alkene: 2-methyl-2-hexene.
       b.  five-carbon chain: 2-pentene
       c.  Number to put the C=C between C1 and C2, and then give the
           first substituent the lower number: 1,6-dimethylcyclohexene.
       d.  seven-carbon chain: 3-methyl-1-heptyne
13.47

trans

cis

CH₃CH₂CH₂CH₂CH₂ ... CHCHCH₂CH₂CH₂COOH
                           S—CH₂
                           |
                           CHCONHCH₂COOH
                           |
                           NHCOCH₂CH₂CHCOOH
                                         |
                                         NH₂

13.49  cis alkene, cis-4-methyl-2-pentene

13.51  a.
        H        H
         \      /
          C=C
         /      \
       CH₃       CH₂CH₂CH₂CH₂CH₂CH₃
              cis-2-nonene

        H        CH₂CH₂CH₂CH₂CH₂CH₃
         \      /
          C=C
         /      \
       CH₃       H
              trans-2-nonene

       b.
               H        H
                \      /
                 C=C
                /      \
           CH₃CH        CH₂CH₂CH₃
              |
              CH₃
            cis-2-methyl-3-heptene

               H        CH₂CH₂CH₃
                \      /
                 C=C
                /      \
           CH₃CH        H
              |
              CH₃
            trans-2-methyl-3-heptene

13.53  Constitutional isomers have the same molecular formula but have
       the atoms bonded to different atoms. Stereoisomers have atoms
       bonded to the same atoms but in a different three-dimensional
       arrangement.
13.55  a.  identical       b.  constitutional isomers

13.57  a.  CH₃CH₂CH₂CH₂CH₂CH₃       c.  (cyclohexane with CH₃)

       b.  (CH₃)₂CHCH₂CH₂CH₂CH₃     d.  (cyclohexane with H, CH₃)

13.59  a.  (cyclobutane with Cl)     c.  CH₃CHCH₂CH(CH₃)₂
                                              |
                                              Cl

       b.  (CH₃)₂C—C(CH₃)₂           d.  (cyclohexane with CH₃, Cl)
               |   |
               Cl  H

13.61  a.  (cyclohexane with CH₂CH₃, H, H)
       b.  (cyclohexane with Cl, CH₂CH₃, Cl, H)
       c.  (cyclohexane with Br, CH₂CH₃, Br, H)
       d.  (cyclohexane with Cl, CH₂CH₃, H, H)
       e.  (cyclohexane with Br, CH₂CH₃, H, H)
       f.  (cyclohexane with OH, CH₂CH₃, H, H)

13.63  $CH_2\!=\!CH_2$    reagent: HBr

reagent: HCl

reagent: $Cl_2$

$CH_2\!=\!CHCH_2CH(CH_3)_2$    reagent: $Br_2$

13.65  a. HCl    d. HBr
b. $H_2$, Pd    e. $Br_2$
c. $H_2O$, $H_2SO_4$    f. $Cl_2$

13.67

13.69  a.    c.

b.

13.71

13.73

13.75  a. *p*-chloroethylbenzene    b. *o*-bromofluorobenzene
13.77  a. *m*-chloronitrobenzene
b. *p*-nitroaniline
c. *o*-butylethylbenzene
d. 2,5-dichlorophenol

13.79

*o*-chloroaniline

*p*-chloroaniline

*m*-chloroaniline

13.81  a.    d.

b.    e.

c.

13.83  a.    c.

b.

13.85

13.87  Vitamin E is an antioxidant.
13.89  Methoxychlor is more water soluble. The $OCH_3$ groups can
hydrogen bond to water. This increase in water solubility makes
methoxychlor more biodegradable.
13.91  a.

b. $CH_3CH_2CH_2CH_2CH_2CH_2CH_2CH_2CH_2CH_2CH_2CH_2CH_2CH_2CH_2CH_2CH_2CH_2COOH$

c.
one possibility:

13.93 c.

13.95 Benzene is converted to a more water-soluble compound that can then be excreted in the urine.

13.97 a.

CH$_3$(CH$_2$)$_5$    (CH$_2$)$_7$COOH

b.

CH$_3$(CH$_2$)$_5$    (CH$_2$)$_7$COOH

c.

CH$_3$(CH$_2$)$_4$    (CH$_2$)$_8$COOH    is one possibility

13.99 All the carbons in benzene are trigonal planar with 120° bond angles, resulting in a flat ring. In cyclohexane, all the carbons are tetrahedral so the ring is puckered.

13.101 a. CH$_2$=CH(CH$_2$)$_4$CH$_3$   1-heptene
b. CH$_3$(CH$_2$)$_5$CH$_3$
c. CH$_3$CH(OH)CH$_2$CH$_2$CH$_2$CH$_2$CH$_3$

d. ⊦CH$_2$C—CH$_2$C—CH$_2$C⊣   R = (CH$_2$)$_4$CH$_3$

13.103 They are constitutional isomers because the double bond is located in a different place on the carbon chain.

## CHAPTER 14

14.1 a.

b. The OH on the benzene ring of salmeterol is part of a phenol.

14.3 a. 3°     b. 1°     c. 2°

14.5 a.

b. (CH$_3$)$_3$C—OH

14.7 a. 2-heptanol          c. 2-methylcyclohexanol
b. 4-ethyl-3-hexanol       d. 5-ethyl-6-methyl-3-nonanol

14.9 a. CH$_3$—C=CH$_2$  b. ⬡—CH=CH$_2$  c. ⬠
         |
         H

14.11 **B** has no H on the carbon adjacent to the carbon with the OH group, so H$_2$O cannot be lost.

14.12 a. CH$_3$CCH$_2$CH$_2$CH$_3$       c. ⬠=O
          ‖
          O

b. (CH$_3$)$_3$CCH$_2$C—OH     d. no reaction

14.13 H—C—C—H  which is further oxidized to  HO—C—C—OH

14.15 a. CH$_3$(CH$_2$)$_5$OCH$_3$     c. CH$_3$(CH$_2$)$_6$OH

b.     d. CH$_3$(CH$_2$)$_5$OCH$_3$

14.17 a. 1-methoxybutane (or butyl methyl ether)
b. methoxycyclohexane
c. dipropyl ether

14.19

14.21 a. 3°
b. 2° OH on six-membered ring, 3° OH on five-membered ring, 1° OH bonded to CH$_2$ group

14.23 a. 2-bromohexane
b. 3-chloro-2-methylpentane
c. 1-bromo-2-methylcyclohexane

14.25 a. CFC     b. HCFC     c. HFC

14.26 a. 3-pentanethiol
b. cyclohexanethiol
c. 5-ethyl-1-heptanethiol

14.27

14.29 a. 1°   b. 3°   c. 2°   d. 2°
14.31 a. 2°   b. 3°   c. 2°   d. 1°

14.33 a. CH$_3$CH$_2$CHCH$_2$CH$_2$CH$_3$       c. CH$_3$CH$_2$C—Br
            |                                        |
            OH                                      CH$_3$   (with CH$_3$ top)

b. CH$_3$—O—CH$_2$CH$_2$CH$_2$CH$_2$CH$_3$

14.35

CH$_3$—O—CHCH$_2$CH$_3$    CH$_3$—O—CH$_2$CH$_2$CH$_2$CH$_3$    CH$_3$—C—O—CH$_3$
            |                                                              |
            CH$_3$                                                       CH$_3$

CH$_3$CH$_2$CH$_2$OCH$_2$CH$_3$    CH$_3$—C—O—CH$_2$CH$_3$    (CH$_3$)$_2$CHCH$_2$OCH$_3$
                                        |
                                        H

14.37 a. 2-methyl-3-pentanol      b. 1-chloro-2-methylcyclopentane
14.39 a. CH$_3$CH$_2$C(CH$_3$)$_2$CH(OH)CH$_3$
b. 2°
c. 3,3-dimethyl-2-pentanol

14.41 a. 2-pentanol
b. 3,3-dimethyl-2-hexanol
c. 4-ethyl-6-methyl-1-heptanol
d. 4-butylcyclohexanol
e. 2,2-dimethylcyclobutanol
f. 2,5-diethylcyclopentanol

14.43  a. CH$_3$CH$_2$CHCH$_2$CH$_2$CH$_3$ (with OH on the CH)

b. CH$_3$CH$_2$CH$_2$OH

c. cyclopropane with OH and CH$_3$ substituents

d. CH$_2$CHCH$_2$CH$_3$ (with OH OH on first two carbons)

e. CH$_3$CH$_2$—C—C—C—CH$_2$CH$_3$ (with CH$_3$ CH$_3$ H on top; H CH$_3$ OH on bottom)

f. HOCH$_2$CH$_2$CCH$_2$CCH$_2$CH$_3$ (with H H on top; CH$_3$ CH$_3$ on bottom)

14.45  a. 1-ethoxybutane (or butyl ethyl ether)
b. 2-ethoxypentane
c. ethoxycyclopentane

14.47  2-methoxy-2-methylpropane

14.49  CH$_3$CH$_2$CH$_2$CH$_2$CH$_2$CH$_2$CH$_2$OH     1-heptanol

CH$_3$CH$_2$CH$_2$CH$_2$CH$_2$CHCH$_3$ (with OH)     2-heptanol

CH$_3$CH$_2$CH$_2$CH$_2$CHCH$_2$CH$_3$ (with OH)     3-heptanol

CH$_3$CH$_2$CH$_2$CHCH$_2$CH$_2$CH$_3$ (with OH)     4-heptanol

14.51  a. 4-bromoheptane
b. 1-chloro-3-methylcyclobutane
c. 1-pentanethiol

14.53  a. CH$_3$—C—CH$_3$ (with OCH$_3$ on top, H on bottom)      d. CH$_3$CH$_2$CH$_2$CH$_2$Cl

b. cyclobutane with OCH$_2$CH$_3$

e. cyclohexane with SH and CH$_3$ substituents

c. cyclohexane with OCH$_2$CH$_3$ and CH$_2$CH$_3$ substituents

f. cyclobutane with CH$_2$CH$_3$ and F substituents

14.55  a. CH$_3$CH$_2$CH$_2$I      b. HOCH$_2$CH$_2$OH      c. CH$_3$CH$_2$CH$_2$OH

14.57  Ethanol is a polar molecule capable of hydrogen bonding with itself and water. The greater intermolecular forces make its boiling point higher. Both ethanol and dimethyl ether have only two carbons and can hydrogen bond to H$_2$O, so both are water soluble.

14.59  1-Butanol is capable of hydrogen bonding with H$_2$O and is therefore water soluble. 1-Butene is not polar and cannot hydrogen bond with H$_2$O, so it is not water soluble.

14.61  a. cyclobutene (square with double bond)

b. benzene ring with —CH=CHCH$_3$

c. CH$_3$CH=CHCH$_2$CH$_2$CH$_3$   (major product)   +   CH$_2$=CH(CH$_2$)$_3$CH$_3$

d. CH$_3$CH=CCH$_2$CH$_3$ (with CH$_3$)   (major product)   +   CH$_3$CH$_2$CCH$_2$CH$_3$ (with CH$_2$)

14.63  a. CH$_3$CH=CHCH$_2$CH$_2$CH$_3$   and   CH$_3$CH$_2$CH=CHCH$_2$CH$_3$

b. The carbons of both double bonds are bonded to an equal number of H's; therefore, equal amounts of both isomers are formed.

14.65  a. two phenyl groups attached to —C—C— (with H H on top; OH H on bottom)

b. cyclooctane with OH

14.67  CH$_3$CH$_2$CH$_2$OH   and   CH$_3$CHCH$_3$ (with OH)

14.69  a. CH$_3$(CH$_2$)$_6$COH (with O double bond)

c. CH$_3$CH$_2$CHCOH (with O double bond; CH$_3$ below)

b. CH$_3$CH$_2$CCH$_2$CH$_3$ (with O double bond)      d. no reaction

14.71  (steroid structure with CH$_3$, O, OH, C—COH groups)

14.73  a. cycloheptane with —OH

b. CH$_3$—C—CH (with CH$_3$ OH on top; CH$_3$ CH$_3$ on bottom)

c. benzene ring with C—H (with OH on top, H on bottom)

14.75  a. CH$_3$CH$_2$CH$_2$CH=CHCH$_2$CH$_3$

b. CH$_3$CH$_2$CH$_2$CCH$_2$CH$_2$CH$_3$ (with O double bond)

14.77  a. two cyclohexane rings connected by —S—S—

b. CH$_3$(CH$_2$)$_4$S—S(CH$_2$)$_4$CH$_3$

14.79  a. CH$_3$SH   and   HSCH$_2$CH$_2$CH$_3$
b. CH$_2$=CHCH$_2$SH   and   HSCH$_2$CH$_2$CH$_3$

14.81  C$_4$H$_{10}$O + 6 O$_2$ $\longrightarrow$ 4 CO$_2$ + 5 H$_2$O

14.83  a. CFCs are chlorofluorocarbons with a general formula of CF$_x$Cl$_{4-x}$, HCFCs have fluorine, chlorine, and hydrogen bonded to carbons, and HFCs have only hydrogen and fluorine bonded to carbon.

b. CFCs interact and destroy the ozone layer, whereas HCFCs and HFCs decompose before ascending to the ozone layer.

14.85  PEG is capable of hydrogen bonding with water and this makes it water soluble. PVC cannot hydrogen bond to water so it is water insoluble.

**14.87**

$$CH_3CH_2OH + K_2Cr_2O_7 \longrightarrow CH_3\overset{O}{\overset{\|}{C}}OH + Cr^{3+} \quad \text{(green color)}$$
(orange)

The greater the blood alcohol level, the greater the color change from red-orange to green on the Breathalyzer.

**14.89** $CH_3\overset{O}{\overset{\|}{C}}-\overset{O}{\overset{\|}{C}}OH$

pyruvic acid

**14.91**

$CH_3CH_2OH \longrightarrow$ acetaldehyde $\overset{O}{\overset{\|}{C}}$ $CH_3$ H $\xrightarrow{\text{Antabuse (blocks conversion)}}$ acetic acid $\overset{O}{\overset{\|}{C}}$ $CH_3$ OH

Antabuse blocks the conversion of acetaldehyde to acetic acid and the accumulation of acetaldehyde makes people ill.

**14.93** $(CH_3)_3COH$

**14.95** Ether molecules have no H's on O's capable of hydrogen bonding to other ether molecules, but the hydrogens in water can hydrogen bond to the oxygen of the ether.

**14.97**
a. 3-ethylcyclopentanol
b. 2°
c. [cyclopentene with CH₂CH₃] and [cyclopentene with CH₂CH₃]
d. [cyclopentanone with CH₂CH₃]
e. [cyclopentane with CH₂CH₃ and OH]
f. [cyclopentane with OCH₂CH₃]

**14.99** a. $CH_3CH_2\overset{CH_3}{\overset{|}{C}}CH_2OH$ **A**   b. $CH_3CH=\overset{CH_3}{\overset{|}{C}}-CH_3$
   $\overset{|}{H}$

$CH_3CH_2\overset{CH_3}{\underset{OH}{\overset{|}{C}}}CH_3$ **B**

# CHAPTER 15

**15.1**
a. constitutional isomers     c. identical
b. stereoisomers     d. constitutional isomers

**15.3** a, d: achiral     b, c: chiral

**15.5** a. $CH_3\overset{}{\underset{Cl}{\overset{|}{C}}HCH_2CH_3}$     c. $CH_2=CHCHCH_3$ $\overset{}{\underset{OH}{}}$

b. none     d. [benzene ring]$\overset{H}{\underset{Br}{\overset{|}{C}}}-CH_3$

**15.7**   a. $CH_3CH_2CH_2-\overset{H}{\underset{OH}{\overset{|}{C}}}-CH_3$

b. $H_2N-\overset{COOH}{\overset{|}{C}}-H$
   $CH_3-\overset{|}{\underset{|}{C}}-H$
   $\overset{|}{CH_2CH_3}$

c. $CH_3CH_2-\overset{Br}{\underset{H}{\overset{|}{C}}}-CH_2CH_2-\overset{Cl}{\underset{H}{\overset{|}{C}}}-CH_3$

**15.9** a. $\overset{CH_3}{\underset{Cl\ \ \ CH_2CH_3}{C}}H$   $\overset{CH_3}{\underset{CH_3CH_2\ \ \ Cl}{C}}H$

b. $\overset{OH}{\underset{H\ \ CH_2CH_3}{C}}$ $\overset{}{\underset{CH_2OH}{}}$   $\overset{HO}{\underset{CH_3CH_2\ \ H}{C}}$ $\overset{}{\underset{HOCH_2}{}}$

**15.11** $CH_3NH-$ [tetrahydronaphthalene ring system linked to dichlorophenyl, Cl, Cl]

**15.13** a. $\overset{CH_3}{\underset{Cl}{\overset{|}{\underset{}{H-\!\!\!-Br}}}}$   b. $\overset{COOH}{\underset{CH_2Cl}{\overset{|}{\underset{}{H-\!\!\!-OH}}}}$

**15.15** a. $CH_3-\overset{H}{\underset{OH}{|}}-CH_2CH_2CH_3$   $CH_3CH_2CH_2-\overset{H}{\underset{OH}{|}}-CH_3$

b. $ClCH_2-\overset{H}{\underset{Cl}{|}}-CH_2CH_3$   $CH_3CH_2-\overset{H}{\underset{Cl}{|}}-CH_2Cl$

**15.16** b. optically active; a, c, d: optically inactive
**15.17** optically inactive
**15.18** a. levorotatory     b. +32
**15.19** a. $\overset{COO^-}{\underset{H_3N^+}{\overset{|}{\underset{}{H\cdots C\cdots CH_3}}}}$   b. 297 °C   c. −8.5

(R)-alanine

**15.20** a. **Z**   b. **Y**   c. **Z** and **W**   d. **Y** and **X**

**15.21**

| $CH_3$ | $CH_3$ | $CH_3$ | $CH_3$ |
|---|---|---|---|
| H—Cl | H—Cl | Cl—H | Cl—H |
| H—Br | Br—H | H—Br | Br—H |
| $CH_2CH_3$ | $CH_2CH_3$ | $CH_2CH_3$ | $CH_2CH_3$ |
| **W** | **X** | **Y** | **Z** |

**15.23** a, d: achiral     b, c: chiral
**15.25** Butane does not have an enantiomer since the molecule and its mirror image *are* superimposable and therefore not enantiomers.

**15.27** a. $\overset{CF_3}{\underset{Cl\ \ H\ \ Br}{C}}$   b. $H-\overset{H}{\underset{Cl}{\overset{|}{\underset{}{C}}}}-Cl$

chiral     achiral

**15.29**  **B** enantiomer; **C** identical

**15.31**  a. none                  c. none

b. $CH_3CHCHCl_2$ (with Cl below)

d. $CH_3CCH_2CHCH_3$ (with $CH_3$, Cl above, H below)

**15.33**  a. none

c. (cyclopentene ring with $CH_3$)

b. (cyclohexene ring with OH)

d. none

**15.35**  a. $CH_3CH_2-\overset{\underset{|}{CH_3}}{\underset{H}{C}}-CH_2CH_2CH_3$

b. $CH_3CH_2-\overset{\underset{|}{OH}}{\underset{H}{C}}-CH_2CH_2CH_3$

**15.37**  A chirality center must have a carbon bonded to four groups and a carbonyl carbon has only three groups.

**15.39**  a. (pyridine-pyrrolidine structure with N–CH₃)

b. $HO_2CCH_2\overset{\underset{|}{NH_2}}{CH}\overset{\underset{||}{O}}{C}NH\overset{\underset{|}{CO_2CH_3}}{CH}CH_2-$ (phenyl)

**15.41**  (benzene)–$CH_2\overset{\underset{|}{H}}{C}\overset{\underset{|}{N}}{H}N CH_3$ with $CH_3$

(two structures with CH₃, H, CH₂, NHCH₃ and CH₃NH)

**15.43**  a. identical        b, c: enantiomers

**15.45**  a. constitutional isomers        c. identical
           b. enantiomers                  d. diastereomers

**15.47**  a. $CH_3CH_2\overset{\underset{|}{H}}{C}COOH$ with $CH_3$

c. $CH_3CH_2\overset{\underset{|}{OH}}{CH}CH_2\overset{\underset{||}{O}}{CH}$

b. $CH_3CH_2CH_2CH_2COOH$

**15.49**  $CH_3-\overset{\underset{|}{CHO}}{\underset{CH_3}{C}}-CH_3$        $CH_3-\overset{\underset{|}{CHO}}{\underset{H}{C}}\blacktriangleleft CH_2CH_3$  chirality center

$CH_3CH_2CH_2CH_2CHO$        $CH_3CHCH_2CHO$ with $CH_3$

**15.51**  $Br-\overset{\underset{|}{CHO}}{\underset{CH_3}{\phantom{C}}}-H$

**15.53**  a. $H-\overset{\underset{|}{CHO}}{\underset{CH_3}{C}}-OH$     b. $CH_3-\overset{\underset{|}{OCH_3}}{\underset{CH_2CH_3}{C}}-\overset{H}{OH}$

**15.55**  a. $H\blacktriangleright\overset{\underset{|}{CH_3}}{\underset{CH(CH_3)_2}{C}}\blacktriangleleft F$   b. $H\blacktriangleright\overset{\underset{|}{COOH}}{\underset{CH_2CH_3}{C}}\blacktriangleleft NH_2$ (with $CH_3\blacktriangleright C\blacktriangleleft H$)

**15.57**  a, d: identical        b, c: enantiomers

**15.59**  a. An optically active compound rotates the plane of polarized light. An optically inactive compound does not rotate the plane of polarized light.

b. one possibility: $CH_3CH_2CH_2CH_2OH$

c. one possibility:

$CH_3CH_2\overset{\underset{}{C}}{\phantom{x}}\overset{CH_3}{\underset{OH}{\phantom{x}}}H$

chiral and optically active

**15.61**  a. optically active        b, c: optically inactive

**15.63**  a. dextrorotatory        b. −52        c. 22 g

**15.65**  Enantiomers are stereoisomers that are nonsuperimposable mirror images of one another, whereas diastereomers are stereoisomers that are not mirror images of one another.

**15.67**  a. 1, 2, 5, 6: diastereomers        3, 4: enantiomers

b. $\underset{CH_2OH}{\overset{\underset{|}{C=O}}{\underset{|}{H\blacktriangleright C\blacktriangleleft OH}}}$ (with $CH_2OH$)

**15.69**  They are diastereomers because they are not mirror images of one another.

**15.71**  a. $CH_3CHCO_2H$ with $OH$

b. $CH_3\blacktriangleright\overset{\underset{|}{H}}{\underset{OH}{C}}\blacktriangleleft COOH$   $HOOC\blacktriangleright\overset{\underset{|}{H}}{\underset{OH}{C}}\blacktriangleleft CH_3$

c. $CH_3-\overset{\underset{|}{H}}{\underset{OH}{C}}-COOH$   $HOOC-\overset{\underset{|}{H}}{\underset{OH}{C}}-CH_3$

**15.73**  a. $CH_3\overset{\underset{|}{OH}}{C}CH_2CH_2CH_2\overset{\underset{|}{CH_3}}{CH}-CH_2CHO$

b. $CH_3\overset{\underset{|}{HO}}{C}CH_2CH_2CH_2\blacktriangleright\overset{\underset{|}{CH_3}}{\underset{H}{C}}\blacktriangleleft CH_2CHO$   $OHCCH_2\blacktriangleright\overset{\underset{|}{CH_3}}{\underset{H}{C}}\blacktriangleleft CH_2CH_2CH_2\overset{\underset{|}{OH}}{\underset{CH_3}{C}}CH_3$

c. $CH_3\overset{\underset{|}{HO}}{\underset{CH_3}{C}}CH_2CH_2CH_2-\overset{\underset{|}{CH_3}}{\underset{H}{\phantom{C}}}-CH_2CHO$   $OHCCH_2-\overset{\underset{|}{CH_3}}{\underset{H}{\phantom{C}}}-CH_2CH_2CH_2\overset{\underset{|}{OH}}{\underset{CH_3}{C}}CH_3$

**15.75** a.

$CH_3CH_2CO_2$—C (with $CH_2$–phenyl above, phenyl to the right)
$CH_3$—C—H
$CH_2N(CH_3)_2$

b.

$CH_2$ (phenyl above), phenyl to left, C—$O_2CCH_2CH_3$
H—C—$CH_3$
$CH_2N(CH_3)_2$

c.

$CH_3CH_2CO_2$—C ($CH_2$-phenyl above, phenyl right)
H—C—$CH_3$
$CH_2N(CH_3)_2$

d.

$CH_2$ (phenyl above), $CH_3$—C—phenyl
$CH_3CH_2CO_2$—C—H
$CH_2N(CH_3)_2$

e.

$CH_3CH_2CO_2$—C ($CH_2$-phenyl above, phenyl right)
$CH_3$—C—H
$CH_2N(CH_3)_2$

**15.77** ✶ = chirality center

HOCH₂ / HO / HO / OH ring with HOCH₂, OH, OH, O, CH₂OH, CH₂OH ring (disaccharide structure with chirality centers marked ✶)

# CHAPTER 16

**16.1** a.

$CH_3CH_2$—C(=O)—H    aldehyde

b.

$CH_3CH_2$—C(=O)—$CH_3$    ketone

c.

$(CH_3)_3C$—C(=O)—$CH_3$    ketone

d.

$(CH_3CH_2)_2CH$—C(=O)—H    aldehyde

**16.3** (terpene structure with cyclohexene ring, $CH_3$ groups, conjugated double bonds, terminal CHO — retinal-like structure)

**16.4** a. 5-methylhexanal
b. 3,3,4,4-tetramethylpentanal
c. 2,5,6-trimethyloctanal

**16.5** a. $CH_3CHClCHO$ (Cl on the carbon)

b. $CH_3CH_2CHCHCHCH_2CHO$ with $CH_3CH_2$, $CH_2CH_3$ substituents and $CH_2CH_3$

c. $CH_3CH_2CH_2CHCH_2CH_2CHCHCH_2CHO$ with $CH_2CH_3$ and $CH_2CH_3$ substituents

d. (benzene ring)—CHO with $CH_2CH_3$ ortho substituent

**16.7** a. 4-methyl-3-heptanone
b. 2-methylcyclopentanone
c. 2,2-dimethyl-3-heptanone

**16.9** a. (cyclohexanone ring)=O
b. $(CH_3CH_2)_2CO$
c. (cyclohexane ring)—OH
d. $CH_3(CH_2)_5CHO$

**16.11** Hexane is soluble in acetone because both compounds are organic and "like dissolves like." Water is soluble in acetone because acetone has a short hydrocarbon chain and is capable of hydrogen bonding with water.

**16.13** a.

$CH_3CH_2$—C(=O)—OH

b. no reaction

c. $CH_3C{=}CHCH_2CH_2CHCH_2C$—OH with two $CH_3$ groups and C(=O)

**16.14** a. $CH_3(CH_2)_6C(=O)$—OH

c. (cyclopentane ring)—C(=O)—OH

b, d: no reaction

**16.15**  a. $CH_3CH_2CH_2CH_2$—OH    c. $CH_3CHCH_2CH_3$ (OH)

b. cyclopentane with OH and $CH_3$ substituents

d. benzene ring—$CH_2OH$

**16.17**  a. stereoisomers    b. not isomers    c. stereoisomers

**16.18**  a. $CH_3\overset{OCH_3}{\underset{H}{C}}OH$    $CH_3\overset{OCH_3}{\underset{H}{C}}OCH_3$

      hemiacetal      acetal

b. $(CH_3CH_2)_2\overset{OCH_3}{C}OH$    $(CH_3CH_2)_2\overset{OCH_3}{C}OCH_3$

      hemiacetal      acetal

c. benzene—$\overset{OCH_2CH_3}{C}HOH$    benzene—$\overset{OCH_2CH_3}{C}HOCH_2CH_3$

      hemiacetal      acetal

**16.19**  a. ether    b. acetal    c. hemiacetal    d. acetal

**16.20**  a. sugar ring structure (hemiacetal indicated)

b. sugar ring structure (acetal indicated)

**16.21**  a. tetrahydropyran ring with $OCH_2CH_3$

b. tetrahydrofuran ring with O—cyclohexyl

**16.22**  a. $CH_3\overset{O}{\underset{}{C}}CH_2CH_2CH_3$  +  2 $CH_3OH$

b. cyclohexanone  +  2 $CH_3CH_2OH$

c. cyclohexyl—$\overset{O}{\underset{H}{C}}$  +  2 $CH_3OH$

**16.23**  a. $CH_3CH_2CH_2\overset{CH_2CH_3}{CH}CH_2CHO$    c. cyclopentanone

b. $CH_3CH_2\overset{O}{C}\overset{}{CH}CH_3$ (with $CH_3$)    d. cyclopentane—$\overset{O}{\underset{H}{C}}$

**16.25**  a. Both are trigonal planar.
b. C=O is polar and C=C is not.
c. Both functional groups undergo addition reactions.

**16.27**  No, it cannot. $C_5H_{12}O$ has too many H's. Since an aldehyde has a double bond, the number of C's and H's resembles an alkene, not an alkane. A compound with 5 C's would have to be $C_5H_{10}O$.

**16.29**  a. 2-methylpentanal    b. 3-ethylcyclohexanone

**16.31**  a. 3-methylhexanal
b. 3,5-dimethylheptanal
c. 3-propylhexanal
d. 6,6-diethyl-2,2-dimethyloctanal
e. p-chlorobenzaldehyde

**16.33**  a. $CH_3CH_2\overset{Cl}{\underset{Cl}{C}}CH_2CHO$    c. benzene ring with CHO and Br

b. $CH_3CH_2\overset{CH_3}{CH}\underset{CH_3}{CH}CH_2CHO$    d. $CH_3CH_2CH_2\overset{OH}{CH}CH_2CH_2CHO$

**16.35**  a. 4-methyl-2-pentanone
b. 2,6-dimethylcyclohexanone
c. o-butylacetophenone
d. 2,4-dimethyl-3-hexanone
e. 3-chlorocyclopentanone

**16.37**  a. $CH_3CH_2CH_2\overset{CH_3}{\underset{CH_3}{C}}\overset{O}{C}CH_3$    c. benzene ring with $\overset{O}{C}CH_3$ and $CH_2CH_3$

b. $CH_3\overset{O}{C}CH_2CH_2CH_3$    d. cyclohexanone ring with $CH_2CH_3$, $CH_3CH_2$, $CH_2CH_3$

**16.39**  $CH_3CH_2\overset{CH_3}{\underset{CH_3}{C}}CHO$    $CH_3\overset{CH_3}{\underset{CH_3}{C}}CH_2CHO$
    2,2-dimethylbutanal    3,3-dimethylbutanal

$CH_3\overset{CH_3}{CH}\underset{CH_3}{CH}CHO$    $CH_3CH_2\overset{CH_2CH_3}{CH}CHO$
    2,3-dimethylbutanal    2-ethylbutanal

**16.41**  a. $CH_3CH_2CH_2CH_2\overset{O}{CH}$    c. $CH_3CH_2CH_2\overset{O}{C}\underset{CH_3}{CH}CCH_3$
    pentanal

                          3-methyl-2-hexanone

b. $CH_3CH_2CH_2\overset{O}{C}CH_2CH_3$    d. $CH_3CH_2CH_2CH_2CH_2CH_2\overset{O}{CH}\underset{CH_3}{CH}$
    3-hexanone

                          2-methyloctanal

**16.43**

**16.45** a. $(CH_3)_3CCH_2CHO$

b. (cyclopentyl)—$CH_2CH_2OH$

**16.47** —$CH_3$   =O   —OH

**16.49** a. insoluble   b. soluble   c. insoluble

**16.51** 2,3-Butanedione has two carbonyl groups capable of hydrogen bonding, whereas acetone has one carbonyl group. It would be soluble in diethyl ether.

**16.53** a. $CH_3(CH_2)_4COOH$   c. no reaction

b. —$CH_2COOH$   d. $CH_3(CH_2)_4COOH$

**16.55** a. $CH_3(CH_2)_4COOH$   c. no reaction

b. —$CH_2COOH$   d. no reaction

**16.57** a, b:

$$HOCH_2-\overset{O}{\underset{}{C}}-\overset{OH}{\underset{}{CH}}-CH_2OH$$
ketone   2°   1°

c. no reaction

d. $$HO_2C-\overset{O}{\underset{}{C}}-\overset{O}{\underset{}{C}}-CO_2H$$

**16.59** a. $CH_3CH_2\overset{CH_3}{\underset{}{CH}}CH_2CHO$   c. $CH_3CH_2\overset{}{\underset{CHO}{CH}}CH_2CH_3$

b. $CH_3$——CHO

**16.61** a. $CH_3CH_2$——$CH_2OH$   b.

**16.63** a, b: $CH_3CH_2-\overset{CH_3}{\underset{}{CH}}-(CH_2)_4CHO$
chirality center

c. $CH_3CH_2-\overset{CH_3}{\underset{}{CH}}-(CH_2)_4CH_2OH$

**16.65** a. $CH_3CH_2CH_2CH_2\overset{O}{\underset{}{C}}H$   b.

**16.67** 1-Methylcyclohexanol is a 3° alcohol and cannot be produced from the reduction of a carbonyl compound.

**16.69** a. $CH_3CH_2-O-\overset{H}{\underset{H}{C}}-O-CH_2CH_3$

b. $CH_3-\overset{H}{\underset{OH}{C}}-O-CH_2CH_2CH_3$

c. $CH_3CH_2-O-\overset{H}{\underset{H}{C}}-\overset{H}{\underset{H}{C}}-O-CH_3$

d. $CH_3-\overset{H}{\underset{H}{C}}-O-\overset{H}{\underset{H}{C}}-\overset{OH}{\underset{H}{C}}-CH_3$

**16.71** a. $CH_3-\overset{OCH_3}{\underset{OCH_3}{C}}-H$  acetal

c. $HOCH_2\overset{OCH_3}{\underset{}{CH}}CH_2CH_3$  ether, alcohol

b. $CH_3-\overset{OCH_2CH_3}{\underset{OH}{C}}-H$  hemiacetal

d. ether

**16.73** a.

b. $CH_2(OCH_3)_2$

c. $CH_3-\overset{CH_3O}{\underset{CH_2CH_2CH_3}{C}}-OCH_3$

d.

**16.75** a. $CH_3-\overset{OH}{\underset{CH_3}{C}}-O-$

b. $CH_3-\overset{(cyclopentyl-O)}{\underset{CH_3}{C}}-O-$

**16.77** a. hemiacetal carbon

c.

b. $HOCH_2CH_2CH_2\overset{O}{\underset{}{C}}H$

**16.79**

**16.81** a. =O + 2 $HOCH_2CH_2CH_3$

b. $H-\overset{O}{\underset{}{C}}-CH_2CH_2CH_3$ + 2 $HOCH_3$

**16.83**   a. (structure: CH₃–benzene ring–C(=O)–CH₃)    c. seven

b. *p*-methylacetophenone

d. (structure: CH₃–benzene ring–C(OCH₃)₂–CH₃)

**16.85**   a. (benzene ring–CH₂OH)

b. (benzene ring–C(=O)OH)

c. (benzene ring–C(=O)OH)

d. (benzene ring–C(OCH₃)₂–H)

e. (benzene ring–CH(OCH₂CH₃)₂)

f. (benzene ring–C(=O)H)

**16.87**   a. $CH_3-\overset{OH}{\underset{H}{C}}-(CH_2)_4CH_3$

b, c:  no reaction

d. $CH_3-\overset{OCH_3}{\underset{OCH_3}{C}}-(CH_2)_4CH_3$

e. $CH_3-\overset{OCH_2CH_3}{\underset{OCH_2CH_3}{C}}-(CH_2)_4CH_3$

f. $CH_3-\overset{O}{\overset{\|}{C}}-(CH_2)_4CH_3$

**16.89**

$CH_2=CHCH_2CH_2CHO$   $CH_3CH=CHCH_2CHO$   $CH_3CH_2CH=CHCHO$

**16.91**   a. (steroid structure with OH and CH₃ groups, CH₃, HO)

b. (steroid structure with CH₃, O groups)

c. (steroid structure with OCH₃, OCH₃, CH₃, HO)

d. (steroid structure with OCH₂CH₃, OCH₂CH₃, CH₃, HO)

**16.93**   (structure: benzene ring–CH=CH–C(=O)–OH)

**16.95**   (cyclic structure: HOCH₂, ring with O, OH — labeled hemiacetal; alcohol → HO)

**16.97**   The cis double bond in 11-*cis*-retinal produces crowding, making the molecule unstable. Light energy converts this to the more stable trans isomer, and with this conversion an electrical impulse is generated in the optic nerve.

**16.99**   (complex polyether structure with labels: alcohol, carboxylic acid, acetal, ether, hemiacetal, alcohol)

## CHAPTER 17

**17.1**   a. $CH_3CH_2-\overset{O}{\overset{\|}{C}}-OCH_2CH_3$  ester

c. $(CH_3)_3C-\overset{O}{\overset{\|}{C}}-OH$  carboxylic acid

b. $CH_3-\overset{O}{\overset{\|}{C}}-\overset{}{\underset{H}{N}}-CH_3$  amide

d. $(CH_3)_2CH-\overset{O}{\overset{\|}{C}}-N(CH_3)_2$  amide

**17.3**   a. aromatic ring, two carboxyl groups, two amines, one amide
b. nine

**17.4**   a. 3,3-dimethylhexanoic acid      c. 2,4-diethylhexanoic acid
b. 4-chloropentanoic acid

**17.5**   a. $CH_3CH_2\overset{}{\underset{Br}{CH}}-\overset{O}{\overset{\|}{C}}-OH$

b. $CH_3CH_2\overset{CH_3}{\underset{CH_3}{CH}CH}-\overset{O}{\overset{\|}{C}}-OH$

c. $CH_3CH_2CH_2\overset{CH_3}{\underset{CH_3}{C}}CH_2CH_2\overset{}{\underset{CH_2CH_3}{CH}}-\overset{O}{\overset{\|}{C}}-OH$

d. $CH_3CH_2CH_2CH_2\overset{CH_3CH_2}{CH}\overset{CH_2CH_3}{CH}CHCH_2-\overset{O}{\overset{\|}{C}}-OH$ (with CH₃CH₂ and CH₂CH₃ substituents)

**17.6**  a. methyl hexanoate
b. ethyl benzoate
c. propyl pentanoate

**17.7**  a.

$$CH_3CH_2-\overset{\overset{\displaystyle O}{\|}}{C}-OCH_2CH_2CH_3$$

b.

$$CH_3-\overset{\overset{\displaystyle O}{\|}}{C}-OCH_2CH_2CH_2CH_3$$

c.

$$CH_3CH_2CH_2CH_2CH_2-\overset{\overset{\displaystyle O}{\|}}{C}-OCH_2CH_3$$

d.

Ph$-\overset{\overset{\displaystyle O}{\|}}{C}-OCH_3$

**17.8**  a. pentanamide
b. N-methylbenzamide
c. N,N-dipropylformamide

**17.9**  a.

$$CH_3CH_2-\overset{\overset{\displaystyle O}{\|}}{C}-NH_2$$

b.

$$CH_3CH_2CH_2CH_2CH_2-\overset{\overset{\displaystyle O}{\|}}{C}-\overset{\underset{\displaystyle H}{\big|}}{N}-CH_2CH_3$$

c.

$$CH_3-\overset{\overset{\displaystyle O}{\|}}{C}-\overset{\underset{\displaystyle CH_3}{\big|}}{N}-CH_3$$

d.

$$CH_3CH_2CH_2-\overset{\overset{\displaystyle O}{\|}}{C}-\overset{\underset{\displaystyle CH_3}{\big|}}{N}-CH_2CH_2CH_2CH_3$$

**17.11**

cyclohexyl-CH$_2$CH$_2$CH$_2$CH$_3$   cyclohexyl-COOCH$_3$   cyclohexyl-CH$_2$COOH

lowest bp                                    highest bp
least water soluble                          most water soluble

**17.13**  PGF$_{2\alpha}$ is more water soluble since it has a COOH and three OH groups.

**17.15**  a.

cyclohexyl$-\overset{\overset{\displaystyle O}{\|}}{C}-O^-Na^+$  +  $H_2O$

b.

$$CH_3CH_2CH_2-\overset{\overset{\displaystyle O}{\|}}{C}-O^-Na^+ \quad + \quad Na^+HCO_3^-$$

**17.17**  a. sodium butanoate       b. lithium benzoate

**17.19**

$$CH_3CH_2CH_2CH_2CH_2CH_2CH_2CH_2CH_2CH_2CH_2CH_2CH_2CH_2CH_2-\overset{\overset{\displaystyle O}{\|}}{C}-O^-K^+$$

**17.21**  a.

$(CH_3)_2CHCH_2-$〔ring〕$-\overset{\underset{\displaystyle }{}}{\underset{\displaystyle CH_3}{CH}}COOH$  +  NaOH

$\longrightarrow$  $(CH_3)_2CHCH_2-$〔ring〕$-\underset{\displaystyle CH_3}{CH}COO^-Na^+$  +  $H_2O$

b. The neutral form is present in the stomach.
c. The ionized form is present in the small intestines.

**17.22**  a.

$(CH_3)_2CH-\overset{\overset{\displaystyle O}{\|}}{C}-OCH_2CH_3$

b.

$H-\overset{\overset{\displaystyle O}{\|}}{C}-OCH_2CH_3$

c.

$CH_3(CH_2)_6-\overset{\overset{\displaystyle O}{\|}}{C}-OCH_2CH_3$

d.

cyclohexyl$-\overset{\overset{\displaystyle O}{\|}}{C}-OCH_2CH_3$

**17.23**

(2,5-dimethoxyphenyl)$-CH_2O-\overset{\overset{\displaystyle O}{\|}}{C}-CH_2CH(CH_3)_2$

(with OCH$_3$ groups at positions shown and OCH$_3$)

**17.25**  a.

$$CH_3CH_2CH_2CH_2-\overset{\overset{\displaystyle O}{\|}}{C}-NH_2$$

b.

$$CH_3CH_2CH_2CH_2-\overset{\overset{\displaystyle O}{\|}}{C}-\overset{\underset{\displaystyle CH_3}{\big|}}{N}-CH_3$$

c.

$$CH_3CH_2CH_2CH_2-\overset{\overset{\displaystyle O}{\|}}{C}-\overset{\underset{\displaystyle H}{\big|}}{N}-cyclohexyl$$

d.

$$CH_3CH_2CH_2CH_2-\overset{\overset{\displaystyle O}{\|}}{C}-\overset{\underset{\displaystyle H}{\big|}}{N}-CH_3$$

**17.27**  a.

$CH_3(CH_2)_8-\overset{\overset{\displaystyle O}{\|}}{C}-OH$  +  $CH_3OH$

b.

$CH_3CHCH_2-\overset{\overset{\displaystyle O}{\|}}{C}-OH$  +  $CH_3CH_2OH$ (with CH$_3$ branch)

c.

cyclohexyl$-\overset{\overset{\displaystyle O}{\|}}{C}-OH$  +  $CH_3CH_2CH_2OH$

**17.29**

(2-hydroxyphenyl)$-COOH$  +  $CH_3\overset{\overset{\displaystyle O}{\|}}{C}OH$

**17.30 a.** $CH_3(CH_2)_8\overset{O}{\underset{}{C}}OH$ + $NH_4^+\ HSO_4^-$

**b.** $CH_3\underset{CH_3}{\underset{|}{CH}}CH_2\overset{O}{\underset{}{C}}OH$ + $(CH_3NH_3)^+\ HSO_4^-$

**c.** (cyclohexyl)$\overset{O}{\underset{}{C}}OH$ + $\left[(CH_3CH_2CH_2)_2NH_2\right]^+\ HSO_4^-$

**17.31 a.** $CH_3(CH_2)_8\overset{O}{\underset{}{C}}O^-Na^+$ + $NH_3$

**b.** $CH_3\underset{CH_3}{\underset{|}{CH}}CH_2\overset{O}{\underset{}{C}}O^-Na^+$ + $CH_3NH_2$

**c.** (cyclohexyl)$\overset{O}{\underset{}{C}}O^-Na^+$ + $(CH_3CH_2CH_2)_2NH$

**17.33** $H_2N-(CH_2)_6-NH_2$ + $HO-\overset{O}{\underset{}{C}}-(CH_2)_8-\overset{O}{\underset{}{C}}-OH$

**17.35** Polyesters can be converted back to their monomers by acid hydrolysis. The strong C—C bonds in polyethylene are not easily broken.

**17.37 a.** $CH_3\underset{CH_3}{\overset{CH_3}{\underset{|}{\overset{|}{C}}}}CH_2CH_2CH_2\overset{O}{\underset{}{C}}OH$

**c.** (cyclobutyl)$\overset{O}{\underset{}{C}}OCH_3$

**b.** $CH_3CH_2CH_2CH_2\overset{O}{\underset{}{C}}OCH_3$

**d.** (cyclobutyl with $CH_3$)$\overset{O}{\underset{}{C}}OH$

**17.39 a.** $CH_3CH_2CH_2CH_2\overset{O}{\underset{}{C}}NH_2$

**c.** $CH_3CH_2\overset{O}{\underset{}{C}}\underset{CH_3}{\underset{|}{N}}-CH_3$

**b.** $CH_3CH_2\overset{O}{\underset{}{C}}\underset{H}{\underset{|}{N}}-CH_2CH_3$

**17.41** $CH_3CH_2\overset{O}{\underset{}{C}}O-CH_3$   $CH_3\overset{O}{\underset{}{C}}O-CH_2CH_3$

$H\overset{O}{\underset{}{C}}OCH_2CH_2CH_3$   $H\overset{O}{\underset{}{C}}OCH(CH_3)_2$

**17.43** A lactone is a cyclic ester and a lactam is a cyclic amide.

**17.45 a.** 4-methylpentanamide  **c.** *o*-chlorobenzoic acid
**b.** ethyl formate

**17.47 a.** 4-methylpentanoic acid  **c.** 2-ethylheptanoic acid
**b.** 4,5-diethyloctanoic acid

**17.49 a.** propyl butanoate  **b.** butyl benzoate

**17.51 a.** hexanamide
**b.** *N*-ethyl-*N*-methylbenzamide

**17.53 a.** formamide  **c.** 2-hydroxybutanoic acid
**b.** lithium acetate  **d.** propyl propanoate

**17.55 a.** $CH_3CH_2CH_2CH_2CH_2\underset{OH}{\underset{|}{CH}}\overset{O}{\underset{}{C}}OH$

**b.** $CH_3CH_2CH_2CH_2CH_2\underset{Cl}{\underset{|}{CH}}CH_2CH_2\overset{O}{\underset{}{C}}OH$

**c.** (dibromophenyl)$\overset{O}{\underset{}{C}}OH$ with Br, Br

**d.** $CH_3CH_2\overset{O}{\underset{}{C}}O^-Li^+$

**e.** $CH_3CH_2\underset{Br}{\overset{Br}{\underset{|}{\overset{|}{C}}}}\overset{O}{\underset{}{C}}OH$

**f.** $CH_3\underset{CH_3}{\underset{|}{CH}}\overset{O}{\underset{}{C}}O-CH_2CH_3$

**17.57 a.** $H\overset{O}{\underset{}{C}}OCH_2CH_2CH_3$

**b.** $CH_3CH_2CH_2\overset{O}{\underset{}{C}}OCH_2CH_2CH_2CH_3$

**c.** (phenyl)$\overset{O}{\underset{}{C}}OCH_2CH_2CH_2CH_2CH_2CH_2CH_3$

**d.** $CH_3CH_2CH_2CH_2CH_2\overset{O}{\underset{}{C}}NHCH_2CH_3$

**e.** $CH_3CH_2CH_2CH_2CH_2CH_2\overset{O}{\underset{}{C}}\underset{CH_3}{\underset{|}{N}}-CH_2CH_3$

**17.59** $CH_3CH_2CH_2CH_2\overset{O}{\underset{}{C}}OH$   $CH_3\underset{CH_3}{\underset{|}{CH}}CH_2\overset{O}{\underset{}{C}}OH$

pentanoic acid   3-methylbutanoic acid

$CH_3CH_2\underset{CH_3}{\underset{|}{CH}}\overset{O}{\underset{}{C}}OH$   $CH_3\underset{CH_3}{\overset{CH_3}{\underset{|}{\overset{|}{C}}}}\overset{O}{\underset{}{C}}OH$

2-methylbutanoic acid   2,2-dimethylpropanoic acid

17.61 (a) $HCO_2CH_3$ can hydrogen bond to water.
(b) $CH_3CH_2COOH$ can hydrogen bond to itself and to water.

17.63 $CH_3CH_2CH(CH_3)_2 < CH_3CH_2COCH_3 < CH_3CH_2CO_2H$

17.65 $CH_3CH_2CONH_2$ can intermolecularly hydrogen bond, so it has stronger intermolecular forces.

17.67 a. $CH_3(CH_2)_3\overset{\displaystyle O}{\overset{\|}{C}}O^-K^+ \;+\; H_2O$

b. $(CH_3)_2CHCH_2CH_2\overset{\displaystyle O}{\overset{\|}{C}}O^-Na^+ \;+\; NaHCO_3$

17.69 a. $CH_3CH_2CH_2\overset{\displaystyle O}{\overset{\|}{C}}OCH_3$

b. $CH_3CH_2CH_2\overset{\displaystyle O}{\overset{\|}{C}}OCH_2CH_2CH_3$

c. $CH_3CH_2CH_2\overset{\displaystyle O}{\overset{\|}{C}}O-\text{cyclohexyl}$

d. $CH_3CH_2CH_2\overset{\displaystyle O}{\overset{\|}{C}}O-CH_2CH_2-\text{phenyl}$

17.71 $HO-\text{(C}_6\text{H}_4\text{)}-CO_2H$ and $CH_3OH$

17.73 a. $CH_3CH_2CH_2\overset{\displaystyle O}{\overset{\|}{C}}NH_2$

b. $CH_3CH_2CH_2\overset{\displaystyle O}{\overset{\|}{C}}\underset{H}{N}-CH_2CH_3$

c. $CH_3CH_2CH_2\overset{\displaystyle O}{\overset{\|}{C}}\underset{CH_2CH_3}{N}-CH_2CH_3$

d. $CH_3CH_2CH_2\overset{\displaystyle O}{\overset{\|}{C}}\underset{CH_2CH_3}{N}-CH_3$

17.75 a. cyclohexyl$-\overset{\displaystyle O}{\overset{\|}{C}}OH \;+\; CH_3OH$

b. $HO\overset{\displaystyle O}{\overset{\|}{C}}CH_3 \;+\;$ cyclohexyl$-OH$

17.77 $CH_3CH_2O-\text{(C}_6\text{H}_4\text{)}-NH_2 \;+\; HO\overset{\displaystyle O}{\overset{\|}{C}}CH_3$

17.79 a. $CH_3CH_2CH_2\overset{\displaystyle O}{\overset{\|}{C}}OH \;+\; HOCH(CH_3)_2$

b. decalin$-OH \;+\; HO\overset{\displaystyle O}{\overset{\|}{C}}CH_3$

c. cyclohexyl$-CH_2CH_2-OH \;+\; HO-\overset{\displaystyle}{\overset{}{C}}\overset{O}{\underset{H}{}}$

17.81 a. $\text{(benzene ring)}\overset{\displaystyle O}{\overset{\|}{C}}OH \;+\; NH_4^+\,Cl^-$
(with $OCH_3$ substituent)

b. $(CH_3)_3C\overset{\displaystyle O}{\overset{\|}{C}}OH \;+\; [(CH_3)_2NH_2]^+Cl^-$

c. $[\text{cyclohexyl}-NH_3]^+\,Cl^- \;+\; HO\overset{\displaystyle O}{\overset{\|}{C}}CH_3$

17.83 $\text{(phenyl)}-CH_2-\overset{\displaystyle O}{\overset{\|}{C}}OH \;+\; CH_3CH_2OH$

17.85 $HO-\overset{\displaystyle O}{\overset{\|}{C}}-\text{(C}_6\text{H}_4\text{)}-\overset{\displaystyle O}{\overset{\|}{C}}-OH \quad NH_2-(CH_2)_4-NH_2$

17.87 $\{-O-\overset{\displaystyle O}{\overset{\|}{C}}-\text{(C}_6\text{H}_4\text{)}-\overset{\displaystyle O}{\overset{\|}{C}}-OCH_2CH_2CH_2O-\overset{\displaystyle O}{\overset{\|}{C}}-\text{(C}_6\text{H}_4\text{)}-\overset{\displaystyle O}{\overset{\|}{C}}-O-CH_2CH_2CH_2-\}$

17.89 Saponification is the hydrolysis of an ester with strong base and forms a metal salt, $RCOO^-M^+$. Esterification forms a new ester, $RCOOR'$.

17.91 a. $CH_3\overset{\displaystyle O}{\overset{\|}{C}}OCH_3$

b. $(CH_3)_2CHOH \;+\; HO\overset{\displaystyle O}{\overset{\|}{C}}CH_3$

c. $Na^+{}^-O\overset{\displaystyle O}{\overset{\|}{C}}CH(CH_3)_2 \;+\; (CH_3)_2CHCH_2OH$

d. $CH_3(CH_2)_4\overset{\displaystyle O}{\overset{\|}{C}}O^-Na^+ \;+\; H_2O$

**17.93** a. 5-methylhexanoic acid

b. $CH_3CH_2CHCH_2CH_2$ — with $CH_3$ branch, $\overset{O}{\underset{}{C}}$—OH

c. $CH_3CH_2CH_2CH_2CH_2$ —$\overset{O}{\underset{}{C}}$—$OCH_3$

d. $CH_3CHCH_2CH_2CH_2$—$\overset{O}{\underset{}{C}}$—$O^-Na^+$ + $H_2O$, with $CH_3$ branch

e. **A** is insoluble in $H_2O$, but soluble in organic solvent.

f. $CH_3CHCH_2CH_2CH_2$—$\overset{O}{\underset{}{C}}$—$OCH_2CH_3$, with $CH_3$ branch

g. $CH_3CHCH_2CH_2CH_2$—$\overset{O}{\underset{}{C}}$—$NHCH_2CH_3$, with $CH_3$ branch

**17.95** b. This is a sodium salt of a long-chain carboxylic acid.

**17.97** a.

b. In the stomach naproxen exists as the neutral carboxylic acid.
c. In the intestines naproxen exists as the ionized carboxylate anion.

**17.99** Aspirin inhibits the production of prostaglandins.

**17.101** The nonpolar end of a soap molecule binds to dirt and hydrocarbons while the polar end then hydrogen bonds with water, thereby rendering the dirt soluble in water.

**17.103**

**17.105** a. b.

## CHAPTER 18

**18.1** a. $\overset{1°}{\downarrow}$ $\overset{2°}{\downarrow}$ $\overset{2°}{\downarrow}$ $\overset{1°}{\downarrow}$
$H_2N(CH_2)_3NH(CH_2)_4NH(CH_2)_3NH_2$

b. $CH_3CH_2O$—$\overset{O}{\underset{}{C}}$—(ring with $C_6H_5$ and $3°$ $N$—$CH_3$)

**18.3** a. 2° amine
b. (1) trigonal planar (2) tetrahedral (3) trigonal pyramidal

**18.4** a. 2-butanamine
b. N-methyl-1-propanamine
c. N,N-dimethylcyclohexanamine
d. dibutylamine

**18.5** a. c.

b. d.

**18.7** a. $(CH_3)_2CHCH_2NH_2$ c.

b. $(CH_3)_2CHCH_2OH$

**18.9** pyridine and pyrrolidine

**18.11** 3°

**18.13** a. 11    b. 9

**18.14** a. $(CH_3CH_2NH_3)^+$ + $Cl^-$

b. $[(CH_3CH_2)_2NH_2]^+$ + $Cl^-$

c. $[(CH_3CH_2)_3NH]^+$ + $Cl^-$

**18.15** a. $(CH_3CH_2CH_2CH_2$—$NH_3)^+$ + $Cl^-$

b. $[(CH_3)_2NH_2]^+$ + $C_6H_5COO^-$

c. + $OH^-$

**18.17** a. methylammonium chloride
b. dipropylammonium bromide
c. ethyldimethylammonium acetate

**18.19** a. $(CH_3CH_2)_3N$    b. $CH_3CH_2NH_2$    c.

**18.21** A quaternary ammonium salt has four R groups bonded to N so there is no proton available that can be removed.

**18.23** COOH must be removed and OH must be added.

**18.25** This would require addition of a methyl group and removal of two OH groups.

**18.27** albuterol: 1° and 2° alcohols, 2° amine
salmeterol: 1° and 2° alcohols, 2° amine

**18.29** 2° amide and 3° amine

**18.31** a. 2°    b. 3°

**18.33** a. $CH_3CH_2CH_2CH_2CH_2NH_2$    c.

b. $CH_3CH_2CH_2\overset{}{\underset{H}{N}}CH_2CH_2CH_3$    d. $\left[ CH_3CH_2\overset{CH_2CH_3}{\underset{CH_2CH_3}{N}}CH_2CH_3 \right]^+$

**18.35** a. cyclohexanamine    b. N-ethyl-N-methylaniline

**18.37** a. diethylamine    c. N-methyl-3-hexanamine
b. 3-octanamine    d. N-ethyl-2-heptanamine

**18.39** a. $CH_3CH_2CH_2CH_2CH_2CH_2CH_2CH_2CH_2CH_2NH_2$

b. (tricyclohexylamine structure — three cyclohexyl groups attached to central N)

c. (4-bromoaniline structure with $NH_2$ and $Br$)

d. $CH_3CHCH_2COOH$ with $NH_2$ on the second carbon

e. $CH_3CH_2CH_2CH_2CH_2CH_2CHCH_3$ with $N(CH_2CH_3)_2$ substituent

f. $CH_3CH_2NHCH_2CH_2CH_2CH_2CH_3$

**18.41** (benzene ring with $N(CH_3)_2$) — *N,N*-dimethylaniline

(benzene ring with $NH_2$, $CH_3CH_2$ and $CH_2CH_3$) — 2,4-diethylaniline

**18.43** a. $[(CH_3CH_2CH_2)_2NH_2]^+$ $Cl^-$

b. $(CH_3CH_2CH_2CH_2NH_3)^+$ $Br^-$

c. $\left[CH_3CH_2N(CH_3)_2\right]^+$ $OH^-$ with H on N

**18.45**

$CH_3$–$N$($CH_3$)–$CH_3$ (trimethylamine)  $CH_3CH_2CH_2NH_2$ (1-propanamine)  $CH_3CH_2NHCH_3$ (*N*-methylethanamine)  $CH_3CHNH_2$ with $CH_3$ (2-propanamine)

trimethylamine    1-propanamine    *N*-methylethanamine    2-propanamine

**18.47** Pyridine is capable of hydrogen bonding with water, so it is more water soluble. Pyridine has a higher boiling point than benzene.

**18.49** a. $CH_3(CH_2)_7NH_2$    c. (cyclohexyl)–$CH_2CH_2CH_2NH_2$

b. $CH_3(CH_2)_6OH$

**18.51** (triethylamine hydrogen bonding structure: $CH_3CH_2$, $CH_3CH_2$, $CH_3CH_2$ on N atoms with H–N and :N–H hydrogen bonds)

**18.53** Primary amines can hydrogen bond to each other, whereas 3° amines cannot. Therefore, 1° amines will have a higher boiling point than 3° amines of similar size. Any amine can hydrogen bond to water so both 1° and 3° amines have similar solubility properties.

**18.55** a. $CH_3CH_2NH_2 + H_2O \longrightarrow (CH_3CH_2NH_3)^+ + OH^-$

b. $(CH_3CH_2)_2NH + H_2O \longrightarrow [(CH_3CH_2)_2NH_2]^+ + OH^-$

c. $(CH_3CH_2)_3N + H_2O \longrightarrow [(CH_3CH_2)_3NH]^+ + OH^-$

**18.57** a. $[CH_3CH_2CH_2NH(CH_3)_2]^+ + Cl^-$

b. $\left[CH_3CH_2CHCH_2CH_3 \text{ with } NH_3 \right]^+ + HSO_4^-$

c. (pyridinium ion with N–H)$^+$ $+ Br^-$

d. $CH_3CH_2$–$N$–$CH_2CH_3$ (with $CH_2CH_3$) $+ H_2O + Na^+$

**18.59** a. (piperidine ring with N–H and $CH_2CH_2CH_3$ substituent, protonated)$^+$ $Cl^-$

b. (morphine-type structure with $HO$, $O$, $N$–$H$, $CH_3$, $HO$ groups, protonated)$^+$ $Cl^-$

**18.61** piperidine

**18.63** Caffeine is a mild stimulant, imparting a feeling of alertness after consumption. It also increases heart rate, dilates airways, and stimulates the secretion of stomach acid. These effects are observed because caffeine increases glucose production, making an individual feel energetic.

**18.65** An alkaloid solution is slightly basic since its amine pulls off a proton from water, forming $OH^-$.

**18.67** Dopamine affects brain processes that control movement, emotions, and pleasure. Normal dopamine levels give an individual a pleasurable, satisfied feeling. Increased levels result in an intense "high." Drugs such as heroin, cocaine, and alcohol increase dopamine levels. When there is too little dopamine in the brain, an individual loses control of fine motor skills and Parkinson's disease results.

**18.69** Serotonin plays an important role in mood, sleep, perception, and temperature regulation. We get sleepy after eating a turkey dinner on Thanksgiving because the unusually high level of tryptophan in turkey is converted to serotonin. A deficiency of serotonin causes depression.

**18.71** Dopamine and norepinephrine are derived from tyrosine, serotonin from tryptophan, and histamine from histidine.

**18.73** a. (benzene ring)–$C(CH_3)_2$–$CH_2N(CH_3)_2$    c. (benzene ring)–$CH_2$–(piperidine ring with HN)

**18.75** (benzene ring)–$C(CH_3)_2$... $CH_2CNH_2$ with $CH_3$ groups

**18.77** Chlorpheniramine is an example of an antihistamine. Antihistamines bind to the H1 histamine receptor, but they evoke a different response. An antihistamine like chlorpheniramine or diphenhydramine, for example, inhibits vasodilation, so it is used to treat the symptoms of the common cold and environmental allergies.

**18.79** a, b:

c.

d.

e.

f.

g.

**18.81** a, b, c, d:

2-phenylethylamine in bold

e.

**18.83**

**18.85** A vasodilator dilates blood vessels and a bronchodilator dilates airways in the lungs. Histamine is a vasodilator and albuterol is a bronchodilator.

**18.87** Albuterol will exist in the ionic form in the stomach and as the neutral form in the intestines.

**18.89** Heroin has two esters, which can be made from the two OH groups in morphine. Add acetic acid ($CH_3COOH$) and $H_2SO_4$ to make the two esters in heroin.

# CHAPTER 19

**19.1** b. and c.

**19.3** a, b:

c. **A** will have the higher melting point because the molecules can pack together better.

**19.5** a. omega-9     b. omega-6

**19.6** a. $CH_3(CH_2)_{16}\overset{O}{\overset{\|}{C}}O(CH_2)_9CH_3$     c. $CH_3(CH_2)_{16}\overset{O}{\overset{\|}{C}}O(CH_2)_{29}CH_3$

      b. $CH_3(CH_2)_{16}\overset{O}{\overset{\|}{C}}O(CH_2)_{11}CH_3$

**19.7**

**19.9**  $CH_3(CH_2)_{12}\overset{\displaystyle O}{\underset{\displaystyle \;}{C}}{-}OH$  +  $HO(CH_2)_{15}CH_3$

**19.10  a.**

$CH_2{-}O{-}\overset{O}{C}{-}(CH_2)_{16}CH_3$
$CH{-}O{-}\overset{O}{C}{-}(CH_2)_{16}CH_3$
$CH_2{-}O{-}\overset{O}{C}{-}(CH_2)_{16}CH_3$

**b.**

$CH_2{-}O{-}\overset{O}{C}{-}(CH_2)_7\overset{H\;\;H}{C{=}C}(CH_2)_7CH_3$
$CH{-}O{-}\overset{O}{C}{-}(CH_2)_7\overset{H\;\;H}{C{=}C}(CH_2)_7CH_3$
$CH_2{-}O{-}\overset{O}{C}{-}(CH_2)_7\overset{H\;\;H}{C{=}C}(CH_2)_7CH_3$

**19.11**

$CH_2{-}O{-}\overset{O}{C}{-}(CH_2)_{16}CH_3$
$CH{-}O{-}\overset{O}{C}{-}(CH_2)_{16}CH_3$
$CH_2{-}O{-}\overset{O}{C}{-}(CH_2)_{14}CH_3$

$CH_2{-}O{-}\overset{O}{C}{-}(CH_2)_{16}CH_3$
$CH{-}O{-}\overset{O}{C}{-}(CH_2)_{14}CH_3$
$CH_2{-}O{-}\overset{O}{C}{-}(CH_2)_{16}CH_3$

**19.13  a.**

$CH_2{-}OH$
$CH{-}OH$   +   $3\ HO{-}\overset{O}{C}{-}(CH_2)_{12}CH_3$
$CH_2{-}OH$

**b.**

$CH_2{-}OH$
$CH{-}OH$   +
$CH_2{-}OH$

$HO{-}\overset{O}{C}{-}(CH_2)_{12}CH_3$
$HO{-}\overset{O}{C}{-}(CH_2)_7CH{=}CH(CH_2)_5CH_3$
$HO{-}\overset{O}{C}{-}(CH_2)_7CH{=}CH(CH_2)_7CH_3$

**19.15  a.**  $3\ Na^+\ {}^-O{-}\overset{O}{C}{-}(CH_2)_{12}CH_3$

**b.**  $Na^+\ {}^-O{-}\overset{O}{C}{-}(CH_2)_{12}CH_3$

$Na^+\ {}^-O{-}\overset{O}{C}{-}(CH_2)_7CH{=}CH(CH_2)_5CH_3$

$Na^+\ {}^-O{-}\overset{O}{C}{-}(CH_2)_7CH{=}CH(CH_2)_7CH_3$

**19.16**

$CH_2{-}O{-}\overset{O}{C}{-}(CH_2)_{14}CH_3$
$CH{-}O{-}\overset{O}{C}{-}(CH_2)_7\overset{H\;\;H}{C{=}C}(CH_2)_7CH_3$
$CH_2{-}O{-}\overset{O}{P}{-}O{-}CH_2CH_2\overset{+}{N}H_3$
$\phantom{CH_2{-}O{-}}O^-$

$CH_2{-}O{-}\overset{O}{C}{-}(CH_2)_7\overset{H\;\;H}{C{=}C}(CH_2)_7CH_3$
$CH{-}O{-}\overset{O}{C}{-}(CH_2)_{14}CH_3$
$CH_2{-}O{-}\overset{O}{P}{-}O{-}CH_2CH_2\overset{+}{N}H_3$
$\phantom{CH_2{-}O{-}}O^-$

**19.17  a.** phosphoacylglycerol, cephalin

[glycerol]
$CH_2{-}O{-}\overset{O}{C}{-}(CH_2)_{12}CH_3$  ← fatty acids
$CH{-}O{-}\overset{O}{C}{-}(CH_2)_{12}CH_3$
$CH_2{-}O{-}\overset{O}{P}{-}O{-}CH_2CH_2\overset{+}{N}H_3$
$\phantom{CH_2{-}O{-}}O^-$
phosphate          ethanolamine

**b.** triacylglycerol

[glycerol]
$CH_2{-}O{-}\overset{O}{C}{-}(CH_2)_{12}CH_3$
$CH{-}O{-}\overset{O}{C}{-}(CH_2)_7CH{=}CH(CH_2)_5CH_3$  ← fatty acids
$CH_2{-}O{-}\overset{O}{C}{-}(CH_2)_{12}CH_3$

**c.** sphingomyelin

[sphingosine]
$HO{-}CH{-}CH{=}CH(CH_2)_{12}CH_3$
$CH{-}NH{-}\overset{O}{C}{-}(CH_2)_{12}CH_3$  ← amide formed with myristic acid
$CH_2{-}O{-}\overset{O}{P}{-}O{-}CH_2CH_2\overset{+}{N}(CH_3)_3$
$\phantom{CH_2{-}O{-}}O^-$
phosphate          derived from choline

**19.19** Membrane **A** will be more fluid or pliable as it contains unsaturated fatty acids.

**19.21** Cholesterol is a lipid since it contains many C—C and C—H bonds and it is not water soluble.

**19.23** Triacylglycerols would be found in the interior, hydrophobic portion of lipoproteins.

**19.25  a.** Estrone has a phenol (a benzene ring with a hydroxyl group) and progesterone has a ketone and C=C in ring A. Progesterone also has a methyl group bonded to C10.
**b.** Estrone has a ketone at C17 and progesterone has a C—C bond, which is attached to a ketone.

**19.27** Testosterone has a methyl group at C10 that nandrolone lacks.

**19.29  a.**

ketone
carboxylic acid
$CH_2CH{=}CH(CH_2)_3COOH$
alkene
$CH{=}CHCH(CH_2)_4CH_3$
HO         OH
alcohol

**b.**

O
COOH
HO         OH

**19.31** b, e, f: hydrolyzable          a, c, d, g: nonhydrolyzable
**19.33** b. and c.

19.35 a. $CH_3(CH_2)_3CH=CH(CH_2)_7COOH$,
$CH_3(CH_2)_{12}COOH$, $CH_3(CH_2)_{14}COOH$
b. $CH_3(CH_2)_5CH=CH(CH_2)_7COOH$,
$CH_3(CH_2)_7CH=CH(CH_2)_7COOH$, $CH_3(CH_2)_{16}COOH$

19.37 a. Increasing the number of carbon atoms increases the melting point.
b. Increasing the number of double bonds decreases the melting point.

19.39 a, b:

hydrophilic

hydrophobic

c. The melting point would be lower than the melting point of the trans isomer.
d. liquid
e. omega-3 fatty acid

19.41 a.

b. omega-3 acid

c.

d.

19.43 a. $CH_3(CH_2)_{14}\overset{O}{\underset{||}{C}}O(CH_2)_{21}CH_3$    c. $CH_3(CH_2)_{14}\overset{O}{\underset{||}{C}}O(CH_2)_9CH_3$

b. $CH_3(CH_2)_{14}\overset{O}{\underset{||}{C}}O(CH_2)_{11}CH_3$

19.45 a. $CH_3(CH_2)_{16}COOH + HO(CH_2)_{17}CH_3$
b. $CH_3(CH_2)_{12}COOH + HO(CH_2)_{25}CH_3$
c. $CH_3(CH_2)_{14}COOH + HO(CH_2)_{27}CH_3$
d. $CH_3(CH_2)_{22}COOH + HO(CH_2)_{13}CH_3$

19.47 a.

b.

c.

d.

19.49

19.51

| Compound | a. General Structure | b. Example | c. Water Soluble (Y/N) | d. Hexane Soluble (Y/N) |
|---|---|---|---|---|
| [1] Fatty acid | RCOOH | | N | Y |
| [2] Soap | RCOO⁻ Na⁺ | | Y | N |
| [3] Wax | RCOOR' | | N | Y |
| [4] Triacylglycerol | | | N | Y |

**19.53** a. arachidic acid, stearic acid, and lauric acid
b. solid
c. The long hydrocarbon chains are hydrophobic.
d. The ester linkages are hydrophilic.

e. $CH_2-OH$   $HOOC(CH_2)_{10}CH_3$
$CH-OH$ + $HOOC(CH_2)_{16}CH_3$
$CH_2-OH$   $HOOC(CH_2)_{18}CH_3$

**19.55** a.   [1] water and $H_2SO_4$

$CH_2-OH$   $2\ HOC-(CH_2)_{14}CH_3$
$CH-OH$ +
$CH_2-OH$   $HOC-(CH_2)_{16}CH_3$

[2] water and NaOH

$CH_2-OH$   $2\ Na^+{}^-OC-(CH_2)_{14}CH_3$
$CH-OH$ +
$CH_2-OH$   $Na^+{}^-OC-(CH_2)_{16}CH_3$

b.   [1] water and $H_2SO_4$

$CH_2-OH$   $HOC-(CH_2)_7CH=CH(CH_2)_7CH_3$
$CH-OH$ + $HOC-(CH_2)_{14}CH_3$
$CH_2-OH$   $HOC-(CH_2)_7CH=CH(CH_2)_5CH_3$

[2] water and NaOH

$CH_2-OH$   $Na^+{}^-OC-(CH_2)_7CH=CH(CH_2)_7CH_3$
$CH-OH$ + $Na^+{}^-OC-(CH_2)_{14}CH_3$
$CH_2-OH$   $Na^+{}^-OC-(CH_2)_7CH=CH(CH_2)_5CH_3$

**19.57** c.

$CH_2-O-C-(CH_2)_7CH=CH(CH_2)_5CH_3$
**19.59** a. $CH-O-C-(CH_2)_7CH=CH(CH_2)_5CH_3$
$CH_2-O-P-O-CH_2CH_2NH_3^+$
$O^-$

$CH_2-O-C-(CH_2)_{10}CH_3$
b. $CH-O-C-(CH_2)_{10}CH_3$
$CH_2-O-P-O-CH_2CH_2N^+(CH_3)_3$
$O^-$

c.
$HO-CH-CH=CH(CH_2)_{12}CH_3$
$CH-NH-C-(CH_2)_{16}CH_3$
$CH_2-O-P-O-CH_2CH_2NH_3^+$
$O^-$

**19.61** Triacylglycerols do not have a strongly hydrophilic region contained in a polar head.

**19.63** Diffusion is the movement of small molecules through a membrane along a concentration gradient. Facilitated transport is the transport of molecules through channels in a cell membrane. $O_2$ and $CO_2$ move by diffusion whereas glucose and $Cl^-$ move by facilitated transport.

**19.65**

**19.67** Cholesterol is insoluble in the aqueous medium of the bloodstream. By being bound to a lipoprotein particle, it can be transported in the aqueous solution.

**19.69** Low-density lipoproteins (LDLs) transport cholesterol from the liver to the tissues where it is incorporated in cell membranes. High-density lipoproteins (HDLs) transport cholesterol from the tissues back to the liver. When LDLs supply more cholesterol than is needed, LDLs deposit cholesterol on the wall of arteries, forming plaque. Atherosclerosis is a disease that results from the buildup of these fatty deposits, restricting the flow of blood, increasing blood pressure, and increasing the likelihood of a heart attack or stroke. As a result, LDL cholesterol is often called "bad" cholesterol.

**19.71** a.

estrone                testosterone

b. The estrogen (left) and androgen (right) both contain the four rings of the steroid skeleton. Both contain a methyl group bonded to C13.
c. The estrogen has an aromatic A ring and a hydroxyl group on this ring. The androgen has a carbonyl on the A ring but does not contain an aromatic ring. The androgen also contains a C=C in the A ring and an additional $CH_3$ group at C10. The D rings are also different. The estrogen contains a carbonyl at C17 and the androgen has an OH group.
d. Estrogens, synthesized in the ovaries, control the menstrual cycle and secondary sexual characteristics of females. Androgens, synthesized in the testes, control the development of male secondary sexual characteristics.

**19.73** Prostaglandins and leukotrienes are two types of eicosanoids, a group of biologically active compounds containing 20 carbon atoms derived from the fatty acid arachidonic acid. Prostaglandins are a group of carboxylic acids that contain a five-membered ring. Leukotrienes do not contain a ring. They both mediate biological activity at the site where they are formed. Prostaglandins mediate inflammation and uterine contractions. Leukotrienes stimulate smooth muscle contraction in the lungs and lead to the narrowing of airways as associated with asthma.

**19.75** Prostaglandins contain a five-membered ring and a carboxyl group (COOH).

**19.77** Aspirin inhibits the activity of both COX-1 and COX-2 enzymes, whereas celecoxib inhibits the activity of only COX-2.

**19.79** Vitamins are organic compounds required in small quantities for normal metabolism and must be obtained in the diet since our cells cannot synthesize these compounds.

**19.81**

|   | Vitamin A | Vitamin D |
|---|-----------|-----------|
| a. | 10 | 21 |
| b. | 10 | 6 |
| e. | Required for normal vision | Regulates calcium and phosphorus metabolism |
| f. | Night blindness | Rickets and skeletal deformities |
| g. | Liver, kidney, oily fish, dairy | Milk and breakfast cereals |

c. and d.

**19.83** a.

b. $CH_3(CH_2)_{12}COO(CH_2)_{15}CH_3$

c.

d.

**19.85** **A:** a, c, e     **B:** a, c, d     **C:** b, c

**19.87** They contain an ionic head, making them more polar than triacylglycerols.

**19.89** The hydrocarbon chains have only 12 carbons in them, making them short enough so that the triacylglycerol remains a liquid at room temperature.

**19.91** Vegetable oils are composed of triacylglycerols while motor oil, derived from petroleum, is mostly alkanes and other long-chain hydrocarbons.

**19.93** No, certain fatty acids and fat-soluble vitamins are required in the diet.

**19.95** Saturated fats are more likely to lead to atherosclerosis and heart disease.

**19.97** The unsaturated fats have lower melting points, thus remaining liquid at low temperatures. These unsaturated fats allow the cells to remain more fluid with less rigid cell membranes than saturated triacylglycerols would allow for.

**19.99** a. reduction      b. oxidation      c. reduction

## CHAPTER 20

**20.1**

**20.3** a. aldopentose      b. aldotetrose      c. ketotetrose

**20.5** Hexane < 1-decanol < glucose. Hexane is a nonpolar hydrocarbon, insoluble in water. 1-Decanol is a long-chain alcohol and minimally soluble in water, due to the polar OH group. Glucose, with multiple hydroxyl groups, is water soluble.

**20.7** a.

b.

c.

\* chirality center

**20.9** D-Glucose and D-fructose are constitutional isomers. D-Galactose and D-fructose are also constitutional isomers.

20.23 Cellulose is water insoluble because the many OH groups are already hydrogen bonded to other OH groups in the three-dimensional structure. The OH groups are therefore less available for hydrogen bonding to water.

**20.27** Aldoses are monosaccharides with a carbonyl group at C1, forming an aldehyde, and ketoses are monosaccharides with a carbonyl group at C2, forming a ketone.

CH$_2$OH
CHO                     C=O
H—C—OH              HO—C—H
H—C—OH              H—C—OH
H—C—OH              H—C—OH
CH$_2$OH              CH$_2$OH
ribose, an aldose    fructose, a ketose

**20.29** a.
CHO
H—C—OH
H—C—OH
HO—C—H
CH$_2$OH

b.
CHO
H—C—OH
H—C—OH
CH$_2$OH

c.
CH$_2$OH
H—C—OH
H—C—OH
HO—C—H
CH$_2$OH

**20.31** α-D-Glucose and β-D-glucose are not enantiomers because they differ in the orientation of only one OH at C1.

**20.33** a. aldotetrose   b. aldohexose   c. ketopentose

**20.35** a.
CHO
H——OH
CH$_2$OH

b. aldotriose

**20.37** a.
CHO
HO—C*—H
HO—C*—H
CH$_2$OH
L-tetrose

CHO
H—C—OH
H—C—OH
CH$_2$OH
enantiomer

CHO
HO——H
HO——H
CH$_2$OH
Fischer projection

b.
CHO
HO—C*—H
HO—C*—H
HO—C*—H
H—C*—OH
CH$_2$OH
D-hexose

CHO
H—C—OH
H—C—OH
H—C—OH
HO—C—H
CH$_2$OH
enantiomer

CHO
HO——H
HO——H
HO——H
H——OH
CH$_2$OH
Fischer projection

c.
CH$_2$OH
C=O
H—C*—OH
HO—C*—H
CH$_2$OH
L-pentose

CH$_2$OH
C=O
HO—C—H
H—C—OH
CH$_2$OH
enantiomer

CH$_2$OH
C=O
H——OH
HO——H
CH$_2$OH
Fischer projection

* chirality center

**20.39** a. **A** and **B**
b. **B** and **C** (or **A** and **C**)
c.
CHO
HO—C—H
H—C—OH
CH$_2$OH

d.
CHO
H——OH
H——OH
CH$_2$OH

**20.41**
CH$_2$OH
HO          O    OH
H          H
H        OH
OH    H
β anomer

CH$_2$OH
HO          O    H
H          H
H        OH
OH    H
OH
α anomer

**20.43** Using a skeletal structure:

1° HO—
hemiacetal C
2° HO—          —OH ← OH on the anomeric C
HO      OH
2°        2°

**20.45**
CH$_2$OH
OH          O    OH
H
OH      OH
H          H
H          H

a. hemiacetal carbon
b. β anomer

c.
CH$_2$OH
OH          O    H
H
OH      OH
H          OH
H          H

d.
CH$_2$OH
OH          O    OH
H
OH      H
H          H
H          OH

**20.47** a.
CH$_2$OH
H          O    OH
H          H
HO          H
OH      OH
← hemiacetal anomeric carbon β anomer

b.
CH$_2$OH  O   CH$_2$OH
OH          H
H          OH
H          OH
← hemiacetal anomeric carbon α anomer

**20.49** A ketotriose has no stereoisomers.

**20.51** a.

hemiacetal
β anomer

b.

hemiacetal
α anomer

**20.53**

alditol          aldonic acid

**20.55** a.

[1]      [2]

b.

[1]      [2]

c.

[1]      [2]

**20.57** a.          b.

**20.59** Reducing sugars are carbohydrates that are oxidized with Benedict's reagent ($Cu^{2+}$). Glucose, an aldohexose, is a reducing sugar.

**20.61** a.

b.

**20.63** An α anomer has a hydroxyl at C1, the hemiacetal C, in the down position. An α glycoside has the glycosidic linkage in the down position.

**20.65**

**20.67** a, b:

acetal

hemiacetal

c. 1→6-α-glycosidic linkage

d. β anomer

e.

α anomer          β anomer

**20.69**

**20.71** Cellulose and amylose are both composed of repeating glucose units. In cellulose the glucose units are joined by a 1→4-β-glycosidic linkage, but in amylose they are joined by an α-(1→4) linkage. This leads to very different three-dimensional shapes, with cellulose forming sheets and amylose forming helices.

**20.73**

**20.75** a. D sugar

b. aldohexose

c.
```
        CHO
   H—C—OH
   H—C—OH
   H—C—OH
  HO—C—H
      CH₂OH
    enantiomer
```

d.
```
        CHO
  HO—C*—H
  HO—C*—H
  HO—C*—H
   H—C*—OH
      CH₂OH
  * chirality center
```

e.
```
      CH₂OH
     OH     O    H
        H
      OH    OH
    H              OH
       H    H
```

f.
```
        COOH
  HO—C—H
  HO—C—H
  HO—C—H
   H—C—OH
      CH₂OH
```

g.
```
       CH₂OH
  HO—C—H
  HO—C—H
  HO—C—H
   H—C—OH
      CH₂OH
```

h. a reducing sugar

**20.77** Lactose intolerance results from a lack of the enzyme lactase. It results in abdominal cramping and diarrhea. Galactosemia results from the inability to metabolize galactose. Therefore, it accumulates in the liver, causing cirrhosis, and in the brain, leading to mental retardation.

**20.79** Fructose is a naturally occurring sugar with more perceived sweetness per gram than sucrose. Sucralose is a synthetic sweetener; that is, it is not naturally occurring.

**20.81** An individual with type A blood can receive only blood types A and O, because he or she will produce antibodies and an immune response to B or AB blood. He or she can donate to individuals with either type A or AB blood as the type A polysaccharides are common to both and no immune response will be generated.

**20.83** The long sheets of polysaccharides in chitin, similar to cellulose, have β glycosidic linkages and will not be digestible.

**20.85** Hyaluronate is found in the extracellular fluid that lubricates joints and the vitreous humor of the eye. Chondroitin is a component of cartilage and tendons. Heparin is stored in the mast cells of the liver and other organs and prevents blood clotting.

**20.87**
```
   CH₂OH                    CH₂OH          CH₂OH
    C=O                 HO—C—H        H—C—OH
 HO—C—H    reduction   HO—C—H       HO—C—H
  H—C—OH     ———→       H—C—OH    +   H—C—OH
  H—C—OH                 H—C—OH        H—C—OH
   CH₂OH                  CH₂OH          CH₂OH
  fructose               stereoisomers
```
They differ in configuration at a single carbon.

# CHAPTER 21

**21.1** a. amide      b. alcohol      c. thiol

**21.3** a.
```
       COO⁻              COO⁻
  H₃N⁺—C—H         H—C—NH₃⁺
       CH₂              CH₂

       L                 D
```

b.
```
       COO⁻              COO⁻
  H₃N⁺——H           H——NH₃⁺
    CH₂CH₂SCH₃       CH₂CH₂SCH₃
       L                 D
```

**21.5** a.
```
       H
  H₃N⁺—C—COO⁻
       CH(CH₃)₂
  predominant at pI
```
c.
```
       H
  H₂N—C—COO⁻
       CH(CH₃)₂
```

b.
```
       H
  H₃N⁺—C—COOH
       CH(CH₃)₂
```

**21.7**
a. N-terminal: leucine        C-terminal: alanine
b. N-terminal: arginine       C-terminal: tyrosine
c. N-terminal: phenylalanine  C-terminal: glutamine
d. N-terminal: valine         C-terminal: phenylalanine

**21.9** a.
```
       H  O        H
  H₃N⁺—C—C—N—C—COO⁻
       H  |  H  CH₂—⬡
```

b.
```
       H  O        H
  H₃N⁺—C—C—N—C—COO⁻
       CH₂  H  CH(CH₃)CH₂CH₃
      CH₂CONH₂
```

c.
```
       H  O        H
  H₃N⁺—C—C—N—C—COO⁻
       CH₂  H  CH₂SH
      CH(CH₃)₂
```

**21.11** a. alanine and isoleucine: Ala–Ile
b. tyrosine and valine: Tyr–Val

**21.12**

serine          glycine

21.13   a.

$H_3N^+$—CH—C—N—CH—C—N—CH—C—N—CH—C—N—CH—C—O$^-$
with side chains $CH_2$ (tyrosine, OH), H, H, $CH_2$ (phenyl), $CH_2CH_2SCH_3$; the C=O carbons marked with *

\* amide bonds

   b.  tyrosine
   c.  3

21.15   Yes, the amino acids may be ordered differently.

21.17   Glycine has no large side chain and this allows for the β-sheets to stack well together.

21.19   a.

$H_3N^+$—C—COO$^-$  with side chain $CH_3$
$H_3N^+$—C—COO$^-$  with side chain $CH_2CH(CH_3)_2$
$H_3N^+$—C—COO$^-$  with side chain H

   b.

$H_3N^+$—C—COO$^-$  with side chain $CH_2OH$
$H_3N^+$—C—COO$^-$  with side chain $CH(OH)CH_3$
$H_3N^+$—C—COO$^-$  with side chain $CH_2$—phenyl

   c.

$H_3N^+$—C—COO$^-$  with side chain $CH_2CH(CH_3)_2$
$H_3N^+$—C—COO$^-$  with side chain $CH_2$—phenyl—OH
$H_3N^+$—C—COO$^-$  with side chain $CH_2CONH_2$

21.21   b, d, e

21.23

substrate

Inhibitor blocks substrate access to the active site.

enzyme

21.25   Fibrin and thrombin circulate as inactive zymogens so that the blood does not clot unnecessarily. They are activated as required at a bleeding point to form a clot.

21.27   The L designation refers to the configuration at the chirality center. With a vertical carbon chain in the Fischer projection, the L isomer has the –NH$_3^+$ drawn on the left side. The α-amino acid designation indicates that the amino group is bonded to the carbon adjacent to the carbonyl group.

21.29   Alanine is an ionic salt with strong electrostatic forces, leading to its high melting point, and making it a solid at room temperature. Pyruvic acid has much weaker intermolecular forces so it is a liquid at room temperature.

21.31   a.  $H_3N^+$—C—COO$^-$  with side chain $CH_2OH$
   c.  $H_3N^+$—C—COO$^-$  with side chain $CH_2$—phenyl

   b.  $H_3N^+$—C—COO$^-$  with side chain $CH_2CONH_2$
   d.  $H_3N^+$—C—COO$^-$  with side chain $CH(CH_3)_2$

21.33   isoleucine and threonine

|  | [1] | [2] | [3] | [4] |
|---|---|---|---|---|
| 21.35  a. | $H_3N^+$—C—H, COO$^-$, $CH_2CH(CH_3)_2$ | neutral | Leu | L |
| b. | $H_3N^+$—C—H, COO$^-$, $CH_2$-indole | neutral | Trp | W |
| c. | $H_3N^+$—C—H, COO$^-$, $(CH_2)_4NH_3^+$ | basic | Lys | K |
| d. | $H_3N^+$—C—H, COO$^-$, $CH_2COO^-$ | acidic | Asp | D |

21.37   a.  $H_3N^+$—C—H, COO$^-$, $CH_2CH_2SCH_3$  (L)     H—C—NH$_3^+$, COO$^-$, $CH_2CH_2SCH_3$  (D)

   b.  $H_3N^+$—C—H, COO$^-$, $CH_2CONH_2$  (L)     H—C—NH$_3^+$, COO$^-$, $CH_2CONH_2$  (D)

|  | [1] | [2] | [3] | [4] |
|---|---|---|---|---|
| 21.39  a. | glutamine | Gln | Q | neutral |
| b. | tyrosine | Tyr | Y | neutral |

21.41   a.  $H_3N^+$—C—COO$^-$  with side chain $CH_2CH(CH_3)_2$
predominant form at p$I$

   c.  $H_3N^+$—C—COOH  with side chain $CH_2CH(CH_3)_2$

   b.  $H_2N$—C—COO$^-$  with side chain $CH_2CH(CH_3)_2$

**21.43**

neutral
predominant form at p$I$

positive charge
pH = 1

negative charge
pH = 11

**21.45**

phenylalanine

peptide bond

alanine

Phe–Ala

**21.47** a, b, c:

N-terminal amino acid

Val–Phe

C-terminal amino acid

Phe–Val

**21.49** a. [1] $H_3\overset{+}{N}$–C–C*–N–C–C*–N–C–COO⁻ ...

[2] * amide bonds labeled

[3] N-terminal: leucine
C-terminal: tryptophan

[4] Leu–Val–Trp

b. [1] $H_3\overset{+}{N}$–C–C*–N–C–C*–N–C–COO⁻ ...

[2] * amide bonds labeled

[3] N-terminal: phenylalanine
C-terminal: threonine

[4] Phe–Ser–Thr

**21.51** a. [1], [2] valine: N-terminal, glycine, phenylalanine:
C-terminal [3] Val–Gly–Phe

b. [1], [2] leucine: N-terminal, tyrosine, methionine:
C-terminal [3] Leu–Tyr–Met

**21.53**

Ser–Ala–Ser

Ala–Ser–Ser

Ser–Ser–Ala

**21.55** alanine, cysteine, glycine

**21.57** a.

b.

**21.59**

3 moles Pro

H₃N⁺—C(H)—COO⁻ with (CH₂)₃—N(H)—C(=NH₂⁺)—NH₂     H₃N⁺—C(H)—COO⁻ with CH₂—(phenyl)     2 moles each, Arg and Phe

H₃N⁺—C(H)(H)—COO⁻     H₃N⁺—C(H)—COO⁻ with CH₂OH     1 mole each, Gly and Ser

**21.61**

H₃N⁺—C(H)(H)—C(=O)—N(H)—C(H)(CH₂—phenyl—OH)—COO⁻

Gly–Tyr

H₃N⁺—C(H)(CH(CH₃)₂)—COO⁻

Val

H₃N⁺—C(H)(H)—C(=O)—N(H)—C(H)(CH₃)—C(=O)—N(H)—C(H)(CH₂—phenyl)—COO⁻

Gly–Ala–Phe

**21.63** The primary structure of a protein is the order of its amino acids. The secondary structure refers to the three-dimensional arrangements of regions within the protein.

**21.65**
a. London dispersion forces
b. London dispersion forces
c. electrostatic
d. electrostatic

**21.67**

H₃N⁺—C(H)—COO⁻ with CH₂, C=O, H—N:----H (hydrogen bonding), then O, CH₂, H₃N⁺—C(H)—COO⁻

**21.69**

α-helix, random, β-sheet, random, β-sheet, random, α-helix

**21.71**

| | a. Secondary Structure | b. H₂O Solubility | c. Function | d. Location |
|---|---|---|---|---|
| Hemoglobin | Globular with much α-helix | Soluble | Carries oxygen to tissues | Blood |
| Keratin | α-Helix | Insoluble | Firm tissues | Nail, hair |

**21.73** When heated, a protein's primary structure is unaffected. The 2°, 3°, and 4° structures may be altered.

**21.75**
a. Insulin is a hormone that controls glucose levels.
b. Myoglobin stores oxygen in muscle.
c. α-Keratin forms hard tissues such as hair and nails.
d. Chymotrypsin is a protease that hydrolyzes peptide bonds.
e. Oxytocin is a hormone that stimulates uterine contractions and induces the release of breast milk.

**21.77** Reversible enzyme inhibition occurs when an enzyme's activity is restored when an inhibitor is released. Irreversible inhibition renders an enzyme incapable of further activity.

**21.79** Captopril inhibits the angiotensin-converting enzyme, blocking the conversion of angiotensinogen to angiotensin. This reduces the concentration of angiotensin, which in turn lowers blood pressure.

**21.81**

substrate

active site

enzyme

inhibitor

The inhibitor alters active site configuration and the substrate cannot enter.

**21.83** The α-keratin in nails has more cysteine residues to form disulfide bonds. The larger the number of disulfide bonds, the harder the substance.

**21.85** Humans cannot synthesize the amino acids methionine and lysine. Diets that include animal products readily supply all the needed amino acids, but no one plant source has sufficient amounts of all the essential amino acids. Grains—wheat, rice, and corn—are low in lysine, and legumes—beans, peas, and peanuts—are low in methionine, but a combination of these foods provides all the needed amino acids.

**21.87** Cauterization denatures the proteins in a wound.

**21.89** In sickle hemoglobin there is a substitution of a single amino acid, valine for glutamic acid.

**21.91** Penicillin inhibits the formation of the bacterial cell wall by irreversibly binding to an enzyme needed for its construction. It does not affect humans since human cells have a cell membrane, but not a rigid cell wall. Sulfanilamide inhibits the production of folic acid and therefore reproduction in bacteria, but humans do not synthesize folic acid (they must ingest it instead), so it does not affect humans.

21.93 Both aspartic acid and glutamic acid have two carboxylic acid groups. At low pH they have a +1 charge with both acid groups protonated, but at a high pH both acid groups are ionized, leading to a net charge of –2.

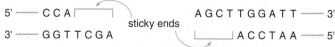

$$H_3\overset{+}{N}-\overset{\underset{|}{H}}{\underset{|}{C}}-COOH \qquad H_2N-\overset{\underset{|}{H}}{\underset{|}{C}}-COO^-$$
$$\overset{|}{C}H_2COOH \qquad\qquad \overset{|}{C}H_2COO^-$$

Form of Asp          Form of Asp
at low pH            at high pH

## CHAPTER 22

22.1  a. base = uracil, sugar = D-ribose, nucleoside = uridine
      b. base = guanine, sugar = D-2-deoxyribose, nucleoside = deoxyguanosine

22.3  a. base = uracil, sugar = ribose, uridine 5'-monophosphate, UMP
      b. base = thymine, sugar = D-2-deoxyribose, deoxythymidine 5'-monophosphate, dTMP

22.5  a.

UMP

b.

dTMP

c.

AMP

22.7

22.9  a. 3'-TTTGCAGG-5'        c. 3'-TAACGTGGGCG-5'
      b. 3'-ATATGCGG-5'        d. 3'-GTGAACTAGCC-5'

22.10 a. 5'-TCTCAGAG-3'        c. 5'-TAGGACATG-3'
      b. 3'-TAACGAG-5'         d. 3'-CCGGTATGAG-5'

22.11 a. [1] 5'-ACGGAUUGC-3'        [2] 5'-ACGGATTGC-3'
      b. [1] 5'-CUGAGG-3'           [2] 5'-CTGAGG-3'
      c. [1] 5'-AAUUGCGCU-3'        [2] 5'-AATTGCGCT-3'
      d. [1] 5'-GUCACUGGCAUG-3'     [2] 5'-GTCACTGGCATG-3'

22.13 a. Ala      c. Leu      e. Gln
      b. Asn      d. Ser      f. Lys

22.15 a. Gln–Glu–Val–Ser–Tyr–Arg
      b. Val–Ile–Trp–Arg–Gly–Ile
      c. Leu–Cys–Ser–Arg–Thr–Pro

22.17 a. 3'-CTC GGG CAT ATG CGG TGC-5'
      b. Glu–Pro–Val–Tyr–Ala–Thr

22.19 a. Pro–Pro–Ala–Asn–Glu–Ala
         GGU GGC CGU UUG CUU CGU
      b. Ala–Pro–Leu–Arg–Asp
         CGU GGU GAU UCU CUG

22.20 a. Arg–Val–Ala–Leu–Leu–Ser
      b. Arg–Gly–Phe–Ile–Val–Asn

22.21 a. Leu–Thr
      b. [1] Leu–Pro
         [2] Stop codon, so no dipeptide is formed.
         [3] Leu–Thr

22.23

5' ∼∼∼ C C A ⌐‾‾⌐              A G C T T G G A T T ∼∼∼ 3'
                    sticky ends
3' ∼∼∼ G G T T C G A              ⌐__⌐ A C C T A A ∼∼∼ 5'

22.25 A ribonucleoside contains ribose (a monosaccharide) and a nitrogen-containing base (A, G, C, or U), and a ribonucleotide has these components plus a phosphate group attached to the 5' position of the ribose.

uridine
a ribonucleoside

cytidine 5'-monophosphate
a ribonucleotide

22.27 A gene is a portion of the DNA molecule responsible for the synthesis of a single protein. Many genes form each chromosome.

22.29 a, c: DNA      b. both      d. RNA

22.31 a. base: cytosine
         monosaccharide: 2'-deoxyribose
         deoxycytidine
      b. base: guanine
         monosaccharide: ribose
         guanosine 5'-monophosphate

22.33 a.

b.

c.

d.

22.35 a.

b.

c.

d.

22.37 a. uracil, adenine
b. The 5' end has the free phosphate and the 3' end has two OH groups on the five-membered sugar ring.
c. UMP, AMP
d. This dinucleotide is a ribonucleotide because the sugar rings contain an OH group on C2'.
e. UA

22.39

22.41 a.

b.

22.43

22.45  a. The DNA double helix has 2-deoxyribose as the only sugar. The sugar–phosphate groups are on the outside of the helix.
b. The 5' end has a phosphate and the 3' end has an OH group.
c. Hydrogen bonding occurs in the interior of the helix between base pairs: A pairs with T and G pairs with C.

22.47  a. 3'-TTTATTG-5'          c. 3'-GCTATAGGGC-5'
b. 3'-TGACCTGA-5'         d. 3'-AAGGGCCCTAT-5'

22.49  27% T, 23% G, 23% C

22.51  G and C

22.53  5'-TACCGGATACGCTA-3'

22.55  Replication occurs in only one direction, from the 3' end to the 5' end of the template strand, but the strands of DNA run in opposite directions. The leading strand can be formed continuously from the 3' end as it is unwound. The lagging strand runs in the opposite direction, so it must be formed in segments that are then joined by DNA ligase.

22.57  Messenger RNA carries the specific sequence of the DNA code from the cell nucleus to the ribosomes in the cytoplasm to make a protein. Each transfer RNA brings a specific amino acid to the growing protein chain on the ribosome according to the sequence specified by the mRNA.

22.59  a. 3'-UUUAUUG-5'          c. 3'-GCUAUAGGGC-5'
b. 3'-UGACCUGA-5'         d. 3'-AAGGGCCCUAU-5'

22.61  a. [1] 5'-UACCGAAU-3'          [2] 5'-TACCGAAT-3'
b. [1] 5'-GCCGCGAAU-3'        [2] 5'-GCCGCGAAT-3'
c. [1] 5'-CCAUAUGGC-3'        [2] 5'-CCATATGGC-3'
d. [1] 5'-AUCCGGCAU-3'        [2] 5'-ATCCGGCAT-3'

22.63  a. GAC: Leu     b. AAA: Phe     c. UUC: Lys     d. CGU: Ala

22.65  anticodon: CGC; amino acid: alanine

22.67  a. Pro–Thr–Trp–Val–Glu
b. Met–Phe–Leu–Trp–Trp
c. Val–Asp–Glu–Pro–Gln

22.69  a. AUU AUG AAA AGU UAU
b. CCU CAA GAA GAU UUU
c. ACU AGU AAU CGU

22.71  a. [1] 3' ATA AGT TAT TTT TTG 5'
[2] Tyr–Ser–Ile–Lys–Asn
b. [1] 3' CTA CAT TTG TTC GGC 5'
[2] Asp–Val–Asn–Lys–Pro

22.73  A point mutation results in the substitution of one nucleotide for another in a DNA molecule. A silent mutation is a point mutation in DNA that results in no change in an amino acid sequence.

22.75  a. Leu–Gln–His
b. Leu–Gln–Asn
c. Leu–Gln–His, no change
d. This is a stop codon so the chain is terminated.
e. A dipeptide, Ser–Ala, is synthesized.

22.77  a. Asn–Ala     b. Asn–Ala     c. Asn–Gly     d. Asn–Ser

22.79  A restriction endonuclease is an enzyme that cleaves plasmid DNA at a specific site.

22.81

5' ∼∼∼ C C G G T T G ⌐‾‾‾⌐ → ⌐ G A T C C T T ∼∼∼ 3'
                          sticky ends
3' ∼∼∼ G G C C A A C T A G         ⌐‾‾‾⌐ G A A ∼∼∼ 5'

22.83  Circular plasmid DNA is isolated from bacteria and cleaved at a specific site with a restriction endonuclease. This forms "sticky ends" of DNA that are then combined with another DNA source, perhaps human, with complementary "sticky ends" to the plasmid DNA. These DNA strands come together and then a DNA ligase is used to re-form a circular DNA that is then reproduced by the bacteria.

22.85  a. Lanes 3 and 5 represent DNA of children that share both parents because they both have DNA fragments common to both parents.
b. Lane 4 represents DNA from an adopted child because the DNA fragments have little relationship to the parental DNA fragments.

22.87  a. cytidine
b. Lamivudine is a nucleoside analogue that gets incorporated into a DNA chain, but since it does not contain a 3' hydroxyl group, synthesis is terminated.

22.89  a. 5' GTT ACA TAA AAA CGA 3'
b. 5' GUU ACA UAA AAA CGA 3'
c. Val–Thr

22.91

| DNA informational strand: | 5' end | AAC | TAT | CCA | ACG | AAG | ATG | 3' end |
|---|---|---|---|---|---|---|---|---|
| DNA template strand: | 3' end | TTG | ATA | GGT | TGC | TTC | TAC | 5' end |
| mRNA codons: | 5' end | AAC | UAU | CCA | ACG | AAG | AUG | 3' end |
| tRNA anticodons: |  | UUG | AUA | GGU | UGC | UUC | UAC |  |
| Polypeptide: |  | Asn | Tyr | Pro | Thr | Lys | Met |  |

22.93

| DNA informational strand: | 5' end | AAC | GTA | TCA | ACT | CAC | ATG | 3' end |
|---|---|---|---|---|---|---|---|---|
| DNA template strand: | 3' end | TTG | CAT | AGT | TGA | GTG | TAC | 5' end |
| mRNA codons: | 5' end | AAC | GUA | UCA | ACU | CAC | AUG | 3' end |
| tRNA anticodons: |  | UUG | CAU | AGU | UGA | GUG | UAC |  |
| Polypeptide: |  | Asn | Val | Ser | Thr | His | Met |  |

22.95  975

22.97  ATA CCA CCA AAA TAC

22.99  TAA CCT AAA

## CHAPTER 23

**23.1** This makes it possible to use the same reactions and the same enzyme systems to metabolize all types of biomolecules.

**23.3** a. glucose + ATP $\longrightarrow$ glucose 1-phosphate + ADP
b. $-2.3$ kcal/mol

**23.5** $-3.0$ kcal/mol of energy released

**23.6** a. reduction using NADH    b. oxidation using $NAD^+$

**23.7** Riboflavin has numerous polar groups (OH and NH) that can hydrogen bond to water, making it water soluble.

**23.9**
$$CH_3CH_2CH_2\overset{\overset{\displaystyle O}{\|}}{C}O^- \quad + \quad HSCoA$$

**23.10** a.
b. oxidation

**23.11** Succinate dehydrogenase is so named because the elements of hydrogen ($H_2$) are removed from succinate.

**23.13** a. reduction    b. oxidizing agent

**23.15** Mitochondria contain an outer membrane and an inner membrane with many folds. The area between these two membranes is called the intermembrane space. Energy production occurs within the matrix, the area surrounded by the inner membrane.

**23.17** hydrolysis of starch, the conversion of glucose to acetyl CoA, the citric acid cycle, electron transport chain, oxidative phosphorylation

**23.19** a. stage [1]    c. stage [3]    e. stage [1]
b. stage [2]    d. stage [4]

**23.21** Coupled reactions are pairs of reactions that occur together. The energy released by one reaction provides the energy to drive the other reaction.

**23.23**
$$CH_3\overset{\overset{\displaystyle O}{\|}}{C}O^- \quad + \quad HPO_4^{2-}$$

**23.25** a.

| | Energy change |
|---|---|
| ATP + succinate + HSCoA $\longrightarrow$ succinyl CoA + ADP + $HPO_4^{2-}$ | $+2.1$ kcal/mol |

b. The reaction is not energetically favored because an input of energy is required.

**23.27** a. glucose + $HPO_4^{2-}$ $\longrightarrow$ glucose 1-phosphate + $H_2O$
b. glucose + ATP $\longrightarrow$ glucose 1-phosphate + ADP
c. $-2.3$ kcal/mol

**23.29** a. $-3.9$ kcal/mol
b.
fructose 6-phosphate + $HPO_4^{2-}$
$\longrightarrow$ fructose 1,6-bisphosphate + $H_2O$

ATP + $H_2O$ $\longrightarrow$ ADP + $HPO_4^{2-}$
―――――――――――――――――――――
fructose 6-phosphate + ATP
$\longrightarrow$ fructose 1,6-bisphosphate + ADP

c. $+3.9 + (-7.3) = -3.4$ kcal/mol

**23.31** a. 1,3-bisphosphoglycerate + ADP
$\longrightarrow$ 3-phosphoglycerate + ATP
b. $-4.5$ kcal/mol
c. Yes, this is an energetically favorable coupled reaction that could be used to synthesize ATP from ADP.

**23.33**

a.
GTP

b.
GDP

**23.35** a. reducing agent    b. neither    c. oxidizing agent

**23.37** When a substrate is oxidized, $NAD^+$ is reduced. $NAD^+$ is an oxidizing agent.

**23.39** a.

b.

**23.41** a. steps [3], [4], and [8]    c. step [6]
b. steps [3] and [4]    d. step [1]

**23.43** a.
fumarate
b. succinate    c. malate

**23.45** a. isocitrate    b. malate, isocitrate

**23.47** a. oxidation    b. decarboxylation    c. step [3a]
d. The elements of $H_2$ (hydrogen) are removed in converting isocitrate to oxalosuccinate.

**23.49** step [7]

**23.51** They require oxygen.

**23.53** a. $FADH_2$ donates electrons to the electron transport chain.
b. ADP is a substrate for the formation of ATP.
c. ATP synthase catalyzes the formation of ATP from ADP.
d. The inner mitochondrial membrane contains the four complexes for the electron transport chain. ATP synthase is also embedded in the membrane and contains the $H^+$ ion channel that allows $H^+$ to return to the matrix.

**23.55** $NAD^+$, FAD, and $H_2O$

**23.57** $FADH_2$ enters the electron transport chain at complex II, whereas NADH enters at complex I.

23.59  a. Pepsin catalyzes the hydrolysis of proteins to amino acids in the stomach.
      b. Succinate dehydrogenase catalyzes the conversion of succinate to fumarate in step [6] of the citric acid cycle.
      c. ATP synthase catalyzes the oxidative phosphorylation of ADP to ATP.

23.61  Each two-carbon fragment of acetyl CoA that enters the citric acid cycle produces three molecules of NADH and one molecule of $FADH_2$. These then enter the electron transport chain and serve as reducing agents. For each NADH that enters the electron transport chain, there are 2.5 ATPs produced, and for each $FADH_2$, there are 1.5 ATPs produced. In addition, there is one GTP (an ATP equivalent) produced in the citric acid cycle.

In total:
$$3 \text{ NADH} \times 2.5 \text{ ATP/NADH} = 7.5 \text{ ATP}$$
$$1 \text{ FADH}_2 \times 1.5 \text{ ATP/FADH}_2 = 1.5 \text{ ATP}$$
$$1 \text{ GTP (ATP equivalent)} = \underline{1 \quad \text{ATP}}$$
$$10 \quad \text{ATP}$$

23.63  ATP has three phosphate groups and ADP has two.

23.65  a. and b.

glucose 1-phosphate

23.67  The citric acid cycle generates the reducing agents NADH and $FADH_2$ that then enter the electron transport chain.

23.69  There would be more mitochondria in the heart because it has far more metabolic needs than bone.

23.71  Creatine phosphate, stored in muscles, is a high-energy phosphate that generates energy upon hydrolysis.

23.73  68 moles, $4.1 \times 10^{25}$ molecules of ATP

## CHAPTER 24

24.1  The reactant and product are constitutional isomers that differ in the location of a carbonyl and hydroxyl group. Thus, an isomerase enzyme converts one isomer to another.

24.3  They are constitutional isomers with a different arrangement of atoms but the same molecular formula.

24.5  step [1]: glucose; step [3]: fructose 6-phosphate; step [7]: ADP; step [10]: ADP

24.7  The rate of glycolysis would decrease.

24.9  NADH serves as the reducing agent for the conversion of pyruvate to both lactate and ethanol. The $NAD^+$ formed in the process can then be used as the oxidant in step [6] of glycolysis, making the process anaerobic.

24.11  a. Both use NADH to generate a reduced compound.
      b. Ethanol is a two-carbon product formed by decarboxylation, whereas lactate is a three-carbon compound.

24.13  the conversion of pyruvate to acetyl CoA and steps [3] and [4] of the citric acid cycle

24.15

|   | Starting Material | Product |
|---|---|---|
| a. | Pyruvate | Phosphoenolpyruvate |
| b. | 2-Phosphoglycerate | 3-Phosphoglycerate |
| c. | Glucose 6-phosphate | Glucose |

24.17  a. [1] 10; [2] 9 cycles      b. [1] 8; [2] 7 cycles

24.18  106

24.19  134

24.21  a. 5.3 ATP/carbon in glucose
      b. 6.7 ATP/carbon in stearic acid
      c. supports

24.23  β-Hydroxybutyrate contains an alcohol and a carboxylate anion, but no ketone.

24.25  An increased concentration of acetyl CoA increases the production of ketone bodies.

24.26  a.

      b.

      c.

24.27  a.

      b.

      c.

24.29  a. Oxidation occurs with loss of hydrogen by a dehydrogenase enzyme. The coenzyme $NAD^+$ serves as an oxidant.
      b. Transfer of phosphate from GTP to the reactant occurs, forming GDP. The loss of carbon dioxide takes place with the carboxykinase enzyme.

24.31  This reaction converts one isomer to another, so there is a change in position of the phosphate; thus, the enzyme is called a "mutase."

24.33  a.      b. 2-phosphoglycerate      c. pyruvate

phosphoenolpyruvate

24.35  Energy-investment phase:
      a. glucose, glyceraldehyde 3-phosphate
      b. 2 ATP utilized
      c. no coenzymes used or formed
      Energy-generating phase:
      a. glyceraldehyde 3-phosphate, pyruvate
      b. 4 ATP/glucose produced
      c. 2 $NAD^+$ used and 2 NADH produced per glucose

**24.37**　a. 7, 10　　b. 1, 3　　c. 6　　d. 4

**24.39**　The conversion of pyruvate to acetyl CoA forms one $CO_2$ for each pyruvate.
The conversion of isocitrate to α-ketoglutarate and α-ketoglutarate to succinyl CoA in the citric acid cycle forms one $CO_2$ for each acetyl CoA.

**24.41**　a.

$$C_6H_{12}O_6 + 2\,NAD^+ \xrightarrow{\;\;2\,ADP\quad 2\,ATP\;\;} 2\,CH_3COCO_2^- + 2\,NADH + 2\,H^+$$
glucose　　　　　　　　　　　　　　　　　　　pyruvate

b.

$$C_6H_{12}O_6 \xrightarrow{\;\;2\,ADP\quad 2\,ATP\;\;} 2\,CH_3CH_2OH + 2\,CO_2$$
glucose　　　　　　　　　　　　ethanol

c.

$$CH_3-\overset{O}{\underset{}{C}}-\overset{O}{\underset{}{C}}-O^- \xrightarrow{\;NADH+H^+\quad NAD^+\;} CH_3-\overset{OH}{\underset{H}{C}}-\overset{O}{\underset{}{C}}-O^-$$
pyruvate　　　　　　　　　　　　　　　　　　lactate

**24.43**　a. aerobic: $CO_2$
　　anaerobic: lactate
　b. aerobic: $NAD^+$ and FAD are used and NADH and $FADH_2$ are formed.
　　anaerobic: NADH is used to convert pyruvate to lactate and $NAD^+$ is formed.

**24.45**　Glycolysis takes glucose and breaks it into smaller units, producing pyruvate. Gluconeogenesis is the synthesis of glucose from lactate, amino acids, and glycerol.

**24.47**　a. increased　　　c. increased
　b. decreased　　　d. decreased

**24.49**　In the Cori cycle, glucose in muscle is catabolized to pyruvate and then converted to lactate, which is transported to the liver. In the liver, lactate is converted to glucose by gluconeogenesis and then transported back to the muscle.

**24.51**　a. lactate　　b. ethanol　　c. $CO_2$

**24.53**　During glycolysis: 2 ATP and 2 NADH generated.
　　Each NADH in turn leads to 2.5 ATP,
　　so glycolysis leads to:　　　　　　　　　　total 7 ATP
　　Conversion of 2 pyruvate to 2 acetyl CoA
　　yields 2 NADH, which leads to:　　　　　　　5 ATP
　　In the citric acid cycle, 20 additional ATP
　　are formed for 2 $CH_3COSCoA$:
　　　　2 GTP (ATP), 6 NADH ⟶ 15 ATP,
　　　　2 $FADH_2$ ⟶ 3 ATP:　　　　　　　total 20 ATP
　　　　　　　　　　　　　　　　　　　　　　= 32 ATP

**24.55**　two carbons in two molecules of $CO_2$ and four in two molecules of $CH_3CH_2OH$

**24.57**　Two phosphate bonds of ATP are hydrolyzed forming AMP; therefore, 2 ATP equivalents are used.

**24.59**　a. 7　　b. 6

**24.61**　a. 3　　b. 2

**24.63**　92

**24.65**

$$C_{15}H_{31}CO_2H \longrightarrow CH_3(CH_2)_{12}-CH_2-CH_2-\overset{O}{\underset{}{C}}-SCoA$$
$C_{16}$ acyl CoA

acyl CoA dehydrogenase　⟍ FAD ⟍ FADH₂　　① **Oxidation**

$$CH_3(CH_2)_{12}-CH=CH-\overset{O}{\underset{}{C}}-SCoA$$

enoyl CoA hydratase　⟍ $H_2O$　　② **Hydration**

$$CH_3(CH_2)_{12}-\overset{OH}{\underset{}{C}}H-\overset{H}{\underset{}{C}}H-\overset{O}{\underset{}{C}}-SCoA$$

β-hydroxyacyl CoA dehydrogenase　⟍ $NAD^+$ ⟍ $NADH+H^+$　　③ **Oxidation**

$$CH_3(CH_2)_{12}-\overset{O}{\underset{}{C}}-CH_2-\overset{O}{\underset{}{C}}-SCoA$$

acyl CoA acyltransferase　⟍ HSCoA　　④ **Cleavage**

$$CH_3(CH_2)_{12}-\overset{O}{\underset{}{C}}-SCoA + CH_3-\overset{O}{\underset{}{C}}-SCoA$$
$C_{14}$ acyl CoA　　　　　　　2 C's

**24.67**　a. $CH_3(CH_2)_6-\underset{\beta}{CH_2}-\underset{\alpha}{CH_2}-\overset{O}{\underset{}{C}}-OH$

b. $CH_3(CH_2)_6-\underset{\beta}{CH_2}-\underset{\alpha}{CH_2}-\overset{O}{\underset{}{C}}-SCoA$

c. 5　　d. 4　　e. 64

**24.69**　0.37 mol ATP/g decanoic acid

**24.71**　Ketosis is the condition under which ketone bodies accumulate. Ketogenesis is the synthesis of ketone bodies from acetyl CoA.

**24.73**　In poorly controlled diabetes, glucose cannot be metabolized. Fatty acids are used for metabolism and ketone bodies are formed to a greater extent.

**24.75**　Ketogenic amino acids are converted to acetyl CoA or a related thioester and can be converted to ketone bodies. Glucogenic amino acids are catabolized to pyruvate or another intermediate in the citric acid cycle.

**24.77**　a. $H-\overset{O}{\underset{}{C}}-CO_2^-$　　b. ⟨benzene ring⟩$-CH_2-\overset{O}{\underset{}{C}}-CO_2^-$

**24.79**   a.   $CH_3-\overset{\overset{\displaystyle O}{\|}}{C}-CO_2^-$   +   $^-O_2CCH_2-\overset{\overset{\displaystyle +NH_3}{|}}{\underset{\underset{\displaystyle H}{|}}{C}}-CO_2^-$

      b.   $(CH_3)_2CHCH_2-\overset{\overset{\displaystyle O}{\|}}{C}-CO_2^-$   +   $^-O_2CCH_2-\overset{\overset{\displaystyle +NH_3}{|}}{\underset{\underset{\displaystyle H}{|}}{C}}-CO_2^-$

**24.81**   a.   $(CH_3)_2CHCH_2-\overset{\overset{\displaystyle O}{\|}}{C}-CO_2^-$   +   $NH_4^+$

      b.   ⟨benzene ring⟩$-CH_2-\overset{\overset{\displaystyle O}{\|}}{C}-CO_2^-$   +   $NH_4^+$

**24.83**   a.   acetoacetyl CoA, fumarate
      b.   α-ketoglutarate
      c.   oxaloacetate
      d.   pyruvate

**24.85**   Yes, phenylalanine, for example, can be degraded by multiple routes and can be both ketogenic and glucogenic.

**24.87**   A spiral pathway involves the same set of reactions repeated on increasingly smaller substrates; example: β-oxidation of fatty acids. A cyclic pathway is a series of reactions that regenerates the first reactant; example: citric acid cycle.

**24.89**   Glucose is metabolized anaerobically to form $CO_2$ and ethanol. The $CO_2$ causes bread to rise.

**24.91**   Pyruvate is metabolized anaerobically to lactate.

**24.93**   The diet calls for ingestion of protein and fat, so in the absence of carbohydrates to be metabolized, ketone bodies are formed.

**24.95**   a. kinase      b. dehydrogenase      c. carboxylase

**24.97**   18.5 ATP

**24.99**   One gram of arachidic acid produces more ATP than one gram of glucose (0.429 mol/g compared to 0.18 mol/g). This result supports the fact that lipids are more efficient at storing energy than carbohydrates.

# Glossary

## A

**Acetal** (16.8) A compound that contains two OR groups (alkoxy groups) bonded to the same carbon; general formula $R_2C(OR)_2$.

**Acetyl CoA** (23.4) A compound formed when an acetyl group ($CH_3CO–$) is bonded to coenzyme A (HS–CoA); $CH_3COSCoA$.

**Achiral** (15.2) Being superimposable on a mirror image.

**Acid** (9.1) In the Arrhenius definition, a substance that contains a hydrogen atom and dissolves in water to form a hydrogen ion, $H^+$.

**Acid dissociation constant, $K_a$** (9.4) A constant, $K_a$, related to acid strength. The stronger the acid (HA), the larger the value of $K_a$; $K_a = [H_3O^+][A:^-]/[HA]$.

**Acidic solution** (9.5) A solution in which $[H_3O^+] > [OH^-]$; thus, $[H_3O^+] > 10^{-7}$ M.

**Actinides** (2.4) A group of elements in the periodic table beginning with thorium ($Z = 90$), and immediately following the element actinium (Ac).

**Active site** (6.4, 21.9) The region in an enzyme that binds a substrate, which then undergoes a very specific reaction with an enhanced rate.

**Active transport** (19.7) The process of moving an ion across a cell membrane that requires energy input.

**Actual yield** (5.7) The amount of product formed in a reaction, determined by weighing the product on a balance.

**Acyclic alkane** (12.1) An alkane with molecular formula $C_nH_{2n+2}$, which contains a chain of carbon atoms but no rings. An acyclic alkane is also called a saturated hydrocarbon.

**Acyl CoA** (24.7) The thioester formed from a fatty acid and coenzyme A that undergoes $\beta$-oxidation in mitochondria; general structure RCOSCoA.

**Acyl group** (17.1) A substituent having the formula RCO–.

**Addition reaction** (13.6) A reaction in which elements are added to a compound.

**Adenosine 5'-diphosphate** (ADP, 23.3) A nucleoside diphosphate formed by adding two phosphates to the 5'-OH group of adenosine.

**Adenosine 5'-triphosphate** (ATP, 23.3) A nucleoside triphosphate formed by adding three phosphates to the 5'-OH group of adenosine. ATP is the most prominent member of a group of "high-energy" molecules that release energy by cleavage of a P–O bond during hydrolysis.

**Adrenal cortical steroid** (19.9) A steroid hormone synthesized in the outer layer of the adrenal gland.

**Alcohol** (11.5) A compound containing a hydroxyl group (OH) bonded to a tetrahedral carbon atom; general formula ROH.

**Aldehyde** (11.5) A compound that has a hydrogen atom bonded directly to a carbonyl carbon; general formula RCHO.

**Alditol** (20.4) A compound produced when the carbonyl group of an aldose is reduced to a 1° alcohol.

**Aldonic acid** (20.4) A compound produced when the aldehyde carbonyl of an aldose is oxidized to a carboxyl group.

**Aldose** (20.2) A monosaccharide with an aldehyde carbonyl group at C1.

**Alkali metal** (2.4) An element located in group 1A (group 1) of the periodic table. Alkali metals include lithium (Li), sodium (Na), potassium (K), rubidium (Rb), cesium (Cs), and francium (Fr).

**Alkaline earth element** (2.4) An element located in group 2A (group 2) of the periodic table. Alkaline earth elements include beryllium (Be), magnesium (Mg), calcium (Ca), strontium (Sr), barium (Ba), and radium (Ra).

**Alkaloid** (18.4) A naturally occurring amine derived from a plant source.

**Alkane** (11.5) A compound having only C–C and C–H single bonds.

**Alkene** (11.5) A compound having a carbon–carbon double bond.

**Alkoxy group** (14.7) An OR group. An alkoxy group is named by changing the -yl ending of an alkyl group to -oxy.

**Alkyl group** (12.4) A group formed by removing one hydrogen from an alkane.

**Alkyl halide** (11.5) A compound with the general structure R–X that contains a halogen atom (X = F, Cl, Br, or I) bonded to a tetrahedral carbon.

**Alkyne** (11.5) A compound with a carbon–carbon triple bond.

**Alpha ($\alpha$) carbon** (17.2) The carbon adjacent to a carbonyl group.

**Alpha ($\alpha$) particle** (10.1) A high-energy particle that is emitted from a radioactive nucleus and contains two protons and two neutrons.

**Amide** (11.5) A compound that contains a nitrogen atom bonded directly to a carbonyl carbon; general structure $RCONR'_2$, where R' = H or alkyl.

**Amine** (11.5) An organic compound that contains a nitrogen atom bonded to one, two, or three alkyl groups; general structure $RNH_2$, $R_2NH$, or $R_3N$.

**Amino acid** (21.2) A compound that contains two functional groups—an amino group ($NH_2$) and a carboxyl group (COOH) bonded to the same carbon.

**Amino group** (11.5) An $–NH_2$ group.

**Ammonium ion** (3.6) An $NH_4^+$ ion.

**Ammonium salt** (18.6) An ionic compound that contains a positively charged ammonium ion and an anion. $(CH_3CH_2CH_2NH_3)^+Cl^-$ is an ammonium salt.

**Amorphous solid** (7.9) A solid with no regular arrangement of its particles.

**Amphoteric compound** (9.2) A compound that contains both a hydrogen atom and a lone pair of electrons so that it can be either an acid or a base.

**Anabolic steroid** (19.9) A synthetic androgen analogue that promotes muscle growth.

**Anabolism** (23.1) The synthesis of large molecules from smaller ones in a metabolic pathway.

**Androgen** (19.9) A hormone that controls the development of secondary sex characteristics in males.

**Anion** (3.2) A negatively charged ion with more electrons than protons.

**$\alpha$ Anomer** (20.3) The cyclic form of a monosaccharide that contains a hemiacetal with the OH group drawn down, below the ring.

**$\beta$ Anomer** (20.3) The cyclic form of a monosaccharide that contains a hemiacetal with the OH group drawn up, above the ring.

**Anomeric carbon** (20.3) The carbon atom that is part of the hemiacetal in a cyclic monosaccharide.

**Anticodon** (22.8) Three nucleotides in a tRNA molecule that are complementary to the codon in mRNA and identify an individual amino acid.

**Antihistamine** (18.10) A compound that binds to the H1 histamine receptor and prevents the action of histamine.

**Antioxidant** (13.4) A compound that prevents an unwanted oxidation reaction from occurring.

**Anti-ulcer drug** (18.10) A drug that binds to the H2 histamine receptor, thus reducing acid secretion in the stomach.

**Aqueous solution** (8.1) A solution with water as the solvent.

**Aromatic compound** (11.5) A compound that contains a benzene ring, a six-membered ring with three double bonds.

**Aryl halide** (13.13) An organic halide with the halogen bonded directly to a benzene ring.

**Atmosphere** (7.2) A unit used to measure pressure; 1 atm = 760 mm Hg.

**Atom** (2.2) The basic building block of matter composed of a nucleus and an electron cloud.

**Atomic mass unit** (2.2) A unit abbreviated as amu, which equals one-twelfth the mass of a carbon atom that has six protons and six neutrons; 1 amu = $1.661 \times 10^{-24}$ g.

**Atomic number** (2.2) The number of protons in the nucleus of an atom; symbolized as $Z$.

**Atomic weight** (2.3) The weighted average of the mass of all naturally occurring isotopes of a particular element, reported in atomic mass units.

**Avogadro's law** (7.4) A gas law that states that the volume of a gas is proportional to the number of moles present when the pressure and temperature are held constant.

**Avogadro's number** (5.3) A quantity that contains $6.02 \times 10^{23}$ items—usually atoms, molecules, or ions.

**Axon** (18.8) The long stem that protrudes from the cell body of a neuron.

# B

**Balanced chemical equation** (5.2) An equation written so that an equal number of atoms of each element is present on both sides.

**Barometer** (7.2) A device for measuring atmospheric pressure.

**Base** (9.1) In the Arrhenius definition, a substance that contains hydroxide and dissolves in water to form $OH^-$.

**Basic solution** (9.5) A solution in which $[OH^-] > [H_3O^+]$; thus, $[OH^-] > 10^{-7}$ M.

**Becquerel** (10.4) An SI unit used to measure radioactivity, abbreviated as Bq; 1 Bq = 1 disintegration/s.

**Benedict's reagent** (20.4) A $Cu^{2+}$ reagent that oxidizes the aldehyde carbonyl of an aldose to a carboxyl group, yielding an aldonic acid.

**Beta (β) carbon** (17.2) The carbon bonded to the α (alpha) carbon and located two carbons from a carbonyl group.

**Beta (β) particle** (10.1) A high-energy electron emitted from a radioactive nucleus.

**Boiling point** (bp, 7.7) The temperature at which a liquid is converted to the gas phase.

**Boiling point elevation** (8.7) The increase in the boiling point of a liquid solution due to the presence of a dissolved nonvolatile solute.

**Bond dissociation energy** (6.2) The energy needed to break a covalent bond by equally dividing the electrons between the two atoms in the bond.

**Bonding** (3.1) The joining of two atoms in a stable arrangement.

**Boyle's law** (7.3) A gas law that relates pressure and volume. Boyle's law states that for a fixed amount of gas at constant temperature, the pressure and volume of the gas are inversely related.

**Branched-chain alkane** (12.2) An alkane that contains one or more carbon branches bonded to a carbon chain.

**Brønsted–Lowry acid** (9.1) A proton donor.

**Brønsted–Lowry base** (9.1) A proton acceptor.

**Buffer** (9.10) A solution whose pH changes very little when acid or base is added. Most buffers are solutions composed of approximately equal amounts of a weak acid and the salt of its conjugate base.

**Building-block element** (2.1) One of the four nonmetals—oxygen, carbon, hydrogen, and nitrogen—that comprise 96% of the mass of the human body.

# C

**Calorie** (6.1) A unit of energy that equals the amount of energy needed to raise the temperature of 1 g of water by 1 °C; abbreviated as cal, where 1 cal = 4.184 J.

**Carbohydrate** (20.1) A polyhydroxy aldehyde or ketone, or a compound that can be hydrolyzed to a polyhydroxy aldehyde or ketone.

**Carbonate** (3.6) A polyatomic anion with the structure $CO_3^{2-}$.

**Carbonyl group** (11.5) A carbon–oxygen double bond (C=O).

**Carboxylate anion** (17.6) The conjugate base of a carboxylic acid; general structure $RCOO^-$.

**Carboxyl group** (17.1) A COOH group.

**Carboxylic acid** (11.5) A compound that contains an OH group bonded directly to the carbonyl carbon; general structure RCOOH or $RCO_2H$.

**Catabolism** (23.1) The breakdown of large molecules into smaller ones during metabolism.

**Catalyst** (6.4) A substance that increases the rate of a reaction but is recovered unchanged at the end of the reaction.

**Cation** (2.8) A positively charged particle with fewer electrons than protons.

**Cell membrane** (19.7) The semipermeable membrane that surrounds the cell, composed of a lipid bilayer.

**Celsius scale** (1.9) One of three temperature scales in which water freezes at 0 °C and boils at 100 °C.

**Cephalin** (19.6) A phosphoacylglycerol in which the identity of the R group esterified to the phosphodiester is $-CH_2CH_2NH_3^+$. A cephalin is also called a phosphatidylethanolamine.

**Chain reaction** (10.6) The process by which each neutron produced during fission can go on to bombard three other nuclei to produce more nuclei and more neutrons.

**Charles's law** (7.3) A gas law that states that for a fixed amount of gas at constant pressure, the volume of the gas is proportional to its Kelvin temperature.

**Chemical equation** (5.1) An expression that uses chemical formulas and other symbols to illustrate what reactants constitute the starting materials in a reaction and what products are formed.

**Chemical formula** (2.1) A representation that uses element symbols to show the identity of elements in a compound, and subscripts to show the number of atoms of each element contained in the compound.

**Chemical properties** (1.2) Those properties that determine how a substance can be converted to another substance by a chemical reaction.

**Chemistry** (1.1) The study of matter—its composition, properties, and transformations.

**Chiral** (15.2) Not superimposable on a mirror image.

**Chirality center** (15.2) A carbon atom bonded to four different groups.

**Chlorination** (13.13) A reaction with chlorine in which a Cl atom substitutes for a hydrogen atom.

**Chlorofluorocarbon** (14.9) A halogen-containing compound having the general molecular formula $CF_xCl_{4-x}$.

**Cis isomer** (13.3) An alkene with two R groups on the same side of the double bond.

**Citric acid cycle** (23.5) A cyclic metabolic pathway that begins with the addition of acetyl CoA to a four-carbon substrate and ends when the same four-carbon compound is formed as a product eight steps later.

**Codon** (22.7) A sequence of three nucleotides (triplet) in mRNA that codes for a specific amino acid.

**Coenzyme** (14.6, 21.9) An organic molecule needed for an enzyme-catalyzed reaction to occur.

**Coenzyme A** (23.4) A coenzyme that contains a sulfhydryl group (SH group) making it a thiol (RSH), and abbreviated as HS–CoA.

**Cofactor** (21.9) A metal ion or a nonprotein organic molecule needed for an enzyme-catalyzed reaction to occur.

**Colligative properties** (8.7) The properties of a solution that depend on the concentration of the solute but not its identity.

**Colloid** (8.1) A homogeneous mixture with large particles, often having an opaque appearance.

**Combined gas law** (7.3) A gas law that relates pressure, volume, and temperature. For a constant number of moles, the product of pressure and volume divided by temperature is a constant.

**Combustion** (12.8) An oxidation reaction in which carbon-containing compounds react with oxygen to form carbon dioxide ($CO_2$) and water.

**Competitive inhibitor** (21.9) An enzyme inhibitor that has a shape and structure similar to the substrate, and competes with the substrate for binding to the active site.

**Complementary base pairs** (22.3) The predictable pairing of bases between two strands of DNA. Adenine pairs with thymine using two hydrogen bonds, forming an A–T base pair, and cytosine pairs with guanine using three hydrogen bonds, forming a C–G base pair.

**Compound** (1.3) A pure substance formed by chemically combining two or more elements.

**Concentration** (8.4) The amount of solute dissolved in a given amount of solution.

**Condensation** (7.8, 7.10) The conversion of a gas to a liquid.

**Condensation polymer** (17.10) A polymer formed when monomers containing two functional groups come together with loss of a small molecule such as water.

**Condensed structure** (11.4) A representation used for a compound having a chain of atoms bonded together. The atoms are drawn in, but the two-electron bond lines and lone pairs on heteroatoms are generally omitted.

**Conjugate acid** (9.2) The product formed by the gain of a proton by a base.

**Conjugate acid–base pair** (9.2) Two species that differ by the presence of a proton.

**Conjugate base** (9.2) The product formed by loss of a proton from an acid.

**Conjugated protein** (21.7) A compound composed of a protein unit and a nonprotein molecule.

**Constitutional isomers** (12.2) Isomers that differ in the way the atoms are connected to each other.

**Conversion factor** (1.7) A term that converts a quantity in one unit to a quantity in another unit.

**Cooling curve** (7.11) A graph that shows how the temperature of a substance changes as heat is removed.

**Cori cycle** (24.6) The cycling of lactate from the muscle to the liver, where it is re-oxidized to pyruvate and converted to glucose. Glucose is then transported back to the muscle, where it undergoes glycolysis.

**Coupled reactions** (23.3) Pairs of reactions that occur together. The energy released by an energetically favorable reaction drives an energetically unfavorable reaction.

**Covalent bond** (3.1) A chemical bond that results from the sharing of electrons between two atoms.

**Critical mass** (10.6) The amount of a radioactive element required to sustain a chain reaction.

**Cross formula** (15.6) A Fischer projection formula that replaces a chirality center with a cross. The horizontal lines represent wedged bonds and the vertical lines represent dashed bonds.

**Crystalline solid** (7.9) A solid with a regular arrangement of particles—atoms, molecules, or ions—with a repeating structure.

**C-Terminal amino acid** (21.4) In a peptide, the amino acid with the free –$COO^-$ group on the α carbon.

**Cubic centimeter** (1.4) A unit of volume equal to one milliliter; one cubic centimeter = 1 cm$^3$ = 1 cc.

**Curie** (10.4) A unit used to measure radioactivity and equal to $3.7 \times 10^{10}$ disintegrations/s. A curie corresponds to the decay rate of one gram of the element radium.

**Cyclic hemiacetal** (16.8) A compound formed by an intramolecular reaction of a hydroxyl group and an aldehyde or ketone.

**Cycloalkane** (12.1) A compound with the general formula $C_nH_{2n}$ that contains carbons joined in one or more rings.

# D

**Dalton's law** (7.6) A law that states that the total pressure ($P_{total}$) of a gas mixture is equal to the sum of the partial pressures of its component gases.

*d* **Block** (2.6) A group of elements consisting of the 10 columns of transition metals in the periodic table. The *d* subshell is filled last in these elements.

**Decarboxylation** (24.2) The loss of carbon dioxide ($CO_2$) from a compound.

**Dehydration** (14.5) The loss of water ($H_2O$) from a starting material.

**Deletion mutation** (22.9) The loss of one or more nucleotides from a DNA molecule.

**Denaturation** (21.8) The process of altering the shape of a protein without breaking the amide bonds that form the primary structure.

**Dendrites** (18.8) Numerous small filaments at the end of a neuron.

**Density** (1.10) A physical property that relates the mass of a substance to its volume; density = g/(mL or cc).

**Deoxyribonucleic acid** (DNA, 22.1, 22.3) A polymer of deoxyribo-nucleotides that stores the genetic information of an organism and transmits that information from one generation to another.

**Deoxyribonucleoside** (22.1) A compound that contains the monosaccharide 2-deoxyribose and a purine or pyrimidine base.

**Deoxyribonucleotide** (22.1) A compound that contains the monosaccharide 2-deoxyribose bonded to a purine or pyrimidine base, as well as a phosphate at the 5'-OH group.

**Deposition** (7.10) The conversion of a gas directly to a solid.

**Deuterium** (2.3) A hydrogen atom having one proton and one neutron, giving it a mass number of two.

**Dextrorotatory** (15.7) Rotating plane-polarized light in the clockwise direction. The rotation is labeled (+).

**Dialysis** (8.8) A process that involves the selective passage of substances across a semipermeable membrane, called a dialyzing membrane.

**Diastereomers** (15.8) Stereoisomers that are not mirror images of each other.

**Diatomic molecule** (4.1) A molecule that contains two atoms. Hydrogen ($H_2$) is a diatomic molecule.

**Dilution** (8.6) The addition of solvent to a solution to decrease the concentration of solute.

**Diol** (14.3) A compound with two hydroxyl groups, also called a glycol.

**Dipeptide** (21.4) A peptide formed from two amino acids joined together by one amide bond.

**Dipole** (4.7) The separation of charge in a bond or molecule.

**Dipole–dipole interactions** (7.7) The attractive intermolecular forces between the permanent dipoles of two polar molecules.

**Diprotic acid** (9.1) An acid that contains two acidic protons.

**Disaccharide** (20.1) A carbohydrate composed of two monosaccharides joined together.

**Dissociation** (9.3) The splitting apart of a covalent molecule (or an ionic compound) into individual ions.

**Disulfide** (14.10) A compound that contains a sulfur–sulfur bond.

**DNA fingerprinting** (22.10) A technique in which DNA is amplified using PCR and cut into fragments that are separated by size using gel electrophoresis. This forms a set of horizontal bands, each band corresponding to a segment of DNA, sorted from low to high molecular weight.

**Double bond** (4.2) A multiple bond that contains four electrons—that is, two two-electron bonds.

**Double-headed arrow** (13.9) An arrow drawn between resonance structures.

# E

**Eicosanoids** (19.11) A group of biologically active compounds containing 20 carbon atoms derived from arachidonic acid.

**Electrolyte** (8.1) A substance that conducts an electric current in water.

**Electron** (2.2) A negatively charged subatomic particle.

**Electron cloud** (2.2) The space surrounding the nucleus of an atom, which contains electrons and comprises most of the volume of an atom.

**Electron-dot symbol** (2.7) A symbol that shows the number of valence electrons around an atom.

**Electronegativity** (4.7) A measure of an atom's attraction for electrons in a bond.

**Electronic configuration** (2.6) The arrangement of electrons in an atom's orbitals.

**Electron transport chain** (23.6) A series of reactions that transfers electrons from reduced coenzymes to progressively stronger oxidizing agents, ultimately converting oxygen to water.

**Element** (1.3) A pure substance that cannot be broken down into simpler substances by a chemical reaction.

**Elimination** (14.5) A reaction in which elements of the starting material are "lost" and a new multiple bond is formed.

**Enantiomers** (15.2) Mirror images that are not superimposable.

**Endothermic reaction** (6.2) A chemical reaction where $\Delta H$ is positive (+) and energy is absorbed.

**Energy** (6.1) The capacity to do work.

**Energy diagram** (6.3) A schematic representation of the energy changes in a reaction, which plots energy on the vertical axis and the progress of the reaction—the reaction coordinate—on the horizontal axis.

**Energy of activation** (6.3) The difference in energy between the reactants and the transition state; symbolized by $E_a$.

**English system of measurement** (1.4) A system of measurement used primarily in the United States in which units are not systematically related to each other and require memorization.

**Enthalpy change** (6.2) The energy absorbed or released in any reaction—also called the heat of reaction and symbolized by $\Delta H$.

**Enzyme** (6.4, 21.9) A biological catalyst composed of one or more chains of amino acids in a very specific three-dimensional shape.

**Enzyme–substrate complex** (21.9) A structure composed of a substrate bonded to the active site of an enzyme.

**Epoxide** (14.7) A cyclic ether containing an oxygen atom in a three-membered ring.

**Equilibrium** (6.5) A reaction that consists of forward and reverse reactions that have equal reaction rates, so the concentration of each species does not change.

**Equilibrium constant** (6.5) A characteristic value for a reaction at a given temperature and equal to the ratio of the concentrations of the products multiplied together to the concentrations of the reactants multiplied together. Each term is raised to a power equal to its coefficient in the balanced chemical equation.

**Ester** (11.5) A compound that contains an alkoxy group (OR) bonded directly to the carbonyl carbon; general structure RCOOR.

**Estrogen** (19.9) A hormone that controls the development of secondary sex characteristics in females and regulates the menstrual cycle.

**Ether** (14.1) A compound that has two alkyl groups bonded to an oxygen atom; general structure ROR.

**Evaporation** (7.8) The conversion of liquid molecules to gas molecules.

**Exact number** (1.5) A number that results from counting objects or is part of a definition.

**Exothermic reaction** (6.2) A reaction in which energy is released and $\Delta H$ is negative (−).

# F

**Facilitated transport** (19.7) The process by which some ions and molecules travel through the channels in a cell membrane created by integral proteins.

**Factor–label method** (1.7) A method of using conversion factors to convert a quantity in one unit to a quantity in another unit.

**FAD** (flavin adenine dinucleotide, 23.4) A biological oxidizing agent synthesized in cells from vitamin $B_2$, riboflavin. FAD is reduced by adding two hydrogen atoms, forming $FADH_2$.

**$FADH_2$** (23.4) A biological reducing agent and coenzyme formed when FAD is reduced.

**Fahrenheit scale** (1.9) One of three temperature scales in which water freezes at 32 °F and boils at 212 °F.

**Fat** (13.3, 19.4) A triacylglycerol with few double bonds, making it a solid at room temperature.

**Fat-soluble vitamin** (11.7, 19.10) A vitamin that dissolves in an organic solvent but is insoluble in water. Vitamins A, D, E, and K are fat soluble.

**Fatty acid** (13.3, 19.2) A carboxylic acid (RCOOH) with a long carbon chain, usually containing 12–20 carbon atoms.

**$f$ Block** (2.6) A group of elements consisting of the two rows of inner transition metals. The $f$ subshell is filled last in these elements.

**Fermentation** (24.4) The anaerobic conversion of glucose to ethanol and $CO_2$.

**Fibrous protein** (21.7) A water-insoluble protein composed of long linear polypeptide chains that are bundled together to form rods or sheets.

**Fischer esterification** (17.8) Treatment of a carboxylic acid (RCOOH) with an alcohol (R'OH) and an acid catalyst to form an ester (RCOOR').

**Fischer projection formula** (15.6) A method of drawing chiral compounds with the chirality center at the intersection of a cross. The horizontal bonds are assumed to be wedges and the vertical bonds are assumed to be dashed lines.

**Formula weight** (5.4) The sum of the atomic weights of all the atoms in a compound, reported in atomic mass units (amu).

**Forward reaction** (6.5) In equilibrium, a reaction that proceeds from left to right as drawn.

**Freezing** (7.10) The conversion of a liquid to a solid.

**Freezing point depression** (8.7) The decrease in the melting point of a liquid solution due to the presence of a nonvolatile solute.

**Functional group** (11.5) An atom or a group of atoms with characteristic chemical and physical properties.

# G

**Gamma (γ) ray** (10.1) High-energy radiation released from a radioactive nucleus.

**Gas** (1.2) A state of matter that has no definite shape or volume. The particles of a gas move randomly and are separated by a distance much larger than their size.

**Gas laws** (7.3) A series of laws that relate the pressure, volume, and temperature of a gas.

**Gay–Lussac's law** (7.3) A gas law that states for a fixed amount of gas at constant volume, the pressure of the gas is proportional to its Kelvin temperature.

**Geiger counter** (10.4) A small portable device used for measuring radioactivity.

**Gene** (22.1) A portion of a DNA molecule responsible for the synthesis of a single protein.

**Genetic code** (22.7) The sequence of nucleotides in mRNA (coded in triplets) that specifies the amino acid sequence of a protein. Each triplet is called a codon.

**Genetic disease** (22.9) A disease resulting from a mutation that causes a condition to be inherited from one generation to another.

**Genetic engineering** (22.10) The process of manipulating DNA in the laboratory that allows a gene in one organism to be spliced into the DNA of another organism.

**Globular protein** (21.7) A protein that is coiled into a compact shape with a hydrophilic outer surface to make it water soluble.

**Glucogenic amino acid** (24.9) An amino acid that can be used to synthesize glucose.

**Gluconeogenesis** (24.6) The synthesis of glucose from noncarbohydrate sources—lactate, amino acids, or glycerol.

**Glycol** (14.3) A compound with two hydroxyl groups, also called a diol.

**Glycolysis** (24.3) A linear, 10-step pathway that converts glucose, a six-carbon monosaccharide, to two three-carbon pyruvate molecules.

**α Glycoside** (20.5) A monosaccharide with the OR group on the anomeric carbon oriented below the plane of the ring.

**β Glycoside** (20.5) A monosaccharide with the OR group on the anomeric carbon oriented above the plane of the ring.

**Glycosidic linkage** (20.5) The acetal C–O bond that joins two monosaccharides together.

**Gram** (1.4) The basic unit of mass in the metric system; abbreviated as g.

**Gray** (10.4) A unit that measures absorbed radiation; abbreviated as Gy.

**Greenhouse gas** (12.8) A gas that absorbs thermal energy that normally radiates from the earth's surface, and redirects it back to the surface.

**Ground state** (2.6) The lowest energy arrangement of electrons.

**Group** (2.4) A column in the periodic table.

**Group number** (2.4) A number that identifies a particular column in the periodic table.

# H

**Half-life** (10.3) The time it takes for one-half of a sample to decay.

**Half reaction** (5.9) An equation written for an individual oxidation or reduction that shows how many electrons are gained or lost.

**Halogen** (2.4) An element located in group 7A (group 17) of the periodic table. Halogens include fluorine (F), chlorine (Cl), bromine (Br), iodine (I), and astatine (At).

**Halogenation** (13.6) The reaction of a compound with a halogen, $X_2$, such as the addition of $X_2$ to an alkene.

**Hardening** (13.7) The reaction of an unsaturated liquid vegetable oil with hydrogen to form a fat with a higher melting point.

**Haworth projection** (20.3) A planar, six-membered ring used to represent the cyclic hemiacetal of glucose and other sugars.

**Heating curve** (7.11) A graph that shows how the temperature of a substance changes as heat is added.

**Heat of fusion** (7.10) The amount of energy needed to melt one gram of a substance.

**Heat of reaction** (6.2) The energy absorbed or released in any reaction and symbolized by $\Delta H$—also called the enthalpy change.

**Heat of vaporization** (7.10) The amount of energy needed to vaporize one gram of a substance.

**α-Helix** (21.6) A secondary structure of a protein formed when a peptide chain twists into a right-handed or clockwise spiral.

**Heme** (21.7) A complex organic compound containing an $Fe^{2+}$ ion complexed with a large nitrogen-containing ring system.

**Hemiacetal** (16.8) A compound that contains an OH group (hydroxyl) and an OR group (alkoxy) bonded to the same carbon.

**Henry's law** (8.3) A law that states that the solubility of a gas in a liquid is proportional to the partial pressure of the gas above the liquid.

**Heteroatom** (11.2) Any atom in an organic compound that is not carbon or hydrogen.

**Heterocycle** (14.7) A ring that contains a heteroatom.

**Heterogeneous mixture** (8.1) A mixture that does not have a uniform composition throughout a sample.

**Hexose** (20.2) A monosaccharide with six carbons.

**High-density lipoprotein** (19.8) A spherical particle that transports cholesterol from the tissues to the liver.

**Homogeneous mixture** (8.1) A mixture that has a uniform composition throughout a sample.

**Hormone** (18.9, 19.9) A compound synthesized in one part of an organism, which then travels through the bloodstream to elicit a response at a target tissue or organ.

**Hybrid** (13.9) A composite of two or more resonance forms.

**Hydration** (13.6) The addition of water to a molecule.

**Hydrocarbon** (11.5) A compound that contains only the elements of carbon and hydrogen.

**Hydrochlorofluorocarbon** (14.9) A compound such as $CF_3CHCl_2$ that contains the elements of H, Cl, and F bonded to carbon.

**Hydrofluorocarbon** (14.9) A compound such as $FCH_2CF_3$ that contains the elements of H and F bonded to carbon.

**Hydrogenation** (13.6) The addition of hydrogen ($H_2$) to an alkene.

**Hydrogen bonding** (7.7) An attractive intermolecular force that occurs when a hydrogen atom bonded to O, N, or F is electrostatically attracted to an O, N, or F atom in another molecule.

**Hydrohalogenation** (13.6) The addition of HX (X = Cl or Br) to an alkene.

**Hydrolysis** (16.8) A cleavage reaction that uses water.

**Hydrolyzable lipid** (19.1) A lipid that can be converted to smaller molecules by hydrolysis with water.

**Hydronium ion** (3.6) The $H_3O^+$ ion.

**Hydrophilic** (19.2) The polar part of a molecule that is attracted to water.

**Hydrophobic** (19.2) The nonpolar part of a molecule (C–C and C–H bonds) that is not attracted to water.

**Hydroxide** (3.6) The $OH^-$ ion.

**α-Hydroxy acid** (17.4) A compound that contains a hydroxyl group on the α carbon to a carboxyl group.

**Hydroxyl group** (11.5) An OH group.

**Hypertonic solution** (8.8) A solution that has a higher osmotic pressure than body fluids.

**Hypotonic solution** (8.8) A solution that has a lower osmotic pressure than body fluids.

# I

**Ideal gas law** (7.5) A gas law that relates the pressure ($P$), volume ($V$), temperature ($T$), and number of moles ($n$) of a gas in a single equation; $PV = nRT$, where $R$ is a constant.

**Incomplete combustion** (12.8) An oxidation reaction that forms carbon monoxide (CO) instead of carbon dioxide ($CO_2$) because insufficient oxygen is available.

**Induced-fit model** (21.9) The binding of a substrate to an enzyme such that the shape of the active site adjusts to fit the shape of the substrate.

**Inexact number** (1.5) A number that results from a measurement or observation and contains some uncertainty.

**Inhibitor** (21.9) A molecule that causes an enzyme to lose activity.

**Inner transition metal elements** (2.4) A group of elements consisting of the lanthanides and actinides.

**Insertion mutation** (22.9) The addition of one or more nucleotides to a DNA molecule.

**Intermolecular forces** (7.7) The attractive forces that exist between molecules.

**Ion** (3.1) A charged species in which the number of protons and electrons in an atom is not equal.

**Ion–dipole interaction** (8.2) The attraction of an ion to a dipole in another molecule.

**Ionic bond** (3.1) A bond that results from the transfer of electrons from one element to another.

**Ionic solid** (7.9) A solid composed of oppositely charged ions in a regular arrangement.

**Ionization energy** (2.8) The energy needed to remove an electron from a neutral atom.

**Ion–product constant, $K_w$** (9.5) The product of the concentrations of $H_3O^+$ and $OH^-$ in water or an aqueous solution—symbolized by $K_w$ and equal to $1 \times 10^{-14}$.

**Irreversible inhibitor** (21.9) An inhibitor that covalently binds to an enzyme, permanently destroying its activity.

**Isoelectric point** (21.3) The pH at which an amino acid exists primarily in its neutral form; abbreviated as p$I$.

**Isomerase** (24.2) An enzyme that catalyzes the conversion of one isomer to another.

**Isomers** (12.2) Two different compounds with the same molecular formula.

**Isotonic solution** (8.8) Two solutions with the same osmotic pressure.

**Isotopes** (2.3) Atoms of the same element having a different number of neutrons.

**IUPAC nomenclature** (12.3) A systematic method of naming compounds developed by the International Union of Pure and Applied Chemistry.

# J

**Joule** (6.1) A unit of measurement for energy; abbreviated as J, where 1 cal = 4.184 J.

# K

**Kelvin scale** (1.9) A temperature scale commonly used by scientists. The Kelvin scale is divided into kelvins (K); K = °C + 273.

**Ketogenesis** (24.8) The synthesis of ketone bodies from acetyl CoA.

**Ketogenic amino acid** (24.9) An amino acid that cannot be used to synthesize glucose, but can be converted to ketone bodies.

**Ketone** (11.5) A compound that has two alkyl groups bonded to the carbonyl group; general structure RCOR.

**Ketone bodies** (24.8) Three compounds—acetoacetate, β-hydroxybutyrate, and acetone—formed when acetyl CoA levels exceed the capacity of the citric acid cycle.

**Ketose** (20.2) A monosaccharide with a carbonyl group at C2.

**Ketosis** (24.8) The accumulation of ketone bodies during starvation and uncontrolled diabetes.

**Kinase** (24.2) An enzyme that catalyzes the transfer of a phosphate group from one substrate to another.

**Kinetic energy** (6.1) The energy of motion.

**Kinetic-molecular theory** (7.2) A theory that describes the fundamental characteristics of gas particles.

# L

**Lactam** (17.1) A cyclic amide.

**Lactone** (17.1) A cyclic ester.

**Lagging strand** (22.4) The strand of DNA synthesized in small fragments during replication, which are then joined together by a DNA ligase enzyme.

**Lanthanides** (2.4) A group of 14 elements in the periodic table beginning with the element cerium ($Z = 58$) and immediately following the element lanthanum (La).

**Law of conservation of energy** (6.1) A law that states that the total energy in the universe does not change. Energy cannot be created or destroyed.

**Law of conservation of mass** (5.1) A law that states that atoms cannot be created or destroyed in a chemical reaction.

**$LD_{50}$** (10.4) The lethal dose of radiation (or a poison) that kills 50% of a population.

**Leading strand** (22.4) The strand of DNA that grows continuously during replication.

**Le Châtelier's principle** (6.6) A principle that states that if a chemical system at equilibrium is disturbed or stressed, the system will react in the direction that counteracts the disturbance or relieves the stress.

**Lecithin** (19.6) A phosphoacylglycerol in which the identity of the R group esterified to the phosphodiester is $-CH_2CH_2N(CH_3)_3^+$. A lecithin is also called a phosphatidylcholine.

**Leukotriene** (19.11) A molecule synthesized in several steps from arachidonic acid, which contributes to the asthmatic response by constricting smooth muscles, especially in the lungs.

**Levorotatory** (15.7) Rotating plane-polarized light in the counterclockwise direction. The rotation is labeled as (–).

**Lewis structure** (4.1) An electron-dot structure for a molecule that shows the location of all valence electrons in the molecule, both the shared electrons in bonds and the nonbonded electron pairs.

**"Like dissolves like"** (11.6) The principle in solubility that compounds dissolve in solvents having similar types of intermolecular forces.

**Limiting reactant** (5.8) The reactant that is completely used up in a reaction.

**Lipid** (17.9, 19.1) A biomolecule that is soluble in organic solvents and insoluble in water.

**Lipid bilayer** (19.7) The basic structure of the cell membrane formed from two layers of phospholipids having their ionic heads oriented on the outside and their nonpolar tails on the inside.

**Lipoprotein** (19.8) A small water-soluble spherical particle composed of proteins and lipids.

**Liquid** (1.2) A state of matter that has a definite volume, but takes on the shape of the container it occupies. The particles of a liquid are close together but they can randomly move past each other.

**Liter** (1.4) The basic unit of volume in the metric system; abbreviated as L.

**Lock-and-key model** (21.9) The binding of a substrate to a rigid active site, such that the three-dimensional geometry of the substrate exactly matches the shape of the active site.

**London dispersion forces** (7.7) Very weak intermolecular interactions due to the momentary changes in electron density in a molecule.

**Lone pair** (4.1) An unshared electron pair.

**Low-density lipoprotein** (19.8) A spherical particle containing proteins and lipids, which transports cholesterol from the liver to the tissues.

# M

**Main group element** (2.4) An element in groups 1A–8A of the periodic table.

**Major mineral** (macronutrient, 2.1) One of the seven elements present in the body in small amounts (0.1–2% by mass) and needed in the daily diet.

**Markovnikov's rule** (13.6) The rule that states that in the addition of HX to an unsymmetrical alkene, the H atom bonds to the less substituted carbon atom.

**Mass** (1.4) A measure of the amount of matter in an object.

**Mass number** (2.2) The total number of protons and neutrons in a nucleus; symbolized as $A$.

**Matter** (1.1) Anything that has mass and takes up volume.

**Melting** (7.10) The conversion of a solid to a liquid.

**Melting point** (mp, 7.7) The temperature at which a solid is converted to the liquid phase.

**Messenger RNA** (mRNA, 22.5) The carrier of information from DNA (in the cell nucleus) to the ribosomes (in the cell cytoplasm). Each gene of a DNA molecule corresponds to a specific mRNA molecule.

**Metabolism** (23.1) The sum of all of the chemical reactions that take place in an organism.

**Meta isomer** (13.10) A 1,3-disubstituted benzene.

**Metal** (2.1) A shiny element that is a good conductor of heat and electricity.

**Metallic solid** (7.9) A lattice of metal cations surrounded by a cloud of electrons that move freely.

**Metalloid** (2.1) An element with properties intermediate between a metal and a nonmetal. Metalloids include boron (B), silicon (Si), germanium (Ge), arsenic (As), antimony (Sb), tellurium (Te), and astatine (At).

**Meter** (1.4) A unit used to measure length; abbreviated as m.

**Metric system** (1.4) A measurement system in which each type of measurement has a base unit and all other units are related to the base unit by a prefix that indicates if the unit is larger or smaller than the base unit.

**Micelle** (17.6) A spherical droplet formed when soap is dissolved in water. The ionic heads of the soap molecules are oriented on the surface and the nonpolar tails are packed in the interior.

**Millimeters of mercury** (7.2) A unit used to measure pressure; abbreviated as mm Hg and also called "torr."

**Mitochondrion** (23.1) A small sausage-shaped organelle within a cell in which energy production takes place.

**Mixture** (1.3) Matter composed of more than one component.

**Molarity** (8.5) The number of moles of solute per liter of solution; abbreviated as M.

**Molar mass** (5.4) The mass of one mole of any substance, reported in grams per mole.

**Mole** (5.3) A quantity that contains $6.02 \times 10^{23}$ items—usually atoms, molecules, or ions.

**Molecular formula** (4.2) A formula that shows the number and identity of all of the atoms in a compound, but it does not indicate what atoms are bonded to each other.

**Molecular solid** (7.9) A solid composed of individual molecules arranged regularly.

**Molecular weight** (5.4) The formula weight of a covalent compound.

**Molecule** (4.1) A discrete group of atoms that are held together by covalent bonds.

**Monomers** (13.8) Small molecules that covalently bond together to form polymers.

**Monoprotic acid** (9.1) An acid that contains one acidic proton.

**Monosaccharide** (20.1) A carbohydrate that cannot be hydrolyzed to simpler compounds.

**D Monosaccharide** (20.2) A carbohydrate that has the OH group on the chirality center farthest from the carbonyl on the right.

**L Monosaccharide** (20.2) A carbohydrate that has the OH group on the chirality center farthest from the carbonyl on the left.

**Multiple bond** (4.2) A chemical bond that contains four or six electrons—that is, a double or a triple bond.

**Mutarotation** (20.3) The process by which a single anomer of a monosaccharide equilibrates to a mixture of anomers.

**Mutation** (22.9) A change in the nucleotide sequence in a molecule of DNA.

# N

**NAD$^+$** (nicotinamide adenine dinucleotide, 16.6, 23.4) A biological oxidizing agent and coenzyme synthesized from the vitamin niacin. NAD$^+$ and NADH are interconverted by oxidation and reduction reactions.

**NADH** (16.6, 23.4) A biological reducing agent and coenzyme formed when NAD$^+$ is reduced.

**Net ionic equation** (9.7) An equation that contains only the species involved in a reaction.

**Network solid** (7.9) A solid composed of a vast number of atoms covalently bonded together, forming sheets or three-dimensional arrays.

**Neuron** (18.8) A nerve cell.

**Neurotransmitter** (18.8) A chemical messenger that transmits nerve impulses from one nerve cell to another cell.

**Neutralization reaction** (9.7) An acid–base reaction that produces a salt and water as products.

**Neutral solution** (9.5) Any solution that has an equal concentration of $H_3O^+$ and $OH^-$ ions and a pH = 7.

**Neutron** (2.2) A neutral subatomic particle in the nucleus.

**Nitration** (13.13) Substitution of a nitro group ($NO_2$) for a hydrogen.

**Nitro group** (13.13) An $NO_2$ group.

**Noble gases** (2.4) Elements located in group 8A (group 18) of the periodic table. The noble gases are helium (He), neon (Ne), argon (Ar), krypton (Kr), xenon (Xe), and radon (Rn).

**Nomenclature** (3.4) The system of assigning an unambiguous name to a compound.

**Nonbonded electron pair** (4.1) An unshared electron pair or lone pair.

**Noncompetitive inhibitor** (21.9) An inhibitor that binds to an enzyme but does not bind at the active site.

**Nonelectrolyte** (8.1) A substance that does not conduct an electric current when dissolved in water.

**Nonhydrolyzable lipid** (19.1) A lipid that cannot be cleaved into smaller units by aqueous hydrolysis.

**Nonmetal** (2.1) An element that does not have a shiny appearance and poorly conducts heat and electricity.

**Nonpolar bond** (4.7) A bond in which electrons are equally shared.

**Nonpolar molecule** (11.6) A molecule that has no net dipole.

**Nonreducing sugar** (20.4) A sugar that does not react with Benedict's reagent.

**Nonvolatile** (8.7) Not readily vaporized.

**Normal boiling point** (7.8) The temperature at which the vapor pressure above a liquid equals 760 mm Hg.

**N-Terminal amino acid** (21.4) In a peptide, the amino acid with the free $-NH_3^+$ group on the α carbon.

**Nuclear fission** (10.6) The splitting apart of a nucleus into lighter nuclei and neutrons.

**Nuclear fusion** (10.6) The joining together of two nuclei to form a larger nucleus.

**Nuclear reaction** (10.1) A reaction that involves the subatomic particles of the nucleus.

**Nucleic acid** (22.1, 22.2) An unbranched polymer composed of nucleotides. DNA and RNA are nucleic acids.

**Nucleoside** (22.1) A compound formed by joining the anomeric carbon of a monosaccharide with a nitrogen atom of a purine or pyrimidine base.

**Nucleotide** (22.1) A compound formed by adding a phosphate group to the 5'-OH of a nucleoside.

**Nucleus** (2.2) The dense core of the atom that contains protons and neutrons.

**Nylon** (17.10) A condensation polymer that contains many amide bonds.

## O

**Octet rule** (3.2) The rule in bonding that states that main group elements are especially stable when they possess eight electrons (an octet) in the outer shell.

**Oil** (13.3, 19.4) A triacylglycerol that is liquid at room temperature.

**Omega-$n$ acid** (19.2) An unsaturated fatty acid where $n$ is the carbon at which the first double bond occurs in the carbon chain. The numbering begins at the end of the chain with the $CH_3$ group.

**Optically active** (15.7) Able to rotate the plane of polarized light.

**Optically inactive** (15.7) Not able to rotate the plane of polarized light.

**Orbital** (2.5) A region of space where the probability of finding an electron is high.

**Organic chemistry** (11.1) The study of compounds that contain the element carbon.

**Ortho isomer** (13.10) A 1,2-disubstituted benzene.

**Osmosis** (8.8) The selective diffusion of solvent, usually water, across a semipermeable membrane from a less concentrated solution to a more concentrated solution.

**Osmotic pressure** (8.8) The pressure that prevents the flow of additional solvent into a solution on one side of a semipermeable membrane.

**Oxidation** (5.9, 12.8) The loss of electrons from an atom. Oxidation may result in a gain of oxygen atoms or a loss of hydrogen atoms.

**β-Oxidation** (24.7) A process in which two-carbon acetyl CoA units are sequentially cleaved from a fatty acid.

**Oxidative deamination** (24.9) The process by which the C–H and $C-NH_3^+$ bonds on the α carbon of an amino acid are converted to C=O and an ammonium ion ($NH_4^+$).

**Oxidative phosphorylation** (23.6) The process by which the energy released from the oxidation of reduced coenzymes is used to convert ADP to ATP using the enzyme ATP synthase.

**Oxidizing agent** (5.9) A compound that gains electrons (i.e., is reduced), causing another compound to be oxidized.

## P

**Para isomer** (13.10) A 1,4-disubstituted benzene.

**Parent name** (12.4) The root that indicates the number of carbons in the longest continuous carbon chain in a molecule.

**Partial hydrogenation** (13.7) The hydrogenation of some, but not all, of the double bonds in a molecule.

**Partial pressure** (7.6) The pressure exerted by one component of a mixture of gases.

**Parts per million** (8.4) A concentration term (abbreviated ppm)—the number of "parts" in 1,000,000 parts of solution.

**$p$ Block** (2.6) The elements in groups 3A–8A (except helium) in the periodic table. The $p$ subshell is filled last in these elements.

**Penicillin** (17.11) An antibiotic that contains a β-lactam and interferes with the synthesis of the bacterial cell wall.

**Pentose** (20.2) A monosaccharide with five carbons.

**Peptide** (21.4) A compound that contains many amino acids joined together by amide bonds.

**Peptide bond** (21.4) An amide bond in peptides and proteins.

**Percent yield** (5.7) The amount of product actually formed in a particular reaction divided by the theoretical yield, multiplied by 100%.

**Period** (2.4) A row in the periodic table.

**Periodic table** (2.1) A schematic arrangement of all known elements that groups elements with similar properties.

**Petroleum** (12.6) A complex mixture of compounds, most of which are hydrocarbons containing 1–40 carbon atoms.

**Pheromone** (12.1) A chemical substance used for communication in a specific animal species, most commonly an insect population.

**Phosphate** (3.6) A $PO_4^{3-}$ anion.

**Phosphatidylcholine** (19.6) A phosphoacylglycerol in which the identity of the R group esterified to the phosphodiester is $-CH_2CH_2N(CH_3)_3^+$; also called a lecithin.

**Phosphatidylethanolamine** (19.6) A phosphoacylglycerol in which the identity of the R group esterified to the phosphodiester is $-CH_2CH_2NH_3^+$; also called a cephalin.

**Phosphoacylglycerol** (19.6) A lipid with a glycerol backbone that contains two of the hydroxyls esterified with fatty acids and the third hydroxyl as part of a phosphodiester.

**Phosphodiester** (19.6) A derivative of phosphoric acid ($H_3PO_4$) that is formed by replacing two of the H atoms by R groups.

**Phospholipid** (19.6) A lipid that contains a phosphorus atom.

**Phosphorylation** (23.3) A reaction that adds a phosphate group to a molecule.

**pH scale** (9.6) The scale used to report the $H_3O^+$ concentration; $pH = -\log [H_3O^+]$.

**Physical properties** (1.2) Those properties of a substance that can be observed or measured without changing the composition of the material.

**Plane-polarized light** (15.7) Light that consists of waves that oscillate in a single plane. Plane-polarized light arises from passing ordinary light through a polarizer.

**Plasmid** (22.10) A circular, double-stranded DNA molecule isolated from bacteria.

**β-Pleated sheet** (21.6) A secondary structure formed when two or more peptide chains, called strands, line up side-by-side.

**Point mutation** (22.9) The substitution of one nucleotide for another.

**Polar bond** (4.7) A bond in which electrons are unequally shared and pulled towards the more electronegative element.

**Polarimeter** (15.7) An instrument that measures the degree which a compound rotates plane-polarized light.

**Polar molecule** (11.6) A molecule that contains a net dipole.

**Polyamide** (17.10) A class of condensation polymer that contains many amide bonds.

**Polyatomic ion** (3.6) A cation or anion that contains more than one atom.

**Polycyclic aromatic hydrocarbon** (13.11) A compound containing two or more benzene rings that share a carbon–carbon bond.

**Polyester** (17.10) A class of condensation polymer that contains many ester bonds.

**Polymer** (13.8) A large molecule made up of repeating units of smaller molecules—called monomers—covalently bonded together.

**Polymerase chain reaction** (22.10) A technique that produces exact copies of a fragment of DNA.

**Polymerization** (13.8) The joining together of monomers to make polymers.

**Polynucleotide** (22.2) A polymer of nucleotides that contains a sugar–phosphate backbone.

**Polysaccharide** (20.1) Three or more monosaccharides joined together.

*p* **Orbital** (2.5) A dumbbell-shaped orbital higher in energy than an *s* orbital in the same shell.

**Positron** (10.1) A radioactive particle that has a negligible mass and a +1 charge.

**Postsynaptic neuron** (18.8) A nerve cell that contains the receptors that bind a neurotransmitter.

**Potential energy** (6.1) Energy that is stored.

**Pressure** (7.2) The force ($F$) exerted per unit area ($A$); symbolized by $P$.

**Presynaptic neuron** (18.8) A nerve cell that releases a neurotransmitter.

**Primary (1°) alcohol** (14.2) An alcohol having the general structure $RCH_2OH$.

**Primary (1°) alkyl halide** (14.9) An alkyl halide having the general structure $RCH_2X$.

**Primary (1°) amide** (17.1) A compound having the general structure $RCONH_2$.

**Primary (1°) amine** (18.1) A compound having the general structure $RNH_2$.

**Primary (1°) carbon** (12.2) A carbon atom bonded to one other carbon.

**Primary structure** (21.6) The particular sequence of amino acids that are joined together by peptide bonds in a protein.

**Product** (5.1) A substance formed in a chemical reaction.

**Progestin** (19.9) A hormone responsible for the preparation of the uterus for implantation of a fertilized egg.

**Prostaglandins** (17.4, 19.11) A group of carboxylic acids that contain a five-membered ring, are synthesized from arachidonic acid, and have a wide range of biological activities.

**Proteins** (21.1) Biomolecules that contain many amide bonds, formed by joining amino acids together.

**Proton** (2.2) A positively (+) charged subatomic particle that resides in the nucleus of the atom.

**Proton transfer reaction** (9.2) A Brønsted–Lowry acid–base reaction in which a proton is transferred from an acid to a base.

**Pure substance** (1.3) A substance that contains a single component, and has a constant composition regardless of the sample size.

## Q

**Quaternary ammonium ion** (18.1) A cation with the general structure $R_4N^+$.

**Quaternary (4°) carbon** (12.2) A carbon atom that is bonded to four other carbons.

**Quaternary structure** (21.6) The shape adopted when two or more folded polypeptide chains come together into one protein complex.

## R

**Racemic mixture** (15.5) An equal mixture of two enantiomers.

**Rad** (10.4) The <u>ra</u>diation <u>a</u>bsorbed <u>d</u>ose; the amount of radiation absorbed by one gram of a substance.

**Radioactive decay** (10.2) The process by which an unstable radioactive nucleus emits radiation, forming a nucleus of new composition.

**Radioactive isotope** (10.1) An isotope that is unstable and spontaneously emits energy to form a more stable nucleus.

**Radioactivity** (10.1) The energy emitted spontaneously by an unstable radioactive isotope.

**Radiocarbon dating** (10.3) A method to date artifacts that is based on the ratio of the radioactive carbon-14 isotope to the stable carbon-12 isotope.

**Reactant** (5.1) The starting material in a reaction.

**Reaction rate** (6.3) A measure of how fast a chemical reaction occurs.

**Recombinant DNA** (22.10) Synthetic DNA that contains segments from more than one source.

**Redox reaction** (5.9) A reaction that involves the transfer of electrons from one element to another.

**Reducing agent** (5.9) A compound that loses electrons (i.e., is oxidized), causing another compound to be reduced.

**Reducing sugar** (20.4) A carbohydrate that is oxidized with Benedict's reagent.

**Reduction** (5.9, 12.8) The gain of electrons by an atom. Reduction may result in the loss of oxygen atoms or the gain of hydrogen atoms.

**Refining** (12.6) The distillation of crude petroleum to form usable fractions that differ in boiling point.

**Rem** (10.4) The <u>r</u>adiation <u>e</u>quivalent for <u>man</u>; the amount of radiation absorbed by a substance that also factors in its energy and potential to damage tissue.

**Replication** (22.4) The process by which DNA makes a copy of itself when a cell divides.

**Resonance structures** (4.4) Two Lewis structures having the same arrangement of atoms but a different arrangement of electrons.

**Restriction endonuclease** (22.10) An enzyme that cuts DNA at a particular sequence of bases.

**Retrovirus** (22.11) A virus that contains a core of RNA.

**Reverse reaction** (6.5) In equilibrium, a reaction that proceeds from right to left as drawn.

**Reverse transcription** (22.11) A process by which a retrovirus produces DNA from RNA.

**Reversible inhibitor** (21.9) An inhibitor that binds to an enzyme, but enzyme activity is restored when the inhibitor is released.

**Reversible reaction** (6.5) A reaction that can occur in either direction, from reactants to products or from products to reactants.

**Ribonucleic acid** (RNA, 22.1, 22.5) A polymer of ribonucleotides that translates genetic information to protein synthesis.

**Ribonucleoside** (22.1) A compound that contains the monosaccharide ribose and a purine or pyrimidine base.

**Ribonucleotide** (22.1) A compound that contains the monosaccharide ribose bonded to either a purine or pyrimidine base as well as a phosphate at the 5'-OH group.

**Ribosomal RNA** (rRNA, 22.5) The most abundant type of RNA. rRNA is found in the ribosomes of the cell and provides the site where polypeptides are assembled during protein synthesis.

## S

**Saponification** (17.9, 19.5) The basic hydrolysis of an ester.

**Saturated fatty acids** (19.2) Fatty acids that have no double bonds in their long hydrocarbon chains.

**Saturated hydrocarbon** (12.1) An alkane with molecular formula $C_nH_{2n+2}$ that contains a chain of carbon atoms but no rings.

**Saturated solution** (8.2) A solution that has the maximum number of grams of solute that can be dissolved.

*s* **Block** (2.6) Elements located in groups 1A and 2A of the periodic table as well as the element helium. The *s* subshell is filled last in these elements.

**Scientific notation** (1.6) A system in which numbers are written as $y \times 10^x$, where *y* is a number between 1 and 10 and *x* can be either positive or negative.

**Secondary (2°) alcohol** (14.2) An alcohol having the general structure $R_2CHOH$.

**Secondary (2°) alkyl halide** (14.9) An alkyl halide having the general structure $R_2CHX$.

**Secondary (2°) amide** (17.1) A compound that has the general structure RCONHR'.

**Secondary (2°) amine** (18.1) A compound that has the general structure $R_2NH$.

**Secondary (2°) carbon** (12.2) A carbon atom that is bonded to two other carbons.

**Secondary structure** (21.6) The three-dimensional arrangement of localized regions of a protein. The α-helix and β-pleated sheet are two kinds of secondary structure.

**Semipermeable membrane** (8.8) A membrane that allows only certain molecules to pass through.

**Shell** (2.5) A region where an electron that surrounds a nucleus is confined. A shell is also called a principal energy level.

**Sievert** (10.4) A unit that measures absorbed radiation; abbreviated as Sv.

**Significant figures** (1.5) All of the digits in a measured number, including one estimated digit.

**SI units** (1.4) The International System of Units formally adopted as the uniform system of units for the sciences.

**Skeletal structure** (11.4) A shorthand method used to draw organic compounds in which carbon atoms are assumed to be at the junction of any two lines or at the end of a line, and all H's on C's are omitted.

**Soap** (17.6, 19.5) A salt of a long-chain carboxylic acid.

**Solid** (1.2) A state of matter that has a definite shape and volume. The particles of a solid lie close together, and are arranged in a regular, three-dimensional array.

**Solubility** (8.2) The amount of solute that dissolves in a given amount of solvent.

**Solute** (8.1) The substance present in the lesser amount in a solution.

**Solution** (8.1) A homogeneous mixture that contains small particles. Liquid solutions are transparent.

**Solvation** (8.2) The process of surrounding particles of a solute with solvent molecules.

**Solvent** (8.1) The substance present in the larger amount in a solution.

*s* **Orbital** (2.5) A spherical orbital that is lower in energy than other orbitals in the same shell.

**Specific gravity** (1.10) A unitless quantity that compares the density of a substance with the density of water at 4 °C.

**Specific rotation** (15.7) A physical constant for the amount that a chiral compound rotates the plane of polarized light. Specific rotation is defined with a specific sample tube length (usually 10 cm), concentration, temperature (25 °C), and wavelength.

**Spectator ion** (9.7) An ion that appears on both sides of an equation but undergoes no change in a reaction.

**Sphingomyelin** (19.6) A phospholipid derived from sphingosine, which contains a single fatty acid bonded with an amide bond to the carbon backbone.

**SSRI** (18.8) A class of antidepressants that acts by inhibiting the reuptake of serotonin by the presynaptic neuron. SSRI is an abbreviation for "selective serotonin reuptake inhibitor."

**Standard molar volume** (7.4) The volume of one mole of any gas at STP—22.4 L.

**States of matter** (1.2) The forms in which most matter exists—that is, gas, liquid, and solid.

**Stereochemistry** (15.1) The three-dimensional structure of molecules.

**Stereoisomers** (13.3) Isomers that differ only in their three-dimensional arrangement of atoms.

**Steroid** (19.8) A lipid whose carbon skeleton contains three six-membered rings and one five-membered ring.

**STP** (7.4) Standard conditions of temperature and pressure—1 atm (760 mm Hg) for pressure and 273 K (0 °C) for temperature.

**Straight-chain alkane** (12.2) An alkane that has all of its carbons in one continuous chain.

**Sublimation** (7.10) A phase change in which the solid phase enters the gas phase without passing through the liquid state.

**Subshell** (2.5) A sublevel within a shell designated by the letters *s, p, d,* or *f,* and containing one type of orbital.

**Substitution reaction** (13.13) A reaction in which an atom is replaced by another atom or a group of atoms.

**Sulfate** (3.6) An $SO_4^{2-}$ ion.

**Sulfhydryl group** (14.1) An SH group.

**Sulfonation** (13.13) The substitution of $SO_3H$ for a hydrogen.

**Supersaturated solution** (8.3) A solution that contains more than the predicted maximum amount of solute at a given temperature.

**Surface tension** (7.8) A measure of the resistance of a liquid to spread out.

**Synapse** (18.8) The gap between neurons across which neurotransmitters act.

# T

**Temperature** (1.9) A measure of how hot or cold an object is.

**Tertiary (3°) alcohol** (14.2) An alcohol that has the general structure $R_3COH$.

**Tertiary (3°) alkyl halide** (14.9) An alkyl halide that has the general structure $R_3CX$.

**Tertiary (3°) amide** (17.1) A compound that has the general structure $RCONR'_2$.

**Tertiary (3°) amine** (18.1) A compound that has the general structure $R_3N$.

**Tertiary (3°) carbon** (12.2) A carbon atom that is bonded to three other carbons.

**Tertiary structure** (21.6) The three-dimensional shape adopted by an entire peptide chain.

**Tetrose** (20.2) A monosaccharide with four carbons.

**Theoretical yield** (5.7) The amount of product expected from a given amount of reactant based on the coefficients in the balanced chemical equation.

**Thiol** (14.1) A compound that contains a sulfhydryl group (SH group) bonded to a tetrahedral carbon atom; general structure RSH.

**Titration** (9.9) A technique for determining an unknown molarity of an acid by adding a base of known molarity to a known volume of acid.

**Tollens reagent** (16.5) An oxidizing agent that contains silver(I) oxide ($Ag_2O$) in aqueous ammonium hydroxide ($NH_4OH$).

**Trace element** (micronutrient, 2.1) An element required in the daily diet in small quantities—usually less than 15 mg.

**Transamination** (24.9) The transfer of an amino group from an amino acid to an α-keto acid.

**Transcription** (22.6) The process that synthesizes RNA from DNA.

**Transfer RNA** (tRNA, 22.5) The smallest type of RNA, which brings a specific amino acid to the site of protein synthesis on a ribosome.

**Trans isomer** (13.3) An alkene with two R groups on opposite sides of a double bond.

**Transition metal element** (2.4) An element contained in one of the 10 columns in the periodic table numbered 1B–8B.

**Transition state** (6.3) The unstable intermediate located at the top of the energy hill in an energy diagram.

**Translation** (22.8) The synthesis of proteins from RNA.

**Triacylglycerol** (17.9, 19.4) A triester formed from glycerol and three molecules of fatty acids.

**Triol** (14.3) A compound with three hydroxyl groups.

**Triose** (20.2) A monosaccharide with three carbons.

**Tripeptide** (21.4) A peptide that contains three amino acids joined together by two amide bonds.

**Triple bond** (4.2) A multiple bond that contains six electrons—that is, three two-electron bonds.

**Triprotic acid** (9.1) An acid that contains three acidic protons.

**Tritium** (2.3) A hydrogen atom that has one proton and two neutrons, giving it a mass number of three.

# U

**Universal gas constant** (7.5) The constant, symbolized by $R$, that equals the product of the pressure and volume of a gas, divided by the product of the number of moles and Kelvin temperature; $R = PV/nT$.

**Unpaired electron** (2.6) A single electron.

**Unsaturated fatty acid** (19.2) A fatty acid that has one or more double bonds in its long hydrocarbon chain.

**Unsaturated hydrocarbon** (13.1) A compound that contains fewer than the maximum number of hydrogen atoms per carbon.

**Unsaturated solution** (8.2) A solution that has less than the maximum number of grams of solute.

**Urea cycle** (24.9) The process by which an ammonium ion is converted to urea, $(NH_2)_2C{=}O$.

# V

**Valence electron** (2.7) An electron in the outermost shell that takes part in bonding and chemical reactions.

**Valence shell electron pair repulsion (VSEPR) theory** (4.6) A theory that predicts molecular geometry based on the fact that electron pairs repel each other; thus, the most stable arrangement keeps these groups as far away from each other as possible.

**Vapor** (7.8) Gas molecules formed from the evaporation of a liquid.

**Vaporization** (7.10) The conversion of a liquid to a gas.

**Vapor pressure** (7.8) The pressure above a liquid exerted by gas molecules in equilibrium with the liquid phase.

**Vesicle** (18.8) A small packet where neurotransmitters are stored, located in the filaments of the axon of a neuron near the synapse.

**Virus** (22.11) An infectious agent consisting of a DNA or RNA molecule that is contained within a protein coating.

**Viscosity** (7.8) A measure of a fluid's resistance to flow freely.

**Vitamin** (11.7) An organic compound that must be obtained in the diet and is needed in small amounts for normal cell function.

**Volatile** (8.7) Readily vaporized.

**Volume/volume percent concentration** (8.4) The number of milliliters of solute dissolved in 100 mL of solution.

# W

**Water-soluble vitamin** (11.7) A vitamin with many polar bonds that dissolves in water.

**Wax** (19.3) An ester (RCOOR') formed from a fatty acid (RCOOH) and a high molecular weight alcohol (R'OH).

**Weight** (1.4) The force that matter feels due to gravity.

**Weight/volume percent concentration** (8.4) The number of grams of solute dissolved in 100 mL of solution.

# X

**X-ray** (10.7) A high-energy form of radiation.

# Z

**Zaitsev rule** (14.5) A rule that states that the major product in an elimination reaction is the alkene that has more alkyl groups bonded to the double bond.

**Zwitterion** (21.2) A neutral compound that contains both a positive and a negative charge.

**Zymogen** (21.9) The inactive precursor of an enzyme that is then converted to its active form when needed.

# Credits

## Chapter 1

**Opener:** Alexander S. Berk; **1.1a,b:** © The McGraw-Hill Companies, Inc./Jill Braaten, photographer; **1.2a:** © Bob Krist/Corbis; **1.2b:** © Corbis RF; **1.3a:** © Douglas Peebles Photography/Alamy; **1.3b:** Daniel C. Smith; **1.3c:** © Dr. Parvinder Sethi RF; **Page 6(sugar):** Daniel C. Smith; **(water, sugar dissolved in water):** © The McGraw-Hill Companies, Inc./Jill Braaten, photographer; **1.4a:** Daniel C. Smith; **1.4b:** © Richard T. Nowtiz/Photo Researchers, Inc.; **1.5a:** Daniel C. Smith; **1.5b:** © Keith Eng, 2008; **1.5c:** © The McGraw-Hill Companies, Inc./Jill Braaten, photographer; **1.5d:** Daniel C. Smith; **p. 9(top):** © Doug Wilson/Corbis; **(bottom):** © Jill Braaten; **p. 10(top):** © Chuck Savage/Corbis; **(bottom):** © PhotoDisc/Getty RF; **p. 11:** © PhotoDisc/Getty RF; **p. 12 (macadamia nuts):** Zachary D.-K. Smith; **(fish):** Daniel C. Smith; **p. 16:** © Stockbyte/Getty RF; **p. 17:** © Creative Studios/Alamy RF; **p. 20:** © The McGraw-Hill Companies, Inc./Elite Images; **p. 21:** © PhotoDisc/Getty RF; **p. 22, 24 & 26:** © The McGraw-Hill Companies, Inc./Jill Braaten, photographer; **p. 27:** © Photodisc/Getty RF.

## Chapter 2

**Opener:** © Keith Eng. 2008; **p. 33:** © Michael S. Yamashita/Getty Images; **p. 39(top):** © Jill Braaten; **(bottom):** © The McGraw-Hill Companies, Inc./Charles D. Winters/Timeframe Photography, Inc.; **p. 43:** © Steve Snodgrass; **2.4b,c:** © Dr. A. Leger/Phototake; **p. 45:** © Anna Kari - Photojournalist; **p. 48:** © Jill Braaten; **2.6a-c:** © The McGraw-Hill Companies, Inc./Jill Braaten, photographer and Anthony Arena, chemistry consultant; **p. 53:** © Karen Kasmauski/Science Faction/Corbis; **p. 56:** © Dr. Parvinder Sethi; **p. 59:** © Peter Dench/Corbis.

## Chapter 3

**Opener:** © Stockbyte/PunchStock RF; **3.1(Sodium metal & chlorine gas):** © The McGraw-Hill Companies, Inc./Stephen Frisch, photographer; **(sodium chloride crystals):** © Dane S. Johnson/Visuals Unlimited; **p. 69:** © Iconotec/Alamer and Cali, photographers RF; **p. 75:** © The McGraw-Hill Companies, Inc./Jill Braaten, photographer; **p. 79:** © James L. Amos/Photo Researchers, Inc.; **p. 80(both):** © The McGraw-Hill Companies, Inc./Jill Braaten, photographer; **p. 81:** © Digital Vision Ltd./SuperStock RF; **p. 83:** © BananaStock/PunchStock RF; **p. 85:** © The McGraw-Hill Companies, Inc./Jill Braaten, photographer; **p. 87(top):** © The McGraw-Hill Companies, Inc./Elite Images; **(bottom):** © CNRI/Photo Researchers, Inc.; **p. 88(oysters):** © Image Source/Corbis RF; **(tums, maalox, iron):** © The McGraw-Hill Companies, Inc./Jill Braaten, photographer; **p. 89(both):** © Steve Gschmeissner/Photo Researchers, Inc.

## Chapter 4

**Opener:** © The McGraw-Hill Companies, Inc./Elite Images; **p. 96(top):** © Photodisc/Alamy RF; **(middle):** © Grant Heilman Photography/Alamy; **(bottom):** Photo by Tim McCabe, USDA Natural Resources Conservation Service; **p. 100:** U.S. Dept. of Commerce photoset Hawaii Volcanism: Lava Forms; **p. 103:** © Ted Nelson/Dembinsky Photo Associates; **p. 104 & 106:** © Jill Braaten; **p. 109(top):** Daniel C. Smith; **(bottom):** © Image Source Black/Alamy RF; **p. 116(top):** © The McGraw-Hill Companies, Inc./Jill, Braaten, photographer; **(bottom):** © Jill Braaten.

## Chapter 5

**Opener:** © Jill Braaten; **p. 124:** Daniel C. Smith; **5.1(left):** © The McGraw-Hill Companies, Inc./Jill, Braaten, photographer and Anthony Arena, chemistry consultant; **(right):** Daniel C. Smith; **p. 128:** © BananaStock/PunchStock RF; **p. 130:** Scott Bauer/USDA; **5.2b:** © Jack Sullivan/Alamy; **p. 133 & 136:** © The McGraw-Hill Companies, Inc./Jill, Braaten, photographer and Anthony Arena, chemistry consultant; **p. 137:** © Science Photo Library/Getty RF; **p. 139:** © Hisham F. Ibrahim/Getty RF; **p. 140(top):** © Keith Eng, 2008; **(bottom):** © Comstock Images/Punchstock RF; **p. 142:** © Royalty Free/Corbis; **5.3:** © The McGraw-Hill Companies, Inc./Jill, Braaten, photographer and Anthony Arena, chemistry consultant; **p. 145:** © Bob Daemmrich/Stock Boston; **p. 146:** © The McGraw-Hill Companies, Inc./Jill, Braaten, photographer and Anthony Arena, chemistry consultant; **p. 147:** © Ryan McVay/Getty Images RF; **5.4(albuterol & fluoxetine):** © The McGraw-Hill Companies, Inc./Jill, Braaten, photographer; **(atorvastatin):** © Beaconstox/Alamy; **p. 152:** U.S. Department of Energy; **p. 156:** © Jill Braaten, **p. 158(left):** © Tony Cordoza/Alamy RF; **(right):** © Clair Dunn/Alamy; **5.7:** © Keigh Eng, 2008.

## Chapter 6

**Opener:** © UpperCut Images/Alamy RF; **p. 168:** Daniel C. Smith; **p. 169:** © The McGraw-Hill Companies, Inc./Jill, Braaten, photographer; **p. 170:** © Royalty Free/Corbis; **p. 173(top):** © Digital Vision/PunchStock RF; **(bottom):** © Comstock/PunchStock RF; **p. 178:** © Jack Star/PhotoLink/Getty RF; **p. 179 & 6.3:** © The McGraw-Hill Companies, Inc./Jill, Braaten, photographer; **p. 181:** © Ingram Publishing/SuperStock RF; **p. 187:** © Royalty-Free/Corbis.

## Chapter 7

**Opener:** Daniel C. Smith; **7.1:** © Doug Menuez/Getty Images RF; **p. 201:** Daniel C. Smith; **p. 206:** © Open Door/Alamy RF; **p. 209:** © Bill Aron/Photo Edit; **p. 211:** © Jill Braaten; **p. 216:** © National Geographic/Getty Images; **p. 217:** © Spencer Grant/Photo Edit; **p. 218(top):** © Martin Harvey/Corbis; **(bottom):** © Andrew Syred/Photo Researchers, Inc.; **p. 223(chloroethane):** Courtesy of Gebauer Company, Cleveland, Ohio; **(girl drinking):** Daniel C. Smith; **(liquid in a closed container):** © The McGraw-Hill Companies, Inc./Jill, Braaten, photographer; **7.8a:** © The McGraw-Hill Companies, Inc./Jill, Braaten, photographer and Anthony Arena, chemistry consultant; **7.8b:** © blickwinkel/Alamy; **7.9a-d:** © The McGraw-Hill Companies, Inc./Jill, Braaten, photographer; **p. 227(bikers):** © Royalty Free/Corbis; **(glass, ice, liquid water):** © The McGraw-Hill Companies, Inc./Jill Braaten, photographer; **p. 228(both):** © The McGraw-Hill Companies, Inc./Jill Braaten, photographer; **p. 229(all):** © The McGraw-Hill Companies, Inc./Jill Braaten, photographer and Anthony Arena, chemistry consultant.

## Chapter 8

**Opener:** Zachary D.-K. Smith; **p. 242(top):** © Jill Braaten; **8.1a:** © Brian Evans/Photo Researchers, Inc.; **8.1b:** © Digital Vision/Alamy RF; **8.1c:** © Keith Eng, 2008; **p. 243(both):** © The McGraw-Hill Companies, Inc./Jill Braaten, photographer and Anthony Arena, chemistry consultant; **8.3(both):** © The McGraw-Hill Companies, Inc./Jill Braaten, photographer; **8.4:** © Tom Pantages; **p. 247:** © Keith Eng, 2008; **8.5(both):** © The McGraw-Hill Companies, Inc./Jill Braaten, photographer; **p. 249:** © Oliver Anlauf/Getty Images; **p. 250:** © The McGraw-Hill Companies, Inc./Suzie Ross, photographer; **8.6a,b:** © The McGraw-Hill Companies, Inc./Jill Braaten, photographer and Anthony Arena, chemistry consultant; **p. 251:** © BananaStock/PunchStock RF; **p. 252:** © David Hoffman Photo Library/Alamy; **p. 253:** © Comstock/PunchStock RF; **p. 258:** © Jill Braaten; **8.7(both):** © The McGraw-Hill Companies, Inc./Jill Braaten, photographer; **p. 261(top):** © Traverse City Record-Eagle, John L. Russell/AP/Wide World Photos; **(bottom):** © OSF/Doug Allan/Animals Animals; **8.8a-c:** © Dennis Kunkel Microscopy, Inc.

## Chapter 9

**Opener, p. 275(both):** © The McGraw-Hill Companies, Inc./Jill Braaten, photographer and Anthony Arena, chemistry consultant; **9.1a:** © Jill Braaten; **9.1b:** © Photolink/Getty RF; **9.1c:** © BananaStock/PunchStock RF; **9.2a-c:** © The McGraw-Hill Companies, Inc./Jill Braaten, photographer; **p. 280:** © Charles D. Winters/Photo Researchers, Inc.; **9.4, 9.5(all):** © The McGraw-Hill Companies, Inc./Jill Braaten, photographer and Anthony Arena, chemistry consultant; **p. 287:** © Digital Vision Ltd./SuperStock RF; **p. 289:** © The McGraw-Hill Companies, Inc./Jill Braaten, photographer; **p. 291:** © Comstock Images/PictureQuest RF; **p. 293:** © Royalty-Free/Corbis; **9.6a:** © The McGraw-Hill Companies, Inc./Stephen Frisch, photographer; **9.6b:** © Sciencephotos/Alamy; **9.6c:** © Leslie Garland Picture Library/Alamy; **9.7(lemons):** © Humberto Olarte Cupas/Alamy RF; **(strawberries):** © Photolink/Getty RF; **(tomatoes):** © Burke/Triolo/Getty RF; **(milk):** © Mitch Hrdlicka/Getty RF; **(phillips):** © The McGraw-Hill Companies, Inc./Jill Braaten, photographer; **(ammonia):** © The McGraw-Hill Companies, Inc./Terry Wild Studio; **(Clorox):** © The McGraw-Hill Companies, Inc./Jill Braaten, photographer; **p. 295:** © Bruce Heinemann/Getty RF; **p. 298, 299, Fig. 9.9a-c:** © The McGraw-Hill Companies, Inc./Jill Braaten, photographer and Anthony Arena, chemistry consultant; **p. 303:** © Dr. Parvinder Sethi; **p. 309:** © JupiterImages/Brand X/Alamy RF.

## Chapter 10

**Opener:** © Martin Dohrn/Photo Researchers, Inc.; **p. 319(top):** © AFP/Getty Images; **(bottom):** © Cordelia Molloy/Photo Researchers, Inc.; **p. 320:** © S. Wanke/PhotoLink/Getty RF; **10.2a:** © Owen Franken/Corbis; **10.2b,c:** © Custom Medical Stock Photo; **10.3:** © Science VU/Visuals Unlimited; **p. 327(top):** © Hank Morgan/Photo Researchers, Inc.; **(bottom):** Landauer Corporation; **10.4b:** © Living Art Enterprises, LLC/Photo Researchers, Inc.; **10.5a,b:** Daniel C. Smith; **p. 331:** Image courtesy of the Australian Nuclear Science and Technology Organization; **10.7a,c:** Daniel C. Smith; **10.8a:** © Martin Bond/Photo Researchers, Inc.; **10.9a:** © Royalty-Free/Corbis; **10.9b:** © Scott Camazine/Photo Researchers, Inc.; **10.9c:** With permission, Daniel C. Smith.

## Chapter 11

**Opener:** © Corbis RF; **11.1a:** © Comstock/PunchStock RF; **11.1b:** © Corbis Premium RF/Alamy; **11.1c:** © Steven May/Alamy; **11.1d:** © Layna Kennedy/Corbis; **p. 343(methane):** © Ingram Publishing/SuperStock RF; **(ethanol):** © Goodshoot/PunchStock RF; **(capsaicin):** © The McGraw-Hill Companies, Inc./Jill Braaten, photographer; **(caffeine):** © Comstock/PunchStock RF; **p. 346(top):** © Vol. 129 PhotoDisc/Getty RF; **(bottom):** © PhotoDisc/Getty RF; **p. 347:** © Corbis/RF; **p. 350:** John Somerville; **p. 356:** © Ted Kinsman/Photo Researchers, Inc.; **11.3(cherries):** © Brand X Pictures/PunchStock RF; **(bananas):** © Ingram Publishing/SuperStock RF; **(oranges):** © Brand X Pictures/PunchStock RF; **(pineapple):** © Corbis RF; **p. 359:** © Jill Braaten; **p. 360:** © Graham Titchmarsh/Alamy RF; **p. 361:** © National Geographic Image Collection/Alamy RF; **Table 11.5(left):** © PIXTAL/PunchStock RF; **(right):** © Royalty-Free/Corbis; **p. 366:** © The McGraw-Hill Companies, Inc./Jill Braaten, photographer; **p. 367 (top):** © The McGraw-Hill Companies, Inc./John Flournoy, photographer; **(bottom):** Photo by Mary Clay Stensvold, courtesy of Smithsonian Institution.

## Chapter 12

**Opener:** © Bettmann/Corbis; **p. 377(left):** God of Insects; **(right):** © Douglas Peebles/Corbis; **p. 378:** © Bloomberg/Getty Images; **p. 383:** © PhotoDisc Website RF; **p. 384:** © Jill Braaten; **p. 389(left):** © Brand X Pictures/PunchStock RF; **(right):** © The McGraw-Hill Companies, Inc./Suzie Ross, photographer; **12.1a:** © PhotoDisc RF; **p. 393:** © The McGraw-Hill Companies, Inc./Jill Braaten, photographer; **p. 394(top):** © Vince Bevan/Alamy; **(bottom):** © Jill Braaten; **p. 395:** PhotoLink/Getty RF.

## Chapter 13

**Opener, p. 403:** © The McGraw-Hill Companies, Inc./Jill Braaten, photographer; **p. 410:** © Degginger E.R./Animals Animals/Earth Scenes; **p. 411:** © Jill Braaten; **p. 413 (top):** © The McGraw-Hill Companies, Inc./Jill Braaten, photographer; **(bottom):** © Sergio Piumatti; **p. 417:** © 1998 Richard Megna, Fundamental Photographs, NYC; **p. 419(top):** Ethanol Promotion and Information Council (EPIC); **(bottom):** © The McGraw-Hill Companies, Inc./Jill Braaten, photographer; **p. 420:** © Royalty-Free/Corbis; **13.5(both):** © The McGraw-Hill Companies, Inc./Jill Braaten, photographer; **p. 421(both):** © The McGraw-Hill Companies, Inc./Elite Images; **p. 422:** © Jill Braaten; **13.6(PVC):** © The McGraw-Hill Companies, Inc./John Thoeming, photographer; **(balls):** © Dynamicgraphics/Jupiterimages RF; **(blankets):** © Fernando Bengoechea/Corbis; **(styrofoam):** © The McGraw-Hill Companies, Inc./John Thoeming, photographer; **Table 13.2(blood bag):** © Image Source/Getty Images RF; **(syringes):** © Royalty-Free/Corbis; **(dental floss):** © Jill Braaten; **p. 429(sunscreen):** © The McGraw-Hill Companies, Inc./John Thoeming, photographer; **(tobacco plant):** Photo by Bob Nichols, USDA Natural Resources Conservation Service; **(cigarette smoke):** © PhotoAlto/PictureQuest RF; **p. 430(tylenol):** © The McGraw-Hill Companies, Inc./John Thoeming, photographer; **(dentist):** © Mikael Karlsson/Arresting Images RF; **(blowing nose):** © Picture Partners/Alamy; **p. 431(vanilla bean):** © CD16/Author's Image RF; **(cloves):** © Peter Arnold, Inc./Alamy; **(tumeric):** Mr. Napat Kitipanangkul, Science School, Walailak University with financial support by Biodiversity; Research and training program (BRT); **(cell protector):** © The McGraw-Hill Companies, Inc./Elite Images; **p. 432:** © Royalty-Free/Corbis.

## Chapter 14

**Opener:** © John A. Rizzo/Getty Images RF; **p. 444(coffee):** © Creatas/PunchStock RF; **(ether):** © Mira/Alamy; **(tree trunk):** © Greg Vaughn/Alamy; **p. 445:** © Iconotec.com/Pepiera Tom Canabi Hugo RF; **p. 446:** © The McGraw-Hill Companies, Inc./Jill Braaten, photographer; **p. 448:** © Jill Braaten; **14.1(grapes):** © Dynamic Grapics Group/PunchStock RF; **(barrels of wine):** © Goodshoot/PunchStock RF; **(wine bottles):** © BananaStock/RunchStock RF; **p. 450(wheat):** © Vol. 1 PhotoDisc/Getty RF; **(cotton):** © Corbis RF; **14.4:** © The McGraw-Hill Companies, Inc./Elite Images; **p. 457(top):** © BananaStock/PunchStock RF; **(bottom):** Gwinnet County Police Department/Centers for Disease Control and Prevention; **p. 458(top):** © Ed Reschke; **(bottom):** Peter J.S. Franks, Scripps Institution of Oceanography; **p. 461:** The Boston Medical Library in the Francis A. Countway Library of Medicine; **p. 462:** © Jill Braaten; **p. 465(top):** © The McGraw-Hill Companies, Inc./Jill Braaten, photographer; **(bottom):** NASA; **p. 466:** © Mark Downey/Getty Images RF; **14.7(both):** © The McGraw-Hill Companies, Inc./Suzi Ross, photographer.

## Chapter 15

**Opener:** © The McGraw-Hill Companies, Inc./Elite Images; **p. 477:** Daniel C. Smith; **15.1a:** © The McGraw-Hill Companies, Inc./Jill Braaten, photographer; **15.1b:** © Claude Thouvenin/Peter Arnold, Inc.; **p. 482(grapes):** © PhotoDisc/Getty RF; **(ephedrine):** © Henriette Kress; **(greens):** © Comstock/PunchStock RF; **p. 485:** © John Fischer, About.com Hawaii Travel; **p. 486:** © The McGraw-Hill Companies, Inc./Jill Braaten, photographer; **p. 487:** © Nigel Cattlin/Alamy; **p. 492:** © GYRO PHOTOGRAPHY/amanaimages RF; **p. 496(caraway seeds):** © The McGraw-Hill Companies, Inc./Elite Images; **(spearmint leaves):** DAJ/Getty RF.

## Chapter 16

**Opener:** © David Sieren/Visuals Unlimited; **p. 505:** © Iconotec/Alamer and Cali, photographers RF; **p. 507:** © TTH/a.collection/Getty/RF; **p. 510(both), 16.1, p. 511:** © The McGraw-Hill Companies, Inc./Jill Braaten, photographer; **p. 513:** © The McGraw-Hill Companies, Inc./Charles D. Winters/Timeframe Photography, Inc.; **p. 516:** © M.K. Ranjitsinh/Photo Researchers, Inc.; **p. 517(fluoxetine):** © The McGraw-Hill Companies, Inc./Jill Braaten, photographer; **(soybeans):** © PhotoDisc/Getty RF; **523(milk):** © The McGraw-Hill Companies, Inc./Elite Images; **(foxgrove):** © Richo Cech, Horizon Herbs, LLC.

## Chapter 17

**Opener:** © Jill Braaten; **p. 536:** © The McGraw-Hill Companies, Inc./Jill Braaten, photographer; **p. 537:** © Photo Researchers, Inc.; **p. 543:** Photo by Forest and Kim Starr; **p. 544:** © The McGraw-Hill Companies, Inc./Jill Braaten, photographer; **p. 545(mangoes):** © CD16/Author's Image RF; **(apricots):** © Jupiterimages/ImageSource RF; **(wintergreen):** © Westend61 GmbH/Alamy; **(Melatonin & p. 546(both)):** © The McGraw-Hill Companies, Inc./Jill Braaten, photographer; **p. 550(ivory soap ad):** Ivory Soap Advertising Collection, Archives Center, National Museum of American History, Smithsonian Institution; **(willow tree):** © National Geographic/Getty Images; **(meadowsweet):** © Biopix. dkhttp://www.biopix.dk; **p. 553:** © Jill Braaten; **p. 554:** Coby Schal/NC State University; **p. 555:** Photo by Scott Bauer/USDA; **p. 558:** © The McGraw-Hill Companies, Inc./Jill Braaten, photographer; **p. 560(top):** Image courtesy of The Advertising Archives; **(bottom):** © Royalty-Free/Corbis; **p. 561(both):** © The McGraw-Hill Companies, Inc./Jill Braaten, photographer; **17.5a:** © SIU/Visuals Unlimited, Inc.; **17.5b:** © Antonia Reeve/Photo Researchers, Inc.; **p. 563(top):** © Jill Braaten; **(bottom):** Library of Congress.

## Chapter 18

**Opener:** © Taxi/Getty; **p. 572(pepper plant):** © Maximilian Weinzierl/Alamy; **(hemlock):** © D. Hurst/Alamy RF; **p. 574:** © James Forte/Getty RF; **p. 579:** © BananaStock/PunchStock RF; **18.2(coffee plant):** © Mediacolor's/Alamy; **(cup):** © Nick Koudis/Gettty RF; **(coffee cherries):** © Inga Spence/Visuals Unlimited; **p. 580:** © Stockdisc/PunchStock RF; **18.3(tobacco plant):** © Flora Torrance/Life File RF; **(cigarette smoke):** © Nancy R. Cohen/Getty RF; **(dried tobacco leaves):** © Wayne Hutchinson/Alamy; **p. 582(poppy seeds):** © Stockbyte Silver/Getty RF; **(opium poppy):** © Scott Camazine/Photo Researchers, Inc.; **(cinchona tree):** Photo by Forest and Kim Starr; **p. 583(deadly nightshade):** © Werner Arnold; **p. 587:** © The McGraw-Hill Companies, Inc./Jill Braaten, photographer; **p. 591(bufo toad):** © Daniel C. Smith; **(mushrooms):** © IT Stock/age fotostock RF; **p. 593:** © The McGraw-Hill Companies, Inc./Jill Braaten, photographer; **p. 594:** Daniel C. Smith.

## Chapter 19

**Opener:** © Jill Braaten; **p. 602:** © The McGraw-Hill Companies, Inc./Jill Braaten, photographer; **p. 606:** © Brand X Pictures/PunchStock RF; **p. 607(whale):** © Denis Scott/Corbis; **(leaf):** Daniel C. Smith; **(lip gloss):** © The McGraw-Hill Companies, Inc./Jill Braaten, photographer; **(bee's):** © Photodisc/Getty RF; **p. 608:** USDA, ARS, National Genetic Resources Program; **p. 609:** © The McGraw-Hill Companies, Inc./Jill Braaten, photographer; **p. 610(left):** © Ingo Jezierski/Corbis RF; **(right):** © Jupiterimages/ImageSource RF; **p. 611(top):** Daniel C. Smith; **p. 611 (bottom & 19.1(all)):** © The McGraw-Hill Companies, Inc./Jill Braaten, photographer; **p. 614:** Daniel C. Smith; **19.2:** © The McGraw-Hill Companies, Inc./Dennis Strete, photographer; **p. 615:** © AP/Wide World Photos; **p. 616(left):** © Jupiterimages/ImageSource RF; **(right):** © David Buffington/Getty RF; **p. 624:** © Getty RF; **19.8 a,b:** © Ed Reschke; **p. 626:** © Andrew Brookes/Corbis; **p. 628:** © Comstock/JupiterImages RF; **p. 629:** © Jill Braaten; **p. 630(top):** © BananaStock RF; **(middle):** Stockbyte/PunchStock RF; **(bottom):** © IT Stock/PunchStock RF; **p. 631:** © Jill Braaten.

## Chapter 20

**Opener:** © Isabelle Rosenbaum & Frederic Cirou/PhotoAlto/PunchStock RF; **p. 641(top):** © Michelle Garrett/Corbis; **(bottom):** © ImageSource/Corbis RF; **p. 642(top):** Bauer/USDA; **(bottom):** Daniel C. Smith; **p. 643:** © The McGraw-Hill Companies, Inc./Elite Images; **p. 645:** © Photodisc Collection/Getty RF; **p. 647:** © Keith Brofsky/Getty RF; **p. 648(top):** © Comstock/PunchStock RF; **(bottom):** © Jill Braaten; **p. 657, 20.2:** © The McGraw-Hill Companies, Inc./Jill Braaten, photographer; **p. 658:** © Vol. 3/PhotoDisc/Getty RF; **p. 660(left):** © The McGraw-Hill Companies, Inc./Jill Braaten, photographer; **(right):** © D. Hurst/Alamy RF; **p. 661(left):** © David Muench/Corbis; **(right):** © The McGraw-Hill Companies, Inc./Elite Images; **20.3:** © The McGraw-Hill Companies, Inc./Jill Braaten, photographer; **p. 662:** © inga/Alamy; **20.4:** Biophoto Associates/Photo Researchers, Inc.; **20.5(stalks):** © Vol. 1 PhotoDisc/Getty RF; **(kernels):** © Borland/PhotoLink/Getty Images RF; **20.6:** © Dennis Kunkel/Visuals Unlimited; **667(top):** © Geldi/Alamy; **(bottom):** © The McGraw-Hill Companies, Inc./Jill Braaten, photographer; **p. 668:** Comstock Images/PictureQuest RF; **p. 669:** © Royalty-Free/Corbis.

## Chapter 21

**Opener:** © Royalty-Free/Corbis; **p. 677:** © Jill Braaten; **p. 679(top):** © John A. Raineri; **(bottom):** © Jill Braaten; **p. 681:** © Comstock/PunchStock RF; **21.13:** © Image Source/PunchStock RF; **p. 698:** Daniel C. Smith; **p. 699:** © Eye of Science/Photo Researchers, Inc.; **p. 701:** © The McGraw-Hill Companies, Inc./Jill Braaten, photographer; **p. 702:** Daniel C. Smith.

## Chapter 22

**Opener:** © Lawrence Lawry/Getty RF; **22.3a:** ©Photodisc/Jupiterimages RF; **p. 725:** Daniel C. Smith; **22.7b:** © Kenneth Eward/Photo Researchers, Inc.; **p. 738:** Cystic Fibrosis Trust; **22.12:** Courtesy Genelex Corp., www.HealthandDNA.com; **p. 743(top):** © The McGraw-Hill Companies, Inc./Jill Braaten, photographer; **(bottom):** © Time & Life Pictures/Getty Images.

## Chapter 23

**Opener:** © David Stoecklein/Corbis; **23.2(left):** © Royalty-Free/Corbis; **(middle):** © Nancy R. Cohen/Getty RF; **(right):** © PhotoLink/Getty RF; **p. 761:** © Jill Braaten; **p. 764:** © The McGraw-Hill Companies, Inc./Jill Braaten, photographer; **p. 765:** © Digital Vision/Getty RF; **p. 772:** © Connie Brainsilver/Photo Researchers, Inc.; **p. 773:** © The McGraw-Hill Companies, Inc./Jill Braaten, photographer.

## Chapter 24

**Opener:** © Dennis Gray/Cole Group/Getty RF; **p. 787(sugar beets):** © Corbis RF; **(milk):** © Isabelle Rozenbaum Frederic Cirou/PhotoAlto/PunchStock RF; **(cranberries):** © Burke/Triolo/Getty RF; **p. 789:** © Warren Morgan/Corbis; **p. 790:** © John A. Rizzo/Getty RF; **p. 798:** Daniel C. Smith; **p. 799(both):** © The McGraw-Hill Companies, Inc./Jill Braaten, photographer.

# Index